ELEMENTARY AND MIDDLE SCHOOL
MATHEMATICS

Teaching Developmentally

Third Canadian Edition

John A. Van de Walle
Late of Virginia Commonwealth University

Sandra Folk
University of Toronto

Karen S. Karp
University of Louisville

Jennifer M. Bay-Williams
University of Louisville

Pearson Canada
Toronto

Library and Archives Canada Cataloguing in Publication

Elementary and middle school mathematics : teaching developmentally /
  John A. Van de Walle ... [et al.]. —3rd Canadian ed.

First-2nd Canadian eds. written by John A. Van de Walle, Sandra Folk.

Includes bibliographical references and index.

ISBN 978-0-205-67697-2

1. Mathematics—Study and teaching (Elementary). 2. Mathematics—Study and teaching (Middle school).
  I. Van de Walle, John A II. Van de Walle, John A. Elementary and middle school mathematics

QA135.6.E44 2011   372.7'044   C2010-900414-0

ISBN 978-0-205-67697-2

Vice-President, Editorial Director: Gary Bennett
Editor-in-Chief: Ky Pruesse
Acquisitions Editor: David S. Le Gallais
Marketing Manager: Loula March
Developmental Editor: Heather Parker
Production Editor: Lila Campbell
Copy Editor: Marg Bukta
Proofreaders: Valerie Adams, Susan Bindernagel
Production Coordinator: Avinash Chandra
Compositor: Joan M. Wilson/Hermia Chung
Photo Research: Sandy Cooke
Art Director: Julia Hall
Cover and Interior Designer: Anthony Leung
Cover Image: GettyImages

Photo Credits: p. 36: Shutterstock; p. 62: Jupiter Unlimited; p.98: Copyright © Bill Aron / PhotoEdit; p. 107: Jupiter Unlimited; p. 123: Natie/GetStock.com; p. 171: Copyright © Richard Hutchings / PhotoEdit; p. 212: Copyright © Spencer Grant / PhotoEdit; p. 249: Copyright © Myrleen Ferguson Cate / PhotoEdit; p. 266: Copyright © Michael Newman / PhotoEdit; p. 296: Copyright © Spencer Grant / PhotoEdit; p. 340: Ryan Nunn; p. 361: © Nordicphotos / Almay; p. 387: © Leslie Garland Picture Library / Almay; p. 422: a) Simon Hayter/GetStock.com, b) canadabrian/GetStock.com, c) Bill Brooks/GetStock.com; p. 459: Copyright © David Young-Wolff / PhotoEdit; p. 476: © A ROOM WITH VIEWS / Almay; p. 496: a) NASA, ESA, The Hubble Heritage Team (STScI/AURA) and A. Riess (SSTScl), b) Shutterstock.

1 2 3 4 5   14 13 12 11 10

Printed and bound in the United States of America.

Brief Contents

Contents

SECTION I
Foundations of Teaching Mathematics

The fundamental core of effective teaching of mathematics combines an understanding of how children learn, how to promote that learning by teaching through problem solving, and how to plan for and assess that learning on a daily -basis. Introductory chapters in this section provide perspectives on trends in mathematics education and the process of doing mathematics. These chapters develop the core ideas of learning, teaching, planning, and -assessment. Additional perspectives on mathematics for children with diverse backgrounds and the role of technology are also discussed.

CHAPTER 6

Teaching Mathematics Equitably to All Children   93

CHAPTER 7

Technology and School Mathematics   106

SECTION II
Development of Mathematical Concepts and Procedures

This section serves as the application of the core ideas of Section I. Here you will find chapters on every major content area in the pre-K–8 mathematics curriculum. Numerous problem-based activities to engage students are interwoven with a discussion of the mathematical content and how children develop their understanding of that content. At the outset of each chapter, you will find a listing of "Big Ideas," the mathematical umbrella for the chapter. Also included are ideas for incorporating children's literature, technology, and assessment. These chapters are designed to help you develop pedagogical strategies and to serve as a resource for your teaching now and in the future.

CHAPTER 11

Developing Whole-Number Place-Value Concepts   191

CHAPTER 12

Developing Strategies for Whole-Number Computation   221

CHAPTER 13

Using Computational Estimation with Whole Numbers   248

CHAPTER 14

Algebraic Thinking: Generalizations, Patterns, and Functions   262

CHAPTER 15

Developing Fraction Concepts   294

CHAPTER 16

Developing Strategies for Computation with Fractions   320

CHAPTER 17

Decimal and Percent Concepts and Decimal Computation   339

CHAPTER 18

Proportional Reasoning   360

CHAPTER 19

Developing Measurement Concepts   385

CHAPTER 23

Developing Concepts of Exponents, Integers, and Real Numbers   491

APPENDIX

Guide to Blackline Masters   A-1

Preface

TO STUDENTS AND INSTRUCTORS

Learning is not the result of development; learning is development. It requires invention and self-organization on the part of the learner. Thus teachers need to allow learners to raise their own questions, generate their own hypotheses and models as possibilities, and test them for viability.

—*Fosnot (1996, p. 29)*

What is basic in mathematics is as simple as this: Math makes sense! Every child in his or her own way can come to believe this simple truth. More importantly, every child can come to believe that he or she is capable of making sense of mathematics. Every child should leave school confident in his or her ability to understand and do mathematics.

This is the goal of *Elementary and Middle School Mathematics*—to help both you and your students come to believe that math makes sense and that you are capable of making sense of it yourself. As the quotation from Catherine Fosnot suggests, students will have to develop this understanding themselves. Their understanding and, thus, their confidence will grow as a result of being engaged in the doing of mathematics. The subtitle of this book, *Teaching Developmentally*, refers to engaging students where you find them so that they can create or develop new ideas that they can use and understand—so they can see that math makes sense through their own eyes and can believe it because they can do it.

Research in mathematics education has consistently found that understanding and skills are best developed when students are allowed to wrestle with new ideas, to create and defend solutions to problems, and to participate in a mathematical community of learners. This student-centred, problem-based approach to learning is a central theme of this book.

You may be surprised to find that your instructor does not "cover" much more than half of the book. In fact, no course can completely prepare you for all you need to know to help children learn mathematics. However, this book has always been more than a textbook. It is a guide for your ongoing learning as you continue your work with children. For each strand of the mathematics curriculum, you will find a discussion of how children develop that mathematics, along with tasks and activities for helping students learn. Integrated with this discussion you will find a development of the mathematics content you need to be an effective teacher.

Learning how best to help children believe that mathematics makes sense and that they themselves can make sense of mathematics is an exciting endeavour and a lifelong process. It requires the knowledge gained from research, the wisdom shared by professional colleagues, and the insightful ideas that come from your own daily experiences with students.

Believe in kids! Allow them to think, to struggle, and to reason with new ideas as together you find the excitement that happens when mathematics makes sense.

WHAT YOU WILL FIND IN THIS BOOK

If you look at the table of contents, you will see that the chapters are separated into two distinct sections: Foundations of Teaching Mathematics, and Development of Mathematical Concepts and Procedures.

The first section of seven chapters deals with important ideas that cross the boundaries of specific areas of content. The fundamental core of effective teaching of mathematics combines an understanding of how children learn, how to promote that learning by teaching through problem solving, and how to plan for and assess that learning on a daily basis. Introductory chapters in this section provide perspectives on trends in mathematics education and the process of doing mathematics. These chapters develop the core ideas of learning, teaching, planning, and assessment. Additional perspectives on mathematics for children with special needs and the role of technology are also discussed.

Chapters 2 and 3 are the most important. There you will learn about a constructivist view of learning, how that is applied to learning mathematics, and what it means to teach through problem solving. Chapter 4 will help you translate these ideas of how children best learn mathematics into the lessons you will be teaching. Here you will find a practical perspective on planning effective lessons for all children, on the value of drill and practice, and other issues. Sample lesson plans are part of this chapter, as well as in many of the content chapters later in the book and on MyEducationLab. Chapter 5 explores the integration of assessment with instruction to best assist student learning.

Surrounding these central ideas are chapters offering perspectives on the challenging task of helping children learn mathematics. It is important to know where mathematics is going and why so that you will know how to play a professional role in that endeavour. It is also important to have a feel for the discipline of mathematics—to know what it means to "do mathematics." The first chapters address these issues.

In Chapter 6, you will read about working with children whose needs are special, whether they are second-language learners, or gifted, or physically or intellectually challenged.

Chapter 7 provides perspectives on the issues surrounding technology in the teaching of mathematics. A strong case is made for the use of calculators at all grade levels. Guidance is offered for the selection and use of computer software, and suggestions are made to help you find valuable resources on the Internet.

The second section of sixteen chapters offers teaching suggestions for every major topic in the Pre-K–8 mathematics curriculum. This section serves as the application of the core ideas of Section I. At the outset of each chapter, you will find a listing of "Big Ideas," the mathematical umbrella for the chapter. Also included are ideas for incorporating children's literature, technology, and assessment.

Each chapter of Section II provides a perspective on mathematical content, how children best learn that content, and numerous suggestions for problem-based activities to engage children in the development of good mathematics. The problem-based tasks for students are integrated with the text; they are not added on. Many of the activities include accommodations for students who are experiencing mathematical difficulties and for those who are mathematically advanced. Reflecting on the activities as you read can help you think about mathematics from the perspective of the child. Consider them in relation to the chapter content, not as an aside. Like the children you will be teaching, become actively engaged in your learning about children learning mathematics. These chapters are designed to help you develop pedagogical strategies and to serve as a resource for your teaching now and in the future.

SOME SPECIAL FEATURES OF THIS TEXT

By just flipping through the book you will notice many section headings and figures, as well as various icons and special features. They are all there to make the book more useful, both as a textbook and as a resource. Here are some things to look for.

Big Ideas

Much of the literature espousing a student-centred approach suggests that teachers plan their instruction around "big ideas" rather than tiny skills or concepts. Near the start of each chapter in Section II you will find a list of the key mathematical ideas associated with the chapter. Teachers find these lists helpful in order to get a picture quickly of the mathematics they are teaching.

Mathematics Content Connections

Following the Big Ideas lists are brief descriptions of other content areas in mathematics that are related to the content of the current chapter. They are provided to help you become more aware of the potential interaction of content as you plan lessons, diagnose students' difficulties, and learn more about what you are teaching.

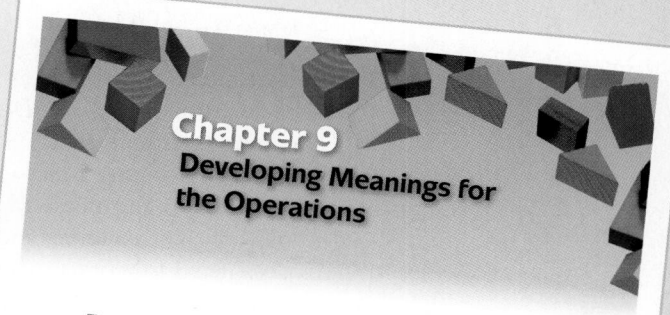

Activities ▶

The numerous activities found in every chapter of Section II are an integral part of the book. Most of these are clearly framed in a box with an accompanying title. Other ideas for activities are described directly in the text or in the illustrations. Every activity is a problem-based task, as described in Chapter 3. Each one is designed to engage students in doing mathematics. Some activities incorporate calculator use; these activities are marked with a calculator icon.

Many activities include an Accommodations section, which offers ideas for how to modify an activity for students who are experiencing difficulty with mathematics or for those who are mathematically advanced.

Investigations in Number, Data, and Space and Connected Mathematics Features ▼

In Chapter 9 you will find a feature describing an activity from the standards-based curriculum *Investigations in Number, Data, and Space* (a K–5 curriculum) and, in Chapters 14 and 18, a feature describing an activity from the standards-based curriculum *Connected Mathematics* (a 6–8 curriculum). The pages include a description of an activity in the program as well as the context of the unit in which it is found. The main purpose of these features is to acquaint you with these materials and to demonstrate how the spirit of the NCTM *Standards* and the constructivist theory, espoused in this book, have been translated into existing commercial curricula.

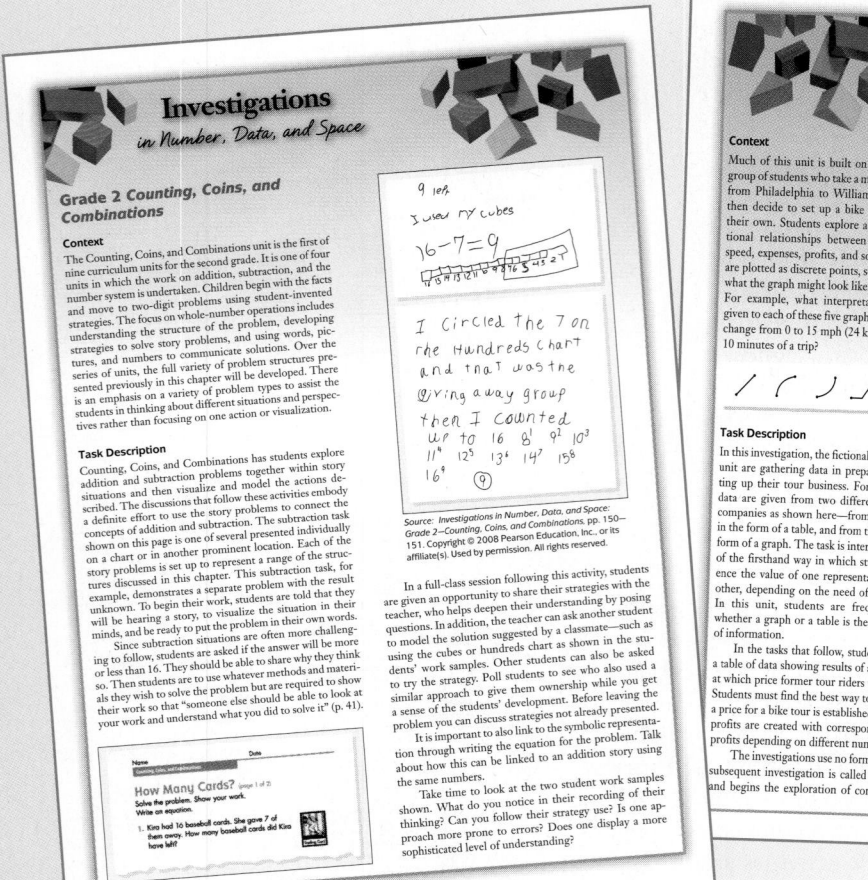

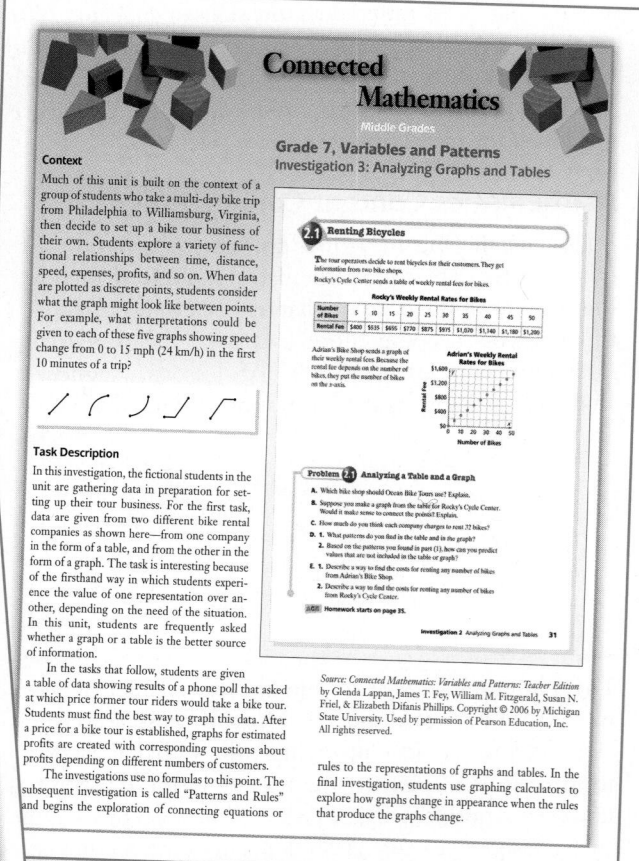

◀ Assessment Notes

Assessment should be an integral part of instruction. Similarly, it makes sense to think about what to be listening and looking for (assessing) as you read about different areas of content development. Throughout the content chapters, you will see assessment icons indicating a short description of things to be looking and listening for as you teach this material. Reading these assessment notes in relation to the text can also help you understand how to help your students.

NCTM Correlations ▶

Throughout the chapters, you will see an icon indicating a reference to NCTM's *Principles and Standards for School Mathematics*. The notes typically consist of a quotation from the *Standards* and/or a summary of what the *Standards* say about a particular topic. These notes point explicitly to the alignment of this book with the *Standards* and we hope they will encourage you to read more about what the authors of that important document have to say.

Technology Notes ▶

When appropriate, a technology icon marks a section discussing how computers can be used profitably to help with the content just discussed. Descriptions of specific software titles and interactive applets available on the Internet are provided. You should not think of these sections as a compendium of available software but as a pointer to the most useful types of computer resources that are available. Inclusion of any title in these notes should not be seen as an endorsement.

The technology icon will also be found with certain activities to indicate the use of computer technology. Similarly, a calculator icon appears with activities that incorporate calculator use.

Chapter End Matter ▶

The end of each chapter is reorganized in this edition to include two major subsections: Reflections, which includes Writing to Learn and For Discussion and Exploration; and Resources, which includes Literature Connections (found in all Section II chapters), Recommendations for Further Reading, and Online Resources.

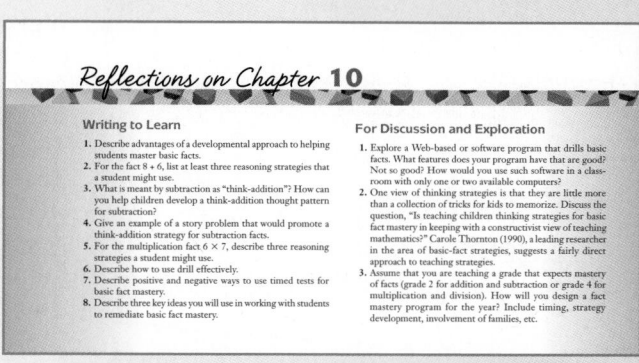

The first section at the end of every chapter, **Reflections**, invites you to reflect on the content of the chapter and to consider and apply what you have learned through writing and discussion activities.

Writing to Learn

To help you focus on the important pedagogical ideas, a list of focusing questions is found at the end of every chapter under the heading "Writing to Learn." These study questions are designed to help you reflect on the main points of the chapter. Actually writing out the answers to these questions in your own words is one of the best ways for you to develop your understanding of each chapter's main ideas.

For Discussion and Exploration

These questions ask you to explore an issue, to reflect on observations in a classroom, to compare text ideas with those found in traditional curriculum materials, or perhaps to take a position on a controversial issue. There are no "right" answers to these questions, but we hope that they will stimulate thought and cause spirited conversations.

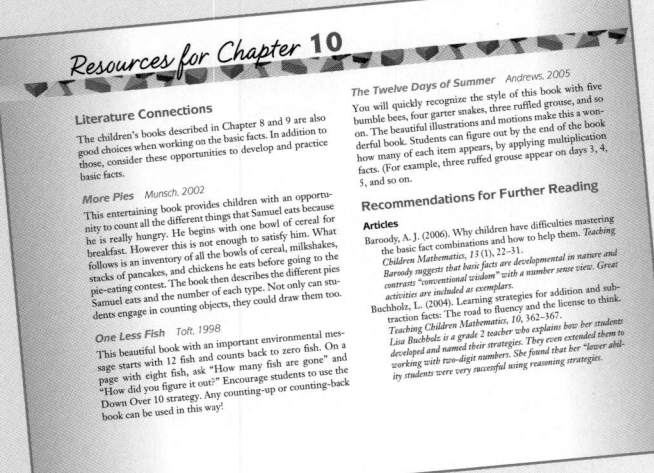

The second section at the end of every chapter, **Resources**, provides lists of resources for use in the classroom and for further learning.

Literature Connections

Most chapters in Section II contain a Literature Connections section. In each of these sections, children's literature titles are suggested along with a brief description of how the mathematics of the chapter can be profitably built on the stories. Though certainly not a comprehensive listing of potential literature, these sections will get you started using this exciting vehicle for teaching mathematics.

Recommendations for Further Reading

Under this heading you will find a short annotated list of articles and books to augment the information found in the chapter. Usually these are taken from NCTM journals and books, and from other professional resources designed for the classroom teacher. (Note that all sources cited within the text proper appear in the References at the end of the book.)

Online Resources

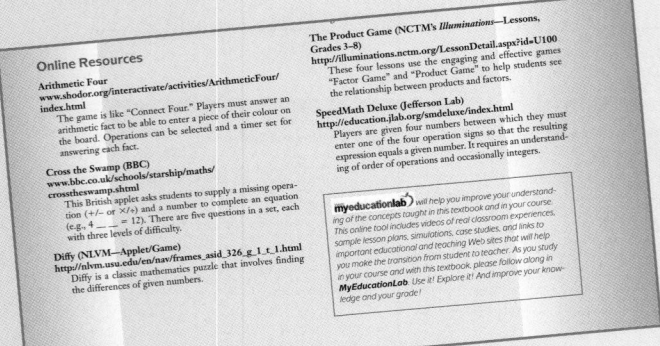

Suggested Applets and Web Links. Today there are many mathematics-learning resources available free on the Internet. Most are in the form of interactive applets that allow students to explore a specific mathematical concept or skill. After each chapter in Section II, you will find an annotated list of some of the best of these resources along with their URLs. Exploring these applets will be a learning experience for you, as well as a way to learn of a valuable resource for students. At the end of Chapter 8 is a list of the broader sites where these and other Web-based resources can be found.

An easy method of accessing these sites is to visit MyEducationLab, where each Web-based resource and applet can be accessed with a simple click of the mouse.

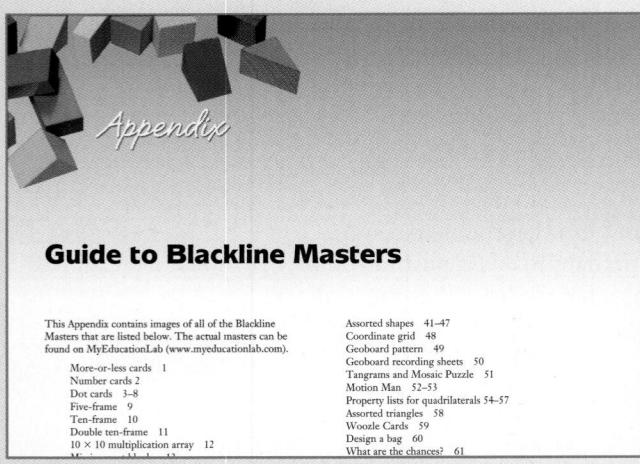

◀ Appendix

The Appendix contains images of all of the Blackline Masters.

Note: NCTM materials included as appendices in previous editions of this text have been moved online. For example, NCTM's *Principles and Standards for School Mathematics* is described in depth in Chapter 1, pointed out periodically by the NCTM Correlations icon, and reflected in spirit throughout the book. On MyEducationLab (www.myeducationlab.com), you will find a copy of the appendix to *Principles and Standards* listing all of the content standards and goals for each of the grade bands (pre-K–2, 3–5, 6–8, and 9–12). You will also find the six Standards for Teaching Mathematics from *Professional Standards for Teaching Mathematics*.

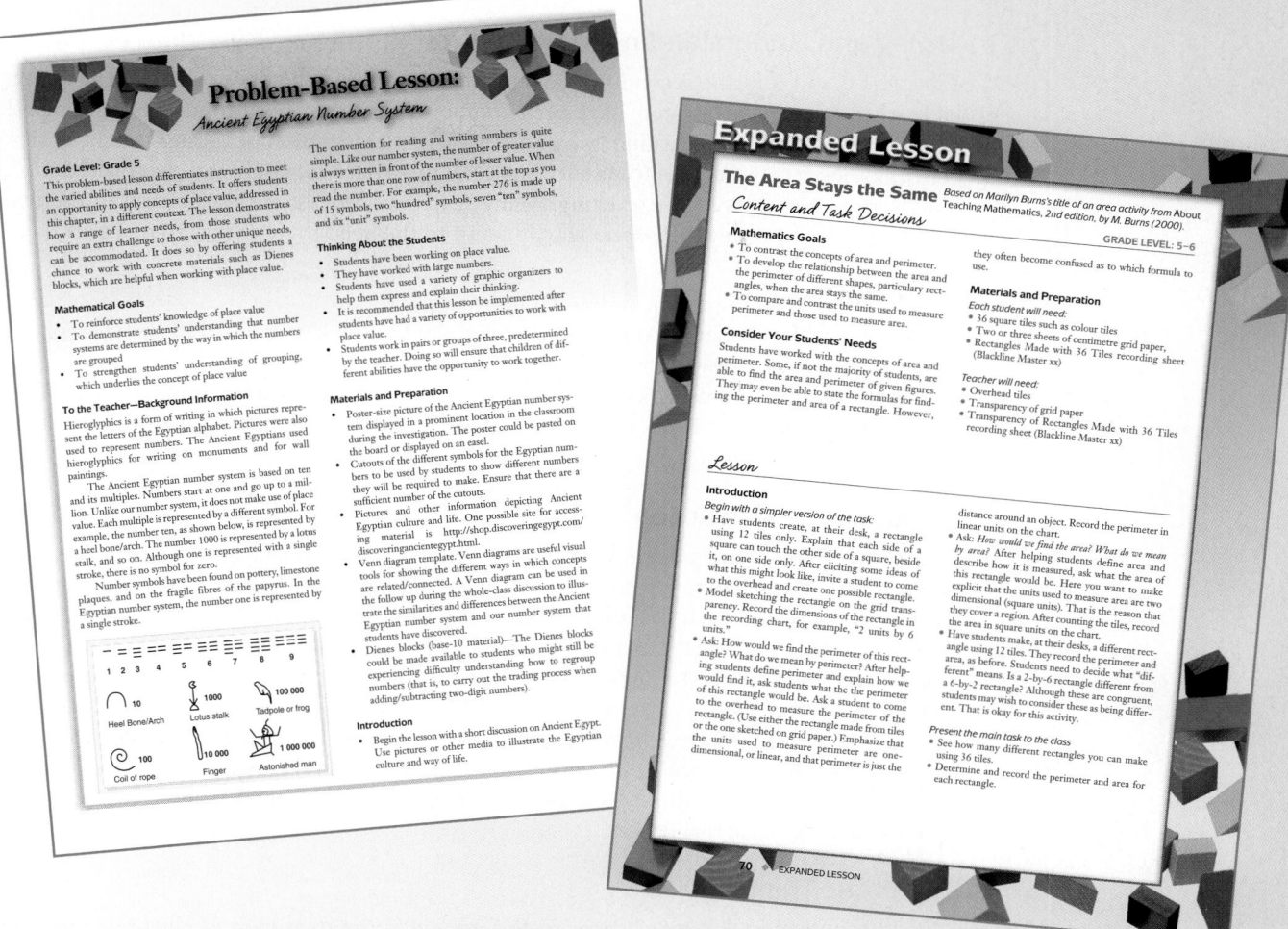

▲ Problem-Based Lessons and Expanded Lessons

Detailed lesson plans can be found in various places in this text.

Problem-Based Lessons can be found in eight of the content chapters. Each of these lessons is designed to show you how a range of learner needs can be met in your classroom. These lessons, which are connected to real-life topics of interest, include a grade-level designation, a list of mathematical goals, and some assessment ideas, in addition to the materials, preparation, and lesson specifics.

As well, two detailed lesson plans that demonstrate how to plan a problem-based lesson, derived from activities in this text have been converted to a similar Expanded Lesson that can be found on MyEducationLab. The Expanded Lessons follow the lesson structure described in Chapter 4. They include mathematical goals, notes on preparation, specific student expectations, notes for assessment, and Blackline Masters, when needed.

CHANGES IN THIS EDITION

Some changes are more obvious, such as the new and engaging photographs spread throughout the text; for others, you have to look more closely. No chapter was left untouched. All features from the second Canadian edition remain, although some have been relocated or altered in format. More books by Canadian authors are listed in the Literature Connections, which are now found at the end of chapters in Section II with the other resources. As well, there is an increased number of Canadian Internet sites listed in the Online Resources sections at the end of chapters. Let us highlight the significant changes in the third Canadian edition.

Doing and Understanding Mathematics

Chapters 2 and 3 in the second Canadian edition separated the doing and understanding of mathematics; these chapters have been combined for this new edition. Now Chapter 2 connects the theories of learning "why do" to the implementation of "doing" mathematics. The theories of constructivism and socio-cultural theory are concisely and clearly described, followed by implications for teaching. Many reviewers requested this melding of the two chapters, and the resulting chapter should point to the need to tie theory to practice.

Problem Solving

Although problem solving is integrated throughout the book, you will find a new emphasis on teaching problem solving with a focus on the work of George Polya. Since we recognize that many teachers are using a curriculum that may not include the same focus on problem solving as espoused in the book, there is an excellent section on how to adapt textbooks to promote problem solving.

Planning for Instruction

Since every lesson should begin with an introduction in which the teacher sets the stage for the learning; a development phase, in which the teacher develops the concepts(s); then a follow-up phase, in which the teacher follows up with reinforcement of the concept(s), the three-phase lesson format has been renamed as Introduction, Development, and Follow Up, to accommodate these phases. This is first introduced in Chapter 3 and discussed in detail in Chapter 4.

Chapter 4, *Planning in the Problem-Based Classroom*, immediately follows with the description of teaching from a student-centred, problem-based perspective. In this chapter, the discussion regarding the steps in planning the three phases of a lesson makes a connection to planning an actual lesson.

Algebraic Thinking

One of the most important changes in this edition is the treatment of algebraic thinking in Chapter 14, *Algebraic Thinking: Generalizations, Patterns, and Functions*. Although revised in the last edition, the chapter is now reorganized around five critical themes of algebraic thinking: generalization from arithmetic and from patterns in all of mathematics, meaningful use of symbols, study of structure in the number system, study of patterns and functions, and the process of mathematical modelling, which integrates the first four. In addition, there is increased attention to developing meaningful contexts for algebraic thinking across grades Pre-K–8, including connections to other subject areas.

Technology

Not surprisingly, there have been many changes in the world of technology since the last edition and it is, and will continue to be, challenging to keep up. In this edition, the definition of technology is more inclusive, including digital tools, collaborative authoring tools, podcasts, and dynamic software. This change is in light of current thinking about Technological Pedagogical Content Knowledge, which reflects the need to infuse technology in every lesson. In Chapter 7, there are guidelines on how to select and evaluate Internet resources, something that readers and reviewers requested. There is a distinct effort throughout the book to focus on software that can be accessed online for free.

Diversity

Chapter 6, *Teaching Mathematics Equitably to All Children*, has been revamped to reflect the diversity of the Canadian school population and the need to teach mathematics equitably to all. It includes discussion about the concept of Universal Design for Learning (UDL), differentiated instruction, teaching to the culturally and linguistically diverse, diverse learning, and strategies for meeting the learning needs of Aboriginal children.

Geometry

In this edition, each of the three van Hiele levels is reflected *within* each geometry strand (shapes and properties, location, transformations, and visualization). The development of the van Hiele theory is highlighted by three activities from the shapes and properties strand. These are now prominently located at the beginning of the chapter.

Other Changes

Although every chapter saw some change, a few specific areas may be worth noting.

- Chapter 5 now includes new perspectives on assessment. The work of Canadian researchers Lorna Earl and Ann Davies on assessment for learning, as learning, and of learning complements *NCTM's Assessment Standards for School Mathematics*.

- Chapter 10, *Helping Children Master the Basic Facts*, has been reorganized to place more emphasis on the Make 10 strategy, which research indicates is most effective. In addition, a new section on what to do and what not to do provides more guidance to teachers about how to implement these strategies.

SUPPLEMENTS

Instructor Supplements

Instructor's Manual

The *Instructor's Manual* for the third Canadian edition includes a wealth of resources designed to help instructors teach the course, along with chapter notes, activity suggestions, suggested essay test questions, and instructor transparency masters.

CourseSmart for Instructors

CourseSmart goes beyond traditional expectations—providing instant, online access to the textbooks and course materials you need at a lower cost for students. And even as students save money, you can save time and hassle with a digital eTextbook that allows you to search for the most relevant content at the very moment you need it. Whether it's evaluating textbooks or creating lecture notes to help students with difficult concepts, CourseSmart can make life a little easier. See how when you visit www.coursesmart.com/instructors.

Student Supplements

MyEducationLab

MyEducationLab (www.myeducationlab.com) will help you improve your understanding of the concepts taught in this textbook and in your course. This online tool includes videos of real classroom experiences, sample lesson plans, simulations, case studies, and links to important educational and teaching Web sites that will help you make the transition from student to teacher. As you study in your course and with this textbook, please follow along in *MyEducationLab*. Use it! Explore it! And improve your knowledge and your grade!

CourseSmart for Students

CourseSmart goes beyond traditional expectations—providing instant, online access to the textbooks and course materials you need at an average savings of 50%. With instant access from any computer and the ability to search your text, you'll find the content you need quickly, no matter where you are. And with online tools like highlighting and note-taking, you can save time and study efficiently. See all the benefits at www.coursesmart.com/students.

ACKNOWLEDGMENTS FROM THE CANADIAN AUTHOR

I would first like to acknowledge Agnes Kieltyka, a doctoral student at the Ontario Institute for Studies in Education at the University of Toronto, a person to whom I am deeply grateful. She has been a tireless and devoted worker (during this edition and the previous one) who was always there to assist, at the drop of a hat. Not only is she responsible for conducting much of the research that went into supporting the content in this Canadian edition, she offered much assistance with chapter 6, an area in which her doctoral studies are focused.

I would also like to thank Rita Cohen, a mathematics coach with the Toronto District School Board who once again assisted with the development of the problem-based lessons for this third Canadian edition. Finally, and most importantly, I would like to thank my husband, Marshall, who is always there to support me with his kind nature, good sense of humour, and great wit.

In preparing this third Canadian edition, the following educators were among those who offered helpful and insightful comments on the previous Canadian edition and/or on the manuscript for the third edition: Jerry Ameis, University of Winnipeg; Norma Fraser, Thomson Rivers University; Audrey Hodgson-Ward, University of Alberta; Wendy Klassen, University of British Columbia, Okanagan; Minnie Liu, Simon Fraser University; Ann McLennan, Mount Royal College; and Leslie Waddington, University of the Fraser Valley.

Chapter 1
Teaching Mathematics in the 21st Century

In this changing world, those who understand and can do mathematics will have significantly enhanced opportunities and options for shaping their futures. Mathematical competence opens doors to productive futures. A lack of mathematical competence keeps those doors closed.... All students should have the opportunity and the support necessary to learn significant mathematics with depth and understanding. There is no conflict between equity and excellence.

NCTM (2000, p. 50)

Someday soon you will find yourself in front of a class of students, or perhaps you are already teaching. What general ideas will guide the way you will teach mathematics to prepare students for the demands of the new knowledge-based economy of the 21st century? What building blocks for success will you provide for students so they become independent thinkers and effective problem solvers? This book will provide you with the necessary learning to help you achieve these goals. As well, it will help you become comfortable with the mathematics of the K–8 curriculum for your provincial or territorial jurisdiction. You will also learn about research-based strategies for helping children come to know mathematics and be confident in their ability to do mathematics. Your knowledge of mathematics and how students learn mathematics is the most important tool you can acquire to be an effective teacher of mathematics. Be aware, though, that outside influences and research will have a strong impact on your teaching of mathematics in the classroom.

For at least two decades, mathematics education has been undergoing slow but steady change. The impetus for the change, in both the content of school mathematics and the way mathematics is best taught, can be traced to a variety of sources, including knowledge gained from research. One significant factor that has played a role in effecting this change is the professional leadership of the National Council of Teachers of Mathematics (NCTM), a U.S.-based organization of teachers and mathematics educators from both the United States and Canada. Another factor is public pressure to change mathematics education, due, in large part, to Canadian students' performance in various international studies. In reaction to these forces, provincial and territorial jurisdictions are pressing for higher levels of achievement, more testing, and increased teacher accountability. The reform agendas of the NCTM and the public sector seem to push teachers in different directions. Although high expectations for students are important, testing alone is not an appropriate answer to improved student learning. The NCTM believes that "Learning mathematics is maximized when teachers focus on mathematical thinking and reasoning" (www.nctm.org). The views of the NCTM are clearly reflected in the ideas discussed in this book.

As you prepare to help children learn mathematics, it is important to have some perspective on the forces that influence change in the mathematics classroom. This chapter addresses the leadership that the NCTM, provincial and territorial ministries, and consortia provide for mathematics education as well as other major pressures on mathematics education.

Ultimately, it is you, the teacher, who will shape mathematics for the children you teach. Your beliefs about what it means to know and do mathematics and how children come to make sense of mathematics will have a significant impact on how you approach instruction. These beliefs will undoubtedly be affected, directly or indirectly, by the strong influences on mathematics education that you will read about in this chapter.

The Leadership of NCTM

In April 2000, the National Council of Teachers of Mathematics released *Principles and Standards for School Mathematics*, an update of its original standards document released 11 years earlier in 1989. With this most important document, the Council continues to guide a revolutionary reform movement in mathematics education, not just in the United States and Canada, but throughout the world.

The momentum for reform in mathematics education began in the early 1980s. Educators were responding to a "back to basics" movement that emphasized "reading, writing, and arithmetic." As a result, problem solving became an important strand in the mathematics curriculum. The work of Piaget and other developmental psychologists helped to focus research on how children can best learn mathematics.

This momentum came to a head in 1989, when the NCTM published *Curriculum and Evaluation Standards for School Mathematics*, and the standards movement or reform era in mathematics began. It continues today. No other document has ever had such an enormous effect on school mathematics or on any other area of the curriculum. In 1991, the NCTM published *Professional Standards for Teaching Mathematics*. *Professional Standards* and the recent revision of *Mathematics Teaching Today* articulate a vision of teaching mathematics and build on the notion, found in the *Curriculum Standards*, that significant mathematics is a vision for all children, not just a few. The NCTM completed the package with *Assessment Standards for School Mathematics* in 1995. *Assessment Standards* shows clearly the necessity for integrating assessment with instruction. It outlines the key role that assessment plays in implementing change. From 1989 to 2000, these three documents guided the reform movement in mathematics education, directly leading, in 2000, to *Principles and Standards for School Mathematics*. *Principles and Standards*, which is an update of all three of these earlier standards documents, further articulates the ideas, processes, and content that should be emphasized in pre-K through grade 12 classrooms and programs.

Much progress has been made in mathematics instruction. However, there is still work to be done in order for the vision of *Standards* to be realized. The sustained hard work of teachers and mathematics educators will help move us forward in order to achieve these goals. In the following section, we discuss *Principles and Standards*, as well as other documents and reports, because their message is critical to your work as a mathematics teacher.

Principles and Standards for School Mathematics

Principles and Standards for School Mathematics (2000) is designed to provide guidance and direction for teachers and other leaders in mathematics education from pre-K to grade 12. It has played a significant role in shaping the philosophy and outcomes of such documents as the *Western and Northern Canadian Protocol Common Curriculum Frameworks for K–12 Mathematics* (www.wncp.ca), *Foundations for the Atlantic Canada Mathematics Curriculum*, and other provincial and territorial curricula. Because it is important that teachers read and reflect on the *Standards* document (as well as their own provincial and territorial documents), the next few pages will provide you with an idea of what you will find there.

The Six Principles

One of the most important features of *Principles and Standards for School Mathematics* is the articulation of six principles fundamental to high-quality mathematics education:

- Equity
- Curriculum
- Teaching
- Learning
- Assessment
- Technology

According to *Principles and Standards*, these principles must be "deeply intertwined with school mathematics programs" (NCTM, 2000, p. 12). The principles make it clear that excellence in mathematics education involves much more than simply listing content objectives.

The Equity Principle

Excellence in mathematics education requires equity—high expectations and strong support for all students.

(NCTM, 2000, p. 12)

The strong message of the Equity Principle is high expectations for all students. All students must have the opportunity and adequate support to learn mathematics "regardless of personal characteristics, backgrounds, or physical challenges" (p. 12). The message of high expectations for all is intertwined with every other principle and the document as a whole.

The Curriculum Principle

A curriculum is more than a collection of activities: it must be coherent, focused on important mathematics, and well articulated across the grades.

(NCTM, 2000, p. 14)

Coherence speaks to the importance of building instruction around "big ideas" both in the curriculum and in daily classroom instruction. Students must be helped to see that mathematics is an integrated whole, not a collection of isolated bits and pieces.

Mathematical ideas are "important" if they help in the development of other ideas, link ideas one to another, or serve to illustrate the discipline of mathematics as a human endeavour.

The Teaching Principle

Effective mathematics teaching requires understanding what students know and need to learn and then challenging and supporting them to learn it well.

(NCTM, 2000, p. 16)

What students learn about mathematics depends almost entirely on the experiences that teachers provide every day in the classroom. To provide high-quality mathematics education, teachers must (1) understand deeply the mathematics they are teaching; (2) understand how children learn mathematics, including having a keen awareness of the individual mathematical development of their own students; and (3) select instructional tasks and strategies that will enhance learning. "Teachers' actions are what encourage students to think, question, solve problems, and discuss their ideas, strategies, and solutions" (p. 18).

The Learning Principle

Students must learn mathematics with understanding, actively building new knowledge from experience and prior knowledge.

(NCTM, 2000, p. 20)

This principle is based on two fundamental ideas. First, learning mathematics with understanding is essential. Mathematics today requires not only computational skills, but also the ability to think and reason mathematically in order to solve the new problems and learn the new ideas that students will face in the future.

Second, the principle states quite clearly that students *can* learn mathematics with understanding. Learning is enhanced in classrooms where students are required to evaluate their own ideas and those of others, are encouraged to make mathematical conjectures and test them, and develop their reasoning skills.

The Assessment Principle

Assessment should support the learning of important mathematics and furnish useful information to both teachers and students.

(NCTM, 2000, p. 22)

In the authors' words, "Assessment should not merely be done *to* students; rather, it should also be done *for* students, to guide and enhance their learning" (p. 22). Ongoing assessment conveys to students what mathematics concepts are important. Assessment that includes ongoing observation and student interaction encourages students to articulate and, thus, clarify their ideas. Feedback from daily assessment helps students establish goals and become more independent learners.

Assessment should also be a major factor in making instructional decisions. By continuously gathering information about student growth and understanding, teachers are able to make better daily decisions that support student learning. For assessment to be effective, teachers must use a variety of assessment techniques, have a deep understanding of their mathematical goals, and have a good idea of how their students may be thinking about the mathematics that is being developed.

The Technology Principle

Technology is essential in teaching and learning mathematics; it influences the mathematics that is taught and enhances students' learning.

(NCTM, 2000, p. 24)

Calculators, computers, and other technologies should be seen as essential tools for doing and learning mathematics in the classroom. Technology permits students to focus on mathematical ideas, to reason, and to solve problems in ways that are often impossible without these tools. Technology enhances the learning of mathematics by allowing for increased exploration and enhanced representation of ideas. It extends the range of problems that can be accessed. It also aids special needs students who might need assistance with certain procedures while working with important mathematical concepts.

The Five Content Standards

Principles and Standards includes four grade bands: pre-K–2, 3–5, 6–8, and 9–12. The new emphasis on preschool recognizes the need to highlight the critical years before children enter kindergarten. Rather than having a different set of mathematical topics for each grade band, the following are a common set of content standards or strands of mathematics that appear throughout the grades:

- Number and Operations
- Algebra
- Geometry
- Measurement
- Data Analysis and Probability

Each content standard includes a small set of goals that are applicable to all grade bands. Each grade-band chapter provides specific expectations for what students should know. These grade-band expectations are listed concisely in the appendix to the *Standards* and in Appendix A of this book.

Although the same five content standards apply across all grades, you should not infer that each strand has equal weight or emphasis in every grade band. Number and Operations is the largest strand from pre-K to grade 5. It continues to be important in the middle grades, with a lesser emphasis in grades 9–12. That same emphasis is reflected in this book, with Chapters 8 to 13 and 15 to 18 addressing content found in the Number and Operations standard.

Algebra is clearly intended as a strand for all grades. This was almost certainly not the case when you were in school. Today, most provincial and territorial school districts include algebra objectives at every level of the curriculum. In this book, Chapter 14 addresses this strand.

Note that Geometry and Measurement are separate strands, suggesting the unique importance of each of these two areas to the elementary school curriculum.

The Five Process Standards

Following the five content standards, *Principles and Standards* lists five process standards:

- Problem Solving
- Reasoning and Proof
- Communication
- Connections
- Representation

The process standards refer to the mathematical processes through which students should acquire and use mathematical knowledge. The statement of the five process standards can be found in Table 1.1.

These five processes should not be regarded as separate content or strands in the mathematics curriculum. Rather, they direct the methods or processes of doing all mathematics. For this reason, they should be viewed as integral components of all mathematics learning and teaching.

To teach in a way that reflects these process standards is one of the best definitions of what it means to teach "according to the *Standards*."

The **Problem Solving** standard clearly views problem solving as the vehicle through which children develop mathematical ideas. Learning and doing mathematics *as you solve problems* is probably the most significant difference in the *Standards* approach compared to previous methodologies.

If problem solving is the focus of mathematics, the **Reasoning and Proof** standard emphasizes the logical thinking that helps us decide if and why our answers make sense. Students need to develop the habit of providing a rationale as an integral part of every answer. It is essential for students to learn the value of justifying ideas through logical arguments.

The **Communication** standard points to the importance of being able to talk about, write about, describe, and explain mathematical ideas. Learning to communicate in mathematics fosters interaction and exploration of ideas in the classroom as students learn in an active, verbal environment. No better way exists for wrestling with an idea than to attempt to articulate it to others.

The **Connections** standard has two separate thrusts. First, it refers to connections within and among mathematical ideas. For example, fractional parts of a whole are connected to concepts of decimals and percents. Students need opportunities to see how mathematical ideas build on one another in a useful network of connected ideas.

Table 1.1

The Five Process Standards from *Principles and Standards for School Mathematics*	
Problem Solving Standard Instructional programs from prekindergarten through grade 12 should enable all students to—	· Build new mathematical knowledge through problem solving · Solve problems that arise in mathematics and in other contexts · Apply and adapt a variety of appropriate strategies to solve problems · Monitor and reflect on the process of mathematical problem solving
Reasoning and Proof Standard Instructional programs from prekindergarten through grade 12 should enable all students to—	· Recognize reasoning and proof as fundamental aspects of mathematics · Make and investigate mathematical conjectures · Develop and evaluate mathematical arguments and proofs · Select and use various types of reasoning and methods of proof
Communication Standard Instructional programs from prekindergarten through grade 12 should enable all students to—	· Organize and consolidate their mathematical thinking through communication · Communicate their mathematical thinking coherently and clearly to peers, teachers, and others · Analyze and evaluate the mathematical thinking and strategies of others · Use the language of mathematics to express mathematical ideas precisely
Connections Standard Instructional programs from prekindergarten through grade 12 should enable all students to—	· Recognize and use connections among mathematical ideas · Understand how mathematical ideas interconnect and build on one another to produce a coherent whole · Recognize and apply mathematics in contexts outside of mathematics
Representation Standard Instructional programs from prekindergarten through grade 12 should enable all students to—	· Create and use representations to organize, record, and communicate mathematical ideas · Select, apply, and translate among mathematical representations to solve problems · Use representations to model and interpret physical, social, and mathematical phenomena

Second, mathematics should be connected to the real world and to other disciplines. Children should see that mathematics plays a significant role in art, science, and social studies. This belief suggests that mathematics should frequently be integrated with other discipline areas and that applications of mathematics in the real world should be explored.

The **Representation** standard emphasizes the use of symbols, charts, graphs, manipulatives, and diagrams as powerful methods for expressing mathematical ideas and relationships. Students need to understand that symbolism in mathematics, along with visual aids such as charts and graphs, are ways of communicating mathematical ideas to other people. Moving from one representation to another is an important way to add depth of understanding to a newly formed idea.

 Throughout this book, this icon will alert you to specific information in *Principles and Standards* that relates to the information you are reading. However, these notes and the brief descriptions you just read should not be a substitute for reading the *Standards* documents. Members of the NCTM have online access to the complete *Principles and Standards* document, as well as to the previous three *Standards* documents. Non-members can sign up for 120 days of free access to the *Principles and Standards* at www.nctm.org. The Web site also contains a number of free applets (referred to as "E-examples"), which are interactive tools for learning about mathematical concepts.

The *Professional Standards for Teaching Mathematics* and *Mathematics Teaching Today*

Although *Principles and Standards* incorporates principles of teaching and assessment, the emphasis is on curriculum. In contrast, *Professional Standards for Teaching Mathematics* (1991) and the second edition, *Mathematics Teaching Today* (2007), focus on teaching. Through detailed classroom stories (vignettes) of real teachers, the document articulates the careful reflective work that must go into the teaching of mathematics.

Shifts in Classroom Environment

The introduction to *Mathematics Teaching Today* lists six major shifts in the environment of the mathematics classroom that are necessary to allow students to develop mathematical understanding. These are:

- Communities that offer an equal opportunity to learn to all students

- A balanced focus on conceptual understanding, as well as on procedural fluency
- Active student engagement in problem solving, reasoning, communicating, making connections, and using multiple representations
- Well-equipped learning centres in which technology is used to enhance understanding
- Incorporation of multiple assessments that are aligned with instructional goals and practices
- Mathematics authority that lies within the power of sound reasoning and mathematical integrity (NCTM, 2007, p. 7).

The Teaching Standards

Mathematics Teaching Today contains chapters on (1) teaching and learning; (2) observation, supervision, and improvement of mathematics teaching; (3) education and continued professional growth of teachers; (4) working together to achieve the vision; and (5) questions for the reflective practitioner. In the teaching and learning section there are seven mathematical teaching standards:

1. Knowledge of Mathematics and General Pedagogy
2. Knowledge of Students' Mathematical Learning
3. Worthwhile Mathematical Tasks
4. Learning Environment
5. Discourse
6. Reflection on Student Learning
7. Reflection on Teaching Practice

Mathematics Teaching Today (or its predecessor) is an excellent resource to help you envision your role as a teacher in creating a classroom that supports *Principles and Standards*.

Influences and Pressures on Mathematics Teaching

The NCTM has provided the major leadership and vision for reform in mathematics education. However, no single factor controls the direction of change. National and international comparisons of student performance continue to make headlines and provoke public opinion, pressuring school boards and districts to ensure that their schools are achieving "above average" marks. Results of provincial and territorial testing add to this situation. The impact of these pressures on schools and ultimately on teachers often leads to instruction that is different from that envisioned in the NCTM *Standards*. The strong influence of the textbook and other teacher materials not necessarily aligned with provincial and territorial standards—and the pressure on teachers to cover the curriculum—also affect the direction of change.

National and International Studies

Large-scale studies that tell the Canadian public how the nation's children are doing in mathematics receive a lot of attention. They influence political decisions as well as provide useful data for mathematics education researchers. Two such studies are the Pan-Canadian Assessment Program (PCAP) (formerly the School Achievement Indicators Program), and the Trends in International Mathematics and Science Study (TIMSS).

The Pan-Canadian Assessment Program (PCAP) The Pan-Canadian Assessment Program (PCAP), formerly the School Achievement Indicators Program (SAIP), is a project of the Council of Ministers of Education, Canada (CMEC) (www.cmec.ca). This cyclical program of pan-Canadian assessments of student achievements in reading, science, and mathematics informs Canadians on how well their education systems are meeting the needs of students and society. Because school programs in the various subject areas from one part of Canada to the other differ, and even though students learn many similar skills, making comparisons of results from these programs is complex. Nevertheless, PCAP assessments will help determine whether students across the country are reaching similar levels of performance in these subject areas, at the same age. The most recent PCAP initiative, conducted in 2007, assessed the reading, mathematics, and science skills of 13- to 15-year-old students. Over 30 000 randomly selected students, from the ten provinces and the Yukon, participated. The results, which are made available to participating schools, students, parents, and the public, will give ministers of education a basis for examining their curricula and other aspects of their school systems.

Results from the 2007 assessment, which reflects the principles of the NCTM *Standards*, indicated that the mean score for Quebec students in mathematics was significantly higher than the average mean score for Canadian students, overall. For Ontario and Alberta students, the mean score was not significantly different from the mean score for Canadian students overall. Results for the other provinces and the Yukon indicate that they were below the mean score for Canadian students.

Trends in International Mathematics and Science Study (TIMSS) The Trends in International Mathematics and Science Study (TIMSS) is the largest and most ambitious study of mathematics and science education ever conducted. Working on a four-year cycle, the first assessment was administered in 1995, with the most current one held in 2007. The study was designed to compare and contrast the teaching and learning of mathematics and science at the elementary and secondary school levels around the world, so that educators might learn more about the kinds of exemplary practices and curricula that contribute to high levels of student achievement. Data are based on the achievement of students in grades 4, 8, and 12.

Canada was one of 41 participating countries in the first cycle of assessment, in 1995. More recently, Canadian participation has declined. In 2003, only Ontario and Quebec participated. The last cycle of assessment, in 2007, was limited to British Columbia, Alberta, Ontario, and Quebec.

In the 2007 assessments, where approximately 60 countries participated, the average grade 4 scale scores ranged from a low of 224 (Yemen) to a high of 607 (Hong Kong). Hong Kong, Singapore, Taipei, and Japan were the top-performing jurisdictions, which showed significantly better achievement than all other jurisdictions. Thirteen jurisdictions had an average scale score higher than those of Ontario, Quebec, British Columbia, and Alberta. Nineteen were lower.

The average grade 8 scale scores ranged from a low of 307 (Qatar) to a high of 598 (Taipei). The top-performing jurisdictions were Taipei, Korea, and Singapore, with significantly better achievement than all other jurisdictions. Although Quebec ranked among the top-performing jurisdictions with a score of 528, Ontario and British Columbia did not. Six jurisdictions had a higher average scale score than these two provinces.

As there is no federal ministry of education, and educational decision making rests with individual provinces, Canadian responses to TIMSS findings vary. For example, in Ontario, the publication of results has offered some direction for the process of curriculum development. In fact, instructional materials were developed as a direct outcome of TIMSS. In British Columbia, results of the study have had an impact on the makeup of British Columbia's mathematics assessment. For Alberta, TIMSS results have helped to reinforce reform (Robitaille, Beaton, & Plomp, 2000).

Responses to TIMSS in the United States have been vigorous and varied. One of the most interesting components of the 1999 study was the inclusion of a video study conducted in grade 8 classrooms in the United States, Australia, and five of the highest-achieving countries. The results indicated that teaching is a cultural activity and the differences for countries were often striking, despite many similarities. In all countries, problems or tasks were often used to begin a lesson. However, as a lesson progressed, the way these problems were handled in the United States was in stark contrast to the ways used in the high-achieving countries. At least in U.S. grade 8 classrooms, it is safe to say that teachers focus on having students follow directions and rules. In high-achieving countries, there is a greater focus on conceptual understanding and true problem solving. Teaching in high-achieving countries more closely resembles the recommendations of the NCTM *Standards* than does the teaching in the United States.

Provincial Assessment Programs

Province-wide testing programs are another means of evaluating Canadian students' knowledge of curriculum. Unlike national and international assessments, these tests generally provide information regarding the achievement of individual students. In a majority of provinces, testing is generally carried out at two key transitional stages in elementary school. In Ontario and Alberta, testing is carried out at grades 3 and 6. In Manitoba, there is one assessment in grade 3 and a middle years assessment in grade 7. In British Columbia, students write provincial tests in numeracy in grades 4 and 7. Unlike the former, mathematical literacy was recently assessed (June 2008) only in grade 3, in Nova Scotia.

Classroom teachers generally play an important role in the development of these programs. The direct link of these tests with regional curriculum documents, as well as public reporting of the test scores, account for their strong influence on school board policy and instructional decision making. The focus on assessment and accountability explains the popularity of provincial and territorial testing and the pressure on teachers to ensure favourable test results.

Curriculum

Mathematics curricula may differ from one part of the country to another, yet a high degree of congruency exists in many of the different areas. Most jurisdictions in Canada regularly renew their curricula or are currently involved in the process of doing so. Although renewal initiatives are designed with the spirit of reform in mind, outcomes do not always reflect intentions. The extensive list of what teachers are expected to cover in class often means that they are pressured to move quickly through the curriculum, detracting from a meaningful approach to instruction. Student learning is focused more on procedures than on conceptual understanding. Consequently, the need to meet test expectations can be another deterrent.

The situation is further complicated by the fact that, in most classrooms, the textbook is the single most influential factor in determining the *what, when, and how* of actual *teaching*. Textbooks are developed by major publishing companies, based on market research. Though they vary in some ways, they share characteristics in common. The textbooks reflect the publishers' efforts to cover a broad range of topics in order to meet the needs of every province's and territory's curriculum. This approach results in a textbook with many topics that do not necessarily fit with a particular province's or territory's curriculum. Because teachers often rely on the textbook as their curriculum and follow it so lessons are covered in a one-a-day fashion, developing students' deep understanding of concepts often goes by the wayside.

Because of the way that textbooks influence teaching practice, teachers need to be selective about how they use them. When planning instruction, it is important to always begin with your regional curriculum document; then consult the textbook or textbooks along with other teacher-based resources to support your objectives for students' learning. There are some excellent materials that promote teaching and learning from a reform-based perspective.

A Changing World Economy

What happens in education today will affect the lives of students and communities for decades to come. Thomas Friedman points out in his book *The World Is Flat* (2007) that people need to have lasting skills that will survive the ever-changing landscape of available jobs. He suggests that if people can fit into several of the broad categories he defines then they will not be challenged by a shifting job market. One of these safety-ensuring categories in his analysis is "math lovers." Friedman points out that in a world that is digitized and surrounded by algorithms, the math lover will always have opportunities and options. It becomes the job of the teacher to develop this passion in students. As Lynn Arthur Steen, a well-known mathematician and educator, states, "As information becomes ever more quantitative and as society relies increasingly on computers and the data they produce, an innumerate citizen today is as vulnerable as the illiterate peasant of Gutenberg's time" (1997, p. xv).

The changing world influences what should be taught in K–8 mathematics classrooms. As we prepare elementary students for the future, we know that there are few jobs where people do just simple computation. No doubt, there will be work that requires interpreting complex data, designing algorithms to make predictions, and approaching new problems in a variety of ways.

An Invitation to Learn and Grow

The mathematics education described in the NCTM *Standards* may not be the same as the mathematics and the mathematics teaching you experienced in kindergarten through grade 8. Along the way, you may have had some excellent teachers who really did reflect the current spirit of reform. You may have benefited from a teacher who taught in this way. But for the most part, the goals of the reform movement at the end of the second decade have not yet been realized in the large majority of school boards and districts in North America.

As a practising or prospective teacher facing the challenge of teaching from a reform perspective, this book may require you to confront some of your personal beliefs—

about what it means to *do mathematics*, how one goes about *learning mathematics*, how to *teach mathematics through problem solving*, and what it means to *assess mathematics* integrated with instruction. The next four chapters of this book will help you develop these foundational ideas for teaching. Chapters 6 and 7 discuss other topics that influence mathematics teaching across all strands and grade levels: the equitable teaching of all children in mathematics and the role of technology.

Section II of the book examines the teaching and learning of specific topics in mathematics. The chapters in the second section are designed not only as text material but also as a source of instructional tasks for your future or current teaching.

Teaching mathematics can be an exciting adventure. Perhaps the most exciting part is that you will grow and learn along with your students. Enjoy the journey!

Reflections on Chapter **1**

Writing to Learn

At the end of each chapter of this book, you will find a series of questions under this heading. The questions are designed to help you reflect on the most important ideas of the chapter. Writing (or talking aloud with a peer) is an excellent way to explore new ideas and incorporate them into your own knowledge base. The writing (or discussion) will help make the ideas your own. After you have written your responses in your own words, compare what you have written with what is written in the book. Make changes, if necessary, or discuss differences with your instructor.

1. What are the five content strands (standards) defined by *Principles and Standards*?
2. Among the ideas in *Mathematics Teaching Today* are six shifts in the classroom environment. Examine these six shifts, and describe in a few sentences what aspects of each shift seem most significant to you.
3. What are some of the implications of the results of the Pan-Canadian Assessment Program (PCAP) data?
4. Describe results derived from Trends in International Mathematics and Science Study (TIMSS) data. What are the implications?
5. Describe the influence of province-wide assessment on classroom mathematics education.

For Discussion and Exploration

1. In recent years, the outcry for "basics" was again being heard from a loud and very political public. The debate between reform and the basics is both important and interesting. For an engaging discussion of the reform movement in light of the "back to basics" outcry, read one or more of the first five articles in the February 1999 edition of the *Phi Delta Kappan*. Where do you stand on the issue of reform versus the basics?
2. Examine a conventional textbook for a grade level of your choice. If possible, use a teacher's edition. Turn through the pages of any chapter and look for signs of the five process standards. To what extent are children who are being taught from this book likely to be doing and learning mathematics in ways described by those processes? What might you do to change the general approach of this text, if necessary?
3. Examine your regional curriculum document to see how it reflects the NCTM vision of reform, especially in regard to the five process standards. Discuss whether or not it achieves this goal.

Resources for Chapter 1

Recommendations for Further Reading

Articles

Hoffman, L., & Brahier, D. (2008). Improving the planning and teaching of mathematics by reflecting on research. *Mathematics Teaching in the Middle School, 13* (7), 412–417.

This article addresses how these teachers' philosophies and beliefs influenced their mathematics instruction. Using TIMSS and NAEP studies as a foundation, the authors talk about posing higher-level problems, asking thought-provoking questions, facing students' frustrations, and using mistakes to enhance understanding of concepts. They pose a set of reflective questions that are good for self-assessment or discussion with peers.

Books

Ferrini-Mundy, J. (2000). The standards movement in mathematics education: Reflections and hopes. In M. J. Burke (Ed.), *Learning mathematics for a new century* (pp. 37–50). Reston, VA: National Council of Teachers of Mathematics.

In this chapter, written before the Standards *was released, the author shares her unique and very well-informed view of this important publication, how it came to be, the impact of the earlier document, the political climate in which the* Standards *was released, and the intentions that the NCTM had for the document. This article will provide an understanding of the* Standards *that is impossible to get from the document itself.*

Hiebert, J. (2003). What research says about the NCTM standards. In J. Kilpatrick, W. G. Martin, & D. Schifter (Eds.), *A research companion to Principles and Standards for School Mathematics* (pp. 5–23). Reston, VA: National Council of Teachers of Mathematics.

This chapter provides one of the best perspectives on what we have learned since the Standards *was released. It also offers some perspective into typical U.S. classrooms and offers contrasts between conventional mathematics programs and those referred to as "standards-based."*

National Research Council (2001). *Adding it up: Helping children learn mathematics.* J. Kilpatrick, J. Swaffor, & B. Findell (Eds.). Mathematics Learning Study Committee, Center for Education, Division of Behavioral and Social Sciences and Education. Washington, DC: National Academy Press.

This book is the effort of a select committee representing mathematics educators, mathematicians, school administrators, and industry. A hallmark of this book is the formulation of five strands of "mathematical proficiency": conceptual understanding, procedural fluency, strategic competence, adaptive reasoning, and productive disposition. Educators and policy makers will cite this book for many years to come.

Online Resources

Illuminations
http://illuminations.nctm.org

A companion Web site to NCTM, sponsored by NCTM and Marcopolo. Provides lessons, interactive applets, and links to Web sites for learning and teaching mathematics.

Key Issues in Math
www.mathforum.org/social/index.html

Part of the Math Forum at Drexel University, this page lists numerous questions concerning issues in mathematics education with answers supplied by experts in short articles or excerpts.

National Council of Teachers of Mathematics
www.nctm.org

Here you can find out all about NCTM, its belief statements, and positions on important topics. Also find an overview of *Principles and Standards* and free access to interactive applets (see Standards—Electronics), membership and conference information, publications catalogue, links to related sites, and much more. Members have access to even more information.

Pan-Canadian Assessment Program (PCAP)
(formerly SAIP)
www.cmec.ca/pcap/index.stm

Here you will be able to find out more about national assessments, who the Council of Ministers of Education, Canada, are, and their policy and projects.

TIMSS (Trends in International Mathematics and Science Study)
http://timss.bc.edu/
http://nces.ed.gov/timss

Here you will be able to access articles and data from TIMSS.

myeducationlab *will help you improve your understanding of the concepts taught in this textbook and in your course. This online tool includes videos of real classroom experiences, sample lesson plans, simulations, case studies, and links to important educational and teaching Web sites that will help you make the transition from student to teacher. As you study in your course and with this textbook, please follow along in **MyEducationLab**. Use it! Explore it! And improve your knowledge and your grade!*

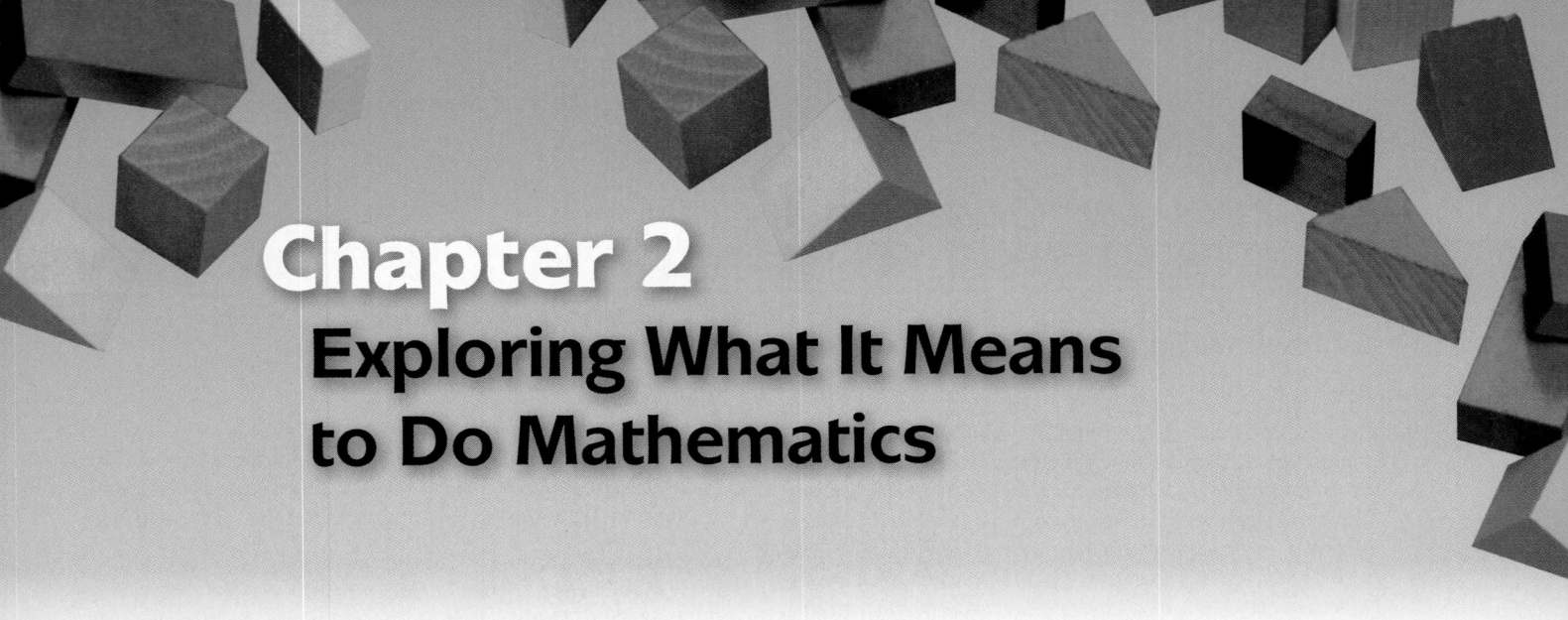

Chapter 2
Exploring What It Means to Do Mathematics

No matter how lucidly and patiently teachers explain to their students, they cannot understand for their students.

Schifter and Fosnot (1993, p. 9)

What does it mean to know a mathematics topic? Take division of fractions, for example. If you know this topic well, what do you know? The answer is broader than knowing a procedure (invert the second fraction and multiply) you may have memorized. Knowing division of fractions means that, not only are you able to think of examples that fit division of fractions, you are also able to think of alternative strategies for solving problems, as well as estimate an answer or draw a diagram to show what happens when a number is divided by a fraction. Unfortunately, too much mathematics instruction is limited to teaching simple algorithms without providing students with an opportunity to develop a deep understanding of different topics.

This chapter is about learning the theory of teaching developmentally and the knowledge necessary for students to learn mathematics with understanding. You might consider this chapter the what, why, and how of teaching mathematics. The "how" is addressed first—how should mathematics be experienced by a learner? Second, "why" should mathematics look this way? Third, "what" does it mean to understand mathematics?

What Does It Mean to Do Mathematics?

Stop for a moment and write a few sentences about what it means to know and do mathematics, based on your own experiences. Then put your paper aside until you have finished this chapter.

The description of doing mathematics presented here may not match your personal experiences. That's okay! However, it is *not* okay to be closed off to new ideas that may clash with your perceptions or to refuse to acknowledge that teaching mathematics could be dramatically different from your previous experience.

Mathematics is more than completing sets of exercises or mimicking processes the teacher explains. Doing mathematics means generating strategies for solving problems, applying those approaches, seeing if they lead to solutions, checking to see if your answers make sense. Doing mathematics in classrooms should closely model the act of doing mathematics in the real world.

Mathematics Is the Science of Pattern and Order

This wonderfully simple description of mathematics, found in the thought-provoking publication *Everybody Counts* (MSEB, 1989; see also Schoenfeld, 1992), challenges the popular view of mathematics as a discipline dominated by computation and rules without reasons. Science is a process of figuring out or making sense of things. It begins with problem-based situations. Although you may never have thought of it in quite this way, mathematics is a science of concepts and processes that have a pattern of regularity and a logical order. Finding and exploring this regularity or order, then making sense of it, is what doing mathematics is all about.

Even the youngest schoolchildren can and should be involved in the science of pattern and order. Have you ever noticed that 6 + 7 is the same as 5 + 8 and 4 + 9? What is the pattern? What are the relationships? When two odd numbers are multiplied, the result is also odd, but if the same numbers are added or subtracted, the result is even.

While studying patterns and algebraic relations, students learn how to graph linear functions (e.g., functions that can be represented in the form of $y = mx + b$). Graphing functions can be narrowly explored by following a set of steps or rules. However, understanding why certain forms of equations, situations, or models are growing in a linear manner involves a search for patterns. Discovering what types of real-world relationships are represented by linear graphs is more scientific—and infinitely more valuable—than creating a graph from an equation without connection to the real world.

Engaging in the science of pattern and order—doing mathematics—takes time and effort. Consider topics that appear on lists of "basic skills," such as knowing basic facts for addition and multiplication and having efficient methods for computing whole numbers, fractions, and decimal numbers. Studying interrelationships on the multiplication chart or analyzing patterns in place value (discussed in detail in the related content chapters) helps students understand what they are doing, therefore increasing their accuracy and retention. To master these topics as facts and procedures by memorization alone is no more doing mathematics than playing scales on the piano is making music.

❚❚ ———————— *Pause and Reflect*

Envision for a moment an elementary mathematics class where students are doing mathematics as "a study of patterns." What action verbs would students use to describe what they are doing? Make a short list before reading further.

A Classroom Environment for Doing Mathematics

To create a setting where students are "doing mathematics" means making a shift in the way that tasks are presented to students and how classrooms are organized for mathematics lessons. Doing mathematics begins with posing worthwhile tasks; then creating a risk-taking environment where students share and defend mathematical ideas.

The Language of Doing Mathematics

Children in traditional mathematics classes often describe mathematics as "work" or "getting answers." They talk about "plussing" and "doing times" (multiplication). They talk about "plussing" and "timings" (multiplication). In contrast, the following collection of verbs can be found in most of the literature describing the authentic work of doing mathematics, and all are used in *Principles and Standards* (NCTM, 2000):

explore	represent	explain
investigate	formulate	predict
conjecture	discover	develop
solve	construct	describe
justify	verify	use

These verbs suggest higher-level thinking. They engender the process of "making sense" and "figuring out." Children engaged in these actions in mathematics classes will be actively thinking about the mathematical ideas that are involved. Contrast these verbs with the ones that might reflect the traditional mathematics classroom: listen, copy, memorize, drill. These are lower-level thinking activities that do not adequately prepare students for the real act of doing mathematics.

Mathematics requires effort and it is important that students, parents, and the community acknowledge and honour the fact that effort is what leads to learning in mathematics (National Mathematics Advisory Panel, 2008). In classrooms where higher-level mathematics activities are pursued on a daily basis, students receive an empowering message: "You are capable of making sense of this—you are capable of doing mathematics!

Every idea introduced in the mathematics classroom can and should be understood by every child. There are no exceptions! All children are capable of learning the mathematics we want them to learn. And learning is meaningful when they are taught to perform challenging and engaging mathematics, using the verbs listed here.

The Setting for Doing Mathematics

The teacher's role is to create a spirit of inquiry, trust, and expectation. Within this environment, students are invited to do mathematics. Teachers pose problems; students then wrestle with ideas to find solutions. The focus in on active engagement. Students test ideas, make conjectures, develop reasons, and offer explanations. In *Classroom Discussions*, a teacher resource describing how to implement effective discourse in the classroom, Chapin, O'Conner, and Anderson (2003) write, "When a teacher succeeds in setting up a classroom in which students feel obligated to listen to one another, to make their own contributions clear and comprehensible, and to provide evidence for their claims, that teacher has set in place a powerful context for student learning." (p. 9)

In the classic book, *Making Sense* (Hiebert et al., 1997), the authors describe four features of a productive classroom culture for mathematics in which students can learn from each other.

1. *Ideas are the currency of the classroom.* Ideas, expressed by any student in the classroom, have the potential to contribute to everyone's learning. Consequently, they warrant respect and response.

2. *Students have autonomy with respect to the methods used to solve problems.* Students must respect that everyone has their own methods for solving problems. They must also recognize that there are often a variety of methods that will lead to a solution.

3. *The classroom culture exhibits an appreciation for mistakes as opportunities to learn.* Student errors afford opportunities for everyone to examine faulty reasoning, thereby raising each person's level of analysis. Mistakes are not covered up; they are to be used constructively.

4. *The authority for reasonability and correctness lies in the logic and structure of the subject, rather than in the social status of the participants.* The persuasiveness of an explanation or the correctness of a solution depends on the mathematical sense it makes, not on the popularity of the presenter.

In classrooms that embrace this culture for learning, the way students think about mathematics changes. Rather than students asking (or thinking), "What do you want me to do?" problem ownership shifts the situation to "I think I am going to ... " (Baker & Baker, 1990). In the latter situation, the student feels empowered to come up with her or his own approach, rather than relying on the teacher to offer an approach. This is key for creating an environment for doing mathematics. More information on creating a community of learners is found in Chapter 4.

An Invitation to Do Mathematics

If your goal is to create a classroom environment where children are truly doing mathematics, it is important that you have a personal feel for doing mathematics. The purpose of this section is to provide you with opportunities to engage in the science of pattern and order—to do some mathematics. If possible, find one or two peers to work with you so that you can experience a sharing and an interchange of ideas.

Don't read too much at once. Some hints and suggestions follow each task. Do as much as you can, until you and your group are stuck—really stuck; then read a bit more.

Let's Do Some Mathematics!

We will explore four different problems. Each is independent of the others. None requires any sophisticated mathematics, not even algebra. But, they do require higher-level thinking and reasoning. Try out your ideas! Devote time and effort—persist—these are the key ideas for being successful at mathematics. Have fun!

Start and Jump Numbers: Searching for Patterns

You will need to make a list of numbers that begin with a "start number" and increase by a fixed amount we will call the "jump number." First try 3 as the start number and 5 as the jump number. Write the start number at the top of your list, then 8, 13, and so on, "jumping" by 5 each time until your list extends to about 130.

Your task is to examine this list of numbers and find as many patterns as you possibly can. Share your ideas with the group, and write down every pattern you agree really is a pattern.

 Do not read on until you have listed as many patterns as you can identify.

A Few Ideas. Here are some things you might consider:

- There is at least one alternating pattern.
- Have you looked at odd and even numbers?
- What can you say about the number in the tens place?
- How did you think about the first two numbers with no tens-place digits?
- What happens when the numbers go above 100? (There are two ways to think about that.)
- Have you tried doing any adding of numbers? Numbers in the list? Digits in the numbers?

 If there is an idea in this list that you haven't tried, try it now.

Remember to think about what happens to your patterns after the numbers go over 100. In what ways might you think/express 113? One way you might think of it is: 1 hundred, 1 ten, and 3 ones. Of course, it could also be "eleventy-three," where the tens digit has gone from 9 to 10 to 11. How do these different perspectives affect your patterns? What would happen after 999?

When you added the *digits* in the numbers, the sums are 3, 8, 4, 9, 5, 10, 6, 11, 7, 12, 8,.... Did you look at every other number in this string? And what is the sum for 113? Is it 5 or is it 14? (There is no "right" answer here. But it is interesting to consider different possibilities.)

Next Steps. Sometimes when you have discovered some patterns in mathematics, it is a good idea to make some changes and see how the changes affect the patterns. What changes might you make in this problem?

STOP
_____

Try some ideas now before going on.

_____

Your changes may be even more interesting than the following suggestions. But here are some ideas that seem a bit more obvious than others:

- Change the start number but keep the jump number equal to 5. What is the same and what is different?
- Try keeping the start number the same and examine different jump numbers. You will find out that changing jump numbers really "messes things up" a lot compared to changing the start numbers.
- If you have patterns for several different jump numbers, what can you figure out about how a jump number affects the patterns? For example, when the jump number was 5, the ones-digit pattern repeated every two numbers—it had a "pattern length" of two. Yet, when the jump number is 3, the length of the ones-digit pattern is ten! Do other jump numbers create different pattern lengths?
- For a jump number of 3, how is the ones-digit pattern related to the circle of numbers in Figure 2.1? Are there other circles of numbers for other jump numbers?
- Using the circle of numbers for 3, find the pattern for jumps of multiples of 3, that is, jumps of 6, 9, or 12.

Figure 2.1 For jumps of 3, this cycle of digits will occur in the ones place. The start number determines where the cycle begins.

Using Technology. You may want to explore this problem using a calculator, which can make the list generation accessible to young children who can't skip count yet. Also, it opens the door for students to work with bigger jump numbers, such as 25 or 36. Most simple calculators have an automatic constant feature that will add the same number successively. For example, if you press 3 ⊞ 5 ⊟ and then keep pressing ⊟, the calculator will count by 5s (the first sequence of numbers you wrote.). This also works for the other three operations.

Two Machines, One Job

When Ron started Ron's Recycle Shop he bought a used paper-shredding machine. Business was good, so Ron bought a new shredding machine. The old machine could shred a truckload of paper in 4 hours. The new machine could shred the same truckload in only 2 hours. How long will it take to shred a truckload of paper if Ron runs both shredders at the same time?

 STOP
_____

Do not read until you either get an answer or get stuck. Can you check that you are correct? Are you sure you are stuck?

_____

A Few Ideas. Are you overlooking any assumptions made in the problem? Do the machines run simultaneously? The problem says "at the same time." Do they run just as fast when working together as when they work alone?

 STOP
_____

If this gives you an idea, pursue it before reading more.

_____

Have you tried to predict approximately how much time you think it should take the two machines? Just make an estimate using rounded numbers. For example, will it be closer to 1 hour or closer to 4 hours? What causes you to answer as you have? Can you tell if your "guesstimate" makes sense or is at least in the ballpark? Checking a guess in this way sometimes leads to a new insight.

Some people draw pictures to solve problems. Others like to use something they can move or change. For example, you might draw a rectangle or a line segment to stand for the truckload of paper, or you might get some counters (chips, plastic cubes, pennies) and make a collection that stands for the truckload.

STOP
_____

Go back and try some more.

_____

Consider the Solutions of Others. Here are solutions of teachers who worked on this problem. (Adapted from Schifter & Fosnot, 1993, pp. 24–27.) Here is Luiza's solution (she teaches grade 6):

> Luiza holds up a bar of plastic cubes. "Let's say these 16 cubes are the truckload of paper. In 1 hour, the new machine shreds 8 cubes and the old machine 4 cubes." Luiza breaks off 8 cubes and then 4 cubes. "That leaves these 4 cubes. If the new machine did 8 cubes' worth in 1 hour, it can do 2 cubes' worth in 15 minutes. The old machine does half as much, or 1 cube." As she says this, she breaks off 3 more cubes. "That is 1 hour and 15 minutes, and we still have 1 cube left." Long pause. "Well, the new machine did 2 cubes in 15 minutes, so it will do this cube in $7\frac{1}{4}$ minutes. Add that onto the 1 hour and 15 minutes. The total time will be 1 hour $22\frac{1}{2}$ minutes" (See Figure 2.2.)

Cindy teaches grade 4. She disagrees with Luiza. Here is Cindy's proposal:

> "This rectangle [see Figure 2.3] stands for the whole truckload. In 1 hour, the new machine will do half of this." The rectangle is divided in half. "In 1 hour, the old machine could do $1/4$ of the paper." The rectangle is divided accordingly. "So in 1 hour, the two machines have done $3/4$ of the truck, and there is $1/4$ left. What is left is $1/3$ as much as what they already did, so it should take the two machines $1/3$ as long to do that part as it took to do the first part. One-third of an hour is 20 minutes. That means it takes 1 hour and 20 minutes to do it all."

Jeff teaches grade 3. He and his partner have come up with the following strategy:

> At first, we solved the problem by averaging. We decided that it would take 3 hours because that's the average. Then Samantha asked how we knew to average. We thought we had a reason, but then Samantha asked how Ron would feel if his two machines together took longer than just the new one that could do the job in only 2 hours. So we can see that 3 hours doesn't make sense. So we still don't know whether it's 1 hour and 20 minutes or 1 hour and $22\frac{1}{2}$ minutes.

As with the teachers in these examples, it is important to decide if your solution is correct, then articulate why you did it in this way, as this reflects real problem solving. After you have justified that you solved the problem correctly (rather than checking with an answer key), try to find other ways to reach the correct solution or try to understand others' approaches to solving the problem. In considering other ways, you can expand your repertoire of problem-solving strategies.

One Up, One Down

For Grades 1–3. **When you add 7 to itself, you get 14. When you make the first number 1 more and the second number 1 less, you get the same answer:**

7 + 7 = 14 has the same answer as 8 + 6 = 14

It works for 5 + 5 too:

5 + 5 = 10 has the same answer as 6 + 4 = 10

What can you find out about this?

For Grades 4–8. **What happens when you change addition to multiplication in this exploration?**

7 × 7 = 49 has an answer that is one more than 6 × 8 = 48

It works for 5 × 5 too:

5 × 5 = 25 has an answer that is one more than 6 × 4 = 24

What can you find out about this situation? Can this pattern be extended to other situations?

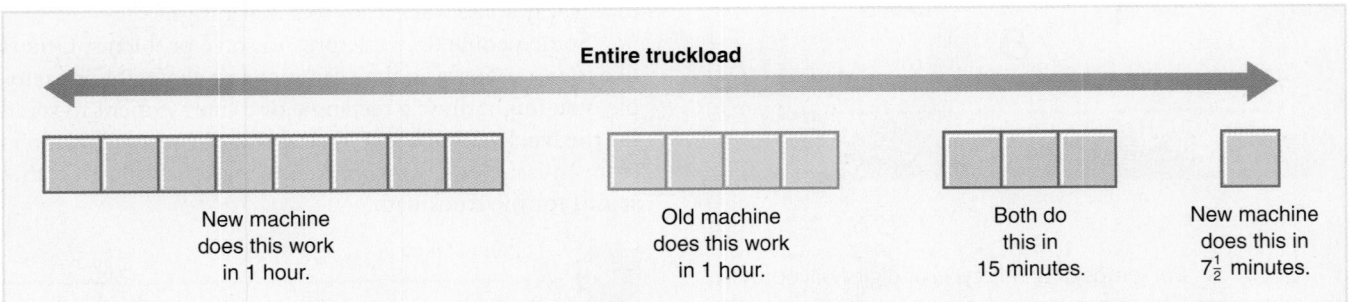

Entire truckload

New machine does this work in 1 hour.

Old machine does this work in 1 hour.

Both do this in 15 minutes.

New machine does this in $7\frac{1}{2}$ minutes.

Figure 2.2 Luiza's solution to the paper-shredding problem.

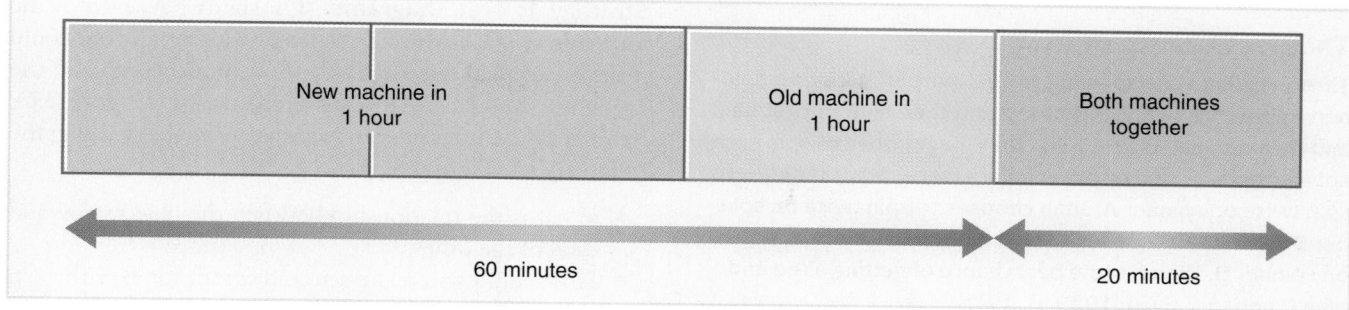

Figure 2.3 Cindy's solution to the paper-shredding problem.

🛑

Work on the multiplication pattern. Explore until you have developed some ideas. Write down whatever ideas you discover.

A Few Ideas. Use a physical model or picture. You have probably found some interesting patterns. Can you tell why these patterns work? In the case of addition, it is fairly easy to see that when you take from one number and give to the other, the total stays the same. This is not the case with multiplication. Why? One way to explore this is to draw rectangles where the length and height represent each factor (e.g., for the first problem, a 7 by 7 unit rectangle and a 6 by 4 unit rectangle). See how the rectangles compare (Figure 2.4a).

You may prefer to think of multiplication as equal sets. For example, using stacks of chips, 7 × 7 is seven stacks with seven chips in each stack (set). The expression 8 × 6 is represented by eight stacks of six (six stacks of eight is also a possible interpretation). See how the stacks for each expression compare (Figure 2.4b).

🛑

Work with one or both of these approaches to see if you get any insights.

Additional Patterns to Explore. There is a lot to find out about multiplication patterns. Think of the many "what ifs" that are possible. Here are a few. If you have found other ones—great! There are many ways to explore this problem.

- Have you looked at how the first two numbers are related? For example, 7 × 7, 5 × 5, and 9 × 9 are all products with like factors. How do those results differ when the two factors are 1 apart from each other (8 × 7 or 13 × 12)? What about when the factors differ by 2 or by 3?

- Think about adjusting factors by numbers other than 1. What if you adjust up 2 and down 2 (e.g., 7 × 7 to 9 × 5)?
- What happens if you use big numbers instead of small ones (e.g., 30 ×30)?
- What if *both* factors increase? Is there a pattern?

We hope you have made your own conjectures and explored them or, at least, added to the "what if?" list. Scientists (including mathematicians) explore new ideas that strike them as interesting and promising, rather than blindly following the direction of others.

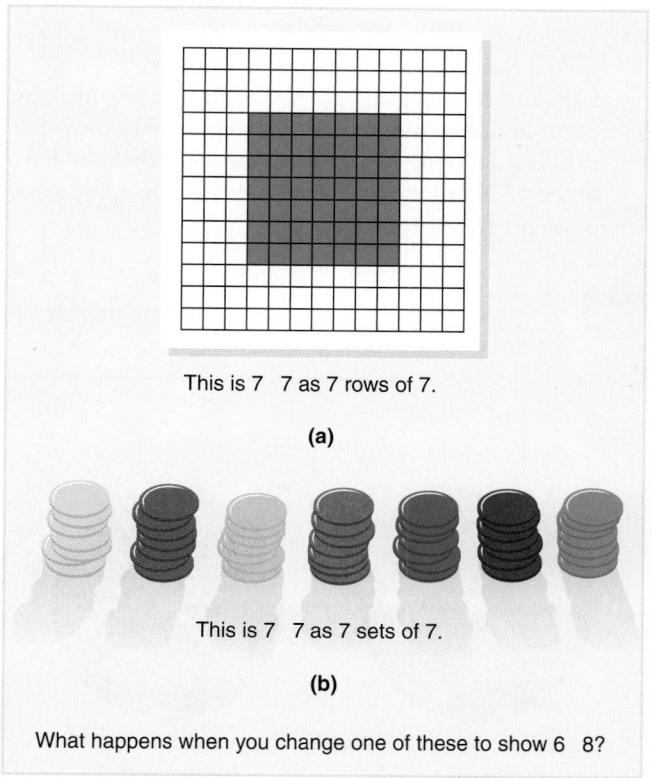

This is 7   7 as 7 rows of 7.

(a)

This is 7   7 as 7 sets of 7.

(b)

What happens when you change one of these to show 6   8?

Figure 2.4 Two physical ways to think about multiplication that might help in the exploration.

The Best Chance of Purple

Three students are spinning to "get purple" with two spinners (either by spinning first red and then blue or first blue and then red; see Figure 2.5). They may choose to spin each spinner once or one of the spinners twice. Mary chooses to spin twice on spinner A; John chooses to spin twice on spinner B; and Susan chooses to spin first on spinner A and then on spinner B. Who has the best chance of getting a red and a blue (Lappan & Even, 1989, p. 17)?

Think about the problem and what you know. Experiment.

A Few Ideas. Sometimes it is tough to get a feel for problems that seem too abstract or complex. In situations involving chance, find a way to experiment and see what happens. For this problem, you can easily make spinners using a freehand drawing on paper, a paper clip, and a pencil. Put your pencil point through the loop of the clip, then place it, point down, on the centre of your spinner. Now you can spin the paper clip "pointer" with a flick of your fingers. Try at least 20 pairs of spins for each choice and keep track of what happens.

- For Susan's choice (A then B), would it matter if she spun B first and then A? Why or why not?
- Explain why you think purple is more or less likely to occur in one of the three cases, compared to the other two. It sometimes helps to talk through what you have observed in order to come up with a way to apply some more precise reasoning.

Try these suggestions before reading on.

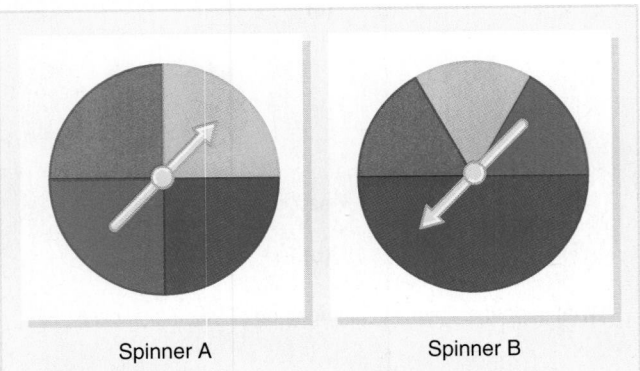

Figure 2.5 You may spin A twice, B twice, or A then B. Which option gives you the best chance of spinning a red and a blue?

Strategy 1: Tree Diagrams On spinner A, each of the four colours has the same chance of coming up. You could make a tree diagram for A with four branches, and all the branches would have the same chance (see Figure 2.6). Spinner B has different size sections, which begs asking the following questions:

- What is the relationship between the blue region and each of the others?
- How could you make a tree diagram for B with each branch having the same chance?
- How can you add to the diagram for spinner A so that it represents spinning A twice in succession?
- Which branches on your diagram represent getting purple?
- How could you make tree diagrams for John's and Susan's choices? Why do they make sense?

Test your ideas by actually spinning the spinner or spinners.

Tree diagrams are only one way to approach this. You may have a different way. As long as your way seems to be getting you somewhere, stick with it. There is one more suggestion to follow, but don't read further if you are ready to solve the problem.

Strategy 2: Grids Suppose that you had a square that represented all the possible outcomes for spinner A and a similar square for spinner B. Although there are many ways to divide a square into four equal parts, if you use lines all going in the same direction, you could compare all the outcomes of one event (one whole square) with the outcomes of another event (drawn on a different square). When the second event (here the second spin) follows the first event, make the lines on the second square go in the opposite direction from the lines in the first square. Then, make a tracing of one square in Figure 2.7 and place it on the other. You end up with 24 little sections.

Why are there six subdivisions for the square that represents spinner B? What does each of the 24 little

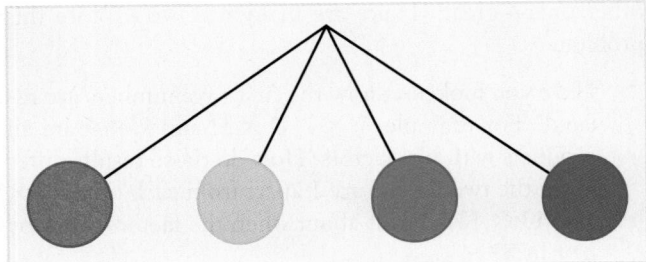

Figure 2.6 A tree diagram for spinner A in Figure 2.5.

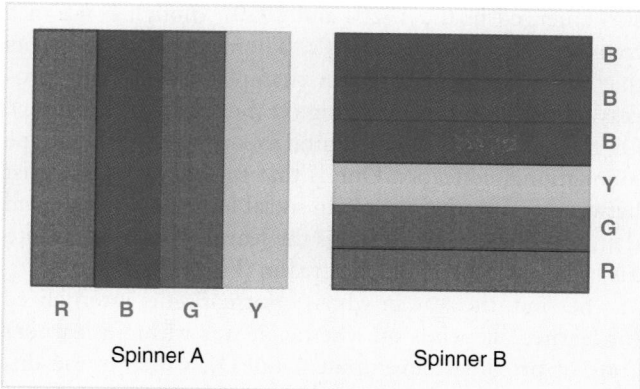

Figure 2.7 A square shows the chance of obtaining each color for the spinners in Figure 2.5.

rectangles stand for? What sections would represent purple? In any other method you have been trying, did 24 come into play when spinner A was followed by spinner B?

Where Are the Answers?

No answers or solutions are given in this text. How do you feel about that? What about the "right" answers? Are your answers correct? What makes the solution to any investigation "correct"?

In the classroom, the ready availability of the answer book or the teacher's willingness to provide the solution or verify that the answer is correct sends a clear message to children about doing mathematics: "Your job is to find the answers that the teacher already has." In the real world of problem solving outside the classroom, there are no teachers with answers and no answer books. Doing mathematics includes deciding if an answer is correct and being able to justify your reasoning to others.

What Does It Mean to Learn Mathematics?

Now that you have had the chance to experience doing mathematics, you may have a series of questions: Can students solve such challenging tasks? Why take the time to solve these problems? Why should students be doing problems like this, especially if they are reluctant to do so? Collectively, these questions could be summarized as "How does 'doing mathematics' relate to student learning?" The answer lies in current theory and research on how people learn, as discussed in the following sections. The experiences we provide in classrooms should be designed to maximize learning opportunities for students.

Constructivist Theory

Constructivism is rooted in the cognitive school of psychology and in the work of Jean Piaget, who introduced the notion of mental schema, developing a theory of cognitive development in the 1930s (translated into English in the 1950s). At the heart of constructivism is the notion that children are not blank slates but the creators of their own learning. Integrated networks, or *cognitive schemas*, are both the product of constructing knowledge and the tools with which additional new knowledge can be constructed. As learning occurs, the networks are rearranged, added to, or otherwise modified. Piaget suggested that schemas can be changed in two ways—by *assimilation* and *accommodation*. Assimilation occurs when a new concept "fits" with prior knowledge and the new information expands an existing network. Accommodation takes place when the new concept does not "fit" with the existing network, so the brain revamps or replaces existing schema. Through *reflective* (or purposeful) *thought*, people may modify their existing schemas to incorporate new ideas (Fosnot, 1996). Reflective thought involves sifting through existing ideas (also called prior knowledge) to find those that seem to be related to the current thought, idea, or task.

The basic tenet of constructivism is that people construct their own knowledge based on their prior knowledge (Pirie and Kieren, 1992). Existing schemas are often referred to as prior knowledge. All people, all of the time, construct or give meaning to things they perceive or think about. As you read these words, you are giving meaning to them. Whether listening passively to a lecture or actively engaging in synthesizing findings in a project, your brain is applying prior knowledge to make sense of this information.

Construction of Ideas. To construct or build something in the physical world requires tools, materials, and effort. How we construct ideas can be viewed in an analogous manner. The tools we use to build understanding are our existing ideas and knowledge. The materials we use to build understanding may be things we see, hear, or touch—elements of our physical surroundings. Sometimes the materials are our own thoughts and ideas. The effort required is active and reflective thought.

In Figure 2.8 blue and red dots are used as symbols for ideas. Consider the picture to be a small section of our cognitive makeup. The blue dots represent existing ideas. The lines joining the ideas represent our logical connections or relationships that have developed between and among ideas. The red dot is an emerging idea, one that is being constructed. Whatever existing ideas (blue dots) are used in the construction will necessarily be connected to the new idea (red dot) because those were the ideas that gave meaning to it. If a potentially relevant idea (blue dot) is not accessed by the learner when learning a new concept (red dot), then that potential connection will not be made.

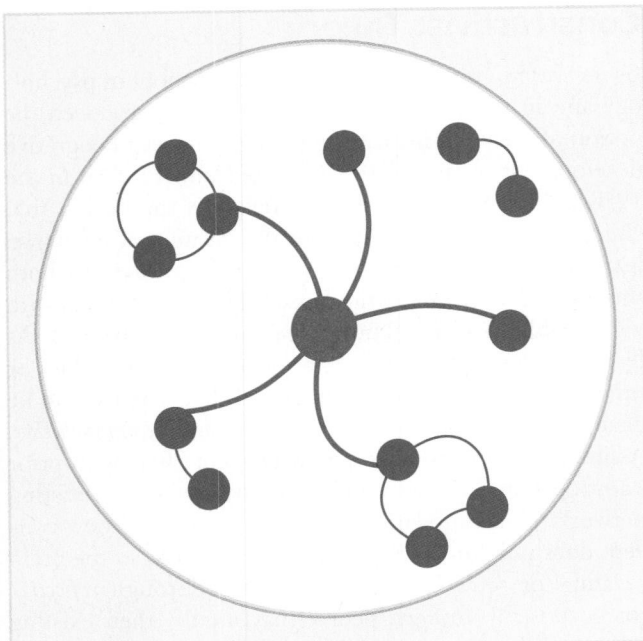

Figure 2.8 We use the ideas we already have (blue dots) to construct a new idea (red dot), developing in the process a network of connections between ideas. The more ideas used and the more connections made, the better we understand.

Constructing knowledge is an extremely active endeavour on the part of the learner (Baroody, 1987; Cobb, 1988; Fosnot, 1996; Pirie & Kieren, 1992; von Glasersfeld, 1990, 1996). To construct and understand a new idea requires actively thinking about it. "How does this idea fit with what I already know?" "How can I understand this idea in the context of my current understanding of this idea?" Mathematical knowledge cannot be "poured into" a learner. Put simply, constructing knowledge requires *reflective thought*, actively thinking about or mentally working on an idea.

Learners will vary in the number and nature of connections they make between a new idea (red dot) and existing ideas (blue dots). Moreover, different learners will use different ideas (blue dots) to give meaning to the same new idea (red dot). The construction of an idea is almost certainly going to be different for every learner, even within the same environment or classroom.

Though learning is constructed within the self, the classroom culture contributes to learning while the learner contributes to the culture of the classroom (Yackel & Cobb, 1996). Cobb argues that the learner and the culture of the classroom are reflexively related—one influencing the other.

Sociocultural Theory of Learning

In the same way that the work of Piaget led to constructivism, the work of Lev Vygotsky, a Russian psychologist, has greatly influenced sociocultural theory. Vygotksy's work

also emerged in the 1920s and 1930s, though it was not translated until the late 1970s. There are many concepts that these theories share (for example, the learning process as active meaning-seeking on the part of the learner). On the other hand, sociocultural theory has several unique foundational concepts. One is that mental processes exist between and among people in social learning settings, and that from these social settings the learner moves ideas into his or her own psychological realm (Forman, 2003).

Second, the way in which information is internalized (or learned) depends on whether it was within a learner's zone of proximal development (ZPD), which is the difference between a learner's assisted and unassisted performance on a task (Vygotksy, 1978). Simply put, the ZPD refers to a "range" of knowledge that may be out of reach for a person to learn on their own, but is accessible if the learner has the support of peers or more knowledgeable others. "[T]he ZPD is not a physical space, but a symbolic space created through the interaction of learners with more knowledgeable others and the culture that precedes them" (Goos, 2004, p. 262). Both Cobb (1994) and Goos (2004) suggest that in a true mathematical community of learners there is something of a common ZPD that emerges across learners, as well as the ZPDs of individual learners.

Another major concept in sociocultural theory is semiotic mediation, a term used to describe how information moves from the social plane to the individual plane. It is defined as the "mechanism by which individual beliefs, attitudes, and goals simultaneously affected and affect sociocultural practices and institutions" (Forman & McPhail, 1993, p. 134). Semiotic mediation involves interaction through language but also through diagrams, pictures, and actions. Language and these other objects and actions are considered the "tools" of mediation.

Social interaction is essential for mediation. The nature of the community of learners is affected not only by the culture the teacher created, but also by the broader social and historical culture of the members of the classroom (Forman, 2003). In summary, from a sociocultural perspective, learning is dependent on the learner (working within his or her ZPD), the social interactions in the classroom, and the culture within and beyond the classroom.

Implications for Teaching Mathematics

It is not necessary to choose between a social constructivist theory that favours the views of Vygotsky and a cognitive constructivist perspective that is built on the theories of Piaget (Cobb, 1996). In fact, when considering classroom practices that maximize opportunities to construct ideas or to provide tools to promote mediation, they are quite similar. Classroom discussion based on students' own ideas and solutions to problems is absolutely "foundational to children's learning" (Wood & Turner-Vorbeck, 2001, p. 186).

It is important to restate that a learning theory is not a teaching strategy. A theory *informs* practice, whereas a strategy offers a way or method for teaching. In this section, teaching strategies that reflect constructivist and sociocultural perspectives are discussed briefly. You will find these strategies revisited in Chapters 3 and 4, where a problem-based model for instruction is discussed, and in the content chapters, where you will learn how to apply these ideas to specific areas of mathematics.

Build New Knowledge from Prior Knowledge

Consider the following task posed to a class of fourth grade students who are learning division of whole numbers.

Four children had 3 bags of M&Ms. The children decided to open all 3 bags of candy and share them fairly. There were 52 candies in each bag. How many candies did each child get?" (Campbell & Johnson, 1995, pp. 35–36).

Note: You may want to select a non-food context, such as sets of cards or any other culturally relevant or interesting item that would come in similar quantities.

STOP

Consider, as a teacher whose work is grounded in constructivist learning theory, how you might introduce division to fourth grade students. What might your expectations be for this problem?

The student work samples in Figure 2.9 are from a classroom that is grounded in constructivist ideas where students have the opportunity to develop or invent strategies for doing mathematics using their prior knowledge. In so doing, they make connections among mathematical concepts.

Marlena interpreted the task as "How many sets of 4 can be made from 156?" She first used facts that were either easy or available to her: 10×4 and 4×4. She subtracted these totals from 156 until she arrived at 100. This seemed to cue her to use 25 fours. She added the number of sets of 4 that she found in 156 and knew the answer was 39 candies for each child. Marlena is using an equal subtraction approach and known multiplication facts. Note that she is connecting the "blue dots" in order to begin learning about the newer concept of division. While this is not the most efficient approach, it demonstrates that Marlena understands the concept of division and can move toward more efficient approaches.

Darrell's approach was more directly related to the sharing context of the problem. He formed four columns and distributed amounts to each, accumulating the amounts mentally and orally as he wrote the numbers. Darrell used a counting-up approach, first giving each student 20 candies. Seeing they could get more, he distributed 5 more,

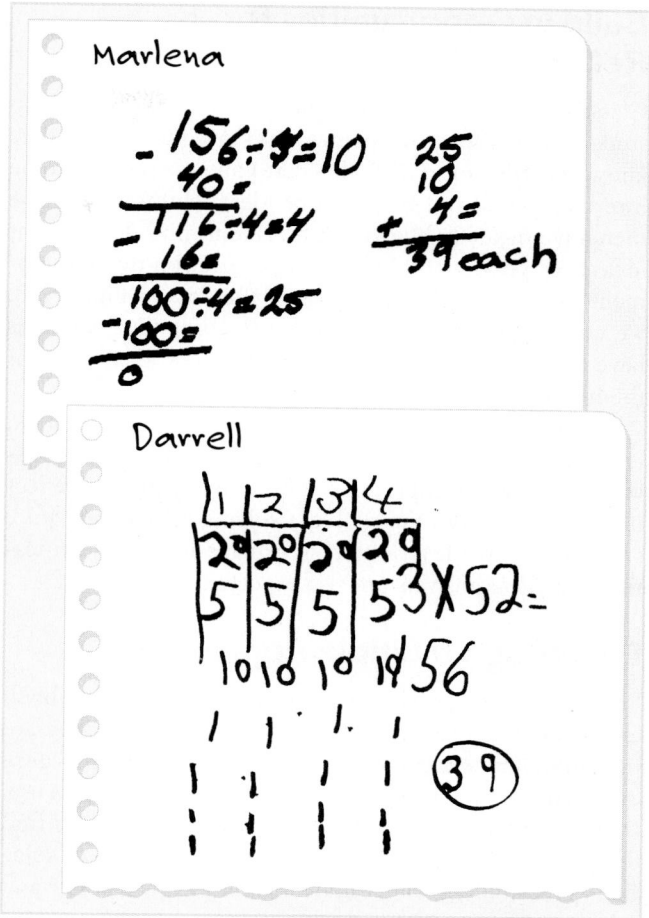

Figure 2.9 Two grade 4 children construct unique solutions to a computation.

Source: Reprinted with permission from P. F. Campbell and M. L. Johnson, "How Primary Students Think and Learn," in I. M. Carl (Ed.), *Prospects for School Mathematics* (pp. 21—42), copyright © 1995 by the National Council of Teachers of Mathematics.

then another 10, then a series of ones until he reached the total. Like Marlena, Darrell used facts and procedures that he knew. The context of sharing was the "blue dot" for Darrell, as he was able to think about the problem in terms of equal distribution.

Provide Opportunities to Talk About Mathematics

Learning is enhanced when the learner is engaged with others to work on the same idea. A worthwhile goal is to create an environment in which students interact with each other and with you, the teacher. The rich interaction in such a classroom allows students to engage in reflective thinking and to internalize concepts that may not be attainable, without the interaction and input from peers and the teacher. In discussions with peers, students will be adapting and expanding on their existing networks of concepts.

Build in Opportunities for Reflective Thought

Classrooms need to provide structures and supports to help students make sense of mathematics in light of what they know. In order for a new idea that you are teaching to be interconnected in a rich web of ideas, children must be mentally engaged. They must be able to find the relevant ideas they possess and bring them to bear on the development of the new idea. In terms of the dots in Figure 2.8, we want to activate every blue dot (existing idea) students have that is related to the new red dot (new idea) we want them to learn.

As you will see in Chapter 3 and throughout this book, engaging students in problem solving, which requires activating prior knowledge, is key for getting them to be reflective. Not only does the problem-solving approach require students to provide answers, but explanations and justifications for these answers are also expected.

Encourage Multiple Approaches

Teachers need to provide opportunities for students to build connections between what they know and what they are learning. The student whose work is presented in Figure 2.10 may not understand the algorithm she is trying to use. If she were encouraged to use her own approach to find the difference, she might be able to find a correct solution, thus building on her understanding of place value and subtraction.

Even learning a basic multiplication fact, such as 7×8, can yield better results if a teacher promotes the use of multiple strategies. Imagine a classroom where children discuss and share clever ways to figure out the product. One child might think of 5 eights, then 2 more eights. Another child may have learned $7 \times 7 = 49$ and add on one more 7.

Figure 2.10 Children sometimes invent incorrect meanings by extending poorly understood rules.

Still, another may take half of the sevens (4×7, because 2 fours are 8) and double that. A class discussion sharing these ideas brings to the fore a wide range of useful mathematical "dots" relating addition and multiplication concepts.

In contrast, multiplication facts such as 7×8 can be learned solely by rote (memorized). While the knowledge is still constructed, it is not connected to other knowledge. Rote learning can be thought of as a "weak construction" (Noddings, 1993). Students can recall the information if they remember it, but if they forget they don't have 7×8 connected to other knowledge pieces that would allow them to access the fact.

Treat Errors as Opportunities for Learning

When students make errors, it might mean there is an inappropriate application of prior knowledge in the new situation. Remember, from a constructivist perspective, the mind is sifting through what it knows in order to find useful approaches for the new situation. Knowing that children rarely give random responses (Ginsburg, 1977; Labinowciz, 1985) gives insight into addressing student misconceptions and helping students accommodate new learning. For example, students comparing decimal numbers may incorrectly apply "rules" of whole numbers, such as "the longer the number the bigger" (Martinie, 2007; Nesher, Leonard, Magone, Omanson, & Peled, 1989).

Figure 2.10 is an example of a student who incorrectly applies what she learned about regrouping. If the teacher tries to help the student by re-explaining the "right" way to do the problem, the student loses the opportunity to rethink what she did and correct her faulty thinking. If instead, the teacher asks the student to explain her method of regrouping, the student must engage in reflective thought and think about what was grouped and how to keep the number equivalent.

Scaffold New Content   The concept of *scaffolding*, which derives from sociocultural theory, is based on the idea that a task, otherwise outside of a student's ZPD, can become accessible if it is carefully structured. For concepts completely new to students, the learning requires more structure or assistance, including the use of tools like manipulatives or more assistance from peers. As students become more comfortable with the content, the scaffolds are removed and the student becomes more independent. Scaffolding can provide support for those students who may not have a robust collection of "blue dots."

Honour Diversity   Finally, and importantly, these theories emphasize that each learner is unique, possessing a different collection of prior knowledge and cultural experiences. Since new knowledge is built on existing knowledge and experience, effective teaching incorporates and builds on the knowledge and experiences students bring to the classroom. In this way, lessons begin by eliciting prior experiences and understandings, and contexts for lessons are selected based on students' knowledge and experiences. Some students will not have the "blue dots" (existing ideas) they need. It is your job, as teacher, to provide experiences where those blue dots are developed, then connected to the concept being learned (red dot).

Classroom culture influences the individual learning of your students. As stated previously, you should support a range of approaches and strategies for doing mathematics. Students' ideas should be valued and included in classroom discussion of the mathematics. This shift in practice, away from the teacher telling one way to do the problem, establishes a classroom culture where ideas are valued. This approach values the uniqueness of each individual.

What Does It Mean to Understand Mathematics?

Both constructivist and sociocultural theories emphasize the learner building connections (blue dots to the red dots) among existing and new ideas. So you might be asking, "What is it they should be learning and connecting?" Or, "What are those blue dots?" This section focuses on mathematics content required in today's classrooms.

It is possible to say that we know something but we do not necessarily understand it. Knowledge is something we either have or don't have. Understanding is another matter. For example, most students in grade 4 or 5 know something about fractions. Given the fraction $6/8$, they will likely be able to read the fraction correctly and identify the 6 and 8 as the numerator and denominator, respectively. They may or may not be able to explain what the 6 and the 8 tell us about the fraction. Many students will know that this fraction is more than $1/2$. Some will think that it is a "big" fraction because the numbers are both somewhat big compared to the numbers in $1/2$ or $2/3$. That the fraction is equivalent

to $3/4$ is also a reasonably common connection for grade 5 students to make.

However, students may have different understandings of what it means to be equivalent. They may know that $6/8$ can be simplified to $3/4$ but not understand that $6/8$ and $3/4$ are identical in value; it may be more difficult for them to see the equivalence of $6/8$ to $9/12$. Some may think that simplifying $6/8$ to $3/4$ makes it a smaller number. Those with a better understanding will be able to create pictures or models to illustrate equivalent fractions or will have many examples of how $6/8$ is used outside of class. In summary, there is a range of ideas that students often connect to their individualized understanding of a fraction—each student brings a different set of blue dots to her or his knowledge of what a fraction is.

Understanding can be defined as a measure of the quality and quantity of connections that an idea has with existing ideas. Understanding is never an all-or-nothing proposition. It depends on the existence of appropriate ideas and on the creation of new connections, varying with each person (Backhouse, Haggarty, Pirie, & Stratton, 1992; Davis, 1986; Hiebert & Carpenter, 1992; Janvier, 1987; Schroeder & Lester, 1989).

One way that we can think about understanding is that it exists along a continuum (see Figure 2.11). At one extreme is a very rich set of connections. The understood idea is associated with many other existing ideas in a meaningful network of concepts and procedures. Understanding at this rich, interconnected end of the continuum can be referred to as *relational understanding*, a term borrowed from Richard Skemp (1978), an educational psychologist who had a major influence on mathematics education. *Instrumental understanding* (Skemp, 1978), at the other end of the continuum, refers to ideas that are isolated; thus, essentially without meaning. Knowledge learned by rote is at the isolated end of the continuum.

In the previous $6/8$ example, the student who can draw diagrams, gives examples, find equivalencies, and approximate the size of $6/8$ possesses a richer understanding, bordering on the relational end of the continuum, than the student who only knows the names and a procedure for

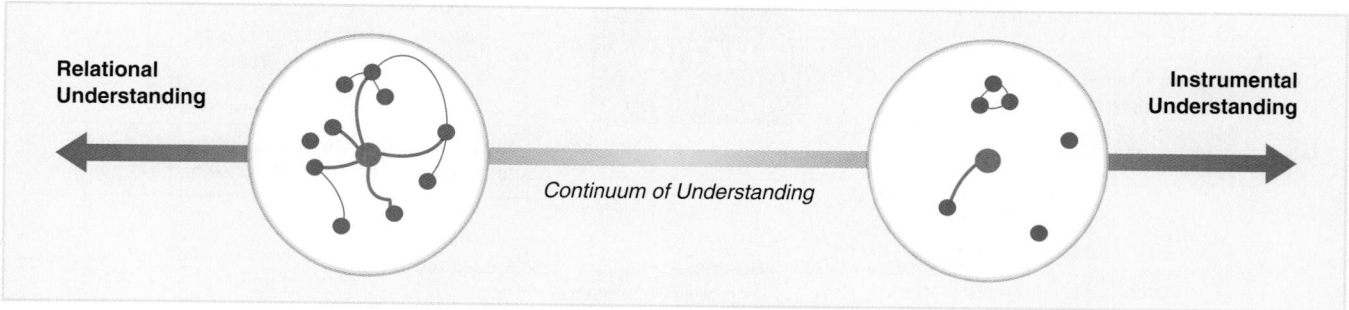

Figure 2.11 Understanding is a measure of the quality and quantity of connections that a new idea has with existing ideas. The greater the number of connections to a network of ideas, the better the understanding.

simplifying $^6/_8$ to $^3/_4$. The latter student's understanding hovers more on the instrumental end of the continuum.

Mathematics Proficiency

Much work has emerged since Skemp's classic work on relational and instrumental understanding focusing on what mathematics should be learned, all of it based on the need to include more than learning procedures.

Conceptual and Procedural Knowledge   For some time now, mathematics educators have found it useful to distinguish between two types of mathematical knowledge: conceptual knowledge and procedural knowledge (Hiebert & Lindquist, 1990).

Conceptual knowledge is knowledge that consists of rich relationships or webs of ideas (Hiebert & Lefevre, 1986). It is knowledge about the relationships or foundational ideas of a topic. *Procedural knowledge*, on the other hand, is knowledge of the rules and the procedures used in carrying out routine mathematical tasks and of the symbolism used to represent mathematics. Consider the task of multiplying 47×21. A student with a conceptual understanding of this problem would know that multiplication is repeated addition, that it could represent the area of a rectangle with dimensions of 47 and 21; that it is 20 groups of 47 and 1 more or to find the answer, you could multiply 47 by 10, double it, then add one more 47. The ability to employ invented strategies requires a deep understanding of place value and multiplication.

A student with procedural knowledge would know the step-by-step procedures for performing a task such as multiplying 47×21. For example, the student might say, "To multiply these two 2-digit numbers, first multiply 7 by 1. Then multiply 7 by 2 and carry the 1. Then multiply 4 by 2 and add the 1."

Interdependence of Conceptual and Procedural Knowledge   It is well established in research on mathematics learning that conceptual understanding is an important component of procedural proficiency (National Mathematics Advisory Panel, 2008; NCTM, 2000; Bransford, Brown, and Cocking, 2000). Mathematical procedures need to be connected to the conceptual ideas that explain why they work. *Principles and Standards*, Learning Principles states it well:

 "The alliance of factual knowledge, procedural proficiency and conceptual understanding makes all three components usable in powerful ways." (p. 19)

Recall the two students who used their own invented procedure to solve $156 \div 4$ (see Figure 2.9). Clearly, there was an active and useful interaction between the procedures the children invented and the ideas they knew about multiplication and were constructing about division.

The common practice of teaching procedures in the absence of concepts leads to errors and a dislike of mathematics. One way to help your students (and you) think about all the interrelated ideas for a concept is to create a network of web of associations, as demonstrated in Figure 2.12, for the concept of ratio. Note how much is involved in having a relational understanding of ratio. Compare that to the instrumental way in which ratio is presented in some textbooks. A single lesson on the topic is presented with prompts such as "If the ratio of girls to boys is 3 to 4, how many girls are there if there are 24 boys?"

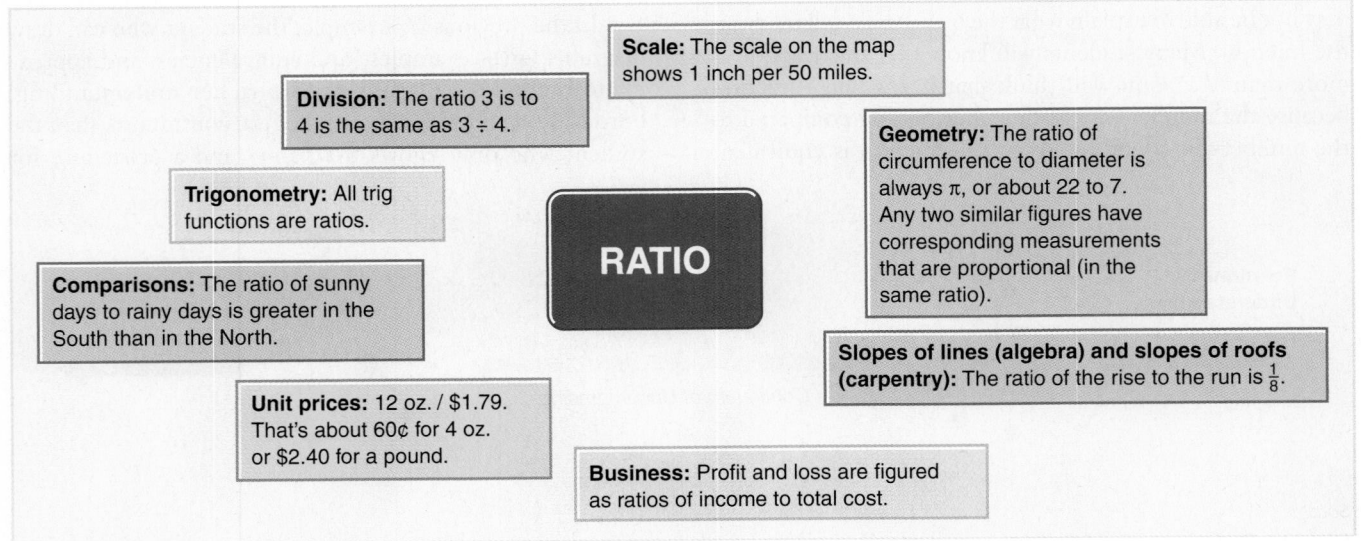

Figure 2.12 Potential web of associations that could contribute to the understanding of "ratio."

Five Strands of Mathematical Proficiency. While conceptual and procedural understanding of any concept are essential, they are not sufficient. Being mathematically proficient means that a person exhibits behaviours and dispositions as they are "doing mathematics." *Adding It Up* (NRC, 2001), an influential report on how students learn mathematics, describes five strands involved in being mathematically proficient: (1) conceptual understanding, (2) procedural fluency, (3) strategic competence, (4) adaptive reasoning, and (5) productive disposition. Figure 2.13 illustrates these interrelated and interwoven strands, providing a definition of each.

Recall the problems that you solved in the "Let's Do Some Mathematics" section. In approaching each problem, if you felt like you could design a strategy to solve it (or try new approaches if one didn't work), then that is evidence of strategic competence. In each of the problems selected, you were asked to explain or justify solutions. If you were able to reason about a pattern and tell how you knew it would work, this is evidence of adaptive reasoning. Finally, if you were committed to making sense of and solving those tasks, knowing that if you kept at it, you would get to a solution, then you have a productive disposition.

The last three of the five strands develop only when students have experiences that involve these processes. We hope you have noticed that the terms used here are very similar to the ones in the previous learning theory discussion. Reflection, using prior knowledge, social interaction, and solving problems in a variety of ways, among other strategies, are essential to learning; therefore, to becoming mathematically proficient.

Implications for Teaching Mathematics

If we accept the notion that understanding has both qualitative and quantitative differences, the question "Does she know it?" must be replaced with "How does she understand it?" "What ideas does she connect with it?" In the following examples, you will see how different children may well develop different ideas about the same knowledge, and thus have different understandings.

Early Number Concepts Consider the concept of "7" as constructed by a child in grade 1. A grade 1 student will most likely connect "7" to the counting procedure and the construct of "more than," probably understanding it as less than 10 and more than 2. What else will this child eventually connect to the concept of 7, as it now exists? Seven is 1 more than 6; it is 2 less than 9; it is the combination of 3 and 4 or 2 and 5; it is odd; it is small compared to 73 and large compared to one-tenth; it is the number of days in a week; it is "lucky"; it is prime; and on and on. The web of potential ideas connected to a number can grow large and involved.

Computation Computation is much more than memorizing a procedure. Analyzing a student's strategy provides a good opportunity to see how understanding can differ from one child to another. For addition and subtraction with two- or three-digit numbers, a flexible and rich understanding of numbers and place value is very helpful. How might different children approach the task of finding the sum of 37 and 28? For children whose understanding of 37 is based only on counting, the use of counters and a count-all procedure is likely. (See Figure 2.14a.) A student may use the traditional algorithm, lining up the digits and adding the ones, then the tens, but not understand why he or she is carrying the one. When procedures are not connected to concepts (in this case, place-value concepts), errors and unreasonable answers such as ending up with an answer of 515 (See Figure 2.14b) are more common.

Consider students who can solve the problem using invented approaches (see Figure 2.14c and d). The strategies used here show that the students know that numbers can be broken apart in many different ways and that the sum of two numbers remains the same if you add something to one number and subtract an equal amount from the other. These students can add in *flexible* ways.

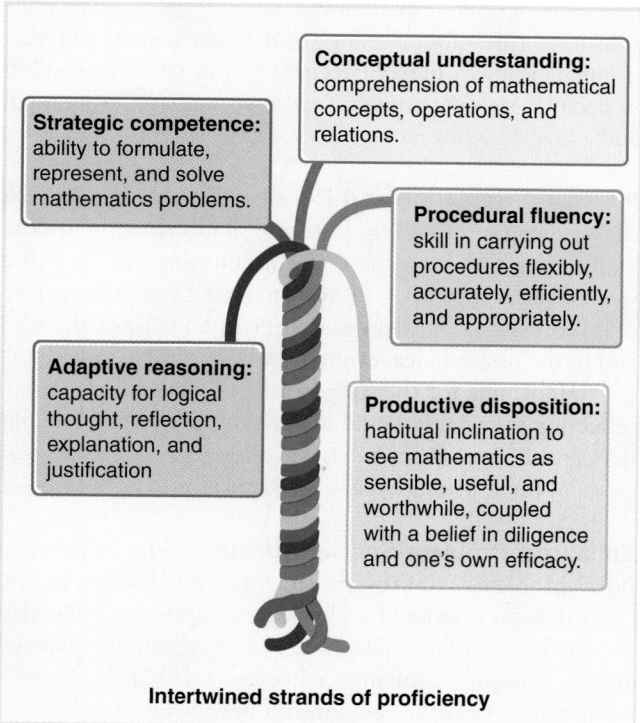

Intertwined strands of proficiency

Conceptual understanding: comprehension of mathematical concepts, operations, and relations.

Strategic competence: ability to formulate, represent, and solve mathematics problems.

Procedural fluency: skill in carrying out procedures flexibly, accurately, efficiently, and appropriately.

Adaptive reasoning: capacity for logical thought, reflection, explanation, and justification

Productive disposition: habitual inclination to see mathematics as sensible, useful, and worthwhile, coupled with a belief in diligence and one's own efficacy.

Figure 2.13 *Adding It Up* describes five strands of mathematical proficiency.
Source: Adding It Up: Helping Children Learn Mathematics, p. 5. Reprinted with permission from the National Academies Press, copyright © 2001, National Academy of Sciences.

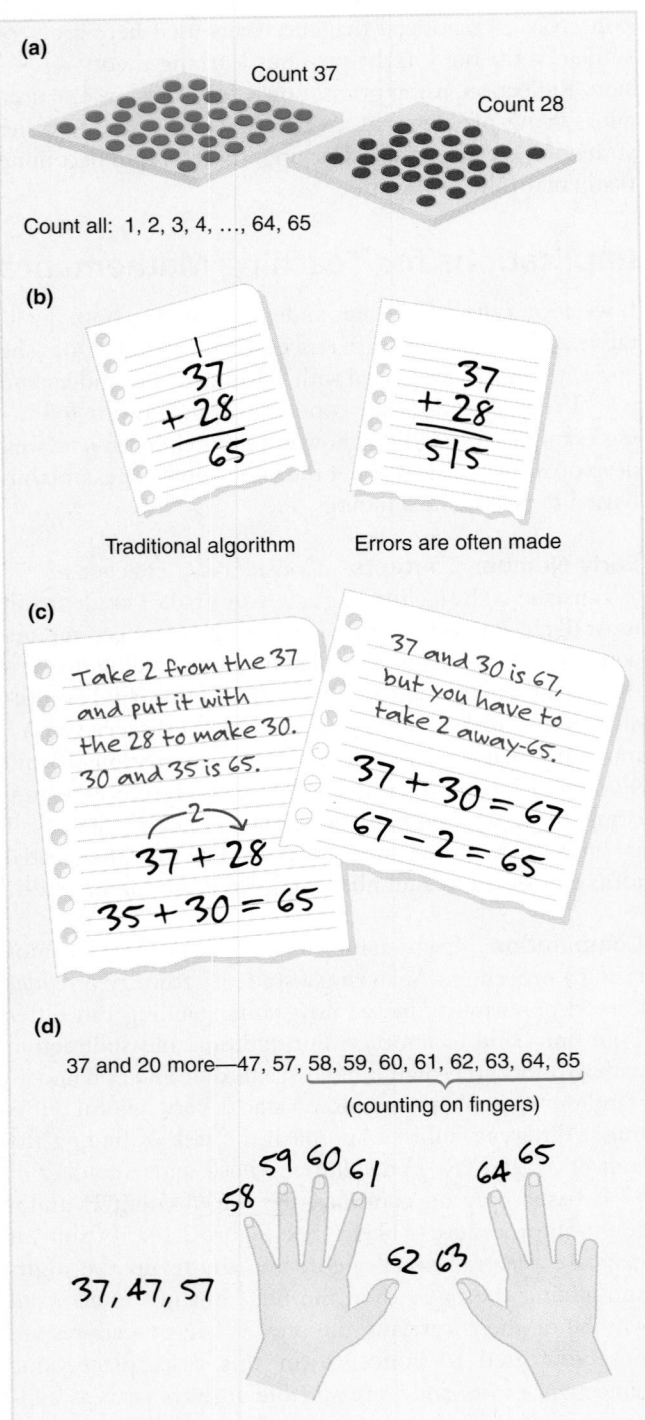

Figure 2.14 A range of computational examples showing different levels of understanding.

Benefits of a Relational Understanding

To teach for a rich or relational understanding requires a lot of work and effort. Concepts and connections develop over time, not in a day. Tasks must be selected that help

students build connections. The important benefits to be derived from relational understanding make the effort not only worthwhile, but also essential.

Effective Learning of New Concepts and Procedures Recall what learning theory tells us—students are actively building on their existing knowledge. The more robust their understanding of a concept, the more connections students are building, and the more likely it is they can connect new ideas to the existing conceptual webs they have. Fraction knowledge and place-value knowledge come together to make decimal learning easier, and decimal concepts directly enhance an understanding of percentage concepts and procedures. Without these and many other connections, children will need to learn each new piece of information they encounter as a separate, unrelated idea.

Less to Remember When mathematics is learned in an instrumental manner, it can seem like an endless list of isolated skills, concepts, rules, and symbols that often are overwhelming to keep straight. Constructivists talk about teaching "big ideas" (Brooks & Brooks, 1993; Hiebert et al., 1996; Schifter & Fosnot, 1993). Big ideas are really just large networks of interrelated concepts. Frequently, the network is so well constructed that whole chunks of information are stored and retrieved as single entities, rather than isolated bits. For example, knowledge of place value subsumes rules about lining up decimal points, ordering decimal numbers, moving decimal points to the right or left in decimal–percent conversions, rounding and estimating, and a host of other ideas.

Increased Retention and Recall Memory is a process of retrieving information. Retrieval of information is more likely when you have the concept connected to an entire web of ideas. If what you need to recall doesn't come to mind, reflecting on ideas that are related will usually lead you to the desired idea, eventually. For example, if you forget the formula for the surface area of a rectangular solid, reflecting on what it would look like unfolded and laid out flat can help you remember that there are six rectangular faces, in three pairs, that are the same size.

Enhanced Problem-Solving Abilities The solution of novel problems requires transferring ideas learned in one context to new situations. When concepts are embedded in a rich network, transferability is significantly enhanced and so is problem solving (Schoenfeld, 1992). When students understand the relationship between a situation and a context, they are going to know when to use a particular approach to solve a problem. While many students may be able to do this with whole number computation, once problems increase in difficulty and numbers move to rational numbers or unknowns, students without a relational understanding of the concepts are not able to apply the skills they learned to solve the new problem.

Results from the Pan-Canadian Assessment Program (2001) illustrated that significantly more 13-year-old Canadian students improved in problem solving as well as in mathematical content, compared to results of earlier assessments. It is suggested that exposure to curricula with an emphasis on understanding may have played a role in students' improvement (Council of Ministers of Education, 2001).

Improved Attitudes and Beliefs Relational understanding has an affective as well as a cognitive effect on the learner. When ideas are well understood and make sense, a learner tends to develop a positive self-concept about her or his ability to learn and understand mathematics. There is a definite feeling of "I can do this! I understand!" There is no reason to fear or to be in awe of knowledge learned relationally. At the other end of the continuum, instrumental understanding has the potential of producing mathematics anxiety, a real phenomenon that involves fear and avoidance behaviour.

Multiple Representations to Support Relational Understanding

The more ways that children are given to think about and test an emerging idea, the better chance they will correctly form and integrate it into a rich web of concepts, thus developing a relational understanding. Lesh, Post, and Behr (1987) talk about five "representations" for concepts (see Figure 2.15). Their research has found that children who have difficulty translating a concept from one representation also have difficulty solving problems and understanding computations. Strengthening the ability to move between and among these representations improves student understanding and retention. Discussion of oral language, real-world situations, and written symbols is woven into this chapter. However, it is also important that you understand how manipulatives and models can either help or fail children as they learn to construct ideas.

Models and Manipulatives

A *model for a mathematical concept* refers to any object, picture, or drawing that represents the concept, or onto which the relationship for that concept can be imposed. In this sense, any group of 100 objects can be a model for the concept "hundred" because we can impose the 100-to-1 relationship on the group and a single element of the group.

Manipulatives are physical objects that students and teachers can use to illustrate and discover mathematical concepts, whether made specifically for mathematics, like interlocking cubes, or objects that were created for other purposes.

It is incorrect to say that a model "illustrates" a concept. To illustrate implies showing. It would mean that when you looked at the model, you would see an example of the concept. Technically, all that you actually see is the physical object. Only your mind can impose the mathematical relationship on the object (Thompson, 1994).

Models can be a testing ground for emerging ideas. It is sometimes difficult for students (of all ages) to think about and test abstract relationships using only words or symbols. For example, to explore the area of a parallelogram requires the use of pictures and/or manipulatives to build connections. A variety of models should be accessible for students to select and use freely. You will undoubtedly encounter situations in which you use a model that you think clearly illustrates an idea, but a student just doesn't get it. However, when you use a different model, it is very helpful.

Examples of Models Physical materials or manipulatives, from common objects such as lima beans, used as counters, to commercially produced materials such as Dienes' blocks or pattern blocks have become enormously popular as tools for teaching mathematics. Figure 2.16 shows six models for six different concepts, giving a glimpse into the many ways each manipulative can be used to support the development of mathematical concepts and procedures.

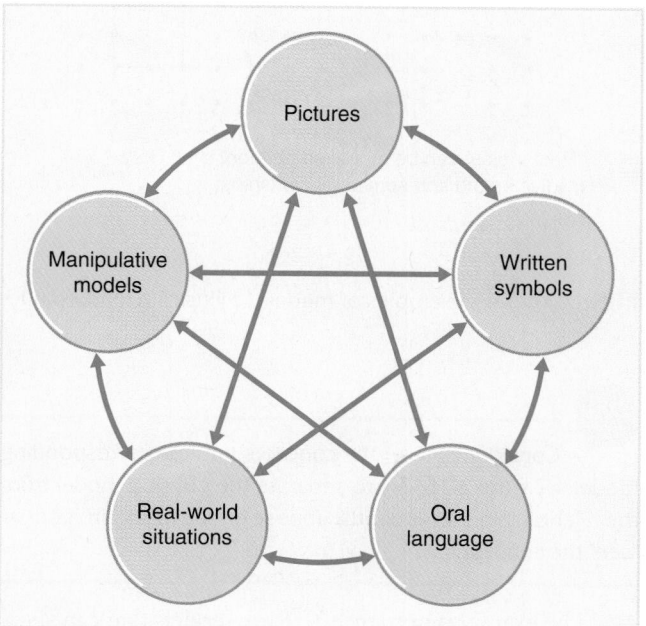

Figure 2.15 Five different representations of mathematical ideas. Translations between and within each can help develop new concepts.

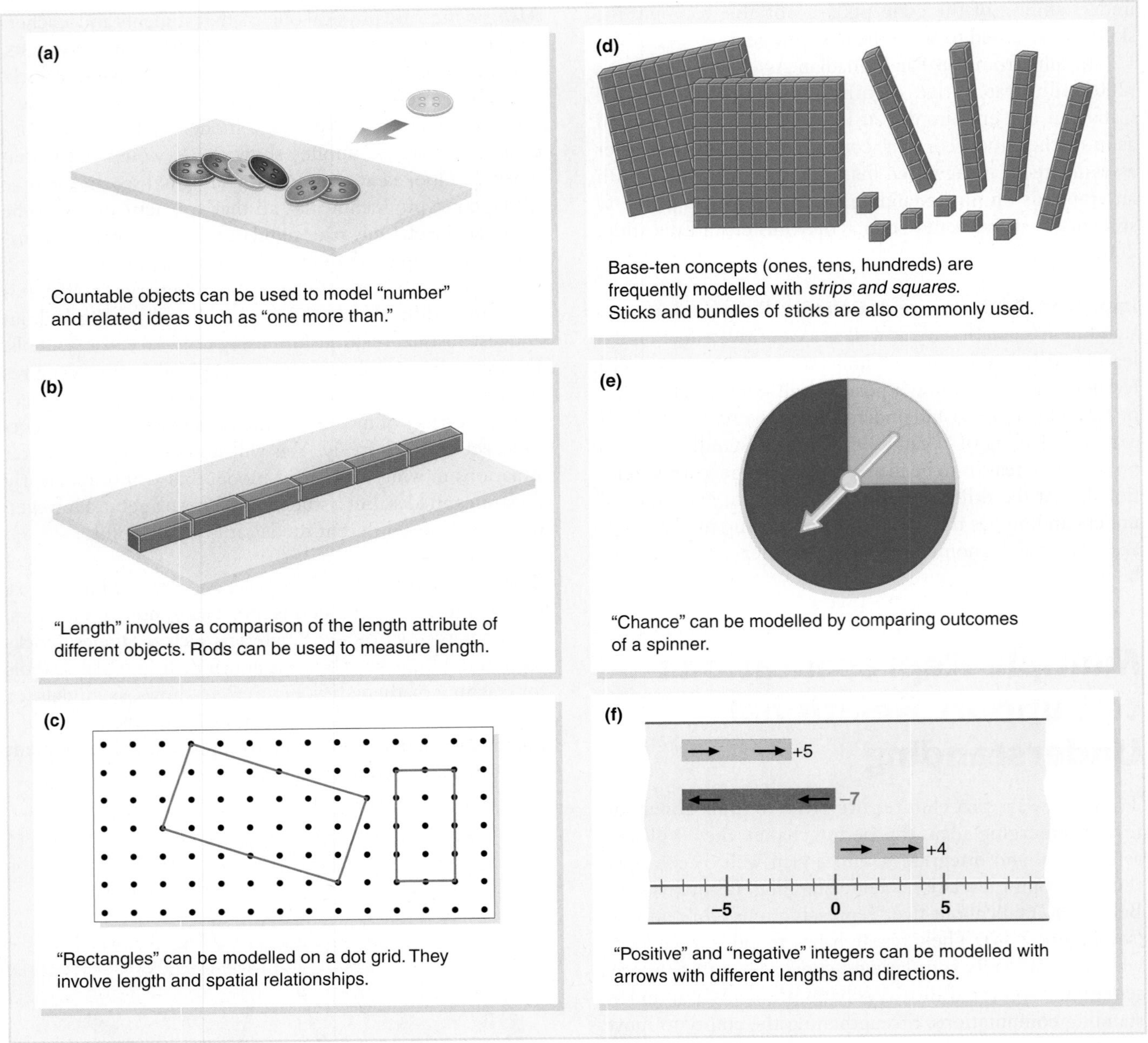

(a)

Countable objects can be used to model "number" and related ideas such as "one more than."

(b)

"Length" involves a comparison of the length attribute of different objects. Rods can be used to measure length.

(c)

"Rectangles" can be modelled on a dot grid. They involve length and spatial relationships.

(d)

Base-ten concepts (ones, tens, hundreds) are frequently modelled with *strips and squares*. Sticks and bundles of sticks are also commonly used.

(e)

"Chance" can be modelled by comparing outcomes of a spinner.

(f)

"Positive" and "negative" integers can be modelled with arrows with different lengths and directions.

Figure 2.16 Examples of models to illustrate mathematics concepts.

STOP

Consider each of the concepts and the corresponding model in Figure 2.16. Try to separate the physical model from the relationship that you must impose on the model in order to "see" the concept.

The examples in Figure 2.16 are models that can show the following concepts:

(a) The concept of "six" is a relationship between sets that can be matched to the words *one, two, three, four, five, six*. Changing a set of counters by adding one alters the relationship. The difference between the set of 6 and the set of 7 is the relationship "one more than."

(b) The concept of "measure of length" is a comparison of the length attribute of different objects. The length measure of an object is a comparison relationship of the length of the object to the length of the unit.

(c) The concept of "rectangle" includes both spatial and length relationships. The opposite sides are equal in length and parallel and the adjacent sides meet at right angles.

(d) The concept of "hundred" is not in the larger square but in the relationship of that square to the rod ("ten") and to the little cube ("one").

(e) "Chance" is a relationship between the frequency of an event's occurrence compared with all possible outcomes. The spinner can be used to create relative frequencies. These can be predicted by observing relationships that exist between sectors of the spinner.

(f) The concept of a "negative integer" is based on the relationships of "magnitude" and "is the opposite of." Negative quantities exist only in relation to positive quantities. Arrows on the number line model opposite relationships, in terms of direction and size or magnitude, according to length.

Ineffective Use of Models and Manipulatives In addition to not making the distinction between a model and the concept it is used to represent, there are other ways that models or manipulatives can be used ineffectively. One of the most widespread misuses occurs when the teacher tells students, "Do as I do." There is a natural temptation to get out the materials and show children exactly how to use them. Children will blindly follow the teacher's directions, and it may even look as if they understand. It is just as possible to get students to move blocks around mindlessly as it is to teach them to "invert and multiply" mindlessly. Neither promotes thinking or aids in the development of concepts (Ball, 1992; Clements & Battista, 1990; Stein & Bovalino, 2001).

A natural result of over direction with the use of models is that children begin to use them as answer-getting devices, rather than as tools for exploring a concept. For example, if you have carefully shown and explained to students how to get an answer to a multiplication problem with a set of base-ten blocks, they may then set up the blocks to get the answer. However, they fail to focus on the patterns or processes that can be seen in modelling the problem with the blocks. A mindless procedure with a good manipulative is still just a mindless procedure.

Conversely, leaving students with insufficient focus or guidance results in non-productive and unsystematic investigation (Stein & Bovalino, 2001). Students may be engaged in conversations about the model they are using, but if they do not know what the mathematical goal is, the manipulative is not serving as a tool for developing the concept.

Technology-Based Models Technology provides another source of models and manipulatives. There are Web sites that have a range of virtual manipulatives available (e.g., geoboards, base-ten blocks, spinners, number lines, etc.). Virtual manipulatives are a good addition to physical models, because some students will prefer the electronic version. Moreover, they can have access to these tools outside the classroom.

It is important to include calculators in any list of common models. The calculator models a wide variety of numeric relationships by quickly and easily demonstrating the effects of these ideas. For example, if the calculator is made to count by increments of 0.01 (press ⊞ 0.01 ⊟), the relationship of one-hundredth to one whole is illustrated. Press 3 ⊞ 0.01. How many presses of ⊟ are required to get from 3 to 4? Doing the required 100 presses and observing how the display changes along the way is quite impressive. Especially note what happens after 3.19, 3.29, and so on.

Connecting the Dots

It seems appropriate to close this chapter by connecting some dots, especially because the ideas represented here are the foundation for the approach to each topic in the content chapters. This chapter began with discussing what *doing* mathematics is and challenged you to do some mathematics. Each of the tasks offered opportunities to make connections among mathematical concepts—connecting the blue dots.

Second, you read about learning theory—the importance of having opportunities to connect the dots. The best learning opportunities, according to constructivism and sociocultural theories, are those that engage the learner in using her or his own knowledge and experience to solve problems through social interaction and reflection. This is what you were to do in the four tasks. Did you learn something new about mathematics? Did you connect an idea that you had not previously connected?

Finally, you read about understanding—that relational knowledge (knowledge where blue dots are well connected) requires conceptual and procedural understanding, as well as other proficiencies. The problems that you solved in the first section included a focus on concepts and procedures while placing you in a position to use strategic competence, adaptive reasoning, and productive disposition.

In conclusion, this chapter focused on connecting the dots between theory and practice—building a case for teaching that focuses on opportunities for students to develop their own networks of blue dots. As you plan and design instruction, you should constantly reflect on how to elicit prior knowledge by designing tasks that reflect the social and cultural backgrounds of students, to challenge students to think critically and creatively, and to include a comprehensive treatment of mathematics.

Reflections on Chapter 2

Writing to Learn

1. How would you describe what it means to "do mathematics?"
2. Explain why we should assume that each child's knowledge and understanding of an idea are unique for that child.
3. What is reflective thought? Why is reflective thinking so important in the development of conceptual ideas in mathematics?
4. What does it mean to say that understanding exists on a continuum, ranging from relational to instrumental? Give an example of an idea, and explain how a student's understanding might fall on either end of the continuum of understanding, be it learned by rote or with understanding.
5. Explain why a model for a mathematical idea is not really an example of the idea. If it is not an example of the concept, what does it mean when we say we "see" the concept when we look at the model?

For Discussion and Exploration

1. Read the following problem and respond to the items:
   - Solve it using a strategy of choice.
   - Explain in words how you solved it.
   - Justify that your solution is correct.

> Some people say that to add four consecutive numbers, you add the first and last numbers and multiply by 2. Is this always true? How do you know? (Stoessiger & Edmunds, 1992).

2. Consider your most recent classroom experience in which mathematics was being taught. Would you say that the teaching reflected a constructivist view of learning? Why or why not? Did the teaching reflect a sociocultural view of learning?
3. Not every educator believes in Constructivism. A common argument goes something like this: "There is not enough time to let children discover everything. Basic facts and ideas are more efficiently taught through careful, well-planned, and meaningful explanations. Students should not have to 'reinvent the wheel.'" How would you respond to someone with this perception of school and learning?

Resources for Chapter 2

Recommendations for Further Reading

Articles

Ball, D. L. (1997). From the general to the particular: Knowing our own students as learners of mathematics. *Mathematics Teacher, 90,* 732–737.
Deborah Ball, one of the leading advocates for classroom discourse and listening to children, offers a thought-provoking example of third-grade thinking about fractions while raising our awareness of how difficult it is to see into the minds of children.

Berkman, R. M. (2006). One, some, or none: Finding beauty in ambiguity. *Mathematics Teaching in the Middle School, 11* (7), 324–327.
This article offers a great teaching strategy for nurturing relational thinking. Examples of the engaging "one, some, or none" activity are given for geometry, number, and algebra activities.

Buschman, L. (2003). Children who enjoy problem solving. *Teaching Children Mathematics, 9,* 539–544.
The focus of this article is the enjoyment that students achieve when they are making sense of mathematics themselves rather than following rules.

Flores, A. & Klein, E. (2005). From students' problem solving strategies to connections with fractions. *Teaching Children Mathematics, 11* (9), 452–457.
This outstanding article focuses on fractions, a topic for which students (and adults) often lack relational understanding. It also describes how connections can be made to other concepts.

Hedges, M., Huinker, D., & Steinmeyer, M. (2005). Unpacking division to build teachers' mathematical knowledge. *Teaching Children Mathematics 11* (9), 478–483.
Like the Flores and Klein article, this article offers a wonderful explanation of the concepts related to division. Student strategies are examined. From that, a collection of related concepts are proposed.

Lampert, M. (1990). When the problem is not the question and the solution is not the answer: Mathematical knowing and teaching. *American Educational Research Journal, 27,* 29–63. Reprinted in T. P. Carpenter, J. A. Dossey, & J. L. Koehler (Eds.), *Classics in mathematics education research* (pp. 152–171). Reston, VA: National Council of Teachers of Mathematics.

Magdelene Lampert is one of mathematics education's most articulate voices for making shifts toward classrooms as communities where children do mathematics. In this article, she articulates how the spirit of the traditional classroom adversely affects teachers' and students' concepts of mathematics.

Suh, J. (2007). Tying it all together: Classroom practices that promote mathematical proficiency for all students. *Teaching Children Mathematics, 14* (3), 163–169.

This is an excellent resource for teachers wanting to implement strategies for developing the five strands of mathematics proficiency described in Adding It Up *(NRC, 2001).*

Books

Lampert, M. (2001). *Teaching problems and the problems of teaching.* New Haven, CT: Yale University Press.

Lampert reflects on her personal experiences teaching grade 5 and shares with us her perspectives on the many issues and complexities of teaching. It is wonderfully written and easily accessed at any point in the book.

Mokros, J., Russell, S. J., & Economopoulos, K. (1995). *Beyond arithmetic: Changing mathematics in the elementary classroom.* Palo Alto, CA: Dale Seymour Publications.

These authors/researchers of the Investigation in Number, Data, and Space *curriculum use numerous examples from the elementary classroom to develop an image of teaching mathematics from a problem-solving perspective. In looking at teaching, curriculum, and assessment, the importance of problem solving as a way of learning mathematics is quite clear.*

Online Resources

A Maths Dictionary for Kids
www.amathsdictionaryforkids.com
This site features an extensive dictionary, with each word illustrated by way of a small interactive explanation.

Classic Problems
www.mathforum.org/dr.math/faq/faq.classic.problems.html
A nice collection of well-known problems (Train A leaves the station at...) along with discussion, solutions, and extensions.

Constructivism
http://carbon.ucdenver.edu/~mryder/itc_data/ constructivism.html
Based at the University of Colorado, Denver, this site lists definitions and numerous papers on constructivist theories from Dewey to von Glasersfeld and Vygotsky.

Constructivism in the Classroom
http://mathforum.org/mathed/constructivism.html
Provided by the Math Forum, this page contains links to numerous sites concerning constructivism as well as articles written by researchers.

Mathematically Sane: Analysis
http://mathematicallysane.com/analysis.asp
This site features articles by authors who have analyzed issues in mathematics education.

Utah State University National Library of Virtual Manipulatives
http://nlvm.usu.edu/en/nav/vlibrary.html
A robust collection of virtual manipulatives. A great site to bookmark and use. Here are two favourite applets to check out from this site:

Circle 21
http://nlvm.usu.edu/en/nav/frames_asid_188_g_2_t_1.html
A puzzle that involves adding positive and negative integers to add to 21.

How High?
http://nlvm.usu.edu/en/nav/category_g_3_t_3.html
This is a conservation of volume activity. The student predicts what the height of liquid from one container will be when it is poured into a second container.

---

myeducationlab *will help you improve your understanding of the concepts taught in this textbook and in your course. This online tool includes videos of real classroom experiences, sample lesson plans, simulations, case studies, and links to important educational and teaching Web sites that will help you make the transition from student to teacher. As you study in your course and with this textbook, please follow along in* **MyEducationLab**. *Use it! Explore it! And improve your knowledge and your grade!*

Chapter 3
Teaching Through Problem Solving

Allowing the subject to be problematic means allowing students to wonder why things are, to inquire, to search for solutions, and to resolve incongruities. It means that both the curriculum and instruction should begin with problems, dilemmas, and questions for students.

Hiebert et al. (1996, p. 12)

For over two decades since publication of the original NCTM Standards document (1989), evidence has continued to mount that problem solving is a powerful and effective vehicle for learning. As Principles and Standards (2000) states:

> Solving problems is not only a goal of learning mathematics but also a major means of doing so.... Problem solving is an integral part of all mathematics learning, and so it should not be an isolated part of the mathematics program. Problem solving in mathematics should involve all the five content areas described in these Standards.... Good problems will integrate multiple topics and will involve significant mathematics. (p. 52)

In a classic publication (Schroeder & Lester, 1989), two researchers in the area of problem solving in mathematics identified three ways that problem solving might be incorporated into mathematics instruction.

1. *Teaching for problem solving.* This approach follows the format of many textbooks where a skill, which can be used later to problem solve, is taught first. Rather than building on prior knowledge, teaching for problem solving often starts with learning the abstract concept, then moves to solving problems as a way to apply the learned skill. For example, students learn the algorithm for adding fractions. Once this is mastered, they solve story problems that involve adding fractions.

2. *Teaching about problem solving.* This second approach involves teaching students how to problem solve. This approach can include teaching the process (understand the problem, develop a strategy, implement the strategy, look back) or the strategies for problem solving. An example of a strategy is "draw a picture." Here, students draw a picture or a diagram to help solve the problem. Strategies such as this one are discussed in more detail later in this chapter, in the section "Teaching about Problem Solving."

3. *Teaching through problem solving.* In this approach, students generally learn mathematics *through* real life contexts, problems, situations, and models. The contexts and models allow students to build meaning for the concepts so that they can then move to abstract concepts. Teaching *through* problem solving might be described as upside down from teaching *for* problem solving—with the problem(s) presented at the beginning of a lesson and skills emerging from working with the problem(s). For example, exploring the situation of combining $1/2$ hour and $1/3$ hour to figure out how much time the class spent on a mathematics project that morning, would lead students to discover a procedure for adding fractions.

Learning through problem solving is the topic of this chapter and a central theme of this book.

Teaching Through Problem Solving

Most, if not all, important mathematical concepts and procedures can best be taught through problem solving. This statement is a reflection of the views promoted in the *Principles and Standards* document, the *Foundation for the Atlantic Canada Mathematics Curriculum*, the *Common Curriculum Framework of the Western and Northern Canadian Protocol*, and other regional documents. As well, it represents current thinking of researchers in mathematics education.

Tasks or problems can and should be posed that engage students in thinking about and developing the important mathematics they need to learn. Let's examine why this approach better supports student learning.

Problems and Tasks for Learning Mathematics

A *problem* is defined here as any task or activity for which the students have no prescribed or memorized rules or methods, nor is there a perception by students that there is a specific "correct" solution method (Hiebert et al., 1997).

A *problem* for learning mathematics also has these features:

- *It must begin where the students are.* The design or selection of the task must take into consideration the students' current understanding. Students should have the appropriate ideas to engage and solve the problem; yet still find it challenging and interesting.
- *The problematic or engaging aspect of the problem must be due to the mathematics that the students are to learn.* In solving the problem or doing the activity, students should be concerned primarily with making sense of the mathematics involved; thereby developing their understanding of those ideas. Although it is desirable to have contexts for problems that make them interesting, these aspects should not be the focus of the activity. Nor should non-mathematical activity (e.g., cutting and pasting, colouring graphs, etc.) detract from the mathematics involved.
- *It must require justifications and explanations for answers and methods.* Students should understand that the responsibility for determining whether answers are correct and why they are correct rests with them, not the teacher. Justification should be an integral part of their solutions.

It is important to understand that mathematics is to be taught *through* problem solving. That is, problem-based tasks or activities are the vehicle by which the desired curriculum is developed. The learning is an outcome of the problem-solving process.

A Shift in the Role of Problems

Schroeder's and Lester's first suggestion, teaching for problem solving (described earlier), as a way to incorporate problem solving into instruction, is strongly engrained in our culture as the way to teach mathematics. The teacher presents the mathematics, the students practise the skill, then they use the new skill for solving story problems. Unfortunately, this approach to teaching mathematics has not been successful in supporting student learning and retention of mathematical concepts.

- The approach assumes that all students have necessary prior knowledge (the blue dots described in Chapter 2) to make sense of the teacher's explanation.
- The teacher usually presents only one way to do a problem, communicating that this is the only way to solve the problem, even though this is not necessarily the case. Moreover, solving the problem in this way may or may not be the most accessible approach for all students.
- A show-and-tell approach places students in the role of passive learners, dependent on the teacher to present ideas, rather than allowing them to be independent thinkers, who use their knowledge to develop their own approaches to solving problems.
- When problem solving is not an inherent part of skills and concepts development, mathematics learning is diminished. Not only do students feel that they are not capable of solving these problems, but they do not see the connections.
- Students accustomed to being told how to do mathematics are unlikely to attempt a new problem without explicit instructions regarding how to solve it. Yet, that's what doing mathematics is all about—figuring out an approach for solving the problem at hand.

Some teachers may think that showing students how to solve a set of problems, rather than letting them struggle, and thereby saving time, is the best approach. However, students are not learning content for deep understanding, often forgetting what they have learned. A more effective approach to learning mathematics is needed.

Effective lessons begin where the students are, not where teachers are. That is, teaching should begin with the ideas that children already have, the ideas they will use to create new ones. To engage students requires tasks or activities that are problem based and require thought. Students learn mathematics as a *result* of solving problems. Mathematical ideas are the *outcomes* of the problem-solving experience, rather than elements that must be taught before problem solving occurs (Hiebert et al., 1996, 1997). Furthermore, the process of solving problems is now completely interwoven with the learning; children are *learning* mathematics by *doing* mathematics!

The Value of Teaching Through Problem Solving

Teaching through problem solving requires a paradigm shift, which means that a teacher needs to change more than a few things about her teaching. She needs to change her philosophy regarding how she thinks children learn and how she can best help them to learn. At first glance, it may seem that the teacher's role is less demanding because the students are doing the thinking. However, the reverse is actually the case.

Teachers must select quality tasks that provide students with the opportunity to learn the content by figuring out their own strategies and solutions. They must then prompt and ask high quality questions that allow students to verify and relate their strategies. Engaging in this process allows students to gain a deeper understanding of mathematical concepts and ideas. There are good reasons to go to the effort involved in teaching through problem solving.

- *It focuses students' attention on ideas and sense making.* When solving problems, students are necessarily reflecting on the concepts inherent in the problems. Emerging ideas are more likely to be integrated with existing ones, thereby improving understanding. By contrast, no matter how skillfully a teacher provides explanations and directions, students will attend to the directions but rarely to the concepts and the connections.
- *It develops students' confidence and beliefs that they are capable of doing mathematics and that mathematics makes sense.* Every time teachers pose a problem-based task and expect a solution, they say to students, "I believe you can do this." Every time the class solves a problem and students develop their understanding, confidence and self-worth are enhanced.
- *It provides a context to help students build meaning for the concept.* Providing a context, especially when that context is grounded in an experience familiar to students, supports the development of mathematical concepts. Such an approach provides students access to the mathematics, allowing them to successfully learn the content.
- *It allows an entry point for a wide range of students.* Good problem-based tasks have multiple paths to the solution. Students may solve 42 − 26 by counting out a set of 42 counters and removing 26; by adding onto 26 in various ways; to get to 42, by subtracting 20 from 42, then taking off 6 more; by counting forward (or backward) on a hundreds chart; or by using a standard computational method. Each student gets to make sense of the task using his or her own ideas. Furthermore, students expand on these ideas and grow in their understanding as they hear and reflect on the solution strategies of others. In contrast, the teacher-directed approach ignores diversity, to the detriment of most students.
- *It provides ongoing assessment data useful for making instructional decisions, helping students succeed, and informing parents.* As students discuss ideas, draw pictures or use manipulatives, defend their solutions and evaluate those of others, and write reports and explanations, they provide the teacher with a steady stream of valuable information. These products provide rich evidence of how students are solving problems, what misconceptions they might have, and how they are connecting and applying new concepts. With a better understanding of what students know, a teacher can plan more effectively and accommodate each student's learning needs.
- *It allows for extensions and elaboration.* Extensions and "what if" questions can motivate advanced learners or quick finishers, resulting in increased learning and enthusiasm for doing mathematics. Such problems can be configured to meet the needs of a range of learners.
- *It engages students so that there are fewer discipline problems.* Many discipline issues in a classroom are the result of students becoming bored, not understanding the teacher's directions, or simply finding little relevance in the task. Most students like to be challenged and enjoy being permitted to solve problems in ways that make sense to them. Hence, there is less reason to act out or to cause trouble.
- It *develops "mathematical power."* Students solving problems in class will be engaged in all five of the processes of doing mathematics, problem solving, reasoning, communication, connections, and representation, as described in Mathematical Processes, in the *Principles and Standards* document.
- *It is a lot of fun!* Teachers who teach through problem solving never return to a teach-by-telling mode. The excitement of students developing understanding through their own reasoning is worth all the effort.

Examples of Problem-Based Tasks

In Chapter 2, you saw that mathematical knowledge could be categorized as conceptual or procedural. Students can learn both types of knowledge through problem-based activities. Here are some examples in each category.

Conceptual Mathematics

As described in Chapter 2, concepts are the foundational ideas on which understanding builds. For example, concepts related to multiplication include the ideas of repeated addition ($4 \times 5 = 5 + 5 + 5 + 5$) and area (a carpet that is 4 metres by 5 metres has an area of 20 square metres, m^2). The following two examples briefly describe how concepts can be presented through problem solving.

Concept: Partitioning

Grades: K–1

Think about the number 6 broken into two different amounts. Draw a picture to show a way that six things can be broken into two parts. Think up a story to go with your picture.

At the kindergarten or grade 1 level, the teacher may want students simply to think about different parts of 6 and to connect these ideas into a context. In grade 1 or 2, the teacher may challenge children to find all of the combinations rather than focus on the story or context. There is a nice relationship and pattern to be constructed. In a class discussion following work on the task, students are likely to develop an orderly process for listing all seven of the combinations: As one part grows from 0 to 6, the other part begins at 6 and shrinks by ones to 0.

The second task focuses on the approximate size of a fraction, a concept that is poorly understood by most students.

Concept: Estimating Fractions Greater Than 1

Grades: 4–6

Place an X on the number line about where $1\frac{1}{8}$ would be. Explain why you put your X where you did. Perhaps you will want to draw and label other points on the line to help explain your answer.

Note that the task includes a suggestion for how to respond but does not specify exactly what must be done. Students are able to use their own level of reasoning and understanding to justify their answers. In the follow-up discussion, the teacher may well expect to see a variety of justifications from which to help the class refine ideas about fractions that are greater than 1.

Concept: Comparing Ratios and Proportional Reasoning

Grades: 6–8

Jack and Jill were at the bottom of a hill, hoping to fetch a pail of water. Jack walks uphill at the rate of 5 steps every 25 seconds, while Jill walks at a rate of 3 steps every 10 seconds. Assuming each keeps a constant walking rate, who will get the pail of water first?

This problem can be used as one of a number of tasks for introducing proportional reasoning. Students can solve the problem in a variety of ways, including setting up ratios. Students may also use a rate approach. The discussion about this task and others that may be used will focus on the ways that students compared the ratios, which is the essence of proportional reasoning.

Algorithms and Processes

Some teachers falsely assume that procedures must be taught through direct instruction. In reality, students can develop algorithms via a problem-solving approach. The distinction between direct instruction and the problem-solving approach is in who determines the approach to solving the problem. When students learn computation through problem solving, they figure out how they will solve the problem. This is a major shift from showing students only one algorithm that they are to use. The following two examples demonstrate this approach.

The first example is a grade 1–2 lesson on two-digit addition. The lesson begins with the teacher posing the following questions: What is the sum of 48 and 25? How did you figure it out? Even though there is no story or situation to resolve, this is a problem because students must figure out how they are going to approach the task. Students work on the problem using manipulatives, pictures, or other tools. After students have solved the problem in their own way, the teacher gathers the students together to hear one another's strategies and solutions.

In one grade 2 classroom, students offered at least seven different solution methods (Russell, 1997). Two children employed two different counting techniques using a hundreds chart (a 10 by 10 chart numbered from 1 in the box, at the top left corner, in the first row to 100 in the box, in the bottom right corner, in the last row) for assistance. Here are solutions of some of the others:

$4\boxed{8} + 2\boxed{5}$ (Boxed digits help "hold" them.)

$40 + 20 = 60$

$8 + 2 = 10$ $\boxed{3}$ (The 3 is left from the 5.)

$60 + 10 = 70$

$70 + 3 = 73$

$40 + 20 = 60$

$60 + 8 = 68$

$68 + 5 = 73$

$48 + 20 = 68$

$68 + 2$ ("*from the 5*") $= 70$

"*Then I still have that 3 from the 5.*"

$70 + 3 = 73$

$$25 + 25 = 50 \quad \boxed{23}$$
$$50 + 23 = 73$$

Teacher: Where does the 23 come from?

"It's sort of from the 48."

How did you split up the 48?

"20 and 20 and I split the 8 into 5 and 3."

$$48 - 3 = 45 \quad \boxed{3}$$
$$45 + 25 = 70$$
$$70 + 3 = 73$$

The students in this class show a variety of levels of thinking and many interesting techniques. They had learned from each other the trick of placing numbers in "hold boxes," although not everyone used it. The children who are counting on the hundreds chart are showing that they may not yet have developed adequate place-value tools to understand these more sophisticated methods. Or the class discussion may help them activate those ideas or "dots" they simply had not considered. One question asks, "Are these invented methods efficient or adequate?" Students need to consider a variety of methods and make their determinations.

Imagine for yourself what might happen if grade 5 students were asked to add $3.72 + 1.6$ before being told about lining up decimal points. Many students would do it incorrectly, perhaps aligning the 2 and 6 or the 3 and 1. The decimal may be placed in various places. But students attempting to defend their solutions will need to confront the size of the answer and the meaning of the digits in each position. A class of practised problem solvers will soon develop a solid approach for adding decimals.

Gary Tsuruda is a teacher of grades 7 and 8, who wrote a book about his successful problem-based mathematics classroom (Tsuruda, 1994). His classes frequently work in small groups to solve problems. The following example (Figure 3.1) is a lesson on the formula for the area of a trapezoid. Rather than state the algorithm and have students plug numbers into the formula, students use a problem-based approach that fosters understanding of the formula. Notice that the initial questions bring requisite ideas needed for the task to the students' conscious level. Next they are asked to do some exploration and look for patterns. From these explorations the group must come up with a formula, test it, describe how it was developed, and illustrate its use.

Tsuruda (1994) reports that every group was able to produce a formula. "Not all the formulas looked like the typical textbook formula, but they were all correct, and more important, each formula made sense according to the way the students in that group had constructed the knowledge from the data they themselves had generated" (p. 6).

TRAPEZOID AREA

Problem: *Find an easy way to determine the area of any trapezoid.*

Be sure that you understand the answers to each of these questions:

1. What does "area" mean?
2. What is a trapezoid?
3. How do you find the area of other polygons? Show as many different ways as you can.

Now see if your group can find an easy way to determine the area of any trapezoid.

Hints:

1. Draw several trapezoids on dot paper and find their areas. Look for patterns.
2. Consider how you find the area of other polygons. Are any of the key ideas similar?
3. You might try cutting out trapezoids and piecing them together.
4. If you find a way to determine the area, make sure it is as easy as you can make it and that it works for *any* trapezoid.

Write-up:

1. Explain your answers to the first three questions in detail. Tell how your group reached agreement on the answers.
2. Tell what you did to get your formula for the area of any trapezoid. Did you use any of the hints? How did they help you?
3. Show your formula and give an illustration of how it works.

Figure 3.1 A middle school example in which students are required to construct a formula.

Source: From *Putting It Together: Middle School Math in Transition* (p. 7), by G. Tsuruda, 1994, Portsmouth, NH: Heinemann, a division of Reed Elsevier Inc. Reprinted by permission of Gary Tsuruda.

In all of these examples of problem-based lessons, the students are very much engaged in the processes of doing mathematics—figuring out procedures, not accepting them blindly. What is abundantly clear is that the more problem solving students do, the more willing and confident they become about solving problems and the more methods they develop for attacking future problems (Campbell, 1996; Lester, 1994; Rowan & Bourne, 1994; Schifter & Fosnot, 1993; Silver, Smith, & Nelson, 1995; Silver & Stein, 1996; Wood, Cobb, Yackel, & Dillon, 1993).

Selecting or Designing Problem-Based Tasks and Lessons

A key element in teaching with problems is the selection of appropriate problems or tasks. A task is effective when it helps students learn the ideas you want them to learn. It must be the mathematics in the task that makes it problematic for the students so that the mathematical ideas are their primary concern. Therefore, the first and most important consideration for selecting any task for your class must be the mathematics. That said, where do you look for tasks?

Multiple Entry Points

One of the advantages of a problem-based approach is that it can help accommodate the diversity of learners in every classroom. A problem-based approach does not dictate how a child must think about a problem in order to solve it. When a task is posed, students are told, in essence, "Use the ideas *you* own to solve this problem." Because of the range of students' mental tools, concepts, and ideas, many students in a class will have different ideas about the best way to complete a task. Thus, access to the problem by all students demands that there be multiple entry points— different places to "get on the ramp"—to reach solutions.

Once we stop thinking that there is only one way to solve a problem, it is not quite as difficult to develop good "ramp-up problems" or problems with multiple entry points. Although many problems have singular correct answers, there are often many ways to get there. Nearly all the problems presented in this chapter have multiple entry points, as in the following two examples.

Concept: Area

Grades: 3–4

Find the area of the cover of your math book. That is, how many square tiles will fit on the cover of the book?

Concept: Division of Fractions

Grades: 5-6

Clara has two whole pizzas and $1/3$ of another. All the pizzas are the same size. If each of her friends will want to eat $1/4$ of a pizza, how many friends will she be able to feed with the $2\frac{1}{3}$ pizzas?

❚❚ ————————— *Pause and Reflect*

See if you can think of more than one path to the solution for these two problems. Try to think of an approach that is near the bottom of the "ramp" (less sophisticated) and another that is closer to the middle or the top of the "ramp." Do this now before reading further.

The area problem can be solved with materials that directly attack the meaning of the problem. The cover of the book can be completely covered with tiles, which can

then be counted one at a time. Moving slightly up the ramp to a higher entry point, a child may cover the book with tiles but count only the length of the row and the number of rows, multiplying to get the total. Another child may place tiles only along the edges of the book and multiply. Yet another child may use a ruler to measure the book edges, noting that the tiles are 2 cm on each side.

For the pizza task, a direct approach is also possible. Plastic circular fraction pieces (or a drawing) can be used to represent $2\frac{1}{3}$ pizzas, and pieces equal to $1/4$ can be placed on top of these until no more will fit. Another child may know that four-fourths make a whole; therefore, two of the pizzas will feed eight friends. Children may or may not know how many fourths they can get from the $1/3$ piece and will have to tackle that part accordingly. A guess-and-check approach is possible, starting with perhaps six children, then seven, and so on until the pizza is gone. A few children may have learned a computational method for dividing $2\frac{1}{3}$ by $1/4$.

Having thought about these possible entry points, the teacher will be better prepared to suggest appropriate hints for students who are "stuck," depending on what they bring to the task.

Creating Meaningful and Engaging Contexts

Certainly one of the most powerful features of teaching through problem solving is that you can begin a lesson with a problem that gets students excited about learning mathematics. Compare these grade 5–6 introductory lessons on two-dimensional shapes:

> "Today we are going to identify and classify two-dimensional shapes by geometric properties related to symmetry, angles, and sides."
>
> "Today we're going to make tangrams from this lovely coloured paper, after I read you the book, *Grandfather Tang's Story*. Does anyone know what a tangram is?"

Contexts that provide opportunities for students to learn about different cultures, particularly those of their classmates, can be used for promoting teaching through problem solving. Connecting mathematics to other subject areas, as shown in the following sections, is another way. Children's literature, culturally relevant applications, and linking to other disciplines (e.g., science) are explored here for their potential to engage students in learning mathematics.

NCTM *Standards* "By analyzing and adapting a problem, anticipating the mathematical ideas that can be brought out by working on the problem, and anticipating students' questions, teachers can decide if particular problems will help to further their mathematical goals for the class" (NCTM, 2000, p. 53).

Children's Literature

Children's literature is a rich source of problems at all levels, not just primary. Children's stories can be used in numerous ways to create reflective tasks at all grade levels, and there are many excellent books to help you in this area (Ward, 2006, Bay-Williams & Martinie, 2004; Whitin & Whitin, 2004; Theissen, Matthias, & Smith, 1998; Karp, Brown, Allen, & Allen, 1998; Bresser, 1995; Sheffield, 1995; Burns, 1992; Welchman-Tischler, 1992; Whitin & Wilde, 1992, 1995).

By way of example, a very popular children's book, *The Doorbell Rang* (Hutchins, 1986), can be used to explore different concepts at various grade levels. The story is a sequential tale of children sharing 12 cookies. On each page, more children come to the kitchen, and the 12 cookies must be redistributed. This simple yet engaging story can lead to exploring ways to make equal parts of almost any number for children at the K–2 level. It is a springboard for multiplication and division at the 3–4 level. It can also be used to explore fraction concepts at the 4–6 level.

For older students, the novel, *The Mob*, the first of a trilogy entitled *Feather and Bone, The Crow Chronicles* by Calgary-based Canadian author Clem Martini, also offers an excellent opportunity for students to engage in mathematics. Migration experiences are central to this novel, which focuses on a crow family, the Kinaars, faced with troubled times. Students in grade 6 could investigate the migratory patterns of crows and design migratory time lines on butcher-block paper. This would require them to calculate how long it takes and the places that crows pass through in their migratory flights. They could also do this for other birds mentioned in the book and compare these migratory time lines with that of crows. Students in grades 7–8 could calculate distances travelled in relation to time spent traveling for crows and other birds of interest. They could then figure out average time/per day spent in migra-

Teachers may use children's literature as a rich source of problems. Literature may also be used in numerous ways to create reflective tasks at all grade levels.

tion. A comparison chart could be created to compare this data. Students might then compare how long it might take them to travel these routes using different modes of transportation and calculate costs to travel these distances.

Several recent teacher resources focus on using non-fiction literature for teaching mathematics (Bay-Williams & Martinie, 2008; Petersen, 2004; Sheffield & Gallagher, 2004). Non-fiction literature can include newspapers, magazines, and the Web—all great sources for problems that have the added benefit of students learning about the world around them.

For example, an article appeared on the Web site of the *Manchester Evening News*, in England (Leeming, 2007), explaining that the Cool Cash Lottery Scratchcard, created by a company named Camelot, had to be recalled because the integer values were too difficult for many people:

> To qualify for a prize, users had to scratch a window to reveal a temperature lower than the value displayed on each card. As the game had a winter theme, the temperature was usually below freezing. Camelot received dozens of complaints on the first day from players who could not understand how, for example, –5 is higher than –6.... [One person] said, "On one of my cards it said I had to find temperatures lower than –8. The numbers I uncovered were –6 and –7 so I thought I had won and so did the woman in the shop. But when she scanned the card the machine said I hadn't.

Can you think of a good problem, using a non-fiction resource, to pose to students? One task could be to ask students to prepare an illustration with an explanation that could help adults such as these understand the value of negative numbers.

The end of the chapters in Section 2 include a section titled "Literature Connections" that suggests picture books, poetry, and novels that could be used to explore the mathematics of that chapter. Literature ideas are often found in the articles of NCTM's journals and in provincial mathematics association periodicals. It is an exciting approach to creating lessons with a problem-solving scenario.

Links to Other Disciplines

Finding relevant contexts for engaging the diversity of learners in a class can be challenging. However, using contexts familiar to all students can be effective. An excellent source for problems is other subject matter that students are studying. Ideas can be taken from topics being taught in social studies, science, and language arts. Other familiar contexts for older children, such as art, sports, and pop culture, can also be valuable.

In kindergarten, the study of life sciences and mathematics can be integrated by having children sort leaves based on a range of rules such as colour, smooth or jagged edges, feel of the leaf, and shape. Students learn about rules for sorting and about observing and analyzing what is the same and different about leaves from different trees. Sorting and measuring, topics in mathematics and science, are concepts that can be explored in other grades. Older students can classify plants and animals according to external and internal features. In mathematics, they can investigate and compare animals according to size and/or mass. Patterning is another area where mathematics can be integrated with other subject areas. Students can use patterns found in charts and tables to explore the world around them in both mathematics and science, as well as in social studies.

Visual arts offers many opportunities for making real life connections with mathematics. It also offers excellent ways to explore the multicultural aspects of mathematics. This is an excellent way to make the study of mathematics more inclusive. Students can explore patterns in art and architecture of different cultures, connecting it to the study of tessellations in geometry.

Different architectural structures can be examined as part of the study of the characteristics and features of three-dimensional shapes.

 The Equity Principle challenges teachers to believe that every student brings something of value to the tasks that they pose to their classes. The Teaching Principle calls for teachers to select tasks that "can be solved in more than one way, such as using an arithmetic counting approach, drawing a geometric diagram and enumerating possibilities, or using algebraic equations [so that tasks are] accessible to students with varied prior knowledge and experience" (NCTM, 2000, p. 19).

How to Find Quality Tasks and Problem-Based Lessons

Abundant mathematics teaching resources are available in print along with a nearly endless supply of ideas on the Web. Searching for the right task for a particular lesson can be a time-consuming task. Knowing what makes a good task and where to start looking can be helpful.

A Task Selection Guide

Throughout this book, in every student textbook, and in every article you read or in-service workshop you attend, you will find suggestions for activities, problems, tasks, or explorations that someone believes are effective in helping children learn some aspect of mathematics. As well-known mathematics educators, Lappan and Briars (1995) contend that selecting activities or tasks is the most significant decision teachers make that affect students' learning. Figure 3.2 shows a four-step guide you can use when considering a new activity for your students.

Activity Evaluation and Selection Guide

STEP 1: How Is the Activity Done?

Actually do the activity. Try to get "inside" the task or activity to see how it is done and what thinking might go on.

How would *children* do the activity or solve the problem?

- What materials are needed?
- What is written down or recorded?
- What misconceptions may emerge?

STEP 2: What Is the Purpose of the Activity?

What *mathematical ideas* will the activity develop?

- Are the ideas concepts or procedural skills?
- Will there be connections to other related ideas?

STEP 3: Can the Activity Accomplish Your Learning Goals?

What is *problematic* about the activity? Is the problematic aspect related to the mathematics you identified in the purpose?

What *must* children reflect on or think about to complete the activity? (Don't rely on wishful thinking.)

Is it possible to complete the activity without much reflective thought? If so, can it be modified so that students will be required to think about the mathematics?

STEP 4: What Must You Do?

What will you need to do in the *before* portion of your lesson?

- How will you activate students' prior knowledge?
- What will the students be expected to produce?

What might you anticipate seeing and asking in the *during* portion of your lesson?

What will you want to focus on in the *after* portion of your lesson?

Figure 3.2 A process for selecting effective tasks, mathematics, or activities.

The third step in Figure 3.2 is the most important point in determining if the activity is a good fit for the content you are teaching. What is problematic about the activity? How will the activity improve the chances that the children will be mentally active, reflecting on and constructing the ideas you identified for the lesson?

Try to predict what students will do with the activity. Think about how students might have difficulty with the task. Difficulties are usually the best opportunities for learning, but you would like to anticipate them if possible.

Practise using this evaluation and selection guide with activities throughout this book. Work toward thinking about tasks or activities from the view of what is likely to happen inside children's minds, not just what they are doing with their hands. Good tasks are minds-on activities, not just hands-on activities.

⏸ *Pause and Reflect*

Suppose your goal is for students to learn some of the more challenging multiplication facts they had not yet mastered (grades 3 or 4). You pose the task on page 46 about finding a helping fact. Think about the questions in step 3 of Figure 3.2. Do you think this will be an effective activity for your students? Why? Can you make it better? How?

Illuminations, the resource Web site of the NCTM, is perhaps the best portal for finding high-quality lessons on the Internet. Besides over 100 posted activities that use engaging applets, there are more than 500 full lesson plans as well as links to many high-quality Web sites, searchable by content and by grade level. A definite site to bookmark on your computer is http://illuminations.nctm.org.

Another excellent source for finding lesson plans, activities, and applets can be found in your provincial and territorial curriculum documents and mathematics association.

Standards-Based Programs

If your school is using a "standards-based" mathematics program, then you will likely find that most of the lessons are already geared to a problem-solving mode. Your main difficulty may be assuring yourself that all the skills and concepts of your local curriculum are appropriately emphasized. Some units may need additional activities or modifications based on the needs of your students; others you may decide to skip.

Teaching about Problem Solving

As discussed in the first section of this chapter, teaching about problem solving means explicitly teaching students how to solve problems. Although this is also part of teaching through problem solving, there are times when a teacher's goal needs to focus on teaching students a particular problem-solving strategy, such as "Make an Organized List." In teaching about problem solving, it is not only important to have students understand the process for solving problems; it is also important to teach general strategies that can be used for solving these problems.

Four-Step Problem-Solving Process

In his classic book, *How to Solve It*, which first appeared in 1945, George Polya, a famous mathematician, outlined four steps for solving mathematical problems. These widely adopted steps for solving problems continue to appear in many books and textbooks. Explicitly teaching these four steps to students can improve their ability to solve problems. The four steps are described very briefly in the following list:

1. *Understand the problem.* Briefly, this means figuring out what the problem is about, that is, identifying what question or problem is being posed.
2. *Devise a plan.* In this phase, you need to think about how to solve the problem. Will you want to write an equation? Will you want to model the problem with a manipulative? (See the next section, "Problem-Solving Strategies," for more on this one.)
3. *Carry out the plan.* This is the implementation phase of your plan.
4. *Look back.* This phase is arguably the most important, as well as the one most skipped by students. It is the moment you determine if your solution from step 3 answers the problem as originally understood in step 1. This is where you ask yourself "Does my answer make sense?"

As you teach through problem solving, using these steps to help guide your students will foster success. Your first step, once you pose a problem to students, is to be sure they understand it, the first step of Polya's process. You may also ask students for ideas on which strategies might work for the problem in order to get some ideas started for step 2. In this phase of the lesson, students are devising and carrying out a strategy they have selected (steps 2 and 3). Then, they look back to see if their solution makes sense (step 4). In the final stage of the lesson students share their strategy (step 2), how they solved the problem (step 3), and how they know it is correct (step 4). The beauty of Polya's framework is its generality. It can and should be applied to many different types of problems, from simple computational exercises to difficult multi-step problems.

Problem-Solving Strategies

Strategies for solving problems are identifiable methods for approaching a task that are completely independent of the specific topic or subject matter. Students select or design a strategy as they devise a plan (step 2). When students discover important or especially useful strategies, they should be identified, highlighted, and discussed. Labelling a strategy provides a useful means for students to talk about their methods and for you to provide hints and suggestions in the initial and development phases of a lesson. The following strategies are generally introduced in K–8 mathematics, though some may not be used at every grade level.

- *Draw a picture, act it out, use a model.* This is the strategy of using models and manipulatives described in Chapter 2. "Act It Out" extends models to a real interpretation of the problem situation.

- *Look for a pattern.* Pattern searching is at the heart of many problem-based tasks, especially in the algebraic reasoning strand. Patterns in number and in operations play a huge role in helping students learn about and master basic facts and continue to be a major factor into the middle- and high-school years.
- *Guess and check.* This might be called "Try and see what you can find out." A good way to work on a task that has you stumped is to try something. Make an attempt! Reflection even on a failed attempt can lead to a better idea.
- *Make a table or chart.* Charts of data, function tables, tables for operations, and tables involving ratios or measurements are a major form of analysis and communication. The use of a chart is often combined with pattern searching as a means of solving problems or constructing new ideas.
- *Try a simpler form of the problem.* Here the general idea is to modify or simplify the quantities in a problem so that the resulting task is easier to understand and analyze. Solving the easier problem can sometimes lead to insights that can then be used to solve the original, more complex problem.
- *Make an organized list.* Systematically accounting for all possible outcomes in a situation can show the number of possibilities there are or verify that all possible outcomes have been included. One subject area where organized lists are essential is probability.
- *Write an equation.* As it implies, in this strategy, the story is converted into numbers and symbols. The resulting equation is then solved.

It is important not to "proceduralize" problem solving. In other words, don't take the problem solving out of problem solving by telling students the strategy they should choose and how to do it. Instead, pose a problem that lends itself to the strategy you would like them to develop (e.g., make an organized list) and allow students to solve the problem any way they like. During the sharing of results, highlight student work that uses a list, or if no one uses a list, ask, "Could we have made an organized list to solve the problem more efficiently? What would that look like? Give it a try!"

 The first two goals of the problem-solving standard concern teaching through problem solving. The third and fourth goals refer to students learning about problem solving. It would be beneficial to check these goals for the grade that interests you most.

You might also check your provincial or territorial curriculum documents to see what it recommends for teaching problem solving for the particular grade which interests you.

Teaching in a Problem-Based Classroom

The ideas expressed throughout this chapter have been gathered from the research literature on teaching through problem solving and from elementary and middle school teachers who have been working hard at developing a problem-based approach in their classrooms. The following are important distinctions and considerations in planning for such a mathematics classroom.

Let Students Do the Talking

The value of classroom discussion of ideas cannot be overemphasized. As students describe and evaluate solutions to tasks, share approaches, and make conjectures, learning will occur in ways that are unlikely to occur, otherwise. Students begin to take ownership of ideas and develop a sense of power in making sense of mathematics.

When students are given a task, they should understand that one of their responsibilities is to prepare for a discussion that will occur after they have had an opportunity to work on the problem. One grade 4 teacher discovered that she was too involved in her class discussions. The students tended to wait for her questions rather than tell about their solutions. To help her students be more personally responsible, she devised three posters, inscribed as follows:

1. How did you solve the problem?
2. Why did you solve it this way?
3. Why do you think your solution is correct and makes sense?

In the beginning, students referred to the posters as they made presentations to the class, but soon that was not necessary. They continued to refer to the posters as they wrote up the solutions to problems during lesson development. Students began to prompt presenters: "You didn't answer the second question on the poster." One of the best results of these posters was that they helped remove the teacher from the content of the discussions.

Regardless of the exact structure or timeframe for a lesson, an opportunity for discourse should always be built in. After students have played a game, worked in a learning centre, completed a challenging worksheet, or engaged in a mental math activity with a full class, they can still discuss their activity: *What strategies worked well in the game? What did you find out in the learning centre? What are different ways to do this exercise?*

How Much to Tell and Not to Tell

When teaching through problem solving, one of the most perplexing dilemmas is how much to tell. On one hand, telling diminishes student reflection. Students who sense that the teacher has a preferred method or approach are more reluctant to use their own strategies. Nor will students develop self-confidence and problem-solving abilities by watching the teacher do the thinking. On the other hand, to tell too little can sometimes leave students floundering and waste precious class time.

While noting that there will never be a simple solution to this dilemma, researchers offered the following guidance: Teachers should feel free to share relevant information as long as the mathematics in the task remains problematic for the students (Hiebert et al., 1997). That is, "information can and should be shared as long as it does not solve the problem [and] does not take away the need for students to reflect on the situation and develop solution methods they understand" (p. 36). They go on to suggest three types of information that teachers should provide to their students:

- *Mathematical conventions.* The social conventions of symbolism and terminology that are important in mathematics will never be developed through reflective thought. For example, representing "three and five equals eight" as "$3 + 5 = 8$" is a convention. Definitions and labels are also conventions. It is important to offer these symbols and words only when students need them or will find them useful. As a rule of thumb, symbolism and terminology should be introduced *after* concepts have been developed and then specifically as a means of expressing or labelling ideas.
- *Alternative methods.* You can, with care, suggest to students an alternative method or approach for solving a problem. You may also suggest more efficient recording procedures for student-invented computational methods. For example, suggesting students draw a vertical line between the tens and ones place as a way of keeping track of the value of digits can be effective for students who have difficulty organizing information and possibly understanding place value. The value of a procedure should be grounded in both accuracy and efficiency. Engage students in evaluating procedures by asking whether their procedure always works and if it is efficient. Encourage students to decide which procedure they might use the next time they encounter a similar problem.
- *Clarification of students' methods.* You should help students clarify or interpret their ideas and perhaps point out related ideas. A student may add 38 and 5 by noting that 38 and 2 more is 40 with 3 more making 43. This strategy can be related to the make-ten strategy used to add 8 + 3. The selection of 40 as a midpoint in this procedure is an important place-value concept. Such clarifications are reinforcing for the students who have the ideas. Discussion or clarification of students' ideas

focuses attention on ideas you want the class to learn. Teacher attention to one method should not be done in such a way as to suggest that it is the preferred approach.

The Importance of Student Writing

There are many reasons to use writing in a mathematics classroom. The most important is that it improves student learning and understanding (Bell & Bell, 1985; Pugalee, 2005; Steele, 2007). There are other important related reasons, as well.

- *The act of writing is a reflective process.* As students make an effort to explain their thinking and defend their answers, they will spend more focused time thinking about the ideas involved.
- *Writing explanations allows students to think of themselves as mathematical thinkers.* When we provide experiences for students to write in mathematics, students begin to think about abstract ideas in a more meaningful way and to make connections between what they already know and what they are learning (Marks-Krpan, 2001).
- *A written report is a rehearsal for the discussion period.* It is difficult for students to explain how they solved a problem 15 minutes after they have done so. Students can always refer to a written report when asked to share. Even a kindergarten child can show a picture and talk about it. When every student has written about her or his solution, you need not ask for volunteers to share ideas.
- *A written report is also a written record that remains when the lesson is finished.* The reports can be collected and looked at later. The information can be used for planning, for finding out who needs help or opportunities to extend their knowledge, and for evaluation and teacher conferences.

It is important to help students understand what they are trying to accomplish in their written report. When you ask students to explain how they got their answer, they may just repeat each step, rather than explaining why they did what they did. Figures 3.3 and 3.4 illustrate a range of quality explanations. Modelling for students how to explain their thinking is essential. Using student work samples, such as those illustrated, can help students understand your expectations for them. To help elicit better explanations, you might consider the following two possible types of directions:

- Give students the following template to begin their report: "I (We) think the answer is ____. We think this because ____."
- "Use words, pictures, and numbers to explain how you got your answer and why you think your answer makes sense and is correct."

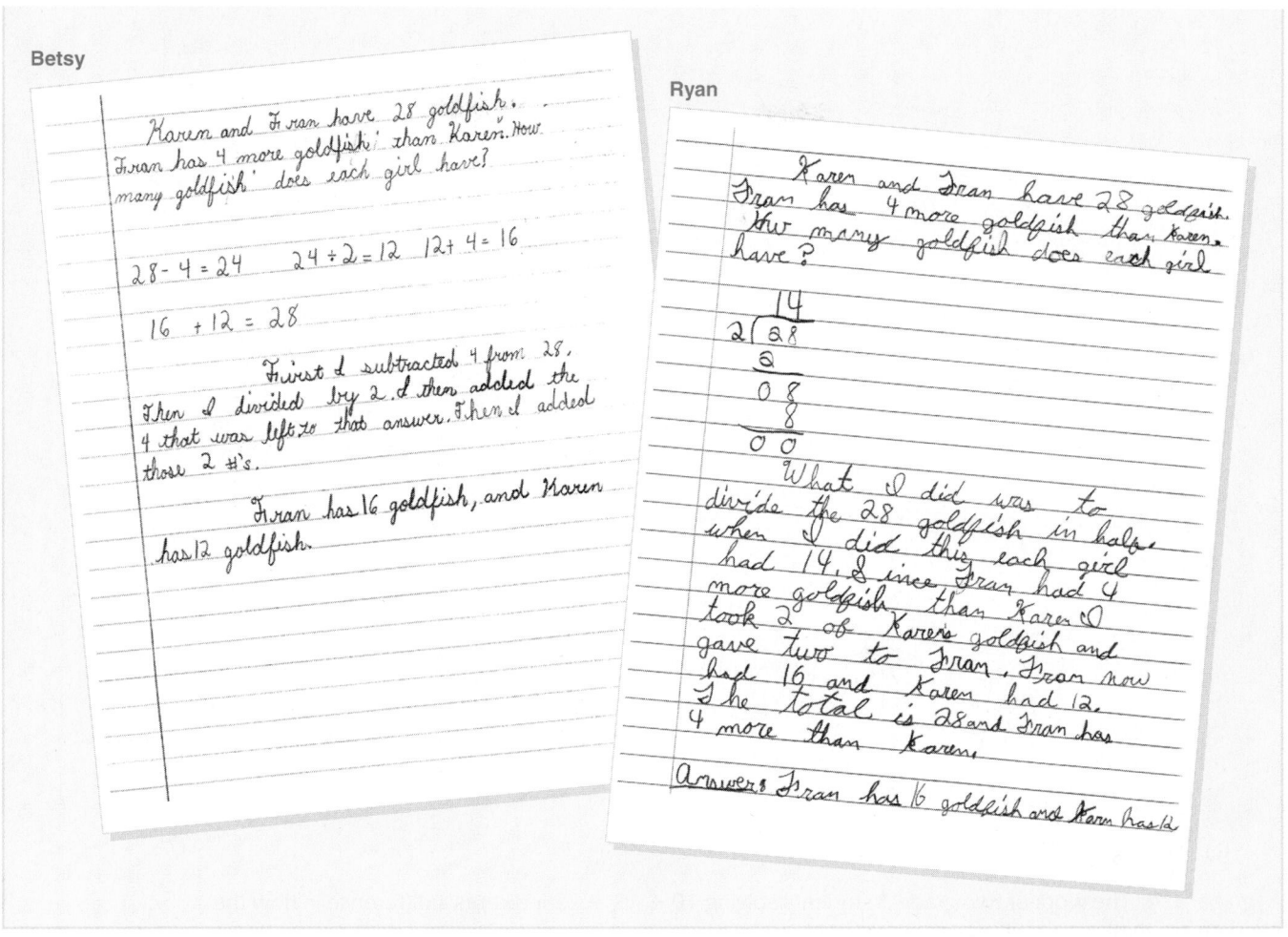

Figure 3.3 Betsy tells each step in her solution but provides no explanation. In contrast, Ryan's work includes reasons for his steps.

Technology Tools in Writing. Take advantage of the following free programs as part of allowing students to write, edit, and submit work to you electronically:

Text Editing
(real-time, collaborative tools)
- Google Docs & Spreadsheets (http://docs.google.com)
- Synchroedit (www.synchroedit.com)
- OpenEffort (www.openeffort.com/oe)
- Zoho Writer (http://zoho.com)

Wikis
(free, asynchronous, collaborative Web site creation tools)
- Wikispaces—includes ability to use math equations (www.wikispaces.com)
- Wiki-site—includes ability to use math equations (www.wiki-site.com)

- WikiLot—includes ability to use math equations (www. wikilot.com)
- XWiki—includes ability to use math equations (www.xwiki.com/xwiki/bin/view/Main/WebHome)
- Wikidot—includes ability to use math equations no ads (www.wikidot.com)

Blogging Tools
- Blogger (www.blogger.com)
- WordPress (wordpress.com)

Web-based tools such as these can be used inside and outside the (physical) mathematics classroom to allow students and teachers to collaboratively draft, read, and edit each other's mathematical ideas. Students who are reluctant to write by hand or in a word document could be motivated by the more interactive technologies, increasing the likelihood that they will produce quality written explanations and illustrations.

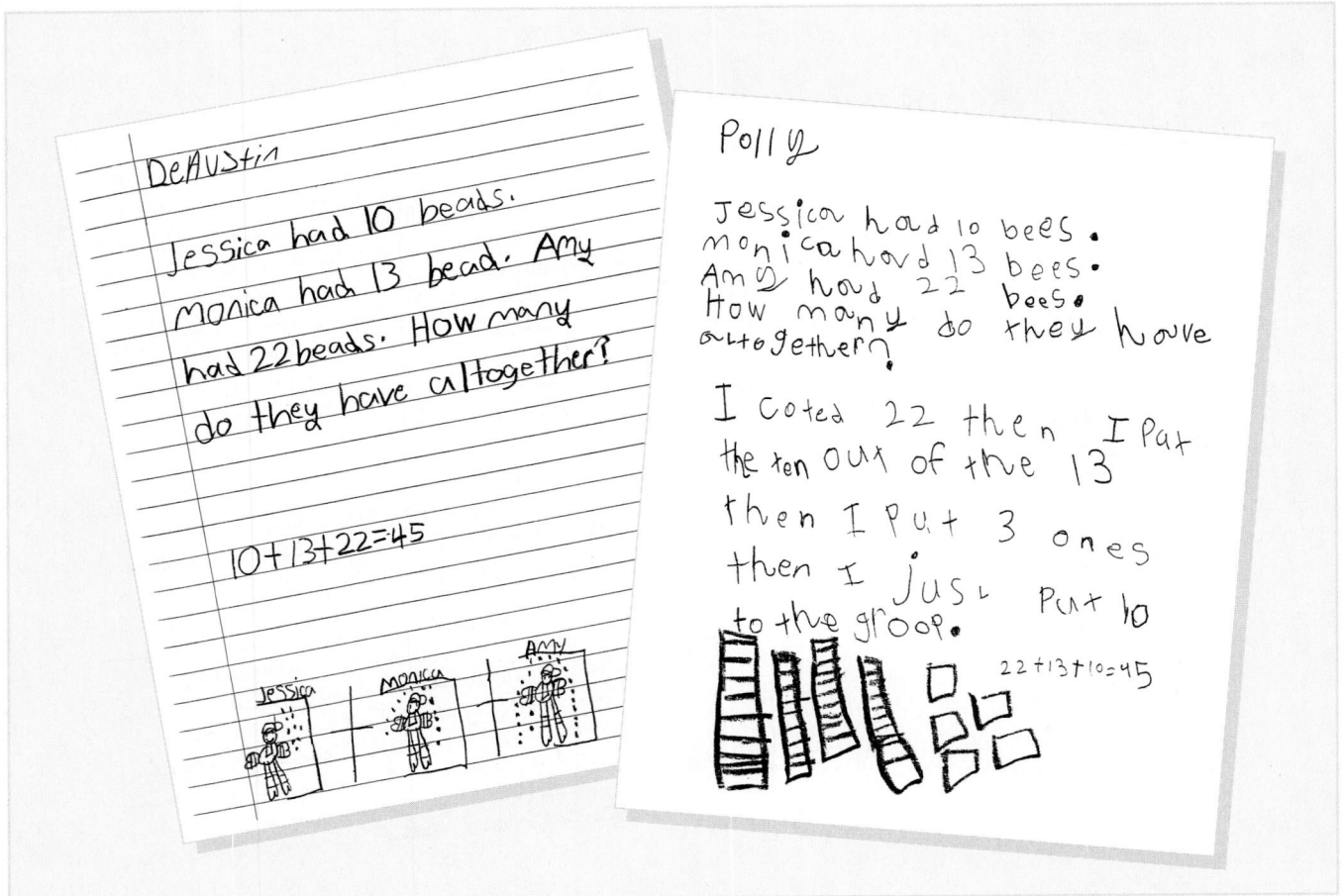

Figure 3.4 The work of two grade 1 students solving 10 + 13 + 22 indicates a difference in how the children are thinking about two-digit numbers.

Metacognition

Metacognition refers to conscious monitoring (being aware of how and why you are doing something) and regulation (choosing to do something or deciding to make changes) of your own thought process. Good problem solvers monitor their thinking regularly and automatically. They recognize when they are stuck or do not fully understand. They make conscious decisions to switch strategies, rethink the problem, search for related content knowledge that may help, or simply start afresh (Schoenfeld, 1992).

There is evidence that metacognitive behaviour can be learned (Campione, Brown, & Connell, 1989; Garofalo, 1987; Lester, 1989). Furthermore, students who learn to monitor and regulate their own problem-solving behaviours do show improvement in problem solving.

We know that it is important to help students learn to monitor and control their own progress in problem solving. A simple formula that can be employed consists of three questions: *What* are you doing? *Why* are you doing it? *How* does it help you? These three questions are elab-

orated in the THINK framework proposed by Thomas (2006):

> *Talk* about the problem.
> *How* can it be solved?
> *Identify* a strategy to solve the problem.
> *Notice* how your strategy helped you solve the problem.
> *Keep* thinking about the problem. Does it make sense?
> *Is* there another way to solve it?

Students who used the THINK framework improved in their problem solving over those who did not use it (Thomas, 2006). The key to success is being intentional and consciously developing the metacognitive skills to monitor and reflect on the problems being solved.

You can foster metacognition during a lesson by doing the following. In the beginning stages of a lesson, have students address *what* strategies they are using and *why*. As you move into the development phase of your lesson, they can then consider *what*, *why*, and even *how*. You can support metacognition by using prompts that will help students use the THINK framework. You can ask the questions as you interact with individuals or small groups. By joining a group, you can model questions you want students to ask each other and themselves. In the upper grades, each group can have a designated monitor, whose job is to be the reflective questioner that you have modelled when working with the group.

You can also help students develop self-monitoring habits after their problem-solving activity is over. A brief discussion after a problem can focus on what types of things were done to solve the problem. In addition to discussing solution strategies, the follow-up phase of the lesson should include opportunities to reflect on the metacognitive questions noted previously. This can be accomplished through journals (Roberts and Tayeh, 2007) or through classroom discussions prompted by questions such as the following:

- What did you do that helped you understand the problem?
- Did you find any numbers or information you didn't need?
- How did you decide what to do?
- Did you think about your answer after you got it?
- How did you decide your answer was right?
- Did you try something that didn't work? How did you figure it was not going to work?
- Can something you did in this problem help you solve other problems?

As students become more independent in their study of mathematics, they are less likely to need support of the teacher to solve problems. Their attitudes and dispositions will shift related to what they think mathematics is and how competent they feel about doing mathematics.

Disposition

Disposition refers to the attitudes and beliefs that students possess about mathematics. Students' beliefs concerning their abilities to do mathematics and to understand the nature of mathematics have a significant effect on how they approach problems and ultimately on how well they succeed.

Students who enjoy solving problems and feel satisfaction or pleasure at conquering a perplexing problem are much more likely to persevere, make second and third attempts, and even search out new problems. Negative attitudes have just the opposite effect.

Attitudinal Goals

- *Gain confidence and belief in abilities*—to develop students' confidence in their ability to do mathematics and to confront unfamiliar tasks

- *Be willing to take risks and to persevere*—to improve students' willingness to attempt unfamiliar problems and to develop their perseverance in solving problems without being discouraged by initial setbacks
- *Enjoy doing mathematics*—to help students learn to enjoy and sense personal reward in the process of thinking, searching for patterns, and solving problems

A classroom environment built on high expectations for all students and respect for each student's thoughts will go a long way toward achieving the attitudinal goals. Here are some additional ideas to help with these goals for all students:

- *Build in success.* In the beginning of the year, plan problems that you are confident your students can solve. Avoid creating false success that depends on your showing the way at every step and barrier.
- *Praise efforts and risk taking.* Students need to hear frequently that they are "good thinkers" capable of good, productive thought. When students volunteer ideas, listen carefully and actively to each idea, and give credit for the thinking and the risk that children take by venturing to speak out. Be careful to focus praise on the risk or effort and not the products of that effort, regardless of the quality of the ideas.
- *Listen to all students.* Avoid ending a discussion with the first correct answer. As you make non-evaluative responses, you will find many children repeating the same idea. Were they just copying a known leader? Perhaps, but more likely they were busy thinking and did not even hear what had already been said by those who were a bit faster. Don't forget the suggestion made earlier to call on less secure students early in a discussion, so that the most obvious ideas are not taken by the more assertive students.
- *Provide special successes for special children.* Not all children will develop the same problem-solving abilities, but all have abilities and can contribute. This must be something you truly believe, because it is difficult to fake. One way to provide success for students who are slower or not as strong is to involve them in groups with strong and supportive children or to ask easier questions early in discussions. In group settings, all children can be made to feel the success of the group work.

When students have confidence, show perseverance, and enjoy mathematics, it makes sense they will achieve at a higher level and want to continue learning about mathematics—opening many doors for them in the future. As noted earlier, though, teaching in this manner requires a complete re-conceptualization of your role as the teacher and the students' role as student. In considering such a transformation, questions are likely to arise.

Even if you feel these methods contain really good ideas, you may be wondering how to accomplish some of the recommendations and how to fit new approaches into a lesson. In the following section, a three-phase lesson plan model is explained. This model will enable you to engage students in learning through problem solving, as well as learning about problem solving.

A Three-Phase Lesson Format

Often teachers typically spend a small portion of a lesson explaining or reviewing an idea and then go into "production mode," where students wade through a set of exercises. Lessons organized in this explain-then-practise pattern condition students to focus on procedures so that they can finish the exercises. Teachers find themselves going from desk to desk re-teaching and explaining to individuals. This approach is in significant contrast to a problem-based lesson that tends to be built around a single problem (Sawada, 1999, 1997).

It is useful to think of a lesson consisting of three simple parts: *introduction*, *development*, and *follow up*. (See Figure 3.5.) If time is allotted for each segment, one problem may take a full day or even longer. There are times when a task may not merit a full lesson; a mental mathematics activity is a good example. Even here, it is useful to keep the same three components of a lesson in mind. Each part of the lesson has a specific agenda. How you attend to these agendas in each portion of the lesson may vary depending on the class, the problem itself, and the purpose of the lesson.

The Introduction Phase of a Lesson

There are three related agendas for the *introduction* phase of a lesson. They are as follows:

1. Get students mentally prepared to work on the problem and think about the previous knowledge they have that will be most helpful.

2. Be sure that students understand the problem so that you will not need to clarify or explain to individuals later in the lesson.

3. Clarify your expectations to students before they begin working on the problem. This includes both how they will be working (individually, or in pairs or small groups) and what product you expect in addition to an answer.

These *introduction* phase agendas need not be addressed in the order listed. For example, for some lessons you will do a short activity to activate students' prior knowledge for

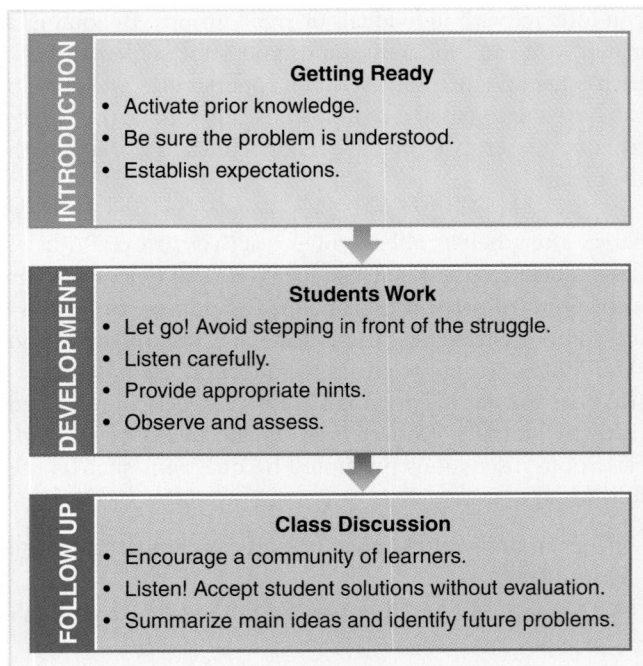

Figure 3.5 Teaching through problem solving suggests a simple three-part structure for lessons.

the problem, then present the problem and clarify expectations. Other lessons may begin with a statement of the problem and may or may not have a readiness activity.

Teacher Actions in the *Introduction* Phase

The kinds of things you do in the *introduction* phase of a lesson will vary with the task. Some tasks you can begin with immediately. For example, if your students are used to solving story problems and know they are expected to use words, pictures, and numbers to explain their solutions in writing, all that may be required is to read through the problem with them and be sure all understand it. The actual presentation of the task or problem may occur at the beginning or at the end of your *introductory* actions.

1. Activate Prior Knowledge Activate specific prior knowledge related to the concept on which you are focusing that day. The form this preparatory activity might take will vary with the topic, as shown in the following examples.

Begin with a Simple Version of the Task. Suppose that you are interested in developing some ideas about area and perimeter in grade 4 or 5. This is the task you plan to present (Lappan & Even, 1989).

Concept: Perimeter

Grades: 4–6

Assume that the edge of a square is 1 unit. Add squares to this shape so that it has a perimeter of 18.

Instead of beginning your lesson with this problem, you might consider activating prior knowledge in one of the following ways:

- Draw a 3-by-5 rectangle of squares on the board and ask students what they know about the shape. (It's a rectangle. It has squares. There are 15 squares. There are 3 rows of 5.) If no one mentions the words *area* and *perimeter*, you could write those words on the board and ask if those words can be used in talking about this figure.
- Provide students with some square tiles or grid paper. "I want everyone to make a shape that has a perimeter of 12 units. After you make your shape, find out what its area is." After a short time, have several students share their shapes.

Each of these "warm-ups" uses the vocabulary needed for the problem-solving task. The second activity suggests the tiles as a possible model that students may elect to use. It also introduces the idea that there are different figures with the same perimeter.

The following problem is designed to help students use addition to solve a subtraction problem.

Concept: Subtraction

Grades: 3–4

Dad says that it is 403 km to the ski hills in Mont-Sainte-Anne. When we stopped for gas, we had gone 167 km. How much farther do we have to drive?

Before presenting this problem, you can elicit prior knowledge by asking students to supply the missing part of 100 after you give one part. Try numbers like 80 or 30 at first; then try 47 or 62. When you present the actual task, you might ask students if the answer to the problem is more or less than 200 kilometres.

Brainstorm Solutions. The following problem is designed to address ratios and proportion, as well as data analysis.

Concepts: Ratios and Statistics

Grades: 7–8

The following enrollment data compare information about students and their families in one class with information about the whole school:

	In School	In Class 8B
Number of Siblings		
One	89	7
Two	134	12
More than two	103	8
Country of Birth		
India	23	2
Hong Kong	5	10
Taiwan	107	9
Italy	28	0
Canada	109	11
Travel-to-School Method		
Walk	205	20
Bus	145	12
Other	12	0

If someone asked you how typical class 8B was of the rest of the school, how would you answer? Write an explanation for your answer. Include one or more charts or graphs that you think would support your conclusion.

This problem does not lend itself to posing a simpler problem. Rather it solicits students' prior knowledge during their thinking about how to approach the problem. For example, students might discuss in a think–pair–share what "typical" means and how they might determine what a typical class is. The teacher can list ideas on the board for students to consider when they move into the *development* phase of the lesson.

Estimate or Use Mental Computation. When the task is aimed at the development of a computational procedure, a useful *introductory* action is to have students actually do the computation mentally or suggest an estimated answer. This practice will not spoil the problem for the class. In fact it may raise curiosity as to what the answer might be. This technique is appropriate for the earlier problem concerning how many more kilometres to go to the ski hills. The following task is another example in which preliminary estimates or mental computations would activate prior knowledge.

Concepts: Multiplication

Grades: 5–6

How many small unit squares will fit in a rectangle that is 54 units long and 36 units wide? Use base-ten blocks to help you with your solution. (Note that base-ten blocks come in ones (one cube), tens (a rod of ten cubes), and hundreds (a ten-by-ten square of cubes).

Make a plan for figuring out the total number of squares without doing too much counting. Explain how your plan would work on a rectangle that is 27 units by 42 units.

Prior to estimation or mental computation for this problem, beginning with several simpler problems will help. For example, rectangles such as 30 by 8 or 40 by 60 could be explored.

2. Be Sure the Task Is Understood Understanding the problem is not optional! You must always be sure that students understand the problem before setting them to work. It is important for you to analyze the problem in order to anticipate student approaches and possible misinterpretations or misconceptions (Wallace, 2007). Time spent at this stage of the problem-solving process is critical to the rest of the lesson. You can ask questions to clarify student understanding of the problem (i.e., knowing what it means rather than how they will solve it). For example, ask, "What do you know?" and "What do you need to know?" Wallace, a mathematics researcher and teacher, notes, "The more I questioned *prior* to giving the problem, the less help the students needed from me *during* problem solving" (p. 510).

Consider a problem-based approach to mastering the multiplication facts, a term used for the basic multiplication tables. The most difficult facts can each be connected or related to an easier fact already learned.

Concept: Multiplication Facts

Grades: 3–4

Use a multiplication fact you already know (a "helping fact") to help you solve each of these facts: 4×6, 6×8, 7×6, 3×8.

For this task, it is essential that students understand the idea of using a helping fact. They have most likely used helping facts in addition. You can build on this prior knowledge by asking, "When you were learning addition facts, how could knowing $6 + 6$ help you figure out $6 + 7$?" You may also need to help students understand what is meant by a fact they know—one they have mastered and know without counting.

When using a word problem like the one that follows, it is important to help students understand the meaning of the sentences without giving away how to solve the problem.

Concept: Multiplication

Grades: 4–6

The local convenience store purchases chocolate bars in cartons holding 12 boxes per carton. The price paid for one carton is $42.50. Each box contains 8 chocolate bars that the store plans to sell individually. What is the convenience store's cost for each chocolate bar?

Questions might include: "What did the convenience store do? What is in a carton? What is in a box? What is the price of one carton? What does the problem mean when it says 'each box'?" The last question here is to identify vocabulary that may be misunderstood. It is also useful to be sure students can explain to you what the problem is asking. Having students re-read a problem does little good, but having students restate the problem in their own words helps them figure out what the problem is asking.

3. Establish Clear Expectations There are two components to establishing expectations: how students are to work and what products they are to prepare for the discussion in the third part of the lesson. Each of these is essential; they cannot be skipped.

Whether or not you have students work in groups, it is always a good idea for students to have some opportunity to discuss their ideas with one or more classmates prior to sharing their thoughts in the *follow-up* phase of the lesson. When students work alone, they have no one to look to for an idea or a way to get started if they are stuck. On the other hand, when students work in groups, there is always the possibility of students not contributing or of a dominating student being overly leading.

Buschman (2003b), a leader in mathematics education, suggests the *think–write–pair–share* approach, adding that students should first write or illustrate their solutions to the problem before sharing with a partner. With written work to share, the two students have something to talk about. Although appropriate for all students, the think–write–pair–share method is especially helpful for K–1 students, who often do not know how to go about discussing a solution or even how to work together.

Teaching through problems requires that students focus not just on the solution, but also how they reached that solution. Therefore, it is important to model and explain your expectations for their final product. One expectation might be a written explanation for their solution. Writing supports students' learning in mathematics (Pugalee, 2005; Steele, 2007) and it can assist students during discussions. They can use their own explanations to assist them. Students may also choose to prepare an illustration, a diagram, or a graph to use with their written explanation or they may use one of the ways shown in Figure 3.6 instead. This example shows one young student's solution for ways to make 5. Teachers also need to discuss with students what they might draw that will show their thinking. Along with ascertaining that students understand the problem, it is also important to make sure that they have a clear understanding of the expectations for the product they will share in the *development* phase (the next stage) of the lesson.

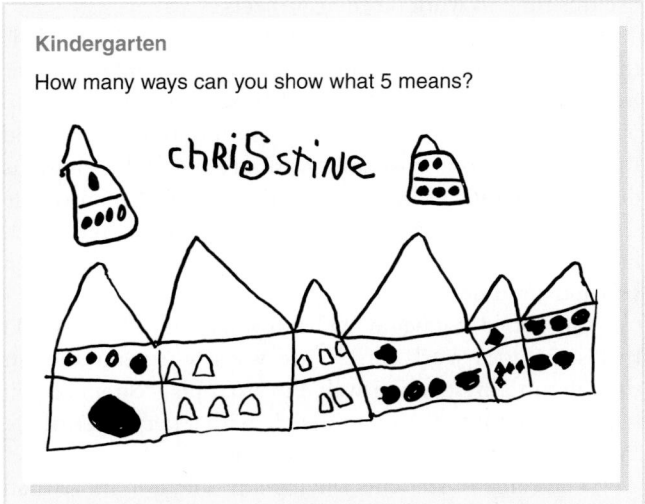

Kindergarten

How many ways can you show what 5 means?

Figure 3.6 A kindergarten student shows her thinking about ways to make 5.

The *Development* Phase of a Lesson

In the *development* phase students explore the task on which the lesson focuses. They may work alone, with partners, or in small groups. There are clear agendas to which you will need to attend:

1. *Let go*! Give students a chance to work without too much guidance. Allow and encourage students to embrace the struggle. It is an important part of doing mathematics.
2. *Listen actively.* Take this time to find out how different students are thinking, what ideas they are using, and how they are approaching the problem. This is a time for observation and assessment—not teaching.
3. *Provide appropriate hints.* Base any hints on students' ideas and ways of thinking. Be careful not to imply that you have the *correct* method of solving the problem.
4. *Provide worthwhile extensions.* Have something ready for students who finish quickly.

Teacher Actions in the *Development* Phase

With the exception of preparing for early finishers, these agendas can challenge teachers who tend to help too much.

1. Let Go! Once students understand what the problem is asking, it is time to LET GO. While students are ready to work on the task, it is time to let go. It is tempting to "step in front of the struggle," at this phase of the lesson, but you need to hold back. Doing mathematics takes time and solutions are not always obvious. It is important to communicate to students that spending time on a task, trying different approaches, and consulting each other is important to learning and understanding mathematics. When students are stuck, you could ask questions such as "Is this like any other problem we have solved?" "Did you try to making a diagram or a picture?" "What is it about this problem that seems to be difficult for you?" This approach is effective for helping students because you are supporting their thinking, yet you are not telling them how to solve the problem.

Students will look to you for approval of their ideas and results. Avoid being the source of right and wrong. When asked if a method or result is correct, respond by saying, "How can you decide?" or "Why do you think that is right?" or "Is there some way that you can check to see if it is right?" Asking, "How can we tell if that makes sense?" reminds students that answers without understanding are not acceptable.

Letting go also means allowing students to make mistakes. When you observe an error or incorrect thinking, do not correct it at this point. Students must learn from the very beginning that their mistakes can be profitable

(Boaler & Humphreys, 2005). The best discussions occur when students disagree.

When students make mistakes, ask them to explain their process or approach to you. They may catch their own mistake. In addition, in the follow-up portion of the lesson, students will have an opportunity to explain, justify, defend, and challenge strategies and solutions. This process provides an opportunity for mistakes and misconceptions to be treated as opportunities for learning.

2. Listen Actively   "Listening actively" means that you are trying to understand a student's approach to a problem. Consequently, your questions must probe your students' thinking; the result may be unexpected. This is different from listening for a particular response or for what you know to be the answer and trying to elicit that response. This process is referred to as "funnelling" students toward a response that approaches what you have in mind.

The *development* phase is one of two opportunities you have (the other is in the *follow-up* phase) to find out what your students know, how they think, and how they are approaching the task you have given them. You might sit down with a group and simply listen for a while, letting the students explain what they are doing as you take occasional notes. If you want further information, try saying, "Tell me what you are doing," or "I see you have started to multiply these numbers. Can you tell me why you are multiplying?" You want to convey a genuine interest in what students are doing and thinking. This is *not* the time to evaluate or to tell students how to solve the problem.

"It's easy. Let me help you." These two simple sentences send two disastrous messages to the student who hears them. For the student who asks for help, it is *not* easy! Students may think, "If it's easy and I can't get it, I must be stupid." The second sentence can also send a negative message. It implies, "You are not capable of doing this on your own. I have to help you."

Listening actively includes asking questions, such as the following:

- What do you think this problem is asking?
- What ideas have you tried so far?
- Can you tell me more about...?
- Why did you....?
- How did you solve it?

By asking questions, you find out where students are in their understanding of the concepts.

3. Provide Appropriate Hints   If a group or student is searching for a place to begin, a hint may be appropriate. You might suggest that the students try using a particular manipulative, drawing a picture, or making a table if one of these ideas seems appropriate. You might also ask questions like those mentioned in the "Let Go" section.

Concept: Percent Increase and Decrease

Grades: 7–8

In Fern's Furniture Store, Fern has priced all of her furniture at 20 percent over wholesale. In preparation for a sale, she tells her staff to cut all prices by 10 percent. Will Fern be making 10 percent profit, less than 10 percent profit, or more than 10 percent profit? Explain your answer.

For this problem, consider the following hints:

- Try drawing a picture or a diagram of something that shows what 10 percent off means.
- Try drawing a picture or a diagram that shows what 20 percent more means.
- Maybe you could pick a sample price of something and see what happens when you add 20 percent and then reduce 10 percent.
- Let's try a simpler problem. Suppose that you had 8 blocks and got 25 percent more. Then you lost 25 percent of the new collection.

Notice that these suggestions are not directive; rather, they serve as starters. Even here, the choice of a hint is best made after listening carefully to what the student has been trying or thinking. After offering a hint, walk away. Don't hover or the student is apt to wait for even further direction.

4. Provide Worthwhile Extensions   Some students will always finish well before others. Early finishers can often be challenged in some manner connected to the problem just solved, without it seeming like extra work. (See Chapter 6 for discussion of strategies for talented and gifted students.) Ongoing extended projects should be used as another part of your mathematics program. Students finishing early can use this time to work on their projects.

Many good problems are simple on the surface. It is the extensions that are challenging. The area and perimeter task is a case in point. Many students will quickly come up with one or two solutions. "I see you found one way to do this. Are there any other solutions? Are any of the solutions different or more interesting than others? Which of the shapes with a perimeter of 18 has the largest area and which has the smallest? Does the perimeter always change when you add another tile?"

Questions that begin "What if you tried...?" or "Would that same idea work for...?" are ways to extend student thinking in a motivating way. For example, "Suppose you tried to find all the shapes possible with a perimeter of 18. What could you find out about the areas?"

The value of students solving a problem in more than one way cannot be overestimated. It shifts the value system in the classroom from answers to processes and thinking. It is a good way for students to make new and different connections.

For example, consider this grade 7 problem.

Concept: Percent Increase and Decrease

Grades 7–8

The regular price of the dress Shakra purchased for her party was $90. If the sale price was 25 percent off the regular price, how much did it cost?

This is an example of a straightforward problem with a single answer. Many students will solve it by multiplying by 0.25 and subtracting the result from $90. The suggestion to find another way may be all that is necessary. Others may require specific directions: "How would you do it with fractions instead of decimals?" "Draw me a diagram that explains what you did." "How could this be done in just one step?" "Think of a way that you could do this mentally."

Grade 2 students will frequently solve the next problem by counting or using addition.

Concept: Addition and Subtraction

Grades: K–2

Molly had saved up $9. The next day she received her allowance. She then had $12. How much allowance did she get?

"How would you do that on a calculator?" and "Can you write two equations that represent this situation?" are ways of encouraging children to connect $9 + ? = 12$ with $12 - 9$.

The *Follow-up* Phase of a Lesson

In the *follow-up* phase of the lesson, your students will work as a community of learners, discussing, justifying, and challenging various solutions to the problem all have just worked on. Here is where much of the learning will occur as students reflect individually and collectively on the ideas they have explored. It is challenging but critical that you make sufficient time for a discussion and make sure the *development* portion does not go on too long. The agendas for the *follow-up* phase are easily stated but more difficult to achieve:

1. *Promote a mathematical community of learners.* Include all learners. Engage the class in productive discussion, helping students work together as a community of learners.
2. *Listen actively without evaluation.* Take this second major opportunity to find out how students are thinking—how they are approaching the problem. Evaluating methods and solutions is the duty of your students.
3. *Summarize main ideas and identify problems for future exploration.* You can lay the groundwork for future activities as a natural part of this phase.

Teacher Actions in the *Follow-up* Phase

Be certain to plan ample time for this portion of the lesson and then be certain to *save* the time. Twenty minutes or more is not at all unreasonable for a good class discussion and sharing of ideas. It is not necessary for every student to have finished. This is not a time to check answers but for the class to share ideas.

Over time, you will develop your class into a mathematical community of learners, where students feel comfortable taking risks and sharing ideas, where students and the teacher respect one another's ideas even when they disagree, where ideas are defended and challenged respectfully, and where logical or mathematical reasoning is valued above all. This atmosphere will not develop easily or quickly. You must teach your students about your expectations for this time and how to interact with their peers.

1. Promote a Mathematical Community of Learners That Includes All Children NCTM in its *Standards* documents is very clear in expressing the belief that all children can learn important mathematics. This view is supported by a number of prominent mathematics educators who have worked extensively with at-risk populations (Campbell, 1996; NCTM, 1989, 1991; Silver & Stein, 1996; Trafton & Claus, 1994).

Because the needs and abilities of children are different, conducting a large group discussion that is balanced and that includes all children requires skill and practice. Rowan and Bourne (1994) offer excellent suggestions based on their work in an urban, multi-ethnic, low-socioeconomic school district. They emphasize that the most important factor is to be clear about the purpose of group discussion—that is, to share and explore the variety of strategies, ideas, and solutions generated by the class and to learn to communicate these ideas in a rich mathematical discourse. Every class has a handful of students who are always ready to respond. Other children learn to be passive or do not participate. So rule number one is to be sure the discussion involves all students.

Considerable research into how mathematical communities develop and operate provides us with additional insight for developing effective classroom discourse (e.g., see Rasmussen, Yackel, & King, 2003; Stephan & Whitenack, 2003; Wood, Williams, & McNeal, 2006; Yackel & Cobb, 1996). Suggestions from this research include the following:

- Encourage student–student dialogue rather than student–teacher conversations that exclude the class. "Juanita, can you answer Lora's question?" "Devon, can you explain that so that La Toya and Kei can understand what you are saying?" When students have differing solutions, have students work these ideas out as a class. "Memona, I noticed that you got an answer different from Alia's. What do you think about her explanation?"

- Request explanations to accompany *all* answers. Soon the request for an explanation will not signal an incorrect response, as children will initially believe. Correct answers may not represent the conceptual thinking you assumed. Incorrect answers may only be the result of an easily corrected error. By requiring explanations, students learn that reasoning in mathematics is important and useful.
- Call on students for their ideas, often calling first on the children who tend to be shy or lack the ability to express themselves well. When asked to participate early and given sufficient time to formulate their thoughts, these reticent children can more easily participate and thus be valued. Asking, "Who wants to explain their solution?" will result in the same three or four eager students raising their hands. Other students tend to accept that these students are generally correct and may be reluctant to offer ideas that are different from the well-known leaders. Use the *development* portion of a lesson to walk around the room and identify interesting solutions that will add to your discussion—including those that are incorrect. All students should be prepared to share as part of their everyday expectations.
- Encourage students to ask questions. "Ilana, did you understand how they did that? Do you want to ask Antonio a question?"
- Be certain that your students also understand what you understand. Your knowledge of the topic may cause you to accept a less than clear explanation because you hear what the student means to say. Select important points in a student's explanation and express your own "confusion." "Faiza, I don't quite get why you subtracted 9 here in this step. Can you tell us why you did that?" Demonstrate to students that it is okay to be confused and that asking clarifying questions is appropriate. An important instructional goal is for students to ask these questions without your input.
- Occasionally, ask those who understand to offer explanations for others. "Rajdeep, perhaps you can explain this idea in your own words so that some of the rest of us can understand better." Don't assume that a student who says he or she understands really does.
- Move students to more conceptually based explanations when appropriate. For example, if a student says that he knows 4.17 is more than 4.1638, you can ask her (or another student) to explain why this is so. Another technique is to use a "fooler." With pretend confusion, ask, "How can this be? It seems like the longer decimal ought to be a larger number." Similarly, move students

away from simply listing steps in their solutions. "I see *what* you did but I think some of us are confused about *why* you did it that way and why you think that will give us the correct solution."

2. Listen Actively Without Evaluating By being a facilitator rather than an evaluator, students will be more willing to share their ideas during discussions. This is your window into their thinking. Listen carefully to the discussion without too much interference. You can use this information to plan for tomorrow's lesson and in general to decide on the direction you wish to take in your current unit.

Try to take a neutral position with respect to *all* responses. Resist the temptation to judge the correctness of an answer. You can ask questions to help clarify a response—both right and wrong. When you say, "That's correct, Benjamin," there is no longer a reason for students to evaluate the response. Had students disagreed with Benjamin's response or had a question about it, they will not challenge or question it since you've said it was correct. As a result, you will not have the chance to hear and learn from them. You can support student thinking without evaluation. "Does someone have a different idea or want to comment on what Benjamin just said?"

Use praise cautiously. Praise offered for correct solutions or excitement over interesting ideas suggests that the students did something unusual or unexpected. This can be negative feedback for those who do not get praise. Comments such as "Good job!" and "Super work!" roll off the tongue easily. However, there is evidence to suggest that we should be careful with expressions of praise, especially with respect to student products and solutions (Kohn, 1993; Schwartz, 1996).

In place of praise that is judgmental, Schwartz (1996) suggests comments of interest and extension: "I wonder what would happen if you tried..." or "Please tell me how you figured that out." Notice that these phrases express interest and value the child's thinking.

There will be times when a student will get stuck in the middle of an explanation or when a response is simply not forthcoming. Be sensitive about calling on someone else to "help out." You may be communicating that the child is not capable on his or her own. Always allow ample time. You can sometimes suggest taking additional time to get thoughts together and promise to return to the student later—and then be *certain* to hear what the student figured out.

3. Summarize Main Ideas and Identify Hypotheses
A wide variety of approaches can be used to summarize ideas. A whole class discussion can bring to light main ideas in students' words and help to make sure that all students understand. There are numerous ways to share ideas orally. One example is a partner exchange where one partner tells one key idea and the other partner gives an example.

Following oral summaries with individual written summaries is important to ensure that you know what each child has learned from the lesson. Exit activities, such "Ticket Out the Door," provide students with a ticket (handout) with one or two prompts that ask students to explain the main idea(s) of the lesson (or ask for pictures from younger students). These are handed in as an exit from the math lesson. Another strategy is to ask students to write a newspaper headline and a brief column to describe the day's activity. There are many different templates and writing starters that could be engaging for your students.

When ideas have been well developed, reinforce appropriate terminology, definitions, or symbolism. Vocabulary should come after ideas have been established, not before. If a problem involves creating a procedure such as a method of computing, a strategy for basic facts, or a formula in measurement, record useful methods on the board. These can be labelled with the student's name and an example. These strategies are then available in future lessons for students to try.

Often someone will make a generalization or an observation that he or she strongly believes in but cannot completely justify. Untested ideas can be written on the board with the name of the student who proposed the conjecture, for example. "Andrew's Hypothesis." Explain the meaning of *hypothesis* as an idea that may or may not be true. Testing the hypothesis may become the problem for another day, or the hypothesis may simply be kept on the board until additional evidence comes up that either supports or disproves it. For example, when comparing fractions, suppose that a group makes this generalization and you write it on the board: *When deciding which fraction is larger, the fraction in which the bottom number is closer to the top number is the larger fraction. Example: $^4/_7$ is not as big as $^7/_8$ because 7 is only 1 from 8 but 4 is 3 away from 7.* This is not an unusual conclusion, but it is not correct in all instances. A problem for a subsequent day would be to decide if the hypothesis is always right or to find fractions for which it is not right (counterexamples).

Even when students have not suggested hypotheses, discussions will often turn up interesting questions that can profitably be used for tasks to help clarify an emerging idea.

Frequently Asked Questions

The following are questions teachers have asked about implementing a teaching through problem-solving approach to instruction.

1. *How can I teach all the basic skills I have to teach?* It is tempting, especially with the pressures of provincial and territorial testing programs, to resort to rote drill and practice to teach "basic skills." Some people believe that mastery of the basics is incompatible with a problem-based approach. However, the evidence strongly suggests otherwise. In fact, drill-oriented approaches have consistently produced poor results (Battista, 1999; Kamii & Dominick, 1998; O'Brien, 1999). Short-term gains on low-level skills may possibly result from drill, but more is required if students are to be successful, as testing programs such as the TIMSS (2007) and the PCAP (2007) have demonstrated.

   Second, research data indicate that students in programs based on a problem-based approach do as well on basic skills or better than students in traditional programs, as measured by standardized tests (Campbell, 1995; Carpenter, Franke, Jacobs, Fennema, & Empson, 1998; Hiebert, 2003; Hiebert & Wearne, 1996; Silver & Stein, 1996; Riordan & Noyce, 2001). Any deficit in skill development is more than outweighed by strength in concepts and problem solving.

   Finally, traditional skills such as basic fact mastery and computation can be effectively taught in a problem-solving approach (for example, see Campbell, Rowan, & Suarez, 1998; Huinker, 1998).

2. *Why is it often better for students, than for me, to "tell" or "explain"?* First, students' explanations are grounded in their own understanding. Second, as students communicate their mathematical ideas in their own words, they are solidifying their own understanding. Third are the implications for creating a community of learners. Students will question their peers when an explanation does not make sense to them, whereas explanations from the teacher are usually accepted without scrutiny (and possibly without understanding). Finally, when students are responsible for explaining, the class members develop a sense of pride and confidence that *they* can figure things out and make sense of mathematics. *They* have power and ability.

3. *Is it okay to help students who have difficulty solving a problem?* Of course, you will want to help students who are struggling. However, as Buschman (2003b) suggests, rather than suggesting how to solve a problem, a better approach is to try to find out *why* the student is having difficulty. If you jump in with help, you may not even be addressing the real reason the student is struggling. It may be as simple as not understanding the problem or as complex as a lack of understanding of a fundamental concept. "Tell me what you are thinking" is a good beginning.

   Recall the negative consequences of the two simple sentences: *It's easy! Let me help you* in our previous discussion. Rather, try to build on the student's knowledge. Do not rob students of the feeling of accomplishment and the true growth in understanding that come from solving a problem themselves.

4. *Where can I find the time to cover everything?* Mathematics is much more connected and integrated than the

itemized objectives found in many provincial and territorial curriculum documents. To deal with coverage, the first suggestion is to teach with a goal of developing the "big ideas," the main concepts in a unit or chapter. Most of the skills and ideas on your list of objectives will be addressed as you progress. If you focus separately on each item on the list, then big ideas and connections, the essence of understanding, are unlikely to develop. Secondly, we spend far too much time re-teaching because students don't retain ideas. Time spent up front to help students develop meaningful networks of ideas drastically reduces the need for re-teaching and remediation, thus creating time in the long term.

5. *How much time does it take for students to become a community of learners and really begin to share and discuss ideas?* It generally takes more time than we anticipate and discussions may seem strained or unproductive at first. Students have to be coached in how to participate in a classroom discussion about a problem and how to work collaboratively in small groups. For the first weeks of school, time must be devoted to explicitly teaching and modelling these skills. Frequent reinforcement of participation and listening is needed initially. Support then becomes necessary as the community is established. Students in the primary grades will adapt much more quickly than students in the higher grades, as they have not yet developed a firm belief that mathematics class is about sitting quietly and following the rules. You might expect it to take as long as six weeks before students begin to assume responsibility for making sense of mathematics. Probing and asking good questions and developing a community of learners requires a long-term commitment. Don't give up!

6. *Can I use a combination of student-oriented, problem-based teaching with a teacher-directed approach?* Switching instructional approaches is not recommended. Switching methods confuses students as to what is expected of them. More importantly, students will come to believe that their own ideas do not really matter because the teacher will eventually tell them the "right" way to do it (Mokros, Russell, & Economopoulos, 1995). In order for students to become invested in a problem-based approach, they must deeply believe that their ideas are important and that the source of their knowledge is themselves— every day.

7. *Is there any place for drill and practice?* Absolutely! The error is to believe that drill is a method of developing or reinforcing concepts. Drill is only appropriate when (a) the desired concepts have been meaningfully developed, (b) flexible and useful procedures have been developed, *and* (c) speed and accuracy are needed. With drill and practice, the important thing is to remember a little goes a long way. Drilling of basic facts should take no more than 10 minutes in one sitting. Five multiplication problems can be as sufficient in assessing student understanding of the procedure as 25 problems. Not much is gained from the additional 20 problems. Also, when students are making mistakes, more drill and practice is not the solution—identifying and addressing misunderstandings or misconceptions is far more effective. For example, some students in grade 7 or 8 still do not know their multiplication facts. Drilling the 144 facts won't nearly help as much as working on strategies for the targeted facts (e.g., helping facts) a student is forgetting. (See Chapter 10 for many more strategies for basic facts.)

8. *What do I do when a problem-based lesson bombs?* It will happen, although not as often as you think, that students just do not know what to do with a problem you pose, no matter how many hints and suggestions you offer. Do not give in to the temptation to "tell them." Set it aside for the moment. Ask yourself why it didn't work well. Did the students have the prior knowledge they needed? Was the task too advanced? Often we need to regroup and offer students a simpler related task that gets them prepared for the one that proved too difficult. When you sense that a task is not going anywhere, regroup! Don't spend days just hoping that something wonderful might happen. If you listen to your students, you will know where to go next.

Reflections on Chapter 3

Writing to Learn

1. Which of the benefits of teaching with problems resonates with you? Why?
2. Describe what is meant by tasks or problems that can be used for teaching mathematics. Be sure to include the three important features that are required to make this method effective.
3. Polya's four-step process maps on to the three-phase (*introduction, development, follow-up*) lesson plan model. What questions might you ask students to support their thinking in each of the four steps?
4. Discuss the benefits of using literature in teaching mathematics.
5. What are some of the benefits of having students write in mathematics class? When should the writing take place? How can very young students "write"?
6. Describe in your own words what is meant by a "mathematical community of learners."
7. What is the teacher's purpose or agenda in each of the three parts of a lesson—*introduction, development,* and *follow-up?*
8. Describe the kinds of actions or things that a teacher should be doing in each of the three parts of a lesson. (Note that not all of these would be done in every lesson.) Which actions should you use almost all the time?
9. "It's easy! Let me help you." Not a good idea? What is a better way of helping a student who is having difficulty solving a problem?

For Discussion and Exploration

1. If you were to begin teaching through a problem-based approach to students who had never experienced learning mathematics in this way, they would likely not know how to work effectively with a partner, or to engage in a classroom discussion. How would you deal with these and other challenges related to this approach so that students would develop an understanding of their role in the classroom?
2. Select an activity from any chapter in Section 2 of this text. How can the activity be used as a problem or task for the purpose of instruction, as described in this chapter? If you were using this activity in the classroom, what specifically would you do during the introductory section of the lesson?

Resources for Chapter 3

Recommendations for Further Reading

Articles

Buschman, L. E. (2005). Isn't that interesting! *Teaching Children Mathematics, 12* (1), 34–40.

Buschman uses the prompt that is the title of this article to get his students to articulate their mathematics processes. In this article he shares several rich tasks and the different ways that students approach the problems. The tasks themselves are worthy of a look, and the discussion of what he learned by asking for elaboration highlights the fact that as teachers we can jump to incorrect conclusions if we don't listen carefully.

Hartweg, K. & Heisler, M. (2007). No tears here! Third grade problem solvers. *Teaching Children Mathematics, 13* (7), 362–368.

This article is a great complement to this chapter. The authors elaborate on how they have implemented a three-phase lesson approach to instruction. They offer suggestions for supporting student understanding of the problem, questioning, and templates for student writing. The data they gathered on the responses of teachers and students is also impressive.

Reinhart, S. C. (2000). Never say anything a kid can say! *Mathematics Teaching in the Middle School, 5,* 478–483.

The author is an experienced middle school teacher who questioned his own "masterpiece" lesson after realizing that his students were often confused. The article is a result of the realization that he was doing the talking and explaining, and that was causing the confusion. Reinhart's suggestions for questioning techniques and involving students are superb.

Rigelman, N. R. (2007). Fostering mathematical thinking and problem solving: The teacher's role. *Teaching Children Mathematics, 13* (6), 308–314.

This is a wonderful article for illustrating the subtle (and not so subtle) differences between true problem solving and "proceduralizing" problem solving—in other words, showing students how to solve problems. Because two contrasting vignettes are offered, it gives an excellent opportunity for discussing how the two teachers differ philosophically and in practice.

Books

Boaler, J., & Humphreys, C. (2005). *Connecting mathematical ideas: Middle school video cases to support teaching and learning.* Portsmouth, NH: Heinemann.

Cathy Humphreys teaches grade 7. Jo Boaler is a respected researcher who is interested in the impact of different teaching approaches. This book offers cases, based on different content areas and issues in teaching, from Cathy's classroom. Each case is followed by Jo's commentary and expert perspective. Accompanying the book are two CDs that provide videos of the cases.

Buschman, L. (2003). *Share and compare: A teacher's story about helping children become problem solvers in mathematics.* Reston, VA: National Council of Teachers of Mathematics.

Larry Buschman is an experienced elementary teacher who has taught with a problem-based approach for many years. In this book he describes in detail how he makes this work in his classroom. Much of the book is written as if a teacher were interviewing Larry as he answers the kinds of questions you will undoubtedly have as you begin to teach.

Flewelling, G., & Higginson, W. (2000). *Realizing a vision of tomorrow's mathematics classroom: A handbook on rich learning tasks.* Kingston, ON: Centre for Mathematics, Science and Technology Education.

This handbook gives educators an understanding of the nature and assessment of rich learning tasks and of new ways to nourish the teaching and learning process. It provides teachers with sample tasks, along with accompanying rubrics that reflect the type of problem solving recommended in this chapter.

Hiebert, J., Carpenter, T. P., Fennema, E., Fuson, K., Wearne, D., Murray, H., Olivier, A., & Human, P. (1997). *Making sense: Teaching and learning mathematics with understanding.* Portsmouth, NH: Heinemann.

The authors of this significant book are each connected to one of four problem-based, long-term research projects. They make one of the best cases currently in print for developing mathematics via problem-based tasks.

Lester, F. K., & Charles, R. I. (Eds.). (2003). *Teaching mathematics through problem solving: Pre-K to 6.* Reston, VA: National Council of Teachers of Mathematics.

This is an important and valuable publication from the council. The 17 chapters, all written by top authors in the field, provide an in-depth examination of using a problem-based approach to teaching for understanding.

Saskhaug, L. E.. & Olsen, J. (2002). *Children are mathematical problem solvers.* Reston, VA: National Council of Teachers of Mathematics.

This excellent problem-solving collection includes 29 tasks that appeared in Teaching Children Mathematics' *Problem Solvers column. Each task is followed by student solutions, the problem, and a reflection on what these students are telling us.*

Online Resources

Annenberg/CPB
www.learner.org/index.html
A unit of the Annenberg Foundation, Annenberg/CPB offers professional development information and useful information for teachers who want to learn about and teach mathematics.

Math Solution Lessons from the Classroom.
www.mathsolutions.com/index.cfm?page=wp9&crid=56
This is a great collection of lessons for teaching through problem solving.

ENC Online (Eisenhower National Clearinghouse)
www.enc.org
Click on Digital Dozen, Lessons and Activities, or Web Links. The ENC site is full of useful information for teachers who are planning lessons and activities or searching for professional development resources.

Writing and Communication in Mathematics
http://mathforum.org/library/ed_topics/writing_in_math/
This Math Forum page lists numerous articles and Web links concerning the value of writing in mathematics at all levels.

PEARSON **myeducationlab** *will help you improve your understanding of the concepts taught in this textbook and in your course. This online tool includes videos of real classroom experiences, sample lesson plans, simulations, case studies, and links to important educational and teaching Web sites that will help you make the transition from student to teacher. As you study in your course and with this textbook, please follow along in* **MyEducationLab**. *Use it! Explore it! And improve your knowledge and your grade!*

Chapter 4
Planning in the Problem-Based Classroom

Natural learning ... doesn't happen on a time schedule and often requires more time than schools are organized to provide. Problem-solving experiences take time. It's essential that teachers provide the time that's needed for children to work through activities on their own and that teachers not slip into teaching-by-telling for the sake of efficiency.

Burns (1992, p. 30)

The three-phase lesson format described in Chapter 3 provides a basic structure for problem-based lessons. It is grounded in the need for students to be engaged in problems followed by time for discussion and reflection. However, to successfully implement this instructional model, it is necessary to consider a range of pragmatic issues.

This chapter begins with a step-by-step guide for planning problem-based lessons. Also explored here are some variations of the three-part structure, tips for dealing with diversity in the classroom, issues of drill and practice, homework, textbooks, and grading. In short, this chapter discusses the "nuts and bolts" of effective teaching.

Planning a Problem-Based Lesson

Regardless of your experience, it is crucial that you give substantial thought to the planning of your lessons. There is no such thing as a "teacher-proof" mathematics program—where you can simply teach every lesson as planned and in the order it appears. Every class of students is different. Choices of which tasks to use and how they are presented must be made daily to best fit the diverse needs of your students and the objectives of your provincial and territorial curriculum guidelines.

Planning Process for Developing a Lesson

Planning lessons is usually a constituent part of planning an instructional unit. Each lesson builds from the previous to accomplish the goals and objectives of the unit. This book does not address unit development. Instead, it focuses on how to develop a problem-based lesson within a unit. Figure 4.1 provides an outline of the important steps to consider in planning a lesson. Content and task decisions (the first column) are the most crucial part of the planning process. Often, they are overlooked when lessons are planned, without considering the content expectations and needs of the students. Once these decisions are made, the lesson is ready to be designed (See the purple shaded steps in the second column, Figure 4.1.). Here, the focus is on designing activities for students that accomplish the goals outlined in Chapter 3 for the three phases of a lesson (*introduction, development,* and *follow up*). It is through these three phases that content goals are accomplished. Once the plan is drafted, it is important to review and finalize the plan, taking into consideration the flow of the lesson, the anticipated challenges, expected responses from students, and the questions or prompts that can best support the lesson. Each of these steps, under consideration in planning a problem-based lesson, is discussed briefly in this section. An example of a problem-based lesson, The Area Stays the Same (an adaptation of a Marilyn Burns activity, Burns, 2004) is used as a basis for brief discussion, as each step is addressed, to illustrate how the process is implemented. The actual lesson can be found at the end of the chapter in the Expanded Lesson section.

Step 1: Determine the Mathematics and the Learning Goals How do you decide what mathematics your students need to learn? Prior to planning this lesson, either you or

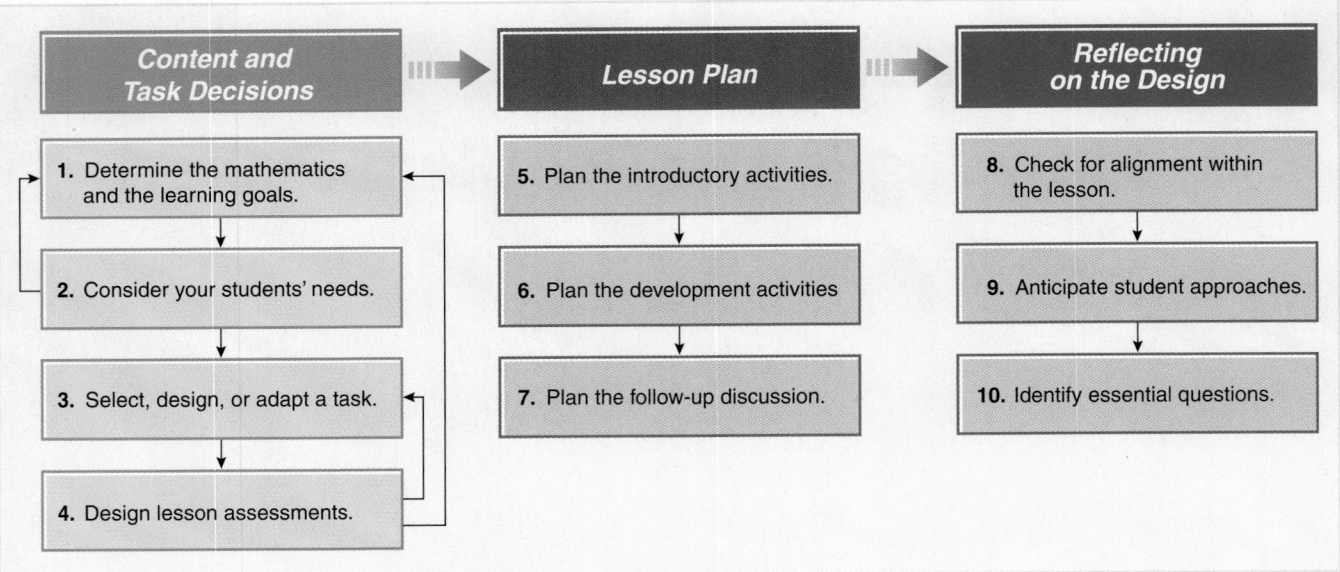

Figure 4.1 Planning steps for thinking through a problem-based lesson.

you and your colleagues would have identified your mathematical goals for the year. You would also have identified the mathematical concepts on which you want to focus in the current unit. At the lesson level, you first need to consult your local curriculum guide, for your grade level, and ask yourself, "What is it that my students should be able to do when this lesson is over?" Keep in mind that the lesson can take several days to accomplish. As you respond to this question, be sure you are focused, at this point, on the important mathematical learning and not the activity you want to do.

Lesson Connection: The Area Stays the Same

In looking at your curriculum expectations for measurement (grade 5), you are likely to see that students are required to learn about area and perimeter of two-dimensional shapes, namely rectangles. A possible goal for one lesson on the topic of area and perimeter is for students to explore the relationship between the two measures, specifically that one can change while the other stays the same.

This goal leads to the development of *observable* and *measurable* outcomes/objectives. The outcomes/objectives are the very things you want to see your students *do* or *say* to demonstrate what they know. Although different formats are used for expressing lesson objectives, there is consensus that an objective must clearly state what the student will do.

Lesson Connection: The Area Stays the Same

The following objectives are intended to help you see what students will *do* or *say* to demonstrate what they know.

Students will be able to draw a variety of possible rectangles for a given area and determine the perimeter.

Students will be able to describe the relationship between area and perimeter.

Students will describe a process (their own algorithm) for finding perimeter of a rectangle.

Students will understand that the perimeter can change at the same time that the area stays the same.

Although the last objective, unlike the first three, is not an outcome you can see or hear, it is a reasonable goal to guide you in your planning.

Step 2: Consider Your Students' Needs What do your students already know or understand about the mathematical concepts on which you chose to focus? Are they ready to tackle this bit of mathematics or are there some background ideas that they have not yet developed? Perhaps they already have some knowledge of the content you have been working on, at which this lesson is aimed at expanding or refining. Be sure that the mathematics you identified in step 1 includes something new or at least slightly unfamiliar to your students. At the same time, be certain that your objectives are not out of reach.

Consider the individual needs of each student i.e., possible learning challenges, learning styles, as well as each person's strengths and weaknesses. Language and culture are also important considerations. Ask yourself, "What might students already know about this topic that serves as a launching point for the lesson? What context might be engaging for the range of learners in the classroom? What learning gaps or misconceptions might need to be addressed? What visuals or models (manipulatives) might support student understanding? What vocabulary might be needed?"

Lesson Connection: The Area Stays the Same

Students are likely to have prior knowledge of the terms perimeter and area. At the same time though, they may confuse the meaning of the two. They may not have a good understanding of the concepts. They may also believe that, for a given area, there can only be one perimeter, or vice versa.

Step 3: Select, Design, or Adapt a Task With your goals in mind, you are now ready to consider what task or activity will be the focus of your lesson. You might choose a task or activity, or exercises from your textbook. At this stage of the planning, the question to ask yourself is "Does the task you are considering (from the textbook or any other source) accomplish the content goals (step 1) and the content needs (step 2) of my students?" If the answer is yes, then any adaptations, such as using a context students would find more engaging or including a literature connection, that you decide to incorporate, will serve as minor ways to enhance the lesson. Next you will need to consider each of your students and think how you will adapt the lesson to fit their particular needs. Karp and Howell (2004) offer three questions to consider when thinking about the needs of students with special needs. These questions can be a good basis when thinking about the needs of any student:

1. What organizational, behavioural, and cognitive skills are necessary in order for students with special needs to derive meaning from this activity?
2. Which students have important weaknesses in any of these skills?
3. How can I provide support in these areas of weakness so that students with special needs can focus on the conceptual tasks at hand?

If you look at the given lesson tasks and find that they do not fit your content and student needs, then you will need to either make substantial modifications to the lesson or find an appropriate substitute.

Good tasks need not be elaborate. Often a simple story problem is all that is needed, as long as the solution involves children in the intended mathematics for the lesson.

Chapter 3 gave examples of tasks and suggestions for creating or selecting them. This book is full of tasks, especially the problem-based lessons in Section II. The more experience you have with the content in step 1 and the longer you have to build a repertoire of tasks gleaned from journals, resource books, conferences, and professional development, the easier this important step in planning will become.

Step 4: Design Lesson Assessments You might wonder why you are thinking about assessment before you have even introduced the lesson. But, thinking about what it is you want students to know and how they are going to

show that to you *is* assessment. The sentence you just read may give you a déjà-vu experience related to the section on objectives—and so it should. Your assessments are derived from your objectives. It is important to assess in a variety of ways—see Chapter 5 for extended discussion of assessment strategies. Formative assessment is the type of information gathering that lets you know how students are doing on each of the objectives during the lesson. This information can be used for adjusting the lesson midstream or making changes for the next day. Formative assessment also informs the questions you pose in the discussion that you hold with your students about the task, in the follow-up phase of the lesson. Summative assessment lets you know whether the students have learned the objectives you have listed for the lesson (or the unit).

Lesson Connection: The Area Stays the Same

Outcome/Objective 1: **Students will be able to draw a sufficient variety of possible rectangles for a given area and determine their perimeters.**

***Assessment:* In the *development* phase of the lesson, I will use a checklist to determine if each student is able to create at least three different rectangles with given area and accurately record their perimeters.**

Outcome/Objective 2: **Students will be able to describe the relationship between area and perimeter.**

***Assessment*: In the *development* phase of the lesson, I will ask individuals, "What have you noticed about the relationship between the area and the perimeter of the rectangles?" [formative] I will also use an exit slip where students will explain the relationship between area and perimeter of a rectangle and draw pictures to support their explanation. An exit slip is a written response that is turned in at the end of the class—as an "exit" to the lesson. [formative]**

Outcome/Objective 3: **Students will describe a process (their own algorithm) for finding perimeter of a rectangle.**

***Assessment*: In the *development* phase of the lesson, I will ask "How are you finding perimeter? Are you seeing any patterns or shortcuts? Explain it to me." [formative]. This will be the focus of the discussion in the *follow-up* phase of the lesson. [formative]**

Steps 1 through 4 define the heart of your lesson. The next three steps explain how you will carry out the plan in your classroom.

Step 5: Plan the Introduction Phase of the Lesson As discussed in Chapter 3, in the section titled "Teacher Actions in the *Introduction* Phase," the beginning of the lesson should elicit students' prior knowledge, provide context, and establish expectations. You need to think about the task you have selected and how you will introduce it. What terminology and background might students need in order to be ready for the task? Will you read a children's book that connects to the task and builds interest for students? Is there a current or popular event that could be used to introduce the topic? Sometimes you can just simply begin with the task and articulate what students' responsibilities are. But, in many instances, you will want to prepare students by posing a related task or some related warm-up exercise that builds background and elicits prior knowledge.

Consider how you will present the task. Options include having it written on paper, taken from their texts, shown on the overhead, or written on the board or on chart paper. Be sure to tell the students about their responsibilities. For nearly every task, you want students to be able to tell you

- What they did to get the answer.
- Why they did it that way.
- Why they think the solution is correct or reasonable.

Decide how you want students to supply this information. If responding in writing, will students write individually or prepare a group presentation? Will they write in their journals, on paper to be turned in, on a worksheet, on chart paper for presentation to the class, or on acetate to use on the overhead? Will they prepare a PowerPoint presentation?

Estimate how much time you think students should be given for the task. It is useful to tell students in advance. Some teachers set timers that all students can see. Plan to be somewhat flexible, but do not give up your discussion period.

Lesson Connection: The Area Stays the Same

Connecting with the sustainable growth project that the grade 5 class is doing for environmental studies, you might begin with the following context. The garden that we will be planting has an area of 36 square metres. Students will explain what the perimeter and the area of the garden are. The teacher will then draw and label this information on the board or on chart paper. A good question to focus students' attention and to raise their curiosity is: Given that the area is 36 square metres, does it matter what length and width the garden has? Would one rectangular shape be better or worse than another? Let's see what the possibilities are. Then, we can pick one that we think will serve us best.

Step 6: Plan the Development Phase of the Lesson   While it may seem that this phase occurs when the students are working independently, this is a critical time for teaching. The teacher's role is to monitor and assess student progress and to provide hints as necessary. For example, you might make one quick visit to each group to verify that each understands the task and is engaged in solving the problem.

What hints or assists can you plan in advance for students who may be stuck or who may need accommodations? Are there particular groups or individual students you wish to specially observe or assess during this lesson? Make a note to do so. Think of extensions or challenges you can pose to gifted students or others who finish early.

After the initial round to see that each group has started, the next rounds are your opportunity to learn what your students know and can do (see planning steps 1 and 4). Students should become accustomed to the fact that in the *development* phase of the lesson you will be asking them to explain what they are thinking and doing. This phase is also a time for you to see which groups or individuals should be sharing their work in the *follow-up* phase of the lesson.

Lesson Connection: The Area Stays the Same

After distributing 36 tiles to each pair of students, make one trip around the room to see that students are actually building a rectangle, recording its dimensions on the grid sheet accurately, and labelling each side. After confirming that all students have completed this for the first rectangle, make more trips around asking the assessment questions. The goal is to get each student to explain how they found the perimeter of the rectangles and what patterns they are noticing. But if you can't get to everyone, target those that you miss in the next lesson.

Step 7: Plan the Follow-up Phase of the Lesson   How will you begin your discussion? One option is to simply list all the different answers from groups or individuals, doing so without comment. Then, return to students or groups to explain their solutions and justify their answers. You may also begin with full explanations from each group or student before you get all the answers. If you accept oral reports, think about how you will record on the board what is being said.

Plan an adequate amount of time for your discussion. Five minutes is almost never sufficient. A rich problem can take about 15 to 20 minutes to discuss.

Lesson Connection: The Area Stays the Same

First, post all the possibilities for rectangles with a given area. Have an overhead copy of grid paper and have each group report one that they found. Quickly sketch and label the dimensions of each one. Second, ask different groups to report on the perimeter and area of each one; then go back and add this information. This visual will stay posted for the focus discussion:

- How did you find the perimeters of these rectangles? (Collect different ideas—look for shortcuts and note those responses in words and symbols on the board.)

◆ **What do you notice about the relationship between area and perimeter? (Students should notice that there are a number of possible perimeters for a given area and that the perimeter is less when the shape is more "square").**
◆ **If you were a garden designer, which of the rectangles would you pick and why?**

After the discussion, distribute an exit slip titled "Advice to the Designer" that asks students to explain the second question, using illustrations to support the explanation, to the garden designer.

Steps 5, 6, and 7 will result in a tentative instructional plan. The next three steps are designed to review this tentative plan in light of some critical considerations, making changes or additions as needed.

Step 8: Check for Alignment Within the Lesson A well-prepared lesson that maximizes the opportunity for students to learn must be focused and aligned. There is often a temptation to do a series of "fun" activities that seem to relate to a topic but that are intended for slightly different learning goals. First, look to see that three parts of the plan: the objectives, the assessment, and the questions asked in the *development* and *follow-up* phases are clearly aligned, sometimes nearly identical. If the questions are all focused on only one objective, add questions to address each objective or remove the objective that is not addressed.

Second, the lesson should have a reasonable flow to it, building in sophistication. The *introductory* activity should be related to the focus task in the *development* phase, but will likely be less involved. The *follow-up* phase should take students from looking at the task itself to generalizing ideas about mathematics concepts. If you feel like you are doing one activity, then switching to another, and you don't know how to pull it together in the end, it may be that the lesson is not aligned. Look back to the outcomes/objectives and make sure all activities support these outcomes/objectives and build in critical thinking and challenges.

Lesson Connection: The Area Stays the Same

The area lesson demonstrates alignment. The outcomes/objectives were used to write the assessment employed and the assessment questions were written to match the phases of the lesson. The lesson starts with an example to get students thinking about the use of area and perimeter. It then builds on this foundation by having them create as many rectangles as they can, with an area of 36 square units. They then engage in discussion by focusing on generalized ideas of the relationship between area and perimeter and ways to find the perimeter.

Step 9: Anticipate Student Approaches In reflecting on the task that is chosen, it is important to consider what strategies students might use and how you might respond. What misconceptions might students have? What common barriers might need to be addressed? Which of these do you want to address prior to starting the activity and which ones do you want to see emerge from their work?

Lesson Connection: The Area Stays the Same

Students are likely to debate about whether the 6-by-6 square should be considered as one of their rectangles. This will not be addressed up front, as a conversation around whether a square is a rectangle is a worthy class discussion. Secondly, students may initially consider a 4-by-9 rectangle different from a 9-by-4 rectangle. To prevent students getting bogged down making too many rectangles, this issue will be addressed in the *introductory phase*. They will be acknowledged as the same. Students may confuse the terms *perimeter* and *area*. To deal with this problem, discuss strategies for remembering which is which in the *introductory* phase. Also, students will be encouraged to use these appropriate terms, as they work with their partner.

Step 10: Identify the Essential Question While this might sound redundant after the previous steps, the quality of your questioning in a lesson is so critically important to the potential learning that it is a fitting last step. Using your outcomes/objectives as the focus, review the lesson to see that in the *introductory* phase you are posing questions that focus students' attention and raise curiosity about how to solve the problem. In the *development* and *follow-up* phases, you are using questions based on the outcomes/objectives to focus students' thinking on the salient features of the task and what you want them to learn. Research on questioning indicates that teachers rarely ask higher-level questions—this is your chance to review and be sure that you have included some challenging questions that ask students to extend, analyze, compare, generalize, and synthesize. These questions help students understand the concepts they are studying, more deeply.

Lesson Connection: The Area Stays the Same

Higher-level questions based on the objectives are posed to students in the *development* and *follow-up* phases. Some additional questions to have ready for the discussion or for early finishers or advanced students include the following:

What if the perimeter was set at 36 meters? Would there be different possible areas?
Which one might a garden designer prefer for a garden?
Is a square a rectangle? Explain using what you know about the characteristics of the different shapes.

Applying the Planning Process

The importance of the planning process cannot be over-emphasized. Sometimes teachers have a tendency to spend more time doing marking than preparing lessons for upcoming concepts. This may result in poor quality lessons resulting in less being learned. The teacher then has even more work trying to remediate students and respond to their misunderstandings and confusion. A finished lesson plan often has the following components, though the order may vary:

- Provincial and territorial mathematics outcomes/expectations
- Lesson goals and learning objectives
- Assessment(s)
- Materials needed
- *Introductory* phase
- *Development* phase
- *Follow-up* phase

Examples of Lessons: Expanded Lesson

Attention to the first two planning steps (the mathematics in your curriculum and the particular needs of your students, relative to the mathematics) is critical to a successful lesson. Therefore, to plan a lesson without a real class in mind is somewhat artificial. The Expanded Lesson, The Area Stays the Same, that served as an example for each of the planning steps in a problem-based lesson on area and perimeter, can be found at the end of this chapter. It illustrates, in detail, the thinking involved in planning a problem-based lesson. It is designed as a full class lesson for grade five. In addition to this sample lesson, the MyEducationLab (www.myeducationlab.com) has Expanded Lessons that elaborate on activities from each content chapter in Section II of this book.

Look for this icon **EXPANDED LESSON** indicating that a lesson related to a given activity or concept is offered on the Web site.

Variations of the Three-Phase Lesson

The basic lesson structure we have been discussing assumes that a class will be given a task or problem, allowed to work on it, and end with a discussion. Certainly, not every lesson is developed around a task given to a full class. However, the basic concept of tasks and discussions can be adapted to most any problem-based lesson.

Minilessons   Many tasks do not require the full period. The three-part format can be compressed to as little as 10 minutes. You might plan two or three cycles in a single lesson. For example, consider these tasks:

Grades K–1:   Make up two questions that we can answer using the information in our graph.

Grades 2–3:   If you have forgotten the answer to the addition fact $9 + 5$, how might you figure it out in your head?

Grades 4–5:   On your geoboard, make a figure that has line symmetry but not rotational symmetry. Make a second figure that has rotational symmetry but not line symmetry.

Grades 6–7:   Without finding the common denominator, find a way to determine which of the fractions in the pair is larger. Explain your strategy.

$\frac{1}{8}$ and $\frac{1}{10}$ $\frac{9}{20}$ and $\frac{13}{25}$ $\frac{3}{4}$ and $\frac{3}{8}$ $\frac{9}{10}$ and $\frac{10}{11}$

These are worthwhile tasks but probably would not require a full period to do and discuss.

An effective strategy for short tasks is *think–pair–share*. Students are first directed to spend a minute developing their own thoughts and ideas on how to approach the task or even on what they think may be a good solution. Then they pair with a classmate and discuss each other's ideas. This strategy provides an opportunity to test out ideas and to practise articulating them. The last step is to share the idea with the rest of the class. The pair may actually have two ideas or can be told to come to a single decision. The entire process, including some discussion, may take less than 15 minutes.

Stations   It is often useful for students to work at different tasks or games at various locations around the room. Stations are also a good way to manage materials without the need to distribute and collect them. They also help when it is impossible for all students to have access to the required materials for an activity. Because good computer tasks are available, especially applets found on the Web, one station can be a computer station allowing all students an opportunity to have a turn on the computer. Stations also allow you to differentiate tasks when your students are at different stages in their conceptual understanding.

You may want students to work at stations in small groups or individually. Therefore, for a given topic you might prepare from four to eight different activities. Not every station has to be different. Materials required for the activity or game, including any special recording sheets, are placed in a container or folder for quick distribution at different locations around the classroom.

A good idea for younger children or for games and computer activities is to explain or teach the activity to the full class ahead of time, in addition to having the instructions at the station. In this way, students will not waste time when they get to the station and you will not have to run around the room explaining what to do. The first sample lesson at the end of the chapter is an example of using stations.

A good task for a station activity is one that can be profitably repeated several times. For example, students might play a "game" where one student covers part of a known number of counters and the other student names the covered part. The game "Fraction Game" in the NCTM *Illuminations Lessons* (http://illuminations.nctm.org/ActivityDetail.aspx?ID=18) can be played repeatedly, each time strengthening students' understanding of fractions.

A game or other repeatable activity may not seem to incorporate a problem, but it can nonetheless be a problem-based task. The determining factor is whether the activity causes students to be reflective about new or developing mathematical relationships. Remember that it is reflective thought that leads to growth in understanding and resultant learning. If the activity merely has students repeating a procedure without wrestling with an emerging idea, then it is not a problem-based experience. The few examples just mentioned, and many others, do have children thinking through concepts that they have not yet developed well. In this sense, they fit the definition of a problem-based task.

The time during which students are working at stations is analogous to the *development* portion of a lesson. What kinds of things could you do for the *follow-up* portion of the lesson? Discussions with students who have been working on a task are just as important for games and stations. These discussions might take place in small groups. For example, you might sit down with students at a station and ask about what they have been doing, what strategies they have discovered, or how they have been going about the activity in general. Try to get at the reasoning behind what they are doing. Another possibility is to wait until all in the class have worked at the same game or station. Then, you can have a full class discussion about the mathematics concepts embedded in the activities.

Just as with any task, some form of recording or writing should be included with stations whenever possible. Students solving a problem on a computer can write up what they did and explain what they learned. Students playing a game can keep records and then tell how they played the game and what thinking or strategies they used.

Textbooks as Resources

The textbook remains the most significant factor influencing instruction in the elementary and middle school classroom. To make decisions about the use of a textbook, it is good to have an objective view of textbooks and the role they can serve in instruction. Our task as teachers is to help children construct relationships and ideas, not to get them to "do pages." We should look on the textbook as simply one of a variety of teaching resources available in the classroom, not as the object of instruction. Yet, most teachers use their textbook as the main guide for their day-to-day curriculum. Although they are a useful resource, they should not be your only source for the lessons you teach. When teachers let the text determine the next lesson, they assume that children learned from each page what was intended. Avoid the "myth of coverage": If we covered it, they must have learned it. Good teachers use their text and accompanying teacher's resources to support their curriculum guideline. In the face of the current pressures from provincial and territorial assessments, the curriculum guideline is extremely important.

The textbook can be a source of ideas for designing lessons rather than prescriptions for what each lesson will be. Here are some suggestions:

- Teach to the big ideas or concepts, not the pages of the textbook. The chapter or unit viewpoint will help focus on the big ideas rather than on the activity required to complete a page.
- Consider the conceptual portions of lessons as ideas or inspirations for planning more problem-based activities. The students do not actually have to do the activity on that page.
- Let the pace of your lessons through a unit be determined by student performance and understanding rather than on the artificial norm of a lesson a day.
- Remember, there is no law saying every page must be done or every exercise completed. Select lessons or activities that suit your curriculum guidelines, your instructional goals, and students, rather than designing instructions that are text based. Omit pages activities you believe to be inappropriate and use only what is needed.

Planning for All Learners

Perhaps one of the most important challenges for teachers today is to reach all the students in their increasingly diverse classrooms. Every teacher faces this dilemma because every classroom contains a range of student abilities and backgrounds.

Interestingly and perhaps surprisingly to some, the problem-based approach to teaching is the best way to teach mathematics and attend to the range of students. In the problem-based classroom, children are making sense of the mathematics in *their* way, bringing to the problems only the skills and ideas that they own. In contrast, in a traditional, highly directed lesson, it is often assumed that all students will understand and use the same approach and the same ideas, as determined by the teacher or the textbook. Students not ready to understand the ideas presented must focus their attention on following the teacher's rules or directions in an instrumental manner (i.e., without conceptual understanding). This, of course, leads to endless difficulties and leaves many students behind or in need of serious remediation.

In addition to using a problem-based approach, there are specific things you can do to help attend to the diversity of learners in your classroom: Chapter 6 offers strategies for the diverse range of learners you will have in your classroom. In this chapter, the focus is specifically on the planning steps during the development of a problem-based lesson that are essential if you are to do the best for all learners. Specifically, this section briefly discusses:

- Accommodations and modifications
- Differentiated instruction
- Flexible groupings
- Examples of accommodating a lesson: English Language Learners (ELLs)

Make Accommodations and Modifications

There are two paths to making a given task accessible to all students: *accommodation* and *modification*. An *accommodation* is a change to teaching, student responding, and the classroom environment that increases students' access to the curriculum. For example, you might write down instructions instead of just saying them orally. Students may use a calculator or computer or work with the assistance of a translator or a person who can scribe a student's responses. Accommodations do not alter the task.

A *modification* refers to a change in the problem or task itself. For example, suppose the task begins with finding the area of a compound shape as shown here.

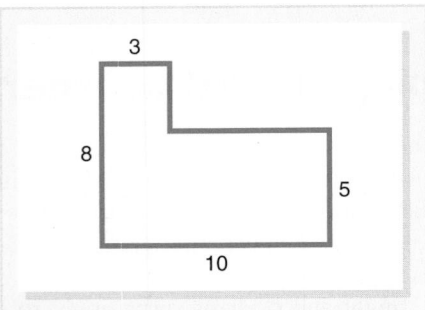

If you decide instead to focus on simple rectangular regions, then that is a modification. However, if you decide to begin with rectangular regions and build to connected compound shapes composed of rectangles, you have *scaffolded* the lesson in a way to ramp up to the original task. Scaffolding a task in this manner is an accommodation. In planning accommodations and modifications, the goal is to enable each child to successfully reach your learning objectives, not to change the objectives. This is how equity is achieved in the classroom.

Choices regarding which tasks to use and how to present them must be made daily to best fit the diverse needs of your students, as well as the objectives of your provincial or territorial curriculum guidelines.

Differentiating Instruction

Differentiating instruction means that a teacher's plan includes strategies to support the range of different academic backgrounds that frequently exist in classrooms. These may be academically, culturally, and linguistically heterogeneous (Tomlinson, 1999).

When considering what to differentiate, consider the learning profiles of each student, student interest, and student readiness. Second, consider what can be differentiated across three critical elements: content (what do you want each student to be able to do), process (how will you engage them in learning), and product (what will they have to show for what they have learned when the lesson is over). Third, consider how the physical learning environment might be adapted. This might include seating arrangement, specific grouping strategies, and access to materials. Some common ways to differentiate include adapting the task to different levels (tiered lessons) and using centres or stations.

Tiered Lessons In a tiered lesson, the teacher determines the learning goals for all students. Then the level of difficulty of the task is adapted up and down to meet the range of learners. The challenge of each of the defined tiers in a lesson is designed to best the meet the learning needs of students in the classroom (Kingore, 2006; Tomlinson, 1999). The level of difficulty is not just about the content. It can be about any of the following:

1. *The degree to which the teacher provides assistance.* This might include providing examples or partnering students.

2. *How structured the lesson is.* Students with special needs, for example, benefit from a highly structured task, whereas gifted students often benefit from a more open-ended structure.
3. *The complexity of the given task(s).* This can include making a task more concrete or more abstract or including more difficult problems or applications.
4. *The complexity of the process.* This includes how quickly paced the lesson is, how many instructions you give at one time, and how many higher-level thinking questions are included as part of the task.

Consider the following task for grades 1–2, focused on the concepts of addition.

Original Task

George had 9 toy cars. Keisha came over to play and brought 8 cars. Can you figure out how many cars George and Keisha have together? Explain how you know.

The teacher has distributed cubes to the students to model the problem. She also provides paper and pencil so students can illustrate and record how they solved the problem. She asks students to model the problem and to be ready to explain their solution.

Adapted Task

George had some toy cars. Keisha came over to play and brought her cars. Can you figure out how many cars George and Keisha have together? Explain how you know.

The teacher asks students what is happening in this problem and what they are going to be doing to solve this problem. She then distributes Task Cards that tell how many cars George and Keisha have. She has varied the difficulty of the numbers, giving the struggling students numbers less than ten. The more advanced students are given numbers greater than ten.

Card 1 (easier)

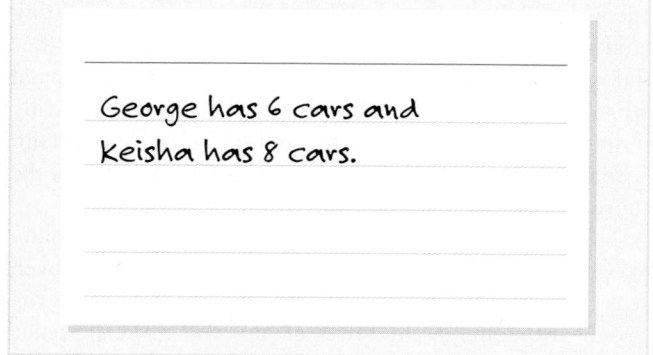

George has 6 cars and
Keisha has 8 cars.

Card 2 (middle)

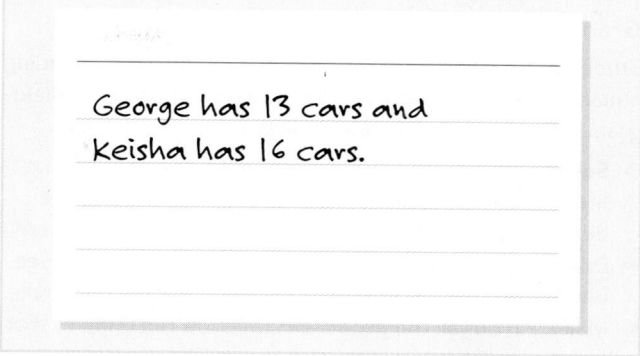

George has 13 cars and
Keisha has 16 cars.

Card 3 (advanced)

George has ___ cars and
Keisha has ___ cars. Together
they have 25 cars. How many
cars might George have and
how many cars might Keisha have?

In each case, students must use models, pictures, words, or numbers on paper to illustrate how they solved the problem. Various tools are provided (interlocking cubes, sticks, and hundreds charts) for their use.

In this adapted lesson, there are several options for how to organize the use of the Task Cards. First, the teacher can give everyone the cards in order. Second, the teacher can give students only one card, based on their current academic readiness (e.g., easy cards to those that have not yet mastered addition of single digit numbers). Third, the teacher can give out cards 1 and 2 based on ability, and use card 3 as an extension for those who have successfully completed card 1 or 2. In each of the three cases, the teacher will know at the end of the lesson which students are able to model and explain addition problems and will plan the next lesson accordingly.

There are several other ways you can effectively differentiate a task. One way to differentiate a task is to present a situation with related but different questions that can be asked. The situation might be data in a chart or graph, a measurement task, or a geometry task. Here is an example.

Topic: Properties of a Parallelogram

Grades: 6–8

Students are given a collection of parallelograms, including squares and rectangles as well as non-rectangular parallelograms. These questions can be posed:

◆ Select a shape and draw at least three new shapes that are like it in some way. Tell how your new shapes are both similar to and different from the shape you selected.

◆ Draw diagonals in these shapes and measure them. See what relationships you can discover about the diagonals.

◆ Make a list of all the properties that you can think of that every parallelogram in this set has.

In this task, there is a challenge to engage nearly every student.

For many problems involving computation, you can insert multiple sets of numbers. In the following problem students are permitted to select the first, second, or third number in each bracket.

Topic: Subtraction

Grades: 2–3

Sam had {12, 60, 121} marbles. He gave Rhosnee {5, 15, 46} marbles. How many marbles does Sam have now?

Students tend to select the numbers that provide them with the greatest challenge without being too difficult. In the discussions, all children benefit and feel as though they worked on the same task.

Pause and Reflect

How might you change the parallelogram task to adjust the level of difficulty, giving consideration to the four levels of difficulty (Kingore, 2006) described earlier?

Flexible Groupings

Allowing students to collaborate on tasks is both supportive and challenging for them. It increases their chance to communicate about mathematics and to build understanding. Collaboration is also an important life skill. "Flexible grouping" means that the size and makeup of the small groups are varied in a purposeful and strategic manner. This means that sometimes students work with partners because the task is best suited to only two people working together. At other times, students might work in groups of four because the task has enough jobs or roles to warrant a larger team. Also, groups are selected based on students' academic abilities, language needs, social dynamics, and

behaviour. It is often most effective to use mixed ability (heterogeneous) groups, strategically placing students who are more challenged with those who are more capable and likely to be helpful.

Groups may stay the same for a full unit so that the students become skilled at working with one another. If students are seated with their groups in clusters of four, they can still pair with another person from the group if the task is better suited for only two people.

Regardless of whether groups have two or four members or whether they have been grouped according to mixed ability or similar ability (homogeneous), the key to successful grouping is *individual accountability*. This means that while the group is working together on a product, each member of the group must be able to explain the process, the content, and the product. While this concept may sound easy, it is not. Second, and equally challenging, is building a sense of *shared responsibility* within a group. At the start of the year, it is important to do team building activities and to set the standard that all members will participate and that all team members are responsible for making sure that all the people in their group understand the process, the content, and the product.

Good resources for team building activities (though there are many) include *Reaching All by Creating Tribes Learning Communities* by Jeanne Gibbs (2006); *Team Building Activities for Every Group* by Alanna Jones (1999); and *Feeding the Zircon Gorilla and Other Team Building Activities* by Sam Sikes (1995). For a free downloadable collection, Tom Hecks has created eight fun activities, all done with shoestrings, in the e-book *Team Building Games on a Shoestring* (www.teachmeteamwork.com).

To reinforce individual accountability and shared responsibility means a shift in your role as teacher. When a member of a small group asks you a question, your response is not to answer the question but to ask the whole group what they think. Students will soon learn that they use their teammates as their first resource and seek teacher help only when the whole group needs it. Also, when observing groups, rather than ask Jamal what he is doing, you can ask Leah what she is doing, or you can ask Jamal to explain what Leah is doing. Having all students participate in their oral report to the whole class also builds individual accountability. Letting students know that you may call on them to explain what they did is a good way to be sure all group members understand what they did. Additionally, having students individually write and record their strategies and solutions is important. The more you use these strategies and others like them, the more successfully students will learn the concepts.

Avoid ability grouping! Trying to split a class into ability groups is futile. Every group will still be diverse. Moreover, it is demeaning to those students who are not in the top groups. Students in the lower groups will not experience the thinking and language of the top group. Concomitantly, top students will not hear the thoughts of students in the lower group, which may provide unconventional, yet interesting approaches to the problem. Furthermore, having two or more groups requires that you reduce the time you spend with each group.

Example of Accommodating a Lesson for English Language Learners (ELLs or ESLs) We have already

seen some strategies that promote equity for all students. To be an equitable teacher, you must keep your eye on the mathematical goals for your lessons and at the same time attend to the specific learning needs of each child. Attention to the needs of students who are learning English (ELLs) must be considered at each step of the ten-step planning guide detailed in Table 4.1.

Table 4.1

An At-a-Glance Look at General Planning Steps and Additional Considerations for ELLs		
Steps	**General Description**	**Additional Considerations for English Language Learners**
1. Determine the mathematics and goals	• Identify the mathematical concepts that align with provincial and territorial standards. • Formulate learning objectives.	• Establish language objectives (e.g., include reading, writing, speaking, and listening) in the lesson plan. • Post content and language objectives, using child-friendly words.
2. Consider your students' needs	• Relate concepts to previously learned concepts and experiences.	• Consider students' social/cultural backgrounds and previously learned content and vocabulary.
3. Select, design, or adapt a task	• Select a task that will enable students to explore the concept(s) selected in step 1.	• Include a context that is meaningful to the students' culture and background. • Analyze the task for language pitfalls. Identify words that need to be discussed and eliminate terms that are not necessary to the lesson. • Watch for homonyms, homophones, and words that have special meanings in math (e.g., *mean, similar, product*).
4. Design lesson assessments	• Determine the types of assessments that will be used for each objective. • Use a variety of assessments.	• Build in questions to diagnose understanding. Use translators if necessary. • If a student is not succeeding, seek alternative strategies to diagnose if the problem is with language, content, or both.
5. Plan the introductory activities	• Determine how you will introduce the task. • Consider warm-ups that orient student thinking.	• Build background! Link task to prior learning and to familiar contexts. • Review key vocabulary needed for the task. List key vocabulary in a prominent location. • Provide visuals and real objects related to the selected task. • Set the task in written and oral format. • Check for understanding (e.g., ask students to pair-share what they are supposed to do).
6. Plan the questions and extensions for the *development* phase	• Think about hints or assists you might give as students work. • Consider extensions or challenges.	• Group students for both academic and language support. • Encourage students to draw pictures, make diagrams, and/or use manipulatives/models. • Maximize language. Ask students to explain and defend. • Consider using a graphic organizer. Ideas include: sentence starters (e.g., "I solved the problem by …"), recording tables, and concept maps. • Maximize language use in non-threatening ways (e.g., think–pair–share).
7. Plan the follow-up discussion	• Decide how students will report their findings. • Determine how you will format the discussion of the task.	• Encourage students to use visuals in reports. • Give advance notice that students will be speaking, so they can plan. • Encourage students to choose the language they wish to use, using a translator if possible. • Provide appropriate wait time.
8. Check for agreement within the lesson	• Check that all aspects of the lesson target the objectives.	• Review lesson phases to see if key vocabulary is supported throughout the lesson. • Review lesson phases to see that visuals and other supports are in place.
9. Anticipate student approaches	• Reflect on how students will respond to the task and what misunderstandings may occur. • Determine how to address these issues.	• Consider approaches that might be used in other countries and encourage students to share different approaches. • Encourage pictures to replace words, as appropriate for age and language proficiency.
10. Identify essential questions	• Using your objectives as a guide, what questions will you ask in each phase of the lesson?	• If possible, translate essential questions to diagnose understanding. • Use straightforward, simple sentence structures to word questions.

In the NCTM Equity Principle, the two phrases "high expectations" and "strong support" are one idea, not two. In the following example, the teacher uses several techniques that provide support for her ESL learners while keeping expectations high.

Ms. Nygard is working on a grade 4 geometry lesson that requires students to apply their knowledge of the geometric properties of three-dimensional shapes (polyhedra) to identify *prisms* and *pyramids* by their distinguishing features (e.g., three-dimensional shape of and number of faces). The task requires students to examine a set of face cards for a three-dimensional shape, decide which shape it is, and then check the correctness of their answer by comparing with an actual model. Ms. Nygard has a student from Ethiopia who has been in Canada for only eight months and knows very little English, and a student from Sri Lanka who has been here for about two years. These two students may not be familiar with the terms *prism* and *pyramid* and will have difficulty identifying which set of face cards represents a *prism* and which one represents a *pyramid*. The student from Ethiopia may also be confused by the word *face*, which in common English usage has a different meaning.

To ensure that these students (as well as the rest of the class) are familiar with the words *prism* and *pyramid*, Ms. Nygard addresses their meaning before launching into the lesson. She writes the words *prism* and *pyramid* on the board and asks students what they are. She allows time for students to discuss their meaning with a partner, then to share their answers with the whole class. Ms. Nygard makes sure that she has different *prisms* and *pyramids* displayed at the front of the room. Students also discuss the use of the word *face* so that her English Language Learners appreciate its use in the context of geometry, as well as in everyday life. Upon completion of the discussions, Ms. Nygard explains to the class that today they are going to apply their knowledge of the properties of three-dimensional shapes to identify prisms and pyramids. Ms. Nygard models how the task is to be carried out. First, she lays out a set of cards for the class and asks them, "What three-dimensional shape do you think this is? Can you tell us why you think it is?" She has students discuss with a partner. She makes certain that the two English Language Learners are paired with a partner who can offer necessary language support. Then, a student is invited to give an answer and an explanation for her or his choice. The student's response is checked for correctness by comparing with the *prisms* and *pyramids* displayed. Now, she has them ready to begin the activity, working in partners.

❚❚ ———————— *Pause and Reflect*

Review Ms. Nygard's lesson. What specific strategies to support students who are learning English (ELLs) can you identify?

Discussion of the words *prism*, *pyramid*, and *face* using a think–pair–share technique recognized the potential language confusion. Doing so allowed students the chance to talk about terms, before becoming perplexed by the task. Using visuals and concrete models (the cards and the 3-D shapes) also provided support, so the ELL students could succeed in this task. As well, she had ELL students work with a partner who could offer language support as they carried out the task. Most importantly, Ms. Nygard did not diminish the challenge of the task with these strategies. If she had altered the task, for example, by using simpler shapes, she would have lowered her expectations. Conversely, if she had simply posed the problem without taking time to discuss the meanings of the words, provide visuals, and model the task, she would have kept her expectations high but failed to provide the support that would enable her students to succeed. Instead, she took the necessary steps to ensure that all students would be successful.

❚❚ ———————— *Pause and Reflect*

Examine the Expanded Lesson at the end of the chapter. Look for evidence within the lesson that there is already support for students who are learning English (ELLs). What additional opportunities can you find in the lessons to provide support for them?

Additional information for working mathematics with students who are learning English can be found in Chapter 6.

Drill or Practice?

Drill and practice, if not a hallmark of Canadian instructional methods in mathematics, is present, to at least some degree, in the classroom. The use of drill-and-practice workbooks and computer drill programs tend to be plentiful. This repetitive procedural work is supposed to cement the ideas just learned. On the surface, this idea seems to make sense.

A question worth asking is, "What has all of this drill gotten us?" It has been an ever-present component of mathematics classes for decades and yet the adult population is replete with those who almost proudly proclaim "I was never any good at mathematics" and who understand little more about the subject than arithmetic. This section offers a different perspective.

New Definitions of Drill and Practice

The phrase "drill and practice" slips off the tongue so rapidly that the two words *drill* and *practice* appear to be synonyms—and, for the most part, they have been. In the interest of developing a new or different perspective on drill and practice, consider definitions that differentiate between these terms as different types of activities rather than link them together.

> *Practice* refers to different problem-based tasks or experiences, spread over numerous class periods, each addressing the same basic ideas.
>
> *Drill* refers to repetitive, *non*–problem-based exercises designed to improve skills or procedures already acquired.

Pause and Reflect

How are these two definitions different? Which is more in keeping with the view of drill and practice (as a singular term) with which you are familiar? How do each of these align with what we know about how people learn? (See Chapter 2.)

Using these definitions as a point of departure, it is now useful to examine what benefits we can get from each and when each is appropriate.

What Drill Provides

Drill can provide students with the following:

- An increased facility with a procedure but *only* with a procedure already learned
- A review of facts or procedures so they are not forgotten

Limitations of drill include:

- A focus on a singular method and an exclusion of flexible alternatives
- A false appearance of understanding
- A rule-oriented or procedural view of what mathematics is about

The popular belief is that somehow students learn through drill. In reality, drill can only help students get faster at what they already know. Students who count on their fingers to answer basic fact questions only get very good at counting on their fingers. Drill is not a reflective activity. The nature of drill asks students to do what they already know how to do, even if they just learned it. The focus of drill is on procedural skill.

For most school-level mathematics, including computation, there are numerous ways of getting answers. For example, how many different mental methods can you think

of to add 48 + 35? To find 25 percent of $84 you can divide by 4 and subtract rather than multiplying by 0.25. What approach would you use to find 17 percent of $84? Similar examples of the value of flexible thinking are easily found. Drill has a tendency to narrow one's thinking rather than promote flexibility.

When students successfully complete a page of routine exercises, teachers (and even students) often believe that this is an indication that they've "got it." In fact, what they most often have is a very temporary ability to reproduce a procedure recently shown to them. The short-term memory required of a student to complete the exercises at the end of a traditional lesson is no indication of understanding. Superficially learned procedures are easily and quickly forgotten and confused. As noted in Chapter 6, one of the obstacles for special needs students is memorization. An approach to instruction where students are asked to memorize and drill a fact or procedure is not in the best interests of students, as well as for the students who are not good at memorizing. Yet, they are good thinkers.

When drill is such a prevalent component of the mathematics classroom, it is no wonder that so many students and adults dislike mathematics. Real mathematics is about sense making and reasoning—it is a science of pattern and order. Students cannot possibly obtain this view of the discipline when constantly being asked to repeat procedural skills over and over.

What is most important to understand is this: Drill will *not* help with conceptual understanding. Drill will *not* provide any new skills or strategies. Drill focuses only on what is already known.

What Practice Provides

In essence, practice is what this book is about—providing students with ample and varied opportunities to reflect on or create new ideas through problem-based tasks. The following list of outcomes of practice should not be surprising:

- An increased opportunity to develop conceptual ideas and more elaborate and useful connections
- An opportunity to develop alternative and flexible strategies
- A greater chance for all students to understand, particularly students with special needs
- A clear message that mathematics is about figuring things out and making sense

Each of the preceding benefits has been explored in this or previous chapters and should require no further discussion. However, it is important to point out that practice can and does develop skills. The fear that without extensive drill students will not master "basic skills" is not supported by current research.

When Is Drill Appropriate?

Yes, there is a place for drill in mathematics, but it need not occur nearly as frequently, or be as lengthy, as is often the case. Consider these two proposed criteria for the profitable use of drill:

- An efficient strategy for the skill to be drilled is already in place.
- Automaticity with the skill or strategy is a desired outcome, which means that the skill is being performed efficiently and effectively.

Is it possible to have a skill and still need to perfect it or to drill it? Clearly, this happens outside of mathematics, with sports and music as good examples. We learn how to dribble a soccer ball or play the chords shown on a sheet of music. At the outset of instruction, we are given the necessary bits of information to perform these skills. Initially, the skills are weak and unperfected. They must be repeated in order to hone them to a state of efficiency. However, if the skill is not there to begin with, no amount of drill will create it.

When drill is appropriate—for example, practising the basic facts—a little goes along way. Practising a set of ten facts is more effective than a page of 50 facts that have to be completed within a set time frame. (See Chapter 10 for an elaboration of effective teaching of the basic facts.) Because drill is basically a review, it is best limited to 5 to 10 minutes. Devoting extensive time to repeating a procedure is not effective and can negatively affect a student's perception, motivation, and understanding.

Finally, students often quit thinking when they have to solve problem after problem the same way. Consider the problem 301 − 298. Students who find themselves solving large sets of these will perform the algorithm for subtraction here, borrowing from the 3 across the zero, which often times results in an error. They don't stop to see that these numbers are only three apart and the difference is therefore 3. In fact, they don't need to follow an algorithm at all.

❚❚ ───── *Pause and Reflect*

Stop and make a mental list of the things in K–8 mathematics with which you think students should have automaticity.

Probably your list includes how to count, read, and write numbers. It should include mastery of basic facts (e.g., 3 + 9 or 8 × 6). If you are like most people, you may have computation with whole numbers and even with fractions and decimals on your list. Certainly we want students to be fluent in computation but not limited to a single method or one that does not make sense. There are more items that are candidates for the list of skills with desired automaticity,

but generally these will be small bits of mathematics, not big ideas. In fact, the list of things for which automaticity is truly required is actually quite short and these topics should reflect this.

Students Who Don't Get It

As discussed earlier, the diversity in classrooms is a challenge for all teachers. For those students who don't pick up new ideas as quickly as most in the class, there is an overwhelming temptation to give in and "just drill 'em." Before committing to this solution, ask yourself these two questions: *Will drill build understanding? What is this telling the child?* The child who has difficulties has certainly been drilled in the past. It is naive to believe that the drill you provide will be more beneficial than the drills this child has undoubtedly endured in the past. Although drill may provide some very short-term success, an honest reflection will suggest that it probably will have little effect in the long run. What these children learn from more drill is simple: "I'm no good at math. I don't like math. Math is rules."

The earlier section of this chapter, "Planning for All Learners," suggests strongly that a conceptual approach is the best way to help students who struggle. Drill is simply not the answer.

Homework

How much homework is assigned and its value has been a hotly debated topic for many years (Gill & Schlossman, 2003). Even though most school districts have homework policies, individual schools will have their own guidelines. According to results of a recent national survey (Gill & Schlossman, 2004), many parents expect to see homework and most teachers do assign it.

But what should homework in a problem-based curriculum consist of? How do you effectively support students and their families to be successful with homework? The distinction between drill and practice as described in the previous section provides a useful lens for looking at homework.

Practice as Homework

Homework is a perfectly appropriate way to engage students in problem-based activities—in practice. A problem-based task similar to those described in Chapter 3 can be assigned for homework, provided that the difficulty of the task is within reach of most of the students. The difference is that, when at home, students will be working alone rather than with a partner or group.

The process of giving homework can mimic the three-phase lesson model. Carry out a brief version of the introductory phase of a lesson to be sure the task is understood before students go home with it. At home, students complete the development phase. When they return with the completed work, apply the sharing techniques of the follow-up phase of the lesson. They can even practise the discussion/sharing follow-up phase with their family. However, this would have to be encouraged via parent/guardian communication. Some form of written work must be required so that students are held responsible for the task and are prepared for the class discussion.

Homework of this nature communicates to families the problem-based or sense-making nature of your classroom and can help them see the value in this approach. Families want to see homework, but some will not have any experience with the type of instruction about which you have been reading. Providing guidance and support to families can make a big difference in their understanding of the approach and their ability to help their student(s).

Drill as Homework

Do not assign drill as a substitute for practice or before the requisite concepts have been developed. When assigning drill for homework, here are some things to think about:

- Keep it short. Lengthy drill is not productive.
- Provide an answer key. At grade 3 and above, students are capable of checking their own work. They should not change their answers but should repeat the missed exercises and/or write a short note indicating where they had difficulty and what they do not understand. If you respond to these notes with assistance, students will begin to understand that homework drills are a way for them to receive help.
- Never grade homework based on correctness. Instead, grade only that it was or was not completed. Rather than penalizing wrong answers, use wrong answers as an opportunity to assist students and promote growth. This suggestion applies equally well to practice homework.

These guiding questions are designed for helping your child think through their math homework problems:

- What do you need to figure out? What is the problem about?
- What words are confusing? What words are familiar?
- Did you solve problems like this one in class today?
- What have you tried so far?
- Can you make a drawing to help you think about the problem?
- Does your answer make sense?
- Is there more than one answer?

Figure 4.2 Questions for families for helping with homework.

- Do not waste valuable classroom time going over drill homework. Especially if the last two suggestions are followed, simply observing that it is complete is all that is required.

Provide Homework Support

Families also benefit from strategies for doing homework problems. Providing guiding questions for parents or guardians can help them help their child. It will also help them understand your emphasis on a problem-based approach to instruction. Figure 4.2 provides some guiding questions that can be included in the students' notebooks and shared with parents or guardians.

Check to see what online resources your textbook provides. Sometimes textbook Web sites have online resources for homework and for parents and guardians, including flash-based tutorials, video resources, resources for parents or guardians, connections to careers and real applications, multilingual glossaries, audio podcasts, and more.

Expanded Lesson

The Area Stays the Same

Based on Marilyn Burns's title of an area activity from About Teaching Mathematics, *2nd edition, by M. Burns (2000).*

Content and Task Decisions

Mathematics Goals

- To contrast the concepts of area and perimeter.
- To develop the relationship between the area and the perimeter of different shapes, particulary rectangles, when the area stays the same.
- To compare and contrast the units used to measure perimeter and those used to measure area.

Consider Your Students' Needs

Students have worked with the concepts of area and perimeter. Some, if not the majority of students, are able to find the area and perimeter of given figures. They may even be able to state the formulas for finding the perimeter and area of a rectangle. However, they often become confused as to which formula to use.

Materials and Preparation

Each student will need:
- 36 square tiles such as colour tiles
- Two or three sheets of centimetre grid paper,
- Rectangles Made with 36 Tiles recording sheet (Blackline Master 62)

Teacher will need:
- Overhead tiles
- Transparency of grid paper
- Transparency of Rectangles Made with 36 Tiles recording sheet (Blackline Master 62)

Lesson

Introduction

Begin with a simpler version of the task:

- Have students create, at their desk, a rectangle using 12 tiles only. Explain that each side of a square can touch the other side of a square, beside it, on one side only. After eliciting some ideas of what this might look like, invite a student to come to the overhead and create one possible rectangle.
- Model sketching the rectangle on the grid transparency. Record the dimensions of the rectangle in the recording chart, for example, "2 units by 6 units."
- Ask: How would we find the perimeter of this rectangle? What do we mean by perimeter? After helping students define perimeter and explain how we would find it, ask students what the the perimeter of this rectangle would be. Ask a student to come to the overhead to measure the perimeter of the rectangle. (Use either the rectangle made from tiles or the one sketched on grid paper.) Emphasize that the units used to measure perimeter are one-dimensional, or linear, and that perimeter is just the distance around an object. Record the perimeter in linear units on the chart.
- Ask: *How would we find the area? What do we mean by area?* After helping students define area and describe how it is measured, ask what the area of this rectangle would be. Here you want to make explicit that the units used to measure area are two dimensional (square units). That is the reason that they cover a region. After counting the tiles, record the area in square units on the chart.
- Have students make, at their desks, a different rectangle using 12 tiles. They record the perimeter and area, as before. Students need to decide what "different" means. Is a 2-by-6 rectangle different from a 6-by-2 rectangle? Although these are congruent, students may wish to consider these as being different. That is okay for this activity.

Present the main task to the class
- See how many different rectangles you can make using 36 tiles.
- Determine and record the perimeter and area for each rectangle.

Provide clear expectations

- Write the following directions on the board:

  1. Find a rectangle using *all* 36 tiles.
  2. Sketch the rectangle on the grid paper.
  3. Measure and record the perimeter and area of the rectangle on the recording chart.
  4. Find a new rectangle using *all* 36 tiles and repeat steps 2–4.

- Place students in pairs to work collaboratively, but have each student draw her or his own sketches and use her or his own recording sheets.

Development

Initially

- Question students to be sure they understand the task and the meaning of *area* and *perimeter*. Look for students who are confusing these terms.
- Be sure students are both drawing the rectangles and recording their dimensions, area, and perimeter appropriately in the chart.

Ongoing

Observe students as they work and ask questions to assess their understanding. Pose one or two to a student as you move around the room (see "Assessment" below).

Follow up

- Bring the class together to share and discuss the task.
- Ask students what they have found out about perimeter and area. Ask: Did the perimeter stay the same? Is that what you expected? When is the perimeter big and when is it small?
- Ask students how they can be sure they have all the possible rectangles.
- Ask students to describe what happens to the perimeter as the length and width change. (The perimeter gets shorter as the rectangle gets fatter. The square has the shortest perimeter.) Provide time to share ideas.

Assessment

Observe

- Are students confusing perimeter and area?
- As students form new rectangles, are they aware that the area is not changing because they are using the same number of tiles each time? These students may not know what area is, or they may be confusing it with perimeter.
- Are students looking for patterns for how to find the perimeter?
- Are students discussing important concepts or patterns with their partners?

Ask

- What is the area of the rectangle you just made?
- What is the perimeter of the rectangle you just made?
- How is area different from perimeter?
- How do you measure the area of a rectangle? The perimeter?

Reflections on Chapter 4

Writing to Learn

1. Not every lesson will be built around a single task. What are other ways to structure problem-based activities in the class?
2. How can a game be considered a problem-based task?
3. How do you do the *follow-up* portion of a lesson when students are working at stations?
4. Why is a problem-based approach a good way to reach all students in a diverse classroom?
5. Discuss what is meant by (a) tasks with multiple entry points, and (b) differentiated tasks.
6. What teacher actions are needed for groups to function effectively?
7. What is the difference between making an accommodation for students and making a modification in a lesson? Explain why this distinction is important.
8. This chapter suggests a possible distinction between drill and practice. Explain the difference and what each can provide.
9. Is it ever appropriate to assign problem-based tasks for homework? Explain.

For Discussion and Exploration

1. Examine a textbook for any grade level. Look at a topic for a whole chapter, and determine the two or three main objectives or big ideas covered in the chapter. Restrict yourself to no more than three. Now look at the individual lessons. Are the lessons really aimed at the big ideas you have identified? Will the lessons effectively develop the big ideas for this chapter? Are the lessons problem-based? If not, how can they be adapted to be problem-based?
2. Using the Expanded Lesson at the end of this chapter, describe the adaptations you would incorporate for English Language Learners (ELLs). Use the key ideas outlined in Table 4.1 to help you.

Resources for Chapter 4

Recommendations for Further Reading

Articles

Holden, B. (2008). Preparing for problem solving. *Teaching Children Mathematics*, *14* (5), 290–295.
   This excellent how to article shares how a first grade teacher working in an urban high-poverty setting incorporated differentiated instruction. Holden describes how she prepared her classroom and her students to be successful through six specific steps. For new and experienced teachers, this article provides great insights into how to structure a successful problem-based classroom.

Reeves, C. A., & Reeves, R. (2003). Encouraging students to think about how they think! *Mathematics Teaching in the Middle School*, *8*, 374–377.
   When students (and also adults) get into a habit of mind—or in this case, a pattern for solving a problem—they often continue to use this pattern even when much easier methods are available. The authors explore this idea with some simple tasks that you can try. The point is that too much drill with little variability may have negative effects.

Williams, L. (2008). Tiering and scaffolding: Two strategies for providing access to important mathematics. *Teaching Children Mathematics*, *14* (6), 324–330.

Using a grade 2 fraction lesson and a grade 3 geometry lesson as examples, Williams shares how they were tiered and then how scaffolds, or supports, were built into the lesson. The focus on individual learners and equity make this a very worthwhile article to read.

Books

Burns, M., & Silbey, R. (2000). *So you have to teach math? Sound advice for K–6 teachers*. Sausalito, CA: Math Solutions Publications.
   This is a must-read for new teachers and also for veteran teachers who are switching grades. Burns and Silbey offer practical advice on leading class discussions, using manipulatives, incorporating writing into your classroom, creating useful homework, working with families, and more. Each topical chapter is organized by questions teachers typically ask. Filled with practical tips, this will be a resource to come back to often.

Litton, N. (1998). *Getting your math message out to parents: A K–6 resource*. Sausalito, CA: Math Solutions Publications.
   Well-meaning parents and other family members who remember mathematics to be dominated by memorization and work sheets often challenge a constructivist, student-oriented approach to teaching. Litton is a classroom teacher who has practical suggestions for communicating with family members. The book includes chapters on parent conferences, newsletters, homework, and family math night.

Online Resources

Math Central
http://mathcentral.uregina.ca/mp/current/
This site, maintained by faculty and students at the University of Regina, is a good resource for problems that can be incorporated into lesson planning. It also is an excellent resource for other math-related information and organizations.

Illuminations
www.illuminations.nctm.org
This is a favourite of many math teachers. Click on "Lessons." You can then select the grade band and the content to search for lessons—all of them excellent!

The Math Forum: Internet Mathematics Library
http://mathforum.org/library
Here you will find links to all sorts of information that will be useful in both planning and assessment in a problem-based classroom.

Ask Dr. Math
http://mathforum.org/dr.math
Ask Dr. Math is a great homework resource for families, students, and teachers. Dr. Math has answers to all the classic math questions students have, such as why a negative times a negative is a positive.

myeducationlab will help you improve your understanding of the concepts taught in this textbook and in your course. This online tool includes videos of real classroom experiences, sample lesson plans, simulations, case studies, and links to important educational and teaching Web sites that will help you make the transition from student to teacher. As you study in your course and with this textbook, please follow along in *MyEducationLab*. Use it! Explore it! And improve your knowledge and your grade!

Chapter 5
Building Assessment into Instruction

Assessment should be the servant of teaching and learning. Without information about their students' skills, understanding, and individual approaches to mathematics, teachers have nothing to guide their work.

Mokros, Russell, and Economopoulos (1995, p. 84)

What ideas about assessment come to mind from your personal experiences? Tests? Pop quizzes? Grades? Studying? Anxiety? Getting the correct answers? All these are typical. Now suppose that you are told that assessment in the classroom should be designed to help students learn and to help teachers teach. It is an integral part of regular classroom activity, occurring daily. Differentiating instruction and facilitating student learning is an important part of this process (Western and Northern Canadian Protocol for Collaboration in Education [WNCP], 2006). How can assessment do these things?

Integrating Assessment into Instruction

The Assessment Principle in *Principles and Standards* stresses two main ideas: (1) assessment should enhance students' learning, and (2) assessment is a valuable tool for making instructional decisions. Lorna Earl, a noted researcher in the area of assessment, points out that assessment influences learning when teachers use it for the following:

1. To become aware of the knowledge and beliefs that their students bring to a learning task
2. To use this knowledge about their students as a starting point for new instruction
3. To monitor students' changing perceptions as instruction proceeds

(Earl, 2006, pp. 116–122)

Assessment can be either formative or summative. In *Rethinking Classroom Assessment with Purpose in Mind* (WNCP, 2006), formative assessment is defined as assessment that takes place during teaching to make adjustments to the teaching process. It is a planned process of regularly checking students' understanding during instructional activities (Popham, 2008; Williams, 2008). When implemented well, formative assessment can dramatically increase the speed of student learning (Nyquist, 2003; William, 2007). This requires providing feedback that promotes learning and using the results and evidence collected to improve instruction—either for the whole class or for individual students.

Summative assessment, on the other hand, is assessment that takes place at the end of a unit or term in order to convey student progress. These cumulative assessments might generate a single score from an end-of-a-unit test or the standardized test that is used in your province or territory. If summative assessment could be described as a digital snapshot, formative assessment is like video streaming. One is a picture of what a student knows that is captured in a single moment of time. The other is a moving picture that demonstrates active student thinking and reasoning.

In the following pages we will examine different perspectives on assessment. We will also discuss several formative assessment approaches that include performance-based tasks, journals observations of students solving problems, and student diagnostic interviews. The role of summative assessment will also be considered.

What Is Assessment?

The term *assessment* is defined in the NCTM *Assessment Standards* as "the process of gathering evidence about a student's knowledge of, ability to use, and disposition toward mathematics and of making inferences from that evidence for a variety of purposes" (NCTM, 1995, p. 3). It is important to note that "gathering evidence" is not the same as giving a test or quiz. As noted previously, assessment can and should happen every day as an integral part of instruction. If you restrict your view of assessment to tests and quizzes, you will miss seeing how assessment can help students grow and inform instruction.

Perspectives on Assessment

Assessment is a complex process that can be approached in a number of different ways.

Assessment *for*, *as*, and *of* Learning　Assessment can be viewed as three distinct but interrelated processes: assessment *for* learning, assessment *as* learning, and assessment *of* learning (Earl, 2006; Davies, 2007). They provide a framework for how to select or develop assessment tasks, how to use them and how to communicate with students, parents, and others about them (WNCP, 2006). All have an important role to play in supporting and improving student learning and must be appropriately balanced.

Assessment *for* learning is formative in nature. It is designed to help teachers gain insight into what students understand. Teachers can then use this information to modify and differentiate teaching and learning activities and provide helpful feedback to students. It is not used to evaluate students. Rather, it is used to help learners learn better (Davies, 2007).

Assessment *as* learning is also formative in nature. It focuses on the importance of student self-monitoring in the process of learning. Students are the critical connector between assessment and learning. They develop an awareness of how they learn and use that awareness to adjust and advance their learning, taking an increased responsibility for their learning. Teachers need to help students develop, practise, and become comfortable with reflection and with a critical analysis of their own learning.

Assessment *of* learning is summative in nature. It informs students, teachers, and parents, as well as the broader educational community, of what students know and can do to demonstrate whether they have achieved curriculum outcomes. Recipients of the information use it to plan interventions and support continued progress. (www.edu.gov.mb.ca/k12/assess/docs/my_ policy/my_policy_doc.pdf).

The *Assessment Standards*

Assessment Standards was developed as a guide for examining assessment practices and planning assessment systems. The *Standards* reflects the shift from assessing what students do not know (how many wrong answers) to what students do know (what ideas they bring to a task, how they reason, what process they used), called for in the 1989 *Curriculum Standards*. An important theme of the *Standards* is that assessment of students' achievement should be based on information from a variety sources, and that much of this

Table 5.1

The NCTM Assessment Standards	
The Mathematics Standard	• Use NCTM and local standards [curricula] to establish what mathematics students should know and be able to do and base assessments on those essential concepts and processes • Develop assessments that encourage the application of mathematics to real and sometimes novel situations • Focus on significant and correct mathematics
The Learning Standard	• Incorporate assessment as an integral part of instruction and not an interruption or a singular event at the end of a unit of study • Inform students about what content is important and what is valued by emphasizing those ideas in your instruction and matching your assessments to the models and methods used • Listen thoughtfully to your students so that further instruction will not be based on guesswork but instead on evidence of students' misunderstandings or needs
The Equity Standard	• Respect the unique qualities, experiences, and expertise of all students • Maintain high expectations for students while recognizing their individual needs • Incorporate multiple approaches to assessing students, including the provision of accommodations and modifications for students with special needs
The Openness Standard	• Establish with students the expectations for their performance and how they can demonstrate what they know • Avoid just looking at answers and give attention to the examination of the thinking processes students used • Provide students with examples of responses that meet expectations and those that don't meet expectations
The Inferences Standard	• Reflect seriously and honestly on what students are revealing about what they know • Use multiple assessments (e.g., observations, interviews, tasks, tests) to draw conclusions about students' performance • Avoid bias by establishing a rubric that describes the evidence needed and the value of each component used for scoring
The Coherence Standard	• Match your assessment techniques with both the objectives of your instruction and the methods of your instruction • Ensure that assessments are a reflection of the content you want students to learn • Develop a system of assessment that allows you to use the results to inform your instruction in a feedback loop

information should be gathered by teachers during the process of instruction. These ideas are also consistent with the *Principles for Fair Student Assessment Practices for Education in Canada* (Rogers, 1996). They provide a basis for the development of provincial and territorial assessment programs that assess students' progress and knowledge of regional curricula. A full description of assessment practices of different jurisdictions can be found in *Student Assessment in Canada* (Taylor and Tubosa, 2001) or by contacting your local ministry or department of education.

Assessment Standards contains six standards for assessment. (See Table 5.1) Four purposes of assessment, along with examples for each, are also included. The standards are not prescriptions for how to create assessments; rather they act as a benchmark for judging your own assessment practices. A cursory glance at these six assessment standards suggests a complete integration of assessment and instruction.

Four Purposes of Assesment

The four purposes of assessment contained in the *Assessment Standards* are discussed according to the objectives to be achieved and the results obtained. These are depicted in Figure 5.1. With each purpose, an arrow points to a corresponding result on the outside ring.

Monitoring Student Progress   Assessment should provide both teacher and students with ongoing feedback concerning progress toward lesson objectives and long-term goals. Assessment during instruction should inform each individual student and the teacher about that student's problem-solving ability and growth toward the understanding of mathematical concepts, not just the mastery of procedural skills.

Making Instructional Decisions   Teachers planning tasks to develop student understanding must have information about how students are thinking and what ideas they are using and developing. Daily problem solving and discussion provide a much richer and more useful array of data than can ever be gathered from a chapter test. This gathering of evidence comes at a time when you can formulate plans to help students develop ideas rather than remediate after the fact.

Evaluating Student Achievement   *Evaluation* differs from assessment. Evaluation is "the process of determining the worth of, or assigning a value to, something on the basis of careful examination and judgment" (NCTM, 1995, p. 3). Evaluation involves the collection of evidence in order for a teacher to make an informed judgment about a student's demonstrated understanding. It may include test data but should take into account a wide variety of sources and types of information gathered during the course of instruction. Most importantly, evaluation should reflect performance criteria about what students know and understand; it should not be used to compare one student with another.

Evaluating Programs   Assessment data should be used as one component in answering the question "How well did this program work to achieve my goals?" For the classroom teacher, this includes selection of tasks, sequence of activities, kinds of questions developed, and use of models.

What Should Be Assessed?

The broader view of assessment promoted here and by the NCTM requires that appropriate assessment reflect the full range of mathematical concepts and procedures, mathematical processes, and even students' disposition to mathematics.

Concepts and Procedures

A good assessment strategy provides the opportunity for students to demonstrate how they understand the concepts under discussion. A poorly designed test generally targets only one way to know an idea—the way determined by the test designer of the assessment. If you collect formative information from students as they complete an activity, while it is being discussed, as results are justified—in short,

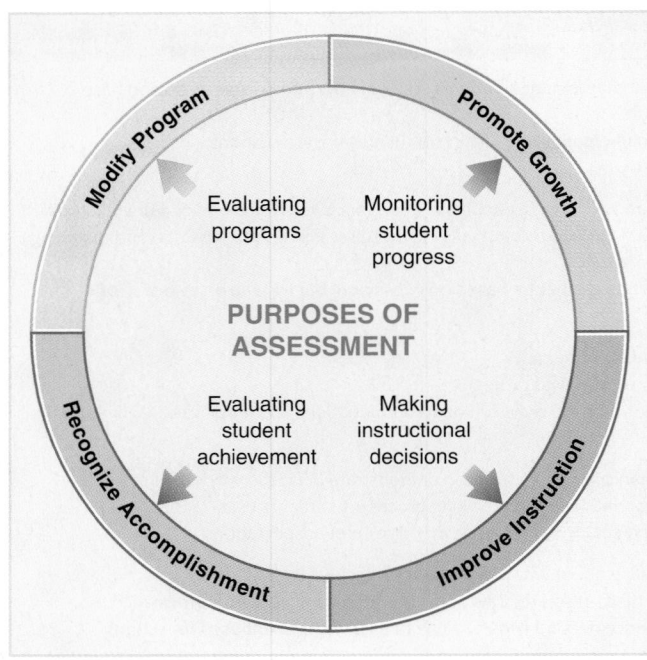

Figure 5.1 Four purposes of assessment and their results.
Source: Adapted from NCTM (1995, p. 25). Used with permission.

while students are *doing* mathematics—you will gain information that provides insight into the nature of the students' understanding of that idea.

Procedural knowledge, including skill proficiency, should also be assessed. However, if a student can compute with fractions yet has no idea of why he or she needs a common denominator for addition but not for multiplication, then the rules that have been "mastered" are poorly connected to meaning. This would indicate only the most tenuous presence of a skill. Whereas a routine skill can be checked easily with a simple fact-based test, the desired conceptual connections require different assessments.

Mathematical Processes

Guidelines for defining the specifics of mathematical power can be found in the five process standards of *Principles and Standards*. Be aware; it is not reasonable to try to assess all these processes at the same time, and certainly not every day. For each grade band, *Principles and Standards* describes what the process standards might look like at that level. Use these descriptions to craft statements about doing mathematics that your students can understand. Here are a few examples, but you should write your own or use those provided by your school system or by provincial or territorial guidelines.

Problem Solving

- ■ Works to fully understand a problem before beginning work

- ■ Uses drawings, graphs, and physical models to help with solving problems

- ■ Knows a variety of strategies

- ■ Uses appropriate strategies for solving problems

- ■ Assesses the reasonableness of answers

Reasoning

- ■ Justifies solution methods and results

- ■ Makes conjectures based on reasoning

- ■ Observes and uses patterns in mathematics

Communication

- ■ Explains ideas in writing using words, pictures, and numbers

- ■ Communicates ideas clearly in class discussions

These statements should be discussed with your students to help them understand what it means to do mathematics and to let them know that these are processes you value. Periodically, use the statements to evaluate students'

mathematical processes based on their individual work, group work, and participation in class discussions. If you use portfolios consisting of work developed and collected over time, assessment that focuses on process should be considered. Processes must also be assessed as part of your grading or evaluation scheme, or students will not take them seriously.

Productive Disposition

Collecting data on students' confidence and beliefs in their own mathematical abilities, as well as their likes and dislikes about mathematics, is also an important aspect of assessment. This information is most easily obtained with self-reported checklists, interviews, and journal writing. Information on perseverance and willingness to attempt problems is available to you every day when using a problem-solving approach.

 "Assessment should not merely be done to students; rather, it should also be done for students" (p. 22). "Assessment should become a routine part of the ongoing classroom activity, rather than an interruption" (p. 23).

Performance-Based Assessment

Recall from Chapter 3 that a problem is any task or activity for which the students have no prescribed or memorized rules or solution method. The same definition should be used for assessment tasks. Perhaps you have heard about *performance assessment tasks* or *alternative assessments*. These terms refer to tasks that are connected to actual problem-solving activities used in instruction. A good problem-based task designed to promote learning is also the best type of task for assessment.

Good tasks should permit every student in the class, regardless of mathematical prowess, to demonstrate some knowledge, skill, or understanding. Students who are struggling should be encouraged to use their own ideas to work on a problem, even if they are not the same skills or strategies used by others in the room.

Often assessment tasks include real-world, or authentic, contexts for problems. Although contextual situations are often important, how a student completes a task and justifies the solution should inform us about her or his understanding of the mathematics. That agenda should not be overshadowed because of difficulties that may arise from context, especially for English Language Learners (ELL students).

The justifications for answers, even when given orally, will almost certainly provide more information than the answers alone. Perhaps no better method exists for getting at student understanding.

Examples of Performance-Based Tasks

Each of the following tasks provides ample opportunity for students to learn. At the same time, each will provide data for the teacher to use in assessment. Notice that these are not elaborate tasks; yet, when followed by a discussion, each could engage students for most of a period. What mathematical ideas are required to successfully respond to each of these tasks? Will the task help you understand how well students understand these ideas?

Shares (Grades K–3)

Leila has 6 gumdrops, April has 2, and Melissa has 4. They want to share them equally. How will they do it? Draw a picture to help explain your answer.

In grade 2 or 3, the numbers in this "shares" task would probably be larger. What additional concepts would be involved if the task was about cookies and the total number of cookies was 14?

Subtraction (Grades 1–2)

If you did not know the answer to 12 − 7, what are some ways you could find the answer?

How Much? (Grades 1–2)

Jelena has saved $15 to buy a game that she wants. The game costs $23. How much money does Jelena still need? Explain how you got your answer.

These two problems are similar in that they involve subtraction and allow the teacher to see what strategies a student might use. In the second problem, the context increases the chances that students will use an "add-on" approach (15 and how much more make 23?). Contrast the benefits of using these tasks with simply giving the corresponding computations.

The Whole Set (Grades 3–5)

When Naomi counted the leftover cupcakes from the batch her mother made for the picnic, there were 15. "We've already eaten two-fifths," she noted. How many cupcakes did her mother bake?

This problem could easily have been posed without any context. What is the value of context in tasks such as these?

In the following task, students are asked to judge the performance of other students. Analysis of student performance is a good way to create tasks.

Decimals (Grades 4–6)

Lee Cheng tried to make a decimal number as close to 50 as she could, using the digits 1, 4, 5, and 9. She arranged them in this order: 51.49. Natasha thinks she can arrange the same digits to get a number that is even closer to 50. Do you agree or disagree? Explain.

Mental Math (Grades 4–8)

Explain two different ways to multiply 4×276 in your head. Which way is easier? Would you use a different way to multiply 5×98? Explain why you would use the same method or a different method.

Mental computation tasks should be done frequently at all grade levels, beginning about grade 2. As students share their methods in class, others will pick up them up. The explanations also offer evidence about students' understanding of concepts and strategies used. This observational information can be recorded over time in a variety of ways.

Two Triangles (Grades 4–8)

Tell everything you can about these two triangles.

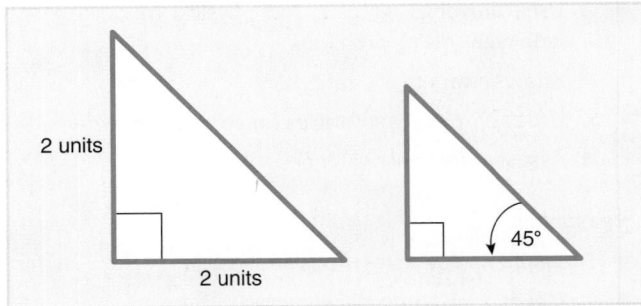

This task is a good example of an open-ended assessment. Consider how much more valuable this task is than asking for the angle measure in the triangle on the left.

Algebra: Graphing (Grades 7–8)

Does the graph of $y = x^2$ ever intersect the graph of $y = x^2 + 2$? What are some ways that you could test your idea?

Even with a graphing calculator, proving that these two graphs will not intersect requires reasoning and an understanding of how graphs are related to equations and tables.

Thoughts About Assessment Tasks

In some instances, the real value of the task or what can be learned about students will come only in the discussion that follows the work. For others, the information will be in the written report. In many of Marilyn Burns's books, you will see the phrase "We think the answer is.... We think this because...." Students must develop the habit of sharing, writing, and listening to justifications. If providing explanations is not a regular practice in your room, it may be unrealistic to expect students to offer good explanations in assessments.

Some excellent examples of realistic problems that also serve as excellent assessment tasks can be found in the *Handbook on Rich Learning Tasks* (Flewelling & Higginson, 2002). Although real-world contexts do not necessarily guarantee that students will be engaged in constructing mathematics, the *Handbook of Rich Learning Tasks* demonstrates how open-ended tasks make it possible without sacrificing the mathematics.

Many activities have no written component and no set "answer" or result. For example, students may be playing a game in which dice or dominoes are being used. A teacher who sits in on the game will see great differences in how children use numbers. Some will count every dot on the card or domino. Others will use a counting-on strategy. (A student using a counting-on strategy to find the total on a domino, for example, will see four dots on one side. He or she will then count on from four to tally the total number.) Some will recognize certain patterns without counting. Others may be unsure if 13 beats 11. This evidence differentiates students relative to their understanding of number concepts. Data gathered from listening to a pair of children working on a simple activity or an extended project provide significantly greater insight into students' thinking than almost any written test we could devise. Data from student conversations and observations of student behaviour can be recorded and used for the same purposes as written data, or for evaluation or grading. Especially in the case of grading, it is important to keep dated, written anecdotal notes that can be referred to later. (See the section "Anecdotal Notes" later in this chapter.)

You can move from instruction to assessment and make performance-based tasks into evaluation tools aligned with your goals. The process of moving from teaching tasks to assessment tasks involves the addition of rubrics. The next section will explain how you can create and use both generic rubrics that describe general qualities of performance and topic-specific rubrics that include criteria based on your particular lesson objectives.

Rubrics and Performance Indicators

Problem-based tasks may tell us a great deal about what students know, but how do we handle this information? Often there is only one problem for students to work on in a given period. There is no way to simply count the percent correct and put a mark in the grade book. It may be helpful to make a distinction between *scoring* and *grading*. "*Scoring* is comparing students' work to criteria or rubrics that describe what we expect the work to be. *Grading* is the result of accumulating scores and other information about a student's work for the purpose of summarizing and communicating to others" (Stenmark & Bush, 2001, p. 118). The scores can be used (or perhaps not used) along with other information to create a grade. One valuable tool for scoring is a rubric.

A *rubric* is a framework that can be designed or adapted by the teacher for a particular group of students or a particular mathematical task (Kulm, 1994). A rubric consists of a three- to six-point scale that is used as a rating of performance on a single task, rather than a count of how many items in a series of exercises are correct or incorrect. The rating or score is applied by examining total performance on a task.

Simple Rubrics

Table 5.2 presents a simple four-point rubric (designed to assess performance in language arts) that was developed by the Saskatchewan Professional Development Unit as one of a number of tools for assessing children in multi-level classrooms. This rubric, created to measure depths of student understanding, allows a teacher to rate performance using the criteria illustrated in Table 5.2. The relatively simple scale and general nature of the categories makes this rating scale a good starting point for working with rubrics. It can easily be adapted to mathematics.

A teacher might prefer to use a three-point rubric, such as the following, to rate a student's problem-solving performance:

3 Above and beyond—uses exemplary methods, shows creativity, goes beyond the requirements of the problem

2 On target—completes the task with no more than minor errors, uses expected approaches

1 Not there yet—makes significant errors or omissions, uses inappropriate approaches

These relatively simple scales are *general* rubrics. They label general categories of performance but do not define the specific criteria for a particular task. For any given task or process, it is usually helpful to create performance indicators for each level.

Table 5.2

Example of a Four-Point Rubric	
Powerful	The response is personalized and thoughtful. The student integrates previous experience and includes specific references to the text. The ideas expressed go beyond the text, describe the comparisons or metaphors, and indicate a relatively deep and sophisticated understanding of the selection.
Competent	The response is consistent and logical, features some integration of previous experience, and includes text references. The student may focus on one aspect of the poem, or may describe the metaphor or deal with the idea on a surface level.
Partial	Some inconsistencies are apparent, suggesting a partial or incomplete understanding of the poem. Typically the student makes less frequent use of images, emotions, and specific text references.
Undeveloped	The response is inconsistent or illogical. The student may offer broad general statements without explanation. If any references are included, they may be inappropriate or illogical.

Performance Indicators

Performance indicators are task-specific statements that describe what performance looks like at each level of the rubric. In so doing, they establish criteria for acceptable performance. The language used should clearly describe each level of performance (Rolheiser, Bower, & Stevahn, 2000). Indicators that are well designed reflect appropriate levels of student work for different ages and abilities. They also help students to see how performance at each level varies and to distinguish between acceptable and unacceptable performance (Horsman, 1997).

A rubric and its performance indicators should focus you and your students on the objectives and away from the self-limiting question, "How many can you miss and still get an A?" Like athletes who continually strive for better performances rather than "good enough," students should always see the possibility to excel. When you take into account the total performance (processes, answers, justifications, extension, and so on), it is always possible to "go beyond."

When you create your task-specific rubric, what performance at different levels of your rubric will or should look like may be difficult to predict. Much depends on your experience with children at that grade level, your past experiences with students working on the same task, and your insights about the task itself. One important part of helping you set performance levels is students' common misconceptions or the expected thinking or approaches to the same or similar problem.

If possible, it is good to write out indicators of "proficient" or "on target" performances before you use the task in class. This is an excellent self-check to ensure that the task is likely to accomplish its original purpose. Think about your process goals as well as your content goals. Think about how children are likely to approach the activity.

Remember that topic-specific rubrics are applied to performance on a single task, even though the task may have multiple components. If you find yourself writing performance indicators in terms of the number of correct responses, you are most likely looking at drill exercises and not the performance-based tasks for which a rubric is appropriate. Examples of task-specific scoring rubrics can be found on provincial or territorial ministry Web sites. For example, rubrics used for scoring student responses in numeracy for the Foundation Skills Assessment can be found on the British Columbia Ministry of Education Web site at www.bced.gov.bc.ca/assessment/fsa/en_samples/09_rubric_samp_resp.pdf.

⏸ *Pause and Reflect*

Consider the fraction problem titled "The Whole Set," found on page 78. Assume you are teaching grade 4 and wish to write performance indicators that you can share with your students using a four-point rubric (Table 5.2). What indicators would you use for level-3 and level-4 performances? Start with a level-3 performance; then think about level 4. Try this before reading further.

Determining performance indicators is always a subjective process, based on your professional judgment. Here is one possible set of indicators for "The Whole Set" task.

3   Determines the correct answer or uses an approach that would yield a correct answer, if not for minor errors. An explanation is either missing or incorrect. Giving a correct response for the number eaten, but an incorrect response for the total baked, would also be a level-3 performance.

4   Determines the total number baked and uses words, pictures, and numbers to explain and justify the result and how it was obtained. Demonstrates a knowledge of fractional parts and the relation to the whole.

Indicators such as these should be shared ahead of time with students. Sharing indicators before working on a task clearly conveys what is valued and expected. If you review the indicators with students when you return papers, try including the correct answers and some examples of successful responses. This will help students understand how they might have done better. Often it is useful to show work from classmates (anonymously) or from a prior class. Students need to see models of what a top performance looks like.

What about level-1 and level-2 performances? Here are suggestions for the same task:

2   Uses some aspect of fractions appropriately (e.g., divides the 15 into 5 groups instead of 3) but fails to illustrate an understanding of how to determine

the whole. The meanings of numerator and denominator are incorrect or confused.

1 Shows some effort but little or no understanding of a fractional part relative to the whole.

For the most part, it is not necessary to share indicators for level-1 and level-2 performances unless, of course, students or parents request further explanation. However, it would be helpful if you articulated the differences between these performances so students' growth can be documented.

Unexpected methods and solutions happen. Don't box students into demonstrating their understanding, according to your way of thinking, when there is evidence that they are accomplishing your objectives in different ways. Such occurrences can help you revise or refine your rubric for future use.

When you have finished your sorting process, use the results to write additional rubric indicators for the task. Keep the descriptions as general as possible. These indicators can then be shared with students when you return the papers. Keep the revised rubric and indicators in a file with the task for future use.

Student Involvement with Rubrics

In the beginning of the year, discuss your general rubric with the class. Post it prominently. Many teachers use the same rubric for all subjects; others prefer to use a special rubric for mathematics. In your discussion, let students know that, as they do activities and solve problems in class, you will look at their work, listen to their explanations, and then provide them with feedback in terms of the rubric, rather than as a letter grade or a percentage.

When students start to understand what the rubric really means, begin to discuss performance on tasks in terms of the general rubric. You might have students assess their own work using the general rubric and explain their reasons for the rating. Older students can do this in written form and you can respond in writing. For all students, you can have class discussions about a task they have completed and what might constitute proficient and excellent performance.

Observation Tools

All teachers learn useful bits of information about their students every day. When the three-part lesson format suggested in Chapter 3 is used, the flow of evidence about student performance increases dramatically, especially in the *development* and *follow-up* portions of lessons. If you have a systematic plan for gathering this information while observing and listening to students, at least two very valuable results occur. First, information that may have otherwise gone unnoticed is suddenly visible and important.

Second, observational data, gathered systematically, can be added to other data and used in planning lessons, providing feedback to students, conducting parent conferences, and determining grades.

Depending on the kind of information you may be trying to gather, a single observation of a whole class may require several days before all students have been observed. Shorter periods of observation will focus on a particular cluster of concepts or skills or on particular students. Over longer periods, you can note growth in mathematical processes, such as problem solving, representation, reasoning, or communication. To use observation effectively as a means for gathering assessment data from performance tasks, you should take the following maxim seriously: *Do not attempt to record data for every student in a single class period.*

Observation methods will vary with the purposes for which they are used. Further, formats and methods of gathering observation data are going to be influenced by your individual teaching style and habits.

Anecdotal Notes

One system for recording observations is to write short notes either during or immediately after a lesson in a brief narrative style. One possibility is to have a card for each student. Some teachers keep the cards on a clipboard with each taped at the top edge (see Figure 5.2).

Another option is to focus your observations on about five students a day. On another day, different students are selected. The students selected may be members of one or two cooperative groups. An alternative to cards is the use of large peel-off file labels, possibly pre-printed with student names on your computer. The label notes are then moved to a more permanent notebook page for each student.

Observation Rubric

Another possibility is to use your three- or four-point general rubric on a reusable form as in Figure 5.3. Include space for content-specific indicators and another column to jot down names of students. A quick note or comment may be added to a name. This method is especially useful for planning purposes.

Checklists for Individuals

To cut down on writing and to help focus your attention, a checklist with several specific processes or content areas of interest can be devised and duplicated for each student (see Figure 5.4). Some teachers have found methods of printing these on their computer, perhaps on sticky labels. Once a computer format is worked out, it is easy to change the items on the checklist without retyping all the student names. Regardless of the checklist form, a place for comments should be included.

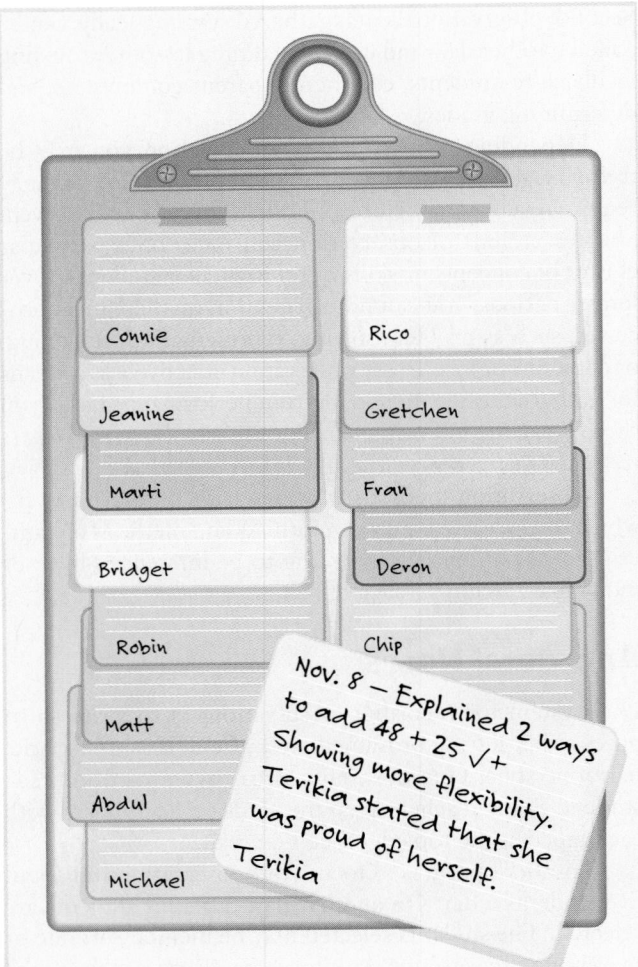

Connie
Jeanine
Marti
Bridget
Robin
Matt
Abdul
Michael

Rico
Gretchen
Fran
Deron
Chip

*Nov. 8 — Explained 2 ways to add 48 + 25 ✓+ Showing more flexibility. Terikia stated that she was proud of herself.
Terikia*

Figure 5.2 Preprinted cards for observation notes can be taped to a clipboard or folder for quick access.

Observation Rubric
Making Whole Given Fraction Part   (3/17)

Above and Beyond Clear understanding. Communicates concept in multiple representations. Shows evidence of using idea without prompting. *Fraction whole made from part in rods and in sets. Explains easily.*	Sally ✓ Latania ✓+ Greg Zal
On Target Understands or is developing well. Uses designated models. *Can make whole in either <u>rod</u> or <u>set</u> format (note). Hesitant. Needs prompt to get unit fraction.*	Lavant Tanisha Julie Lee George J.B. Maria John H.
Not There Yet Some confusion or misunderstands. Only models idea with help. *Needs help to do activity. No confidence.*	John S. Mary

Figure 5.3 Record names in a rubric during an activity or for a single topic over several days.

Checklists for Full Classes

Another format involves listing all students in a class on a single page or not more than three pages (see Figure 5.5). Across the top of the page are specific abilities or deficiencies for which to look. Pluses and minuses, checks, or codes corresponding to your general rubric can be entered in the grid. A space left for comments is useful. A full-class checklist is more likely to be used for long-term objectives. Topics that might be appropriate for this format include problem-solving processes, communication skills, and such subject areas as basic facts or estimation. Dating entries or noting specific activities observed is also helpful.

Writing and Journals

We have been emphasizing that instruction and assessment should be integrated. This is never more evident than in students' writing. Writing is both a learning and an assess-

ment opportunity. Though some students initially have difficulty writing in mathematics, persistence pays off and students come to see writing as a natural part of the mathematics class.

The Value of Writing

When students write, they express their own ideas and use their own words and language. It is personal. In contrast, oral communication in the classroom is very public. Ideas "pop out" without editing or revision. Meaning is negotiated or elaborated on by the class as a whole. The individual reflective quality of writing compared to the spontaneous nature of classroom discourse is an important factor in considering its value in mathematics.

The process of writing requires gathering, organizing, and clarifying thoughts. It demands finding out what you know and don't know. It calls for clear thinking. Similarly, doing mathematics depends on gathering, organizing, and clarifying thoughts, finding out what you know and don't know, and thinking clearly. Although the final representation of a mathematical pursuit looks very different from

NAME: *Sharon V.*	NOT THERE YET	ON TARGET	ABVE AND BEYOND	COMMENTS
FRACTIONS				
Understands numerator/denominator		✓		
Area models		✓		
Set models	✓			
Uses fractions in real contexts	✓			
Estimates fraction quantities		✓		*getting better*
PROBLEM SOLVING				
Understands problem before beginning work		✓		*this is good*
Is willing to take risks	✓			*problem area*
Justifies results				

Figure 5.4 A focused computer-generated checklist and rubric can be printed for each student.

the final product of a writing effort, the mental journey is, at its base, the same—making sense of an idea and presenting it effectively. (Burns, 1995b, p. 3)

As an assessment tool, writing provides a unique window into students' perceptions and their thinking about an idea. Even a kindergarten child can express ideas in drawings or other markings on paper and begin to explain what he or she is thinking. Finally, student thinking is an excellent form of communication with parents during conferences. Writing shows evidence of students' thinking to their parents or guardian, telling them much more than any grade or test score.

When students write about their solutions to a task, prior to a class discussion, the writing can serve as a rehearsal for the conversation about the work. Students who otherwise have difficulty thinking on their feet will now have a script to support their contributions. This practice circumvents having a few verbal students providing all the input during a discussion. Call on these more reluctant talkers first so that their ideas will be heard and valued.

Journals

Journals are a way to make written communication a regular part of doing mathematics. The feedback you provide to students should move their learning forward. Journals are a place for students to write about various aspects of their mathematical experiences:

- Their conceptual understandings and problem solving, including descriptions of ideas, solutions, and justifications of problems, graphs, charts, and observations

Topic: Mental Computation + of 2 – dig. nos.	Not Yet *Can't do mentally*	On Target *Has at least one strategy*	Wow! *Uses different methods with different numbers*	Comments
Names				
Lalie		✓ 3-18 -21		
Pete	✓ 3-20			*Needs place value help*
Sid			✓ + 3-20	*Super*
Lakeshia		✓		*Good*
George		✓		
Pam	✓			*Close – getting a tens first idea*
Maria		✓ 3-24		*Finally!*

Figure 5.5 A full-class observation checklist can be used for longer-term objectives or for several days to cover a short-term objective.

- Their questions concerning the current topic, an idea that they may need help with, or an area they don't quite understand
- Their attitudes toward mathematics, their confidence in their understanding, or their fears of being wrong

Even if you have students write in their journals regularly, be sure that these journals are special places for writing about mathematics thinking. Drill or lengthy projects done over several days are not best carried out in journals. A performance-based assessment task you plan to use primarily for evaluation purposes should probably not be in a journal. But the work for many of your instructional tasks can and should go in the journal, communicating that the work is important and you do want to see it even if you are not going to grade it.

Grading journals would communicate that there is a specific "right" response you are seeking. It is essential, however, that you read and respond to journal writing. One form of response for a performance task would be to use the classroom's general rubric along with a helpful comment. It is another way to distinguish between rubrics and grades and still provide feedback.

Writing Prompts and Ideas

Students should always have a clear, well-defined purpose for writing in their journals. They need to know exactly what to write about and who the audience is (you, a student in a lower grade, an adult, a new student to the school), and they should be given a definite time frame within which to write. Journal writing that is completely open-ended without a stated goal or purpose will not be a good use of time. Here are some suggestions for writing prompts to get you thinking; however, the possibilities are endless.

Concepts and Processes

- ◼ "I think the answer is…. I think this because…." (The journal can be used to solve and explain any problem. Some teachers duplicate the problem and have students tape it into the journal to save time and effort.)

- ◼ Write an explanation for a new or younger student, telling why 4×7 is the same as 7×4 and why this would work for 6×49 and 49×6.

- ◼ Explain to a student in a different grade or class (or who was absent today) what you learned about decimals.

- ◼ What mathematics work that we did today was easy? What was hard? What do you still have questions about?

- ◼ If you got stuck today in solving a problem, where in the problem did you get stuck? Why do you think you had trouble there?

- ◼ After you got the answer to today's problem, what did you do so that you were convinced your answer was correct? How sure are you that you got the correct answer?

- ◼ Write a story problem that goes with this picture (this graph, this diagram, this equation).

Productive Dispositions

- ◼ "What I like most (or least) about mathematics is…."

- ◼ Write a mathematics autobiography. Tell about your experiences in mathematics outside of school and how you feel about the subject.

- ◼ What was the most interesting mathematics idea you learned this week?

Journals for Early Learners

If you are interested in working with K–1 children, the writing prompts presented may have sounded too advanced. It is difficult for pre-writers and beginning writers to express ideas like those suggested. There are specific techniques for journals in kindergarten and grade 1 that have been used successfully.

The Giant Journal To begin the development of the writing-in-mathematics process, one kindergarten teacher uses a language experience approach. After an activity, she writes "Giant Journal" and a topic or prompt on a large flipchart. Students respond to the prompt, and she writes their ideas, adding the contributor's name and even drawings when appropriate, as in Figure 5.6.

Drawings and Early Writing All students can draw pictures of some sort to describe what they have done. Dots can represent counters or blocks. Shapes and special figures can be cut out from duplicated sheets and pasted onto the journal page.

The "writing" should be a record of something the student has just done and with which he or she is comfortable. Figure 5.7 shows problems solved in grades 1 and 2. Do not be concerned about invented spellings to communicate ideas. Have students read their papers to you.

Student Self-Assessment

Stenmark (1989) notes that "the capability and willingness to assess their own progress and learning is one of the great-

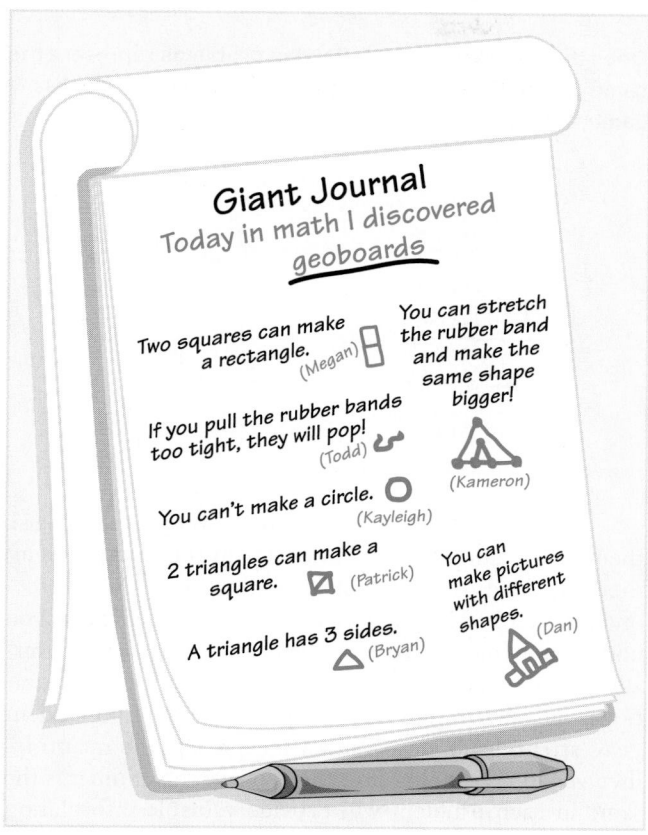

Figure 5.6 A journal in kindergarten may be a class product on a flipchart.

est gifts students can develop.... Mathematical power comes with knowing how much we know and what to do to learn more" (p. 26). Student self-assessment should not be your only measure of students' learning or disposition, rather it should be a record of how *they perceive* these things.

As you plan for a self-assessment, consider how you want the assessment to help you as a teacher. Tell your students why you are having them do this activity. Encourage them to be honest and candid.

You can gather self-assessment data in several ways. An open-ended writing prompt, as suggested earlier for journals, is a successful method of getting self-assessment data:

- How well do you think you understand the work we have been doing on fractions during the last few days? If there is something that is causing you difficulty with fractions, please tell me what it is.
- Write one thing you liked and one thing you did not like about class today (or this week).
- As you worked in your group today, what was your contribution?

Another method is to use some form of questionnaire to which students respond. These can have open-ended

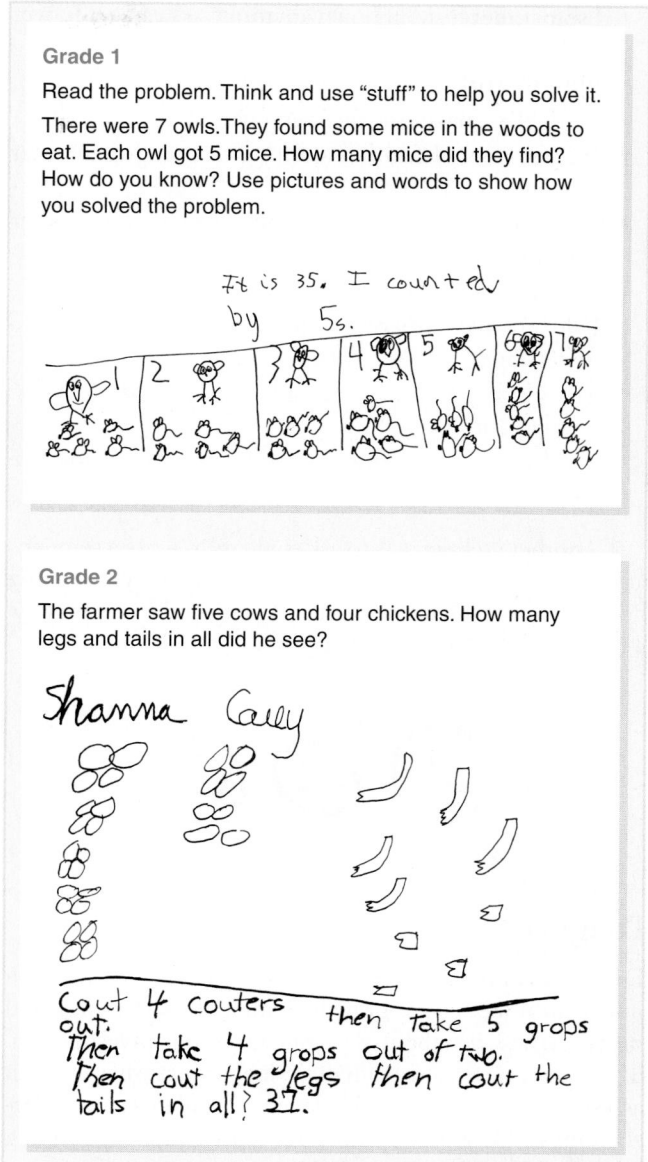

Figure 5.7 Journal entries of children in grades 1 and 2.

questions, response choices (e.g., *seldom, sometimes, often; disagree, don't care, agree*), mind maps, drawings, and so on. Many such instruments appear in the literature, and many textbook publishers provide examples. Whenever you use a form or questionnaire that someone else has devised, be certain that it serves the purpose you intend.

Students may find it difficult to write about attitudes and beliefs. A questionnaire where they can respond "yes," "maybe," or "no" to a series of statements is often a successful approach. Encourage students to add comments under an item if they wish. Here are some items you could use to build such a questionnaire:

- I feel sure of myself when I get an answer to a problem.

- I sometimes just put down anything so I can get it over with.
- I like to work on really hard math problems.
- Math class makes me feel nervous.
- If I get stuck, I feel like quitting or going to another problem.
- I am not as good in mathematics as most of the other students in this class.
- Mathematics is my favourite subject.
- I do not like to work at problems that are hard to understand.
- Memorizing rules is the only way I know to learn mathematics.
- I will work a long time at a problem until I think I've solved it.

Another technique is to ask students to write a sentence at the end of any work they do in mathematics class saying how the activity made them feel. Young children can draw a face on each page to tell you about their feelings.

Diagnostic Interviews

Diagnostic interviews are a means of getting in-depth information about an individual student's knowledge and mental strategies about the concept under investigation. These interviews, although often labour intensive, are rich assessments that provide evidence of students' misunderstandings. They also explore students' ways of thinking about important concepts. In each case a student is given a problem and asked to articulate his or her thinking at points in the process. Sometimes students correct a mistake. More frequently though, teachers can unearth students' misunderstandings or reveal what strategies the students have mastered.

The problems you select should match the essential understanding for the topic your students are studying. In every case, have paper, pencils, and a variety of materials available, particularly those you have been using during instruction. It is often useful to have a scoring guide or rubric available to jot down notes about emerging understandings, common methods you expect to see used, or common misunderstandings that may come to light.

Here are suggested problems that can be used for diagnostic interviews.

Does the 1 in each of the following problems represent the same amount? (Phillipp, Schappelle, Siegfried, Jacobs, & Lamb, 2008)

$$
\begin{array}{r}
2\overset{1}{5}9 \\
+\ 38 \\
\hline
297
\end{array}
\qquad
\begin{array}{r}
\overset{3}{\cancel{4}}\overset{1}{2}9 \\
-\ 34 \\
\hline
395
\end{array}
$$

After students have given their answer you should ask them to explain why in addition (as in the first problem) the 1 is added to the 5, but in subtraction (as in the second problem) 10 is added to the 2. This problem helps you understand whether your students are working procedurally or if they possess conceptual knowledge of the operations of addition and subtraction. Whether the student gives attention to place-value concepts and the quantities involved in regrouping or if they believe the number is the same in each problem will provide valuable information that enhances professional judgment for your subsequent instructional decisions.

The following problem can be used in an interview to assess knowledge of comparing fractions. Figure 5.8 shows students work comparing $\frac{4}{4}$ and $\frac{4}{8}$.

Which is more—$\frac{4}{4}$ or $\frac{4}{8}$? (Ball, 2008)

In this case, students should be encouraged to show their thinking about this comparison. Possibly they will select an area model or a number line in their attempt to make their mental processes apparent and justify their answer. Some students may draw diagrams of different size rectangles, revealing their understanding or misunderstanding about the whole as a constant unit for this comparison. For example, in a presentation by Deborah Ball, a noted mathematics educator, one of the children in her class drew an area model of the four-fourths, then used the same size pieces to draw four-eights. This resulted in a whole that was twice the size of the original (2008). He then corrected himself when he saw another student who had drawn two rectangles of the same size. One was divided into fourths, with all four part shaded. The other was divided into eighths, with only four of the eight parts (or half) shaded. During a diagnostic interview the students will not be able to benefit from the explanations of other students. However, these are the

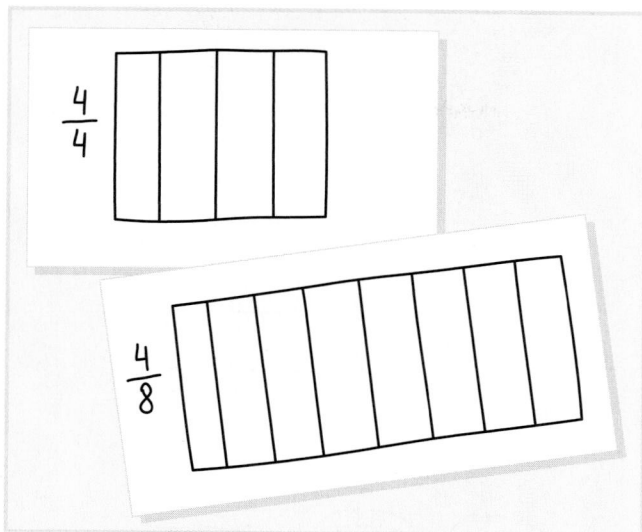

Figure 5.8 Student work comparing fractions.

discoveries and results that can inform and improve your instruction. This information will also help you in redirecting or reinforcing students' thinking and strategies.

Portfolios

Portfolios offer an excellent way for students to communicate their learning to teachers, as well as to parents or guardians. This systematic collection of work, selected by the student, with input from the teacher, provides a holistic view of mathematical learning. Materials, selected over time, may include assignments, projects, reports, student writing, worksheets from texts or other sources, comments by teachers, observations from interviews, and self-evaluations of group and individual efforts. A portfolio should demonstrate and help students reflect on their progress and growth in problem-solving and mathematical understanding.

Your own portfolio program should serve the particular goals you have in mind and communicate achievement of these goals to students and parents. These plans and goals should be discussed with your students from the outset and revisited periodically, so that the students are fully involved in the process. To assist you with setting up a portfolio program for a class, here are some ideas found in Rolheiser, Bower, & Stevahn (2000).

- Set up a folder (a working portfolio) for each student to place potential entries of their choice. Teacher observation notes and feedback are also included here.
- Have a class discussion about how to select items and what the items should show.
- At the end of a unit or grading period, students clip together items from the working portfolio that tell

about themselves in mathematics (their strengths, weaknesses, successes, areas that need work) to include in their final portfolio.

- A student-written cover letter that discusses the content and other items such as personal perspective on unit skills, confidence and attitudes, and growth in understanding is included in the final portfolio.
- Portfolios are then evaluated and feedback provided. They are now ready for sharing with parents or guardians. Rubrics can be used for evaluation.

Tests

Tests will always be a part of assessment and evaluation no matter how adept we become at blending assessment with instruction. However, a test need not be a collection of low-level skill exercises. Although simple tests of computational skills may have some role in your classroom, the use of such tests should be only one aspect of your assessment. Like all other forms of assessment, tests should reflect the goals of your instruction. Tests can be designed to find out what concepts students understand and how their ideas are connected. Tests of procedural knowledge should go beyond just knowing how to perform an algorithm. They should allow and oblige students to demonstrate a conceptual basis for the process. The following examples will illustrate these ideas.

1. Write a multiplication problem that has an answer between the answers to these two problems:

$$\begin{array}{cc} 49 & 45 \\ \times\ 25 & \times\ 30 \end{array}$$

2. **a.** In this division exercise, what number tells how many tens were shared among the 6 sets?
   b. Instead of writing the remainder as "R 2," Jasmine writes " $\frac{1}{3}$." Explain the difference between these two ways of handling the leftover part.

$$\begin{array}{cc} 49\text{R2} & 49\frac{1}{3} \\ 6\overline{)296} & 6\overline{)296} \end{array}$$

3. On the grid, draw two figures with the same area but different perimeters. List the area and perimeter of each.

4. For each subtraction fact, write an addition fact that helps you think of the answer to the subtraction.

$$\begin{array}{cccc} 12 & 9 & 9 & 14 \\ -3 & +3 & -4 & -7 \\ \hline 9 & 12 & & \end{array}$$

5. Draw pictures of arrows to show why $-3 + (-4)$ is the same as $-3 - (4)$.

If a test is well constructed, much more information can be gathered than simply the number of correct or incorrect answers. The following considerations can help maximize the value of your tests:

1. *Permit students to use calculators.* Except for tests of computational skills, calculators allow students to focus on what you really want to test. Permitting calculators also communicates a positive attitude about calculator use to your students.

2. *Use manipulatives and drawings.* Students can use appropriate models to work on test questions, especially when those same models have been used during instruction to develop concepts. (Note the use of grids and drawings in previous examples.) Simple drawings can be used to represent counters, base-ten pieces, fraction pieces, and the like (see Figure 5.9). Be sure to provide examples in class of how to draw the models before you ask students to draw on a test.

3. *Include opportunities for explanations.*

4. *Avoid always using "pre-answered" tests.* These are tests in which questions have only one correct answer, whether it is a calculation, a multiple-choice question, or a fill-in-the-blank question. Tests of this type tend to fragment what children have learned and hide most of what they know. Rather, construct tests that allow students the opportunity to show what they know.

Standardized Testing

Standardized tests are firmly in place in school systems throughout Canada. In particular, standardized curriculum-based provincial and territorial tests, as noted in Chapter 1, are designed to provide information regarding the achievement of individual students in the different school districts or boards of a province or territory. While assessment practices may differ somewhat among provinces, testing is designed to assess students' knowledge of curriculum expectations and provide feedback to teachers, parents, students, and the general public. See Table 5.3 for provincial or territorial mathematics assessment schedules for students in elementary and middle school. In some provinces, such as Ontario and Alberta, testing is carried out at key transitional stages (grades 3 and 6) in elementary school. In others, such as Saskatchewan, province-wide testing is carried out biennially. In Nova Scotia, mathematics literacy testing is done annually in grades 3. Results of curriculum-based testing play an important role in school board or district policy and instructional decision-making. They form the basis of school improvement plans. They are also used to develop plans for identifying students' individual needs and developing intervention strategies for improvement, among a variety of other purposes.

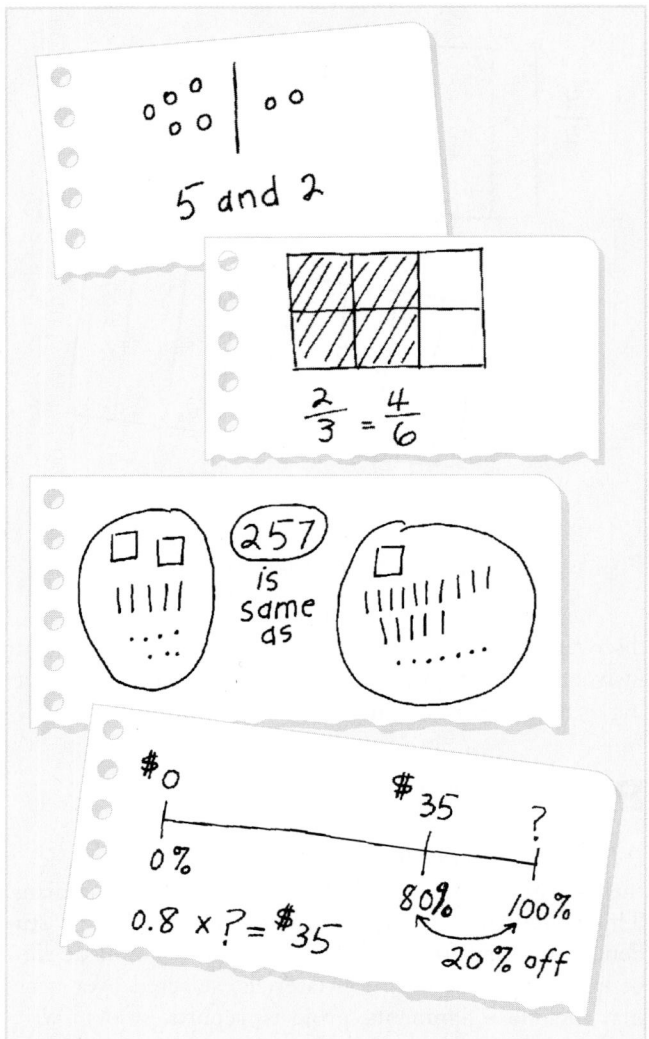

Figure 5.9 Students can use drawings to illustrate concepts on tests.

These external tests (originating from outside the classroom) impose significant pressure on school boards and districts, which in turn puts pressure on principals, who impose this pressure on teachers. External tests make the pressure of testing significant for both students (Will I pass? Will my parents be upset?) and teachers (Will my class meet proficiency levels? My students' scores have been below passing—I've got to get them up.) The pressure certainly has an effect on instruction. Since you will not be able to avoid the pressures of this type of testing, the question is, "How will I respond?"

Teach Fundamental Concepts and Processes

Regardless of the province or territory, the nature of the tests, or the consequences, the best advice is to teach to the

Table 5.3

Province	Program	Students tested	Frequency
British Columbia	Foundation Skills Assessment (FSA)	All students in grades 4 and 7	Annual
	Provincial Learning Assessments (for subjects or for cross-curricular areas not covered by the FSA)	Sample of students in grades 4 and 7	Occasional
Alberta	Provincial Achievement Testing Program	All students in grades 3 and 6	Annual
Saskatchewan	Assessment for Learning Program	Random sample of students in grades 5 and 8	Every two years
Manitoba	Grade 3 assessment and Middle years assessment (This is not a test—the assessment is based on classroom work)	All students in grades 3 and 7	Annual
Ontario	Education Quality and Accountability Office (EQAO) Assessments	All students in grades 3 and 6	Annual
Quebec	Complementary exam	All students in grade 6	Annual
New Brunswick	Provincial Mathematics Assessment	All students in grades 5 and 8	Annual
Nova Scotia	Program of Learning Assessment for Nova Scotia (PLANS)	All students in grades 3 (and an assessment for grade 6 is in development)	Annual
Prince Edward Island	No current provincial assessment program; may use the assessment program of the Council of Atlantic Ministers of Education and Training (CAMET) once it is developed		
Newfoundland and Labrador	No current provincial assessment program; plans to use the CAMET assessment program once it is developed		
The Yukon	Yukon Achievement Tests	All students in grades 3 and 6	Annual
Northwest Territories	No territorial assessment program, although 5 of 8 school boards annually administer the Alberta Achievement Tests to all students in grades 3 and 6		
Nunavut	No territorial assessment program		

big ideas in mathematics that are aligned with your provincial or territorial curriculum and local standards. Students who have a strong relational understanding of the main ideas in mathematics and have learned the processes of doing mathematics will perform well on tests, regardless of the format or specific objectives.

Examine the skills and objectives of your mathematics curriculum and identify the broader conceptual foundations on which they depend. At the start of each chapter of Section II of this book, you will find a short list of Big Ideas followed by a section called "Mathematics Content Connections." These will help you identify the broader ideas behind the objectives that you need to teach so you can help students deepen their understanding of connecting ideas and strands. All programs should have a common focus on conceptual development, problem solving, reasoning, and communication of mathematical understanding. In short, a problem-based approach is the best course of action for raising scores.

Test-Taking Strategies

Another common approach to raising test scores is to teach students specific strategies, unrelated to content, useful for test taking. With a healthy dose of caution and keeping in mind the following caveats, this approach may help some students. First, if the students have not developed the concepts, the test strategies will be completely useless. Second, time spent teaching test strategies is best done shortly before a test. Here are a few strategies that may have some positive effect:

- *Familiarize students with different question formats.* Research the types of formats the standardized test will employ, and be sure to use these question formats regularly (not exclusively) in class.
- *Teach test-taking strategies.* Students are often not very efficient test-takers, so helping them learn to take tests can result in benefits. Here are some teachable strategies:
  - Read questions carefully. Practise identifying what questions are asking and what information is given to get the answer.
  - Estimate the answer before spending time with computation. On multiple-choice tests, estimation and good number sense are often all that are needed to select the correct answer.
  - Eliminate choices. Look at the available options. Some will almost certainly be unreasonable. Does a choice make sense? Can looking at the ones digit eliminate answers?
  - Work backward from an answer.

Remember! Successful test-taking strategies require understanding concepts, and having skills and number sense.

Grading

A grade is a statistic used to communicate to others the achievement level that a student has attained in a particular area of study. The accuracy or validity of the grade is dependent on the information that is used to generate the grade, the professional judgment of the teacher, and the alignment of the assessments with the true goals and objectives of the course. Look again at the definition of grading on page 79. Notice that it says scores are used along with "other information about a student's work" to determine a grade. There is no mention of averaging scores.

Most experienced teachers will tell you that they know a great deal about their students in terms of what the students know, how they perform in different situations, their attitudes and beliefs, and their various levels of skill attainment. Effective teachers have always been engaged in ongoing performance assessment, albeit informal and sometimes with no recording. A better approach is to record all important assessment information that reflects an accurate picture of your students' performance.

The practice of grading by statistical number crunching is so firmly ingrained in schooling at all levels that you may find it hard to abandon. One idea that should be clear from the discussions in this chapter is that it is quite useful to gather a wide variety of rich information about students' understanding, problem-solving processes, and attitudes and beliefs. To ignore all this information in favour of a handful of numbers based on tests, especially those that may focus on low-level skills, is unfair to students, to parents, and to you as the teacher.

Grading Issues

For effective use of the assessment information gathered from problems, tasks, and other appropriate methods for assigning grades, some hard decisions are inevitable. Some are philosophical, some require school or board/district policies about grades, and all require us to examine what we value and the objectives we communicate to students and parents.

What Gets Graded Gets Valued   Among the many components of the grading process, one truth is undeniable: *What gets graded* by teachers *is what gets valued* by students. Using rubric scores to provide feedback and to encourage a pursuit of excellence must also relate to grades. However, "converting four out of five [on a rubric score] to 80 percent or three out of four [on a rubric] to a grade of C can destroy the entire purpose of alternative assessment and the use of scoring rubrics" (Kulm, 1994, p. 99). Kulm explains that directly translating rubric scores to grades focuses attention on the grades and away from the purpose of every good problem-solving activity—to strive for an excellent performance. When papers are returned with less than a top rating, the purpose of detailed rubric indicators is to instruct students on what is needed in order to achieve at a higher level. Early on, there should be opportunities to improve, based on feedback. When a grade of 75 percent

or a C– is returned, all the student knows is that he or she did poorly. If, for example, a student's ability to justify her or his answers and solutions has improved, should he or she be penalized in the process of averaging numbers with a weaker performance early in the marking period?

What this means is that grading must be based on the performance tasks and other activities to which you assigned rubric ratings; otherwise, students will soon realize that these scores are not important. At the same time, these ratings need not be added or averaged in any numerical manner. The grade at the end of the marking period should reflect a holistic view of where the student is now relative to your goals and your value system.

From Assessment Tools to Grades   The grades you assign should reflect all your objectives. Procedural skills remain important but should be proportional to other goals. If you are restricted to assigning a single grade for mathematics, you will need to decide what weight or value different factors have in making up the grade. Student X may be stronger at reasoning and truly love mathematics, yet be weak in computational skills. Student Y may be mediocre in problem solving but possess good skills in communicating her mathematical thinking. How much weight should you give to cooperation in groups, to written versus oral reports, to computational skills? There are no simple answers to these questions. However, they should be addressed at the beginning of the grading period and not the night you set out to assign report card grades.

A multi-dimensional reporting system that relies on multiple assessments is important for improving the validity of a grading system. If you can assign several grades for mathematics and not just one, your report to families will be more meaningful. Even if the school's report card does not permit multiple grades, you can devise a supplement indicating several ratings for different objectives. A place for comments is also helpful. This form can be shared with students periodically during a grading period and can easily accompany a report card.

The process of grading your students using multiple forms of assessments has the potential to enhance your students' achievement. As you develop your own tools to match your instruction and provide valuable evidence of your students' understanding, work with colleagues. In small groups or with a grade-level partner, you can share tasks, look at samples of students' work to try and decipher errors, or to celebrate a student's novel approach. You can also engage in discussions with your colleagues about their responses to similar student misconceptions and misunderstandings. Working as a team to create and implement sound assessments will enrich your ability to select and administer meaningful performance-based questions or tasks. It will also enhance your professional judgment by questioning or confirming your thinking.

Reflections on Chapter 5

Writing to Learn

1. What is the difference between formative and summative assessment? Give examples of each.
2. What is the difference between scoring and grading? What is the purpose of a score if it is not a grade?
3. Describe the essential features of a rubric. What are performance indicators?
4. How can students be involved in understanding and using rubrics to help with their learning?
5. How can you incorporate observational assessments into your daily lessons? What is at least one method for getting observations recorded? Do you have to observe every student?
6. How can children with limited writing skills "write" in mathematics journals?
7. How do diagnostic interviews help to capture student thinking?

For Discussion and Exploration

1. Examine a few end-of-chapter tests in various mathematics textbooks. How well do the tests assess what is important in the chapter? Concepts and understanding? Mathematical processes?
2. Access your province's or territory's ministry of education Web site and find a few released test items used on provincial or territorial testing. For the released test items, first decide if they are good problem-based assessments that would help you find out about student understanding of the concepts involved. If they are not, try to improve each item so that it becomes a problem-based assessment that would be useful in the classroom.
3. How are teachers in your area responding to the pressures of provincial or territorial testing programs? What are they doing to improve students' performance on these tests?

Resources for Chapter 5

Recommendations for Further Reading

Articles

Kitchen, R., Cherrington, A., Gates, J., Hitchings, J., Majka, M., Merk, M., & Trubow, G. (2002). Supporting reform through performance assessment. *Mathematics Teaching in the Middle School, 8,* 24–30.

Six of the seven authors are middle school teachers working together in the same school. As part of implementing a standards-based curriculum in a school that had recently dropped tracking, these teachers wrote and refined assessments that they believed would help promote higher-order thinking. The article includes interesting examples and provides useful and inspiring information that is applicable across the grades.

Leatham, K. R., Lawrence, K., & Mewborn, D. (2005). Getting started with open-ended assessment. *Teaching Children Mathematics, 11,* 413–419.

In this article, the definition of an open-ended assessment item includes the potential for a range of responses and a balance between too much and too little information given. Examples are included. The teacher–author (Lawrence) talks personally about getting started in her grade 3–4 class of "culturally and economically diverse" students and the values that accrued for both her and her class.

Books

Glanfield, F., Bush, W. S., & Stenmark, J. K. (Eds.). (2003). *Mathematics assessment: A practical handbook for grades K–2.* Reston, VA: National Council of Teachers of Mathematics.

Stenmark, J. K., & Bush, W. S. (Eds.). (2001). *Mathematics assessment: A practical handbook for grades 3–5.* Reston, VA: National Council of Teachers of Mathematics.

Bush, W. S., & Leinwand, S. (Eds.). (2000). *Mathematics assessment: A practical handbook for grades 6–8.* Reston, VA: National Council of Teachers of Mathematics.

These three NCTM books are part of a K–12 series on assessment. The handbooks offer practical advice for classroom teachers that is considerably beyond the scope of this chapter. The four chapters in each book essentially cover the kinds of assessment options that are best used, practical guidelines for implementing a quality assessment program in your classroom, and suggestions for dealing with the assessment data once gathered.

Western and Northern Canadian Protocol for Collaboration in Education (WNCP). (2006). *Rethinking classroom assessment with purpose in mind.*

This excellent document developed by the WNCP in conjunction with Dr. Lorna Earl, a recognized expert on assessment, is concerned with classroom assessment. The document focuses on the kind of assessment that is an integral part of regular classroom activity. The latest detailed information is provided on the three purposes of assessment: assessment for learning, assessment as learning, assessment of learning.

Wright, R., Martland, J., & Stafford, A. (2006). *Early Numeracy: Assessment for teaching and intervention.* London: Paul Chapman Educational Publishing.

This book includes six diagnostic interviews for assessing young children's knowledge and strategy use related to number and the operations of addition and subtraction. Using a series of frameworks, the authors help teachers pinpoint students' misconception and support appropriate interventions.

Online Resources

Principles for Fair Student Assessment Practices for Education in Canada
www.bced.gov.bc.ca/classroom_assessment/fairstudent.pdf
Principles for Fair Student Assessment Practices in Canada is the product of a comprehensive effort to reach consensus on what constitutes sound principles to guide the fair assessment of students. It was developed by a working group guided by a Joint Advisory Committee from organizations such as Canadian School Boards, Canadian Education Association, Canadian Teachers' Federation, along with representatives from other organizations that have a concerted interest in Canadian education.

NCTM Research Clips and Briefs—Formative Assessment
www.nctm.org/researchbriefs.aspx
NCTM provides information on the definition of formative assessment and Five Key Strategies for effective formative assessment, including an example of a task for a diagnostic interview. They also include an excellent set of references for further investigation.

The Math Forum: Internet Mathematics Library—Assessment
http://mathforum.org/library/ed_topics/assessment
Here you will find links to all sorts of information that will be useful in both planning and assessment.

Building a Rubric Backgrounder @2Learn.ca
www.2learn.ca/construct/rubric/tlcrubricinfo.html
At this site, which is part of www.2learn.ca, you can build printable rubrics that can be duplicated and distributed to students. The site includes strategies and tips for designing and building rubrics.

---

myeducationlab *will help you improve your understanding of the concepts taught in this textbook and in your course. This online tool includes videos of real classroom experiences, sample lesson plans, simulations, case studies, and links to important educational and teaching Web sites that will help you make the transition from student to teacher. As you study in your course and with this textbook, please follow along in **MyEducationLab**. Use it! Explore it! And improve your knowledge and your grade!*

Chapter 6
Teaching Mathematics Equitably to All Children

A society can claim success in eradicating the malady of mathematics illiteracy if and only if all its progeny are able to develop to their fullest potential. If its offspring can become employable workers, wisely choosing consumers, and autonomously thinking citizens who can be contributors in the super symbolic quantitative world they will inherit, then society can say, "Victory is ours!"

Elliott and Garnett (1994, p. 15)

NCTM views the education of every child as its most compelling objective. Its "Every Child" statement says:

By "every child," we mean every child—no exception.

We are particularly concerned about students who have been denied access to educational opportunities for reasons such as language, ethnicity, physical impairment, gender, socioeconomic status, and so on. We emphasize that "every child" includes:

- learners of English as a second language and speakers of English as a first language
- members of underrepresented ethnic groups and members of well-represented groups
- students who are physically challenged and those who are not
- females and males
- students who live in poverty and those who do not
- students who have not been successful and those who have been successful in school and in mathematics (www.nctm.org/about/every_child.htm)

Mathematics for All Children

— *Pause and Reflect*

Stop and think for a minute. Do you personally believe the "Every Child" statement? Children with disabilities, children from impoverished homes, minority children, English language learners—can all of these children learn to think mathematically?

It is the responsibility of all who are concerned with children's mathematical learning to make that vision a reality. Most teachers, particularly new teachers, are committed to supporting each of the children in their classrooms. It is critical that you are equipped with a large collection of strategies you can use in your classroom with children. You might have a strategy that works for one child but is completely ineffective with another, even if the child has the same exceptionality.

In this chapter, we will examine issues of diversity in the mathematics classroom and approaches that could help you to be more successful in reducing these identified differences.

Diversity in Today's Classroom

It is no longer reasonable to talk about the "regular classroom." The range of abilities, disabilities, and socioeconomic circumstances in today's classrooms pose significant challenges for teachers. Addressing the needs of *all* children means providing opportunities for any or all of the following:

- Students who are identified as having a specific learning problem (disability)
- Students who are intellectually challenged
- Students from different cultural backgrounds
- Students who do not speak English
- Students who are female
- Students who are mathematically promising

Meeting the needs of all children requires that we challenge and possibly change many of our long-held assumptions about how mathematics should be taught and about how children should learn mathematics. In Canada, each of the provincial and territorial school systems has a mandate to provide learning for all, so that the differences among learners do not impede their participation in school, their mastery of learning outcomes, or their ability to become contributing members of society (CMEC, 2004, p. 21).

Traditionally, mathematics instruction has broken content into small, bite-sized increments. Each bit is explained, demonstrated, and then practised until mastery is achieved; then the next bit is introduced. The belief is that somehow the essentially passive students will put the bits together into some sort of cohesive whole. In classrooms for learning-disabled or low-average students, this approach has been even more pronounced and resistant to change. Unfortunately, much of the instruction for children experiencing mathematical difficulties is replete with worksheets and rote drill focused on "basic skills." What we know about how children learn would suggest a quite different approach.

There is no reason to believe that children with special needs, regardless of the nature of those needs, should learn any differently than other children (Andrews & Lupart, 2000; Baroody & Hume, 1991; Carey, Fennema, Carpenter, & Franke, 1995; Hutchinson, 2002; Poplin, 1988a, 1988b; Trafton & Claus, 1994; Winzer, 1996). Creating classrooms that respect diversity and foster learning for *all* students is teaching for equity (Hutchinson, 2000). As you read each section in this chapter, you will discover ways to create more equitable classrooms and you will find the means of helping all students become more mathematically literate.

The Goal of Equitable Instruction

The goal of equity is to offer all students access to important mathematics. Yet, inequities exist, even if unintentionally. For example, if a teacher does not build in opportunities for student-to-student interaction in a lesson, he or she may not be addressing the needs of girls, who are often social learners, or English language learners, who need opportunities to talk, listen, and write in small-group situations. It takes more than just wanting to be fair or equitable; it takes knowing the strategies that accommodate each type

of learner and making every effort to incorporate those strategies into your teaching. Although all students should have equal chances to learn grade-level curriculum, equal instruction is not a goal.

Inclusive Education

Canadian law guarantees "universal access" to schooling for all children. What this means is that every child, without exception for disability, has the right to free public schooling. The *Education Act* in each jurisdiction also guarantees this right. The trend today is toward a unified education system, where special and regular education are merged in order to meet the individual learning needs of all students (Andrews & Lupart, 2000). Across Canada, inclusion is the predominant approach, and inclusive schools are a natural part of our education system (Hutchinson, 2002).

Inclusion entitles exceptional students or students with special needs (the term used in British Columbia and Alberta) to have programs adapted to their needs. Exceptional includes giftedness and a wide range of disabilities, such as emotional, sensory, and physical disabilities.

Legal definitions for a wide range of exceptionalities are usually determined by the ministry of education of a provincial or territorial jurisdiction. These definitions, which are included in an Individual Education Plan (IEP), help to determine which children are eligible for special services and what types of services they will receive. The IEP describes in writing the adaptations, modifications, and services to be provided for the student deemed exceptional.

Instructional Principles for Diverse Learners

Across the myriad of diversities of our students, all children essentially learn in the same way (Fuson, 2003). The authors of *Adding It Up* (NRC, 2001) conclude that all children are best served when attention is given to the following three principles:

1. Learning with understanding is based on connecting and organizing knowledge around big conceptual ideas.
2. Learning builds on what students already know.
3. Instruction in school should take advantage of the children's informal knowledge of mathematics.

These principles should come as no surprise. The tenets of constructivism described in Chapter 3 apply to all learners, not just the middle of a so-called typical classroom.

Having said this, it is worth revisiting two ideas from Chapter 4: accommodation and modification, both considered instructional adaptations (see p. 62). An accommodation is a change to teaching, student responding, and the classroom environment that increases students' access to the curriculum. It does not affect the difficulty or grade level of the learning goals or curriculum expectations. A modification is an adjustment to the curriculum expectations or learning goals, either reducing or raising the level of difficulty of the content, skills, or concepts of the original curriculum standards or expectations. In planning accommodations and modifications, the goal is to enable each child to successfully reach your learning objectives. In each chapter in Section II, you will find a special feature, adapting the lesson, which demonstrates how the needs of special learners can be accommodated in a mathematics lesson. You will also find that some chapter activities have been adapted in this way too. This chapter also looks at accommodations and modifications for the diversity of students that are likely to be in your classroom.

Specific Learning Disabilities

The predominant instructional model for students with learning disabilities has historically viewed the learner as passive, with the mastery of skills taking precedence over understanding (Poplin, 1988a). It is this thinking that led to pull-out and self-contained-classroom approaches. Although popular, these skills-oriented models have produced very limited results.

A Perspective on Learning Disabilities

Students with learning disabilities have very specific problems with perceptual or cognitive processing. These problems may affect memory or the ability to speak or to express ideas in writing, to perceive auditory or written information, or to integrate abstract ideas. It is insufficient simply to label a child "LD," learning disabled. The following insights offered by Borasi (1994) are an important point of departure for teachers who have children with learning disabilities in their classes:

- Students with learning disabilities are mentally capable; they are not slow or intellectually disabled.
- The classification of *learning disabled* is not useful to the classroom teacher without a clear understanding of the child's specific learning problem.
- Learning disabilities are not easily remediated, and possibly cannot be remediated.
- Learning disabilities should be compensated for by helping students use their strengths.
- Instructional modifications will be needed to accommodate children with specific learning disabilities.

Borasi suggests that teachers accept the fact that learning disabilities are real in the same sense that being blind or deaf is a real disability. You would not ask a blind person to

"look more closely" or a deaf person to "listen more carefully." Hence, we should never ask a child with learning disabilities to do things that depend heavily on his or her area of deficit.

Adaptations for Specific Learning Difficulties

Note that cognitive deficits or processing disabilities may be present as auditory problems, visual processing problems, or sometimes both. It is important that the teacher have as much detailed information as possible about children who have specific difficulties. If the child has already been evaluated by the school psychologist and other community-based professionals, assessment results would be available in an Individual Education Plan (IEP) to help pinpoint specific weaknesses and strengths. The Plan will also describe ways to adapt instructional strategies to avoid weaknesses and capitalize on strengths.

Adaptations for Perceptual Deficits There are many variations of perceptual problems; some are visual and others auditory. All involve confusion of input in one way or another.

The realm of perceptual problems is perhaps the most apparent where the maxim "avoid weaknesses and capitalize on strengths" is best observed. The following are simply a few specific suggestions:

- Seat the child near you and the chalkboard.
- Keep the child's desk or workspace free of distractions.
- Maintain a moderate voice. Repeat main ideas.
- When using the overhead projector or other technology with the whole class, show only one main idea, problem, or exercise at a time. (Avoid complex visual displays.)
- Maintain a classroom environment that values the importance of only one person talking at a time so that each child's voice is respected and the focus on one person is easier to attend to.
- Enunciate words clearly and attempt to face students when speaking to them.
- Design text or worksheet pages for the child. Provide templates to block out all but one problem or exercise at a time.
- Utilize methods for organizing written work. Have computation work done on centimetre grid paper, writing one number per square. Provide paper with columns or turn notebook paper sideways. Use already drawn templates for traditional algorithms.
- Use a tape recorder (headphones) with instructions explaining what may be difficult to discern from the visual materials.
- Provide geometric models whenever possible instead of relying on pictures. Use geoboards and materials

such as pattern blocks for constructions so that drawing is kept to a minimum.

- Assign a buddy to help read, explain, or repeat directions.

Adaptations for Memory Deficits Memory deficits can also be specifically visual or auditory. Children with *short-term memory* deficits can have trouble recalling things for even a few seconds, when copying from the board, or when recalling information in a word problem or directions. Children with *long-term memory* deficits may show no difficulty with material when it is presented, but may appear to have not learned it at all a day or a week later. Mastery of basic facts is a hallmark problem for children with this disability.

You can diminish the load on a student's short-term memory by breaking tasks and directions into small steps and providing a buddy to help with recall. Long-term memory problems require over-learning, frequent practice, and as many associations with other ideas as possible. The following additional specific suggestions may be useful:

- Rather than presenting a series of instructions, provide only one at a time.
- After giving instructions, ask one or more students to state them in their own words as a way of checking for broad understanding of the instructions and allowing other students to hear them from a peer's perspective.
- Write instructions on the board or make written copies for distribution.
- When working on oral exercises or problems, allow students the option of using the written versions as well.
- For basic facts, use strategies and number relationships to promote memorization (see Chapter 11).
- Allow use of a calculator at all times.
- Use frequent brief reviews—distributed practice.

Memory deficits tend to be exhibited in procedural work. Remember that no routine procedural knowledge, including mastery of basic facts, should prevent a student from progress in mathematical ideas. Exploration of new concepts is never dependent on mastery of skills.

Adaptations for Integrative Deficits Children with integrative problems seem to have difficulty with abstract ideas and conceptualization. These children often have difficulty making the cognitive connections that others may find easy. Children with an integrative disorder may do quite well at rote procedures such as computational algorithms, but these are no longer the focus of the mathematics curriculum. A general principle for helping these children integrate concepts and develop understanding is to use the experiences and ideas most familiar to them: their own invented procedures for solving problems, familiar models

or personal drawings that make sense to them, and their own words in either written or oral form to express their ideas. The following more specific approaches may be helpful for children with integrative difficulties:

- Use familiar physical models for longer than the usual period of time.
- Have students articulate what they do as often as possible using words, pictures, and numbers. Use both written and oral reports.
- Frequently require explanations and justifications. This self-monitoring can heighten the children's awareness of new ideas and assist them in making connections.
- Allow for repetition or practice of new conceptual ideas.
- Encourage students to restate word problems in their own words.
- Provide students with opportunities to teach a concept to a peer or younger child, hence an opportunity to organize and re-conceptualize their own thoughts about the concept.
- Use multiple representations of abstract concepts (e.g., words, symbols, drawings, concrete objects, acting it out).

Adaptations for Attention Deficits In many (not all) instances, students with learning disabilities are also identified as having attention deficit disorder or attention deficit–hyperactivity disorder. These children have chronic difficulties with attention span, impulse control, and sometimes hyperactivity. The following strategies have proven useful:

- Establish simple, predictable routines and discuss them with the child. Make expectations and consequences clear.
- Design learning activities that are active and engaging, rather than tedious or requiring lengthy periods of silent seatwork.
- Plan for the child to do independent work in an environment free of distractions or intense visual stimuli.
- Use highlighters to attract attention to important key ideas in textual material.
- Keep assignments and exercise lists short. Plan smaller sub-tasks within larger explorations or projects.
- Assign a buddy and impress on both that the agenda is to stay on task.
- Instead of placing the child in a cooperative group of three or four, pair the child with a buddy to form a separate group.

Intellectual Disabilities

All of us possess different mental capacities that modify our individual strengths and weaknesses or our learning styles.

Children with moderate or severe intellectual disabilities (generally with IQ scores between 50 and 70) will be limited in the kind and degree of mathematical reasoning they can perform. The essential requirement is that significantly more time is given for learning than under standard circumstances. Although severely disabled children are generally best served in a special classroom, there may be a wide range of intellectual disabilities in the regular classroom.

Modifications in Instruction

Limited cognitive abilities do not in any way alter how children learn, but these limited abilities do alter the means by which children experience and acquire their learning. For example, a child with limited cognitive abilities can learn the part/whole concept of addition just as a child without limitations can. However, much more time, repetition, and use of concrete learning tools will likely be required. In general, these special children learn *much* more slowly than do their peers (Bley, 1994; NRC, 2001).

Though a fast-paced, highly interactive classroom may be somewhat overwhelming for children who need more time to learn, they can benefit from many of the same experiences as the rest of the class. They can and should participate in projects and hands-on activities with their peer group. They can participate in cooperative groups by taking on less demanding roles, such as materials organizer or encourager. They can learn to perform calculations on a calculator and can serve as the person in a group who performs this activity. Many such children are good at drawing or making graphs. These helping roles are potentially consistent with the kinds of jobs they are likely to have in the adult world.

Partner the child with limited abilities with different students periodically, and have the partner help the child with the same task or idea. In this way, there is opportunity for needed repeated exposure or over-learning, and other students also will gain from serving as the explainer. It is important for all children in the room to involve children who need more time to learn in activities and projects. All children gain an appreciation for and acceptance of human differences.

Modifications in Curriculum

Since children with limited abilities need more time to learn than other children, it follows that less content can be learned during the years they are in school. It makes sense to focus the available instructional time on those areas that are going to be of the most value to these students as adults. Computational skill is the most obvious area where changes in curricular expectations should be made. There is no reason to be obsessive about fact mastery. Traditional computational algorithms should be eliminated from their curriculum altogether.

These students should have a calculator handy for all mathematics work. The child with limited abilities should be given careful instruction and lots of practice in using the calculator. A calculator with a printer is useful because it creates a printed record of work done.

Whereas calculations can be mastered via the calculator, the meanings of numbers in the real world cannot. Do not confuse number meaning with place-value concepts. What is important here is to realize that a bag of flour weighs 2.5 kilograms, that $100 buys a pair of fancy shoes, or that it takes about 20 minutes to walk about $1\frac{1}{2}$ kilometres. Numbers in the abstract will be of little use in their conceptual development.

Culturally and Linguistically Diverse Students

Canadian classrooms are increasing in racial, cultural, and linguistic diversity and the trend is expected to continue (Hutchinson, 2002). More than 200 000 immigrants arrive in Canada each year. Most settle in Ontario, Quebec, and British Columbia. Although immigration is increasing, fewer speak English. In 2001, about one-quarter of all children up to the age of 17 in Toronto and Vancouver were themselves recent immigrants or were born to parents who were recent immigrants. Most of these children lived in households in which a language other than English or French was the main language spoken. How best to meet the needs of our increasingly multicultural and multilingual students in our classrooms is a critical question. You will serve the needs of your students better if you create an environment in which students of varied cultures and languages thrive and grow academically and personally, and if you celebrate their presence in your classroom and enrich the learning experience for all students. This section discusses ways to address the needs of these students who are culturally and linguistically diverse.

Culturally Relevant Mathematics Instruction

It may seem that some areas of the classroom curriculum such as social studies and literature can be infused more readily with culturally relevant approaches than subjects such as mathematics and science. This common misconception can lead to inequities in the classroom for culturally and linguistically diverse students. It also tends to ignore the language needs of culturally and linguistically diverse students in mathematics instruction. Achieving a culturally relevant mathematics curriculum is a possibility. Here are three different perspectives on how best to meet the needs of these students and achieve the goal of culturally relevant instruction in mathematics:

1. Integrate ideas that contain representations of the cultural backgrounds of students (Gutstein & Peterson, 2005).
2. Implement the NCTM *Principles and Standards*, using a lot of language-rich tasks.
3. Use a dual-language approach (Ontario Ministry of Education, 2006).

We will look briefly at each of these three approaches.

Classroom experiences must be meaningful in terms of the daily lives and cultures of students. Making connections in mathematics with the real life of students is an effective way to reach students who are culturally and linguistically diverse. Gutstein and Peterson (2005) suggest that teaching mathematics is not neutral, and that grounding story problems in students' culture is one way of achieving this goal. For example, a teacher can teach double-digit multiplication and problem-solving skills by designing problems that highlight important social relations. The authors cite the following example: Factory workers aged 14, 15, and 16 in Honduras make McKids children's clothing for Wal-Mart. Each worker earns 43 cents an hour and works a 14-hour shift each day. How much does each worker make in one day, excluding fees deducted by employers?

The second perspective on teaching culturally and linguistically diverse students is to embrace the recommendations outlined in *Principles and Standards*. A teacher who teaches from a *Standards*-based perspective may use inquiry, student–student interactions (pairs and small groups), discussions, and alternative assessments. All of these can support the learning of a student who is also learning English or who is not familiar with particular aspects of Canadian culture.

Standards-based teaching supports the English language learner more effectively than traditional teaching because many strategies are helpful not only for culturally and linguistically diverse students but for other students as well. For example, *Standards* encourages a learning environment in which students solve a problem using a strategy of their own choosing and later explain how they solved the problem. A student from a different culture may have learned different strategies for that concept or for related skills. In addition, explaining their strategy allows students opportunities to develop their language skills.

Creating effective learning for culturally and linguistically diverse students involves integrating a dual-language approach. Many assignments in mathematics can be adapted and enriched by allowing students to approach them using more than one language. Allowing students to use their first language along with English enables them to draw on their strengths, including their academic, linguistic, and cultural knowledge. For example, English language learners might engage in an activity in which they compare numbers in various languages, or they might do a journal response in their own language.

When teaching from a culturally relevant perspective, it is important to explore how to embrace culture and to support language development. Both are discussed separately in the next two sections, even though they are interrelated and should not be separated for instruction.

Ethnomathematics

The combination of culture, mathematics, and educational activities is often referred to as *ethnomathematics*. Many societies have different mathematical traditions and have developed various strands of mathematical thought. One way to respect the diversity that exists within the classroom is to teach mathematics from a cultural perspective. Actively engage students in mathematics by examining the impact of their own culture on the ways they use, practise, and think about mathematics. A study of mathematics within other cultures provides students with an opportunity to "put faces" on mathematics instead of erroneously thinking that mathematics is a result of some mystical phenomenon.

There are many ways to approach mathematics from a cultural perspective (e.g., biographies of mathematicians, historical development of concepts, games, children's literature, and thematic units). Mathematics is the by-product of human ideas, creativity, problem solving, recreation, beliefs, values, and survival. Contributions to the field of mathematics come from people of diverse cultures all over the world. Many women and people of colour who have made important contributions to mathematics have been overlooked. There are Web sites and resources that provide links to the contributions of these diverse mathematicians and to ideas for teaching ethnomathematics. Two are listed with the resources at the end of the chapter.

The combination of culture, mathematics, and educational activities is often referred to as ethnomathematics. Inviting First Nations or guests from other cultures to class may help students learn and appreciate the different ways people use, practice, and think about mathematics.

English Language Learners

It is well known that English language learners (also known as ESL students or English-as-a-second-language students) enter the mathematics classroom from homes in which English is not their primary language of communication. Although a person might develop conversational English language skills in a few years, it takes as many as seven years to learn the "academic language" that is specific to a content area, such as mathematics (Cummins, 1994). Academic language is harder to learn because it is not used in the student's everyday world. When learning mathematics, students might be learning content in English for which they may not yet have learned words in their native language. For example, in studying the measures of central tendency (*mean, median,* and *mode*), they may not know words for these terms in their first language, thus increasing the challenge for learning academic terms in their second language. Moreover, story problems are difficult for English language learners, not just because of the language, but also because of the fact that sentences in story problems are often structured differently from sentences in conversational English.

Teachers of English to Speakers of Other Languages (TESOL) have developed standards for effective instruction of English as a second language (ESL) to pre-K–12 students. Their vision of effective education for students learning English includes developing proficiency in English and the maintenance and promotion of students' native languages. TESOL standards state that students will use English to:

1. "interact in the classroom,"
2. "obtain, process, construct, and provide subject matter information in spoken and written form," and
3. "use appropriate learning strategies to construct and apply academic knowledge" (TESOL, 1997, p. 9).

Notice that students are to use English in their academic content courses. This does not mean "English only," but rather an approach that encourages the use of native language and the development of English. Also note that the emphasis for English language learners is to provide them with opportunities for reading, writing, speaking, and listening. When these are incorporated effectively into instruction, both mathematical understanding and language can be learned.

Specific Strategies for Teaching Mathematics to English Language Learners

Among the many ways to support English language learners in the classroom, the following six strategies are critical to mathematics instruction. These strategies are among the most frequently mentioned by teachers and researchers as increasing the academic achievement of English language learners in the mathematics classroom.

1. Write and State the Content and Language Objectives Every lesson should begin with telling students what they will be learning. You do not have to give away what they will discover in their exploration. However, you need to state the larger purpose of what they will be doing; in other words, provide a road map. If students know the purpose of the lesson, they are better able to make sense of the details in light of the bigger picture. For example, when teaching a lesson about using different strategies for multiplication and division, you would write student-friendly objectives on the board such as the following:

Today you will:

1. Find different ways to multiply and divide numbers. (content)
2. Explain how you completed a multiplication and division problem when you were given the first step. (language and content)
3. Write the way you would choose to solve the division problem. (language)

2. Build Background This is similar to building on prior knowledge, but it takes into consideration language and culture as well as content. If possible, use a context and any appropriate visuals to help students understand the task you want them to solve. Link the lesson to prior learning: yesterday's lesson, a real-world problem, or something you did earlier in the month. For the non-contextual lesson in "Building on Numbers You Know," you might have a discussion of what 22×37 could refer to (perhaps it refers to the measurements of a picture hanging on the wall or the amount of money it will cost to buy stamps for each member of a class of 22 students).

3. Encourage Use of Native Language Research shows that students' cognitive development proceeds more readily in their native language. In a mathematics classroom, students should be encouraged to communicate in their native language and to continue with their English language development. For example, when students are working in small groups, a good strategy is to have a group of students who speak Mandarin first discuss the problem in Mandarin as they try to solve it. If a student knows enough English, then the presentation during the *follow-up* phase of the lesson can be assigned as "English preferred." If the student knows little or no English, then he or she can explain in Mandarin and have a translator.

4. Comprehensible Input *Comprehensible input,* a term used in bilingual education, means that the message you are communicating is understandable to students. It means to simplify sentence structures and limit the use of non-essential vocabulary; it does not mean to lower the expectations for the lesson. It also means to use strategies to help students understand the language they encounter. Sometimes teachers put many unnecessary words and phrases into questions, making them less clear to non-native speakers. Compare the following two teacher questions:

Not Modified: In front of you, you have an assignment that I just gave out. For every problem, I want you to determine the total area for the shape. You will be working with your partner, but each of you needs to write your answers on your own paper and explain how you got your answers. If you get stuck on a problem raise your hand.

Modified: Please look at your paper. (*Holds paper and points to it. Pointing to the first picture.*) You need to find the area. What does area mean? (*Allows wait time.*) How can you calculate area? Talk to your partners. (*Points to mouth and then to a pair of students as she says this.*) Write your answers. (*Makes a writing motion over paper.*)

Notice that three things have been done: sentences were shortened, unnecessary words were removed, and gestures and motions that link to the vocabulary were used. Also notice the "wait time" the teacher provides. It is very important to provide extra time after posing a question or giving instructions so that English language learners have time to translate and make sense of the request, before participating.

Another way to provide comprehensible input is to use a variety of tools to help students visualize and understand what has been articulated. This is particularly critical for students who may not have strong verbal skills. Modelling is important. In the preceding example, the teacher is modelling the instructions. When introducing a lesson, include pictures, real objects, and diagrams. For example, if you are teaching integers, having a real thermometer, as well as an overhead transparency with a thermometer, will help provide a visual (and a context) for exploring the number line. You might even add pictures of places covered in snow and position them near the low temperatures, and so on. Students should also be expected to include multiple representations in their work. Expect students to draw, write, and explain what they have done. This is helpful to them and to their peers, who will be seeing their solutions. Supplemental materials you should consider using include manipulatives, real objects, pictures, visuals, multimedia, demonstrations, children's books, and adapted text (Echevarria, Vogt, & Short, 2004).

5. Explicitly Teach Vocabulary   One popular tool to reinforce vocabulary development is a mathematics word wall. As you encounter vocabulary essential for learning mathematics, students participate in creating and adding to the word wall. When a word is selected, students can create cards that include the word in English, translations of the word in the languages represented in your classroom, pictures, and a student-made description (not a formal definition) in English or in several languages.

In addition to word walls, there are many ways to teach vocabulary explicitly. For example, students can create concept maps, linking concepts and terms as they study the relationships among fractions, decimals, and percents. Students can keep "personal math dictionaries" of terms they need to know, which include the word, illustrations, and examples of it. As you use a mathematical term that has been previously addressed, stop and make sure that students remember the term. As new terms are introduced, the words should be discussed, and the root and related words shared (Rubenstein, 2000). There are many terms whose meanings in mathematics are different from those used in everyday life. Here are some examples: *product, mean, factor, acute, division, difference, similar,* and *angle.*

6. Use Cooperative Groups   English language learners need opportunities to use language in non-threatening situations. They also need to speak, write, talk, and listen. The best way to accomplish these objectives is through cooperative grouping. When doing so, you must consider a student's language skills. Placing an English language learner with two English-speaking students may result in the English language learner being left out entirely. It is better to place a bilingual student in this group, or to place students that have the same first language together (Garrison, 1997; Khisty, 1997). Pairs may be more appropriate than groups of three or four. As with all group work, rules or structures should be in place to make sure that each student is able to participate and is accountable for the activity assigned.

The single most important thing you can do is to create an environment that is supportive and nurturing and that values a culture where children are willing to risk making mistakes in front of others. English language learners will recognize that you have established such a haven when they find that you see their culture and language as a resource to be valued rather than a drawback to be managed.

From Gender Bias to Gender Equity

Research over the last two decades suggests that gender differences favouring boys in mathematics tends not to appear until high school—in earlier grades, differences are either non-existent or favour girls (Lauzon, 2001). Results of the Trends in International Mathematics and Science Study (TIMSS), 1995, revealed virtually no difference between boys and girls at the grade 4 and 8 levels, with an increasing male advantage developing by the final year of high school. The good news for the TIMSS, 1999, in mathematics, was that most gender differences were negligible. In 2003, on average, across the TIMSS participating countries, there was essentially no difference in achievement between boys and girls at either the grade 4 or grade 8 level (Mullis, Martin, & Foy, 2005). Yet, there persists in our society a common belief that boys are better than girls at mathematics—what Damarin (1995) refers to as the "maleness of mathematics." After high school, more males than females enter fields of study that include heavy emphases on mathematics and science. It remains important to be aware of and address gender equity issues in your classroom.

Possible Causes of Gender Inequity

As Becker and Jacobs (2001) point out, most of the research "is moving away from 'sex differences' to 'gender differences' in acknowledgment that gender is socially constructed and the differences are not biologically determined" (p. 2). We can find some of the causes of gender inequity in the classroom.

Teacher Interactions and Gender Teachers may not consciously seek to stereotype students by gender; however, the gender-based biases of our society often affect teachers' interactions with students (Martin, Sexton, Wagner, & Gerlovich, 1997). For example, observations of teachers' gender-specific interactions in the classroom indicate that boys get more attention and different kinds of attention than girls do. Boys tend to receive more criticism for wrong answers as well as more praise for correct answers. Boys also tend to be more involved in discipline-related attention and have their work monitored more carefully (Campbell, 1995; Leder, 1995). Attention is interpreted as value, with a predictable effect on both sexes. The increased attention, both positive and negative, that teachers unconsciously provide to males contributes to the impression of mathematics as a male domain.

Research has found that teachers wait longer for responses from boys than from girls (Leder, 1995). In one study, females received more wait time on low-level questions concerning facts and procedures, whereas males received longer wait times on more difficult, more challenging, and higher-cognitive questions. Over time, these subtle but real differences suggest to girls that they are not perceived as capable of quality thinking, and they eventually come to believe this of themselves.

Belief Systems Related to Gender The belief that mathematics is a male domain persists in our society and is held by both sexes. In adolescent years, when girls are significantly interested in and influenced by boys, many girls are afraid to act "too smart" for fear of alienating boys.

Campbell (1995) points out that "unless boys as well as girls are convinced that 'real women do math,' efforts toward gender equity in mathematics will encounter obstacles based on stereotyped social roles" (p. 229).

Working Toward Gender Equity: What Can Be Done?

Campbell (1995) makes a compelling argument that we have tended to address gender inequity as a "girl problem." This places the focus of our efforts to solve this problem on girls—to make them somehow like mathematics more or take more courses in mathematics. This approach, she says, makes it seem that there really is something wrong with girls. "If you change a girl so that she 'loves math,' but then you put her back into the same environment and situations that caused her to hate mathematics in the first place, she will revert to hating mathematics" (p. 226). As already noted, the causes of girls' perceptions of themselves vis-à-vis mathematics are largely a function of the educational environment. That is where we should look for solutions.

Become Aware As a teacher, you need to be aware of whether you treat boys and girls differently. Work at ensuring equitable treatment. As you interact with students, try to be aware of the interactions with both gender groups in relationship to the:

- Numbers and types of questions you ask
- Amount of attention given to disturbances
- Kinds and topics of projects and activities assigned
- Praise given in response to students' participation
- Makeup of small groups
- Contexts of problems

Being aware of your gender-specific actions is more difficult than it may sound. To receive feedback, try video-recording a class or two on a periodic basis. Tally the number of questions asked of boys and girls. Also note which students ask questions and what kinds of questions they ask. Think about where you stand in the class. At first, you will be surprised at how gender-biased your interaction is. Awareness takes effort.

Involve All Students Find ways to involve all students in your class, not just those who seem eager. Girls tend to shy away from involvement and are not as quick to seek help. Perhaps the best suggestion for involving students is to follow the tenets of this book—use a problem-based approach to instruction. Mau and Leitze (2001) make the case that when teachers are in a show-and-tell mode, there is significantly more opportunity for the teacher to reinforce the more overt behaviours of boys, allowing the girls to be passive. In a classroom influenced by constructivist theory, all students are expected to both talk and listen. More mathematics is constructed with less teacher intervention. Authority resides in the students and in their arguments. The result is that girls are on an equal footing with the boys.

Pause and Reflect

Stop for a moment and envision the directed teaching that most likely was the model you experienced. Can you see situations in which males are favoured, encouraged, or assisted by the teacher—even without consciously being aware of any differential treatment? How would these differences possibly disappear in a problem-based, student-oriented environment?

Providing for the Mathematically Gifted and Talented

Children who are typically known as "gifted" have special educational needs. They require appropriate educational opportunities and challenges; otherwise, they are vulnerable to the same pitfalls and frustrations that affect other children, becoming bored in environments that are neither stimulating nor motivating (Winzer, 1996). Considerable research is available on the education of the gifted but offers little consensus. Alternative views have typically focused on two major questions: What does it mean to be gifted, and should the program for gifted children focus on acceleration or enrichment? In addition, there are practical considerations, not the least of which is how to deliver an appropriate program. Alternatives include pull-out designs, after-school models, and in-class programs. There are also questions of time, teachers, and materials.

Hutchinson (2002) defines students who are gifted or talented as "[those] who are advanced in one or many areas of development. They exceed teachers' and parents' expectations in specific areas of the school curriculum" (p. 66). In the past, it was thought that gifted students were advanced in all areas. More recent research suggests that gifted learners usually are advanced in specific domains—a view that has been incorporated into provincial and territorial definitions. It is also important to be aware of other characteristics that will help to identify students who may be gifted or talented. Often their vocabulary is advanced for their age; they may show an unusual degree of curiosity and persistence with tasks they enjoy. It might also surprise you that their performance in subjects in which they do not excel will be ordinary. Indeed, there will be some children who are gifted or talented who will not exhibit any of these characteristics and might appear to be average or even below average (British Columbia Special Education Branch, 1995).

Mathematically Promising Students

Rather than *gifted* or *talented*, *promising* is the term preferred by an NCTM Task Force on the Mathematically Promising, for students who are mathematically talented. The term *promising* was chosen because, under common definitions of the gifted and talented, many mathematically adept students have been overlooked or excluded. In Canada, *gifted* and/or *talented* is the term that is still commonly used. The literature on mathematically promising students suggests that they may not be especially talented in other areas. Nor can mathematical promise be equated with general school achievement or facility with computational algorithms. Promising students generally have good verbal skills, curiosity, imagination, analytic thinking skills, and the ability to concentrate and work independently (House, 1999).

What all of this means for the identification of promising students is that simple criteria built on test scores, IQ, or high grades may exclude those who have a high probability of developing into exceptional mathematical students.

Acceleration, Enrichment, and Depth

For years, one of the primary debates related to the talented mathematics student was over the relative merits of acceleration versus enrichment. *Acceleration* is the practice of having students move faster than the normal level of instruction through academic content to meet their needs (British Columbia Special Education Branch, 1995; Winzer, 1996). *Enrichment* refers to the expansion of the regular curriculum to include additional topics. The following are examples of enrichment strategies that can be used for teaching gifted students: telescoping, authentic problem solving, mentor programs, open-ended assignments, tiered assignments, compacting, independent studies, and ability grouping (Hutchinson, 2002).

Acceleration and Enrichment Both acceleration and enrichment deserve merit, at the same time that they warrant caution. Capable and promising students should be challenged to move at an appropriate pace through the curriculum and should be exposed to as much quality mathematics as time permits. Even though the NCTM task force chose not to endorse either approach, this is not necessarily the case for the Canadian context. Daniel Keating, a world-renowned Canadian researcher in the field of children's cognitive and social development, notes that research studies unanimously support the benefits of acceleration to working with gifted children. According to *Gifted Education: A Resource Guide for Teachers* (British Columbia Special Education Branch, 1995), acceleration has been shown to be positive for gifted learners, both achievers and underachievers. Yet, acceleration can have the effect of developing a large array of meaningless skills as students are pushed to learn more without exploring the ideas in a full conceptual manner. Without adequate time, the guidance of a skilled teacher, and the benefit of directed discourse and exploration, students in acceleration programs tend to focus on mechanical skills. This will often be the case as well when students are left to study independently.

Enrichment, the most popular of the various approaches to teaching gifted students, also has its critics. Too often enrichment programs result in little more than "fun math time" with topics such as geometric puzzles, computer games, or the "problem of the day." Although enrichment mathematics activities can be fun, they should accomplish much more. They should broaden students' mathematical horizons, require students to think deeply, make connections to earlier ideas and to real contexts, and challenge them to ask questions, make conjectures, and reason about important ideas.

The Addition of Depth Recognizing the strengths and pitfalls of enrichment and acceleration, Sheffield (1999) argues for a three-dimensional approach: breadth (enrichment), rate (acceleration), and depth or complexity. That is, the benefits of both acceleration and enrichment should be coupled with the opportunity for studying the complexities of new mathematical ideas—those in the regular curriculum and those that go beyond it. Sheffield writes that promising students should be introduced to the "joys and frustrations of thinking deeply about a wide range of original, open-ended, or complex problems that encourage them to respond creatively in ways that are original, fluent, flexible, and elegant" (p. 46).

In the regular classroom, teachers often "reward" highly capable students for finishing routine tasks quickly by having them do more exercises or more tedious exercises than those required of the rest of the class. For example, if the full class is working on the multiplication algorithm for multi-digit numbers, there is no redeeming value in having promising students who complete their work quickly do more exercises or exercises with more digits. However, they may be asked what would produce the largest or smallest products given four distinct digits to make two factors. Is there a general rule? Why does the rule work? Would the rule work if there were five digits?

Even more interesting than the max/min task is that for some products, interchanging the digits in each two-digit factor produces the same result:

$$\begin{array}{cc} 24 & 42 \\ \times\,63 & \times\,36 \\ \hline 1512 & 1512 \end{array}$$

However, this is obviously not always the case, as a little experimentation will quickly show. When will this interchanging of the digits produce equal products and why? Students working on tasks such as these are engaged in a deeper exploration of the multiplication algorithm than simply understanding how it works and being able to use it.

There is no simple formula for adding depth to mathematical explorations, but some valuable insights may be learned from the Japanese. According to Hashimoto and Becker (1999), the Japanese approach to mathematical problem solving involves making the problem open in one of three ways: the process is open (multiple paths to a solution are explored), the end product is open (there are multiple correct answers to be discovered), or the formulation of new problems is open (students explore new problems related to the one solved).

These three approaches to open-ended problem solving are explored in depth in *The Open-Ended Approach: A New Proposal for Teaching Mathematics* (Becker & Shimada, 1997). Application of the open-ended methods is an excellent way to add depth to both acceleration and enrichment for special students.

Reflections on Chapter 6

Writing to Learn

1. How is equity in the classroom different from teaching all students equally?

2. Distinguish between *accommodation* and *modification*. How can a modification be used as a means of scaffolding for the same high expectations held for the whole class?

3. Briefly describe each of the following specific learning disabilities, and give some indication of how the disability may affect mathematics learning or ability. For each disability, also list at least two accommodations that can be used by the classroom teacher to help the child.

   a. Perceptual deficits
   b. Memory deficits (short-term and long-term)
   c. Integrative deficits
   d. Attention deficits

4. For children with intellectual disabilities and special learning needs, how should content and instruction each be modified?

5. Three options were discussed for culturally and linguistically diverse classrooms. The second was to use a standards-based approach—like the one described in this book. The third was to use a dual-language approach. Discuss the benefits and possible shortcomings of these approaches.

6. Describe ethnomathematics in your own words. Why is it important to consider culture in mathematics instruction?

7. What are some of the specific difficulties English language learners may encounter in the mathematics class?

8. TESOL advocates that English language learners use English in their academic classes. How can students who do not know English do this?

9. Six specific strategies were described for teaching mathematics to English language learners. Select three that you think are most important and describe these in your own words.

10. What are some factors that contribute to gender inequity, and what are the long-term effects of that inequity?

11. How can teachers in the elementary or middle school work to erase gender inequity?

12. Describe what is meant by *enrichment* and by *acceleration*. What are the dangers of each for mathematically promising students?

13. In the context of providing for the mathematically promising, what is meant by *depth*? How can the Japanese open-ended approaches help provide depth?

For Discussion and Exploration

1. Two common threads in this chapter are the beliefs that all children will benefit from a developmental or constructivist approach to teaching, and that there is real value in teaching children in diverse, heterogeneous classrooms. Some teachers may argue with this position, contending that it is best for the majority of children if "special needs" students are educated outside the regular classroom environment. Their particular needs would be best met by special teachers in classes with fewer students. Pick a position in this argument, and articulate it in writing or in a classroom discussion.

2. Develop your own philosophical statement for "all students" or "every child." Design a visual representation for your statement. Read the Equity Principle in *Principles and Standards* and see if your position is in accord with that principle.

3. Find and observe a mathematics class in a room that could be described as culturally and linguistically diverse. Identify as many specific adaptations as you can that are made by the teacher in the course of the lesson. Compare these adaptations to those you have found in this chapter. If modifications were made, did these modifications maintain high expectations equal to those for all students?

4. Develop a mathematics lesson plan that reflects a cultural approach to mathematics. What mathematical concepts does your lesson address?

5. What would you do if you found yourself teaching a class with one exceptionally talented child who had no equal in the room? Assume that acceleration to the next grade has been ruled out due to social adjustment factors.

Resources for Chapter 6

Recommendations for Further Reading

Articles

Lee, H., & Jung, W. S. (2004). Limited English-proficient (LEP) students and mathematical understanding. *Mathematics Teaching in the Middle School, 9,* 269–272.

The article is intended to help teachers design instruction to assist students who know little or no English. The article is reflective of the ideas discussed in this chapter. Specific examples will help the reader go beyond guiding principles.

National Council of Teachers of Mathematics. (2004). Teaching mathematics to special needs students [Focus Issue]. *Teaching Children Mathematics, 11.*

The first article in this focus issue by Karp and Howell is worth the rest of the journal by itself. They tackle the reality that children with special needs truly are different and need special help to meet high standards. The suggestions are specific and excellent. Other articles address assessment issues for special students, strategies for differentiation, and more.

Robert, M. (2002). Problem solving and the at-risk students: Making "mathematics for all" a classroom reality. *Teaching Children Mathematics, 8,* 290–295.

This tale of a year in a grade 5 classroom of seriously disadvantaged children, by a teacher who had previously spent two years in an affluent suburban school, will support and sustain teachers who think this class is simply too difficult. Robert tells about how she initially struggled and yet worked throughout the year to use a problem-based approach. Children began to catch on. This is an important story from a teacher for teachers.

Books

Hutchinson, N. L. (2002). *Inclusion of exceptional learners in Canadian schools: A practical handbook for teachers.* Toronto: Prentice Hall.

This book really lives up to the word "practical" in its title. It is an extremely teacher-friendly resource that will assist you in your classroom work. It is up to date and easy to read, with excellent references. Hutchinson provides information regarding useful Web sites, identifies and describes key terms, and includes strategies for working with the varied exceptionalities.

Jordan, A. (2007). *Introduction to inclusive education.* Mississauga, ON: John Wiley & Sons Canada Ltd.

This book offers a series of unique and flexible learning modules designed to introduce special education and to help develop effective teaching methods within an inclusive classroom. This truly modular system offers an interactive model. Each module of text comprises interactive case studies, video clips of real classroom settings, and skill testing questions and evaluative tasks. The modules are available online.

Journal of the Gifted and Talented Education Council of the Alberta Teachers' Association (AGATE)

This journal, which is currently available, is published twice yearly for the Gifted and Talented Education Council (GTEC) of the Alberta Teachers' Association. The journal is devoted exclusively to giftedness. The Special Millennium Issue (volume 14, number 2) focused on gifted education across Canada. Each article in the issue discussed aspects of gifted education in a different province or territory, thus providing a valuable overview.

Secada, W. G. (Series Ed.). (1999–2002). *Changing the faces of mathematics* (6 volumes). Reston, VA: National Council of Teachers of Mathematics.

These six books present perspectives on four categories of cultures: Asian Americans and Pacific Islanders, Native Americans, Latinos, and African Americans. Two volumes address multiculturalism and gender equity. Each culture-specific volume explores curriculum, instruction, and assessment issues relevant to the culture for all grade levels. The authors stress pedagogical strategies, classroom environment, and positive practices that support the learning of students. These are unique, excellent resources.

Sheffield, L.J. (Ed.). (1999). *Developing mathematically promising students.* Reston, VA: National Council of Teachers of Mathematics.

This book is the result of the work of an NCTM Task Force on Mathematically Promising Students. The book has a wealth of ideas and perspectives for working with our most talented students and adds depth to any discussion of mathematics for the talented.

Online Resources

Suggested Applets and Web Links

LD Online
www.ldonline.org

This site offers a vast array of information on a variety of topics related to special students. Click on *LD-InDepth* for articles, research findings, and useful forums, including an area specifically devoted to dyscalculia. Also see *Learning Disorders in Math.*

Special Education Resources on the Internet
http://seriweb.com

SERI is a collection of Internet-accessible information and resources of interest to those involved in fields related to special education.

The International Study Group on Ethnomathematics
www.rpi.edu/~eglash/isgem.htm

The ISGEm is dedicated to the understanding of the cultural diversity of mathematical practices and to applying this knowledge to education and development. Its Web page provides links to other useful sites.

myeducationlab *will help you improve your understanding of the concepts taught in this textbook and in your course. This online tool includes videos of real classroom experiences, sample lesson plans, simulations, case studies, and links to important educational and teaching Web sites that will help you make the transition from student to teacher. As you study in your course and with this textbook, please follow along in **MyEducationLab**. Use it! Explore it! And improve your knowledge and your grade!*

Chapter 7
Technology and School Mathematics

Technology is an essential tool for learning mathematics in the 21st century and all schools must ensure that all their students have access to technology. Effective teachers maximize the potential of technology to develop students' understanding, stimulate their interest, and increase their proficiency in mathematics. When technology is used strategically, it can provide access to mathematics for all students.

NCTM Position Statement on the Role of Technology in the Teaching and Learning of Mathematics (March, 2008)

The term technology in the context of school mathematics refers to digital tools, desktop and laptop computers, calculators and other hand-held devices, collaborative authoring tools, dynamic geometry software, online digital games, podcasts, interactive presentation devices, spreadsheets, as well as the Internet-based resources often available for use with these devices and tools. Technology contributes to the learning of a wide range of mathematical outcomes, and enables students to explore and create patterns, examine relationships, test conjectures, and solve problems (WNCP, 2006, p. 9). The use of technology is an important theme that is integrated throughout the learning outcomes/expectations in this curriculum document.

> Technology contributes to a learning environment in which the curiosity of students can lead to rich mathematical discoveries at all grade levels. While technology can be used in K–3 to enrich learning, it is expected that students will meet all outcomes without the use of technology. (p. 9)

Technology is one of the six principles in the *Principles and Standards* document. The emphasis NCTM places on technology, as an *essential tool* for both learning and teaching mathematics, is further reinforced in the afore-mentioned position statement. Its importance in students' learning of mathematics is also well documented in provincial and territorial curricula. As noted in the Ontario government's elementary mathematics curriculum document, "The computer and the calculator should be seen as important problem-solving tools to be used for many purposes" (Ministry of Education, 2005, p. 15). Thinking of technology as an "extra" added on the list of things you are trying to accomplish in your classroom is not an effective approach. Instead, technology should be seen as an integral part of your instructional arsenal of tools for learning. It can enlarge the scope of the content students can learn and it can broaden the range of problems that students are able to tackle (Ball & Stacey, 2005; NCTM Position Statement, 2008). However, it cannot be a replacement for the full conceptual understanding of mathematics content.

Pedagogical Content Knowledge (PCK) is the intersection of (mathematics) content knowledge with the pedagogical knowledge of teaching and learning (Shulman, 1986). It includes the specific strategies and approaches that teachers use to deliver mathematical content to students. Not all teachers, not even those who are well versed in mathematics, possess this type of knowledge. Technological, pedagogical, and content knowledge (TPACK), as shown in Figure 7.1 describes the infusion of technology to this mix (Mishra & Koehler, 2006; Niess, 2008). We suggest that teachers consider technology as a conscious component of each lesson and each strategy for enhancing student learning. This chapter's emphasis on the importance of technology in instruction is referenced throughout the content chapters, especially in sections highlighted with the technology icon. Its value is obvious when technological features, embedded in a lesson, enhance students' opportunities to learn mathematics. In so doing, it serves as a basic learning tool, rather than an add-on or a once-a-week opportunity in the computer lab.

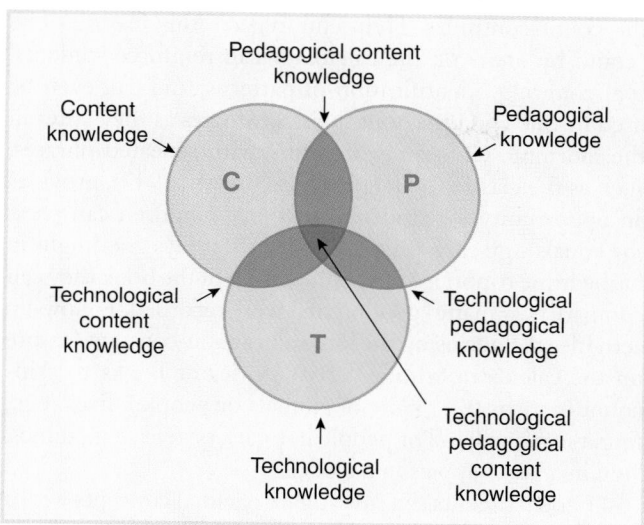

Figure 7.1 TPACK framework.

Calculators are used by almost everyone in every facet of life that involves any sort of exact computation. Students should be taught how to use this commonplace tool effectively. They should also learn to judge when its use is appropriate.

Calculators in Mathematics Instruction

Mathematics educators have long understood the value of calculators in the study of mathematics. Their regular use in the teaching of mathematics at all grade levels is well understood and advocated in Canadian regional curricular documents. Moreover, the importance of calculator use in the curriculum and the development of a variety of computational skills has been a long-standing view of the NCTM (www.nctm.org).

Even with everyday use of calculators in society, and the professional support of calculators in schools, calculator use is not always central to instruction, especially at the elementary level. Resistance to the use of calculators has diminished but not disappeared. Sometimes educators and students' families are concerned that allowing students to just use calculators when solving problems will interfere with them developing computational proficiency. Rather than an either-or choice, just as with the use of the Internet, there are conditions when students should use the technology and times when they must call on their own resources.

Based on efficiency and effectiveness, the student should learn when to use mental mathematics, when to use estimation, when to tackle a problem with paper and pencil, and when to use a calculator. Ignoring the potential benefits of calculators by prohibiting their use entirely can inhibit students' learning. Helping students know when to grab a calculator and when not to use one is precisely the work of the teacher. Sometimes using a calculator during instruction allows students to explore a higher-level topic or identify a complex pattern. Expanding students' abilities to think about challenging mathematics must be balanced with the development of their computational skills.

Help families understand that calculator use will in no way prevent children from learning rigorous mathematics: in fact, calculators used thoughtfully and meaningfully can enhance the learning of mathematics. Furthermore, families should be made aware that calculators and other technologies require students to be problem solvers. Calculators can only calculate according to input entered by humans. In isolation, calculators cannot solve the most meaningful mathematics tasks and they cannot substitute for thinking or understanding. Sending home calculator activities that reinforce important mathematical concepts and including calculator activities on a Family Math Night are ways to educate families about appropriate calculator use.

When to Use a Calculator

If the primary purpose of the instructional activity is to practise computational skills, students should not be using a calculator. On the other hand, students should have full access to calculators when they are exploring patterns, conducting investigations, testing conjectures, and solving problems. Situations involving computation that is beyond students' ability without the aid of a calculator are not necessarily beyond their ability to think about meaningfully.

As students come to fully understand the meanings of the operations, they should be exposed to realistic problems with realistic numbers. For example, young children may want to calculate how many seconds they have been alive. They can think conceptually about how many seconds in a minute, hour, day, and so on. But the actual calculations and those that continue to weeks and years can be done more efficiently on a calculator.

Also include calculators when the goal of the instructional activity is not to compute, but computation is involved in the problem solving. For example, students in the middle grades may be asked to identify the "best buy" when there are different percentages off different merchandise. Whether purchasing a bicycle or getting a deal on ride tickets at the fair, the goal is to figure out the most economical choices, calculating the various percentage discounts with a calculator. Calculators are also valuable for generating and analyzing patterns. For example, when finding the decimal equivalent of $\frac{8}{9}$, $\frac{7}{9}$, $\frac{5}{9}$, and so on, a neat pattern emerges. Let students explore other "ninths" and make conjectures as to why the pattern occurs. Again, the emphasis is not to determine a computational solution but instead to use the calculator to help find a pattern.

Finally, calculators can be used as accommodations for students with special needs. When used for instruction that is not centred on developing computation skills, calculators can help ensure that all students have appropriate access to the curriculum at the maximum extent possible.

Benefits of Calculator Use

Understanding how calculators contribute to the learning of mathematics includes recognizing that the use of "calculators does not threaten the development of basic skills and that it can enhance conceptual understanding, strategic competence, and disposition toward mathematics" (NRC, 2001, p. 354). This includes four-function, scientific, and graphing calculators. A specific discussion of graphing calculators is found later in this chapter.

Calculators Can Be Used to Develop Concepts   The calculator can be much more than a device for calculation. As shown in an analysis of more than 79 research studies, K–12 students (with the exception of grade 4) who used calculators improved their "basic skills with paper-and-pencil tasks both in computational operations and in problem solving" (Hembree & Dessert, 1986; 1992, p. 96). Other researchers confirm that students with long-term experience using calculators performed better overall than children without such experience on both mental computation and paper-and-pencil problems (Ellington, 2003; Smith, 1997b; Wareham, 2005). There has been a call for more studies on the long-term use of calculators (National Mathematics Advisory Panel, 2008), and additional research is likely to result.

Although some worry that calculator use can impede instruction in number and operations, the reverse is actually the case, as shown in the following examples. (Also see the calculator activities in the following chapters, on number and operations. In K–1, children who are exploring concepts of quantity can use the calculator as a counting machine. Using the automatic-constant feature (not all calculators perform this in the same way—so check how it works on your calculator) children can count. For example, press the following keys—⓪ ⊞ ① ⩵ ⩵ ⩵—to count by ones, pressing the equals key for as long as

the count continues. Help children try this feature. The "count by ones" on the calculator can reinforce students' oral counting, identification of patterns, and can even be used by one child to count their classmates as they enter in the morning. Children's literature with repeated phrases, such as the classic *Goodnight Moon* (Brown, 1947), provides an opportunity for students to count. Children can press the equals sign each time the little rabbit says goodnight in his bedtime routine. At the completion of the book they can compare how many "goodnights" were recorded. Follow-up activities include using the same automatic-constant feature on the calculator with different stories or books to skip-count by twos (e.g., pairs of animals or people), fives (e.g., fingers on one hand or people in a car), or tens (e.g., dimes, "ten in a bed," apples in a tree).

Older students can investigate decimal concepts with a calculator, as in the following examples. On the calculator, $796 \div 42 = 18.95348$. Consider the task of using the calculator to determine the whole-number remainder. Another example is to use the calculator to find a number that when multiplied by itself will produce 43. In this situation, a student can press 6.1 ⊠ ⩵ to get the square of 6.1. For students who are just beginning to understand decimals, the activity will demonstrate that numbers such as 6.3 and 6.4 are between 6 and 7. Furthermore, 6.55 is between 6.5 and 6.6. For students who already understand decimals, the same activity serves as a meaningful and conceptual introduction to square roots.

Calculators Can Be Used for Drill   Students who want to practise the multiples of 7 can press 7 ⊠ 3 and delay pressing the ⩵. The challenge is to answer the fact by themselves before pressing the ⩵ key. Subsequent multiples of 7 can be checked by simply pressing the second factor and the ⩵. The TI-10 and TI-15 calculators now have built-in problem-solving modes in which students can practise facts, develop lists of related facts, and test equations or inequalities with arithmetic expressions on both sides of the relationship symbol (http://education. ti.com/educationalportal/sites/US/productCategory/us_ elementary.html).

A class can be split in half, with one half required to use a calculator and the other required to do the computations mentally. For $3000 + 1765$, the group doing it mentally wins every time. They will also win for simple facts and numerous problems that lend themselves to mental computation. Of course, there are many computations, such as 537×32, for which the calculator team will be faster. Not only does this simple exercise provide practice with mental math, it also demonstrates to students that it is not always effective to reach for the calculator.

Calculators Can Improve Attitudes and Motivation   Research results reveal that students who frequently use calculators have better attitudes toward the subject of mathematics (Ellington, 2003). There is also evidence that students are more motivated when their anxiety is reduced; therefore, supporting students during problem-solving activities with calculators is important. A student with special needs who is left out of the problem-solving lesson due to weak knowledge of basic facts will not pursue the worthwhile explorations the teacher plans. That does not excuse them from learning their facts. As we try to increase students' confidence that they can solve challenging mathematics problems we can expand their motivation to be persistent and stay engaged in the process of thinking about numbers. Again, the strategic use of the calculator is guided by the plans of the teacher and the eventual decision making of the students.

Calculators Are Commonly Used in Society Calculators are used in every facet of life that involves any sort of exact computation by almost everyone. Students should be taught how to use this commonplace tool effectively and also learn to judge when its use is appropriate. Many adults have not learned how to use the automatic constant feature of a calculator and are not sufficiently skilled in recognizing common errors that are often made on calculators. Effective use of calculators is an important skill that is best learned by using them regularly in meaningfully problem-solving activities.

Graphing Calculators

Graphing calculators help students visualize concepts as they make real-world connections with data. When students can actually see expressions, formulas, graphs, and the results of changing a variable on those visual representations, a deeper understanding of concepts can result. Graphing calculators are used with upper-elementary-age students to high school students and beyond, but the most common use is at the secondary level.

It is a mistake to think that graphing calculators are only for doing "high-powered" mathematics. The following list demonstrates some features the graphing calculator offers, every one of which is useful within the standard middle school curriculum.

- The display window permits compound expressions such as $3 + 4(5 - 6/7)$ to be shown completely before being evaluated. Furthermore, once evaluated, previous expressions can be recalled and modified. This promotes an understanding of notation and order of operations. The graphing calculator is also a significant tool for exploring patterns and solving problems. Expressions can include exponents, absolute values, and negation signs, with no restrictions on the values used.
- Even without using function definition capability, students can insert values into expressions or formulas without having to enter the entire formula for each new value. The results can be entered into a list or table of values and stored directly on the calculator for further analysis.
- Variables can be used in expressions, then assigned different values to see the effect on expressions. This simple method helps with the idea of a variable as something that varies.
- The distinction between "negative" and "subtract" is clear and very useful. A separate key is used to enter the negative of a quantity. The display shows the negative sign as a superscript. If $^-5$ is stored in the variable (b), then the expression $^-2 - (^- b)$ will be evaluated correctly as $^-7$. This feature is a significant aid in the study of integers and variables.
- Points can be plotted on a coordinate screen either by entering coordinates and seeing the result or by moving the cursor to a particular coordinate on the screen.
- Very large and very small numbers are managed without error. The calculator will quickly compute factorials, even for permutations and combinations. For example, $23! = 1.033314797 \times 10^{40}$.
- Built-in statistical functions allow students to examine the means and medians and standard deviations of large sets of realistic data without a computer. Data are entered, ordered, added to, or changed almost as easily as on a spreadsheet.
- Graphs for data analysis are available, including box-and-whisker plots, histograms, and, on some calculators, pie charts, bar graphs, and pictographs.
- Random number generators allow for the simulation of a variety of probability experiments that would be difficult without such a device.
- Functions can be explored in three modes: equation, table, and graph. Because the calculator easily switches from one to the other and because of the trace feature, the connections between these modes become quite clear.
- The graphing calculator is programmable. Programs are very easily written and understood. For example, a program involving the Pythagorean theorem can be used to find the lengths of sides of right triangles.
- Students can share data programs from one calculator to another, connect their calculators to a classroom display screen, save information on a computer, and download software applications that give additional functionality for special uses.

Most of the ideas on this list are explored briefly in appropriate chapters in this book.

Arguments against graphing calculators are similar to those for other calculators—and are equally unsubstantiated. These amazing tools have the potential of significantly opening up real mathematics for students.

Computers in Mathematics Instruction

A number of powerful tools have been created for use in the mathematics classroom. These exist in two formats: as stand-alone programs that can be purchased from software publishers and as Internet-based applications accessible through Web browsers such as Microsoft Internet Explorer, Apple's Safari, Mozilla's Firefox, and others.

Java applets are much smaller, more targeted programs than commercial software. A significant advantage is that they are freely accessed on the Internet. Many can also be downloaded so that an Internet connection is not required for student use. Some of these applets are described briefly throughout this book and at the end of each chapter. The sites listed at the end of this chapter collectively offer well over 100 applets. You are strongly urged to browse and play. Many of these are a lot of fun!

A mathematical software tool is somewhat like a physical manipulative; by itself, it does not teach. However, the user of a well-designed tool software package has an electronic "thinker toy" with which to explore mathematical ideas.

Tools for Developing Numeration

Programs providing screen versions of popular manipulative models for counting, place value, and fractions are available for students to work with freely without the computer posing problems, evaluating results, or telling the students what to do.

At the earliest level, there are programs that provide "counters" such as coloured tiles, pictures of assorted objects, five/ten frames, and more Typically, students can drag counters to any place on the screen, change the colours, and put them in groupings. Some programs have options that turn on counters for the screen or subsets of the screen. Non-mathematical programs such as *Kidspiration* (Inspiration Software, 2008) can also be used to "stamp" discrete objects on the screen, explore shapes, word process, and more.

Base-ten blocks (ones, tens, and hundreds models) and assorted fraction pieces are available in some software packages as well as in Web-based applets. These include both pure tool programs and instructional software programs that attempt to teach or tutor. Some fraction models are more flexible than physical models. For example, a circular region might be subdivided into many more fractional parts than is reasonable with physical models. When the models are connected with on-screen counters, it is possible with some programs to have fraction or decimal representations shown so that connections between fractions and decimals can be illustrated. *Odyssey Math* (CompassLearning, 2008) or *Destination Math* (Riverdeep Interactive Learning

Limited, 2008) do a nice job of connecting these types of representations for fractions.

Web-based tools or applets exist that are designed so that students may manipulate them without constraint. For example, the Base Ten Block Applet (www.arcytech.org/java/b10blocks/ b10blocks.html) allows children to collect as many flats (hundreds), rods (tens), and units (ones) as they wish, gluing together groups of ten (rods), or breaking a flat (hundreds) into ten rods or a rod into ten units.

The obvious question is, why not simply use the actual physical models? Electronic or virtual manipulatives have some advantages that merit integrating them into your instruction—not just adding them on as extras. Features/characteristics that make their use a worthwhile addition to your mathematics program are:

- *Qualitative Differences in Use.* Usually it is at least as easy to manipulate virtual manipulatives as it is to use their physical counterparts. However, control of materials on the screen requires a different, perhaps more deliberative, mental action that is "more in line with the *mental actions* that we want children to carry out" (Clements & Sarama, 2005, p. 53). For example, the base-ten rod representing a ten can be broken into 10 single blocks by clicking on it with a hammer icon. With physical blocks, the ten must be traded for the equivalent blocks counted out by the student.

- *Connection to Symbolism.* Most virtual manipulatives for number include dynamic numerals or odometers that change as the representation on the screen changes. This direct and immediate connection to numeral representation is impossible with physical models.

- *Unlimited Materials with Easy Cleanup.* With virtual manipulatives, students can easily erase the screen and begin a new problem with the click of a mouse. They will never run out of materials. For place value, even the large 1000 cubes are readily available in quantity. And there is no storage or cleanup to worry about.

- *Accommodations for Special Purposes.* For English language learners or visually impaired students, some programs come with speech enhancements so that the students hear the names of the materials or the numbers. For students with physical disabilities, the computer models are often easier to access and use than physical models.

Many software-based programs also offer a word-processing capability connected to the workspace. This allows students to write a sentence or two to explain what they have done or perhaps to create a story problem to go with their work. Printing a picture of the workspace, with or without a written attachment, creates a record of the work for the teacher or parent that is more challenging with physical models. Note however that Web-based applets typically do not have print capabilities.

Tools for Developing Geometry

Computer tools for geometric exploration are much closer to pure tools than those just described for numeration. That is, students can use most of these tools without any constraints. They typically offer some significant advantages over physical models, although the computerized tools should never replace physical models in the classroom.

Blocks and Tiles Programs that allow students to "stamp" geometric tiles or blocks on the screen are quite common. Typically, there is a palette of blocks, often the same as pattern blocks or tangrams, from which students can choose by clicking the mouse. Often the blocks can be made "magnetic" so that when a block is released close to another, the two will snap together, matching like sides. Blocks can usually be rotated, either freely or in set increments. Figure 7.2 shows a simple yet powerful applet that permits a student to slice any of the three shapes in any place; then manipulate any of the pieces. This is a good example of something a student can do with a computer that would be difficult or impossible with physical models. You may find the following:

- The ability to enlarge or reduce the size of blocks, usually by set increments
- The ability to "glue" blocks together to make new blocks
- The ability to reflect one or more blocks across a line of symmetry or to rotate them about a point

- The ability to measure area or perimeter
- The ability to select polygons with a variable number of sides
- The possibility of creating three-dimensional shapes and rotating them in space

For students who have poor motor coordination or a physical disability that makes block manipulation difficult, the computer versions of blocks are a real plus. Colourful printouts can be displayed, discussed, and taken home if that option is available.

Drawing Programs For younger students, drawing shapes on a grid is much easier and more useful for geometric exploration than free-form drawing. Several programs offer electronic geoboards on which lines can be drawn between points on a grid. When a shape such as a triangle is formed, it can typically be altered just as you would a rubber band on a geoboard. For examples, check the NCTM's *Illuminations* Web site. The electronic geoboard programs offer a larger grid on which to draw, ease of use, and the ability to save and print. Some include measuring capabilities as well as reflection and rotation of shapes, things that are difficult or impossible to do on a physical geoboard. An example of a good Internet applet for drawing is the Isometric Drawing Tool found at NCTM's Web site (see Figure 7.3).

Dynamic Geometry Software Dynamic geometry programs allow students to create shapes on the computer screen and then manipulate and measure them by dragging vertices. The most well-known programs of this type are

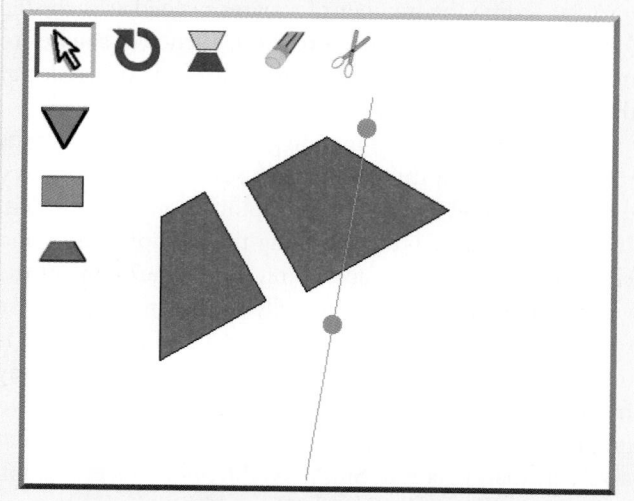

Figure 7.2 The "Cutting Shapes Tool Applet."

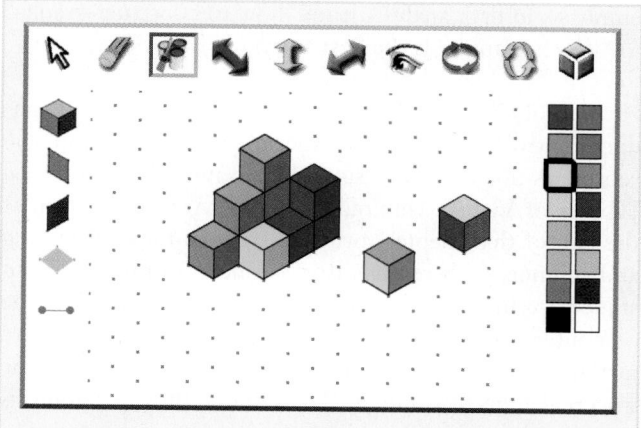

Figure 7.3 The "Isometric Drawing Tool" applet from NCTM's *Illuminations* Web site.

The Geometer's Sketchpad (Key Curriculum Press) and *Cabri Geometry II* (Texas Instruments), and the public domain *Wingeom* (http://math.exeter.edu/rparris/wingeom.html). Dynamic geometry programs allow the creation of geometric objects (lines, circles) so that their relationship to another object is established. For example, a new line can be drawn through a point perpendicular to another line. A midpoint can be established on any line segment. Once created, these relationships are preserved no matter how the objects are moved or altered. Dynamic geometry software can dramatically change and improve the teaching of geometry in grade 3 and beyond. The ability of students to explore geometric relationships with this software is unmatched by any non-computer mode. More detailed discussion of these programs can be found in Chapter 20.

Tools for Developing Probability and Data Analysis

These computer tools allow for the entry of data and a wide choice of graphs for applying this data. In addition, most will produce typical statistics such as mean, median, and range. Some programs are designed for students in the primary grades. Others are more sophisticated and can be used through the middle grades. For example, *Tinkerplots* (Key Curriculum Press, 2005), for students in grades 4–8, can generate graphs in a variety of forms for analyzing data and producing statistics. The dynamic nature of the program allows students to drag an outlier to see how the mean, the median, and the mode change. Using a "stack, order, and separate" framework, the software not only provides a sound approach to thinking about graphs, it gives more than 40 data sets to use for investigating real-world information. These programs make it possible to change the emphasis in data analysis from "how to construct graphs" to "which graph tells the best story."

Probability Tools These programs make it easy to conduct controlled probability experiments and see graphical representations of the results. For example, the National Library of Virtual Manipulatives (see Web site section at the end of this chapter) provides options for coin tossing and spinners with regions that can be customized. Young students using these programs must accept that when the computer "flips a coin" or "spins a spinner," the results are just as random and have the same probabilities as if done with real coins or spinners. The value of these programs is found in the ease with which experiments can be designed and large numbers of trials conducted, allowing more time for analyzing results.

Spreadsheets and Data Graphers *Spreadsheets* are programs that can manipulate rows and columns of numerical data. Values taken from one position in the spreadsheet can be used in formulas to determine entries elsewhere in the spreadsheet. When an entry is changed, the spreadsheet updates all values immediately.

Because the spreadsheet is among the most popular pieces of standard tool software outside of schools, it is often available in integrated packages you may already have on your computer. Students as early as grade 3 can use these programs to organize data, display data graphically in various ways, and do numerical calculations such as finding how changing gas prices can have an impact on the family budget. Students only need to know how to use the capabilities of the spreadsheet they will be using.

The *Illuminations* Web site from NCTM offers a couple of very nice spreadsheet Internet applets, *Spreadsheet* and *Spreadsheet and Graphing Tool*. They can be used while connected to the Internet, or they can be downloaded to your computer.

Tools for Developing Algebra Thinking Very young children can use virtual pattern blocks to create patterns for copying, continuing, transforming, and for analysis (see www.arcytech.org/java/patterns). The unending supply of any pattern block does not restrict children by the number of available materials. Copies of their designs can be printed through a screen capture so that other students can be challenged to identify the pattern. Teachers of older students can use virtual pattern blocks either on their interactive whiteboard or accessed from the National Library of Virtual Manipulatives Web site to create a growing pattern, recording the number of squares needed at each step (or term). Students can explore the sequence of squares to make a conjecture as to how many squares will be needed at the tenth term or the ninth term of the pattern.

For older students, function graphing software permits the user to create the graph of almost any function very quickly. Multiple functions can be plotted on the same axis. It is usually possible to trace along the path of a curve and view the coordinates at any point. The dimensions of the viewing area can be changed easily so that it is just as easy to look at a graph for x and y between -10 and $+10$ as it is to look at a portion of the graph thousands of units away from the origin. By "zooming in" on the intersection of two graphs, it is possible to find points of intersection without algebraic manipulation. Similarly, the point where a graph crosses the axis can be found to as many decimal places as is desired.

The function graphing features just described are available on all graphing calculators. Computer programs can add speed, colour, visual clarity, and a variety of other interesting features to help students analyze functions.

Instructional Software

Instructional software is designed for student interaction in a manner similar to that with a textbook or a tutor. It is designed to teach. The distinction between tool and instructional software is not always clear since some packages include a tool-only component. In the following discussion, the intent is to provide some perspective on the different kinds of input to your mathematics program that instructional software might offer.

Concept Instruction

A growing number of programs make an effort to offer conceptual instruction. Some, like *Mathville* (Courseware Solutions), *Math Trek*, and *Math Strategies* (Nectar Foundation), the *Math Adventures* series of programs (Tom Snyder Productions), and the *Prime Time Math* series (Tom Snyder Productions), rely on real-world contexts to illustrate mathematical ideas. Using problem-solving situations, specific concepts are developed in a guided manner to solve the problem.

What is most often missing is a way to make the mathematics problem-based or to connect the conceptual activity with the symbolic techniques. Furthermore, when students work on a computer, there is little opportunity for discourse, conjecture, or original ideas. Some software even presents concepts in such a fashion as to remove learners from thinking and constructing their own understanding. In some instances, the programs might be best used with the teacher controlling the program on a large display screen with the class. In this way, the teacher can pose questions and entertain discussion that is simply not possible with one student on a computer.

Problem Solving

With the current focus on problem solving, more software publishers purport to teach students to solve problems. The *Mathville* and *Thinkerport* series demonstrate good examples of problem solving. Here the problems are not typical story problems awaiting a computation but more thoughtful stories set in real contexts.

At the other end of the spectrum are programs that offer little more than a large library of typical story problems. Usually, the teacher can control problem difficulty and the operations to be used. These programs would be more valuable if they offered some conceptual assistance if the student gets the problems incorrect, but that is rarely the case.

Logic problem solving is another variant of problem-solving software. This category includes spatial reasoning, as in *Factory Deluxe* (Sunburst) and number patterns and operation sense, as in *Odyssey Math* (CompassLerning), *Destination Math* (Riverdeep), and *Academy of Math* (AutoSkill).

Drill and Reinforcement

Drill programs give students practice with skills assumed to have been taught. In general, a drill program poses questions that are answered by a mechanical response or by selecting from a multiple-choice list. Many of these programs are set in arcade formats that make them exciting for students who like video games; however, the format has nothing to do with the practice involved.

Drill programs evaluate responses immediately. The way in which they respond to a student's first or second incorrect answer is one important distinguishing feature. At one extreme, the answer is simply recorded as wrong. There may be a second or third chance to correct it. At the other extreme, the program may branch to an explanation of the correct response. Others may provide a useful hint or supply a visual model to help with the task. Some programs offer record-keeping features for the teacher to keep track of individual students' progress.

One software feature worth mentioning is differentiated drill as found in *FASTT Math* (Tom Snyder Productions, www.tomsnyder.com/fasttmath/overview.html). The *FASTT Math* (Fluency and Automaticity through Systematic Teaching with Technology) program works to help all students develop fluency with math facts. In short sessions that are customized for individual learners, the software automatically differentiates instruction based on each student's previous performance.

Guidelines for Selecting and Using Software

There is so much software for mathematics today. Commercially published software is becoming increasingly expensive. For this reason, we suggest open-source software where possible. Even though most Internet-based applets are free, schools must still provide for Internet access and the appropriate hardware. In either case, it is important to make informed decisions when investing limited resources.

Guidelines for Using Software

How software is used in mathematics instruction will vary considerably with the topic, the grade level, and the software itself. The following considerations should be kept in mind.

- Software should contribute to the objectives of the lesson or unit. It should not be used as an add-on or substitute for more accessible approaches. Its use should take advantage of what technology can do efficiently and well.
- For individualized or small group use, plan to provide specific instructions for using the software. Also, plan

to provide time for students to freely explore or practise using the software.

- Combine software activities on the computer with activities off the computer (e.g., collect measurement data in the classroom to enter into a spreadsheet).
- Create a management plan for using the software. This could include a schedule for when the software is used (e.g., during centres, during small group work) and ways to assess the effectiveness of software use. Although some software programs include a way to keep track of student performance, you may need to rely on other assessment strategies to determine whether the software is effectively meeting the objectives of the lesson or unit.

How to Select Software

The most important requirement for purchasing effective software is to be well informed about the product and to evaluate its merits in an objective manner.

Gathering Information Some of the best sources of information concerning new software are ministry documents, educational software services sponsored by provincial and territorial ministries of education (e.g., Ontario Educational Software Services), the review section of the NCTM journals, or other journals that you respect. Many Web sites offer reviews on both commercially available software and Internet-based applets. The Math Forum at Drexel University (http://mathforum.org) is one such site.

One important consideration is whether the software is accessible to all students, including individuals with disabilities. Can the text be enlarged or highlighted as it is read aloud? Are the graphics easily recognizable, containing mouse-overs (where the action is written or spoken as the mouse is moved over the image) and not dependent on colour for meaning? Can the software be used with a keyboard instead of a mouse?

TechMatrix at www.techmatrix.org "is a powerful tool for finding educational and assistive technology products for students with special needs" (National Center for Technology Innovation, 2008). Select "mathematics" under the heading "subjects" and take a look at how the learning support "matrix" list indicates the presence of a variety of elements in software programs. The matrix you generate will compare whether different software products for mathematics learning contain such elements as differentiation features, text to speech capability, word prediction, eye-tracking cursors, output options in Braille, voice recognition, and other useful information. Clicking on "Research" and then "Math" at the top of the home page displays a list of research-based reports related to the use of technology in the mathematics classroom for students with and without disabilities.

When selecting any computer-based tool or instructional software, it is important to evaluate it appropriately. Try first to get a preview copy or at least a demonstration version. Take advantage of any option that allows users to download software for 30-day approval.

Before purchasing, try the software with children in the grade that will be using it. Remember, it is the content in which you are interested, not the game the student will be playing.

Criteria The following points are some things to think about as you review software before purchasing it or using it in your classroom:

- What does this software do better than can be done without the computer? Don't select or use software just so your students will have an opportunity to use the computer. Be sure to get past the clever graphics and the games and focus on what students will be learning.
- How are students likely to be engaged with the *content* (not the bells and whistles)? Remember that student reflective thought is the most significant factor in effective instruction. Is the mathematics presented so that it is problematic for the student?
- How easy is the program to use? There should not be so much tedium in using the program that attention is diverted from the content. Otherwise, students will become frustrated.
- How does the program develop conceptual knowledge that supports understanding of ideas? In drill programs, how are wrong answers handled? Will the models or explanations aid student understanding?
- What controls and assessments are provided for the teacher? Are there options that can be turned on and off (e.g., sound, types of feedback or help, levels of difficulty)? Is there a provision for record-keeping so that you will know what progress individual students have made?
- Is a manual or online instruction available? What is the quality of the manual or instructions? Minimally, the manual should make it clear how the program is to operate and provide assistance for troubleshooting.
- Is the program equitable in its consideration of gender and culture?
- What is the nature of the licensing agreement? In the case of purchased software, is a site licence or network licence available? If you purchase a single-user package, it is not legal to install the software on multiple computers. Internet applets require the computer to be connected to the Internet and software such as Java (Sun Microsystems) to view the applets. Do these constraints fit with your school situation?
- Be sure that the program will run on the computers at your school. The software description should indicate

the compatible platform(s) (Windows/Macintosh) and the version of the required operating systems.

Resources on the Internet

In addition to access to Internet-based software applications, or applets, the World Wide Web is a wellspring of information and resources for both teachers and students interested in mathematics and teaching mathematics.

Instead of using a standard search engine to find mathematics-related information, it is better to have some places to begin. Several good Web sites in different categories will usually provide you with more links to other sites than you will have time to search. One source for good Web sites is this book. At the end of the chapter you will find a list of Web-based resources. Although a brief description accompanies each listing, you are encouraged to check these out yourself as Web sites are frequently modified. The types of resources you can expect to find include professional information, teacher resources, digital tools, and open-source software.

How to Select Internet Resources

The massive amount of information available on the Internet must be sifted through for accuracy and sorted by quality when you plan instruction or when the students in your class gather information or research a mathematics topic. For example, identifying a mathematics lesson plan on the Internet does not ensure that it is of high quality, as anyone can publish any idea they have on the Web. When students complete a *WebQuest* (http://webquest.org) about a topic in mathematics, how can they be sure the information is trustworthy? To use the Web as a teaching toolbox for locating successful mathematics tasks, motivating enrichment activities, or supportive strategies to assist struggling learners, it is better to go to trustworthy, high-quality sites than merely plugging a few key words into available search engines. We suggest that you add the end-of-chapter sites in this book to your computer "favourites" and go to them as a first-level source of support and information. If you choose to explore Web pages, Web logs (blogs), or wikis (collaboratively created and updated Web pages) more broadly, take the elements enumerated in Table 7.1 into consideration. These criteria are critical for your use as a discerning educator and can be adapted or simplified for your students as they evaluate material on the Web. The main topics are adapted from a group of considerations suggested by Smith (1997a).

Emerging Technologies

Emerging technologies refers to the ever-changing landscape of technological tools and advances. In our increasingly technological society, we know that we can only do our best in helping students be able to respond to the newest hardware and software with a curious mind and a sensible approach to learning about the innovation. One area of growing interest is Web 2.0 tools that encourage collaboration, communication, and construction of knowledge, including blogs, wikis, and audio or video presentations frequently referred to as podcasts.

Podcasts Podcasts refer to audio or video files that automatically download to subscribers over the Internet and are listened to or watched on mobile media players. Students and teachers create these podcasts so they can replay information related to a particular topic or lesson. Teachers produce podcasts to create downloadable digital instruction that supports classroom lessons. Students develop these as culminating projects, such as a report on the Pythagorean Theorem or a persuasive argument that resulted from collecting data of real-world significance.

Wikis Wikis are Web-based publishing tools built through the combined collective wisdom of multiple contributors. Members of the continuing group add, remove, edit, or otherwise change content. This process of finding authorship can encourage students to find new information, assess and evaluate information already in place, and build new knowledge. Although information that is misleading or inaccurate can get posted, that defect helps to develop the ability to scrutinize Web information as a savvy consumer. You can easily see how a topic in social studies or piece of literature can spark the start of a wiki, too. Numeration systems, geometric transformations, the interpretation of a set of data, or the mathematics in a photograph, book, or movie represent a variety of options for wikis emerging from mathematics lessons.

Web Logs Web logs are electronic documents of Web sites where people discuss events, post comments, or just give opinions about a variety of topics. Sharing resources of thoughts and having others respond is a powerful tool for getting students to communicate and evaluate ideas. At a basic level your class Web log (blog) can archive homework assignments or other materials of interest to families—even a place to post an outstanding assignment. Web logs can also hold portfolios of students' work that can be shared for conferences. They can also just reflect the pattern of growth in mathematics learning throughout a grading period. The site can become a place to store math games, problem of the week, or writing prompts, such as mathematics poetry templates. Remember to develop a policy so that everyone (including family members) understands how the blog should and should not be used.

Table 7.1

	Evaluating Web Resources		
	Criteria	**Justification**	**Evidence/Verification**
Authority	• Page should identify the authors and their qualifications. • Site should be associated with a reputable educational institution or organization.	• Anyone can publish pages on the Web. You want to be assured that the information is from a reliable source and is of high quality.	• Contact information for the author or organization is easily available. Is there a link to the organization's home page? • Do the authors establish their expertise? • Use www.whois.net domain research service to identify the author of the site. • Is the URL domain .org, .edu, .gov, .net, .ca, or .com?
Content	• Site should match topic of interest. • The materials should add depth to your information.	• The information should be useful facts rather than opinions. • The text should be actual information from an expert and not paraphrased from another site.	• Is it a list of links from other sites? • Are the statements verified by footnotes and research articles? • Do the authors indicate criteria for including information?
Objectivity	• Site should not reflect a biased point of view. • Authors should present facts and not try to sway the reader.	• Web sites can try to influence the readers rather than provide independent and evenhanded information sources.	• Are there advertisements or sponsors either on the page or linked to the page? • Does the author discuss multiple theories or points of view?
Accuracy	• Information should be free of errors. • Verification of information confirmed by reviewers or fact-checkers.	• Web sites can be published without reviewers or accuracy checks.	• Does the page contain obvious errors in grammar, spelling, or mathematics? • Are original sources clearly documented in a list of references? • Can the information be cross-checked through another source? • Are charts, graphs, or statistical information labelled clearly?
Currency	• Site should be current and frequently revised.	• Information is changing so rapidly that pages that are not maintained and up-to-date cannot provide the reliable information needed. • Currency is a key advantage of the Web over print sources. If there is no evidence of currency, the site loses its potential to add to knowledge in the field.	• Look for dates and updates for the page. • Links should be current and not lead to dead sites. • References should include recent citations. • Photos and videos should be up-to-date (unless related to a historical topic).
Audience	• Site should clearly target whether it is for your own use or the potential use of students in your classroom. • Site should detail whether it is a self-created site or has been created by others. • Site should be accessible by all learners, particularly those with special needs.	• In education the audience may be students, families, teachers, or administrators. Presenting information for a well-defined audience is critical.	• Check for suggested grade levels or ages. • Does the site allow for easy use through menus or search features that help children find information? • What is the reading level of the narrative? • Are there options for students with special needs? Do they adhere to the principles of universal design by, for example, considering students with visual impairments by using increased font size, synthesized speech, or a screen reader, or considering students with hearing impairments by including captions for video or audio materials? See http://webxact.watchfire.com to assess a Web site for accessibility.

Reflections on Chapter 7

Writing to Learn

1. Technology has affected the mathematics curriculum and how it is taught in many ways. Explain at least three, and give an example to support your explanation. Can you think of examples that are not included in this chapter?
2. Describe some of the benefits of using calculators regularly in the mathematics classroom. Which of these seem to you to be the most compelling? What are some of the arguments against using calculators? Answer each of the arguments against calculators as if you were giving a speech at your PTA meeting or arguing for regular use of calculators before your principal.
3. Name at least three features of graphing calculators that truly improve the learning of mathematics in the middle grades.
4. What are some criteria that seem most important to you when selecting software?
5. What kind of information can you expect to find on the Internet that would be useful for teaching mathematics? How can you evaluate the quality of the information?
6. What are some of the emerging technologies? How can you be ready for new technologies in the future?

For Discussion and Exploration

1. Talk with some teachers about their use or non-use of calculators in the classroom. How do they go about making a decision regarding when to use them? Read the NCTM Position Statement on Computation, Calculators and Common Sense. How do the reasons of the teachers with whom you talked compare to the NCTM position?
2. Among the software kept at your school, find one example of instructional software for mathematics. Try it and decide how it would be used in your classroom (if at all). Be sure to check the documentation for suggested grade levels.
3. Check out at least three of the Web sites suggested below for teacher resources. Be sure to follow some of the links to other sites. Create your own "top ten" to bookmark on your computer as favourites.
4. Explore three or four applets from one or more of the sites listed under Applets (see page 19). Select one and try it with children. Teach a lesson that incorporates the applet as either a teacher tool or student activity.

Resources for Chapter 7

Recommendations for Further Reading
Books

Heide, A., & Henderson, D. (2001). *Active learning in the digital age classroom*. Toronto: Trifolium Books Inc.
This book is the essential "how-to" technology integration resource for K-12 teachers. The authors present a comprehensive, readable, and broadscope overview of technology in the classroom. They offer practical and well-researched ideas, tools, and examples of how classroom teachers can obtain and use a variety of information and communication technologies (ICT) tools with students.

Masalski, W. J., & Elliott, P. C. (Eds.). (2005). *Technology-supported mathematics learning environments: Sixty-seventh yearbook*. Reston, VA: National Council of Teachers of Mathematics.
An excellent collection of perspectives on the use of technology across the grades by noted authorities and practising teachers. Topics include strategies for effective use of technology, examination of virtual manipulatives for young students, dynamic geometry software, the spreadsheet, and much more. A CD is included to illustrate many of the ideas found in the book plus additional sources.

Schwartz, L. M., & Willing, K. R. (2001). *Computer activities for the cooperative classroom*. Markham, Ontario: Pembroke Publishers.

This practical book on integrating computers effectively into your classroom program was developed by two classroom teachers. The authors offer strategies for how to do so and include up-to-date assessment and evaluation techniques, a list of online and paper-based resources, etc. This book is a "must have" that will be well used.

Articles

McGehee, J., & Griffith, L. K. (2004). Technology enhances student learning across the curriculum. *Mathematics Teaching in the Middle School, 9,* 344–349.
Five examples of using technology are explored, including understanding graphs (rate of change), decimals, geometry, measurement, and data analysis. This is a good introduction to the use of technology in any of these domains.

National Council of Teachers of Mathematics. (2002–present). ON-Math is an online NCTM journal that can be accessed on the Web by all NCTM members at www.nctm.org/publications/onmath.aspx.
However, anyone can go into the "Articles by Grade" section and see titles of the variety of articles for pre-K–12 teachers. There are actual classroom activities, enhanced lessons, and more general suggestions for technology use delivered with interactive software, virtual manipulatives, video clips, and sound effects.

Thompson, T., & Sproule, S. (2005). Calculators for students with special needs. *Teaching Children Mathematics, 11,* 391–395.

An excellent argument is made for the use of calculators for students who have learning problems that affect their mathematical skills. A framework or flowchart that is easily used to make decisions about when to allow calculator use is not only appropriate for special students but also for every child. This short article can help counter any objections raised by calculator critics.

Blades, D. (2002). Statistics Canada supports science, mathematics and technology education. *Canadian Journal Science Mathematics and Technology Education, 2* (4) 576–577.

McFarlane, K. (2001). Just another electric circus? Meeting standards for K–12 e-learning classroom resources. *Education Canada, 41* (3), pp. 25–27.

Online Resources

Professional Information

National Council of Teachers of Mathematics (NCTM)
www.nctm.org

The NCTM Web site is a must for every elementary teacher and teacher of mathematics. It includes specific information for teachers, parents, leaders, and researchers. The home page changes almost monthly, providing up-to-date information about conferences, publications, news, and more. The site also provides a mechanism for joining the council, registering for conferences, purchasing publications and products, and linking to the *Illuminations* site (see separate entry). Members can access their journals online, subscribe to a special electronic journal, and renew memberships. You can choose to receive a monthly e-mail update informing you of recent additions to the Web site.

Association for Supervision and Curriculum Development (ACSD)
www.ascd.org

ASCD is an international non-profit educational association that is committed to successful teaching and learning for all.

International Society for Technology in Education (ISTE)
www.iste.org

ISTE is the professional organization for educators interested in infusing technology into instruction. It maintains an exciting set of resources for teachers including Web site links, professional development, and publications. The next generation of ISTE's National Educational Technology Standards (NETS-S) for students can be found by clicking NETS section from the home page. The standards address such topics as creativity and innovation; communication and collaboration; research and information fluency; critical thinking, problem solving and decision making; digital citizenship; and technology operations and concepts.

Teacher Resources

Link To Learning
www.linktolearning.com/math.htm

This site contains many links to other sites that address different strands of the curriculum, appropriate for a variety of grade levels. Some of the activities and resources to which

this site connects are Canadian based (e.g., Learn Alberta; Department of Mathematics, University of Waterloo).

Math Central
http://mathcentral.uregina.ca/

Math Central is an Internet service provided by the Department of Mathematics and Statistics and the Faculty of Education at the University of Regina. There are different components to this site, offered in both French and English. The Resource Room is a place where mathematics educators can share resources, teaching ideas, lesson plans, etc. Other components include Quandaries and Queries, Mathematics with a Human Face, Teachers' Bulletin Board, Math Beyond School, and Problem of the Month.

Math Frog
http://cem2.uwaterloo.ca/mathfrog/

This site assists grade 4, 5, and 6 teachers with integrating technology into their mathematics classrooms. It offers a series of free self-contained lessons, which combine mathematical games and/or technological tools with appropriate printable paper-and-pencil follow-up exercises. It also provides links to a collection of mathematics games, activities, and professional development for teachers. The site can be accessed by teachers, parents, and students.

Wired Math
http://cemc2.math.uwaterloo.ca/wired_math/english/about.shtml

Wired math is another site of the University of Waterloo. However it offers lessons, games, exercises, activities, and extra challenges geared to grades 7, 8, and 9.

NCTM *Illuminations*
http://illuminations.nctm.org

This is an incredible site developed by NCTM to provide Internet resources for teaching and learning intended to "illuminate" *Principles and Standards for School Mathematics*. You can find resources from lesson ideas to "math-lets" (applets designed to provide tools for developing understanding in mathematics). Also at this site are multimedia investigations for students and links to video vignettes designed to promote professional reflection.

The *Illuminations* Web site continues to be updated with the addition of many new lessons. In addition the Illuminations Game Room Project allows students to explore mathematics topics while playing mathematics games with one another over the Web.

The Math Forum
http://mathforum.org

This may be one of your most important sources of information and links to useful sites. The forum has resources (Math Tools) for both teachers and students. There are suggestions for lessons, puzzles, and activities, plus links to other sites with similar information. There are forums where teachers can talk with other teachers. Two pages accept questions about mathematics from students or teachers (Ask Dr. Math) and about teaching mathematics from teachers (Teacher 2 Teacher). Problems are regularly posted, and solutions can be entered via the Internet.

Anneberg/CPB Projects
www.learner.org

The site lists free online learning activities, including information about all sorts of interesting uses of mathematics and science in the real world, resources for free and inexpensive materials from Anneberg, and information about funding opportunities. It is a tremendous resource.

Center for Implementing Technology in Education (CITEd): Math Matrix
www.citeducation.org/mathmatrix/default.asp

CITEd's *Math Matrix* is a useful database of technology products that supports instruction in mathematics for students with special needs. Each product evaluation includes a link to the supplier's Web site.

Environment Canada
www.ec.gc.ca

This site provides a wide source of information on weather and environmental information for Canada. All data are available in French and English.

Stock Market Information
www.globeinvestor.com

This site provides up-to-the-minute Canadian stock market research and information.

Statistics Canada: Learning Resources
www.statcan.gc.ca/edu/index-eng.htm

This site offers valuable statistical data on a variety of topics. Lesson plans, teaching tools, and student activities are available in both French and English. The site is intended to be used both by teachers and students.

The Canadian Encyclopedia
www.thecanadianencyclopedia.com

This interactive Web site offers extensive information on a variety of topics ranging from Canadian history to mathematics. There are French, English, and Junior Edition versions, as well as a student guide.

Applets

http://argyll.epsb.ca/jreed/math7/strand1/1105.htm

The applets at this site were developed by Jim Reed for the Argyll Home Education Services Centre in Alberta. The applets consist of a series of exercises and activities for different topics in the curriculum covered in grades 7, 8, and 9.

National Council of Teachers of Mathematics e-Examples
http://standards.nctm.org/document/eexamples/index.htm

Many of these applets are referenced in and directly support the text of *Principles and Standards for School Mathematics.* They are also available on the CD version of the *Standards.* Most are also available on the *Illuminations* site.

NCTM *Illuminations*
http://illuminations.nctm.org

Check both the i-Math Investigations (interactive math lessons, most built around applets) and Interactive Math-lets (a collection of applets). The Math-let applications cover the K–12 spectrum. They are ordered alphabetically, so be sure to check out the full list. This is a good collection of quality tools. The i-Math Investigations include all of the applets from the e-examples.

The National Library for Virtual Manipulatives (NLVM)
http://nlvm.usu.edu/en/nav/vlibrary.html

This NSF-funded site is located at Utah State University. It contains a huge collection of applets organized by the five content strands of *Standards* and also by the same four grade bands. The eNLVM section contains online units, customizable student activities, and tools to help teachers develop activities collaboratively.

Arcytech
http://arcytech.org/java

This site includes tool applets for base-ten blocks, pattern blocks, Cuisenaire rods, fraction bars, and integer bars. There is also an extended interactive lesson developing the Pythagorean theorem.

Shodor *Interactivate* (Shodor Education Foundation)
www.shodor.org/interactivate

The site contains a huge list of applets that continues to grow. In addition, there are lessons and activities. Applets (referred to as "activities") are arranged by content rather than grade level, so be sure to look through the full list. This is a valuable site, especially for teachers in the upper grades and middle school.

Count On
www.counton.org

This site is sponsored by the National Centre for Excellence in the Teaching of Mathematics and contains all sorts of resources in addition to applets for mathematics. Click on the Explorer button to find a number of applets as well as other useful features such as a mathematics dictionary. Check out other areas of this site as well.

---

myeducationlab *will help you improve your understanding of the concepts taught in this textbook and in your course. This online tool includes videos of real classroom experiences, sample lesson plans, simulations, case studies, and links to important educational and teaching Web sites that will help you make the transition from student to teacher. As you study in your course and with this textbook, please follow along in* **MyEducationLab**. *Use it! Explore it! And improve your knowledge and your grade!*

Chapter 8
Developing Early Number Concepts and Number Sense

Children come to school with many ideas about number. We need to build upon these ideas as we work with them to help them develop new relationships. It is sad to see the large percentage of students in grades 4, 5, and beyond who essentially know little more about number than how to count. It takes time and repeated experiences for children to develop a full understanding of number that will grow and enhance further number-related concepts.

This chapter looks at the development of number ideas for numbers up to about 20. These foundational ideas can all be extended to larger numbers, operations, basic facts, and computation.

Big Ideas

1. Counting tells how many things are in a set. When counting a set of objects, the last word in the counting sequence names the quantity for that set.

2. Numbers are connected to each other through a variety of number relationships. The number 7, for example, is more than 4, is two less than 9, is composed of 3 and 4 as well as 2 and 5, is three away from 10, and can be quickly recognized in several patterned arrangements of dots. These ideas extend to an understanding of 17, 57, and 370.

3. Number concepts are intimately tied to the world around us. Application of number relationships to the real world marks the beginning of making sense of the world mathematically.

Mathematics Content Connections

Early number development is related to other areas of the curriculum in two ways: content that interacts with and enhances the development of number, and content that is directly affected by how well early number concepts have been developed. Measurement, data, and meanings for the operations fall into the first category. Basic facts, place value, and computation fall into the second.

- **Operations** (Chapter 9): As children solve story problems for any of the four operations, they count on, count back, make and count groups, and make comparisons. In the process, they form new relationships and methods of working with numbers.

- **Measurement** (Chapter 19): Determining measures of length, height, size, or mass is an important use of number for the young child. Measurement involves meaningful counting and comparing (number relationships) and connects number to the world in which the child lives.

- **Data** (Chapter 21): Data, like measurement, involve counts and comparisons that aid in developing number and connecting it to the real world.

- **Basic Facts** (Chapter 10): A rich and thorough development of number relationships provides a critical foundation for mastering basic facts. Without these relationships, facts must be memorized or learned by rote. With an understanding of number, facts for addition and subtraction become relatively simple extensions.

- **Place Value and Computation** (Chapters 11 and 12): Many of the ideas that contribute to computational fluency and flexibility with numbers are extensions of how numbers are related to ten and how numbers can be taken apart and recombined in different ways.

Promoting Good Beginnings

In 2002, NCTM and that National Association for the Education of Young Children (NAEYC) collaboratively produced a joint position statement emphasizing that all children need an early start in learning mathematics. *Early Math Strategy, The Report of the Expert Panel on Early Math in Ontario* (www.edu.gov.on.ca, 2003) also supports this view. This emphasis on readiness aligns with the recent findings of the National Mathematics Advisory Panel (2008). The position statement suggests ten research-based recommendations to help teachers develop high-quality learning activities for children aged 3 to 6:

1. Enhance children's natural interest in mathematics and their disposition to use it to make sense of their physical and social worlds.

2. Build on children's experience and knowledge, including their family, linguistic, cultural, and community backgrounds; their individual approaches to learning; and their informal knowledge.

3. Base mathematics curriculum and teaching practices on knowledge of young children's cognitive, linguistic, physical, and social–emotional development.

4. Use curriculum and teaching practices that strengthen children's problem-solving and reasoning processes as well as representing, communicating, and connecting mathematical ideas.

5. Ensure that the curriculum is coherent and compatible with known relationships and sequences of important mathematical ideas.

6. Provide for children's deep and sustained interaction with key mathematical ideas.

7. Integrate mathematics with other activities and other activities with mathematics.

8. Provide ample time, materials, and teacher support for children to engage in play, a context in which they explore and manipulate mathematical ideas with keen interest.

9. Introduce mathematical concepts, methods, and language through a range of appropriate experiences and teaching strategies.

10. Support children's learning by thoughtfully and continually assessing all children's mathematical knowledge, skills, and strategies.

❚❚ ───────── *Pause and Reflect*

Although all these recommendations are critical, which two do you consider most important for you to work on first as you develop as a teacher?

Number Development in Pre-K and Kindergarten

Parents help children count their fingers, toys, people at the table, and other small sets of objects. Questions regarding "Who has more?" or "Are there enough?" are part of the daily lives of children as young as two or three. Considerable evidence indicates that these children have some understanding of the concepts of number and counting (Baroody & Wilkins, 1999; Fuson, 1988; Gelman & Gallistel, 1978; Gelman & Meck, 1986; NRC, 2001). We therefore include abundant activities to support a variety of different experiences that young children need to gain a full understanding of the concepts.

The Relationships of More, Less, and Same

The concepts of "more," "less," and "same" are basic relationships contributing to the overall concept of number. Children begin to develop these relational ideas before they start school. Almost any child entering kindergarten can choose the set that is *more* if presented with two sets that are quite obviously different in number. In fact, Baroody (1987) states, "A child unable to use 'more' in this intuitive manner is at considerable educational risk" (p. 29). Classroom activities should help children build on this basic notion and refine it.

Though the concept of less is logically related to the concept of more (selecting the set with more is the same as *not* selecting the set with less), the word *less* proves to be more difficult for children than *more*. A possible explanation is that children have many opportunities to use the word *more* but have limited exposure to the word *less*. To help children with the concept of less, frequently pair it with the word *more* and make a conscious effort to ask "Which is less?" questions as well as "Which is more?" questions. For example, suppose that your class has correctly selected the set that has more from two that are given. Immediately follow with the question "Which is less?" In this way, the concept can be connected with the better known idea and the term *less* can become more familiar.

For all three concepts (more, less, and same), children should construct sets using counters, as well as make comparisons or choices between two given sets. The following activities should be conducted in a spirit of inquiry accompanied whenever possible with requests for explanations: "Why do you think this set has less?"

Activity **8.1**

Make Sets of More/Less/Same

At a workstation or table, provide about eight cards with sets of 4 to 12 objects, a set of small counters or blocks, and some word cards labelled *More, Less,* and *Same*. Next to each card have students make three collections of counters: a set that is more, one that is less, and one that is the same. The appropriate labels are placed on the sets (see Figure 8.1).

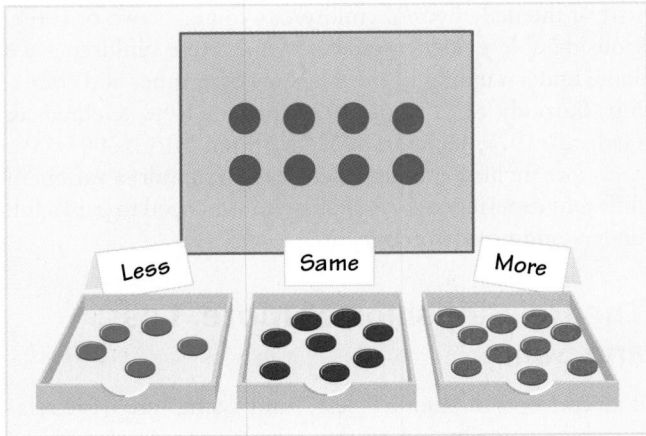

FIGURE 8.1 Making sets that are more, less, and the same.

In Activity 8.1, students create a set with counters; the activity gives them the opportunity to reflect on the sets and adjust them as they work. The next activity is done without counters. Although it addresses the same basic ideas, it provides a different problem situation.

Activity 8.2

Find the Same Amount

Give children a collection of cards with sets on them. Dot cards are one possibility (see the Blackline Masters). Have the children pick up any card in the collection, then find another card with the same amount to form a pair. Children continue to find other pairs until all cards have been played. This activity can be altered to have children find dot cards that are "more" or "less."

Accommodation

For those children who are experiencing difficulty with matching cards, have them use counters to represent the number of dots on each card. They can then compare the number of counters representing the dots on each card to make sure the amounts match.

Observe children as they do this task. Children whose number ideas are completely tied to counting and nothing more will select cards at random and count each dot. Those who begin by selecting a card that appears to have about the same number of dots are at a significantly higher level of understanding. Also observe how the dots are counted. Are the counts made accurately? Is each dot counted only once? Does the child need to touch the dot when counting? A significant milestone for children occurs when they begin recognizing small patterned sets without counting.

⏸ ─────────── *Pause and Reflect*

You have begun to see some of the early foundational ideas about number. Stop now and make a list of all of the important ideas that you think children should know about 8 by the time they finish grade 1. (The number 8 is used as an example. The list could be about any number from, say, 6 to 12.) Put your thoughts aside and we will revisit these ideas later.

Early Counting

Meaningful counting activities begin in preschool. Generally, children at mid-year in kindergarten should have a fair understanding of counting, but they must construct this idea on their own. It cannot be forced. The *meaning* attached to counting is the key conceptual idea on which all other number concepts are developed.

The Development of Counting Skills Counting involves at least two separate skills. First, a child must be able to produce the standard list of counting words in order: "One, two, three, four...." Second, a child must be able to connect this sequence in a one-to-one manner with the items in the set being counted. Each item must get one and only one count.

Experience and guidance are the major factors in the development of counting skills. Many children come to kindergarten able to count sets of ten or beyond. At the same time, children from disadvantaged backgrounds may require considerable practice to make up their experience deficit. Obviously, longer number strings require more practice to learn. The first 12 counts involve no pattern or repetition, and many children do not easily recognize patterns in the teens. Children still learning the skills of counting—that is, matching oral number words with objects—should be given sets of blocks or counters that they can move or pictures of sets that are arranged for easy counting.

Meaning Attached to Counting Fosnot and Dolk (2001) make it very clear that an understanding of cardinality and its connection to counting is not a simple matter for four-year-olds. Children will learn *how* to count (matching counting words with objects) before they understand that the last count word indicates the *amount* of the set or its *cardinality*. Children who have made this connection are said to have the *cardinality principle*, which is a refinement of their early ideas about quantity. Most, but certainly not all, children by age $4\frac{1}{2}$ have made this connection (Fosnot & Dolk, 2001; Fuson & Hall, 1983).

 Young children who can count orally may not have attached meaning to their counts. To determine if a child has attached meaning, show the

child a card with five to nine large dots in a row so that they can be easily counted. Ask the child to count the dots. If the count is accurate, ask, "How many dots are on the card?" Many children will count again. One indication of understanding the first count will be a response that reflects the first count without recounting. Now have the child get that same number of counters from a collection of counters: "Please get the same number of counters as there are dots on the card." There are several indicators to watch for. Will the child recount to know how many to get? Does the child count the counters or place them one-to-one on the dots? Is the child confident that there is the same number of counters as dots? ◆

Fosnot and Dolk talk about a class of four-year-olds in which children who knew that there were 17 students in the class were unsure how many milk cartons they should get so that each could have one.

To develop their understanding of counting, engage children in almost any game or activity that involves counts and comparisons. The following is a simple suggestion.

Perhaps the most common preschool and kindergarten exercises have children match sets of objects with numbers. When children are successful with these activities, it is time to move on to more advanced concepts.

Activity **8.3**

Fill the Chutes

Create a simple game board with four "chutes." Each consists of a column of about twelve 2 cm squares with a star at the top. Children take turns rolling a die and collecting the indicated number of counters. They then place these counters in one of the chutes. The object is to fill all the chutes with counters. An option might be to have the chutes filled exactly. For example, a roll of 5 cannot be used to fill a chute with four spaces.

This "game" provides opportunities for you to talk with children about number and to assess their thinking. Watch how the children count the dots on the die. Ask, "How do you know you have the right number of counters?" and "How many counters did you put in the chute? How many more do you need to fill the chute?"

Activities 8.1 and 8.2 also provide opportunities for formative assessment. Regular classroom activities, such as counting how many napkins are needed at snack time, are additional opportunities for children to learn about number and for teachers to listen to their students' ideas.

Number Writing and Recognition

Helping children read and write single-digit numbers is similar to teaching them to read and write letters of the alphabet. Both have little to do with number concept development. Traditionally, instruction has involved various forms of repetitious practice. Children trace over pages of numbers, repeatedly write the numbers from 0 to 10, make the numbers from clay, trace them in sand, write them on the chalkboard or in the air, and so on.

The calculator is also a good instructional tool for number recognition. In addition to helping children with number recognition, early activities can help develop familiarity with the calculator so that more complex activities are possible.

Activity **8.4**

Find and Press

Every child should have a calculator. Always begin by having the children press the clear key. Then say a number, and have the children press that number on the calculator. If you have an overhead calculator, or interactive white board, you can then show the children the correct key so they can confirm their responses. Otherwise, you can write the number on the board for children to check. Begin with single-digit numbers. Later, progress to two or three numbers called in succession. For example, call, "Three, seven, one." Children then press the complete string of numbers as called.

Accommodation

For those children who are experiencing difficulty when three numbers are called in succession, work only with one or possibly two numbers in succession.

Perhaps the most common preschool and kindergarten exercises have children match sets of objects with numbers. In these exercises, children are given sets of pictures and asked to write or match the number that tells how many.

Alternatively, they may be given a number and told to make or draw a set with that many objects. Many teacher resource books describe learning centre activities that require children to put a number with the correct-sized set, such as numbered frogs on lily pads (with dots). However, it is important to note that these frequently overworked activities involve only the skills of counting sets and number recognition or of number writing. When children are successful with these activities, it is time to move on to more advanced concepts.

 Computer software developed in Canada that can assist with early number development are *Mathville One* (Courseware Solutions), *Math Strategies–Primary* (Nectar Foundation), and *Math Trek 1, 2, 3*, Version 4 (Nectar Foundation). The activities offered in the Counting and Quantity feature in *Math Strategies–Primary* could easily be used to reinforce the concepts of cardinality, counting, developing early number sense, and working with 5 and 10 as benchmarks. ◆

Counting On and Counting Back

Although the forward sequence of numbers is relatively familiar to most young children, counting on and counting back are difficult skills for many. Frequent short practice drills are recommended.

Activity 8.5

Up and Back Counting

Counting up to and back from a target number in a rhythmic fashion is an important counting exercise. For example, line up five children and five chairs in front of the class. As the whole class counts from 1 to 5, the children sit down one at a time. When the target number, 5, is reached, it is repeated; the child who sat on 5 now stands, and the count goes back to 1. As the count goes back, the children stand up one at a time, and so on, "1, 2, 3, 4, 5, 5, 4, 3, 2, 1, 1, 2, …." Preschool, kindergarten, and grade 1 children find exercises such as this both fun and challenging. Any movement (clapping, turning around, doing jumping jacks) can be used as the count goes up and back in a rhythmic manner.

The last activity is designed only to help students become fluent with the number words in both forward and reverse order and to begin counts with numbers other than 1. Although not at all easy for young students, these activities do not address counting on or counting back in a meaningful manner. Fosnot and Dolk (2001) describe the ability to count on as a "landmark" on the path to number sense. The next two activities are designed for that purpose.

Activity 8.6

Counting On with Counters

Give each child a collection of 10 or 12 small counters that they line up from left to right on their desks. Tell them to count four counters and push them under their left hands or place them in a cup (see Figure 8.2). Then say, "Point to your hand. How many are there?" (Four.) "So let's count like this. f-o-u-r (pointing to their hand), five, six …." Repeat the activity with other numbers.

The following activity addresses the same concept in a somewhat more problem-based manner.

Activity 8.7

Real Counting On

This "game" for two children requires a deck of cards with numbers 1 to 7, a die, a paper cup, and some counters. The first player turns over the top number card then places the indicated number of counters in the cup. The card is placed next to the cup as a reminder of how many there are. The second child rolls the die then places that many counters next to the cup. (See Figure 8.3.) Together they decide how many counters in all. A record sheet with columns for "in the Cup," "On the Side," and "In All" is an option. The greatest number in the deck can be adjusted, if needed.

As the children work through this activity, watch how they determine the total amounts. Children who are not yet counting on may want to dump the counters from the cup or they will count up from 1 without dumping out the counters. Be sure to allow them to use these strategies. As children continue to play, they will eventually count on as the strategy becomes meaningful and useful.

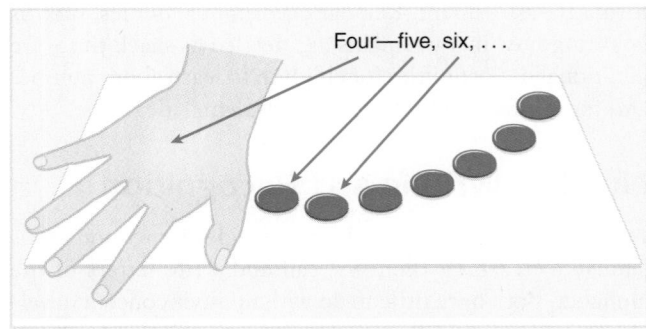

Four—five, six, . . .

Figure 8.2 Counting on: "Hide four. Count, starting from the number of counters that are hidden."

Figure 8.3 How many in all? How do children count to determine the total? Do they dump the counters? Count up from 1 without dumping the counters? Count on?

Early Number Sense

Number sense is a term, although somewhat vague in definition, which became popular in the late 1980s. Howden (1989) described number sense as a "good intuition about numbers and their relationships. It develops gradually as a result of exploring numbers, visualizing them in a variety of contexts, and relating them in ways that are not limited by traditional algorithms" (p. 11). This may still be the best definition.

NCTM Standards In *Principles and Standards*, the term *number sense* is used freely throughout the Number and Operations standard. "As students work with numbers, they gradually develop flexibility in thinking about numbers, which is a hallmark of number sense.... Number sense develops as students understand the size of numbers, develop multiple ways of thinking about and representing numbers, use numbers as referents, and develop accurate perceptions about the effects of operations on numbers" (p. 80).

The discussion of number sense begins here and continues as we look at the kinds of relationships and connections children should be making about smaller numbers up to about 20. But "good intuition about numbers" does not end with these smaller whole numbers. Children continue to develop number sense as they begin to use numbers in operations, build an understanding of place value, and devise flexible methods of computing and making estimates involving large numbers, fractions, decimal numbers, and percents.

The early number ideas that have been discussed to this point in the chapter are the rudimentary aspects of number. Unfortunately, too many conventional programs move directly from these beginning ideas into addition and subtraction, leaving students with a very limited collection of ideas about number to bring to these new topics. Often, the result is that children continue to count by ones to solve simple story problems and have difficulty mastering basic

facts. Early number sense development should be given significantly more attention than it is in most conventional preschool and K–2 programs.

Relationships Among Numbers 1 Through 10

Once children have acquired the concept of cardinality and can meaningfully use their counting skills, little more is to be gained from the kinds of counting activities described so far. More relationships must be created for children to develop number sense, a flexible concept of number not completely tied to counting.

A Collection of Number Relationships

Figure 8.4 illustrates the four different types of relationships that children can and should develop with numbers:

- *Patterned sets:* Children can learn to recognize sets of objects in patterned arrangements and tell how many without counting. For most numbers, there are several common patterns. For smaller numbers, patterns can also be made up of two or more simpler patterns.
- *One and two more, one and two less:* The two-more-than and two-less-than relationships involve more than just the ability to count on two or count back two. Children should know that 7, for example, is one more than 6 and also two less than 9.
- *Anchors or "benchmarks" of 5 and 10:* Since 10 plays such an important role in our number system and because two fives make up 10, it is very useful to develop relationships for the numbers 1 to 10 with 5 and 10 as important anchors.
- *Part–part–whole relationships:* To conceptualize a number as being made up of two or more parts is the most important relationship that can be developed about numbers. For example, 7 can be thought of as a set of 3 and a set of 4 or a set of 2 and a set of 5.

The principal tool that children will use as they construct these relationships is the one number tool they possess, *counting*. Initially, you will notice a lot of counting, and you may wonder if you are making progress. Have patience! Counting will become less and less necessary as children construct these new relationships and begin to use these more powerful ideas.

Patterned Set Recognition

Many children learn to recognize the dot arrangements on standard dice because of the many games they have played that use dice. Similar instant set recognition (also known as *subitizing*) can be developed for other patterns.

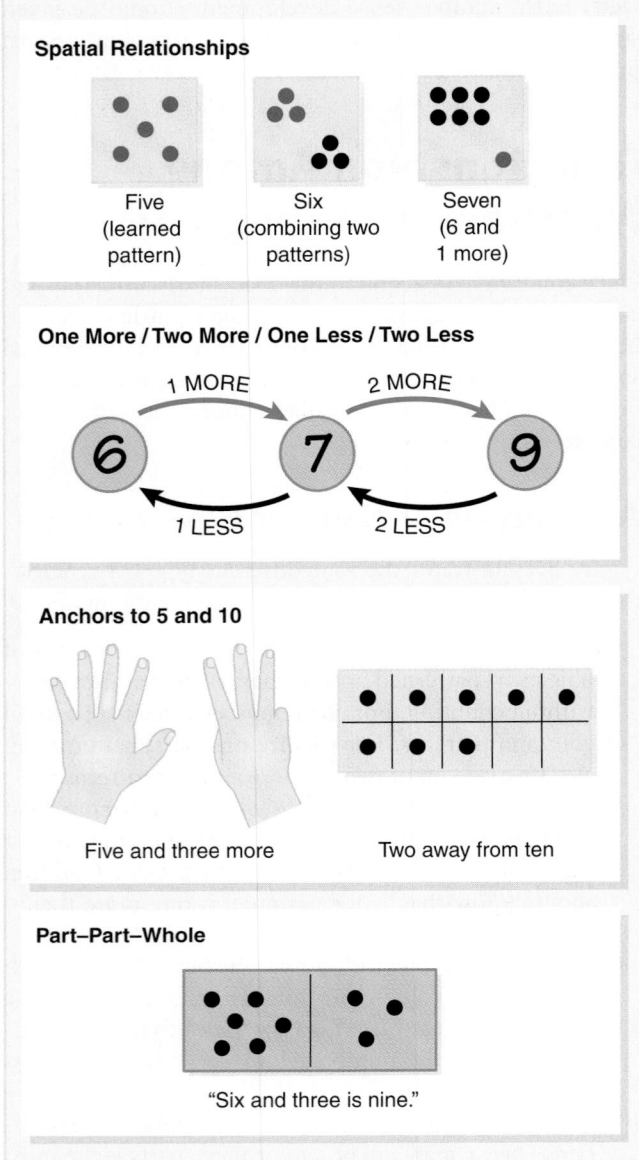

Figure 8.4 Four number relationships to be developed involving small numbers.

The activities suggested here encourage reflective thinking about the patterns so that relationships will be constructed. Naming amounts without the routine of counting can then aid in "counting on" (from a known patterned set) or in learning combinations of numbers (seeing a pattern of two known smaller patterns).

A set of dot plates is good to use for pattern recognition activities. These plates can be made from small paper plates and the peel-off dots commonly available in office supply stores. A collection of patterns is shown in Figure 8.5. Note that some patterns are combinations of two smaller patterns or a pattern with one or two additional dots. These should

be made in two colours. Keep the patterns compact. If the dots are spread out, the patterns are hard to see.

Activity **8.8**

Learning Patterns

To introduce the patterns, provide each student with about ten counters and a piece of construction paper as a mat. Hold up a dot plate for about three seconds. Then say, "Make the pattern you saw on the plate using the counters on the mat." Ask, "How many dots did you see? What did the pattern look like?" Spend some time discussing the configuration of the pattern and the number of dots. Do this with a few new patterns each day.

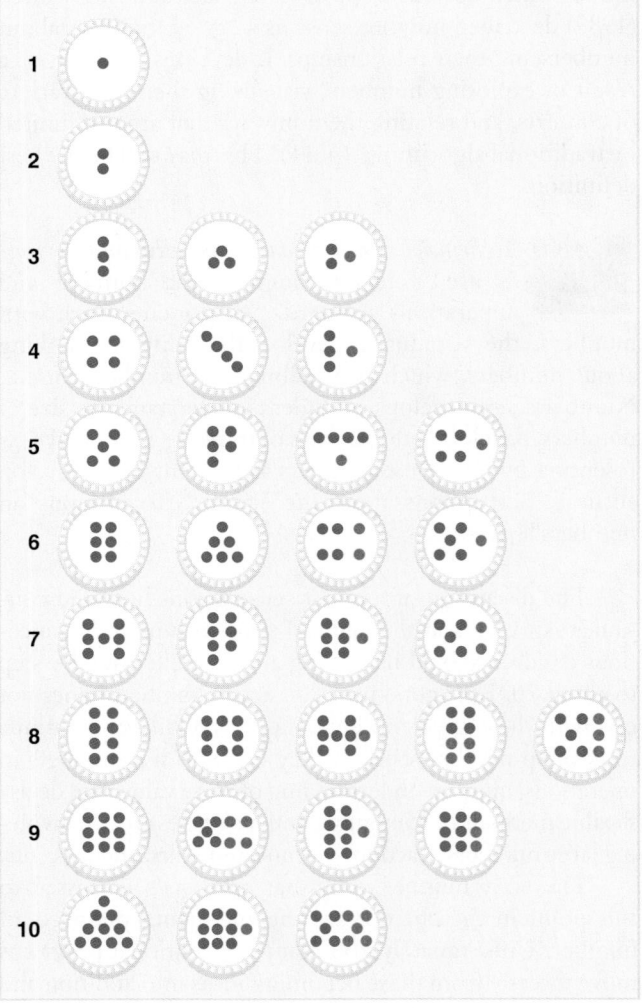

Figure 8.5 A useful collection of dot patterns for "dot plates."

The instant recognition activities with the plates are exciting and can be done in five minutes at any time of day or between lessons. There is value in using them at any primary grade level, at any time of year.

Activity 8.9

Dot Plate Flash

Hold up a dot plate for only one to three seconds. Ask, "How many dots did you see? What did the pattern look like?" Children like to see how quickly they can recognize and say how many dots. Include a lot of easy patterns and a few with more dots as you build their confidence. Students can also flash the dot plates to each other as a workstation activity.

One and Two More, One and Two Less

When children count, they do not necessarily reflect on the way one number is related to another. Their goal is only to match number words with objects until they reach the end of the count. To learn that 6 and 8 are related by the twin relationships of "two more than" and "two less than" requires reflecting on these ideas as they engage in tasks that permit counting. Counting on (or back) one or two counts is a useful tool in constructing these ideas.

Note that the relationship of "two more than" is significantly different than "comes two counts after." The latter relationship is applied to the string of number words, not to the quantities they represent. A comes-two-after relationship can be applied to letters of the alphabet. The letter H comes two after the letter F. However, there is no numerical or quantitative difference between *F* and *H*. The quantity 8 is still two more than 6, even if no number string was used to count these quantities. It is the numerical relationship you want to develop.

The following activity is a good place to begin helping children with these relationships. As described, it focuses on the two-more-than relationship although it can be used just as well for any of the four relationships.

Activity 8.10

Make a Two-More-Than Set

Provide students with about six dot cards. Their task is to construct a set of counters that is two more than the set shown on the card. Similarly, spread out eight to ten dot cards, and ask students to find another card for each that is two less than the card shown. (Omit the 1 and 2 cards for two less than, and so on.)

In activities in which children find a set or make a set, they can add a number card (a small card with a number written on it) to all of the sets involved. They can also be encouraged to take turns reading a number sentence to their partner. If, for example, a set has been made that is two more than a set of four, the child can read this by saying the number sentence, "Two more than four is six" or "Six is two more than four."

The next activity combines these relationships so children will need to be more attentive to which idea they need to be thinking about.

Activity 8.11

More or Less

This is an activity for two players or a small group. Use the Blackline Masters to make a deck of More-or-Less cards as shown in Figure 8.6. Make four or five of each type of card. You will also need a set of cards with the numbers 3 to 10 (two each). One child draws a number card and places it face up where all can see. The child places counters, equivalent to the number on the card, into a cup. Another child then draws one of the More-or-Less cards and places it next to the number card. For the More cards, counters are added accordingly to the cup. For the Less cards, counters are removed from the cup. For Zero cards, no change is made. Once the counters in the cup have been adjusted, each child predicts how many are now in the cup. The counters are then dumped out and counted, ending that round of the game, and a new number card is drawn.

Figure 8.6 Materials to play "More or Less."

"More or Less" can be played as a whole-class activity. Announce to the class how many counters you are placing in the cup, then write this number on the board. Have a student draw a card while the other students predict the new amount. The words *more* and *less* can be paired or substituted with the words *plus* and *minus* to connect these ideas with the arithmetic operations, even if they have not yet been formally introduced.

The calculator can be an exciting device to practise the relationships of one more than, two more than, one less than, and two less than.

Activity 8.12

A Calculator Two-More-Than Machine

Teach children how to make a two-more-than machine. Press 0 ⊞ 2 ⊟. This procedure makes the calculator a two-more-than machine. Now press any number—for example, 5. Children hold their finger over the ⊟ key and predict the number that is two more than 5. Then they press ⊟ to confirm. If they do not press any of the operation keys (⊞ , ⊟ , ⊠ , ⊟) the "machine" will continue to perform in this way.

What is really happening in the two-more-than machine is that the calculator "remembers" or stores the last operation, in this case "+ 2," and adds that to whatever number is in the window when the ⊟ key is pressed. If the child continues to press ⊟ , the calculator will count by twos. At any time, a new number can be pressed followed by the ⊟ key. To make a two-less-than machine, press 2 ⊟ 2 ⊟. (The first pressing of 2 is to avoid a negative number.) In the beginning, students forget and press operation keys, which change what their calculator is doing. Soon, however, they get the hang of using the calculator as a machine.

The calculator two-more-than machine will give the number two more than any number pressed, including those with two or more digits. The two-more-than relationship should be extended to two-digit numbers as soon as students are exposed to them. One way to do this is to ask for the number that is two more than 7. After getting the correct answer, ask "What is two more than 37?" and similarly for other numbers that end in 7. When you try this for 8 or 9, expect difficulties and unusual responses such as two more than 28 is "twenty-ten." In grade 1, this struggle can prove quite valuable. The "More or Less" activity can also be extended to larger numbers if no actual counters are used.

Anchoring Numbers to 5 and 10

Here again, we want to help children relate a given number to other numbers, specifically 5 and 10. These relationships are especially useful in thinking about various combinations of numbers. For example, in each of the following, consider how the knowledge of 8 as "5 and 3 more" and as "2 away from 10" can play a role: 5 + 3, 8 + 6, 8 – 2, 8 – 3, 8 – 4, 13 – 8. (It may be worth stopping here to consider the role of 5 and 10 in each of these examples.) Later, similar relationships can be used in the development of mental computation skills on larger numbers such as 68 + 7.

The most common and perhaps most important model for this relationship is the ten-frame. The ten-frame is simply a 2 × 5 array in which counters or dots are placed to illustrate numbers (see Figure 8.7). Ten-frames can be drawn simply on a full sheet of construction paper (or use the Blackline Master). Nothing fancy is required and each child can have one. The ten-frame has been incorporated into a variety of activities in this book and is now popular in standard textbooks for children.

For children in kindergarten or early grade 1 who have not yet explored a ten-frame, it is a good idea to begin with a five-frame. This row of five sections is also drawn on a sheet of construction paper (or use the Blackline Master). Provide children with about ten counters that will fit in the five-frame sections and conduct the following activity.

Activity 8.13

Five-Frame Tell-About

Explain that only one counter is permitted in each section of the five-frame. No other counters are allowed on the five-frame mat. Have the children show 3 on their five-frame. "What can you tell us about three from looking at your mat?" After hearing from several children, try other numbers from 0 to 5. Children may place their counters on the five-frame in any manner. What they observe will differ a great deal from child to child. For example, with four counters, a child with two on each end may say, "It has a space in the middle" or "It's two and two." There are no wrong answers. Focus attention on how many more counters are needed to make 5 or how far away from 5 a number is. Next, try numbers between 5 and 10. The rule of one counter per section still holds. As shown in Figure 8.8, numbers greater than 5 are shown with a full five-frame and additional counters on the mat but not in the frame. In discussion, focus attention on these larger numbers as 5 and some more: "Eight is five and three more."

Notice that the five-frame really focuses on the relationship to 5, not 10, as an anchor for numbers. When five-frames have been used for a week or so, introduce ten-frames. You may want to play a ten-frame version of "Five-Frame Tell-About." Soon after, introduce the following rule for showing numbers on the ten-frame: *Always fill the top row first, starting on the left, the same way you*

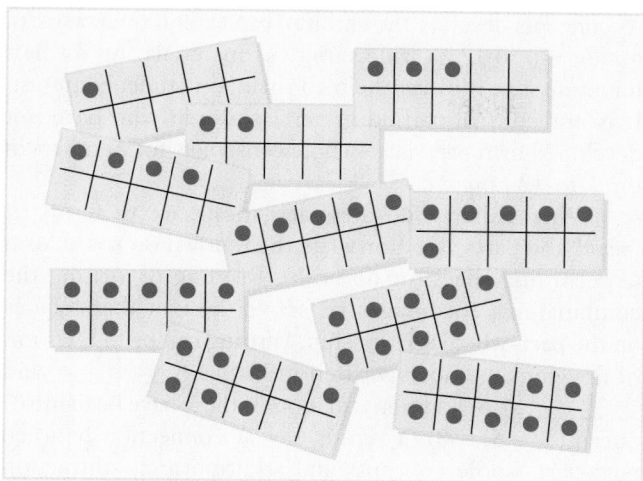

Figure 8.7 Ten-frames.

read. When the top row is full, counters can be placed in the bottom row, also starting from the left. This will produce the "standard" way to show numbers on the ten-frame, as in Figure 8.7.

For a while, many children will count every counter on their ten-frame. Some will take all counters off and begin each number from a blank frame. Others will soon learn to adjust numbers by adding on or taking off only what is required, often capitalizing on a row of five without counting. Do not pressure students. With continued practice, all students will grow. How they use the ten-frame provides insight into students' current number concept development.

Activity 8.14

Crazy Mixed-Up Numbers

This activity is adapted from *Mathematics Their Way* (Baratta-Lorton, 1976). All children make their ten-frame show the same number. The teacher then calls out random numbers between 0 and 10. After each number, the children change their ten-frames to show the new number. Children can play this game independently by preparing lists of about 15 "crazy mixed-up numbers." One child plays "teacher," and the rest use the ten-frames. Children like to make up their own number lists.

"Crazy Mixed-Up Numbers" is much more of a problem than it first appears. How do you decide how to change your ten-frame? Some children will wipe off the entire frame and start over with each numbers. Others will have learned what each number looks like. To add another dimension, have the children tell, *before changing their ten-frames,* how many more counters need to be added ("plus") or removed ("minus"). They then call out plus or minus whatever amount is appropriate. If, for example, the frames

showed 6, and the teacher called out "four," the children would respond, "Minus two!" and then change their ten-frames accordingly. A discussion of how they know what to do is valuable.

Ten-frame flash cards are an important variation of ten-frames. Make cards from tag-board about the size of a small index card, with a ten-frame on each and dots drawn in the frames. A set of 20 cards consists of a 0 card, a 10 card, and two each of the numbers 1 to 9. The cards allow for simple drill activities to reinforce the 5 and 10 anchors, as in the following activity.

Activity 8.15

Ten-Frame Flash

Flash ten-frame cards to the class or group and see how fast the children can tell how many dots are shown. This activity is fast-paced, takes only a few minutes, can be done at any time, and is a lot of fun if you encourage speed.

Important variations of "Ten-Frame Flash" include:

- Saying the number of spaces on the card instead of the number of dots
- Saying one more than the number of dots (or two more, and also less than)
- Saying the "ten fact"—for example, "Six and four make ten"

Ten-frame tasks are surprisingly problematic for students. Students must reflect on the two rows of five, the spaces remaining, and how a particular number is more or less than 5 and how far away from 10. The early discussions of how numbers are seen on the five-frames or ten-frames are examples of brief *follow-up* activities in which students learn from one another.

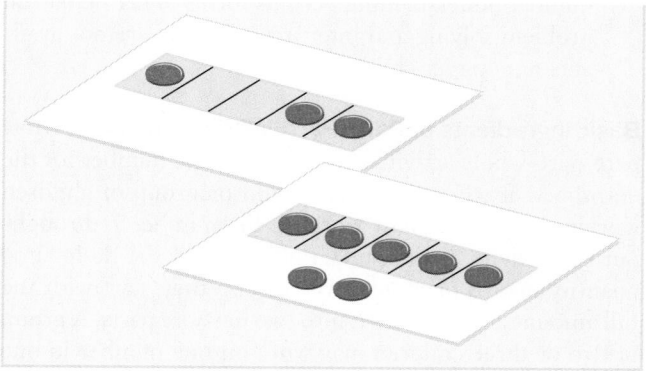

Figure 8.8 A five-frame focuses on 5 as an anchor. Counters are placed one to a section, and students tell how they see their number in the frame.

How well students are able to respond to the cards in "Ten-Frame Flash" is one good indicator of their number concepts and should be included in any quick assessment of a child's current number concept level. Also, include the variations of the activity that were listed. Since the distance to 10 is so important, another assessment is to point to a number less than 10 and ask, "If this many dots were on a ten-frame, how many spaces would there be?" Or you can simply ask, "If I have seven, how many more do I need to make ten?" ◆

Part–Part–Whole Relationships

⏸ ─────────── *Pause and Reflect*

Before reading on, get some simple counters or coins. Count out a set of eight counters as if you were a grade 1 or 2 child counting them.

Any child who has learned how to count meaningfully can count out eight objects as you just did. What is significant about the experience is what it did *not* cause you to think about. Nothing in counting a set of eight objects will cause a child to focus on the fact that it could be made of two parts. For example, separate the counters you just set out into two piles and reflect on the combination. It might be 2 and 6 or 7 and 1 or 4 and 4. Make a change in your two piles of counters and say the new combination to yourself. Focusing on a quantity in terms of its parts has important implications for developing number sense. A noted researcher in children's number concepts, Lauren Resnick (1983), states:

> Probably the major conceptual achievement of the early school years is the interpretation of numbers in terms of part and whole relationships. With the application of a Part–Whole schema to quantity, it becomes possible for children to think about numbers as compositions of other numbers. This enrichment of number understanding permits forms of mathematical problem solving and interpretation that are not available to younger children. (p. 114)

Basic Ingredients of Part–Part–Whole Activities   Most part–part–whole activities focus on a single number for the entire activity. For example, a child or group of children working together might work on the number 7 throughout the activity. Children can either build the designated quantity in two or more parts, or else they start with the full amount and separate it into two or more parts. A group of two or three children may work on one number in one activity for 5 to 20 minutes. Kindergarten children will usually begin these activities working on the number 4 or 5.

As concepts develop, the children can extend their work to numbers 6 to 12. A wide variety of materials and formats for these activities can help to maintain student interest. It is not unusual to find grade 2 children who have not developed firm part–part–whole constructs for numbers in the 7-to-12 range.

When children do these activities, have them say or "read" the parts aloud or write them down on some form of recording sheet (or do both). Reading or writing the combinations encourages reflective thought that focuses on the part–whole relationship. Writing can be in the form of drawings, numbers written in blanks (_____ and _____), or addition equations if these have been introduced ($3 + 5 = 8$). There is a clear connection between part–part–whole concepts and addition and subtraction ideas.

Part–Part–Whole Activities   The following activity and its variations may be considered the "basic" part–part–whole activity.

Activity 8.16

Build It in Parts

Provide children with one type of material, such as interlocking cubes or squares of coloured paper. The task is to see how many different combinations for a particular number they can make using two parts. Each different combination can be displayed on a small mat, such as a quarter-sheet of construction paper. Here are just a few ideas, each of which is illustrated in Figure 8.9.

- **Use two-colour counters such as lima beans spray painted on one side (also available in plastic).**
- **Make bars of connecting cubes. Make each bar with two colours. Keep the colours together.**
- **Make combinations using dot strips, which are strips of poster board with stick-on dots. (Make a lot of strips with one to four dots on them and fewer strips with five to ten dots.)**
- **Make combinations of "two-column strips." Cut these strips from tag-board ruled in 2 cm squares. Except for the single squares, all numbers are cut from two columns of squares.**
- **Colour rows of squares on 2 cm grid paper.**

Accommodation

For children who require an added challenge, have them see how many different combinations for a particular number they can make using more than two parts. They can also work with numbers greater than 15.

As you observe children working on the "Build It in Parts" activity, ask them to "read" a number sentence to go with each of their combinations. Encourage children to read their number sentences to each other. Two or three children working together with the same materials may have quite a large number of combinations including lots of repeats. Remember, the focus of this activity is on the combinations.

The following activity is strictly symbolic. However, children should use counters if they feel they need to.

Activity 8.17

Two Out of Three

Make lists of three numbers, two of which total the whole on which children are focusing. Here is an example of a list for the number 5:

    2—3—4
    5—0—2
    1—3—2
    3—1—4
    2—2—3
    4—3—1

With the list on the board, overhead, or worksheet, children can take turns selecting the two numbers that make the whole. As with all problem-solving activities, children should be challenged to justify their answers.

Accommodation

For children who are experiencing difficulty selecting the two numbers whose sum is 5, have them use one of the materials from "Build It in Parts," Activity 8.16, to make the combinations for 5, to assist them with the selection process.

Missing-Part Activities A special and important variation of part–part–whole activities is referred to as *missing-part* activities. In a missing-part activity, children know the whole amount and use their already developed knowledge of the parts of that whole to try to tell what the covered or hidden part is. If they do not know or are unsure, they simply uncover the unknown part and say the full combination as they would normally. Missing-part activities provide maximum reflection on the combinations for a number. They also serve as the forerunner to subtraction concepts. With a whole of 8 and only 3 showing, the child can later learn to write "8 − 3 = 5."

Missing-part activities require some way for a part to be hidden or unknown. Usually this is done with two children working together or else it can be done in a

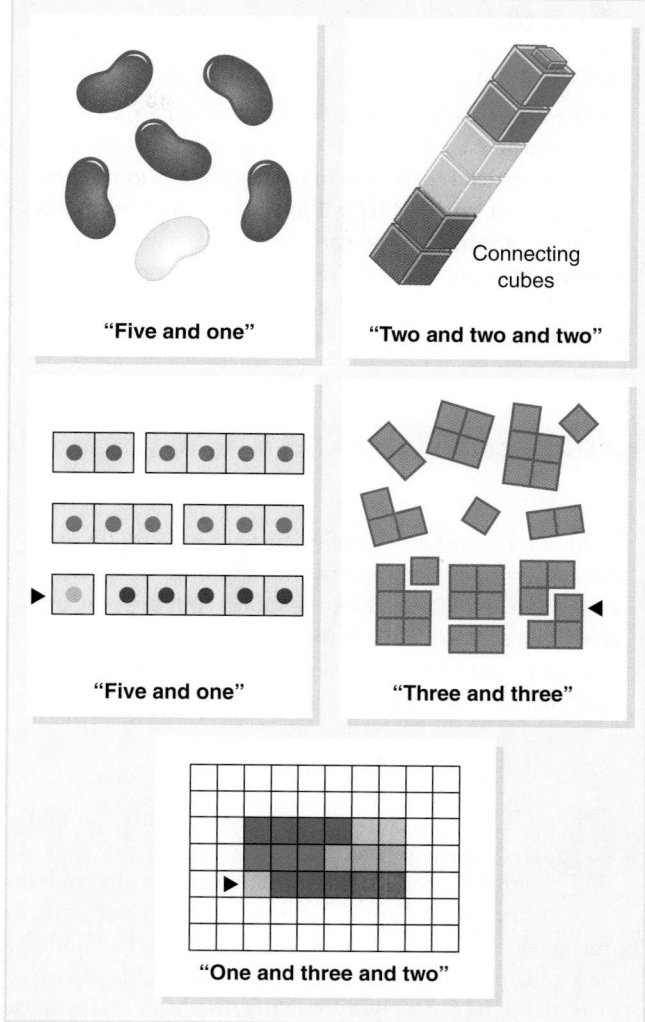

"Five and one"   "Two and two and two"

Connecting cubes

"Five and one"   "Three and three"

"One and three and two"

Figure 8.9 Assorted materials for building parts of 6.

teacher-directed manner with the class. Again, the focus of the activity is on a single designated quantity as the whole. The next four activities illustrate variations of this important idea.

Activity 8.18

Covered Parts

A set of counters equal to the target amount is counted out, and the rest are put aside. One child places the counters under a margarine tub or piece of tag-board. The child then pulls some out into view. (This amount could be none, all, or any amount in between.) For example, if 6 is the whole and 4 are showing, the other child says, "Four and two is six." If there is hesitation or if the hidden part is unknown, the hidden part is immediately shown (see Figure 8.10).

Activity 8.19

Missing-Part Cards

For each number from 4 to 10, make missing-part cards on strips of 7 cm by 22 cm tag-board. Each card has a number, which represents the whole, and two dot sets with one set covered by a flap. For the number 8, for example, you need nine cards with the visible dot set ranging from zero to eight dots. Students use the cards as in "Covered Parts," saying, "Four and two is six" for a card showing four dots and hiding two (see Figure 8.10).

Activity 8.20

I Wish I Had

Hold out a bar of interlocking cubes, a dot strip, a two-column strip, or a dot plate showing 6 or less. Say, "I wish I had six." The children respond with the part that is needed to make 6. Counting on can be used to check. The game can focus on a single whole, or the "I wish I had" number can change each time (see Figure 8.10)

There are lots of ways you can use computer software to create part–part–whole activities. All that is needed is a program that permits students to create sets of objects on the screen. Scott Foresman's *eTools* (Pearson Education, 2004) includes a variety of background screens for counters. This activity is also available free at www.kyrene.org/mathtools. If you use the online version, choose "Counters." Under "workspaces" on the bottom left, select the bucket icon. Then select the bathtub and add boat, duck, or goldfish counters. In the version shown in Figure 8.11, children can stamp these three different types of bathtub toys either in the tub (unseen) or outside the tub. The number on the tub shows how many are in the tub or it can be fixed to show a question mark (?) for missing-part thinking. The total is shown at the bottom. By clicking on the light bulb above the tub, the contents of the tub can be seen (Figure 8.11b). In the hands of a teacher, this program offers a great deal of diversity and challenge for both part–part–whole and missing-part activities. ◆

◼◼ ——————— *Pause and Reflect*

Remember the list you made earlier in the chapter about what children should know about the number 8? Get it out now and see if you would add to it or revise it based on what you have read to this point. Do this before reading on.

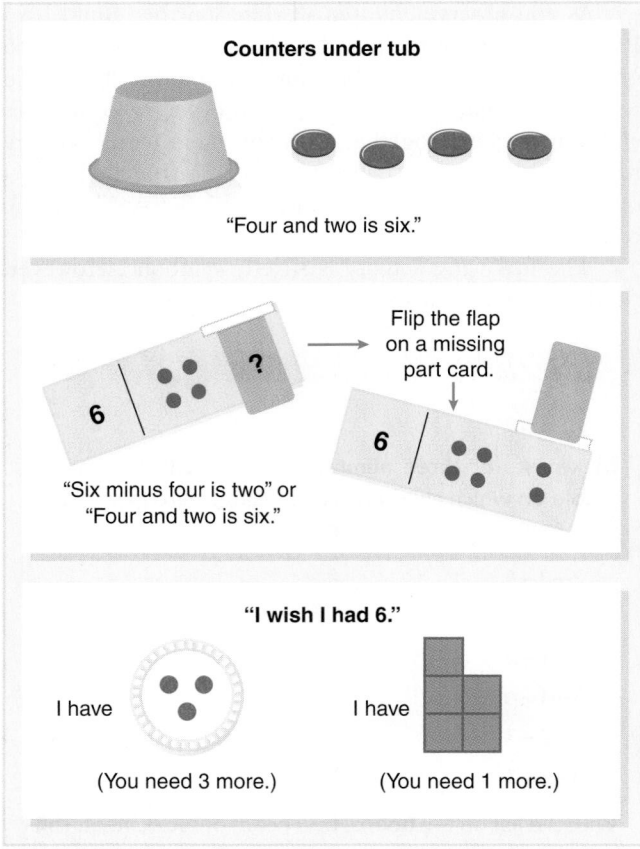

Figure 8.10 Missing-part activities.

Here is a possible list of the kinds of things that children should know about the number 8 (or any number up to about 12) by the end of grade 1. Children should be able to:

- Count to eight (know the number words).
- Count eight objects and know that the last number word tells how many.
- Write the number 8.
- Recognize the number 8.

The preceding list represents the minimal skills children need to work with number. In the following list are the relationships that contribute to number sense students should have:

- More and less by 1 and 2: 8 is one more than 7, one less than 9, two more than 6, and two less than 10.
- Spatial patterns for 8 such as

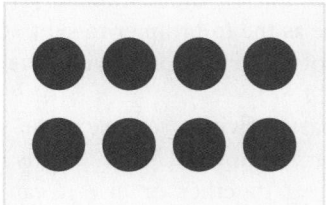

(a)

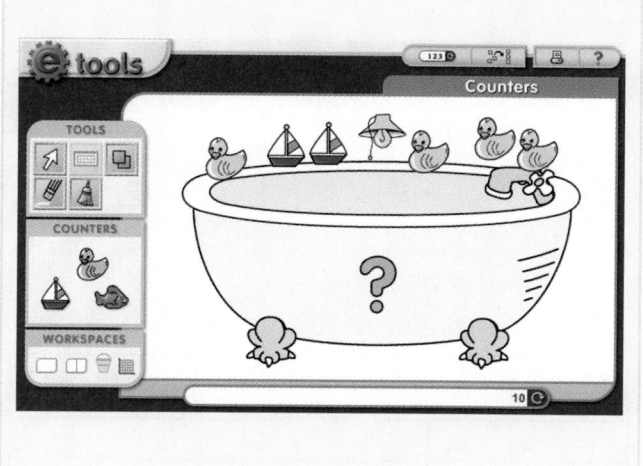

(b)

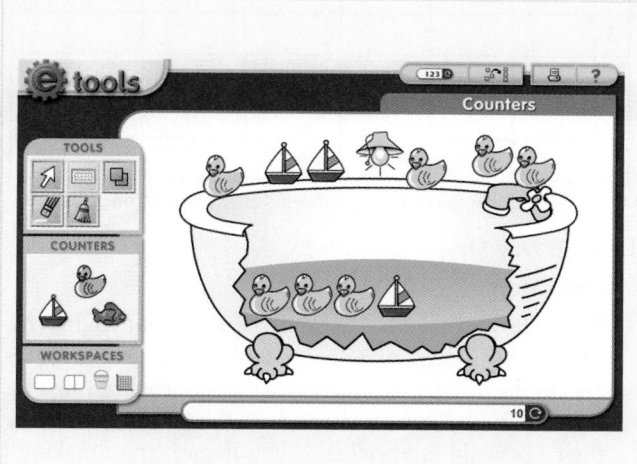

Figure 8.11 The counters tool in Scott Foresman's eTools software (Pearson Education, 2004) is useful for exploring part–part–whole and missing-part ideas as well as earlier number concepts and early addition/subtraction ideas.

- Anchors to 5 and 10: 8 is 5 and 3 more, and 2 away from 10.
- Part–whole relationships: 8 is 5 and 3, 2 and 6, 7 and 1, and so on. This includes knowing the missing part of 8.
- Doubles: double 4 is 8.
- Relationships to the real world: 8 is one more than the days of the week, my brother is 8 years old, my crayons are 8 centimetres long.

Dot Cards as a Model for Teaching Number Relationships

Many good number development activities involve more than one of the relationships discussed so far. As children learn about ten-frames, patterned sets, and other relationships, the dot cards in the Blackline Masters provide a wealth of activities (see Figure 8.12). The cards contain dot patterns, patterns that require counting, combinations of two and three simple patterns, and ten-frames with "standard" as well as unusual placements of dots. When children use these cards for any activity that involves number concepts, the cards make them think about numbers in many different ways. The dot cards add another dimension to many of the activities already described. They can also be used effectively in the following activities.

Activity 8.21

Double War

The game of "Double War" (Kamii, 1985) is played like "War," but on each play, both players turn up two cards instead of one. The winner is the player with the larger total. Children playing the game can use many different number relationships, without actually finding the total number of dots, to determine the winner.

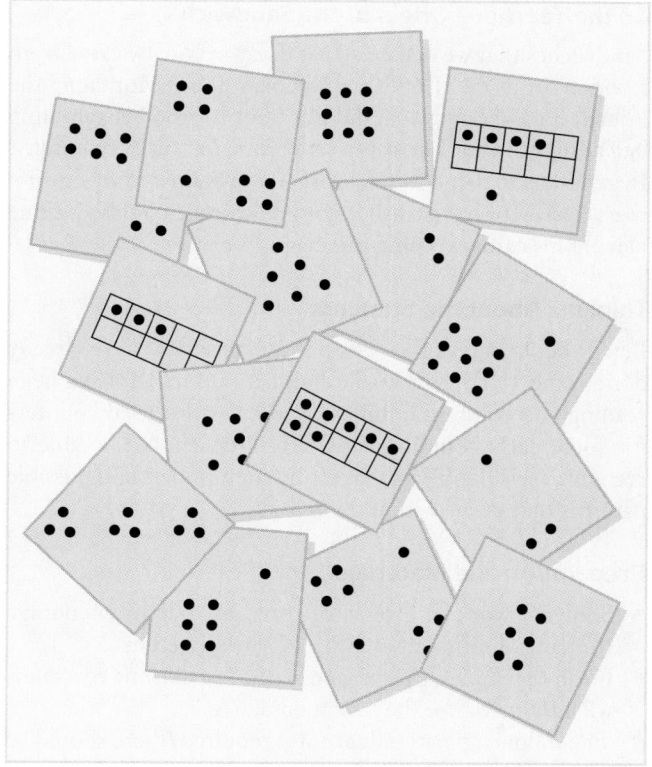

Figure 8.12 Dot cards can be made using the Blackline Masters.

Problem-Based Lesson:
Earl's Sandwich

This problem-based lesson differentiates instruction to meet the varied needs of students. Moreover, it reinforces students' understanding of early number concepts from a problem-based perspective.

The lesson demonstrates how a range of learner needs can be accommodated by having students use manipulatives to represent number ideas developed in the lesson. The open-ended nature of this lesson allows students to work at a pace suited to their level of ability as they create their sandwiches in collaboration with their peers. Ideally, this lesson will extend over two days.

Grade Level: Grade 1 and 2

Mathematical Goals

- Reinforce students' understanding of early number concepts
- Further develop students' counting skills
- Help students connect number concepts to the real world
- Further develop students' understanding of graphing as one way of representing ideas about number
- Engage students in problem solving involving part–whole relationships

To the Teacher—Origin of the Sandwich

Sandwiches that we make and eat today originally came from London in 1762. English nobleman John Montagu, the Fourth Earl of Sandwich, did not want to stop his gambling late at night to eat but at the same time he was very hungry. Legend has it that Montagu ordered a waiter to bring him roast beef between two slices of bread so he could continue playing his cards, keeping one hand free.

Thinking About the Students

Before being taught this lesson students should have already done some work with whole numbers up to 10, have been reading and printing numbers, and have also used counters for some early counting activities. They should be able to recognize sets of objects that represent numbers and possible patterns that occur within them.

Preparation and Materials

- Students work in groups of three or four to encourage students of different abilities to work together.
- Fresh vegetables, cheese, and bread to make one real sandwich to introduce the lesson on day one.
- The following materials are also required (there should be enough for two sandwiches per child): construction paper cutouts of the ingredients (bread, tomato slices, cucumber slices, yellow cheese slices, lettuce leaves) for making

sandwiches. The following chart shows the ingredients with the suggested colour and shape used for each.

Ingredients	Construction Paper Cutouts
1) Bread	Brown rectangles
2) Cheese	Yellow squares
3) Tomato	Red circles
4) Lettuce	Green rectangles
5) Cucumber	White triangles

Number of Ingredients					
6					
5					
4					
3					
2					
1					
	BREAD	CHEESE	TOMATO	LETTUCE	CUCUMBER

(A full-page sample can be found at the end of Appendix A on page A10.)

Lesson: Day One

Introduction

- Begin the lesson with a short discussion about your favourite healthy foods. Include vegetables, fruit, whole grains, etc., in the discussion. Introduce the sandwich as one food that is tasty and nutritious and have the children talk about their favourite sandwiches. Then demonstrate making a tasty and nutritious sandwich using real ingredients.
- Hold up the sandwich made of 6 items: 2 pieces of bread, 1 slice of cheese, and 3 slices of tomato. Together with the class, name the ingredients used to make the sandwich and count how many of each ingredient were used. Place construction paper cutouts representing each ingredient on a paper plate as they are counted. Carry out a second count with the whole class and list the number of each ingredient used on the My Sandwich recipe sheet.
- Make another sandwich with six items (including the bread) together with the children, using only the construction paper cutouts. The sandwich is for a special person named Earl. Invite children to come up and choose the ingredients for the sandwich and place each one on the plate. Then count the ingredients with the whole class and list them on a My Sandwich recipe sheet.
- Some possible questions for discussion are:
    What ingredients did we use to make our sandwich?
    How many slices of cheese are in the sandwich?
    How many slices of tomato?
    Are there fewer slices of cheese than tomato?
    Are there more slices of bread than tomato?

What is another way we can make a six-item sandwich with these ingredients?

The Task

- Students will work in assigned groups of four, as chefs, to make their own sandwiches of six ingredients using the paper cutouts.
- They record the number of each ingredient on the My Sandwich recipe sheet.

Establish Expectations

- Explain to the students that today, while working in groups of four, they will be chefs making their own sandwiches using the paper cutouts laid out on the tables.
- Each sandwich is to have six items including the bread. The number of each ingredient is to be listed on the My Sandwich recipe sheet, which will be displayed in a class cookbook. (As an alternative, the recipes could be displayed on a class bulletin board.) Explain that the recipe sheets will allow others to reproduce their sandwiches.
- Review and display the ingredients: bread, tomato, cheese, lettuce, and cucumber.
- The instructions are listed on experience chart paper, which is readily displayed for the children.

Development

- The children work in their assigned groups, selecting their ingredients for their sandwich and placing them on their paper plates. They then fill in their My Sandwich recipe sheets.
- Invite the earlier finishers who have successfully completed the task to add more ingredients to their sandwich and create a new recipe sheet for their sandwich.
- The students trade sandwiches and recipe sheets to examine each other's sandwiches and to make sure they have recorded the number of items correctly. If time permits the children can make another sandwich with six items that is different from the ones used in the previous sandwich for a family member.

Follow-up

- On completion of the task, the class chefs meet as a whole group to talk about the sandwiches and discuss the different combinations they created, all representing the number six.

Next Steps_____

Assessment Notes

- Which students were early finishers?
- Which ones are still not sure about the combinations that make up the number six?
- Which ones could use larger numbers?

Lesson: Day Two

Introduction

- Together with the class illustrate the ingredients for yesterday's sandwich, created with the class, on the My Sandwich bar graph sheet.

The Task

- The students will illustrate their sandwich ingredients on the My Sandwich bar graph sheets.
- They will work together to match other groups' My Sandwich bar graph sheets with their sandwiches. Note: Each group will ensure that the bar graph sheets are placed in mixed order in the middle of the tables.

Establish Expectations

- Explain to the children that today they will illustrate their sandwich ingredients on the My Sandwich bar graph sheets.
- Their completed graphs, which have been checked by each other, are to be placed in the middle of the table so they are not close to their own sandwich.
- On completion they will move to another table and work together to match up correctly the bar graph sheets with the sandwiches.

Development

- The children work in their assigned groups creating their My Sandwich bar graph sheets. They check each other's sheets.
- They place their bar graph sheets in the middle of the table in a random arrangement so they are not beside their sandwiches.
- The groups then rotate to a different table and together the children work to figure out which graphs match with the appropriate sandwich.
- On completion they place the bar graph sheets in random order in the middle of the table and move to another table.
- On completion of the task, the students meet as a whole group to discuss and compare the number quantities.

Follow-up

- The chefs come together as a whole class to discuss and compare their graphs. The terms *fewer than, more than, different than,* and *same as* are included in the discussion as the numbers are compared.
- Sandwiches with more than six items are included in the discussion.
- As a cross-curricular connection, the story *The Sandwich* by Ian Wallace (ISBN 0-919964-402-8) can be read and discussed with the children. It is the story of a little boy who is teased because of his "stinky sandwiches." Along the way he learns to be proud of his heritage and teaches his class what it truly means to be inclusive.

Activity 8.22

Difference War

Deal out the cards to the two players as in regular "War," and prepare a pile of 30 to 40 counters. On each play, the players turn over their cards as usual. The player with the greater number of dots wins as many counters from the pile as the difference between the two cards. The players keep their cards. The game is over when the counter pile runs out. The player with the most counters wins the game.

Activity 8.23

Number Sandwiches

Select a number between 5 and 12, then find combinations of two cards whose totals equal the number. With the dot side out, students make a "sandwich" with the two cards. When at least ten sandwiches have been found, the next challenge is to name the number on the other side of the sandwich. The sandwich is turned over to confirm. The same pairs can then be used again to name the hidden part.

Use a missing-part diagnostic interview, similar to Activity 8.18 ("Covered Parts"), to assess the important part–whole relationships. Begin

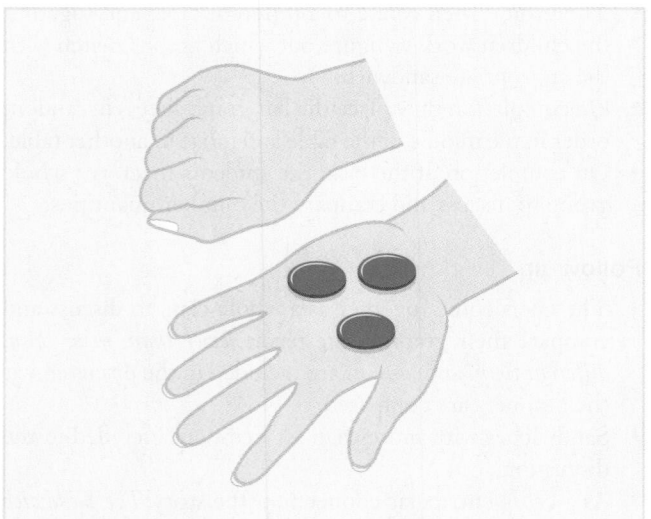

Figure 8.13 A missing-part number assessment. Eight in all. "How many are hidden?"

with a number you believe the child has "mastered," say, 5. Have the child count out that many counters into your open hand. Close your hand around the counters and confirm that the child knows how many are hidden. Then, remove some and show them in the palm of your other hand. (See Figure 8.13.) Ask the child, "How many are hidden?" Repeat the task with different amounts removed, keeping in mind that it is only necessary to check three or four missing parts for each number. If the child responds quickly and correctly and is clearly not counting in any way, call that a "mastered number." If a number is mastered, repeat the entire process with the next higher number. Continue until the child begins to stumble. Early in grade 1, you will find a range in numbers from 4 to 7 or 8 that have been mastered. By spring, most children should have mastered numbers to 10. ◆

Relationships for Numbers 10 to 20

Even though children in kindergarten, grade 1, and grade 2 experience numbers up to 20 and beyond daily, it should not be assumed that they will automatically extend the set of relationships they have developed for smaller numbers to numbers beyond 10. Yet these numbers play a big part in many simple counting activities, in basic facts, and in much of what we do with mental computation. Relationships with these numbers are just as important as relationships involving the numbers through 10.

Pre–Place-Value Concepts

A set of ten should play a major role in children's early understanding of numbers between 10 and 20. When children see a set of six with a set of ten, they should know without counting that the total is 16. It is not appropriate to discuss place-value concepts while working on the numbers between 10 and 20. Prior to a more complete development of place-value concepts (appropriate for grade 2 and beyond), children should not be asked to explain that the 1 in 16 represents "one ten."

Pause and Reflect

Say to yourself, "One ten." Now think about that from the perspective of a child just learning to count to 20! What could one ten possibly mean when ten tells me how many fingers I have and it is the number that comes after nine? How can it be one?

At first, children do not see a numerical pattern in the numbers between 10 and 20. Rather, these number names are simply ten additional words in the number sequence. The concept of a single ten is challenging for a kindergarten or early grade 1 child to grasp. Some would say that it is not appropriate for grade 1 at all (Kamii, 1985). The inappropriateness of discussing "one ten and six ones" (what's a one?) does not negate that a set of ten should not figure prominently in the discussion of numbers in the teens. The following activity illustrates this idea.

Activity 8.24

Ten and Some More

Use a simple two-part mat and have children count out 10 counters on one side. Next, have them put 5 counters on the other side. Together, count all of the counters by ones. Chant the combination: "Ten and five is fifteen." Repeat with other numbers in a random order, without changing the 10 side of the mat.

Activity 8.24 is designed to teach new number names; thus it requires a certain amount of direct teaching. Following this activity, explore numbers to 20 in a more open-ended manner. Provide each child with two ten-frames drawn one under the other on a construction paper mat, or use the Blackline Master provided. In random order, have children show numbers to 20 on their mats. That is, play "Crazy Mixed-Up Numbers" (Activity 8.14) with two ten-frames and numbers to 20. There is no preferred way to do this as long as the number of counters is correct. What is interesting is the discussion regarding how the counters can be arranged on the mat so that it is easy to see how many are there. Have children share their ideas. Not every child will use a full set of ten. But as this idea becomes more popular, the notion that ten and some more is an amount in the teens will soon be developed. As you listen to your children, you may want to begin challenging them to find ways to show 26 counters or even more.

Extending More and Less Relationships

The relationships of one more than, two more than, one less than, and two less than are important for all numbers. These ideas are built on or connected to the same concepts for numbers less than 10. That 17 is one less than 18 is an idea connected to the fact that 7 is one less than 8. Children may need help in making this connection.

Activity 8.25

More and Less Extended

On the overhead or whiteboard, show seven counters, and ask what is two more, one less, and so on. Now add a filled ten-frame to the display (or 10 in any pattern) and repeat the questions. Pair up questions by covering and uncovering the ten-frame as illustrated in Figure 8.14.

Doubles and Near-Doubles

The use of doubles (double 6 is 12) and near-doubles (13 is double 6 and 1 more) is generally considered a strategy for memorizing basic addition facts. There is no reason why children should not begin to develop these relationships long before they are concerned with memorizing basic facts. Doubles and near-doubles are simply special cases of the general part–part–whole construct.

Relate the doubles to special images. Children can draw pictures or make posters that illustrate the doubles for each number. Any images that are strong ideas for your children will be good for them.

Periodically conduct oral exercises in which students double the number you say. Ask children to explain how they knew a particular double. Many will not use the pictures.

Activity 8.26

The Double Maker

Make the calculator into a "double maker" by pressing 2 $\times$ $=$. Now a press of any digit followed by $=$ will produce the double of that number. Children can work in pairs or individually to try to beat the calculator.

As a related oral task, say a number then ask students to tell what double it is. "What is fourteen?" (Double 7.) When students can do this well, use any number up to 20. "What is seventeen?" (Double 8 and 1 more.)

Accommodation

For children who are experiencing difficulty figuring out the number that is doubled to make the given number, provide them with counters so they can divide the given number into two groups. Also, refrain from using numbers that make a double and one more.

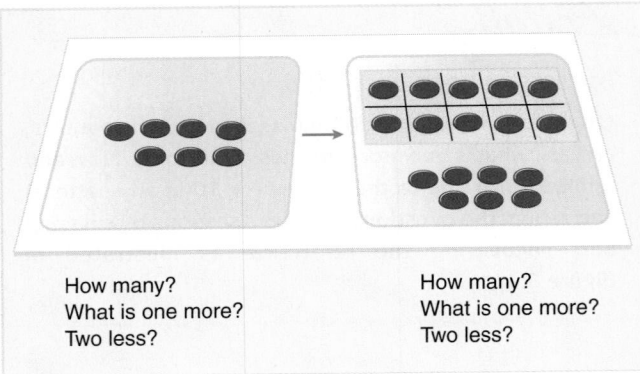

How many?
What is one more?
Two less?

How many?
What is one more?
Two less?

Figure 8.14 Extending relationships to the teens.

Number Sense and the Real World

Here we examine ways to broaden the early knowledge of numbers in a different way. Relationships of numbers to real-world quantities and measures and the use of numbers in simple estimations can help children develop the flexible, intuitive ideas about numbers that are most desired. Here are some activities that can help children connect numbers to real situations.

Activity 8.27

Add a Unit to Your Number

Write a number on the board. Now suggest some units to go with it and ask the children what they can think of that fits. For example, suppose the number is 9. "What do you think of when I say 9 *dollars*? 9 *hours*? 9 *cars*? 9 *kids*? 9 *metres*? 9 *o'clock*? 9 *litres*?" Spend some time discussing each. Let children suggest units as well. Be prepared to explore some of the ideas either immediately or as projects or tasks to share with parents or guardians at home.

Activity 8.28

Is It Reasonable?

Select a number and a unit—for example, 5 metres. Could the teacher be 5 metres tall? Could your living room be 5 metres wide? Can a man jump 5 metres high? Could three children standing side-by-side with their hands touching stretch their arms a distance of 5 metres? Pick any number, large or small, and a unit with which children are familiar; then make up a series of these questions.

Once children are familiar with Activity 8.28, have them select the number and the unit or things (10 kids, 20 bananas, ...), and see what kinds of questions children make up. When a difference of opinion develops, capitalize on the opportunity to explore and experiment. Resist the temptation to supply your adult-level knowledge. Rather, say, "Well, how can we find out if it is or is not reasonable? Who has an idea about what we could do?"

These activities are problem-based in the truest sense. Not only are there no clear answers, but children can easily begin to pose their own questions and explore number in a way that is most interesting to them. Children will not have these real-world connections when you begin, and you may be disappointed in their limited ideas about number. Howden (1989) writes about a grade 1 teacher of children from very impoverished backgrounds. Although resources were scarce, she told Howden, "They all have fingers, the school grounds are strewn with lots of pebbles and leaves, and pinto beans are cheap. So we count, sort, compare, and talk about such objects. We've measured and weighed almost everything in this room and almost everything the children can drag in" (p. 6). This teacher's children had produced a wonderfully rich and long list of responses to the question "What comes to your mind when I say twenty-four?" In another school in a professional community where test scores are high, the same question brought almost no response from a class of grade 3 students. It can be a very rewarding effort to help children connect their number ideas to the real world.

Estimation and Measurement

One of the best ways for children to think of real quantities is to associate numbers with measures of things. In the early grades, measures of length, mass, and time are good places to begin. Just measuring and recording results will not be very effective, since there is no reason for children to be interested in or think about the result. To help children think about or reflect a bit on what number might tell how long the desk is or how heavy the book is, it would be good if they could first write down or tell you an estimate. However, producing an estimate is a very difficult task for young children. They do not grasp the concept of "estimate" or "about." For example, suppose that you have cut out of poster board an ample supply of very large footprints, say, about 36 centimetres long. All are exactly the same size. You would like to ask the class, "About how many footprints will it take to measure the distance across the rug in our reading corner?" The key word here is *about*, and it is one that you will need to spend a lot of time helping children understand. The request for an estimate can be done in ways that help develop an understanding of the concept of "about," while not requiring students to give a specific number.

The following estimation questions can be used with most early estimation activities:

- *More or less than _____?* Will it be more or less than 10 footprints? Will the mass of the apple be more or less than 20 wooden blocks? Are there more or less than 15 connecting cubes in this long bar?

- *Closer to _____ or to _____?* Will it be closer to 5 footprints or closer to 20 footprints? Will the mass of the apple be closer to 10 blocks or closer to 30 blocks? Is this bar closer to 10 cubes or closer to 50 cubes?

- *About _____.* Use one of these numbers: 5, 10, 15, 20, 25, 30, 35, 40, ... About how many footprints? About how many blocks will the mass of the apple be? About how many cubes are in this bar?

Asking for estimates using these formats helps children learn what you mean by "about." Every child can make an estimate without having to pull a number out of the air. Rewarding students for the closest estimate in a competitive fashion will often result in their learning to seek precision and actually estimate. Instead, it is best to discuss all answers that fall into a reasonable range.

To help with numbers and measures, estimate several things in succession using the same unit. For example, suppose that you are estimating and measuring "around things" using a string. To measure, the string is wrapped around the object then measured in some unit such as craft sticks. After measuring the distance around Demetra's head, estimate the distance around the wastebasket or around the globe or around George's wrist. Each successive measure helps children with the new estimates.

Data Collection and Analysis

Graphing activities are another good way to connect children's worlds with number. Chapter 21 discusses ways to make graphs with children in grades K–2. Graphs can be quickly made of almost any data that can be gathered from the students: favourite ice cream, favourite colour, favourite sports team, favourite pet; number of sisters and brothers; children who ride different buses; types of shoes; number of pets; and so on. Graphs can be connected to content in other areas. A unit on water might lead to a graph of items that sink or float.

Once a simple bar graph is made, it is very important to take a few minutes to ask as many number questions as are appropriate for the graph. In the early stages of number development (grades K–1), the use of graphs for teaching number relationships and for connecting numbers to real quantities in the children's environment is a more important reason for building graphs than the graphs themselves.

The graphs focus attention on counts of realistic things. Equally important, bar graphs clearly illustrate comparisons between and among numbers that are rarely evident when only one number or quantity is considered at a time. See Figure 8.15 for an example of a graph and questions that can be asked. At first, children will have trouble with the questions involving differences, but repeated exposure to these ideas in a bar graph format will improve their understanding. These comparison concepts add considerably to children's understanding of number.

 The *Standards* clearly recognizes the value of integrating number development with other areas of the curriculum. "Students' work with numbers should be connected to their work with other mathematical topics. For example, computational fluency ... can both enable and be enabled by students' investigations of data; a knowledge of patterns supports the development of skip counting and algebraic thinking; and experiences with shape, space, and number help students develop estimation skills related to quantity and size" (p. 79).

Extensions to Early Mental Mathematics

Teachers of grades 2 and 3 can capitalize on some of the early number relationships and extend them to numbers up to 100. A useful set of materials to help with these relationships is the little ten-frames found in the Blackline Masters. Each child should have a set of 10 tens and a set of frames for each number 1 to 9, with an extra 5.

The following three ideas can be demonstrated using the little ten-frames in Figure 8.16. First are the relationships of one more than and one less than. If you understand that one more than 6 is 7, in a similar manner, one ten more than 60 is 70. The second idea really looks ahead to fact strategies. If a child has learned to think about adding on to 8 or 9 by first adding up to 10 then adding the rest, the extension to similar two-digit numbers is quite simple; see Figure 8.16b. Finally, the most powerful idea for small numbers is to think of them in parts. It is a very useful idea to take apart larger numbers to begin to develop some flexibility in the same way. Children can begin by thinking of ways to take apart a multiple of 10 such as 80. Once they do it with tens, the challenge can be to think of ways to take apart 80 when one part has a 5 in it, such as 25 or 35.

More will be said about early mental computation in Chapter 12. The point to be made here is that early number relationships have a greater impact on what children know than what may be apparent at first. Even teachers in the upper grades may profitably consider the use of ten-frames and part–part–whole activities.

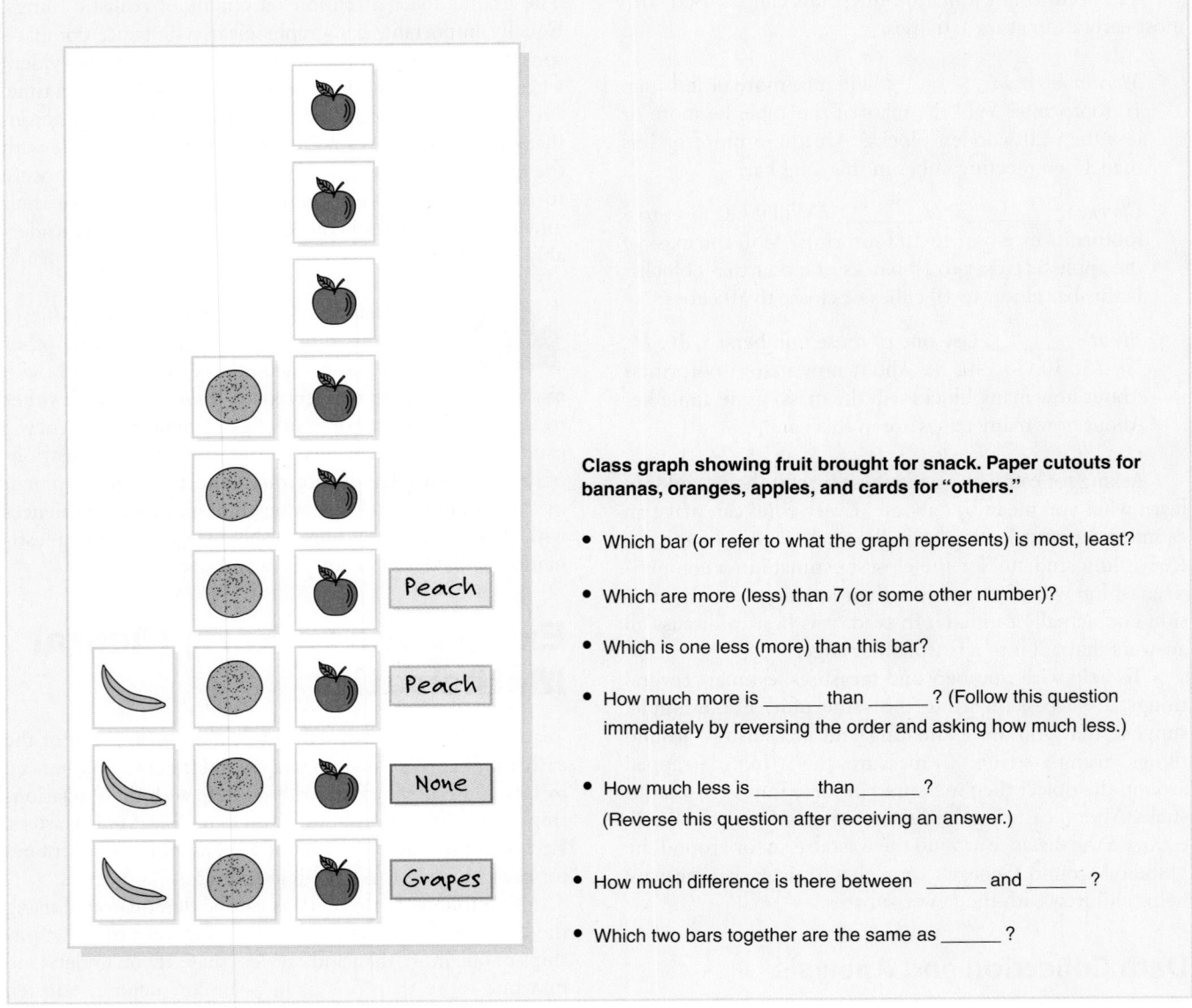

Class graph showing fruit brought for snack. Paper cutouts for bananas, oranges, apples, and cards for "others."

- Which bar (or refer to what the graph represents) is most, least?

- Which are more (less) than 7 (or some other number)?

- Which is one less (more) than this bar?

- How much more is _____ than _____? (Follow this question immediately by reversing the order and asking how much less.)

- How much less is _____ than _____? (Reverse this question after receiving an answer.)

- How much difference is there between _____ and _____?

- Which two bars together are the same as _____?

Figure 8.15 Relationships and number sense in a bar graph.

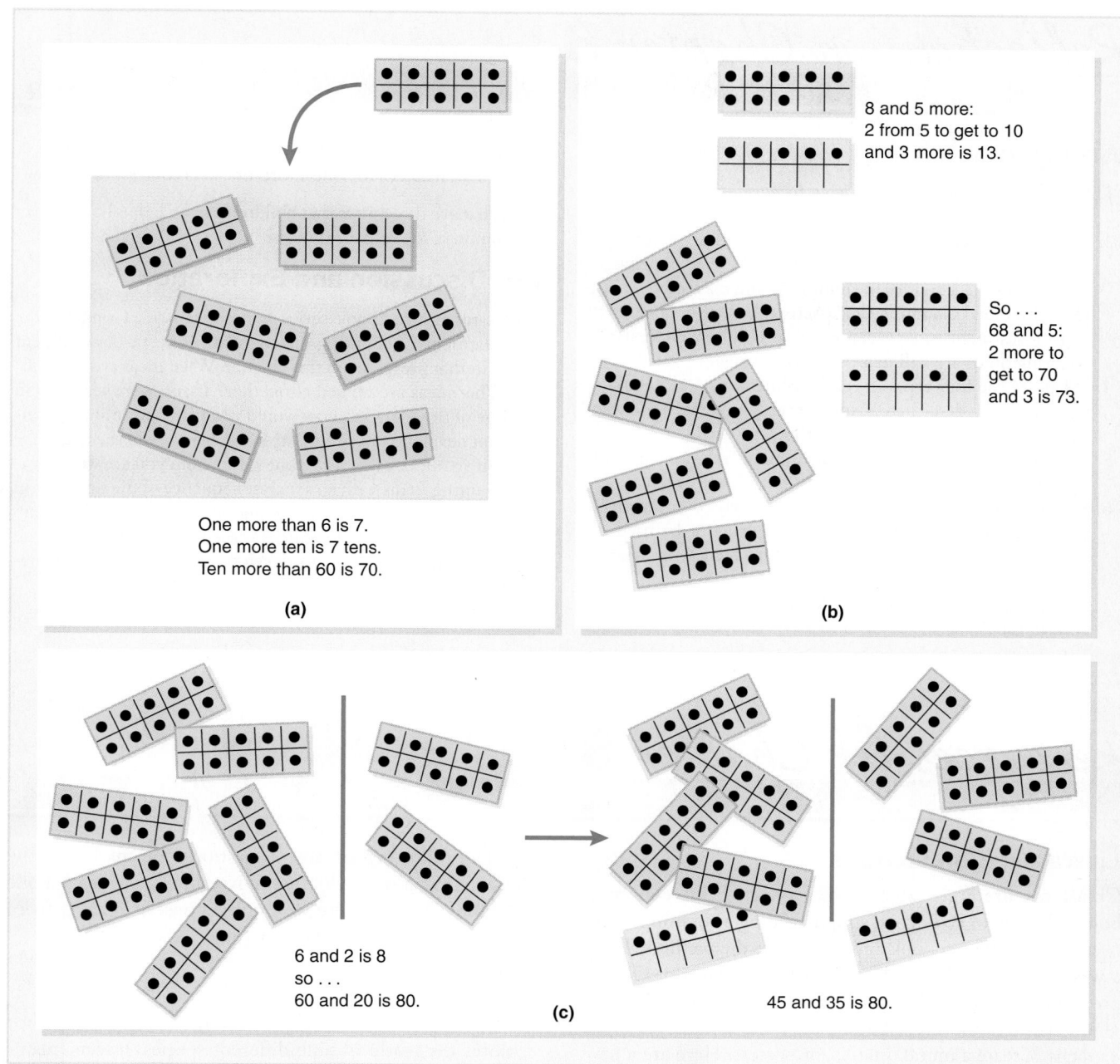

One more than 6 is 7.
One more ten is 7 tens.
Ten more than 60 is 70.

(a)

8 and 5 more:
2 from 5 to get to 10
and 3 more is 13.

So . . .
68 and 5:
2 more to
get to 70
and 3 is 73.

(b)

6 and 2 is 8
so . . .
60 and 20 is 80.

(c)

45 and 35 is 80.

Figure 8.16 Extending early number relationships to mental computation activities.

Reflections on Chapter 8

Writing to Learn

1. What things must a child be able to do in order to count a set accurately?
2. Describe an activity that is a "set-to-number matching" activity. What understandings must a child have in place in order to do the activities meaningfully and correctly?
3. How can "Real Counting On" (Activity 8.7, p. 124) be used as an assessment tool to determine if children understand counting on or are still in a transitional stage?
4. What are the four types of relationships for small numbers that have been described? Explain briefly what each of these means and suggest at least one activity for each.
5. How can a teacher assess the number relationships of part–whole?
6. How can a calculator be used to develop early counting ideas connected with number? How can a calculator be used to help a child practise number relationships such as part–part–whole or one less than?
7. For numbers between 10 and 20, describe how to develop each of these ideas:

a. The idea of the teens as a set of ten and some more
b. Extension of the one-more/one-less concept to the teens

8. What are three ways that children can be helped to connect numbers to real-world ideas?

For Discussion and Exploration

1. Examine a textbook series for grades K–2. Compare the treatment of counting and number concept development with that presented in this chapter. What ideas are stressed? What ideas are missed altogether? If you were teaching in one of these grades, how would you plan your number concept development program? What part would the text play?
2. You've noticed that a student with whom you are working is counting items with an accurate sequence of the numbers in our system, but is not attaching one number to each item. Therefore, the final count is inaccurate. What would you plan to help this students develop a better grasp of the one-to-one correspondence?

Resources for Chapter 8

Literature Connections

Children's literature abounds with wonderful counting books. Be sure to go beyond simply reading a counting book or a number-related book and looking at the pictures. Find a way to connect the book to the children's world. Create problems related to the story. Have children identify the mathematics in the story. Extend the numbers and see what happens. Create a mural, graphs, or posters. Here are a few ideas for making literature connections to number concepts and number sense.

Anno's Counting   *House Anno, 1982*

This book shows ten children in various parts of a house. As the pages are turned, the front of the house covers the children in it so only a few are visible through cut out windows. A second house is on the opposite page. As you move through the book, the children move one at a time to the second house, creating the potential for a 10–0, 9–1, 8–2, ..., 0–10 pattern of pairs. As each page shows part of the group of children through the window, there is an opportunity to discuss how many are in the missing part. Have the children use counters to model the story as you "read" it the second or third time.

The following are some questions you might ask the children: What if the children moved in pairs instead of one at a time? What if there were three houses? What if there were more children? What about your house?

Creatures Great and Small   *Patkau, 2006*

This beautifully illustrated book by a Canadian author explores the world of nine different species: insects, mammals, sea jellies, reptiles, amphibians, birds, crustaceans, arachnids, and mollusks. The concept of scale and proportion are introduced by comparing measurements of animals that are "big" and "really big" to "small" and "really small." The illustrations portray both the oversize and the tiny creatures.

My Arctic 1, 2, 3   *Kusugak, 1996*

This counting book draws on the author's Inuit experiences to weave a fascinating tale that introduces readers to life in Repulse Bay in the Arctic. Students will have a chance to meet and count some of the animals Kusugak and his family watch in the Arctic. This book can easily be used for cross-curricular connections.

Two Ways to Count to Ten   *Dee, 1988*

This Liberian folktale is about King Leopard's search for the best animal to marry his daughter. The task devised involves throwing a spear and counting to 10 before the spear lands. Many animals try and fail. Counting by ones proves too lengthy. Finally, the antelope succeeds by counting "2, 4, 6, 8, 10."

The story is a perfect lead-in to skip counting. Can you count to 10 by threes? How else can you count to 10? In how many ways can you count to 48? What numbers can you reach if you count by fives? A hundreds board or counters are useful in helping with these problems. Be sure to have children write about what they discover in their investigations.

Another amusing book to use is *The King's Commissioners* (Friedman, 1994), a hilarious tale that also opens up opportunities to count by different groupings or skip counting.

Recommendations for Further Reading

Articles

Fuson, K. C., Grandau, L., & Sugiyama, P. A. (2001). Achievable numerical understandings for all young children. *Teaching Children Mathematics, 7*, 522–526.

Researchers who have long worked with the number development of young children provide the reader with a concise overview of number development from ages 3 to 7. This practical reporting of their research is quite useful.

Griffin, S. (2003). Laying the foundation for computational fluency in early childhood. *Teaching Children Mathematics, 9*, 306–309.

This short article clearly lays out five stages of number development based on a simple addition story problem task. This is followed by activities to develop number at each stage. It is a useful article, especially for diagnosis and remediation of early number development.

Losq, C. (2005). Number concepts and special needs students: The power of ten-frame tiles. *Teaching Children Mathematics, 11* (6), 310–315.

This is a very useful article to engage struggling learners in the use of a countable and visually unique model—the ten-frame tile. Losq positions the ten-frames described in this chapter in a vertical position to enhance subitizing, or instant recognition, and provide useful tools for formative assessment.

Books

Fosnot, C. T., & Dolk, M. (2001). *Young mathematicians at work: Constructing number sense, addition, and subtraction.* Portsmouth, NH: Heinemann.

One of three books in a series by these authors, it describes clearly the development of number concepts. Dolk represents the view of the Freudenthal Institute in the Netherlands and Fosnot is a respected mathematician and theoretician in the United States. This book demonstrates a sensitivity for children and a detailed perspective on children's number development.

Richardson, K. (2002). *Assessing math concepts: The hiding assessment.* Rowley, MA: Didax.

This is one of a series of nine assessment books covering number topics from counting through two-digit numbers. The assessments are designed for one-on-one interviews. Extensive explanations and levels with examples are provided. Richardson is a leading expert on early number development and assessment.

Earth math strategy: The report of the expert panel on early math in Ontario (2003). Queen's Printer for Ontario.

This document summarizes the findings of an expert panel of researchers and educators regarding best practices for the teaching and learning of mathematics in the early grades. It includes a list of appropriate materials that should be used in the primary classroom along with the concepts and skills with which they should be employed. There are also some suggestions for instruction and assessment strategies. There is also an accompanying parents' guide and a technical guide for teachers, which provides strategies for instruction and assessment.

Assessing Early Numeracy, Ministry of Education, BC. (2003).

This is one of four documents created through the B.C. Early Numeracy Project. It offers a selection of assessment items, which teachers can use to determine numeracy strengths and weaknesses. It is designed as an assessment learning tool. Supporting Early Numeracy, *a second document, is a companion component of helpful suggestions for ways to address early numeracy difficulties. This component contains activities to support small group intervention. The other two documents are* Whole Group Follow-up, *which provides helpful activities, and* Math for Families: Helping Your Child With Math at Home. *All documents can be found on the B.C. Ministry of Education Web site.*

Online Resources

Count Us In
www.abc.net.au/countusin/default.htm

This site is full of downloadable activities and games for early number development.

Early Years Mathematics Activities and Games
www.edu.gov.mb.ca/k12/cur/math/games/index.html

This is one part of the Manitoba Ministry of Education site. It contains a list of activities and games and a list of blackline masters that teachers can use in the classroom. A third list contains activities and games for home use.

Let's Count to 5 (Grades K–2)
http://illuminations.nctm.org/LessonDetail.aspx?id=U57

This site contains seven lessons with links to resources and downloads for student recording sheets. Children can make sets of zero through five objects and connect number words or numerals to the sets. Familiar songs, rhymes, and a variety of activities that appeal to visual, auditory, and kinesthetic learners are included. In a similar fashion see the following site for higher numbers.

Let's Count to 10 (Grades K–2)
http://illuminations.nctm.org/LessonDetail.aspx?id=U147

Let's Count to 20
http://illuminations.nctm.org/LessonDetail.aspx?id=U153

These lessons emphasize the process standards of Communication and Reasoning.

Toy Shop Numbers (Grades K–2)
http://illuminations.nctm.org/LessonDetail.aspx?id=L216

Using the setting of a toy shop, these activities focus on finding numbers in the real world.

Math Tools: Math 1, Number Sense
http://mathforum.org/mathtools/cell/m1,3.2,ALL,ALL

On this one page of the Math Tools Web site you will find activities and lessons appropriate for grade 1 number sense. Explore other options on the site as well.

O.M.C.A. Must Read List for Early Numeracy/ Mathematics
http://educ.queensu.ca/connectme/weblinks/earlynumeracy/resourcelist.pdf

This site provides a list of books, articles, and resource packages regarding research, strategies, and practical ideas for teaching mathematics to the early learner.

Ten Frame (NCTM illuminations Tools)
http://illuminations.nctm.org/tools/ActivityDetail.aspx?id=75

This applet is a nice manipulative version of the ten-frame. It is probably best used by the teacher because the text is quite small. Students use counters and enter a number that answers a question. There is also a five-frame applet.

---

myeducationlab will help you improve your understanding of the concepts taught in this textbook and in your course. This online tool includes videos of real classroom experiences, sample lesson plans, simulations, case studies, and links to important educational and teaching Web sites that will help you make the transition from student to teacher. As you study in your course and with this textbook, please follow along in *MyEducationLab*. Use it! Explore it! And improve your knowledge and your grade!

Chapter 9
Developing Meanings for the Operations

This chapter is about helping children connect different meanings, interpretations, and relationships to the four operations of addition, subtraction, multiplication, and division so that they can effectively use these operations in real-world settings.

The main thrust of this chapter is helping children develop what might be termed operation sense, a highly integrated understanding of the four operations and the many different but related meanings these operations take on in real contexts.

As you read this chapter, pay special attention to the impact that operation sense has on number development, basic fact mastery, and computation. As children develop their understanding of operations, they can and should simultaneously be developing additional ideas about number and ways to think about basic fact combinations. Story problems that focus on operation meaning are also a means of developing computational skills.

Big Ideas

1. Addition and subtraction are connected. Addition names the whole in terms of the parts, and subtraction names a missing part.

2. Multiplication involves counting groups of like size and determining how many are in all (multiplicative thinking).

3. Multiplication and division are related. Division names a missing factor in terms of the known factor and the product.

4. Models can be used to solve contextual problems for all operations and to figure out what operation is involved in a problem, regardless of the size of the numbers. Models also can be used to give meaning to number sentences.

Mathematics Content Connections

The ideas in this chapter are most directly linked to concepts of numeration and the development of invented computational strategies.

- **Number Development** (Chapter 8): As children learn to think about number in terms of parts and missing parts, they should be relating these ideas to addition and subtraction. Multiplication and division require students to think about numbers as units: In 3 × 6, each of the three sixes is counted as a unit.

- **Basic Facts** (Chapter 10): A good understanding of the operations can firmly connect addition and subtraction so that subtraction facts are a natural consequence of having learned addition. A firm connection between multiplication and division provides a similar benefit.

- **Whole-Number Place Value and Computation** (Chapters 11 and 12): Students work with and develop ideas about the base-ten number system as they solve story problems involving larger numbers. It is reasonable to have children invent strategies for computing with two-digit numbers as they build their understanding of the operations.

- **Algebraic Thinking** (Chapter 14): Representing contextual situations in equations is at the heart of algebraic thinking. This is exactly what students are doing as they learn to write equations to go with their solutions to story problems.

- **Fraction and Decimal Computation** (Chapters 16 and 17): These topics for the middle and upper elementary grades depend on a firm understanding of the operations.

Addition and Subtraction Problem Structures

We begin this chapter with a look at four categories of problem structure for additive situations (which include both addition and subtraction) and later explore four problem structures for multiplicative situations (which include both multiplication and division). Although these categories are not knowledge that students are expected to master, teachers need to have a deep understanding of these categories and know how to teach them in a way that effectively supports and develops students' mathematical learning (Shulman, 1986). Teachers, who are not aware of the variety of situations and structures, may randomly offer problems to students without the proper sequencing to support their full grasp of the meaning of the operation. As a result, students will not be prepared for the variety of real-world contexts they will encounter. By knowing the logical structure of these problems, you will be able to help students interpret a variety of mathematical situations. Students will not need to identify a problem by name, using a "join" or "separate" classification. However, as a teacher, you will need to present a variety of problem types, as well as recognize which structures cause the greatest challenges for students.

Researchers have separated addition and subtraction problems into categories based on the kinds of relationships involved. These include *join* problems, *separate* problems, *part–part–whole* problems, and *compare* problems (Carpenter, Carey, & Kouba, 1990; Carpenter, Fennema, Franke, Levi, & Empson, 1999; Gutstein & Romberg, 1995). The basic structure for each of these four types of problems is illustrated in Figure 9.1. Each structure involves a number "family" such as 3, 5, 8. A different problem is produced depending on which of the three quantities in the structure is unknown.

Examples of Problems for Each Structure

The number family 4, 8, 12 is used in each of the story problems that follow and can be connected to the structure in Figure 9.1. These drawings are not intended for students. They are there to help you, as a teacher. Also note that the problems are described in terms of their structure and interpretation and not as addition or subtraction problems. Contrary to what you may have thought, a joining action does not always mean addition, nor does separate or remove always mean subtraction.

Join Problems For the action of joining, three quantities are involved: an initial or starting amount, a change amount (the part being added or joined), and the resulting amount

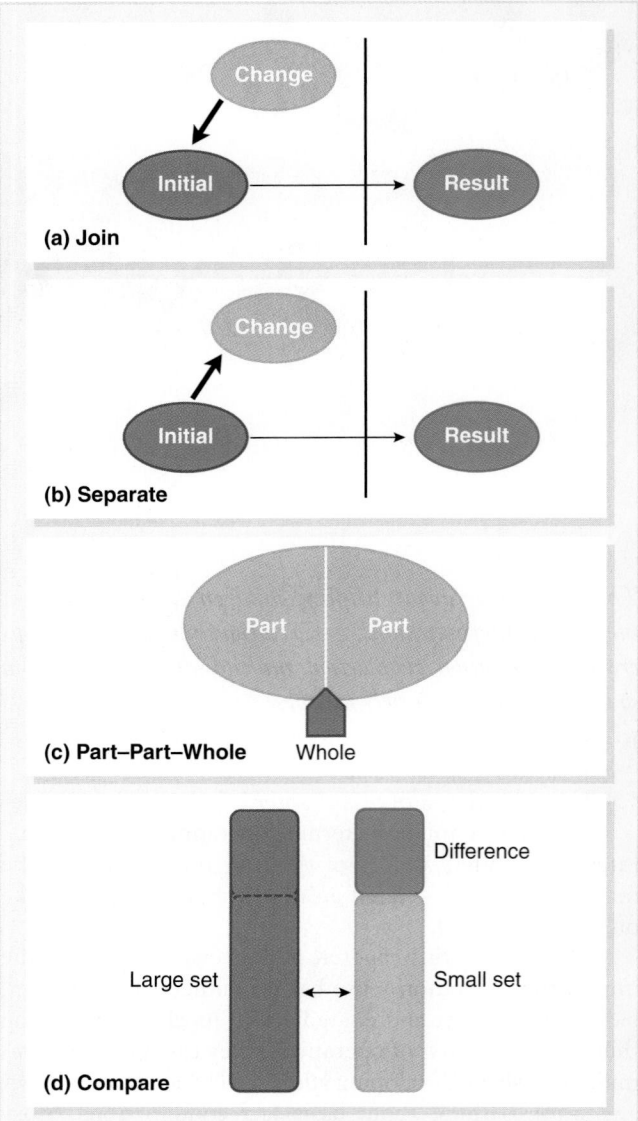

Figure 9.1 Four basic structures for addition and subtraction story problems. Each structure has three numbers. Any one of the three numbers can be the unknown in a story problem.

(the total amount after the action is over). In Figure 9.1a, this is illustrated by the change being "added" to the initial amount. Any one of these three quantities can be unknown in a problem, as shown here.

Join: Result Unknown

Phillippa had 8 pennies. George gave her 4 more. How many pennies does Phillippa have altogether?

Join: Change Unknown

Phillippa had 8 pennies. Sam gave her some more. Now Phillippa has 12 pennies. How many did Sam give her?

Join: Initial Unknown

Phillippa had some pennies. Sam gave her 4 more. Now Phillippa has 12 pennies. How many pennies did Phillippa have to begin with?

Separate Problems Notice that in the "separate" problems, the initial amount is the whole or the largest amount, whereas in the "join" problems, the result is the whole. In "separate" problems, the change is the amount being removed from the initial value. Again, refer to Figure 9.1b as you consider these problems.

Separate: Result Unknown

Phillippa had 12 pennies. She gave 4 pennies to Sam. How many pennies does Phillippa have now?

Separate: Change Unknown

Phillippa had 12 pennies. She gave some to Sam. Now she has 8 pennies. How many did she give to Sam?

Separate: Initial Unknown

Phillippa had some pennies. She gave 4 pennies to Sam. Now Phillippa has 8 pennies left. How many pennies did Phillippa have to begin with?

Part–Part–Whole Problems Part–part–whole problems involve two parts that are combined into one whole, as in Figure 9.1c. The combining may be a physical action or it may be a mental one where the parts are not combined physically.

There is no meaningful distinction between the two parts in a part–part–whole situation, so there is no need to have a different problem for each part as the unknown. For each possibility (whole unknown and part unknown), two problems are given here. The first is a mental combination where there is no action. The second problem involves a physical action.

Part–Part–Whole: Whole Unknown

Sam has 4 pennies and 8 nickels. How many coins does he have?

Sam has 4 pennies and Phillippa has 8 pennies. They put their pennies into a piggy bank. How many pennies did they put into the bank?

Part–Part–Whole: Part Unknown

Sam has 12 coins. Eight of his coins are pennies, and the rest are nickels. How many nickels does Sam have?

Sam and Phillippa put 12 pennies into the piggy bank. Sam put in 4 pennies. How many pennies did Phillippa put in?

Compare Problems Compare problems involve the comparison of two quantities. The third amount does not actually exist but is the difference between the two amounts. Figure 9.1d illustrates the comparison problem types. There are three ways, corresponding to which quantity is unknown (smaller, larger, or difference), to present compare problems. For each of these, two examples are given: one problem in which the difference is stated in terms of more, and another in terms of less.

Compare: Difference Unknown

Sam has 12 pennies and Phillippa has 8 pennies. How many more pennies does Sam have than Phillippa?

Sam has 12 pennies. Phillippa has 8 pennies. How many fewer pennies does Phillippa have than Sam?

Compare: Larger Unknown

Sam has 4 more pennies than Phillippa. Phillippa has 8 pennies. How many pennies does Sam have?

Phillippa has 4 fewer pennies than Sam. Phillippa has 8 pennies. How many pennies does Sam have?

Compare: Smaller Unknown

Sam has 4 more pennies than Phillippa. Sam has 12 pennies. How many pennies does Phillippa have?

Phillippa has 4 fewer pennies than Sam. Sam has 12 pennies. How many pennies does Phillippa have?

Pause and Reflect

Go back through all these problems and match the numbers in the problems with the components of the structures in Figure 9.1. For each problem, do two additional things. First, use a set of counters to model (solve) the problem as you think children in the primary grades might do. Second, for each problem, write either an addition or a subtraction equation that you think best represents the problem as you did it with counters.

In most curricula, the overwhelming emphasis is on the easier join and separate problems with the result unknown. These become the de facto definitions of addition and subtraction: Addition is "put together" and subtraction is "take away." The fact is, these are *not* the definitions of addition and subtraction.

When students develop these limited put-together and take-away definitions for addition and subtraction, they often have difficulty later when addition or subtraction is called for and the structure is other than put together or take away. It is important for children to be exposed to all forms within these four structures.

Problem Difficulty   The various types of problems are not at all equal in difficulty for children. The join or separate problems in which the initial part is unknown are among the most difficult. This is probably due to the fact that children modelling the problems do not know how many counters to put down in the beginning. Problems in which the change amounts are unknown are also difficult.

Many children will solve compare problems as part–part–whole problems, without making separate sets of counters for the two amounts. The whole is used as the large amount, one part for the small amount, and the second part for the difference. Which method did *you* use? There is absolutely no reason this method should be discouraged, as long as children are clear about what they are doing.

As students begin to translate the variety of story problems in the previous pages into equations to solve, they may be challenged to create a matching equation that emphasizes the corresponding operation. This is particularly important as students move into explorations that develop algebraic thinking. The structure of the equations also may cause difficulty for ELL students, who may not initially have the flexibility to create equivalent equations. This is usually due to reading comprehension issues with the situation described in the story. Therefore, we need to look at how knowing about computational and semantic forms of equations will help you help your students.

Computational and Semantic Forms of Equations   If you wrote an equation for each of the problems just suggested, you might have some equations where the unknown quantity is not isolated on one side of the equals sign. For example, a likely equation for the join problem with initial part unknown is $\square + 4 = 12$. This is referred to as the *semantic* equation for the problem since the numbers are listed in the order that follows the meaning of the problem. Figure 9.2 shows the semantic equations for the six join and separate problems on the previous pages. Note that the two result-unknown problems place the unknown alone on one side of the equals sign. An equation that isolates the unknown in this way is referred to as the *computational* form of the equation. When the semantic form is not also the computational form, an equivalent equation can be written.

Quantity Unknown	Join Problems	Separate Problems
Result	8 + 4 = [ ]	12 − 4 = [ ]
Change	8 + [ ] = 12	12 − [ ] = 8
Initial	[ ] + 4 = 12	[ ] − 4 = 8

Figure 9.2 The semantic equation for each of the six join and separate problems on pages 146–147. Notice that, for results-unknown problems, the semantic form is also the computational form. The computational form for the other four problems is an equivalent equation that isolates the unknown quantity.

For example, the equation $\square + 4 = 12$ can also be written in its equivalent form as $12 - 4 = \square$ if you were to solve these equations with a calculator. As numbers increase in size, students must eventually learn to see the equivalence between different forms of the equations.

Teaching Addition and Subtraction

So far you have seen a variety of types of story problems for addition and subtraction and you probably have used some counters to help you understand how these problems can be solved by children. These two approaches, contextual problems and models (counters, drawings, number lines), are important for helping students construct a rich understanding of these two operations. Let's examine how each approach can be used in the classroom. As you move through this section, note that addition and subtraction are taught at the same time.

Contextual Problems

There is more to think about than simply giving students problems to solve. In contrast with the rather sterile story problems in the previous section, consider the following problem.

Yesterday we were measuring how tall we were. Remember that we used the connecting cubes to make a big train that was as long as we were when we were lying down. Rhosnee and Gallina were wondering how many cubes long they would be if they lay down head to foot. Rhosnee measured Gallina; she was 84 cubes long. Gallina measured Rhosnee; she was 102 cubes long. Let's see if we can figure out how long they would be end to end, and then we can check by actually measuring them.

Fosnot and Dolk (2001) point out that in story problems, children tend to focus on getting the answer, probably in the way that the teacher wants. "Context problems, on the other hand, are connected as closely as possible to children's lives, rather than to 'school mathematics.' They are designed to anticipate and to develop children's mathematical modeling of the real world" (p. 24). Contextual problems might be derived from recent experiences in the classroom, a field trip, a discussion you have been having in art or social studies, or children's literature.

Lessons Built on Context or Story Problems There is a tendency to have students solve a lot of problems in a single class period. The focus of these lessons seems to be on how to get answers. In Japan, however, a complete lesson will often revolve around one or two problems and the related discussion (Reys & Reys, 1995).

What might a good lesson built around word problems for grade 2 look like? The answer comes more naturally if you think about students not just solving the problems but also using words, pictures, and numbers to explain how they went about solving the problem and why they think they are correct. Children should be allowed to use whatever physical materials they feel they need to help them, or they can simply draw pictures. Whatever they put on their paper should explain what they did well enough to allow someone else to understand it (allow at least a half page of space for a problem).

The grade 2 Counting, Coins, and Combinations unit of Investigations in Number, Data, and Space places a significant emphasis on connecting addition and subtraction concepts. In the excerpt shown here, you can see an activity that involves word problems for subtraction. Take special note of the way students visualize the situation and put the problem in their own words.

Choosing Numbers for Problems Even pre-K and kindergarten children should be expected to solve story problems. Typically, their methods will involve using counters or actual experiments in a very direct modelling of the problems. This is what makes the join and separate problems with the initial parts unknown so difficult. For these problems, children initially use a trial-and-error approach (Carpenter, Fennema, Franke, Levi, & Empson, 1999).

Although the structure of the problems will influence the difficulty, the numbers in the problems should be in accord with the children's level of number development. Pre-K and kindergarten children can use numbers as large as they can count meaningfully, which is usually to about 10 or 12.

Grade 2 children are also learning about two-digit numbers and are beginning to understand how our base-ten system works. Rather than waiting until students have learned about place value and have developed techniques

for computing numbers, word problems offer a problem-based opportunity to learn about number and computation at the same time. For example, a problem involving the combination of 30 and 42 has the potential to help students focus on sets of ten. As they begin to think of 42 as 40 and 2, it is not at all unreasonable to think that they will add 30 and 40 and then add 2 more. As you learn more about invented strategies for computation in Chapter 12, you will develop a better understanding of how to select numbers for the problems you use in your lessons to aid in computational development.

 The *Standards* authors make clear the value of connecting addition and subtraction. "Teachers should ensure that students repeatedly encounter situations in which the same numbers appear in different contexts. For example, the numbers 3, 4, and 7 may appear in problem-solving situations that could be represented by $4 + 3$, $3 + 4$, or $7 - 3$, or $7 - 4$.... Recognizing the inverse relationship between addition and subtraction can allow students to be flexible in using strategies to solve problems" (p. 83).

Introducing Symbolism Very young children do not need to understand the symbols +, −, and = to learn about addition and subtraction concepts. However, these symbolic conventions are important. When you feel that your students are ready to use these symbols, introduce them in the discussion portion of a lesson in which students have solved story problems. Say, "You had the whole number 12 in your problem and the number 8 was one of the parts of 12. You found out that the part you did not know was 4. Here is a way we can write that: $12 − 8 = 4$." The minus sign should be read as "minus" or "subtract" but not as "take away." The plus sign is easier since it is typically a substitute for "and."

Some care should be taken with the equal sign. The equal sign means "is the same as." However, most children come to think of it as a symbol that tells you that the "answer is coming up." It is interpreted in much the same way as the ▣ on a calculator. That is, it is the key you press to get the answer. An equation such as $4 + 8 = 3 + 9$ has no "answer" and is still true because both sides stand for the same quantity. A good idea is to use the phrase "is the same as" often, in the place of or in conjunction with "equals" as you read equations with students.

Another approach is to think of the equal sign as a balance; whatever is on one side of the equation "balances" or equals what is on the other side. This will support algebraic thinking in future grades if developed early (Knuth, Stephens, McNeil, & Alibali, 2006). (See Chapter 14 for a more detailed look at teaching the equal sign as "is the same as" rather than "give me the answer.")

Investigations
in Number, Data, and Space

Grade 2 *Counting, Coins, and Combinations*

Context

The Counting, Coins, and Combinations unit is the first of nine curriculum units for the second grade. It is one of four units in which the work on addition, subtraction, and the number system is undertaken. Children begin with the facts and move to two-digit problems using student-invented strategies. The focus on whole-number operations includes understanding the structure of the problem, developing strategies to solve story problems, and using words, pictures, and numbers to communicate solutions. Over the series of units, the full variety of problem structures presented previously in this chapter will be developed. There is an emphasis on a variety of problem types to assist the students in thinking about different situations and perspectives rather than focusing on one action or visualization.

Task Description

Counting, Coins, and Combinations has students explore addition and subtraction problems together within story situations and then visualize and model the actions described. The discussions that follow these activities embody a definite effort to use the story problems to connect the concepts of addition and subtraction. The subtraction task shown on this page is one of several presented individually on a chart or in another prominent location. Each of the story problems is set up to represent a range of the structures discussed in this chapter. This subtraction task, for example, demonstrates a separate problem with the result unknown. To begin their work, students are told that they will be hearing a story, to visualize the situation in their minds, and be ready to put the problem in their own words.

Since subtraction situations are often more challenging to follow, students are asked if the answer will be more or less than 16. They should be able to share why they think so. Then students are to use whatever methods and materials they wish to solve the problem but are required to show their work so that "someone else should be able to look at your work and understand what you did to solve it" (p. 41).

In a full-class session following this activity, students are given an opportunity to share their strategies with the teacher, who helps deepen their understanding by posing questions. In addition, the teacher can ask another student to model the solution suggested by a classmate—such as using the cubes or hundreds chart as shown in the students' work samples. Other students can also be asked to try the strategy. Poll students to see who also used a similar approach to give them ownership while you get a sense of the students' development. Before leaving the problem you can discuss strategies not already presented.

It is important to also link to the symbolic representation through writing the equation for the problem. Talk about how this can be linked to an addition story using the same numbers.

Take time to look at the two student work samples shown. What do you notice in their recording of their thinking? Can you follow their strategy use? Is one approach more prone to errors? Does one display a more sophisticated level of understanding?

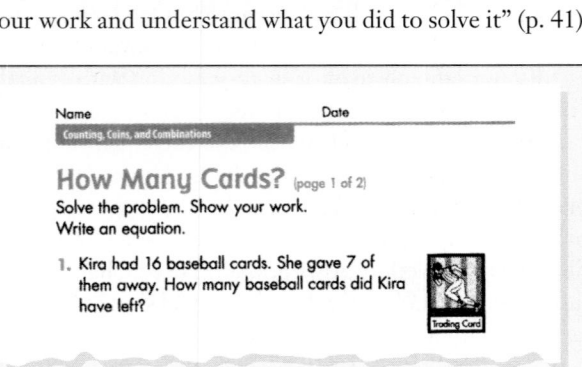

 Watching how children solve story problems will give you a lot of information about children's understanding of number as well as the more obvious information about problem solving and their understanding of addition and subtraction. The CGI project (Carpenter et al., 1999) found that children progress in their problem-solving strategies from kindergarten to grade 2. These strategies are a reflection of students' understanding of number and of their emerging mastery of basic fact strategies. For example, early on, students will use counters and count each addend, then recount the entire set for a join-result-unknown problem. With more practice, they will count on from the first set. This strategy will be modified to count on from the larger set; that is, for 4 + 7, the child will begin with 7 and count on, even though 4 is the initial amount in the problem. Eventually, students will begin to use facts retrieved from memory and rely on counters or other models only when necessary. Watching how students solve problems provides evidence that will help you decide which numbers to use in problems and how to make decisions about what questions to ask students that will focus attention on more efficient strategies. ◆

Model-Based Problems

Many children will use counters or number lines (models) to solve story problems. The model is a thinking tool that helps students understand what is happening in the problem. It is also a means of keeping track of the numbers and solving the problem. Problems where there is no context involved can also be posed using models.

Addition　When the parts of a set are known, addition is used to name the whole in terms of the parts. This simple definition of addition serves both action situations (join and separate) and static or non-action situations.

Each of the part–part–whole models shown in Figure 9.3 is a model for 5 + 3 = 8. Some of these are the result of a definite put-together or joining action, and some are not. Notice that in every example, both of the parts are distinct, even after the parts are joined. If counters are used, the two parts should be kept in separate piles or in separate sections of a mat or should be two distinct colours. For children to see a relationship between the two parts and the whole, the images of the 5 and 3 must be kept as two separate sets. This helps children reflect on the action after it has taken place. "These red chips are the ones I started with. Then I added these five blue ones, and now I have eight all together."

A number line presents some real conceptual difficulties for grades 1 and 2 children. Using it as a model at that level is generally not recommended. A number line measures distances from zero the same way a ruler does.

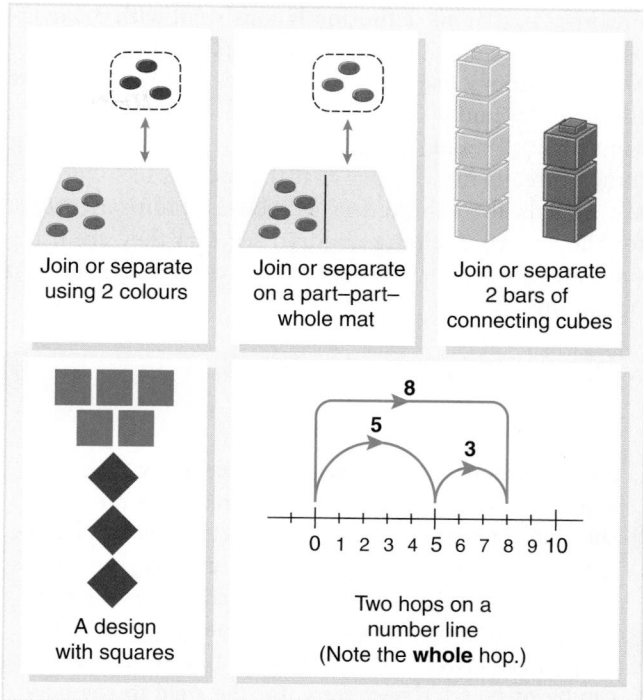

Figure 9.3　Part–part–whole models for 5 + 3 = 8 and 8 − 3 = 5.

In the early grades, children focus on the demarcations or the numbers on a number line, rather than on the spaces in between. However, if arrows (hops) are drawn over the appropriate number of units on the line to represent the numbers in an exercise, the length concept is more clearly illustrated. To model the part–part–whole concept of 5 + 3, start by drawing an arrow from 0 to 5, indicating, "This much is five." Do not point to the dot for 5, saying "This is five."

Activity **9.1**

Up and Down the Line

Create a large number line on the floor of your classroom or hang one on the chalkboard tray. Use an eraser for hopping on the chalkboard tray number line or a student to walk the number line on the floor. Talk about the movement required to represent each of a variety of different addition and subtraction equations. Doing so emphasizes the spaces (the distance between the numbers) on the number line. As well, it is a wonderful mental image for thinking about the meaning of addition and subtraction.

Subtraction　In a part–part–whole model, when the whole and one of the parts are known, subtraction names the other part. This definition is consistent with the over-used language of "take away." If you start with a whole set of 8 and remove a set of 3, the two sets that you know are the sets of 8 and 3. The expression 8 − 3, read as "eight minus three," names the remaining five. Therefore, eight minus three is five. Notice that the models in Figure 9.3 are models for subtraction as well as addition (except for the action). Helping children see that they are using the same models or pictures aids in connecting the two operations.

Activity 9.2

Missing-Part Subtraction

A fixed number of counters is placed on a mat. One child separates the counters into two parts while the other child hides his or her eyes. The first child covers one of the two parts with a sheet of paper, revealing the other part (see Figure 9.4b). The second child says the subtraction sentence. For example, "Nine minus four [the visible part] is five [the covered part]." The covered part can be revealed, if necessary, for the child to say how many are there. Both the subtraction equation and the addition equation can then be written.

Subtraction as Think-Addition   Note that in Activity 9.2 the situation ends with two parts clearly distinct, even when there is a remove action. The part that is removed remains on the mat as a model for an addition equation to be written, after writing the subtraction equation. A discussion of how two equations can be written for the same model situation is an important opportunity to connect addition and subtraction. This modelling and discussion of addition and subtraction connections is significantly better than the traditional activity of "fact families" in which children are given a family of numbers such as 3, 5, and 8. Then they are asked to write two addition equations and two subtraction equations. Very often, this becomes a rote process of dropping numbers into slots.

Thinking about subtraction as "think-addition" rather than "takeaway" is extremely significant for mastering subtraction facts. Because the counters for the remaining or unknown part are left hidden under the cover, when children do these activities, they are encouraged to think about the hidden part: "What goes with the part I see to make the whole?" For example, if the total or whole number of counters is 9 and 6 are removed from under the cover, the child is likely to think in terms of "6 and what makes 9?" or "What goes with 6 to make 9?" The mental activity is a "think-addition" instead of a "count what's left." Later, when working on subtraction facts, a subtraction fact such

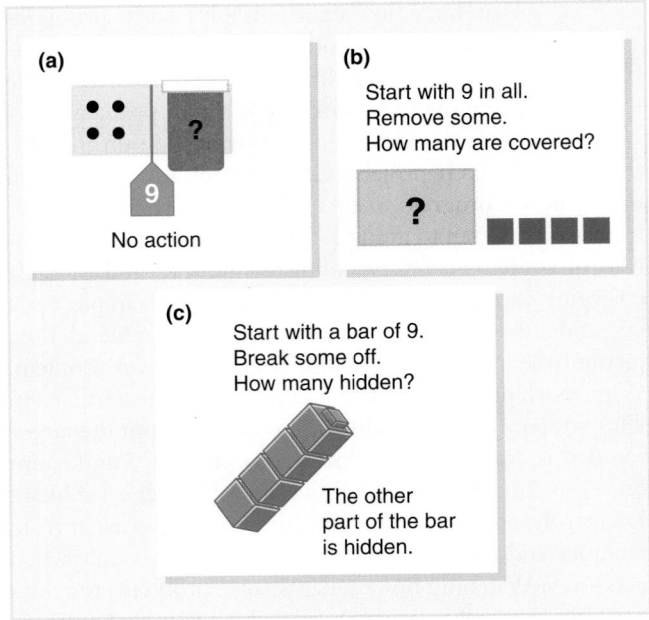

Figure 9.4 Models for 9 − 4 as a missing-part problem.

as 9 − 6 = ☐ should trigger the same thought pattern: "6 and what makes 9?"

Comparison Models   Comparison situations involve two distinct sets or quantities and the difference between them. Several ways of modelling the difference relationship are shown in Figure 9.5. The same model can be used whether the difference or one of the two quantities is unknown.

Note that it is not immediately clear how you would associate either the addition or the subtraction operations with a comparison situation. From an adult vantage point, you can see that if you match part of the larger amount with the smaller amount, the large set is now a part–part–whole model and you can solve the problem. In fact, many children do model compare problems in just this manner. But that is a very difficult idea to show children if they do not construct the idea themselves.

Have children make two amounts, perhaps with two bars of interlocking cubes. Discuss the difference between the two bars in order to generate a third number. For example, if the children make a bar of 10 and a bar of 6, ask, "How many more do we need to match the 10 bar?" The difference is 4. Then ask, "What equations can we make with these three numbers?" Have children make up story problems that involve two amounts of 10 and 6. Discuss which equations go with the problems that are created.

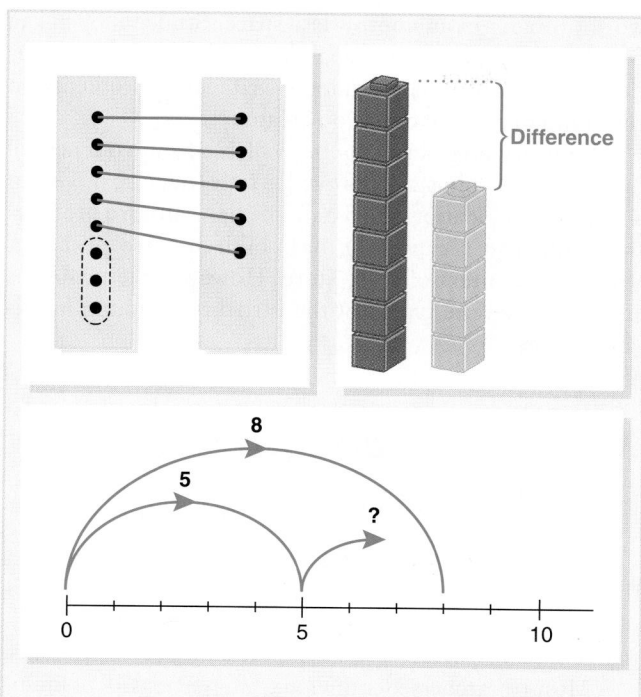

Figure 9.5 Models for the difference between 8 and 5.

Properties of Addition and Subtraction

The Commutative Property for Addition The *commutative* property (or *order* property) for addition says that it makes no difference in which order two numbers are added. Although the commutative property may seem obvious to us (simply reverse the two piles of counters on the part–part–whole mat), it may not be as obvious to children. Because this property is quite useful for problem solving, mastering basic facts, and mental mathematics, there is value in spending some time helping children construct the relationship. Students need to understand this property more than they need to be able to name it.

Schifter (2001) describes a class of early grade 2 students who discovered the "turnaround" property while examining sums to ten. Later, the teacher wondered if they really understood this idea and asked the children if they thought it would always work. Many in the class were unsure if it worked all of the time and were especially unsure about it working with large numbers. The point is that children may see and accept the commutative property for sums they've experienced but not be able to explain or even believe that this simple yet important property works for all addition combinations.

To help children focus on the commutative property, pair problems that have the same addends but in different

orders. The contexts for the problems should be different. For example:

Emily is on page 32 in her book. Tomorrow she hopes to read 15 more pages. What page will she be on if she reads that many pages?

Milk in the cafeteria refrigerator was down to only 15 cartons. Before lunch, more milk was delivered. The refrigerator was filled with 32 more cartons. How many cartons are in the refrigerator now?

Ask if anyone sees how these problems are alike. If done as a pair, some (not all) students will see that having solved one, they essentially have solved the other.

The Associative Property for Addition According to the associative property for addition, when adding three or more numbers, it does not matter whether the beginning two numbers are added first or if you start with any other pair of addends. There is much flexibility in addition. Thus students can change the order in which they group numbers to work with combinations they know. Notice that the following examples involve mentally grouping numbers to add in a different order than just reading the expressions from left to right.

Activity **9.3**

More Than Two Addends

Give students six sums to find, involving three or four addends. Prepare these on a page divided into six sections. Make sure there is enough space to write beneath each sum. Within each section, include at least one pair with a sum of ten or perhaps a double: 4 + 7 + 6, 5 + 9 + 9, or 3 + 4 + 3 + 7. Students should show how they added the numbers. Allow students to find the sums without offering any other directions.

Figure 9.6 illustrates how students might show their thinking. As they share their solutions, almost certainly there will be students who added in a different order but got the same result. From this discussion you can help them conclude that you can add numbers in any order and the result will not change. You are also using the associative property but it is the commutative (order) property that is more important. This is also an excellent number sense activity because many students will find combinations of ten in these sums or will use doubles. Learning to adjust strategies to fit the numbers is the beginning of the road to computational fluency.

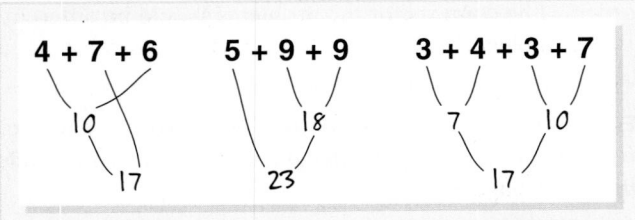

Figure 9.6 Students show how they added.

The Zero Property Story problems involving zero and/or using zeros in the three-addend sums are also a good method for helping students understand how zero works in addition or subtraction (as an identity element). Occasionally, students feel that $6 + 0$ must be more than 6 because "adding makes numbers bigger" or that $12 - 0$ must be 11 because "subtracting makes numbers smaller." Instead of making arbitrary-sounding rules about adding and subtracting zero, build opportunities for discussing zero into the problem-solving routine.

 At present, few software programs offer addition and subtraction word problems with the variety of problem types we have just explored. However, there are other ways that you can take advantage of your classroom computers using almost any basic tool software you happen to have. First, you can develop your own problems using your word-processing software or any program that allows shapes to be easily drawn and words to be typed. Open a new file and write a word problem in an appropriate space. Students open the file and use the drawing capabilities to record their solution. You can also have students write story problems on the computer for pictures you create.

Software programs may be available from your school board that are ministry approved. *Math Trek 1, 2, 3, Version 4* (Nectar Foundation, 2005), a Canadian software program (mentioned in Chapter 7), has children solve problems within the context of a toy store. However, the problems are of the exercise type, not the varied types found in this chapter. ◆

Multiplication and Division Problem Structures

Like addition and subtraction, there are problem structures that will help you, the teacher, formulate and assign multiplication and division tasks. As was the case with the additive problem structures, these are for you, not for students.

Most researchers identify four different classes of multiplicative structures (Greer, 1992). (The term *multiplicative* is used here to describe all types of problems that involve multiplication and division.) The two described in Figure 9.7, *equal groups (repeated addition, rates)* and *multiplicative comparison* are by far the most prevalent in elementary school. Problems matching these structures can be modelled with sets of counters, number lines, or arrays. They represent a large percentage of the multiplicative problems in the real world.

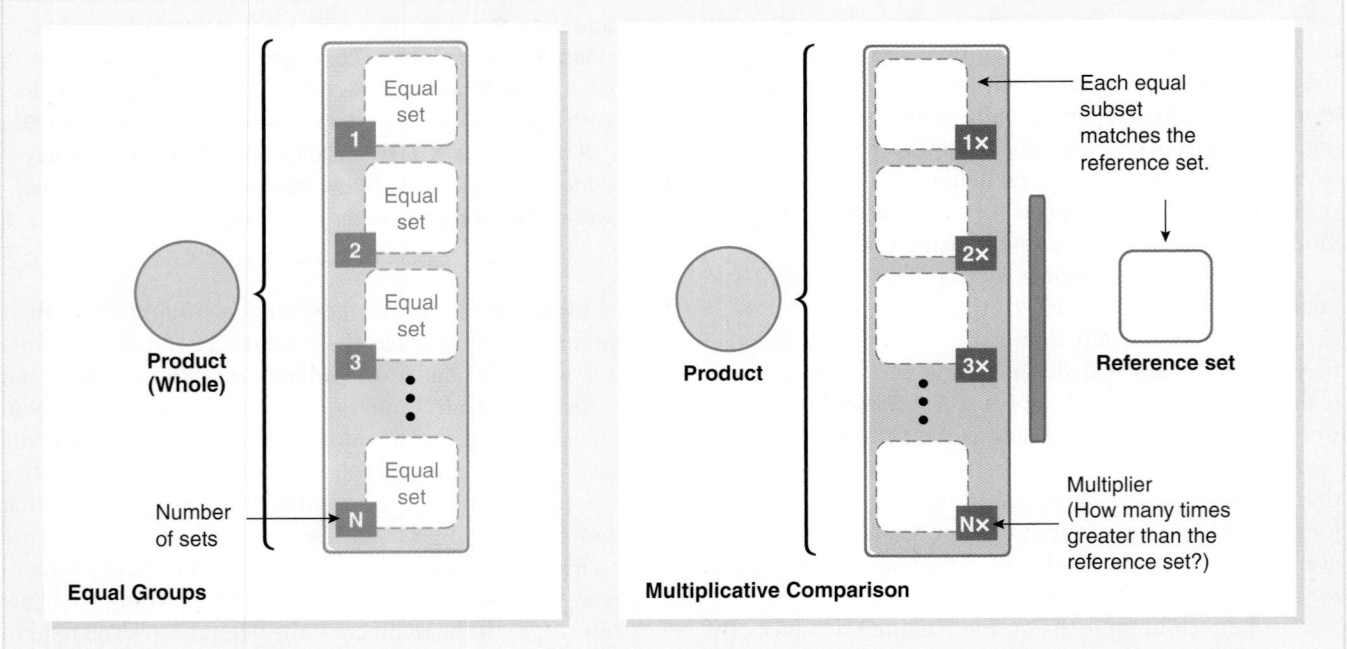

Figure 9.7 Two of the four basic structures for multiplication and division story problems. Each structure has three numbers. Any one of the three numbers can be the unknown in a story problem.

Examples of Problems for Each Structure

In multiplicative problems, one number or *factor* counts how many sets, groups, or parts of equal size are involved. The other factor tells the size of each set or part. The third number in each of these two structures is the *whole* or *product* and is the total of all of the parts. The parts and wholes terminology is useful in making the connection to addition.

Equal-Group Problems   When the number and size of groups are known, the problem is a multiplication situation. When either the number of sets or the size of sets is unknown, the problem is a division situation. But note that these division situations are not alike. Problems in which the size of the sets is unknown are called *fair-sharing* or *partition* problems. The whole is shared or distributed among a known number of sets to determine the size of each. If the number of sets is unknown but the size of the equal sets is known, the problems are called *measurement* or sometimes *repeated-subtraction* problems. The whole is "measured off" in sets of the given size. These terms are used with the examples that follow. Keep in mind the structure in Figure 9.7 to see which numbers are given and which is unknown.

There is also a subtle difference between equal-group problems (also termed *repeated-addition* problems), such as "If 3 children have 4 apples each, how many apples are there?" and those that might be termed *rate* problems "If there are 4 apples per child, how many apples would 3 children have?" For each category, two examples of rate problems are provided.

Equal Groups: Whole Unknown (Multiplication)

Mark has 4 bags of apples. There are 6 apples in each bag. How many apples does Mark have?

If apples cost 32 cents each, how much did Jill have to pay for 5 apples? (*rate*)

Peter walked for 3 hours at 6 kilometres per hour. How far did he walk? (*rate*)

Equal Groups: Size of Groups Unknown (Partition Division)

Mark has 24 apples. He wants to share them equally among his 4 friends. How many apples will each friend receive? (fair sharing)

Jill paid 96 cents for 5 apples. What was the cost of 1 apple? (*rate*)

Peter walked 18 kilometres in 3 hours. How many kilometres per hour (how fast) did he walk? (*rate*)

Equal Groups: Number of Groups Unknown (Measurement Division)

Mark has 24 apples. He put them into bags containing 6 apples each. How many bags did Mark use? (repeated subtraction)

Jill bought apples that cost 32 cents each. The total cost of her apples was 96 cents. How many apples did Jill buy? (rate)

Peter walked 18 kilometres at a rate of 6 kilometres per hour. How many hours did it take Peter to walk the 18 kilometres? (rate)

Comparison Problems   In multiplicative comparison problems, there are really two different sets, as there are with comparison situations for addition and subtraction. One set consists of multiple copies of the other. Two examples of each possibility are provided here. In the former, the comparison is an amount or quantity difference. In multiplicative situations, the comparison is based on one set being a particular multiple of the other.

Comparison: Product Unknown (Multiplication)

Jill picked 6 apples. Mark picked 4 times as many apples as Jill. How many apples did Mark pick?

This month Mark saved 5 times as much money as last month. Last month he saved $15. How much money did Mark save this month?

Comparison: Set Size Unknown (Partition Division)

Mark picked 24 apples. He picked 4 times as many apples as Jill. How many apples did Jill pick?

This month, Mark saved 5 times as much money as he did last month. If he saved $75 this month, how much did he save last month?

Comparison: Multiplier Unknown (Measurement Division)

Mark picked 24 apples, and Jill picked only 6. How many times as many apples did Mark pick as Jill did?

This month Mark saved $75. Last month he saved $15. How much more (many times as much) money did he save this month than (as) last?

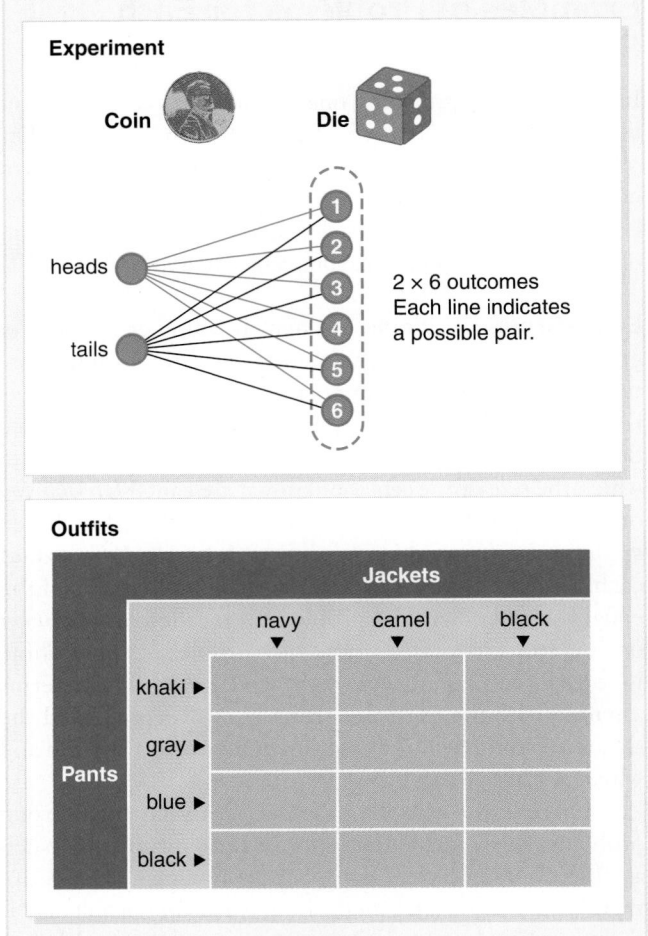

Figure 9.8 Models for combinations situations.

Pause and Reflect

What you just read is a lot to take in without reflection. Stop now and get a collection of counters—at least 75. Use the counters to solve each of the problems. Look first at the equal-group problems and do the "Mark problems" or the first problem in each set. Match the numbers with the structure model in Figure 9.7. How are these problems alike and how are they different, especially the two types of division problems? Repeat the exercise with the "Jill problems" and then the "Peter problems." Can you see how the problems in each group are alike and how the problems across groups are related?

When you are comfortable with the equal-group problems, repeat the same process with the multiplicative comparison problems. Again, start with the first problem in all three sets then the second problem in all three sets. Reflect on the same questions posed earlier.

Although the following two multiplicative structures are slightly more complex, thus not a good introductory point, it is important that you recognize them as two other categories of multiplicative situations.

Combinations or *Cartesian products* and *area* and other *product-of-measures* problems (e.g., length times width equals area) are mentioned less frequently within the multiplication and division sections of most curricula. However, they are used with older-grade elementary students.

Combinations Problems Combinations problems involve counting the number of possible pairings that can be made between two sets. The product consists of pairs of things, one member of each pair taken from each of the two given sets.

Combinations: Product Unknown

Sam bought 4 pairs of pants and 3 jackets, and they all can be worn together. How many different outfits consisting of a pair of pants and a jacket does Sam have?

An experiment involves tossing a coin and rolling a die. How many different possible results or outcomes can this experiment have?

In these two examples, the product is unknown and the size of the two sets is given. It is possible, but rarely, to have related division problems for the combinations concept.

Figure 9.8 shows two common methods of modelling combination problems: an array and a tree diagram. Counting how many combinations of two or more things or events are possible is important in determining prob-

abilities. For example, to determine the probability of a head and either a 1 or a 6, one needs to know that there are 12 possible outcomes for the head and die experiment. The combinations concept is most often found in the probability strand.

Area and Other Product-of-Measures Problems What distinguishes product-of-measures problems from the others is that the product is literally a different type of unit from the other two factors. In a rectangle, the product of two dimensions (length × width) is an area, usually square units. Figure 9.9 illustrates how different the square units are from each of the two factors of length: 4 centimetres times 7 centimetres is not 28 centimetres, rather it is 28 *square* centimetres. The factors are each one-dimensional entities, whereas the product consists of *two*-dimensional (square) units.

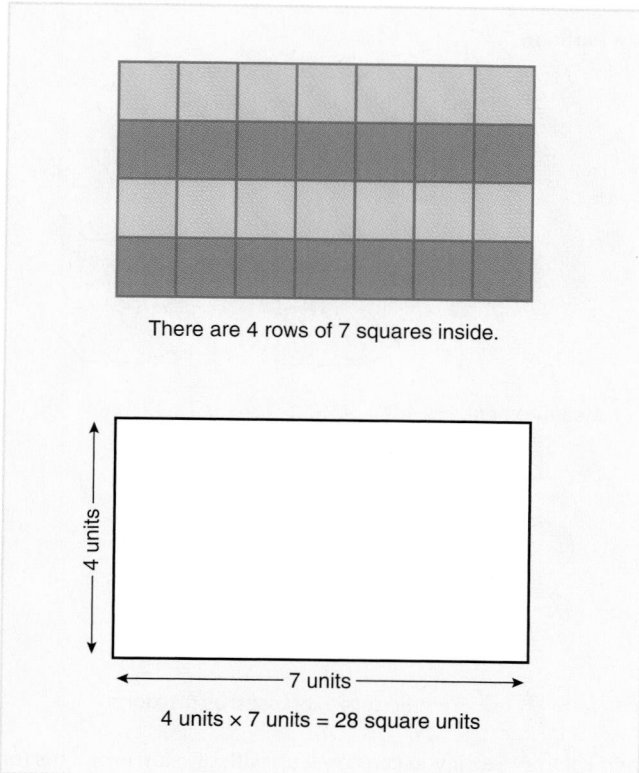

There are 4 rows of 7 squares inside.

4 units

7 units

4 units × 7 units = 28 square units

Figure 9.9 Length times width equals area.

Teaching Multiplication and Division

Multiplication and division are taught separately in most textbooks, with multiplication preceding division. However, it is important to combine multiplication and division soon after multiplication has been introduced so students will see how they are related. These topics are an important focus in most grade 3 curricula, with continued development in grades 4 and 5.

A major conceptual hurdle in working with multiplicative structures is understanding groups of things as single entities while also understanding that a group contains a given number of objects (Clark & Kamii, 1996; Kouba, 1989; Steffe, 1988). Children can solve the problem "*How many apples are in 4 baskets of 8 apples each?*" by counting out four sets of eight counters and then counting all of them. To think multiplicatively about this problem as four *sets of eight* requires children to conceptualize each group of eight as a single item to be counted. Experiences with making and counting groups, especially in contextual situations, are extremely useful. (See the discussion of the book *Each Orange Had 8 Slices* at the end of this chapter.)

Contextual Problems

Many of the issues surrounding addition and subtraction also apply to multiplication and need not be discussed in depth again. It remains important to use contextual problems whenever reasonable instead of more sterile story problems. Just as with additive structures, it is a good idea to build multiplicative lessons around only two or three problems. Students should solve problems using whatever techniques they wish. What is important is that they explain—preferably in writing—what they did and why it makes sense. Words, pictures, and numbers remain important.

Symbolism for Multiplication and Division   When students solve simple multiplication story problems before learning about multiplication symbolism, they will most likely write repeated-addition equations to represent what they did. This is your opportunity to introduce the multiplication sign and explain what the two factors mean.

The usual convention is that 4×8 refers to four sets of eight, not eight sets of four. There is no reason to be rigid about this convention. The important thing is that the students can tell you what each factor in *their* equations represents. In vertical form, it is usually the bottom factor that indicates the number of sets. Again, this distinction is not terribly important.

The quotient 24 divided by 6 is represented in three different ways: $24 \div 6$, $6\overline{)24}$, and $\frac{24}{6}$. Students should understand that these representations are equivalent. The fraction notation becomes important at the middle school level. Children often mistakenly read $6\overline{)24}$ as "6 divided by 24" due to the left–right order of the numbers. Generally, this error does not match what they are thinking.

Compounding the difficulty of division notation is the unfortunate phrase, "six goes into twenty-four." This phrase holds little meaning about division, especially in connection with a fair-sharing or partitioning context. The "goes into" (or "guzinta") terminology is simply engrained in adult parlance and has not been in textbooks for years. If you tend to use that phrase, it is probably a good time to consciously abandon it.

Choosing Numbers for Problems   When selecting numbers for multiplicative story problems or activities, there is a tendency to think that large numbers pose a burden for students or that 3×4 is somehow easier to understand than 4×17. An understanding of products or quotients is not affected by the size of numbers, as long as the numbers are within the grasp of the students. Little is gained by restricting early explorations of multiplication to small numbers. Even in early grade 3, students can work with larger numbers using whatever counting strategies they have at their disposal. A contextual problem involving 14×8 is not at all too large for grade 3 children even before they have learned a computation technique. When given these challenges, children are likely to invent computational strategies.

Remainders

More often than not, division does not result in a simple whole number. For example, problems with 6 as a divisor will "come out even" only one time out of six. In the absence of a context, a remainder can be dealt with in only two ways: (1) It can either remain a quantity left over, or (2) be partitioned into fractions. In Figure 9.10, the problem $11 \div 4$ is modelled to show fractions.

In real contexts, remainders sometimes have three additional effects on answers:

- The remainder is discarded, leaving a smaller whole-number answer.
- The remainder can "force" the answer to the next highest whole number.
- The answer is rounded to the nearest whole number for an approximate result.

The following problems illustrate all five possibilities.

You have 30 pieces of candy to share fairly with 7 children. How many pieces of candy will each child receive?

Answer: 4 pieces of candy and 2 left over. (*left over*)

Each jar holds 4 litres of liquid. If there are 37 litres in the pitcher, how many jars will that be?

Answer: 9 and $\frac{1}{4}$ jars. (*partitioned as a fraction*)

The rope is 25 metres long. How many 2 metre skipping ropes can be made?

Answer: 12 skipping ropes. (*discarded*)

The ferry can hold 8 cars. How many trips will it have to make to carry 25 cars across the river?

Answer: 4 trips. (*forced to next whole number*)

Six children are planning to share a bag of 50 pieces of bubble gum. About how many pieces will each child get?

Answer: About 8 pieces for each child. (*rounded, approximate result*)

Students should not just think of remainders as "R 3" or "left over." Remainders should be put in context and dealt with accordingly.

———— *Pause and Reflect*

It is useful for you to make up problems in different contexts. Include continuous quantities such as length, time,

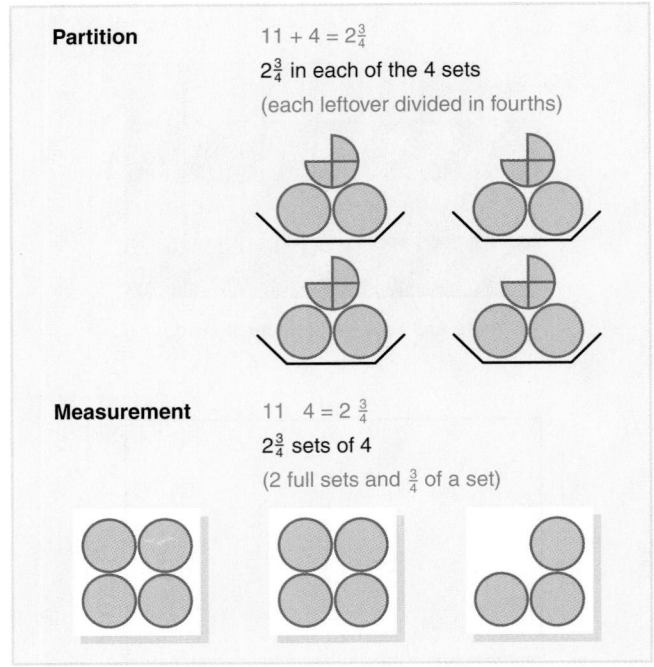

Figure 9.10 Remainders expressed as fractions.

and volume. See if you can come up with division problems for equal-group and comparison structures that would have remainders dealt with as fractions or as rounded-up or rounded-down results.

It is important to provide story problems for both multiplication and division in the same lesson. By doing so you can be certain children are interpreting the meaning of the problems and not simply taking the two numbers and using today's operation.

When children are modelling multiplicative problems or using their own strategies for solving them, they will not always use an approach that matches the problem. For example, if solving a problem involving 12 sets of 4, many children will add 4 twelves instead of 12 fours. Rather than being concerned about this, view it as an indication that students likely accept or understand that 12×4 and 4×12 give the same result. However, when students solve a problem such as this in different ways, it is a great opportunity for profitable discussion. ◆

Model-Based Problems

In the beginning, children will be able to use the same models—sets and number lines—for all four operations. A model not generally used for addition but extremely important and widely used for multiplication and division is the array. An *array* is any arrangement of things in rows and columns, such as a rectangle of square tiles or blocks (see Blackline Master 42).

To make clear the connection to addition, early multiplication activities should also include writing an addition sentence for the same model. A variety of models are shown in Figure 9.11. Notice that the products are not included—only the addition and multiplication "names" are written. This is another way to avoid the tedious counting of large sets. A similar approach is to write one sentence that expresses both concepts at once, for example, $9 + 9 + 9 + 9 = 4 \times 9$.

As with additive problems, children can benefit from a few activities with models and no context. The purpose of such activities is to focus on the meaning of the operation and the associated symbolism. Activity 9.4 effectively reflects the spirit of problem-solving. The language you employ depends on what you have previously used with your children.

Activity 9.4

Finding Factors

Start by assigning a number that has several factors—for example, 12, 18, 24, 30, or 36. Have students find as many possible multiplication expressions for their assigned number. Using counters, students attempt to find a way to separate the counters into equal subsets. With arrays (perhaps made from square tiles or cubes or drawn on grid paper), students try to build rectangles that have the given number of squares. For each such arrangement of sets or appropriate rectangles, both an addition and a multiplication equation should be written. This activity is available as an applet at http://illuminations.nctm.org/ActivityDetail.aspx?id=64

Activity 9.4 can also include division concepts. When children have learned that 3 and 6 are factors of 18, they can write the equations $18 \div 3 = 6$ and $18 \div 6 = 3$ along with $3 \times 6 = 18$ and $6 + 6 + 6 = 18$ (assuming that three sets of six were modelled). The following variation of the same activity focuses on division. Having children create word problems is another excellent way to expand this activity. Require children to explain how their story problems fit with what they did with the counters.

Activity 9.5

Learning About Division

Provide children with an ample supply of counters and a way to place them into small groups. Small paper cups work well. Have children count out a number of counters to represent the whole or total set. They record this number: "Start with 31." Next specify either the number of equal sets to be made or the size of the sets to be made: "Separate your counters into four equal-sized sets," or "Make as many sets of four as possible." Next, have the children write the corresponding multiplication equation for what they see on their materials; under that, have them write the division equation.

Be sure to include both types of exercises: number of equal sets and size of sets. Discuss with the class how these two are different. Yet, each is related to multiplication and each is written as a division equation. You can show both ways to write division equations at this time. Do Activity 9.5 several times. Start with whole quantities that are multiples of the divisor (no remainders), but soon include situations

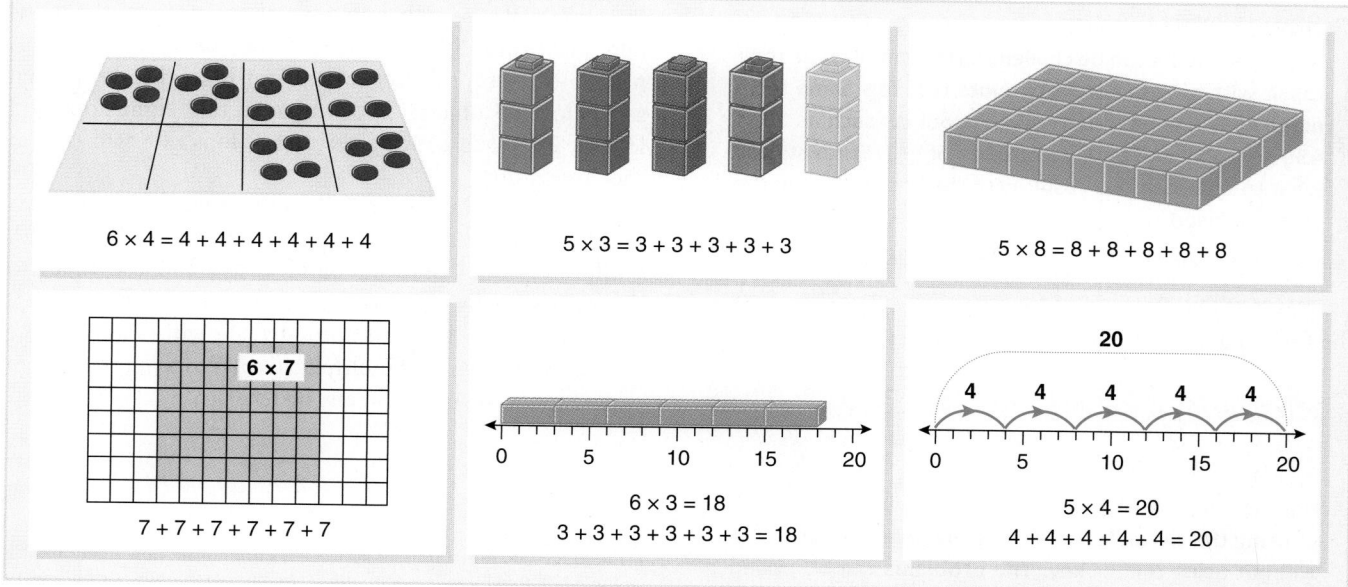

$6 \times 4 = 4 + 4 + 4 + 4 + 4 + 4$

$5 \times 3 = 3 + 3 + 3 + 3 + 3$

$5 \times 8 = 8 + 8 + 8 + 8 + 8$

6 × 7

$7 + 7 + 7 + 7 + 7 + 7$

$6 \times 3 = 18$
$3 + 3 + 3 + 3 + 3 + 3 = 18$

20

4   4   4   4   4

$5 \times 4 = 20$
$4 + 4 + 4 + 4 + 4 = 20$

Figure 9.11 Models for equal-group multiplication.

with remainders. (Note that it is technically incorrect to write $31 \div 4 = 7 \text{ R } 3$. However, in the beginning, that form may be the most appropriate to use.)

The activity can be varied by changing the model. Have children build arrays using square tiles or blocks or have them draw arrays on centimetre grid paper. Present the exercises by specifying how many squares are to be in the array. You can then specify the number of rows that should be made (partition) or the length of each row (measurement). How could children model fractional answers using drawings of arrays on grid paper?

 The applet "Rectangle Division" on the National Library of Virtual Manipulatives (NLVM) Web site (http://nlvm.usu.edu/en/nav/grade_g_2.html) is an excellent interactive illustration of division with remainders. A division problem is presented with an array showing the number of squares in the product. The dimensions of the array can be modified but the number of squares stays constant. If, for example, the task is to show the problem $52 \div 8$, the squares can be adjusted to show an 8 by 6 array with 4 extra squares in a different colour ($8 \times 6 + 4$) as well as any other variation of 52 squares in a rectangle, plus a shorter column for the remainder. This applet very vividly demonstrates how division is related to multiplication. ◆

Activity 9.6

The Broken Multiplication Key

The calculator is a good way to relate multiplication to addition. Students can be asked to find various products on the calculator, without using the ⊠ key. For example, 6 × 4 can be found by pressing ⊞ 4 ⊟. (Successive presses of ⊟ add 4 to the display each time. You began with zero and added 4 six times.) Students can be challenged to demonstrate their result with sets of counters. Note that this same technique can be used to determine products such as 23 × 459 (⊞ 459 and then 23 presses of ⊟). Students will want to compare this result with the product when the ⊠ key is used.

Note: "The Broken Multiplication Key" can profitably be followed by "The Broken Division Key."

Activity 9.7

The Broken Division Key

Have children work in groups to find methods of using the calculator to solve division exercises without using the ⊞ key. The problems can be posed without a story context. "Find at least two ways to figure out $61 \div 14$ without pressing the divide key." If the problem is put in a story context, one method may actually match the problem better than another. Good discussions may follow different solutions with the same answers. Are they both correct? Why or why not?

 *Pause and Reflect*

There is no reason ever to show children how to do Activity 9.7. However, it would be a good idea for *you to see if you can find three ways to solve $61 \div 14$ on a calculator without using the divide key. For a hint, see the footnote.[1]*

 "In grades 3–5, students should focus on the meanings of, and relationship between, multiplication and division. It is important that students understand what each number in a multiplication or division expression represents.... Modeling multiplication problems with pictures, diagrams, or concrete materials helps students learn what the factors and their product represent in various contexts" (p. 51).

Properties of Multiplication and Division

As with addition and subtraction, there are some multiplicative properties that are useful, and thus worthy of attention. The emphasis should be on the ideas, not on the terminology or the definitions.

Commutative and Associative Properties of Multiplication It is not intuitively obvious that 3×8 is the same as 8×3 or that, in general, the order of the numbers makes no difference (the **commutative** property). A picture of 3 sets of 8 objects cannot immediately be seen as 8 piles of 3 objects. It can be seen that eight hops of 3 land at 24, but it is not clear that 3 hops of 8 will land at the same point.

The array, by contrast, is quite powerful in illustrating the commutative property, as is shown in Figure 9.12. Children should draw or build arrays and use them to demonstrate why each array represents two different multiplications with the same product. As with addition, the associative property of multiplication allows numbers in an expression to be paired in any order.

---

[1]There are two measurement approaches to find out how many 14s are in 61. A third way is essentially related to partitioning or finding 14 times what number is close to 61.

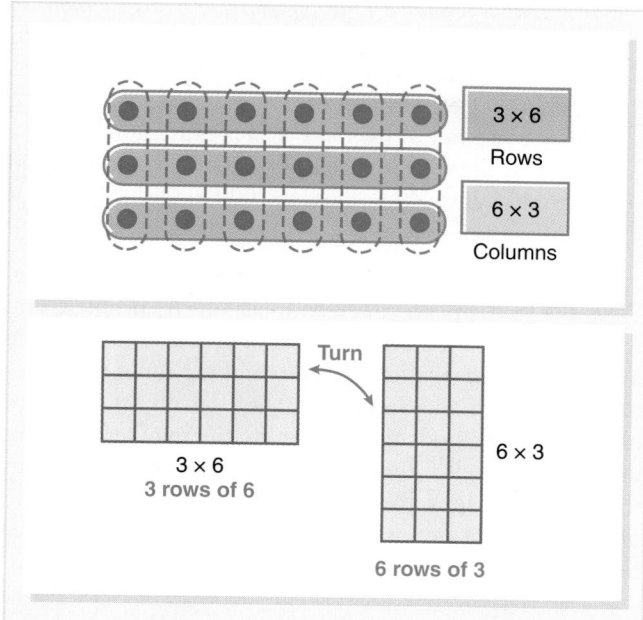

Figure 9.12 Two ways an array can be used to illustrate the order (commutative) property for multiplication.

The Role of Zero and One in Multiplication Zero and, to a lesser extent, 1 as factors often cause conceptual challenges for children. In one grade 3 textbook, a lesson on factors of 0 and 1 has children use a calculator to examine a wide range of products involving 0 or 1 (423×0, 0×28, 1536×1, etc.) and look for patterns. The pattern suggests the rules for multiplication with factors 0 and 1, but not a reason. In the same lesson, a word problem asks how many grams of fat there are in 7 servings of celery with 0 grams of fat in each serving. This approach is far preferable to an arbitrary rule, since it asks students to reason. Make up interesting word problems involving 0 or 1, and discuss the results. Problems with 0 as a first factor are really strange. Note that on a number line, 5 hops of 0 land at 0 (5×0). What would 0 hops of 5 be? Another fun activity is to try to model 6×0 or 0×8 with an array. (Try it!) Arrays for factors of 1 are also worth investigating.

The Distributive Property The *distributive property of multiplication over addition* refers to the idea that one of the two factors in a product can be split into two or more parts. Each part is multiplied separately, then added. The result is the same as when the original factors are multiplied, without splitting any of them. For example, 6×9 is the same as $(6 \times 5) = (6 \times 4)$. The 9 has been split into 5 and 4. The concept involved is very useful for relating one basic fact to another, and it is also involved in the development of two-digit computation. Figure 9.13 illustrates how the array model can be used to illustrate that a product can be broken up into two parts.

The next activity is designed to help children discover how to partition factors or, in other words, to learn about the distributive property of multiplication over addition.

Activity 9.8

Slice It Up

Supply students with several sheets of centimetre grid paper. Assign each pair of students a product such as 6 × 8. (Products can vary across the class or can all be the same.) The task is to construct a rectangle on the grid paper that represents the multiplication of the two factors; then find all the different ways to make a single slice through the rectangle. For each slice, students write an equation. For a slice of one row of 8, students would write 6 × 8 = (5 × 8) + (1 × 8). This might be a good time to discuss order of operations. The individual number phrases can be written in the arrays as shown in Figure 9.13.

Why Not Division by Zero? Often when teachers do not fully understand this concept, some children are simply told, "Division by zero is not allowed" (Quinn, Lamberg, & Perrin, 2008). To avoid an arbitrary rule, pose problems to be modelled that involve zero: "Take 30 counters. How many sets of zero can be made?" or "Put 12 blocks in zero equal groups. How many in each group?"

Math Trek 7, 8 (Nectar Foundation, 2003) an integrated, curriculum-based program offers opportunities for students to solve one- and two-step context-based problems. These problems, along with short quizzes, provide students with an opportunity to practise the operations and apply their knowledge of mathematical concepts presented in the lessons.

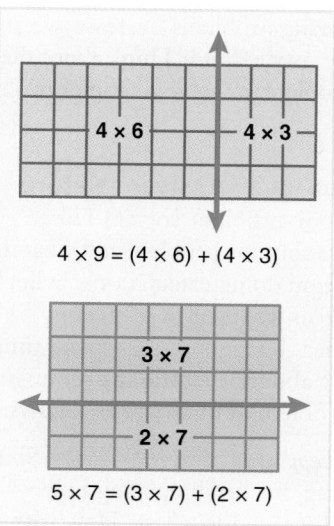

$$4 \times 9 = (4 \times 6) + (4 \times 3)$$

$$5 \times 7 = (3 \times 7) + (2 \times 7)$$

Figure 9.13 Models for the distributive property.

Figure This! is a wonderful collection of explorations available at www.figurethis.org. The 80 challenges are designed for middle-grade students. Although not simple story problems, many involve an understanding of the operations. Each problem has interesting follow-up questions and all are designed to engage students and families in real-world applications of mathematics. ◆

Strategies for Solving Contextual Problems

Often students see context or story problems and are at a loss for what to do. Also, struggling readers or ELL students may need support with understanding the problem. In this section you will learn some techniques for helping them.

Analyzing Context Problems

Consider the following problem:

> In order to build a road through a subdivision, a low section in the land was filled in with dirt that was hauled by trucks. The complete fill required 638 truckloads of dirt. The average truck carried $4\frac{3}{4}$ cubic metres of dirt, with a mass of 15.6 tonnes. How many tonnes of dirt were used for the fill?

Typically, in grade 6–8 textbooks, problems of this type are found as part of a series of problems revolving around a single context or theme. Data may be found in a graph or chart or perhaps a short news item or story. Most likely the problems will include all four of the operations. Students have difficulty deciding on the correct operation and even finding the appropriate data for the problem. Many students will find two numbers in the problem and guess at the correct operation. These children simply do not have any tools for analyzing problems. At least two strategies can be taught that are very helpful: Think about the answer before solving the problem, or solve a simpler problem that is just like this one.

Think About the Answer Before Solving the Problem Poor problem solvers fail to spend adequate time thinking about the problem and what it is about. They rush in and begin doing calculations, believing that "number crunching" is what solves problems. This is simply not the case. Rather, students should spend time talking about (later, thinking about) what the answer might look like. For our sample problem, it might go as follows:

> *What is happening in this problem?* Some trucks were bringing dirt to fill up a big hole.
> *What will the answer tell us?* How many tonnes of dirt were needed to fill the hole.

> *Will that be a small number of tonnes or a large number of tonnes?* Well, each truck carried 15.6 tonnes of dirt, but there were a lot of trucks, not just one. It's probably going to be a lot of tonnes.
> *About how many do you think it will be?* It's going to be a lot. If there were just 100 trucks, it would be 1560 tonnes. It might be close to 2000 tonnes. That's a lot of tonnes!

In this type of discussion, three things are happening. First, the students are asked to focus on the problem and the meaning of the answer instead of on the numbers. The numbers are not significant when thinking about the structure of the problem. Second, with a focus on the structure of the problem, students can identify the numbers that are important, as well as the numbers that are not important to the problem. Third, the thinking leads to a rough estimate of the answer. In any event, thinking about what the answer tells and about how large it might be is a useful first step.

Work a Simpler Problem The reason that models are rarely used with problems such as the dirt problem is that the numbers are impossible to model easily. Dollars and cents, distances in thousands of kilometres, and time in minutes and seconds are all examples of data likely to be found in the upper grades, and all are difficult to model. The general problem-solving strategy of "try a simpler problem" can almost always be applied to problems with unwieldy numbers.

A simple strategy has the following steps:

1. Substitute small whole numbers for all relevant numbers in the problem.
2. Model the problem concretely or pictorially (counters, drawing, number line, array) using the new numbers.
3. Write an equation that solves the small-number version of the problem.
4. Write the corresponding equation with the original numbers where the small-number substitutes were used.
5. Use a calculator to do the computation.
6. Write the answer in a complete sentence, and decide if it makes sense.

Figure 9.14 shows how the dirt problem might be made simpler. It also shows an alternative in which only one of the numbers is made smaller and the other number is illustrated symbolically. Both methods are effective.

The idea is to provide a tool students can use to analyze a problem and not just guess at what computation to do. It is much more useful to have students do a few problems where they must use a model of a drawing to justify their solution than to give them a lot of problems where they guess at a solution but don't know if their guess is correct.

Caution: Avoid the Key Word Strategy! It is often suggested that students should be taught to find "key words"

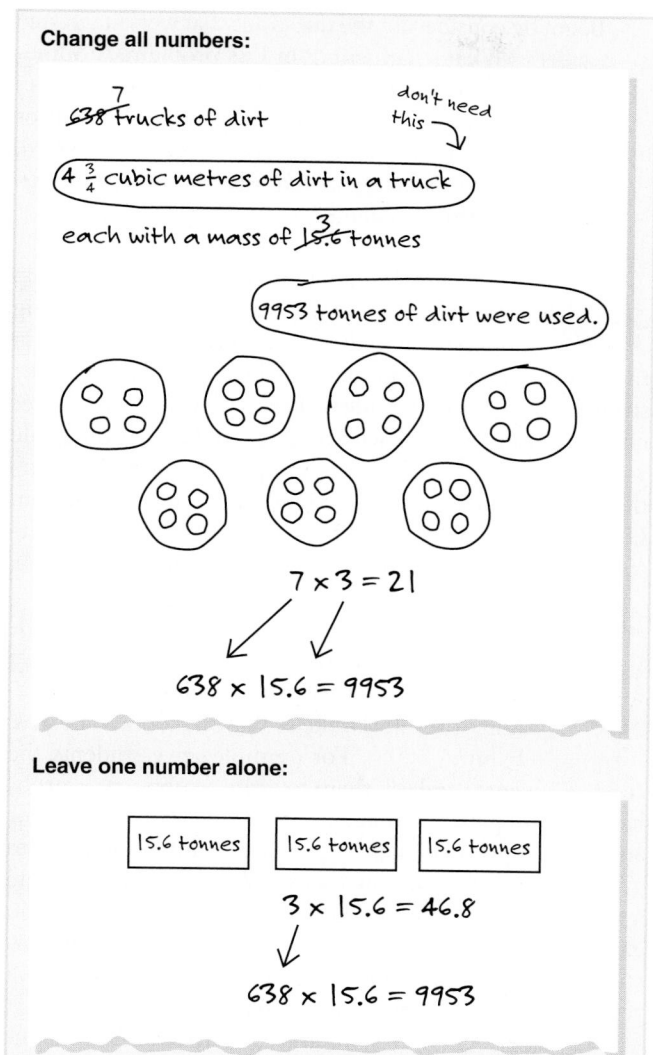

Change all numbers:

~~638~~ 7 Trucks of dirt   don't need this ↓

4 3/4 cubic metres of dirt in a truck

each with a mass of ~~15.6~~ 3 tonnes

9953 tonnes of dirt were used.

$7 \times 3 = 21$

$638 \times 15.6 = 9953$

Leave one number alone:

| 15.6 tonnes | 15.6 tonnes | 15.6 tonnes |

$3 \times 15.6 = 46.8$

$638 \times 15.6 = 9953$

Figure 9.14 Working a simpler problem: two possibilities.

in story problems. Some teachers even post lists of key words with their corresponding meanings. For example, "altogether" and "in all" mean you should add and "left" and "fewer" indicate you should subtract. The word "each" suggests multiplication. To some extent, teachers have been reinforced by the overly simple and formulaic story problems sometimes found in textbooks and other times by their own reading skills (Sulentic-Dowell, Beal, & Capraro, 2006). When problems are written in this way, it may appear that the key word strategy is effective.

In contrast with this belief, researchers and mathematics educators have long cautioned against the strategy of key words (e.g., Burns, 2000; Carpenter, 1985; Clement & Bernhard, 2005; Goldin, 1985; Sowder, 1998). Here are three arguments against the key word approach.

1. Key words are misleading. Often the key word or phrase in a problem suggests an operation that is incor-

rect. The following problem share by Drake and Barlow (2007) demonstrates this possibility.

There are three boxes of chicken nuggets on the table. Each box contains 6 chicken nuggets. How many chicken nuggets are there in all? (p. 272)

Drake and Barlow found that one student generated the answer of 9, using words "how many in all" as a suggestion to add 3 + 6, generating 9 as the answer. Instead of making sense of the situation, the student used the key word approach as a shortcut for making an operational decision.

2. Many problems have no key words. Except for the overly simple problems found in primary textbooks, a large percentage of problems have no key words. A child who has been taught to rely on key words is left with no strategy. For example, both the additive and the multiplicative problems in this chapter include numerous examples of problems with no key words. And these are from a collection of overly simple problems designed to help you with structure.

3. The key word strategy sends a terribly wrong message about doing mathematics. The most important approach to solving any contextual problem is to analyze its structure and make sense of it. The key word approach encourages students to ignore the meaning and structure of the problem and look for an easy way out. Mathematics is about reasoning and making sense of situations. A sense-making strategy will *always* work.

Two-Step Problems

Students often have difficulty with multi-step problems. First, be sure they can analyze one-step problems in the way that we have discussed. The following ideas, adapted from suggestions by Huinker (1994), are designed to help children see how two problems can be linked together.

1. Give students a one-step problem and have them solve it. Before discussing the answer, have each student or group use the answer to the first problem to create a second problem. The rest of the class can then be asked to solve the second problem. Here is an example:

Given problem: It took $3\frac{1}{2}$ hours for the Mercier family to drive the 312 kilometres to Quebec. What was their average speed?

Second problem: The Mercier children remember passing the turkey farm at about 10:30 a.m., or 2 hours after they left home. About how far from home is the turkey farm?

---

2. Make a "hidden question." Repeat the first exercise by beginning with a one-step problem. Give different problems to different groups. This time, have students write a second problem, as before. Then write a single combined problem that leaves out the question from the first problem. That question from the first problem is the "hidden question," as in the following example:

Given problem: Tony bought 3 dozen cookies for 89 cents a dozen, at the bakery outlet. How much was the bill?

Second problem: How much change did Tony get back from $5?

Hidden-question problem: Tony bought 3 dozen cookies for 89 cents a dozen. How much change did Tony get back from $5?

Have other students identify the hidden question. Since all students are working on a similar task but with different problems (be sure to mix the operations), they will be more likely to understand what is meant by a hidden question.

3. Pose standard two-step problems, and have the students identify and answer the hidden question. Consider the following problem:

Willard Sales decides to add DVDs to its line of sale items. To begin with, Willard bought 275 DVDs wholesale for $5.69 each. In the first month, the company sold 205 DVDs at $7.99 each. How much did Willard make or lose on the DVDs? Do you think Willard Sales should continue to sell DVDs?

Begin by considering the questions that were suggested earlier: "What's happening in this problem?" (Something is being bought and sold at two different prices.) "What will the answer tell us?" (How much profit or loss there was.) These questions will get you started. If students are stuck, you can ask, "Is there a hidden question in this problem?"

 The value of student discussions to help develop meaning throughout mathematics including understanding the operations is quite evident in the *Standards*. At the grade K–2 level: "When students struggle to communicate ideas clearly, they develop a better understanding of their own thinking" (p. 129). At the grade 3–5 level: "The use of models and pictures provides a further opportunity for understanding and conversation. Having a concrete referent helps students develop understandings that are clearer and more easily shared" (p. 197).

 One of the best ways to assess students' knowledge of the meaning of the operations is to have them generate story problems for a given equation or result (Drake & Barlow, 2007; Whitin & Whitin, 2008). For example, give students the result "24 cents" and ask them to write a subtraction problem that will generate that answer or a division problem or any other appropriate type of problem. Another option is to give them an expression such as 5×7 and ask them to write a story problem representing the expression. Students who can ably match scenarios to the computation will demonstrate their understanding, whereas struggling students will reveal areas of weakness. Students can also use the context from a piece of children's literature to write word problems that emphasize the meaning of the four operations. ◆

Reflections on Chapter 9

Writing to Learn

1. Make up a comparison word problem. Next change the problem to provide an example of all six different possibilities for comparison problems.

2. Why might a contextual problem be more effective than a simple story problem?

3. Explain how missing-part activities prepare students for mastering subtraction facts.

4. Make up multiplication story problems to illustrate the difference between equal groups and multiplicative comparison. Can you create problems involving rates or continuous quantities?

5. Make up two different word problems for 36 ÷ 9. For one, the modelling should result in four sets of nine, and for the other, the modelling should result in nine sets of four. Which is which? Which of your problems is a measurement problem and which is a partition problem?

6. Make up realistic measurement and partition division problems in which the remainder is dealt with in each of these three ways: (a) it is discarded (but not left over); (b) it is made into a fraction; (c) it forces the answer to the next whole number.

7. Why is the use of key words not a good strategy to teach children?

For Discussion and Exploration

1. *Cognitively Guided Instruction* is not a curriculum program but a professional development program in which teachers learn to use students' thinking to guide instruction. The predominant thrust of CGI is the use of story problems, not only for learning the operations but also for number and fact development and even for computation development with larger numbers. Select either basic fact mastery or computation development and describe how you think these goals might be achieved primarily through story problems. If possible, view some of the video clips on the CD that comes with *Children's Mathematics: Cognitively Guided Instruction* (Carpenter et al., 1999) to compare your thoughts with theirs.

2. See how many different types of story problems you can find in a student textbook. In the primary grades, look for *join*, *remove*, *part–part–whole*, and *compare* problems. For grades 4 and up, look for the four multiplicative types. (Look in the multiplication and division chapters and also at special problem-solving lessons.) Are the various types of problems well represented?

Resources for Chapter 9

Literature Connections

There are many books with stories or pictures concerning sets of things, buying items, measures, and so on, that can be used to pose problems or, better, to stimulate children to invent their own problems. Perhaps the most widely mentioned book in this context is *The Doorbell Rang* by Pat Hutchins (1986). You can check that one out yourself. Here are additional suggestions.

Hannah's Collection   *Jocelyn, 2000*

This colourful book, by Canadian author Jocelyn, captures the charm as well as the skills that make collecting so much fun. The book can serve as a good jumping off point for children to bring their own collections or to reproduce Hannah's. Sorting and grouping objects within a collection or between collections can provide opportunities for adding, subtracting, or grouping objects for multiplication.

How Many Snails?   *Giganti, 1988*

Appropriate for the Pre-K–2 set, this book includes a variety of pictures in which the objects belonging to one collection have various sub-collections (parts and wholes). For example, a sky full of clouds has various types of clouds. The text asks, "How many clouds are there? How many clouds are big and fluffy? How many clouds are big and fluffy and gray?" These pages lead directly to addition and subtraction situations matching the part–part–whole concepts. Of special note is the opportunity to have missing-part thinking for subtraction. Children can then pose their own questions about the drawing, and add appropriate number sentences or draw pictures with sub-collections on their own equation and see how it fits the picture.

One Hundred Hungry Ants   *Pinczes, 1999*

This book, written by a grandmother for her grandchild, helps students explore the operation of multiplication (and division). It tells the tale of 100 ants on a trip to a picnic. In an attempt to speed their travel, the ants move from their single-file line of 100 to two rows of 50, four rows of 25, and so forth. This story uses the visual representation of arrays to explore several options for a group of 100 ants. Students can be given different sizes of ant groups to explore other groupings.

Remainder of One   Pinczes, 1995

Similar to her other book, Elinor Pinczes describes the trials and tribulations of a parade formation of 25 bugs. As the queen is viewing the outline of the parading bugs she notices that one bug is not with the group, trailing behind. The group tries to create different numbers of rows and columns (arrays) but again the one bug is always a "leftover" (remainder). Here too students can be given different parade groups and they can generate formations that will leave one, two, or none out of the group.

The Grapes of Math   Tang 2001

This genuinely clever math book uses rhyming couplets and riddles, as well as visual cues to help the reader find new ways to group numbers for performing addition and/or multiplication. Here the rhyme gives a clue to the new ways of grouping numbers. The extra-large, brightly coloured images leap off the page but never distract from the author's intent. Some riddles are very challenging, but the author provides all the solutions in the back. Children can create their own addition and multiplication stories/riddles using the grouping concept.

Recommendations for Further Reading

Articles

Ameis, J. (2008). A grade 4 adventure with multiplication on the Chinese abacus. *delta-K, 46* (1), 27–36.
   This article explores the experiences of a group of grade 4 students who were developing a functional sense of the distributive property that was then applied to multidigit multiplication. The students extended their understanding by working with the Chinese abacus (suan pan).

Clement, L. & Bernhard, J. (2005). A problem-solving alternative to using key words. *Mathematics Teaching in the Middle School, 10* (7), 360–365.
   This article explores the use of key words as a replacement for sense-making in reading word problems. The authors emphasize the meaning of the operations as they sort out common student misconceptions. They describe ways to emphasize having students understand the quantities and relationships between quantities

Jung, M., Kloosterman, P., & McMullen, M. (2007). Research in review. Young children's intuition for solving problems in mathematics. *Young Children, 62* (5), 50–57.
   This article explores how students in pre-K through the second grade solve problems using the Cognitively Guided Instruction (CGI) approach as a foundation. The authors share classroom vignettes and then they debrief what they learned about children's thinking.

Theis, L. (2007). Helping grade 1 students understand the equals sign: a difficult but not impossible task. *delta-K, 45* (1), 13–20.
   This article focuses on the difficulty that students have developing a proper understanding of the equals sign. It particularly concentrates on the development of grade 1 students' understanding.

Books

Carpenter, T. P., Fennema, E., Franke, M. L., Levi, L., & Empson, S. (1999). *Children's mathematics: Cognitively guided instruction.* Portsmouth, NH: Heinemann. (Also published by NCTM.)
   For teachers, this is the best book available for understanding the CGI approach to operations and the use of story problems to develop number, basic facts, and computational procedures. The classifications of word problems for all operations, as discussed in this chapter, are explained in detail along with methods for using these problems with students. With the book come two CDs, one with classroom clips of CGI classrooms and the other showing children using the various strategies described in the book.

Schifter, D., Bastable, V., & Russell, S. J. (1996b). *Developing mathematical understanding: Numbers and operations, Part 2, Making meaning for operations (Casebook).* Parsippany, NJ: Dale Seymour Publications.
   In this casebook, teachers in grades K–7 share their stories of working with children as they develop meanings for the four operations. The teachers discuss the kinds of actions and situations that students use as they come to understand the operations. This is a companion book to an extended in-service guide. There is also a video available to augment the series. However, the casebook is easily worthwhile by itself.

Online Resources

Can Teach Number Activities
www.canteach.ca/elementary/numbers.html
   At this site, math games and activities that offer practice with performing the operations of addition, subtraction, multiplication, and division can be found.

Link to Learning
www.linktolearning.com/math.htm
   This site contains many links to other sites with activities and resources (both French and English) that could easily be used to reinforce chapter concepts. Some of the activities and resources to which this site links are Canadian-based (e.g., Learn Alberta, The Canadian Government, Department of Mathematics, University of Waterloo).

Broken Calculators
http://my.nctm.org/eresources/view_article.asp?article_id=7457&page= 11 &add=Y
www.fi.uu.nl/toepassingen/00014/toepassing_rekenweb.en.html
   These two applets demonstrate the broken calculator activity as mentioned in Activity 9.6 and 9.7. The first allows for problems at any level, whereas the second is more appropriate for intermediate or middle-grades students, as it includes a problem-solving feature.

Number Line Arithmetic
http://nlvm.usu.edu/en/nav/frames_asid_
156_g_1_t_1.html

This number-line applet can be used to model whole-number operations in addition, subtraction, multiplication, and division.

Thinking Blocks: Addition and Subtraction
www.thinkingblocks.com/ThinkingBlocks_AS/TB_AS_
Main.html

Thinking Blocks: Multiplication and Division
www.thinkingblocks.com/ThinkingBlocks_MD/TB_MD_

www.thinkingblocks.com/ThinkingBlocks_AS/TB_AS_
Main.html http://my.nctm.org/eresources/view_article.
asp?article_ id=7457&page= 11 &add=Y Main.html

This teacher-developed tool links to the various types of problems discussed earlier in the chapter. The difference is the use of two-digit numbers and problems with multiple steps, including compare, part–part–whole, and change examples. There is an emphasis on identifying and solving for an unknown quantity. Because the ideas are presented in game formats, you should view the introduction to be able to play.

All About Multiplication (Grades 3–5)
http://illuminations.nctm.org/LessonDetail.aspx?id=U109

Four lessons with links to other activities and student recording sheets highlight the model of the number line, equal groups, arrays, and balanced equations. Lesson 3 explores the order property, the zero property, and the identity property. Lesson 4 has an engaging applet called the Product Game.

The Factor Game
http://illuminations.nctm.org/ActivityDetail..aspx?ID=12

This game puts two players in competition to collect the factors for given numbers.

myeducationlab *will help you improve your understanding of the concepts taught in this textbook and in your course. This online tool includes videos of real classroom experiences, sample lesson plans, simulations, case studies, and links to important educational and teaching Web sites that will help you make the transition from student to teacher. As you study in your course and with this textbook, please follow along in* **MyEducationLab**. *Use it! Explore it! And improve your knowledge and your grade!*

Chapter 10
Helping Children Master the Basic Facts

Basic facts for addition and multiplication refer to combinations where both addends or both factors are less than 10. Subtraction and division facts correspond to addition and multiplication facts. Thus, $15 - 8 = 7$ is a subtraction fact because both parts are less than 10.

Mastery of a basic fact means that a child can give a quick response (in about 3 seconds) without resorting to non-efficient means, such as counting. Typically, regional curriculum documents indicate that addition and subtraction facts are learned in grade 1, with quick recall mastered in grade 2. Learning of concepts of multiplication and division generally begins in grade 3, with quick recall of the facts mastered in grade 4.

Developing quick and accurate recall with the basic facts is a development process—just like every topic in this book! It is critical that students know their facts well—and teaching them well requires much more than flash cards and timed tests. This chapter explains strategies for helping students learn their facts and instructional approaches to use—and others to avoid.

Big Ideas

1. Number relationships provide the foundation for strategies that help students remember basic facts. For example, knowing how numbers are related to 5 and 10 helps students master facts such as 3 + 5 (think of a ten-frame) and 8 + 6 (since 8 is 2 away from 10, take 2 from 6 to make 10 + 4 = 14).

2. "Think-addition" is the most powerful way to think of subtraction facts. Rather than 13 "take away 6," which requires counting backward while also keeping track of how many counts, students can think 6 and what makes 13. They might add up to 10 or they may think double 6 is 12 so it must be 13.

3. Because mastery of the basic facts is a development process students move through stages, starting with counting, then to more efficient reasoning strategies, and eventually to quick recall. Instruction must help students move through these phases, without rushing them to memorization.

Mathematics Content Connections

As should be clear from the Big Ideas, basic fact mastery is not really new mathematics; rather, it is the development of fluency with ideas that have already been learned.

- **Number and Operations** (Chapters 8 and 9): Fact mastery relies significantly on how well students have constructed relationships about numbers and how well they understand the operations.

  Fluency with basic facts allows for ease of computation, especially mental computations, and, therefore, aids the ability to reason numerically in every number-related area. Although calculators and tedious counting are available to students who do not have command of the facts, relying on these methods for simple number combinations is a serious handicap to mathematical growth.

Developmental Nature of Basic Fact Development

Teaching basic facts well requires the essential understanding that students progress through stages that eventually result in "just knowing" that 2 + 7 is 9 or that 5 × 4 is 20. Arthur Baroody, a mathematics educator who does research on basic facts, describes three phases in this process (2006, p. 22):

Phase 1: Counting Strategies—using object counting (e.g., blocks or fingers) or verbal counting to determine the answer.

Example: 4 + 7. Student starts with 7 and counts on verbally 8, 9, 10, 11.

Phase 2: Reasoning Strategies—using known information to logically determine an unknown combination. Example: 4 + 7. Student knows that 7 + 3 is 10, so 7 + 4 is one more, 11.

Phase 3: Mastery—efficient (fast and accurate) production of answers.

Example 4 + 7. Student quickly responds, "It's 11; I just know it."

Figure 10.1 outlines the methods for solving basic addition and subtraction problems that students move through developmentally.

Much research over many years supports the notion that basic facts mastery is dependent on the development of reasoning strategies (Baroody, 2003, 2006; Brownell & Chazal, 1935; Carpenter & Moser, 1984; Fuson, 1992; Henry & Brown, 2008). This chapter focuses on reasoning strategies and effective ways to teach students to use reasoning to master the basic facts.

Approaches to Fact Mastery

In attempting to help children master their basic facts, three somewhat different approaches can be identified. First is to work on memorization of each fact in isolation. A second approach that can be traced at least as far back as the 1970s (Rathmell, 1978) suggests that for various classes of basic facts we teach students a collection of strategies or thought patterns. These strategies have been found to be efficient and teachable. The third approach, "guided invention," also focuses on the use of strategies for learning facts. However, the strategies are generated or reinvented by students. Each of these approaches is briefly discussed in the following section.

	Addition	Subtraction
Counting	Direct modelling (counting objects and fingers) • Counting all • Counting on from first • Counting on from larger	Counting objects • Separating from • Separating to • Adding on
	Counting abstractly • Counting all • Counting on from first • Counting on from larger	Counting fingers • Counting down • Counting up
		Counting abstractly • Counting down • Counting up
Reasoning	Properties • $a + 0 = a$ • $a + 1$ = next whole number • Commutative property	Properties • $a - 0 = a$ • $a - 1$ = previous whole number
	Known-fact derivations (e.g., 5 + 6 = 5 + 5 + 1; 7 + 6 = 7 + 7 − 1)	Inverses/complement of known addition facts (e.g., 12 − 5 is known because 5 + 7 = 12)
	Redistributed derived facts (e.g., 7 + 5 = 7 + (3 +2) = (7 + 3) + 2 = 10 + 2 = 12)	Redistributed derived facts (e.g., 12 − 5 = (7 + 5) − 5 = 7 + (5 − 5) = 7)
Retrieval	Retrieval from long-term memory	Retrieval from long-term memory

Figure 10.1 The developmental process for basic fact mastery for addition and subtraction.

Source: Henry, V. J., & Brown, R. S. (2008). "First-Grade Basic Facts: An Investigation into Teaching and Learning of an Accelerated, High-Demand Memorization Standard." *Journal for Research in Mathematics Education, 39*(2), p. 156. Reprinted with permission. Copyright © 2008 by the National Council of Teachers of Mathematics, Inc, www.nctm.org. All rights reserved.

Memorizing Facts   Some textbooks and teachers move from presenting concepts of addition and subtraction straight to memorization of facts, skipping the process of developing strategies. This means that students have 100 separate addition facts (0–9) and 100 separate multiplication facts. They may even have to memorize subtraction and division separately. However, the very fact that many students in grades 4 and 5 have not mastered addition and subtraction facts and students in the upper grades do not have a good command of their multiplication facts strongly suggests that this method simply does not work well. You may be tempted to respond that you, as many other students, learned your facts in this manner. Studies by Brownell and Chazal, as long ago as 1935, concluded that children develop a variety of different thought processes or strategies for basic facts in spite of the amount of isolated drill that they experience. Unfortunately, the drill does not encourage or support the refinement of these strategies. Moreover, Arthur Baroody (2006) notes that this approach to basic facts instruction works against the development of the five strands of mathematics proficiency (see Chapter 2), pointing out the following limitations:

- *Inefficiency.* Too many facts to memorize.
- *Inappropriate Applications.* Students misapply the facts and don't check their work.
- *Inflexibility.* Students don't learn flexible strategies for finding the sums (or products) and therefore continue to use counting.

Drill is also an equity issue. Struggling learners and students with learning disabilities have difficulty memorizing so many isolated facts but can be *very* successful at using strategies. In addition, drill can cause unnecessary anxiety—inducing and undermining student interest and confidence in mathematics.

Explicit Strategy Instruction   For approximately three decades, it has been popular to show students an efficient strategy that can be applied to a collection of facts. Students then practise the strategy as it was shown to them. There is strong evidence to indicate that such a method can be effective (e.g., Baroody, 1985; Bley & Thornton, 1995; Fuson, 1984, 1992; Rathmell, 1978; Thornton & Toohey, 1984). Many of the ideas developed and tested by these researchers are discussed in this chapter. However, an all-too-quickly taught version of this approach is found in all conventional textbooks.

Teaching explicit strategies is intended to support student thinking rather than force students to use a strategy they have memorized. Sometimes textbooks or teachers focus on memorizing the strategy and which facts work with that strategy. However, this doesn't work. When students memorize strategies that don't make sense to them they are likely to misapply them. In fact, a recent study found that teachers who relied heavily on textbooks (which

focused on memorizing basic fact strategies) had students with lower number sense proficiency (Henry & Brown, 2008). Moreover, students don't memorize well, so they resort to counting. The key is to help students see the possibilities and then let them choose strategies that help them get to the solution without counting.

Guided Invention   The third option might be called "guided invention" (Gravemeijer & van Galen, 2003). In this effective approach, fact mastery is intricately connected to students' collection of number relationships. Some students may think of 6 + 7 as "double 6 is 12 and 1 more is 13." In the same class, others may note that 7 is 3 away from 10 and so take 3 from the 6 to put with the 7 to make 10. They then add on the remaining 3. Still other students may take 5 from each addend to make 10 and then add the remaining 1 and 2. What is significant is that students are using number combinations and relationships that they own and that make sense to them.

Gravemeijer and van Galen call this approach *guided invention* because many of the strategies that are efficient will not be developed by all students, without some guidance. That is, we simply cannot place all our efforts on developing number relationships and the meanings of the operations and assume that fact mastery will happen by magic. Class discussions based on student solutions to story problems and other number tasks and games will produce a variety of strategies in the classroom. Children then select and adapt the ideas that are meaningful to them. The teacher's job then is to design tasks and problems that will promote the invention of effective strategies and to ensure that these strategies are clearly articulated and shared in the classroom. It is vitally important that teachers develop in students a rich collection of number relationships, as described in Chapter 8.

Guiding Strategy Development

In order for you to guide your students to use effective strategies, you, yourself, need to have a command of as many good strategies as possible. With this knowledge, you will be able to recognize effective strategies as your students develop them; you will also be able to help others capitalize on their ideas.

You need to plan experiences that help students move from counting to strategies to recall. One critical approach uses simple story problems designed in such a manner that students are most likely to develop a strategy as they solve it. In discussing student strategies, you can focus attention on the methods that are most useful.

Second, teach the reasoning strategies. This can help students expand their own collection of mental strategies and move away from counting. We caution, however, that this instruction should be about highlighting strategies, not about having students memorize or be required to use them.

Story Problems Story problems provide context that can help students understand the situation and apply flexible strategies for doing the computation. Consider, for example, that the class is working on × 3 facts. The teacher poses the following question:

In 3 weeks, we will be going to the zoo. How many days until we go to the zoo?

Suppose that Adriana explains how she figured out 3 × 7 by starting with double 7 (14), then adding 7 more. She knew that 6 added onto 14 is 20 and one more is 21. You can then ask another student to explain what Adriana just shared. Doing so requires students to attend to ideas that come from their classmates. Now explore with the class to see what other facts would work with Adriana's strategy. This discussion could go in a variety of directions. Some might notice that all of the facts with a 3 in them will work for the double-and-add-one-more strategy. Others may say that you can always add one more set on, if you know the smaller fact. For example, for 6 × 8 you can start with 5 × 8 and add 8.

The *Thinking with Numbers* program (Rathmell, Leutzinger, & Gabriele, 2000) consists of a large collection of simple story problems developed in sets, designed to promote particular strategies or ways of thinking about a particular collection of facts. Teachers pose one problem each day for students to solve mentally. This routine is followed by a brief discussion of the ideas that students use. There is strong evidence to support the effectiveness of this approach. Research has found that when a strong emphasis is placed on students' solving problems, they not only become better problem solvers, but they also master more basic facts than students in a fact drill program (NRC, 2001).

Reasoning Strategies A second possible approach is to directly model a reasoning strategy. A lesson is created in which students examine a special collection of facts for which a particular type of strategy is appropriate. You then discuss how these facts are all alike in some way, or you might suggest an approach and see if students are able to use it on similar facts.

Avoid the temptation to tell students to use a strategy and then have them practise it. Continue to discuss strategies invented in your class and plan lessons that encourage these strategies. Don't expect to have a strategy introduced and understood with just one word problem or one exposure. Children need a lot of opportunities to make a strategy their own. Many children will simply not be ready to use an idea the first few days. Then, all of a sudden, something will click and a useful idea will be theirs.

It is a good idea to write new strategies on the board or make a poster of strategies students develop. Give the strategies names that make sense. (*Double and add one more set. Adriana's idea. Use with 3s.* Include an example.)

No student should be forced to adopt someone else's strategy, but every student should be encouraged to understand strategies that are brought to the discussion.

Different students will likely invent or adopt different strategies for the same collection of facts. For example, there are several methods or strategies that use 10 when adding 8 or 9. Therefore, a drill that includes all the addition facts with an 8 or a 9 can accommodate any child who has a strategy for that collection. Two children can be playing a spinner drill game, each using different strategies.

 Critics of the reform movement in mathematics education often try to suggest that the *Standards* are "soft on the basics," especially mastery of facts. Nothing could be further from the truth. Among several similar statements that could be selected from the *Standards* document is this quote: "Knowing the basic number combinations—single-digit addition and multiplication pairs and their counterparts for subtraction and division—is essential" (p. 32).

Reasoning Strategies for Addition Facts

The strategies that students can and will invent for addition facts are directly related to one or more number relationships. In Chapter 8, numerous activities were suggested to develop these relationships. Now, the teaching task is to help children connect these number relationships to the basic facts.

The "big idea" behind using reasoning strategies is for students to make use of known facts and relationships to solve basic facts equations. Of the two ways students might do this, one is to use a *known fact* (like 7 + 3 = 10) to solve an unknown fact, such as 7 + 5, which is two more than the

Story problems provide contexts that can help students understand the mathematics and figure out which strategies are needed for completing the computation.

known fact. The second is to use *derived facts*. In this case, the student might solve 7 + 5 by taking 7 apart into 5 + 2, then adding the 5 + 5 and then 2 more (Henry & Brown, 2008). Keep this "big idea" in mind as you review each of the reasoning strategies described in this section.

One-More-Than and Two-More-Than Facts

Each of the 36 facts highlighted in the chart that follows has at least one addend of 1 or 2. These facts are a direct application of the one-more-than and two-more-than relationships.

Story problems in which one of the addends is a 1 or a 2 are easy to create. For example, *When Rachel was at the circus, she saw 7 clowns come out in a little car. Then 2 more clowns came out on bicycles. How many clowns did Rachel see in all?* Ask different students to explain how they got the answer of 9. Some will count on from 7. Some may still need to count 7 and 2 then count all. Others will say they knew that 2 more than 7 is 9. The last response gives you an opportunity to talk about facts where you can use the two-more-than idea.

+	0	1	2	3	4	5	6	7	8	9
0		1	2							
1	1	2	3	4	5	6	7	8	9	10
2	2	3	4	5	6	7	8	9	10	11
3		4	5							
4		5	6							
5		6	7							
6		7	8							
7		8	9							
8		9	10							
9		10	11							

Activity 10.1

How Many Feet in the Bed?

Read *How Many Feet in the Bed?* (This book by Diane Johnston Hamm offers students an opportunity to practise the add-more strategy). On the second time through the book, ask students how many more feet are in the bed when a new person gets in. Ask students to record the equation (e.g., 6 + 2 = 8) and tell how many. Two less can be considered as family members are getting out of the bed.

The different responses will provide you with a lot of information about students' number sense. As students are ready to use the two-more-than idea without "counting all," they can begin to practise with activities such as the following.

Activity 10.2

One-More- and Two-More-Than with Dice and Spinners

Make a die labelled + 1, + 2, + 1, + 2, "one more," and "two more." Use with another die labelled 3, 4, 5, 6, 7, and 8 (or whatever values students need to practise). After each roll of the dice, children should say the complete fact: "Four and two more is six." Alternatively, roll one die and use a spinner with + 1 on one half and + 2 on the other half.

Figure 10.2 illustrates the ideas in Activity 10.2. Notice that activities such as these can be modified for almost all the strategies in the chapter.

Adding with Zero

Nineteen facts have zero as one of the addends. Though such problems are generally easy, some children over-generalize the idea that answers to addition are bigger. Word problems involving zero will be especially helpful. In the discussion, use drawings that show two parts with one part empty.

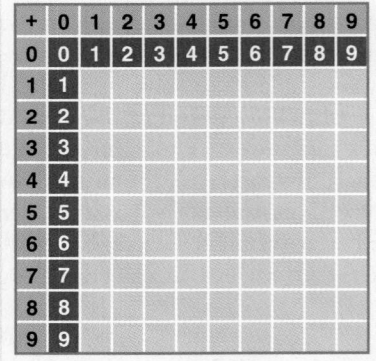

+	0	1	2	3	4	5	6	7	8	9
0	0	1	2	3	4	5	6	7	8	9
1	1									
2	2									
3	3									
4	4									
5	5									
6	6									
7	7									
8	8									
9	9									

Activity 10.3

What's Alike? Zero Facts

Write about ten zero facts on the board, some with the zero first and some with the zero second. Discuss how all of these facts are alike. Have children use counters and a part–part–whole mat to model the facts at their seats.

Using 5 as an Anchor

The use of an anchor is a reasoning strategy that builds on students' knowledge of number relationships. In so doing it helps them derive from these relationships. For example, 7 is 5 + 2, and 6 is 5 + 1. A fact, such as 6 + 7 can then be processed by a student who sees the 5 in each number, along

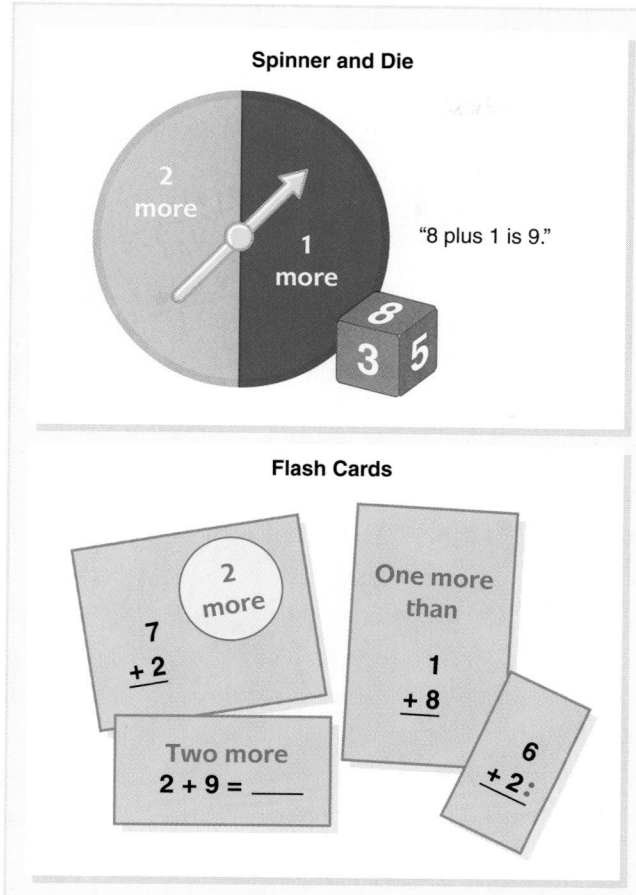

Figure 10.2 One-more and two-more activities.

10 Facts

Perhaps the most important strategy for students to know is the Make 10 strategy, or the combinations that make 10. Story problems using two numbers that make 10 or that ask how many are needed to make 10 can assist this process. The ten-frame is also a very useful tool. Place counters on one ten-frame and ask, "How many more to make ten?" This activity can be done over and over until students have mastered all the combinations to make 10. Knowing combinations that make 10 not only helps with basic facts mastery, it builds foundations for working on addition with higher numbers, as well as understanding place-value concepts.

Up Over 10

Some facts have sums greater than 10. Students use their known facts that equal 10 to solve these basic fact problems. For example, students solving 6 + 8 might start with the larger number and see that it is 2 away from 10. They then take 2 from the 6 to get 10 and add on the remaining 4 to get 14.

with the "extras." In this example the student would add 5 + 5; then add the extra 1 from the 6 and the extra 2 from the 7 to get 13. The ten-frames discussed in Chapter 8 can help students see numbers as 5 and some more.

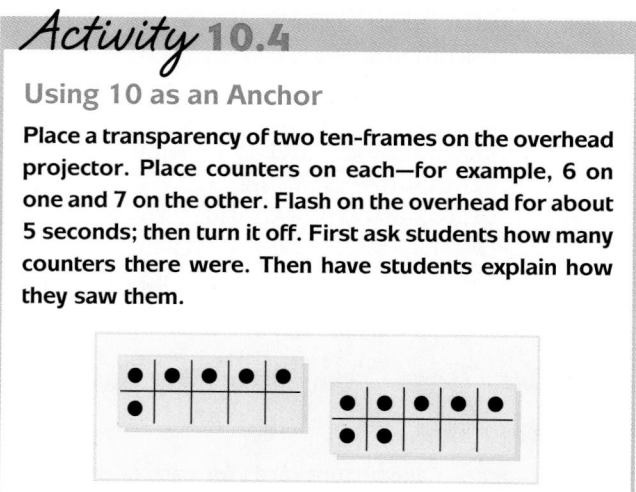

+	0	1	2	3	4	5	6	7	8	9
0										
1										
2										11
3									11	12
4								11	12	13
5							11	12	13	14
6						11	12	13	14	15
7					11	12	13	14	15	16
8				11	12	13	14	15	16	17
9			11	12	13	14	15	16	17	18

This reasoning strategy is extremely important and often not emphasized enough in North American textbooks or classrooms (Henry & Brown, 2008). In fact, this strategy is heavily emphasized in high-performing countries (Korea, China, Taiwan, and Japan) where students memorize facts sooner and more accurately than do North American students. A recent study of California first graders found that the Make 10 strategy contributed more to memorizing over-10 facts (e.g., 7 + 8) than did using doubles (even though using doubles had been emphasized by teachers and textbooks in the study). Also, many of the basic addition facts can be solved using the Make 10 strategy. This strategy can later be applied to adding up over 20 or 50 or other benchmark numbers. Collectively, these considerations argue that this reasoning strategy deserves significant attention in teaching addition (and subtraction) facts.

Activity 10.6

Move to Make

Adapt Activity 10.4 by asking students to visualize moving counters to fill one of the ten-frames to figure out how many. After students have found a total, have students share and record the equations. Alternatively, start with the equation and have students visualize "making 10" and then tell the answer.

Activity 10.7

Make 10 on the Ten-Frame

Give students a mat with two ten-frames. Place flash cards next to the ten-frames, or give facts orally. (Be aware that some children will need to have the visual and will not be able to do the activity if facts are only given orally.) The students model each number in the two ten-frames, then decide on the easiest way to find the total without counting. Get students to explain what they did. Focus especially on the idea that counters can be taken from one of the frames and moved to the other to make 10. Then you have 10 and whatever is left. See Blackline Master 11.

Activity 10.8

Frames and Facts

Use the little ten-frame cards found in the Blackline Masters. Make a transparency set for the overhead. Show an 8 (or 9) card on the overhead. Place other cards beneath it, one at a time, as students respond with the total. Have students say orally what they are thinking. For 8 + 4, they might say, "Take 2 from the 4 and put it with 8 to make 10. Then 10 and 2 left over is 12." Move to harder cards, like 7 + 6. The activity can be done independently with the little ten-frame cards. Ask students to record each equation, as shown in Figure 10.3.

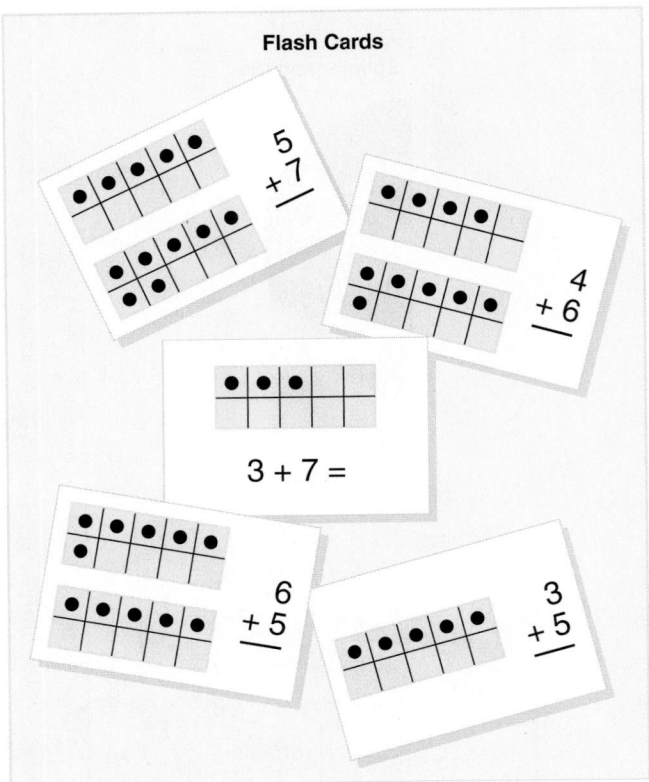

Figure 10.3 Frames and facts.

Doubles

There are only ten doubles facts from 0 + 0 to 9 + 9, as shown here. These ten facts are relatively easy to learn and become a powerful way to learn the near-doubles (addends one apart). Some children use them as anchors for other facts as well.

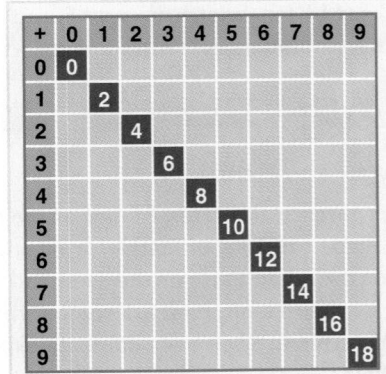

Activity 10.9

Double Images

Have students make picture cards for each of the doubles, and include the basic fact on the card as shown in Figure 10.4.

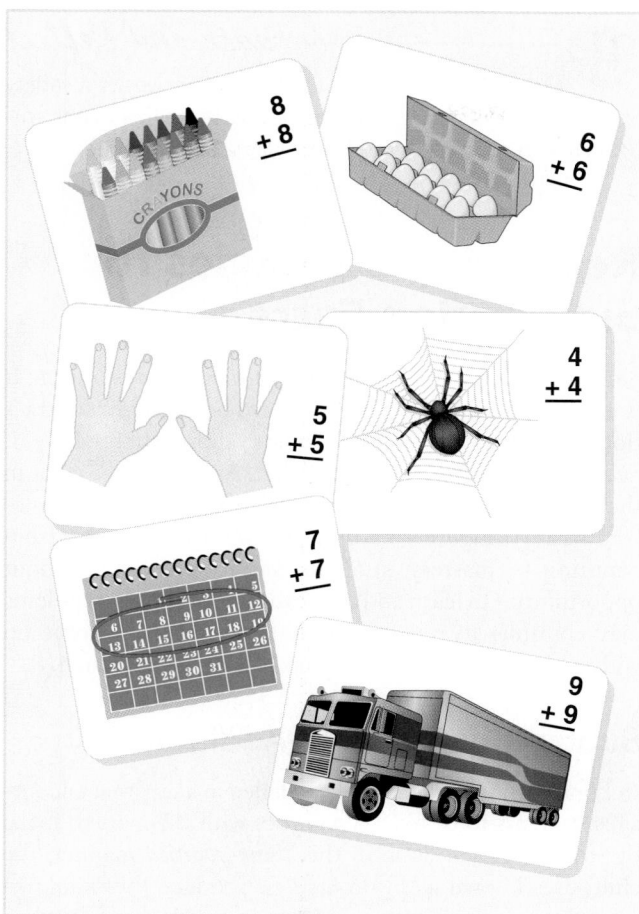

Figure 10.4 Double facts.

Word problems can focus on pairs of like addends. *Alex and Nina each found 7 seashells at the beach. How many did they find all together?*

A simple doubling "machine" can be drawn on the board or created from a shoe box. Cards are made with an "input number" on the front side and the double of the number on the reverse. The card is flipped front to back as it goes "through" the double machine. A pair of students or a small group can use input/output machines, or you can lead the activity with a larger group.

Activity 10.10

Calculator Doubles

Use the calculator and enter the "double maker" (2 ×). Let one child say, for example, "Seven plus seven." The child with the calculator should press 7, try to give the double (14), then press = to see the correct double on the display. (Note that the calculator is also a good way to practise 1 and 2 facts.)

Near-Doubles

Near-doubles are also called the "doubles-plus-one" facts and include all combinations where one addend is one more or less than the other. This is a strategy that uses a known fact to generate an unknown fact. The strategy is to double the smaller number and add 1. Be sure students know the doubles before you focus on this strategy.

+	0	1	2	3	4	5	6	7	8	9
0		1								
1	1		3							
2		3		5						
3			5		7					
4				7		9				
5					9		11			
6						11		13		
7							13		15	
8								15		17
9									17	

In addition to story problems involving near-doubles, you can introduce the strategy to the class by writing about ten near-doubles facts on the board. Use vertical and horizontal formats and vary which addend is the smaller.

Have students work independently to write the answers. Then discuss their ideas for "good" (that is, efficient) methods for answering these facts. Some may double the smaller number and add one. Others may double the larger and subtract. If no one uses a near-double strategy, write the corresponding doubles for some of the facts and ask how these facts could help.

Activity 10.11

On the Double

Create an activity board (on the board or on paper) that illustrates the doubles (see Figure 10.5). Prepare cards with near-doubles (e.g., 4 + 5). Ask students to find the fact that could help them solve the fact they have on the card and place it on that spot. Ask students if there are other doubles that could help.

Reinforcing Reasoning Strategies

Remember that the big idea of developing reasoning strategies is helping students move away from counting and become more efficient until they are able to recall facts quickly and correctly. On a daily basis you can pose short story problems or equations and simply ask, "How did you solve it?" Activity 10.12 is good for helping students realize

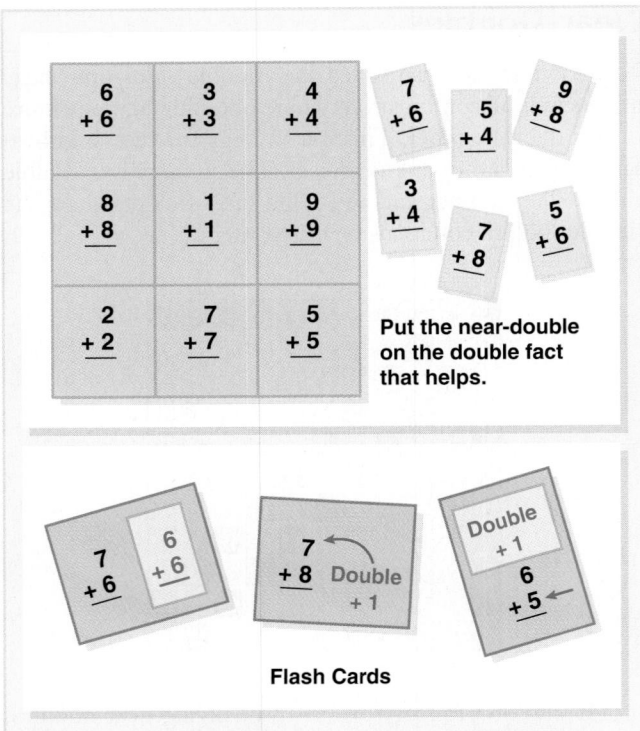

Put the near-double on the double fact that helps.

Flash Cards

Figure 10.5 Near-doubles facts.

that if they don't "just know" a fact, they can fall back on reasoning strategies to figure it out.

Activity 10.12

If You Didn't Know

Pose the following task to the class: **If you did not know the answer to 8 + 5 (or any fact that you want students to think about), what are some really good ways to get the answer?** Explain that "really good" means that you don't have to count and you can do it in your head. Encourage students to come up with more than one way. Use a think-pair-share approach in which students discuss their ideas with a partner before they share them with the class.

 Many students will have latched on to counting strategies for addition facts. Often these children become so adept at counting that you may not be aware that they are doing so. Speed in counting is not a substitute for fact mastery. It is useful to find out just how your students are thinking when they respond to facts. This may require a short diagnostic interview that includes fact groups that you think the student may not have mastered. Once the student records or states the answer, say, "Tell me how you were thinking to get this answer." ◆

Pause and Reflect

Many of the addition facts lend themselves to a variety of different reasoning strategies. What strategies might students use to get the answer 8 + 6? Name at least three.

Reasoning Strategies for Subtraction Facts

Subtraction facts prove to be more difficult than addition. It is especially true when children have been taught subtraction through a "count–count–count" approach; for $13 - 5$, *count* 13, *count* off 5, *count* what's left. As discussed earlier in the chapter, counting is a very early step in reaching basic fact mastery. Figure 10.1 on page 169 lists the ways, from counting to mastery, students might subtract. Without opportunities to learn and use reasoning strategies, students may continue to rely on counting strategies to come up with basic facts, a slow and often inaccurate approach.

Subtraction as Think-Addition

In Figure 10.6, subtraction is modelled in a way that encourages students to think, "What goes with this part to make the total?" When done in this *think-addition* manner, the child uses known addition facts to produce the unknown quantity or part. (You might want to revisit the discussion of missing-part activities in Chapter 8 and part–part–whole subtraction concepts in Chapter 9.) If this important rela-

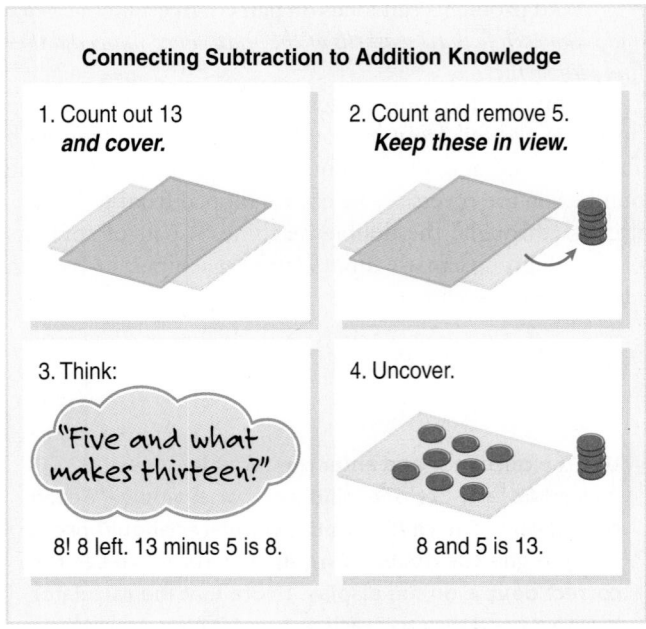

Connecting Subtraction to Addition Knowledge

1. Count out 13 *and cover.*

2. Count and remove 5. *Keep these in view.*

3. Think:

"Five and what makes thirteen?"

8! 8 left. 13 minus 5 is 8.

4. Uncover.

8 and 5 is 13.

Figure 10.6 Using a think-addition model for subtraction.

tionship between parts and wholes—between addition and subtraction—can be made, subtraction facts will be much easier. As with addition facts, it is helpful to begin with the facts that have totals of 10 or less (e.g., 8 – 3, 9 – 7) before working on facts that have a total (minuend) higher than 10 (e.g., 13 – 4).

When children see 9 – 4, you want them to think spontaneously, "Four and *what* makes nine?" By contrast, observe a grade 3 child who struggles with this fact. The idea of thinking addition never occurs to the child. Instead, the child will begin to count either back from 9 or up from 4. The value of think-addition cannot be overstated.

Story problems that promote think-addition are those that sound like addition but have a missing addend: *join, initial part unknown; join, change unknown;* and *part–part–whole, part unknown* (see Chapter 9). Consider this problem: *Aisha had 5 fish in her aquarium. Grandma gave her some more fish. Then she had 12 fish. How many fish did Grandma give Aisha?* Notice that the action is join—thus suggesting addition. There is a high probability that students will think *5 and how many more makes 12.* In the discussion in which you use problems such as this, your task is to connect this thought process with the subtraction fact, 12 – 5.

Down Over 10

⏸ ———————— *Pause and Reflect*

Before reading further, look at the three subtraction facts shown here, and try to reflect on what thought process you use to get the answers. Even if you "just know them," think about what a likely process might be.

$$\begin{array}{ccc} 14 & 12 & 15 \\ -9 & -6 & -6 \end{array}$$

You may have applied a think-addition strategy to any of these. For example, on the first problem counting from 9 up 1 to 10 then 4 more to 14, the difference is 5. If instead, you started with the 14 and counted down, perhaps reasoning that it is 4 down to 10 then down 1 more to get to 9, the total difference is 5. Then, you used a reasoning strategy called Down-Over-Ten. If you didn't already use this strategy, try it with the other two examples.

This reasoning strategy is a derived fact strategy. Students use what they know (that 14 minus 4 is 10). They use that to figure out a related fact (14 – 5). Like the Make Ten strategy discussed in addition facts, this strategy is one emphasized in high-performing countries (Fuson & Kwon, 1992). This strategy shows great promise for helping students move to mastery while supporting their number sense, yet it does not receive the attention in textbooks and classrooms that it should.

A useful story problem for this strategy might be one like the following: *Petra had 16 cents. She spent 7 cents to buy a small toy. How much money does she have left?*

Take from the 10

This strategy is not well known but is used consistently in high-performing countries. It also takes advantage of students' knowledge of the combinations that make 10. It works for all subtraction problems where the starting value (minuend) is over 10. For example, take the problem 16 – 8. Students take the minuend apart into 10 + 6. Subtracting from the 10 (because they know this fact), 10 – 8 is 2. Then they add the 6 back on to get 8. Try it on these examples:

$$15 - 8 = \qquad 17 - 9 = \qquad 14 - 8 =$$

You can see that while this may seem unusual at first, it is a great reasoning strategy. It can be used for all the subtraction facts having minuends greater than 10 (the "toughies") by just knowing how to subtract from 10 and knowing addition facts with sums less than 10.

Activity 10.15

Apples in Two Trees

Adapt Activity 10.13 and explain that each ten-frame is a different tree. Tell students you will tell them how many apples fall out of the "full" tree. They will then tell you how many apples are left (on both trees). Each time ask students to explain their thinking.

Activity 10.16

Missing-Number Cards

Show students families of numbers with the sum circled as in Figure 10.7(a). Ask why they think the numbers go together and why one number is circled. When this number family idea is understood, show some families with one number replaced by a question mark, as in Figure 10.7(b). Ask what number is missing. Ask students how they figured it out. After modelling, students can do this with partners.

When students understand this activity, explain that you have made some missing-number cards based on this idea, as in Figure 10.7(c). Ask students to name the missing number and explain their thinking.

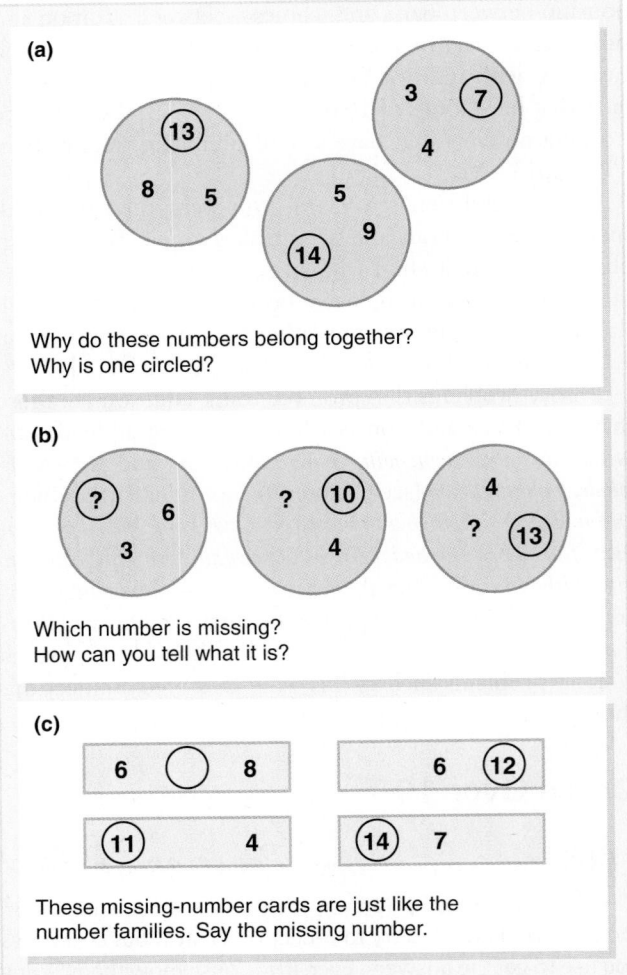

(a)

Why do these numbers belong together?
Why is one circled?

(b)

Which number is missing?
How can you tell what it is?

(c)

These missing-number cards are just like the number families. Say the missing number.

Figure 10.7 Introducing missing-number cards.

Missing Part Worksheet found in Blackline Master 13 can be used to make a wide variety of drill exercises. In a column of 13 "cards," put all the combinations from two families with different numbers missing—some parts and some wholes. Put blanks in different positions. An example is shown in Figure 10.8. After filling in numbers, make copies and have students fill in the missing numbers. Another idea is to group facts from one strategy or number relation, or perhaps mix facts from two strategies on one page.

Have students write an addition fact and a subtraction fact to go with each missing-number card. This is an important step because many children are able to give the missing part in a family but do not connect this knowledge with subtraction. You might accommodate children who are experiencing difficulty with this activity by having them use the ten-frame cards with the counters to figure out the number facts. You might limit how many numbers are missing and their position in the number sentences.

NCTM Standards Teachers often ask when students "should have mastered the addition and subtraction facts?" According to the *Standards*, "By the end of grade 2, students should know the basic addition and subtraction combinations" (p. 35).

Reasoning Strategies for Multiplication Facts

Multiplication facts can also be mastered by relating new facts to existing knowledge. Using a problem-based approach and focusing on reasoning strategies is just as important, if not more so, for developing mastery of the multiplication and related division facts (Baroody, 2006; Wallace & Gurganus, 2005). As with addition and subtraction facts, you should use story problems throughout your work on different reasoning strategies.

It is imperative that students completely understand the commutative property (see page 160 and Figure 9.12). This can be visualized with the use of arrays. For example, a 2 by 8 array can be described as 2 rows of 8 or 8 rows of 2. In both cases, the answer is 16. Having a strong understanding of the commutative property is very important

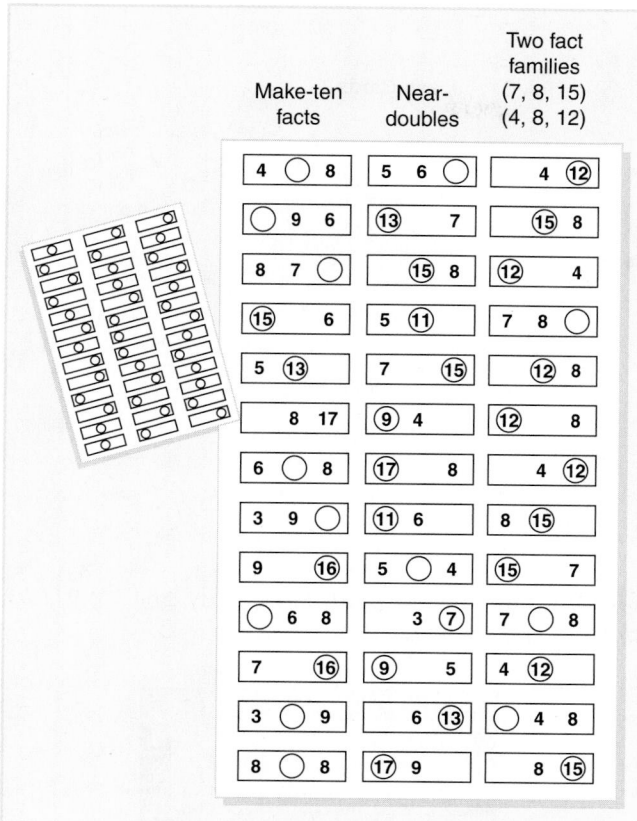

Figure 10.8 Missing-number handouts. The blank version can be used to fill in any sets of facts you wish to emphasize (see Blackline Master 13). Labels (in brackets) are not included on student pages.

for fact mastery, as it cuts in half the facts that need to be memorized.

Of the five reasoning strategies discussed next, the first four are generally easier and cover 75 of the 100 multiplication facts. These strategies are suggestions, not rules, and the instructional approach is to have students discuss ways that *they* use reasoning strategies to determine the basic facts.

Doubles

Facts that have 2 as a factor are equivalent to the addition doubles and should already be known by students who know their addition facts. Help students realize that not only is 2 × 7 double 7, but so is 7 × 2. Try word problems where 2 is the number of sets. Later use problems where 2 is the size of the sets. *George was making sock puppets. Each puppet needed 2 buttons for eyes. If George makes 7 puppets, how many buttons will he need for the eyes?*

×	0	1	2	3	4	5	6	7	8	9
0			0							
1			2							
2	0	2	4	6	8	10	12	14	16	18
3			6							
4			8							
5			10							
6			12							
7			14							
8			16							
9			18							

Fives

This group consists of all facts with 5 as the first or second factor, as shown here.

×	0	1	2	3	4	5	6	7	8	9
0						0				
1						5				
2						10				
3						15				
4						20				
5	0	5	10	15	20	25	30	35	40	45
6						30				
7						35				
8						40				
9						45				

Practise skip counting by fives to at least 45. Connect counting by fives with arrays that have rows of 5 dots. Point out that such an array with six rows is a model for 6 × 5, eight rows is 8 × 5, and so on.

Activity 10.17

Clock Facts

Focus on the minute hand of the clock. When it points to a number, how many minutes after the hour is it? See Figure 10.9(a). Connect this idea to the multiplication facts with 5. Hold up a flash card as in Figure 10(b), then point to the number on the clock corresponding to the other factor. In this way, the five facts become the "clock facts."

Zeros and Ones

Thirty-six facts have at least one factor that is either 0 or 1. These facts, though apparently easy, tend to get confused

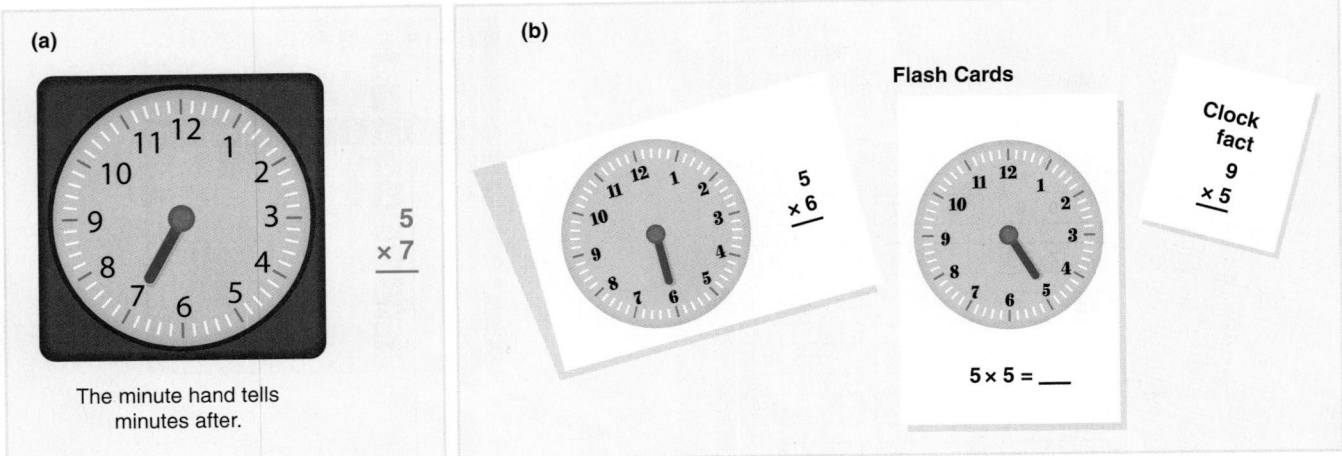

Figure 10.9 Using clocks to help learn five facts.

with "rules" that some children learned for addition. The fact $6 + 0$ stays the same, but 6×0 is always zero. The $1 + 4$ fact is a one-more idea, but 1×4 stays the same. The concepts behind these facts can be developed best through story problems. Alternatively, ask students to put words to the equations. For example, saying that 6×0 is six groups with zero in them (or six rows of chairs with no people in each). For 0×6, there are six in the group, but you have zero groups. For example, you worked 0 hours babysitting at $6 an hour. Avoid rules that sound arbitrary and without reason such as "Any number multiplied by zero is zero."

×	0	1	2	3	4	5	6	7	8	9
0	0	0	0	0	0	0	0	0	0	0
1	0	1	2	3	4	5	6	7	8	9
2	0	2								
3	0	3								
4	0	4								
5	0	5								
6	0	6								
7	0	7								
8	0	8								
9	0	9								

Nifty Nines

Facts with a factor of 9 include the largest products, but can be among the easiest to learn. The table of nines facts includes some nice patterns that are fun to discover. Two of these patterns are useful for mastering the nines: (1) The tens digit of the product is always one less than the "other" factor (the one that is not 9), and (2) the sum of the two digits in the product is always 9. These two ideas can be

used together to get any nine fact quickly. For 7×9, *1 less than 7 is 6; 6 and 3 make 9; so the answer is 63.*

×	0	1	2	3	4	5	6	7	8	9
0										0
1										9
2										18
3										27
4										36
5										45
6										54
7										63
8										72
9	0	9	18	27	36	45	54	63	72	81

Children are not likely to invent this strategy simply by solving word problems involving a factor of 9. Therefore, consider building a lesson around the following task.

Activity **10.18**

Patterns in the Nine Facts

In column form, write the nines table on the board ($9 \times 1 = 9$, $9 \times 2 = 18$, ... $9 \times 9 = 81$). The task is to find as many patterns as possible in the table. (Do not ask students to think of a strategy.) As you listen to the students work on this task, be sure that somewhere in the class the two patterns necessary for the strategy have been found. After discussing all the patterns, a follow-up task is to use the patterns to think of a clever way to figure out a nines fact, if you didn't know it. (Note that even for students who know their nines facts, this remains a valid task.)

Once children have invented a strategy for the nines, practice activities such as those shown in Figure 10.10 are appropriate. Also consider word problems with a factor of 9 and check to see if the strategy is in use.

Warning: Although the nines strategy can be quite successful, it can also cause confusion. Because two separate steps are involved and a conceptual connection is not apparent, children may confuse the two steps or attempt to apply the idea to other facts. It is not, however, a "rule without reason." It is an idea based on a very interesting pattern that exists in the base-ten numeration system. In fact, you can challenge students to think about why this pattern exists.

An alternative strategy for the nines is almost as easy to use. Notice that 7 × 9 is the same as 7 × 10 less one set of 7, or 70 – 7. For students who can easily subtract 6 from 60, 7 from 70, and so on this strategy may be preferable.

You might introduce this idea by showing a set of bars such as those in Figure 10.11 with only the end cube a different colour. After explaining that every bar has ten cubes, ask students if they can think of a good way to figure out how many are yellow.

Using Known Facts to Derive Other Facts

The following chart shows the remaining 25 multiplication facts. It is worth pointing out to children that there are actually only 15 facts remaining to master because 20 of them consist of 10 pairs of turn-arounds.

×	0	1	2	3	4	5	6	7	8	9
0										
1										
2										
3				9	12		18	21	24	
4				12	16		24	28	32	
5										
6				18	24		36	42	48	
7				21	28		42	49	56	
8				24	32		48	56	64	
9										

These 25 facts can be learned by relating each to an already known fact or *helping* fact. If students know their facts for multiplying by 2 (doubling), they can use that known fact to generate facts for multiplying by 3 (× 3) and by 4 (× 4). For example, 3 × 8 is connected to 2 × 8 (double 8 and 8 more). Knowing multiplication by 5 facts or deriving multiplication by 3 (× 3) facts from multiplication by 2 (× 2) facts can lead to other facts. The 6 × 7 fact can be related to either 5 × 7 (5 sevens and 7 more) or to 3 × 7 (double 3 × 7). The helping fact must already be known, and the ability to do the mental addition must also

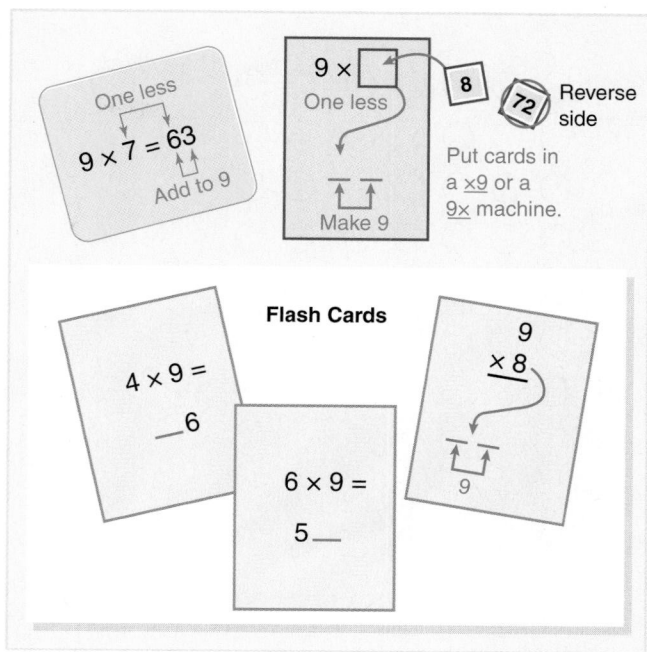

Figure 10.10 "Nifty nines" rule.

be there. For example, to go from 5 × 7 is 35 and then add 7 for 6 × 7, a student must be able to add 35 and 7. If you see finger counting at that stage, suggest that make-ten can be extended: 35 and 5 more is 40 and 2 left makes 42.

Since arrays are a powerful thinking tool for these strategies, provide students with copies of the 10 by 10 dot array (Figure 10.12, also in Blackline Masters). An *L*-shaped tag-board *L* is used to outline specific array products. The intersecting lines in the array make counting the dots easier and often suggest the use of the easier fives facts as helpers. For example, 7 × 7 is 5 × 7 plus double 7 → 35 + 14.

How to find a helping fact that is useful varies with different facts and sometimes depends on which factor you focus on. Figure 10.13 illustrates models for four overlapping groups of facts and the thought process associated with each.

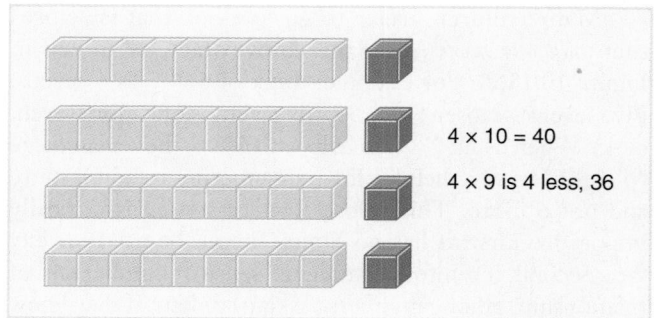

Figure 10.11 Using tens to think of the nines.

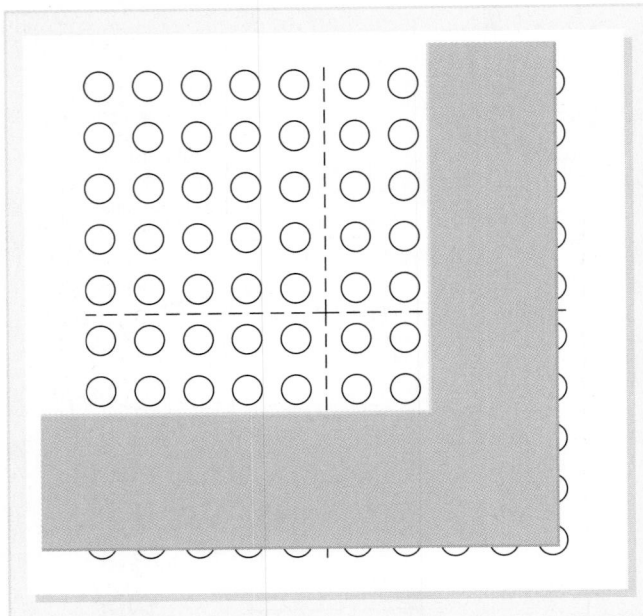

Figure 10.12 An array is a useful model for developing strategies for the hard multiplication facts. See Blackline Master 12.

The *double and double again* strategy shown in Figure 10.13(a) is applicable to all facts with 4 as one of the factors. Remind children that the idea works when 4 is the second factor as well as when it is the first. For 4 × 8, double 16 is also a difficult fact. Help children with this by noting, for example, that 15 + 15 is 30, 16 + 16 is two more, or 32. Adding 16 + 16 on paper defeats the purpose.

The *double and one more set* strategy shown in Figure 10.13(b) is a way to think of facts with one factor of 3. With an array or a set picture, the double part can be circled, and it is clear that there is one more set. Two facts in this group involve more difficult mental additions (8 × 3 and 9 × 3).

If either factor is even, a *half then double* strategy, as shown in Figure 10.13(d) can be used. Select the even factor, and cut it in half. If the smaller fact is known, that product is doubled to get the new fact. For some students, this strategy might prove to be more challenging than the others to understand.

Many children prefer to go to a fact that is "close" then *add one more set* to this known fact, as shown in Figure 10.13(d). For example, think of 6 × 7 as 6 sevens. Five sevens is close: That's 35. Six sevens is one more seven, or 42. When using 5 × 8 to help with 6 × 8, the set language "6 eights" is very helpful for remembering to add 8 more and not 6 more. This "close" fact reasoning is critically important. First, it has no limits—it can be used for any fact. Second, it reinforces students' sense of number and of relationships among numbers. Asking students if they know a nearby fact to derive the new fact over time will become an automatic mental process for students. In fact, many

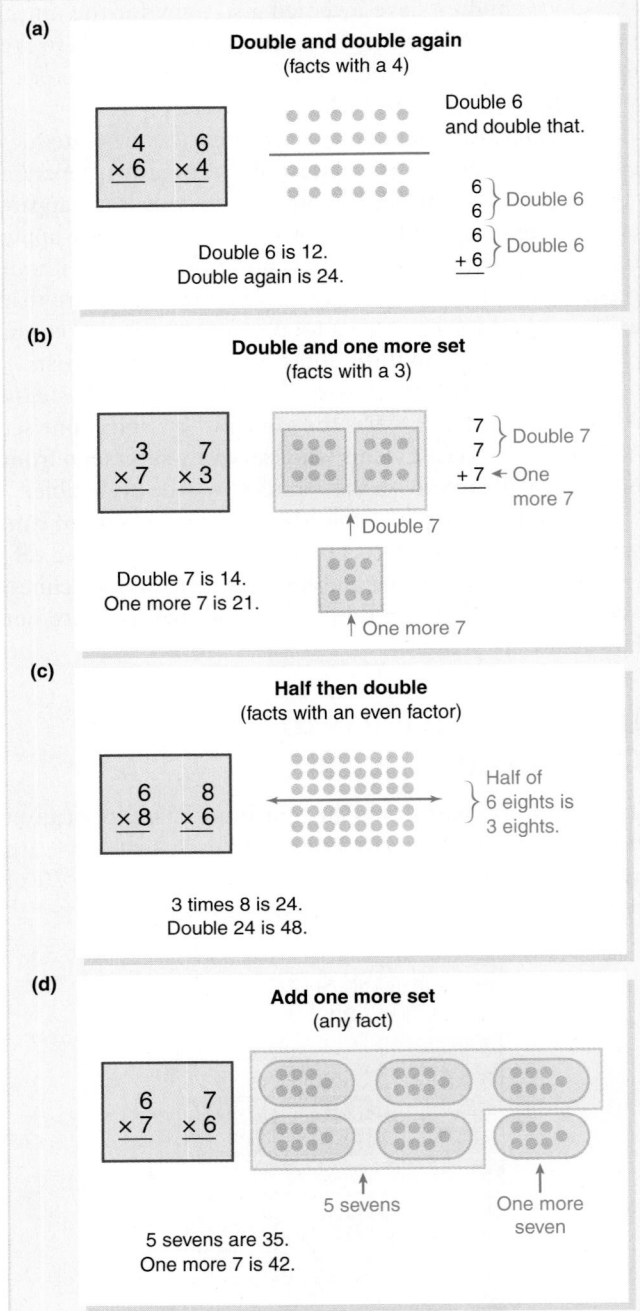

Figure 10.13 Reasoning strategies for using a known fact to derive an unknown fact

adults use this strategy for particularly difficult facts. The mental process goes something like this: "What is seven times eight? Oh, that's 49 and 7 more—56." Similarly students may use 5 facts to generate 4 and 6 facts.

The relationships between easy and hard facts are fertile ground for good problem-based tasks. Rather than telling students what helping facts to use and how to use them, say "If you didn't know what 6 × 8 is, how could you figure it out by using something that you do know?" Students should be challenged to find as many interesting and useful ways as possible to answer a hard multiplication fact.

⏸ *——————————— Pause and Reflect*

Select what you consider a "hard fact" and see how many of the strategies in Figure 10.13 you can use to derive the fact.

Word problems can also be structured to prompt a strategy. *Lauren and Rachel kept their stamps in albums with 8 stamps on each page. Lauren had 6 pages filled. Rachel had 4 pages filled. How many cards did each girl have?* (Do you see the half-then-double strategy?)

It should be clear that the array plays an important role in helping students establish multiplication facts and relationships. The Problem-Based Lesson, Windows Around the World, shows how arrays can be used to represent multiplication. The lesson uses a real world idea to develop the concept.

Division Facts and "Near Facts"

An interesting question to ask is, "When children are working on a page of division facts, are they practising division or multiplication?" There is undoubtedly some value in limited practice of division facts. However, mastery of multiplication facts and connections between multiplication and division are the key elements of division fact mastery. Word problems continue to be a key vehicle to create this connection.

⏸ *——————————— Pause and Reflect*

What thought process do you use to recall facts such as 48 ÷ 6 or 36 ÷9?

If we are trying to think of 36 ÷ 9, we tend to think, "Nine times what is thirty-six?" For most, 42 ÷ 6 is not a separate fact; rather it is closely tied to 6 × 7. (Wouldn't it be wonderful if subtraction were so closely related to addition? It can be!)

Exercises such as 50 ÷ 6 might be called "near facts." Divisions that do not result in a whole number are much more prevalent in computations and in real situations than those that do. To determine the answer to 50 ÷ 6, most people run through a short sequence of the multiplication facts, comparing each product to 50: "6 times 7 (low), 6 times 8 (close), 6 times 9 (high). Must be 8. That's 48 and 2 left over." Children should be able to do problems with

one-digit divisors and one-digit answers with remainders mentally and with reasonable speed.

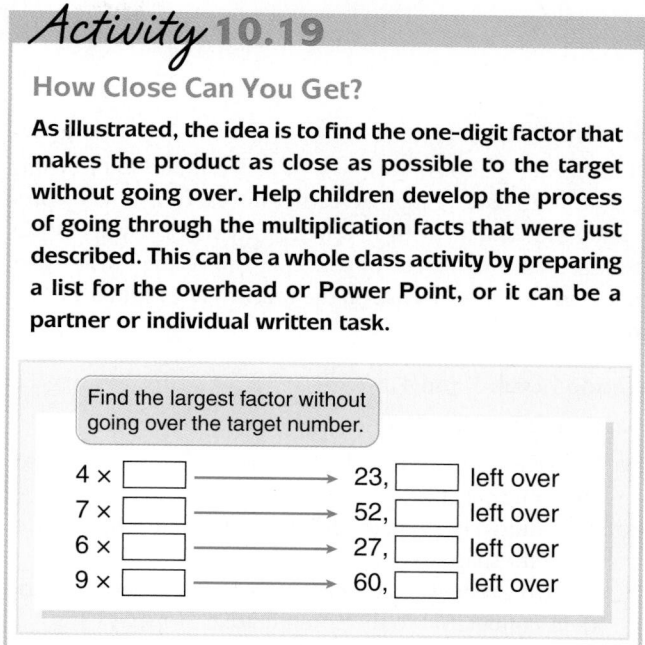

Activity 10.19

How Close Can You Get?

As illustrated, the idea is to find the one-digit factor that makes the product as close as possible to the target without going over. Help children develop the process of going through the multiplication facts that were just described. This can be a whole class activity by preparing a list for the overhead or Power Point, or it can be a partner or individual written task.

Find the largest factor without going over the target number.

4 × ☐ ⟶ 23, ☐ left over
7 × ☐ ⟶ 52, ☐ left over
6 × ☐ ⟶ 27, ☐ left over
9 × ☐ ⟶ 60, ☐ left over

Find the largest factor without going over the target number.

NCTM Standards What does the *Standards* document tell us about multiplication and division facts? "Through skip-counting, using area models, and relating unknown combinations to known ones, students will learn and become fluent with unfamiliar combinations [multiplication facts].... If by the end of grade 4, students are not able to use multiplication and division strategies efficiently, then they must either develop strategies so that they are fluent with these combinations or they must memorize the 'harder' combinations" (p. 153).

Mastering the Basic Facts

There is little doubt that strategy development and general number sense (number relationships and operation meanings) are the best contributors to fact mastery. Drill, in the absence of these factors, has repeatedly been demonstrated as ineffective. However, drill strengthens memory and retrieval capabilities (Ashcraft & Christy, 1995).

Effective Drill

Drill—repetitive non-problem-based activity—is appropriate for children who have a strategy that they understand, like, and know how to use but with which they have not yet become facile. Drill with an in-place strategy focuses

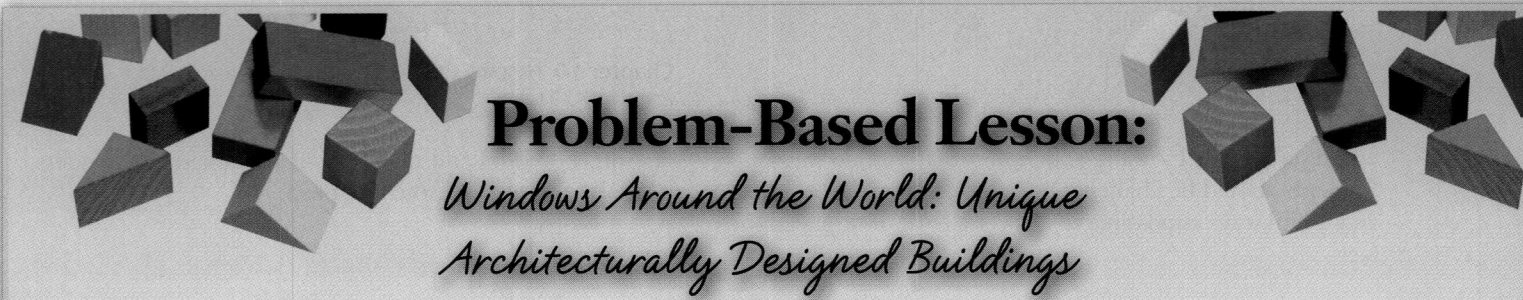

Problem-Based Lesson:
Windows Around the World: Unique Architecturally Designed Buildings

Introduction

This lesson demonstrates how to differentiate the learning to accommodate a range of learner needs. It does so by providing the students with an opportunity to use manipulatives to represent mathematical concepts and related ideas. Also, it allows students to work on the task at a level suited to their particular abilities.

Grade Level: 3 and 4
Mathematical Goals

- To have students learn how arrays can be used to represent multiplication.
- To intuitively prepare children for finding the area of different shapes.
- To have students discover patterns in multiplication and their connection to the commutative property.
- To demonstrate how mathematics and art are connected.

Thinking About the Students

Students are developing their understanding of the meaning of multiplication. They have worked on tasks that look at multiplication as repeated addition and at the equal groups model for multiplication. They have also used number sentences (equations) to represent their ideas.

Materials and Preparation

- Students work in small heterogeneous groups of three or four.
- The following materials are needed for this lesson:

    Small squares of construction paper cutouts for the windows. These will be pasted in the frames.

    Square tiles for students to create arrays before actually pasting the squares on their frames.
    Glue
    Baggies—Each baggy contains a task card and a frame sheet or sheets, onto which the windows are pasted and a number sentence is written to represent what is shown.
    Overhead transparencies of different unique architecturally designed buildings, or
    pictures of various buildings from around the world—please see www.greatbuildings.com.
    A computer and LCD projector would be helpful for viewing the windows.

Possible Suggestions for Unique Architecturally Designed Buildings:

Name of Building	Architect	Location	Photo View	Array Dimensions
Galleria Vittorio Emanuele	Giueseppe Mengoni	Milan, Italy	Inside the covered street space	3 × 2 or 2 × 3
Post Office Savings Bank		,	Exterior, facade overview	4 × 7 or 7 × 4
Majolica House		,	Exterior overview of façade with beautiful textile-style Art Noveau ornamentation	9 × 4 or 4 × 9

http://www.greatbuildings.com/gbc.html
Please note: These are only suggestions for pictures, which have interesting window patterns that look like arrays. Any suitable selection of pictures can be used.

Lesson: Day 1
Introduction

- Display on the overhead projector or LCD projector a variety of pictures of unique architecturally designed buildings.
- Talk with the students about the design, shape, and patterns evident in each of these buildings.
- Draw their attention to the ways that the windows are arranged in these buildings. Discuss any patterns they might see.

The Task

- Students will work in their groups of three or four to create their own window patterns.
- Creating the window patterns should provide students with the chance to see how arrays can assist them with multiplication. It should also help them see the connection of the commutative property to multiplication.
- Early finishers can sketch a picture of a building where they would like these windows placed.

Establish Expectations

- Explain to the students that today they are going to be architects and create their own window patterns for a building they might wish to design.

- In order to create their window patterns, each child will receive a baggy with a task card and a frame onto which they will paste their window pattern or patterns. They will also answer the question on the task card once they have made their window pattern in the frame.
- The construction-paper-square cutouts, the glue, and the square tiles can be found at their group tables.

Development

- The students work at their group tables creating their window patterns with the square tiles according to the instructions on the task cards.
- They then paste the square paper cutouts onto their frame sheet(s) to show the pattern(s) created with the tiles.
- They finish by completing their multiplication sentences (equations) to represent these patterns.
- Students who complete their window patterns early can sketch the building where they would like to place the windows. Note: To ensure that each child has the appropriate task card, the teacher distributes the baggies containing the cards.

Follow-up

- On completion of the task, class architects meet as a whole group to talk about the window patterns they created.
- The different ways of looking at the window patterns and the ways that they can be represented numerically is key to the discussion.
- Some of the important ideas to be discussed are how multiplication can be represented by different array patterns and how the same array can be represented by two different multiplication sentences.

Next Steps _____

Assessment Notes

- Do students' multiplication sentences match the window patterns they created?
- Do they realize that turning their frame sheets 180 degrees allows them to create a multiplication sentence with the same factors, only the order is changed (the principle of the commutative property).
- Do they understand how array patterns are a way of representing multiplication?
- Which students still need additional support?
- Which students could work with two-digit numbers?

Window Pattern Task Cards

Task Card 1

My window pattern has four rows of two windows.
1. Use the tiles to show four rows of two.
2. Paste the window cutouts in the frame to show what you have made.
3. Write a number sentence to represent your window pattern.

Task Card 2

My window pattern has 4×2 windows.
1. Use the tiles to show 4×2.
2. Paste the window cutouts in the frame to show what you have made.
3. Write two number sentences to represent your window pattern.

Task Card 3

My window pattern has 12 windows in all.
1. Use the tiles to show as many different multiplication sentences as you can for 12.
2. Paste the window cutouts in the frame(s) to show what you have made.
3. Write as many different multiplication sentences as you can to represent what you have made.

students' attention on that strategy and helps to make it more automatic. Drill plays a significant role in fact mastery, and the use of methods such as flash cards and fact games can be effective if used wisely.

When you are comfortable that children are able to use a strategy and are beginning to use it mentally, it may be appropriate to create drill activities for special groupings of facts. You might have as many as ten different activities for each strategy or group of facts. File folder or boxed activities can be used by children individually, in pairs, or even in small groups. With a large number of activities, children can work on strategies they understand and on the facts that they need the most.

Flash cards are among the most useful approaches to fact strategy practice. For each strategy or related group of facts, make several sets of flash cards using all of the facts that fit that strategy. On the cards, you can label the strategy or use drawings or cues to remind the children of the strategy. Several such examples have been shown in this chapter.

Drill is appropriate only after students have developed reasoning strategies. Drill can help students move to mastery, but it can also interfere. Therefore, it is important to be aware of methods you should use and others you should avoid.

What to Do When Teaching Basic Facts The following list of recommendations can support the development of quick recall.

1. *Ask students to self-monitor.* The importance of this recommendation cannot be overstated. Across all learning, having a sense of what you don't know and what you need to learn is important. It certainly holds true with memorizing facts. Students should be able to identify their "toughies" and continue to work on reasoning strategies to help them derive those facts.
2. *Focus on self-improvement.* This point follows from self-monitoring. If you are working on improving students' quickness at recalling facts, then the only persons the students should be competing with are themselves. Students can keep track of how long it took them to go through their "four stack" for example, and then, two days later, pull the same stack and see if they are quicker (or more accurate) than the last time.
3. *Drill in short time segments.* You can flash numerous examples on a transparency of double ten-frames in relatively little time. Or you can do a story a day—taking five minutes to share strategies. You can also have each student pull a set of flash cards from storage, pair with another student, and go through each other's set in two minutes. Long periods (ten minutes or more) are not effective. Using the first five to ten minutes of the day, or extra time just before lunch, can provide continued support on fact development without taking up mathematics instructional time better devoted to other topics.

4. *Work on facts over time.* Rather than do a unit on fact memorization, work on facts over months and months, working on reasoning strategies then on memorization, and then continued review and monitoring.
5. *Involve families.* Share the big plan of how you will work on facts over the year. One idea is to let parents or guardians know that during the second semester of second grade (or fourth grade), for example, you will have one or two "Take Home Facts of the Week." Ask family members to help students by using reasoning strategies when they don't know a fact.
6. *Make drill enjoyable.* There are many games designed to reinforce facts that are not competitive or anxiety inducing, as shown in the following activity.

Activity 10.20

Salute!

Place students in groups of three and give each group a deck of cards (without face cards and using aces as 1s). Two of the students draw a card without looking at it and place it on their forehead facing out (so the other two can see it). The student with no card tells the sum (or product). The first of the other two to correctly say what number is on their forehead "wins" the card set. Competition can be removed by having each student write down the card they think they have (within five seconds) and getting a point if they are correct.

7. *Use technology.* When students work on the computer or with the calculator they get immediate feedback and reinforcement, helping them to self-monitor. See the Tech Note below and the Web sites listed at the end of this chapter for ideas.
8. *Emphasize the importance of quick recall of facts.* Without trying to create pressure or anxiety, emphasize to students that in real life and in the rest of mathematics they will be recalling these facts all the time—they really must learn them and learn them well. Celebrate student successes.

 There are literally hundreds of software programs that offer drill of basic facts, but few are developed in Canada. Nearly all of these fact programs offer games or exercises at various levels of difficulty. Unfortunately, there do not seem to be any programs that emphasize strategy development. It should be clear that computerized fact practice should be used only after students have developed reasoning strategies.

A few representative software programs are described here.

Mathville (Courseware Solutions, 2006) is a Canadian-developed program. There are eight different components in the series, each geared to match curriculum expectations for a particular K–8 grade level. Activities are fast-paced, theme-based, and motivating. The program is best suited for use in applying or reinforcing concepts that have been developed in class.

Math Trek (Nectar Foundation, 2006) is another Canadian courseware program. It consists of five different components: *Math Strategies—Primary; Math Trek 1, 2, 3; Math Trek 4, 5, 6;, Math Trek 7, 8;* and *Math Strategies— Understanding Arithmetic, Level 1*. These also fit with elementary curriculum expectations. Each component offers an interactive mathematical tutorial, which teaches a concept. The user then can engage in an activity to reinforce the learning. There is a section with one- and two-step problems to solve, followed by a test section.

In *Math Munchers Deluxe* (Riverdeep Interactive Learning, 2005), students move their muncher in a three-dimensional grid format. By answering questions, they can avoid six Troggles that chase the muncher and try to eat it. *Math Munchers* encourages speed and is highly motivating. It is aimed at grades 3 to 6.

Math Blaster (Knowledge Adventure) promotes speed through an arcade format. Like most programs, *Math Blaster* includes drills for more than just facts, including multi-digit computation, decimals, fractions, percents, estimation, and other topics, all in the same format.

Another example is *FASTT Math* (Tom Snyder Productions software, *not* free). This is a diagnostic tool with ongoing assessment. The program is student paced, provides "self-progress tracking," and includes practice games. See www.tomsnyder.com/products/product. asp?SKU=FASFAS. ◆

What Not to Do When Teaching Basic Facts The following list shows some strategies that may have been designed with good intentions but work against student memorization of the basic facts.

1. *Don't use lengthy timed tests.* Students get distracted by the pressure and abandon their reasoning strategies. If they miss some, they don't get the chance to see which ones they are having trouble with, so the assessment doesn't help them move forward. Students develop anxiety, which works against learning mathematics. Having students self-monitor the time it takes them to go through a small set of facts can help with their speed.

2. *Don't use public comparisons of mastery.* You may have experienced the bulletin board that shows which students are on which step of a staircase to mastering their multiplication facts. Imagine how the student feels who is on their third step when others are on step 6. It is great to celebrate student successes, but avoid comparisons among students.

3. *Don't proceed through facts in order from 0 to 9.* It is better to work on collections based on the strategies and to "knock out" those that students know rather than proceed in a rigid fashion going in order. In reality, the more that facts are mixed up, the more likely it is that students will rely on their reasoning strategies and number sense and not forget the facts mastered last week.

4. *Don't move to memorization too soon.* This has been addressed throughout the chapter, but is worth repeating. Quick recall or mastery can be obtained only after students are ready—meaning they have a robust collection of reasoning strategies to apply as needed.

5. *Don't use facts as a barrier to good mathematics.* Students who have total command of basic facts do not necessarily *reason better* than those who, for whatever reason, have not yet mastered facts. Today, mathematics is not solely about computation, especially pencil-and-paper computation. Mathematics is about reasoning and patterns and making sense of things. Mathematics is problem solving. There is no reason that a child who has not yet mastered all basic facts should be excluded from real mathematical experiences.

 If there is any purpose for a timed test of basic facts, it may be for diagnosis—to determine which combinations are mastered and which remain to be learned. Even for diagnostic purposes there is little reason for a timed test more than once every couple of months. ◆

Fact Remediation

Students who have not mastered their basic facts by grade 5 or 6 need something other than more drill. They have certainly seen and practised facts countless times in previous grades. There is no reason to believe that the drills *you* provide will somehow be more effective than last year's. These students need something better. The following key ideas can guide your efforts to help these older students.

1. *Recognize that more drill will not work.* Students' difficulties with facts are due to a failure to develop or to connect concepts and relationships such as those that have been discussed in this chapter, not a lack of drill. At best, more drill will provide temporary results. At worst, it will cause negative attitudes about mathematics.

2. *Provide hope.* Students who have experienced difficulty with fact mastery often believe that they cannot learn facts, or that they are doomed to finger counting forever. Let these children know that you will help them and that you will provide some new ideas that will

help them as well. Take that burden on yourself, and spare them the prospect of more defeat.

3. *Conduct an inventory of known and unknown facts for each student in need.* Find out from each student which facts are known quickly and comfortably and which are not. Grade 5 or older students can do this diagnosis for you. Provide sheets of all the facts for one operation in random order and have the students circle the facts about which they are hesitant and answer all others. To achieve an honest assessment, emphasize that you need this information so that you can help the student.

4. *Diagnose strengths and weaknesses.* Observe what students do when they encounter one of their unknown facts. Do they count on their fingers? Add up numbers in the margins? Guess? Try to use a related fact? Write down multiplication tables? Are they able to use any of the helpful relationships suggested in this chapter?

You can conduct a ten-minute diagnostic interview with each student in need. Simply pose unknown facts and ask the student how he or she approaches them. Don't try to teach; just find out. Again, students can provide some of this information by writing about what they do when they don't know a fact.

5. *Focus on reasoning strategies.* Using a problem-solving strategy to focus on fact mastery is very effective (Baroody, 2006; Crespo, Kyriakides, & McGee, 2005). Because students will likely be working alone or with a small group in this remediation program, they will have neither the benefit of class discussion nor the time required over weeks and months to develop their own strategies. Therefore, with these students, it is reasonable to share with them strategies that "you have seen other students use." Be certain that they have a conceptual understanding of the strategy and are able to use it.

6. *Build in success.* As you begin a well-designed fact program for a child who has experienced failure, be sure that successes come quickly and easily. Begin with easier and more useful reasoning strategies like "Up Over 10" for addition. Success builds success! With strategies as an added assist, success comes even more quickly. Point out to students how one idea, one strategy, is all that is required to learn many facts. Use fact charts to show sets of facts that you are working

on. It is surprising how the chart quickly fills up with mastered facts. Keep reviewing newly learned facts and those that were already known.

7. Provide engaging activities for drill. See Activity 10.20 as one idea for drill that has an element of fun. The following activity integrates all four operations.

Activity 10.21

Bowl a Fact

In this activity, you draw circles placed in triangular fashion to look like bowling pins, with the front circle labelled 1 and the next labelled consecutively through 10. Take three dice and roll them. Students use the three dice to come up with equations that result in answers that are on the pins. For example, if you roll 4, 2, and 3, they can get 5 by $4 \times 2 - 3$, thereby "knocking down" that "pin." If they can produce equations to knock down all ten pins, they get a strike. If not, roll again and see if they can knock the rest down for a spare. After doing this with the whole class, students can work in small groups. (Adapted from Shoecraft, 1982.)

Your extra effort beyond class time can motivate a student to make some personal effort on his or her own time. During class, these students should continue to work with all students on the regular curriculum. You must believe and communicate to these students that the reason they have not mastered basic facts is not a reflection of their ability. With efficient strategies and individual effort, success will come. Believe!

Reflections on Chapter 10

Writing to Learn

1. Describe advantages of a developmental approach to helping students master basic facts.
2. For the fact 8 + 6, list at least three reasoning strategies that a student might use.
3. What is meant by subtraction as "think-addition"? How can you help children develop a think-addition thought pattern for subtraction?
4. Give an example of a story problem that would promote a think-addition strategy for subtraction facts.
5. For the multiplication fact 6 × 7, describe three reasoning strategies a student might use.
6. Describe how to use drill effectively.
7. Describe positive and negative ways to use timed tests for basic fact mastery.
8. Describe three key ideas you will use in working with students to remediate basic fact mastery.

For Discussion and Exploration

1. Explore a Web-based or software program that drills basic facts. What features does your program have that are good? Not so good? How would you use such software in a classroom with only one or two available computers?
2. One view of thinking strategies is that they are little more than a collection of tricks for kids to memorize. Discuss the question, "Is teaching children thinking strategies for basic fact mastery in keeping with a constructivist view of teaching mathematics?" Carole Thornton (1990), a leading researcher in the area of basic-fact strategies, suggests a fairly direct approach to teaching strategies.
3. Assume that you are teaching a grade that expects mastery of facts (grade 2 for addition and subtraction or grade 4 for multiplication and division). How will you design a fact mastery program for the year? Include timing, strategy development, involvement of families, etc.

Resources for Chapter 10

Literature Connections

The children's books described in Chapter 8 and 9 are also good choices when working on the basic facts. In addition to those, consider these opportunities to develop and practice basic facts.

More Pies   Munsch, 2002

This entertaining book provides children with an opportunity to count all the different things that Samuel eats because he is really hungry. He begins with one bowl of cereal for breakfast. However this is not enough to satisfy him. What follows is an inventory of all the bowls of cereal, milkshakes, stacks of pancakes, and chickens he eats before going to the pie-eating contest. The book then describes the different pies Samuel eats and the number of each type. Not only can students engage in counting objects, they could draw them too.

One Less Fish   Toft, 1998

This beautiful book with an important environmental message starts with 12 fish and counts back to zero fish. On a page with eight fish, ask "How many fish are gone?" and "How did you figure it out?" Encourage students to use the Down Over 10 strategy. Any counting-up or counting-back book can be used in this way!

The Twelve Days of Summer   Andrews, 2005

You will quickly recognize the style of this book with five bumble bees, four garter snakes, three ruffled grouse, and so on. The beautiful illustrations and motions make this a wonderful book. Students can figure out by the end of the book how many of each item appears, by applying multiplication facts. (For example, three ruffed grouse appear on days 3, 4, 5, and so on.

Recommendations for Further Reading

Articles

Baroody, A. J. (2006). Why children have difficulties mastering the basic fact combinations and how to help them. *Teaching Children Mathematics, 13* (1), 22–31.
   Baroody suggests that basic facts are developmental in nature and contrasts "conventional wisdom" with a number sense view. Great activities are included as exemplars.
Buchholz, L. (2004). Learning strategies for addition and subtraction facts: The road to fluency and the license to think. *Teaching Children Mathematics, 10,* 362–367.
   Lisa Buchholz is a grade 2 teacher who explains how her students developed and named their strategies. They even extended them to working with two-digit numbers. She found that her "lower ability students were very successful using reasoning strategies."

Kamii, C., & Anderson, C. (2003). Multiplication games: How we made and used them. *Teaching Children Mathematics, 10,* 135–141.

Constance Kamii, a well-known constructivist teams up with an experienced grade 3 teacher. She describes a collection of games that were used to help Title I school children master multiplication facts.

Books

Baron, C. (2004). *Thinking strategies: Addition. Building mastery of addition facts.* Winnipeg, Manitoba: Portage and Main Press.

This is one of a series of four books, addressing each of the four operations, that contains a sequence of detailed lessons complete with excellent explanations of strategies, as well as pages and pages of useful and practical Blackline Masters. There are many good ideas and games in these books.

Fennema, E., & Carpenter, T. P. (with Levi, L., Franke, M. L., & Empson, S. (1997). *Cognitively guided instruction: Professional development in primary mathematics.* Madison, WI: Wisconsin Center for Education Research.

The CGI program is based on the belief that students develop their own strategies for mastering the basic facts. They are helped in this process by solving well-selected story problems. Teachers listen carefully to students' emerging processes and encourage increasingly efficient methods.

Rathmell, E. C., Leutzinger, L. P., & Gabriele, A. J. (2000). *Thinking with numbers.* Cedar Falls, IA: Thinking with Numbers, Inc.

This resource is a set of small cards, each with several simple story problems. The cards are organized by strategies for each of the operations. As children solve these problems (5 minutes per day), they invent their own strategies and share them with the class.

Online Resources

Arithmetic Four
www.shodor.org/interactivate/activities/ArithmeticFour/index.html
The game is like "Connect Four." Players must answer an arithmetic fact to be able to enter a piece of their colour on the board. Operations can be selected and a timer set for answering each fact.

Cross the Swamp (BBC)
www.bbc.co.uk/schools/starship/maths/crosstheswamp.shtml
This British applet asks students to supply a missing operation (+/– or ×/÷) and a number to complete an equation (e.g., 4 __ __ = 12). There are five questions in a set, each with three levels of difficulty.

Diffy (NLVM—Applet/Game)
http://nlvm.usu.edu/en/nav/frames_asid_326_g_1_t_1.html
Diffy is a classic mathematics puzzle that involves finding the differences of given numbers.

Let's Learn Those Facts (NCTM's *Illuminations—* Lessons, Grades 1–2)
http://illuminations.nctm.org/LessonDetail.aspx?id=U58
These six lessons, including links to resources and student recording sheets, target addition facts.

Math Magician Games
www.linktolearning.com/number_sense.html
Math Magician Games, one of the many links found on this site, provides students with an opportunity to practise basic facts. The site is Canadian, but many of the links are American based.

Multiplication: It's in the Cards (NCTM's *Illuminations—* Lessons, Grades 3–5)
http://illuminations.nctm.org/LessonDetail.aspx?id=U110
These four lessons, including links to resources and student recording sheets, use the properties of multiplication to help students master the multiplication facts. See also "Six and Seven as Factors" (NCTM's *Illuminations*—Lessons, Grades 3–5), two lessons on products where 6 or 7 is a factor (http:// illuminations.nctm.org/LessonDetail.aspx?ID=U150).

Number Invaders
www.mathplayground.com/balloon_invaders.html
This game is like "Space Invaders." Players choose an operation ($\times$, $\div$) and a factor, and use the space bar and arrow keys to launch the "number (product) popper."

Number Puzzles (NLVM—Applet)
http://nlvm.usu.edu/en/nav/frames_asid_157_g_3_t_1.html
In this applet, students are required to arrange numbers in positions in a diagram so that all numbers in a line add up to a given value.

The Product Game (NCTM's *Illuminations*—Lessons, Grades 3–8)
http://illuminations.nctm.org/LessonDetail.aspx?id=U100
These four lessons use the engaging and effective games "Factor Game" and "Product Game" to help students see the relationship between products and factors.

SpeedMath Deluxe (Jefferson Lab)
http://education.jlab.org/smdeluxe/index.html
Players are given four numbers between which they must enter one of the four operation signs so that the resulting expression equals a given number. It requires an understanding of order of operations and occasionally integers.

Chapter 11

Developing Whole-Number Place-Value Concepts

A complete understanding of place value, which extends to decimal numeration, develops across the K–8 grade span. For whole numbers, the most critical period in this development occurs in pre-K to 3. In kindergarten and grade 1, children count and are exposed to patterns in the numbers to 100. Most importantly, they begin to think about groups of ten things as a unit. By grade 2, these initial ideas of patterns and groups of ten are formally connected to our place-value system of numeration. In grades 3 and 4, children extend their understanding to numbers up to 10 000, in a variety of contexts. In grades 4 and 5, the ideas of whole numbers are extended to decimals.

As a significant part of this development, students should begin to work at putting numbers together and taking them apart in a wide variety of ways as they solve addition and subtraction problems with two- and three-digit numbers. Children's struggles with the invention of their own methods of computation will both enhance their understanding of place value and provide a firm foundation for flexible methods of computation.

Big Ideas

1. Sets of ten (and tens of tens) can be perceived as single entities. For example, three sets of ten and two singles is a base-ten method for describing 32 single objects. This is the major principle of *base-ten numeration.*

2. The position of the digits in numbers determines what they represent and which size group they count. This is the major principle of *place-value numeration.*

3. There are patterns to the way that numbers are formed. For example, each decade has a symbolic pattern reflective of the 1-to-9 sequence.

4. The groupings of ones, tens, and hundreds can be taken apart in different ways. For example, 256 can be 1 hundred, 14 tens, and 16 ones, but also 250 and 6. Decomposing and composing multi-digit numbers in flexible ways is a significant skill for computation.

5. "Really big" numbers are best understood in terms of familiar real-world referents. It is difficult to conceptualize quantities as large as 1000 or more. However, the number of people that will fill the local sports arena is, for example, a meaningful concept for those who have experienced that crowd.

Mathematics Content Connections

The base-ten place-value system is the basis for anything we do to communicate and represent ideas about whole numbers and decimals.

⁘ Whole-Number Computation and Number Sense (Chapters 12 and 13): Flexible methods of computation, including various mental methods, pencil-and-paper methods, estimation skills, and even effective use of technology, depend fully on an understanding of place value. Computational strategies for addition and subtraction can and should be developed along with an understanding of place value.

⁘ Decimal and Percent Concepts (Chapter 17): Whole-number place-value ideas are extended to allow for representation of the full range of rational numbers and approximations of irrational numbers.

⁘ Measurement (Chapter 19): Problem-based tasks involving real measures can be used to help students structure ideas about grouping by tens. Through working with measures, people develop benchmarks and meaningful referents for numbers.

Pre–Base-Ten Concepts

Children know a lot about numbers with two digits (10 to 99), even as early as kindergarten. After all, most kindergarten children can and should learn to count to 100 and count out sets of things with as many as 20 or 30 objects. They do daily calendar activities, count children in the room, turn to specified page numbers in their books, and so on. However, their understanding is quite different from yours. It is based on a one-more-than or count-by-ones approach to quantity.

Children's Pre–Base-Ten View of Number

Ask grade 1 or 2 children to count out 53 tiles, and most will be able to do so or will make only careless errors. If you watch closely, you will note that the children count out the tiles one at a time and put them into the pile without using any type of grouping. Have the children write the number that tells how many tiles they just counted. Most children will be able to write it. Some may write "35" instead of "53," a simple reversal.

So far, so good. Now ask the children to write the number that is 10 more than the number they just wrote. Most will begin to count, probably starting from 53. When counting on from 53, they find it necessary to keep track of the counts, probably on their fingers. Many, if not most, children in grade 1 and early grade 2 will not be successful at this task, and very few will know immediately that 10 more is 63. Asking for the number that is 10 less is even more problematic.

Finally, show a large collection of cards, each with a ten-frame on it. Explain that each ten-frame has ten spaces and will hold ten tiles. Demonstrate putting tiles on the cards by filling up one of the ten-frames with tiles. Now ask, "How many cards like this do you think it will take if we want to put all of these tiles [the 53 counted out] on the cards?" A response of "53" is not unusual. Other children will say they do not know, and a few will try to put the tiles on the cards to figure it out.

Counts by Ones

The children just described know that there are 53 tiles "because I counted them." Writing the number and saying the number are usually done correctly, but their understanding of 53 derives from and is connected to counting by ones. Children do not easily or quickly develop a meaningful understanding of groups of ten to represent quantities.

With minimal instruction, children can tell you that in the number 53, the 5 is in the tens place or that there are "3 ones." However, it is likely that this is simply naming the positions with little understanding. If children have been exposed to base-ten materials, they may name a rod of ten as a "ten" and a small cube as a "one." These same children, however, may not readily be able to tell how many ones are required to make a ten. It is easy to attach words to both materials and groups without realizing what the materials or symbols represent.

Children do know that 53 is "a lot" and that it's more than 47 (because you count past 47 to get to 53). They think of the "53" that they write as a single number. They do not know that the 5 represents five groups of ten things and the 3 represents three single things (Fuson et al., 1997; Ross, 1989). Fuson and her colleagues refer to children's pre–base-ten understanding of number as "unitary." That is, there are no groupings of ten, even though a two-digit number is associated with the quantity. They rely on unitary counts to understand quantities.

Basic Ideas of Place Value

Place-value understanding requires an integration of new and difficult-to-construct concepts of grouping by tens (the base-ten concept) with procedural knowledge of how groups are recorded in our place-value scheme, how numbers are written, and how they are spoken.

Integration of Base-Ten Groupings with Counts by Ones

Recognizing that children can count out a set of 53, we want to help them see that making groups of tens with leftovers is a way of counting that same quantity. Each of the groups in Figure 11.1 has 53 tiles. We want children to construct the idea that all of these representations are the same, in that they all stand for the number 53. Also, their sameness is evident by virtue of their groupings.

There is a subtle yet profound difference between children who know that group B is 53 because they understand the idea that five groups of 10 and 3 more is the same amount as 53 counted by ones, and those who simply say, "It's 53," because they have been told that when things are grouped this way, it's called 53. The latter group of children may not be sure how many they will get if they count the tiles in set B by ones, or if the groups were "ungrouped," how many there would then be. The children who understand will see no need to count set B by ones. They understand the "fifty-threeness" of sets A and B to be the same.

❚❚ ——————— *Pause and Reflect*

The ideas in the preceding paragraph are important for you to understand so that the activities discussed later will make sense. Be sure you can talk about those children who do and those who do not understand place value.

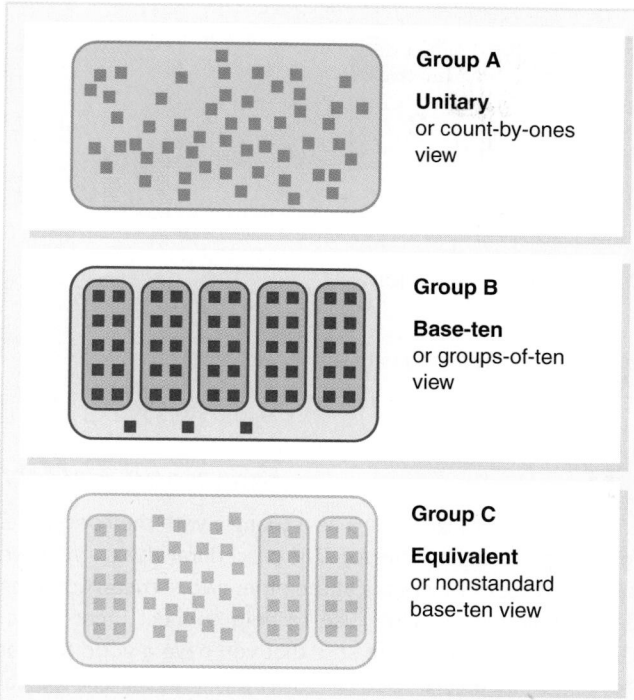

Figure 11.1 Three equivalent representations of 53 objects. Group A is 53 because "I counted them (by ones)." Group B has 5 tens and 3 more. Group C is the same as B, but now some groups are broken into singles.

Recognition of the the equivalence of groups B and C is another step in children's conceptual development. Groupings with fewer than the maximum number of tens can be referred to as *equivalent groupings* or *equivalent representations*. Understanding the equivalence of B and C indicates that grouping by tens is not just a rule that is followed. Rather, it shows an understanding that any grouping by ten, including all or some of the singles (ones), can help tell how many there are. Many computational techniques are based on equivalent representations of numbers.

Role of Counting

Counting plays a key role in constructing base-ten ideas about quantity and connecting these concepts to symbols and oral names for numbers.

Children can count sets such as those in Figure 11.1 in three different ways. Each way helps children think about the quantities in a different way (Thompson, 1990).

1. *Counting by ones.* This is the method children have to begin with. Initially, counting by ones is the only way they are able to name a quantity or "tell how many." All three sets in Figure 11.1 can be counted by ones. Before base-ten ideas develop, counting by ones is the only way children can be convinced that all three sets are the same.

2. *Counting by groups and singles.* In group B in Figure 11.1, counting by groups and singles would go like this: "One, two, three, four, five bunches of ten, and one, two, three singles." Consider how novel this method would be for a child who had never thought about counting a group of things as a single item. Also notice how this counting does not tell directly how many items there are. This counting must be coordinated with a count by ones before it can be a means for telling "how many."

3. *Counting by tens and ones.* This is the way adults would probably count group B and perhaps group C: "Ten, twenty, thirty, forty, fifty, fifty-one, fifty-two, fifty-three." Although this count ends by saying the number that is there, it is not as explicit as the second method for counting the number of groups. Nor will it convey a personal understanding of "how many," unless it is coordinated with the more meaningful counting by ones.

Regardless of the specific activity that you may be doing with children, helping them integrate the grouping-by-tens concept with what they already know about number from counting by ones should be your foremost objective. If first counted by ones, the question might be, "What will happen if we count these by groups and singles (or by tens and ones)?" If a set has been grouped into tens and singles and counted accordingly, "How can we be really certain that there are 53 things here?" or "How many do you think we will get if we count by ones?" It is inadequate to *tell* children that these counts will all be the same. It is a relationship they must construct themselves through reflective thought, not because the teacher says it works that way.

Integration of Groupings with Words

The way we say a number such as "fifty-three" must also be connected with the grouping-by-tens concept. The counting methods provide a connecting mechanism. The count by tens and ones results in saying the number of groups and singles separately: "five tens and three." This is an acceptable, albeit non-standard, way of naming this quantity. Saying the number of tens and singles separately in this fashion can be called *base-ten language* for a number. Children can associate the base-ten language with the usual language: "five tens and three—fifty-three."

There are several variations of the base-ten language for 53—5 tens and 3; 5 tens and 3 ones; 5 groups of ten and 3 leftovers; 5 tens and 3 singles; and so on. Each may be used interchangeably with the standard name, "fifty-three."

It can easily be argued that base-ten language should be used throughout grade 2, even in preference to standard oral names.

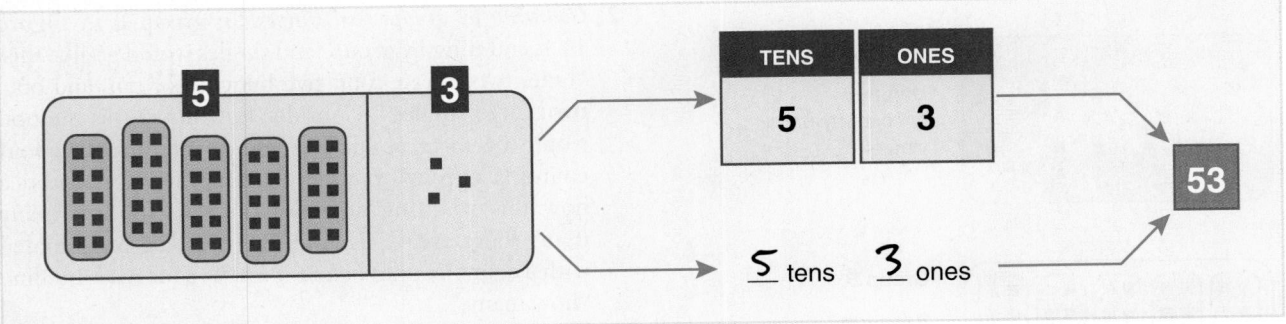

Figure 11.2 Groupings by 10 are matched with numerical representations, coordinated with the correct labelled places, and eventually written in standard form.

Integration of Groupings with Place-Value Notation

In like manner, the symbolic scheme that we use for writing numbers (ones on the right, tens to the left of ones, and so on) must be coordinated with the grouping scheme. Activities can be designed so that children physically associate groupings by tens and ones with the correct recording of the individual digits, as Figure 11.2 indicates.

Language again plays a key role in making these connections. The explicit count by groups and singles matches the individual digits as the number is written in the usual left-to-right manner. A similar coordination is necessary for hundreds.

 "Making a transition from viewing 'ten' as simply the accumulation of 10 ones to seeing it both as 10 ones *and* as 1 ten is an important first step for students toward understanding the structure of the base-ten number system" (p. 33).

Figure 11.3 summarizes the ideas that have been discussed so far.

- The conceptual knowledge of place value is based on the grouping-by-tens ideas.
  - When a collection of objects is grouped in sets of ten and some leftover singles, counting the groups of ten and adding the singles tells how many are in the collection.
  - There can also be equivalent representations where the number of groupings of ten is fewer than the maximum needed to represent the tens digit of a number.
- The base-ten grouping ideas must be integrated with oral and written names for numbers.
- In addition to counting by ones, children use two other ways of counting: by groups and singles separately, and by tens and ones. All three methods of counting are coordinated as the principal method for integrating the concepts, the written names, and the oral names.

Pause and Reflect

Think of Figure 11.3 as a triangle with the conceptual ideas of place value at the top. The procedural ideas of how we say and write numbers are at the other two corners. Counting is the main tool children use to help connect these ideas. Before moving further, be sure that you have a good feel for how these ideas are related. Remember that the conceptual ideas must first be built on the count-by-ones concept of quantity that children bring to this array of ideas.

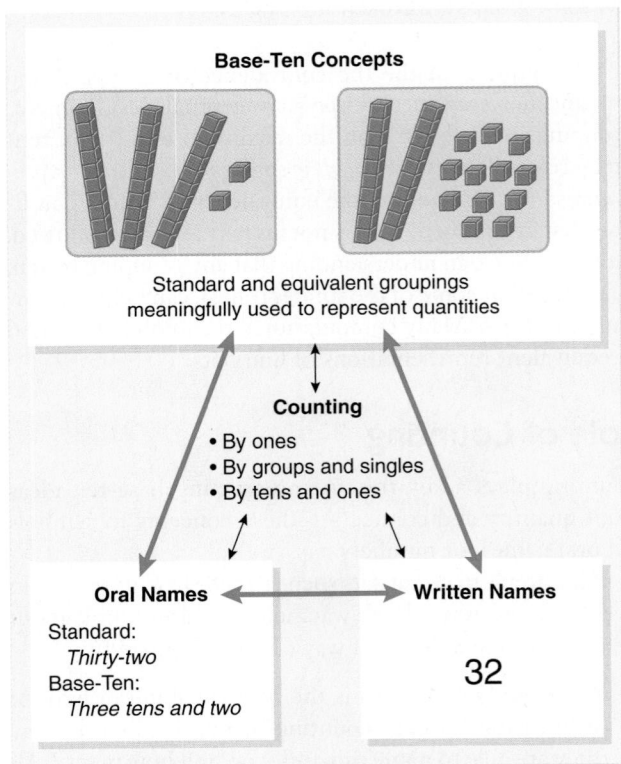

Figure 11.3 Relational understanding of place value integrates three components, shown as the corners of the triangle: base-ten concepts, oral names for numbers, and written names for numbers.

Models for Place Value

Physical models for base-ten concepts can play a key role in helping children develop the idea of "a ten" as both a single entity and as a set of ten units. Remember, though, that the models do not "show" the concept to the children. The children must construct the concept and impose it on the model.

Base-Ten Models and the Ten-Makes-One Relationship

A good base-ten model for ones, tens, and hundreds is *proportional*. That means that there is a one-to-one ratio. A ten model is physically ten times larger than the model for a one, and a hundred model is ten times larger than the ten model. Base-ten models can be categorized as *groupable* and *pregrouped*.

Groupable Models

Models that most clearly reflect the relationships of ones, tens, and hundreds are those for which the ten can actually be made or grouped from the singles. When children put ten beans in a portion cup, the cup of ten literally *is the same as* the ten single beans. Examples of these groupable models are shown in Figure 11.4(a). These could also be called "put-together–take-apart" models.

Of the groupable models, beans or counters in portion cups are the cheapest and easiest for children to use. Plastic connecting cubes are attractive and provide a good transition to pregrouped tens sticks. Bundles of wooden craft sticks or coffee stirrers are a well-known model, but small hands have trouble with rubber bands and actually making the bundles. With most groupable materials, hundreds are possible but generally not as practical for most activities.

As children become more and more familiar with these models, collections of tens can be made in advance by the children and kept as ready-made tens. Lids can be purchased for the plastic portion cups, and the connecting cubes can be left prebundled. This is a good transition into the pregrouped models described next.

Pregrouped or Trading Models

Models that are pregrouped are frequently shown in textbooks and are commonly used in instructional activities. With pregrouped models, such as those in Figure 11.4(b), children cannot always take pieces apart and put them back together. When 10 single pieces are accumulated, they must be exchanged or *traded* for a ten, and likewise, 10 tens must be traded for a hundred.

The chief advantage of these models is their ease of use and the efficient way they model large numbers. A significant disadvantage is the potential for children to use them without reflecting on the ten-to-one relationships or without really understanding what they are doing. For example,

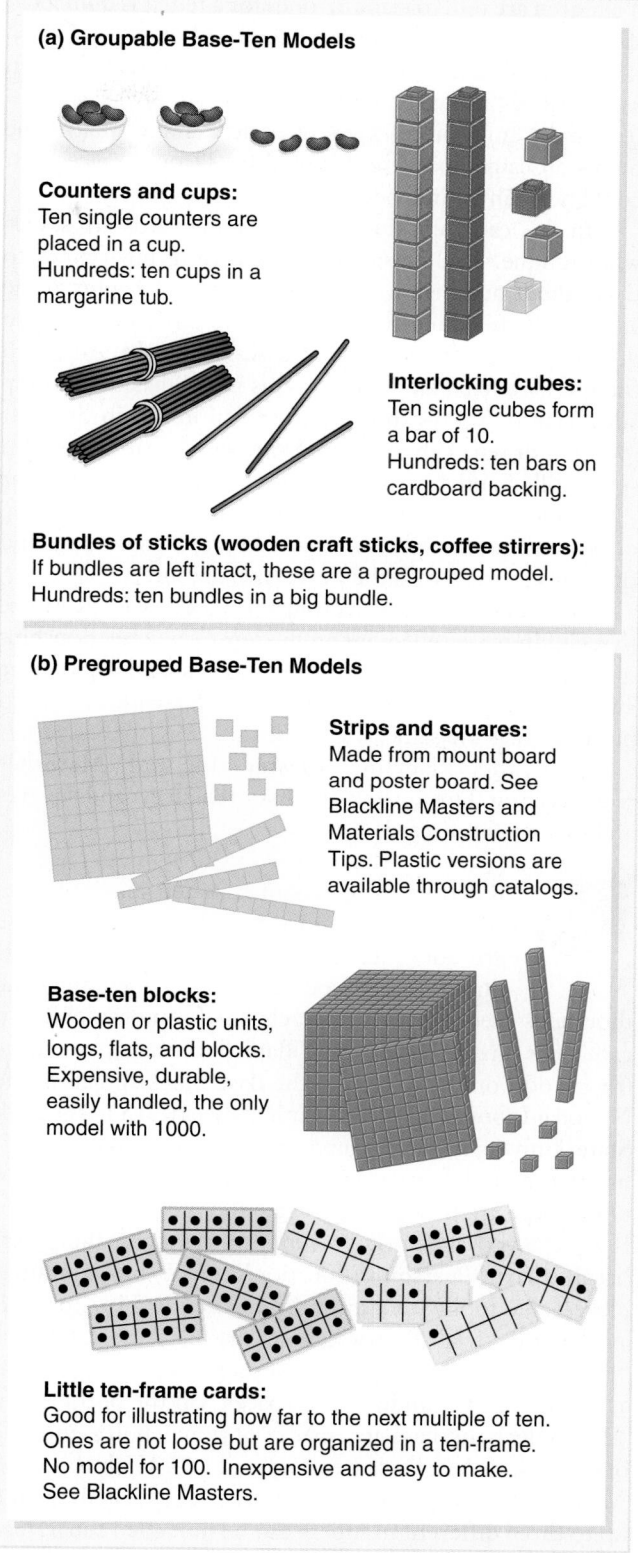

(a) Groupable Base-Ten Models

Counters and cups:
Ten single counters are placed in a cup.
Hundreds: ten cups in a margarine tub.

Interlocking cubes:
Ten single cubes form a bar of 10.
Hundreds: ten bars on cardboard backing.

Bundles of sticks (wooden craft sticks, coffee stirrers):
If bundles are left intact, these are a pregrouped model.
Hundreds: ten bundles in a big bundle.

(b) Pregrouped Base-Ten Models

Strips and squares:
Made from mount board and poster board. See Blackline Masters and Materials Construction Tips. Plastic versions are available through catalogs.

Base-ten blocks:
Wooden or plastic units, longs, flats, and blocks. Expensive, durable, easily handled, the only model with 1000.

Little ten-frame cards:
Good for illustrating how far to the next multiple of ten. Ones are not loose but are organized in a ten-frame. No model for 100. Inexpensive and easy to make. See Blackline Masters.

Figure 11.4 Groupable and pregrouped base-ten models.

if children are told to trade 10 ones for a ten, it is quite possible for them to make this exchange without attending to the "tenness" of the piece they call a ten. Similarly, children can learn to "make the number 42" by simply selecting 4 tens and 2 ones pieces without understanding that if the pieces all came apart there would be 42 ones pieces that could be counted individually.

In this category, the little ten-frame cards are somewhat unique. If children have been using ten-frames to think about numbers to 20, as discussed in Chapter 8, the value of the filled ten-frame may be more meaningful than it is with strips and squares of base-ten blocks. Although the ones are fixed on the cards, this model has the distinct advantage of always showing the relationship to the next multiple of ten. When 47 is shown with 4 cards with ten spaces filled and 1 card with seven spaces filled, it is clear that three more will make 50. With all other models, the ones must continually be counted to tell how many and their relationship with the next ten is obscure.

No model, including a groupable model, will guarantee that children are reflecting on the ten-to-one relationships in the materials. With pregrouped models we need to make an extra effort to see that children understand that a ten piece really is the same as 10 ones.

(See the Blackline Master 14 and Materials Construction Tips for making base-ten strips and squares and the ten-frame cards.)

 Electronic versions of base-ten manipulatives are becoming more popular. Usually, these are computer representations of the three-dimensional base-ten blocks, including the thousands piece. With simple clicks of a mouse children can place units, rods (tens), flats (hundreds), or cubes (thousands) on the screen. In the Base Block applets at the National Library of Virtual Manipulatives (NLVM) at Utah State University (http://matti.usu.edu/nlvm/nav/vlibrary.html), the models are placed on a place-value chart. If ten of one type are lassoed by a rectangle, they snap together. If a piece is dragged one column to the right, the pieces break apart. Pearson Education's *eTools* has a similar place-value tool with a bit more flexibility. This applet is available for free at www.kyrenet.org/mathtools. Choose "Place Value Blocks." If you wish, select the two-part mat as in Figure 11.5 under "workspaces" on the bottom left. Then select the base-ten pieces of your choice and add ones, tens, or hundreds (see Figure 11.5). With the *eTools Number Blocks*, place-value columns can be turned off, and up to three different numbers can be modelled separately. The "odometer" option can show the number 523 as *5 hundreds + 2 tens + 3 ones*, as *500 + 20 + 3*, or as *five hundred twenty-three*. A hammer icon will break a piece into smaller pieces and a glue bottle icon is used to group ten pieces together.

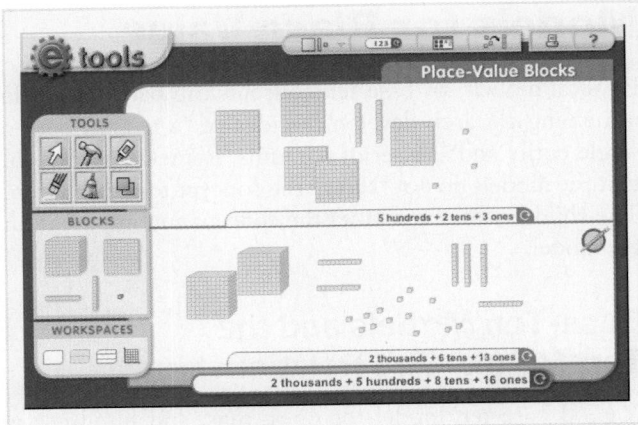

Figure 11.5 Pearson Scott Foresman's *eTools* includes a computer model of base-ten blocks

Source: Scott Foresman Addison-Wesley *Math Electronic-Tools* CD-ROM Grade K Through 6. Copyright © 2004 Pearson Education, Inc., or its affiliate(s). Used by permission. All rights reserved.

Compared to real base-ten models, virtual blocks are free, are easily grouped and ungrouped, can be shown to the full class on a monitor, and are available in "endless" supply, even the thousands blocks. Computer models allow students to print their work, creating a written record of what they've done. On the other hand, the computer model is no more conceptual than a physical model. Like the physical model, it is only a representation for students who understand the relationship involved. ◆

Non-Proportional Models

Non-proportional models can be used by students who no longer need to understand how ten units makes "a ten" or by some students who need to return to place-value concepts as they struggle with more advanced computations. These are models, such as money, that do not show ten as physically ten times larger than the one. Many students can grasp place-value relationships using pennies, dimes, and dollars to represent the ones, tens, and hundreds on their place-value mat. Using coin representations they can display amounts and exchange ten dimes for a dollar and represent and carry out a variety of calculations. Like a bead-frame with same-sized beads on different columns (wires) or coloured chips that are assigned different place values by colour, these non-proportional representations are *not* for introducing place-value concepts. They are used when students already have a conceptual understanding of the numeration system and need additional reinforcement. Often, money is a useful tool for middle- and upper-grade students with special needs who understand the relationships between the place values, yet they need support in developing other mathematical concepts. These older children sometimes do not want to use beans, blocks, and connecting cubes, because they perceive them as tools for much younger children.

Developing Base-Ten Concepts

Now that you have a sense of the task necessary to help children develop place-value concepts, we can begin to focus on activities that can help with this task. This section focuses on the top part of the triangle of ideas in Figure 11.3: base-ten concepts or grouping by tens. The central idea of counting groups of ten to describe quantities is clearly the most important component to be developed. The connection of these critical ideas with the place-value system of writing numbers and the way we say numbers—the bottom two corners of the triangle—are discussed separately to help you focus on the conceptual objective. However, in the classroom, the oral and written names for numbers can and should be developed in concert and nearly always while making connections to conceptual ideas using models.

Grouping Activities

Because children start their development of base-ten concepts with a count-by-ones idea of number, you must begin there. You cannot arbitrarily impose grouping by ten on children. We want children to experiment with showing amounts in groups of like size, and possibly come to an agreement that ten is a very useful size to use. The following activity could be done in late grade 1 or grade 2. It is designed as an example of a first effort at developing grouping concepts.

Activity 11.1

Counting in Groups

Find a collection of things that children might be interested in counting—perhaps the number of eyes in the classroom or the number of shoes, a mystery jar of buttons or cubes, a long chain of plastic links, or the number of crayons in the crayon box. The quantity should be countable, somewhere between 25 and 100. Pose the question, "How could we count our shoes in some way that would be easier than counting by ones?" Whatever suggestions you get, try to implement them. After trying several methods, you can have a discussion of what worked well and what did not. If no one suggests counting by tens, you might casually suggest that as possibly another idea.

One teacher had her grade 2 students find a good way to count all the connecting cubes the children were holding, after each child had been given a cube for each of her or his pockets. The first suggestion was to count by sevens. They tried, but it did not work very well because none of the children could count by sevens. In search of a faster way, the next suggestion was to count by twos. This did not seem to be much better than counting by ones. Finally, they settled on counting by tens and realized that this was a pretty good method, although counting by fives worked well too.

This and similar activities provide you with the opportunity to suggest that materials actually be arranged into groups of tens before the "fast" way of counting is begun. Remember that children may count "ten, twenty, thirty, thirty-one, thirty-two" but not fully realize the "thirty-twoness" of the quantity. To connect the count-by-tens method with their method of counting by ones, the children need to count both ways and discuss why they get the same result.

The idea in the next activity is for children to make groupings of ten and record or say the amounts. Words, rather than numbers, are used so that children will not mechanically match tens and ones with individual digits. It is important that children confront the actual quantity in a manner meaningful to them.

Activity 11.2

Groups of 10

Prepare bags of different types of counters, such as toothpicks, buttons, beans, plastic chips, interlocking cubes, craft sticks, or other items. Children are given a record sheet similar to the top examples in Figure 11.6. The bags can be placed at stations around the room, or given to pairs of children. Children dump out and count the contents. The amount is recorded as a number word. Then the counters are grouped in as many tens as possible. The groupings are recorded on the sheet. Bags are traded, or children move to another station after returning all their counters to the bag.

Variations of the "Groups of 10" activity can be derived from the other recording sheets in Figure 11.6. In "Get This Many," the children first count the dots then count out the corresponding number of counters. Small portion cups in which to put the groups of ten should be provided. Notice that the activity requires students to first count the set in a way they understand, record the amount in words, and then make the groupings. The activity starts with meaningful student counts and develops the idea of groups.

"Fill the Tens" and "Loop This Many" begin with words for numbers (number words). Students then count the indicated amount and make the necessary groups.

 As you watch children do these activities, you will be able to learn a lot about their base-ten concept development. For example, how do children count out the objects? Do they make groupings of ten as they go? Do they count to 10 then start again at 1? Children who do that are already using the base-ten structure. What you are more likely to see early

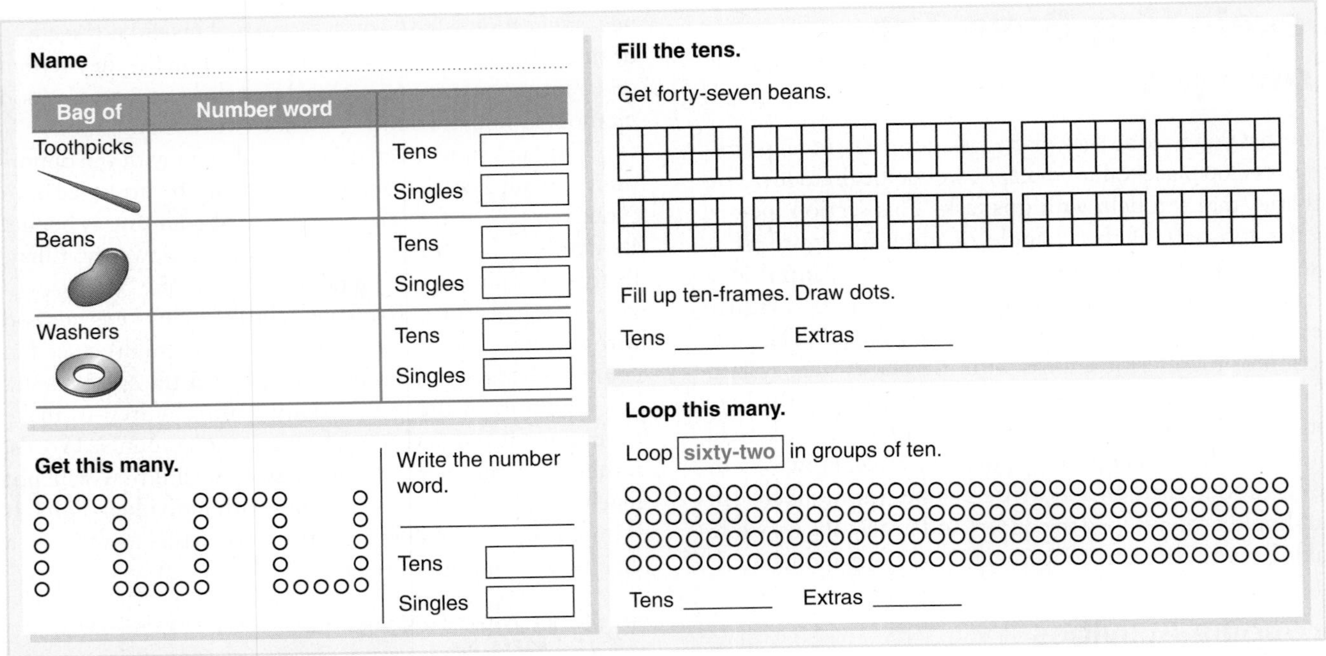

Figure 11.6 Activities involving number words and making groups of 10.

on is children counting a full set without stopping at tens and without any effort to group the materials in piles. A grade 2 teacher had her students count a jar of small beans. After they recorded the number, they were to ask for portion cups in which to make groups of ten. Several children, when asked how many cups they thought they might need, had no idea or made random guesses. What would you know about these students' knowledge of place value? ◆

It is quite easy to integrate grouping concepts along with measurement activities. Doing so will save time as you work through your curriculum. It will also enhance interest in both areas. As you will learn in Chapter 19, adding an estimation component to early measurement activities is important to help students understand measurement concepts. In the following measurement activity, estimation also serves to help students think about quantities as groupings of ten.

Activity 11.3

Estimating Groups of Tens and Ones

Show students a length they are going to measure— for example, the length of a student lying down or the distance around a sheet of newspaper. At one end, line up ten units (e.g., ten cubes in a bar, ten toothpicks, ten rods, or ten blocks). On a recording sheet (see Figure 11.7), students write down a guess of how many groups of ten and ones they think will fit into the length being measured. Next, they find the actual measure by placing units along the full length. These units are counted by ones and also grouped in tens. Both results are recorded.

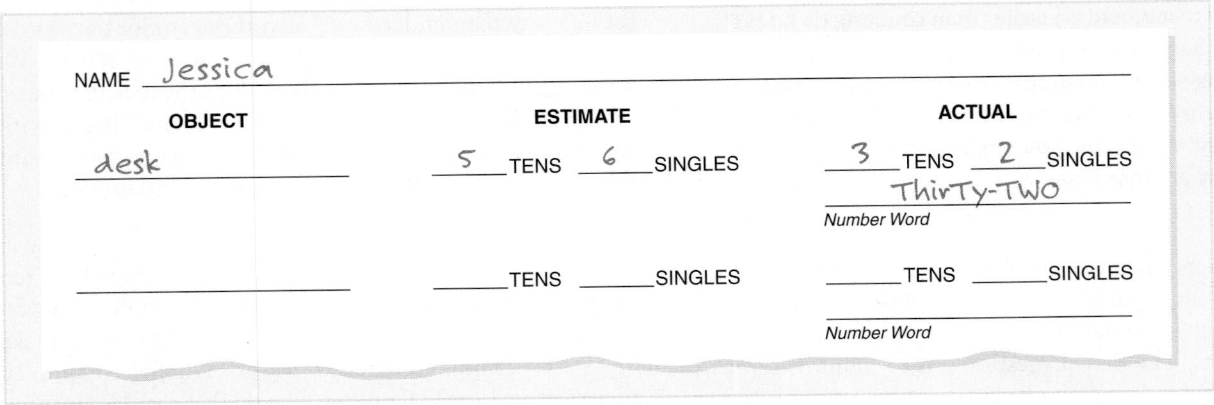

Figure 11.7 Recording sheet for estimating groups of tens and ones.

Notice that all place-value components are included in Activity 11.3. Children can work in pairs to measure several lengths around the room. A similar estimation approach could be added to "Groups of 10" (Activity 11.2), where students first estimate the quantity in the bags. Estimation requires reflective thought concerning quantities expressed in groups.

 Listening to students' estimates is also a useful assessment opportunity that tells you a lot about children's concepts of numbers in the range of your current activities. ◆

The Strangeness of *Ones*, *Tens*, and *Hundreds*

Reflect for a moment on how strange it must sound to say "seven ones." Certainly children have never said they were "seven ones" years old. The use of the word *ten* as a singular group name is even more mysterious. Consider the phrase "Ten ones make one ten." The first *ten* carries the usual meaning of 10 things, the amount that is 1 more than 9 things. But the other *ten* is a singular noun, a thing. How can something the child has known for years as the name for a lot of things suddenly become one thing? Bunches, bundles, cups, and groups of 10 make more sense in the beginning than "a ten."

As students begin to make groupings of 10, the language of these groupings must also be introduced. At the start, language such as "groups of 10 and ones" or "bunches of tens and singles" is most meaningful. For tens, use whatever terminology fits: bars of 10, cups of 10, bundles of 10. Eventually you can abbreviate this simply to "ten." There is no hurry to use the word "ones" for the leftovers. Language such as "four tens and seven" works very well.

The word *hundred* is equally strange yet usually gets less attention. It must be understood in three ways: as 100 single objects, as 10 tens, and as a singular thing. These word names are not as simple as they seem!

Grouping Tens to Make 100

So far we have focused mainly on helping students move from counting by ones to understanding how groups of ten can be used more effectively. In late grade 2 and into grade 3, numbers from 100 to 999 become important. Here the issue is not one of connecting a count-by-ones concept to a group of 100; rather it is seeing how a group of 100 can be understood as a group of 10 tens as well as 100 single ones. This connection is usually illustrated in textbooks on one page showing how 10 sticks of ten can be put together to make 1 hundred. This quick demonstration may be lost on many students.

As a way of introducing hundreds as groups of 10 tens and also 100 singles, consider the following estimation activity.

Activity 11.4

Too Many Tens

Show students any quantity with 150 to 1000 items. For example, you might use a jar of lima beans. Alternatives include a long chain of connecting links or paper clips or a box of Styrofoam packing peanuts. First, have students make and record estimates of how many beans are in the jar. Discuss with students how they came to select their estimates. Give portions of the beans to pairs or triads of students to put into cups of ten beans. Collect leftover beans and put these into groups of ten as well. Now ask, "How can we use these groups of ten to tell how many beans we have? Can we make new groups from the groups of ten? What is 10 groups of ten called?" If using cups of beans, be prepared with some larger containers into which ten cups of ten can be placed. When all groups are made, count the hundreds, the tens, and the ones separately. Record the amount on the board in the following way, "4 hundreds + 7 tens + 8 ones."

In the last activity it is important to use a groupable model so that students can see how the ten groups make the 100 items. This idea is often lost in the rather simple display of a 100 flat or square in the pregrouped base-ten models.

Equivalent Representations

An important variation of the grouping activities is aimed at the equivalent representations of numbers. For example, with children who have just completed the "Groups of 10" activity with a bag of counters, ask, "What is another way you can show your 42 besides 4 groups and 2 singles? Let's see how many ways you can find." Interestingly, most children will go next to 42 singles. The following activities are also directed at the idea of equivalent representations.

Activity 11.5

Odd Groupings

Show a collection of materials partly grouped in sets of ten. For example, you may have 5 chains of 10 links and 17 additional links. Be sure the children understand that each group has ten items. Count the number of groups; also count the singles. Ask, "How many links in all?" Record all responses, and discuss before you count. Let the children use whatever way they wish to count. Next, change the groupings (make a ten from the singles, or break apart one of the tens) and repeat the questions and the discussion. Do not change the total number from one time to the next. Once students begin to understand that the total does not change, ask in what other ways the items could be grouped if you use tens and singles.

If you are teaching grade 3, equivalent representations for hundreds as groups of ten can help with the concept of a hundred as 10 tens. The next activity is similar to "Odd Groupings" but is done using pregrouped materials and includes hundreds.

Activity 11.6

Three Other Ways

Students work in groups or pairs. First they show "four hundred sixty-three" on their desks with strips and squares in the standard representation. Next, they find and record at least three other ways of showing this number.

A variation of "Three Other Ways" is to challenge students to find a way to show an amount with a specific number of pieces. "Can you show 463 with 31 pieces?" (There is more than one way to do this.) Students in grade 3 or 4 can get quite involved with finding all the ways to show a three-digit number.

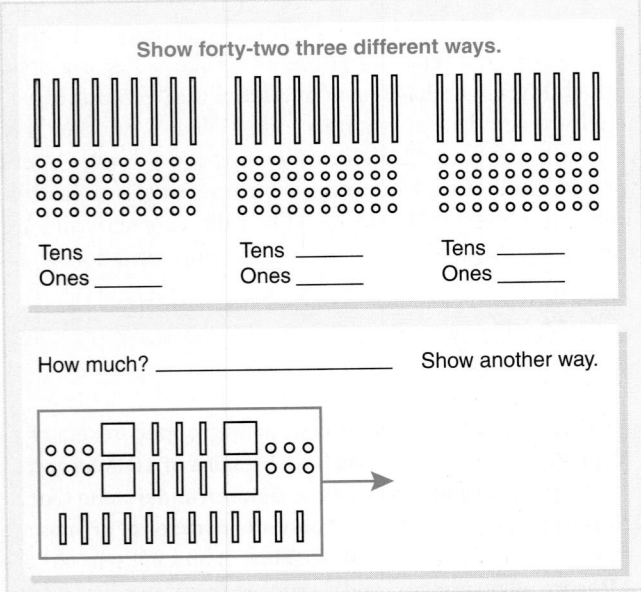

Figure 11.8 Equivalent representation exercises using square-stick-dot pictures.

For children who are still experiencing difficulty with their base-ten concept development, have them show numbers in one way only. As they develop their understanding, have them try showing the number in a different way.

After children have had sufficient experience with pregrouped materials, a "dot, stick, and square" notation can be used for recording ones, tens, and hundreds. By grade 3, children can use small squares for hundreds, as shown in Figure 11.8. Use the drawings as a means for telling the children what materials to take out in order to solve the problems. The drawings will also serve as a way for children to record their results.

The next activity begins to incorporate oral language with equivalent representation ideas.

Activity 11.7

Base-Ten Riddles

Base-ten riddles can be presented orally or in written form. Some children may require both ways. In either case, children should use base-ten materials to help solve them. The examples here illustrate a variety of possibilities with different levels of difficulty. Have children write new riddles when they complete these.

- **I have 23 ones and 4 tens. Who am I?**
- **I have 4 hundreds, 12 tens, and 6 ones. Who am I?**
- **I have 30 ones and 3 hundreds. Who am I?**
- **I am 45. I have 25 ones. How many tens do I have?**
- **I am 341. I have 22 tens. How many hundreds do I have?**
- **I have 13 tens, 2 hundreds, and 21 ones. Who am I?**
- **If you put 3 more tens with me, I would be 115. Who am I?**
- **I have 17 ones. I am between 40 and 50. Who am I?**

Oral and Written Names for Numbers

In this section we focus on helping children connect the bottom two corners of the triangle in Figure 11.3—oral and written names for numbers—with their emerging understanding of base-ten concepts using groups of ten as efficient methods of counting. Note that the ways we say and write numbers are conventions rather than concepts. Students must learn these by being told rather than through problem-based activities. It is also worth remembering that for ELL (ESL) students, the convention or pattern in our English words for numbers is probably not the same as it is in their native language. This is especially true of the numbers 11 to 19.

Two-Digit Number Names

In grade 1 and 2, children need to connect the base-ten concepts with the oral names for numbers they have used many times. They know the words but have not thought of them in terms of tens and ones.

Almost always use base-ten models while teaching the oral names. Rather than using standard number words, initially, a more explicit *base-ten language* can be used. In base-ten language, rather than saying "forty-seven" you would say "four tens and seven ones." Base-ten language is rarely misunderstood as children work with groupings of ten. When it seems appropriate, begin to pair base-ten language with standard language. Emphasize the teens as exceptions. Acknowledge that they are formed "backward" and do not fit the patterns. The next activity is useful for introducing oral names for numbers.

Activity 11.8

Counting Rows of 10

Use a 10 × 10 array of dots on the overhead projector. Cover up all but two rows, as shown in Figure 11.9(a). Ask, "How many tens? (2.) Two tens is called *twenty*." Have the class repeat. Show another row. "Three tens is called *thirty*. Four tens is *forty*. Five tens could have been *fivety* but is just *fifty*." The names *sixty*, *seventy*, *eighty*, and *ninety* all fit the pattern. Slide the cover up and down the array, asking how many tens and the name for that many.

Use the same 10 × 10 array to work on names for tens and ones. Show, for example, four full lines, "forty." Next expose one dot in the fifth row. "Four tens and one. Forty-one." Add more dots one at a time. "Four tens and two. Forty-two." "Four tens and three. Forty-three." This is shown in Figure 11.9(b). When that pattern is established, repeat with other decades from twenty through ninety.

Repeat this basic approach with other base-ten models. The next activity shows how this might be done.

Activity 11.9

Counting with Base-Ten Models

Show some tens pieces on the overhead or electronic whiteboard or just placed on the carpet in a mixed arrangement as shown in Figure 11.10. Ask how many tens. Add a ten or remove a ten and repeat the questions. Next add some ones. Always have children give the base-ten name and the standard name. Continue to make changes in the materials displayed by adding or removing 1 or 2 tens and by adding and removing ones.

By avoiding the standard left-to-right order for tens and ones, the emphasis is on the names of the materials, not their order.

Reverse the activity by having children use base-ten pieces at their desks. For example, you say, "Make 63." The children make the number with the models, then give the base-ten name.

Accommodation

You might wish to work one-on-one to accommodate those children who are experiencing difficulty with the base-ten names. Ask the following questions once they have displayed the number with the materials. "How many tens? How many ones?" Have them count the numbers of tens and ones out loud as you listen.

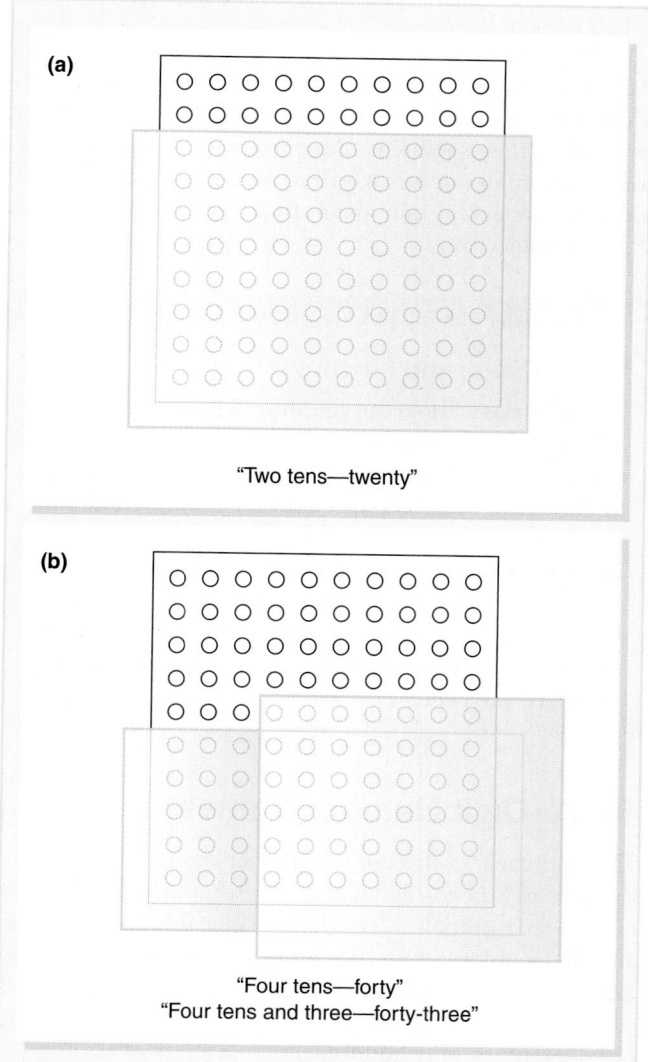

(a)

"Two tens—twenty"

(b)

"Four tens—forty"
"Four tens and three—forty-three"

Figure 11.9 10 × 10 dot arrays are always used to model sets of ten and singles (Blackline Master 12).

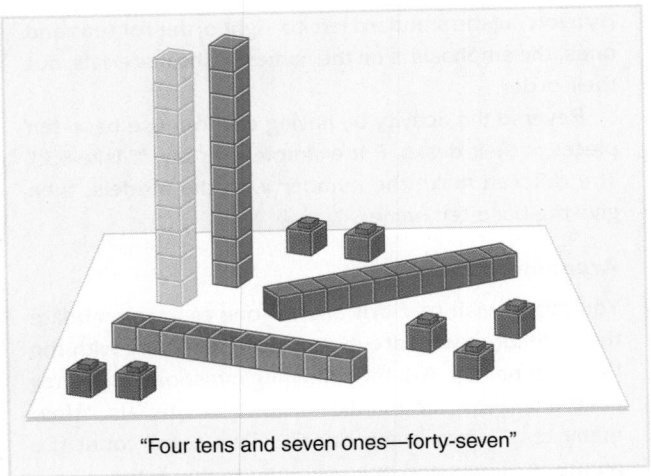

"Four tens and seven ones—forty-seven"

Figure 11.10 Using the base-ten and standard name for 47.

Note that Activities 11.8 and 11.9 will be much enhanced by discussion. Have children explain their thinking. If you don't require children to reflect on these responses, they soon learn how to give the response you want, matching number words to models, without actually thinking about the total quantities. The next activity has the same objective.

Activity 11.10

Tens, Ones, and Fingers

Ask your class, "How can you show 6 [or other amounts less than 10] fingers?" Then ask, "How can you show 37 fingers?" Some children will figure out that at least four children are required. Line up four children and have three hold up 10 fingers while the last child hold up 7 fingers. Have the class count the fingers by tens and ones. Ask for other children to show different numbers. Emphasize the number of sets of 10 fingers and the single fingers (base-ten language) and pair this with the standard language.

Three-Digit Number Names

The approach to three-digit number names is essentially the same as for two-digit names. Show mixed arrangements of base-ten materials. Have children give the base-ten name and the standard name. Vary the arrangement from one example to the next by changing only one type of material (ones, tens, or hundreds). That is, add or remove only ones, or only tens, or only hundreds.

Similarly, have children model at their desks numbers that you give them orally, using standard names. By the time that children are ready for three-digit numbers, the

two-digit number names, including the difficulties with the teens, have usually been mastered. The major difficulty is with numbers where there are no tens, such as 702. As noted earlier, the use of base-ten language is quite helpful here. The zero-tens problem is more pronounced when writing numbers. Children frequently write 7002 for "seven hundred two." The emphasis on the meaning in the oral form of base-ten language will be a significant help.

You might wish to work one-on-one to further assist those children who are still experiencing difficulty with numbers where there are no tens. Use the base-ten language along with the materials to illustrate that there are no tens.

Written Symbols

Place-value mats are simple mats divided into two or three sections where ones and tens or ones, tens, and hundreds pieces can be placed, as shown in Figure 11.11. You can suggest to your students that the mats are a good way to organize their materials when working with base-ten pieces. Explain that the standard way to use a place-value mat is to have the section for the ones on the right with the tens and hundreds places in the sections to the left.

Though not commonly seen in standard textbooks, it is strongly recommended that two ten-frames be drawn in the ones place as shown. (See Blackline Master 17.) That way, the number of ones on the ten-frames is always evident, eliminating the need for frequent and tedious counting. The ten-frame also makes it very clear how many additional

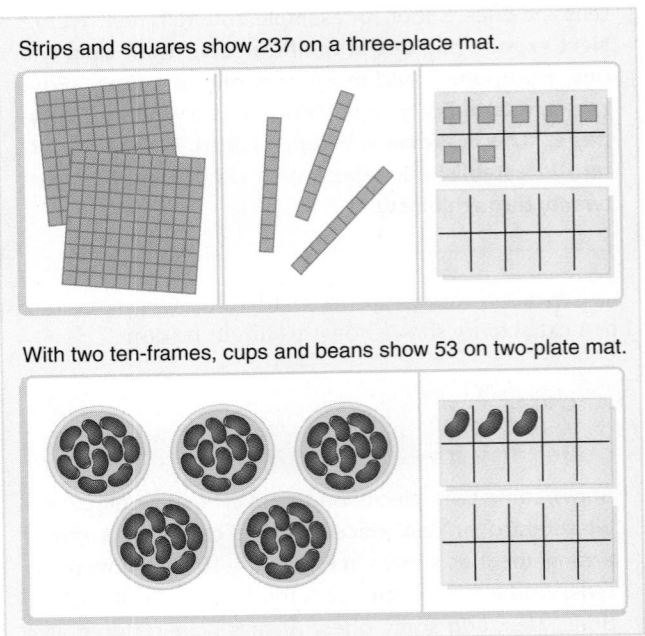

Strips and squares show 237 on a three-place mat.

With two ten-frames, cups and beans show 53 on two-plate mat.

Figure 11.11 Place-value mats with two ten-frames in the ones place to organize the counters and promote the concept of groups of ten.

counters would be needed to make the next set of ten. If children are modelling two numbers at the same time, one ten-frame can be used for each number.

As children use their place-value mats, they can be shown how the left-to-right order of the sections from largest to smallest is also the way that numbers are written. The place-value mat becomes a link between the base-ten models and the written form of the numbers. Once again, be aware of how easy it would be for a child to show a number on a mat using tens and ones pieces and learn to write the number without any understanding of what the number represents. Grade 1 and 2 textbooks often show a model and have children record numbers in this manner:

$$\underline{7}\text{ tens and }\underline{3}\text{ ones is }\underline{73}\text{ in all.}$$

It is all too easy to copy down the number of strips and single squares and rewrite these digits in a single number such as 73 without thinking about what these symbols mean.

The next three activities are designed to help children make connections among all three representations: models, oral language, and written forms. They can be done with two- or three-digit numbers in grades 1 to 4.

Activity 11.11

Say It/Press It

Display some models of ones and tens (and hundreds) in a mixed arrangement (not in the standard left-to-right format) so the class can see. (Use the overhead projector or interactive whiteboard or simply draw on the board using the square-stick-dot method.) Students say the amount shown in base-ten language ("four hundreds, one ten, and five") then in standard language ("four hundred fifteen"). Finally, they enter it on their calculators. Have someone share her or his display and defend it. Change the materials and repeat.

"Say It/Press It" is especially good for helping with teens (note the example in the activity description) and for three-digit numbers with zero tens. If you show 7 hundreds and 4 ones, the class says "seven hundreds, zero tens, and four—seven hundred (*slight pause*) four." The pause and the base-ten language suggests the correct three-digit number to press or write. As mentioned previously, many students have trouble with this example and write "7004," writing exactly what they hear in the standard name. This activity will help. The next activity simply changes the first representation that is presented to the students.

For children who are experiencing difficulty writing numbers such as 704 or 54 correctly, you might have them use the place-value materials to match the digits in the number with the places on the mat.

Activity 11.12

Show It/Press It

Say the standard name for a number (with either two or three digits). (You might need to write the number for some children who need to see it.) At their desks, students use their own base-ten models to show that number and input it on their calculator (or write it). Again, pay special attention to the teens and the case of zero tens.

The following activity has been popular for decades and remains a useful challenge for students in the early stages of place-value development.

Activity 11.13

Digit Change

Have students enter a specific two- or three-digit number on the calculator. The task then is to change one of the digits in the number without having to enter the new number. For example, change 48 to 78. Change 315 to 305 or to 295. Changes can be made simply by adding or subtracting an appropriate amount. Students should write or discuss explanations for their solutions.

Accommodation

For those children who are experiencing difficulty with this activity, work only with two-digit numbers and focus on increments of ten for the changes. For example, have the child change 48 to 58, etc. Later, increase the digit in the tens place that needs to be changed.

For those children who might benefit from an extra challenge, have them work in partners to challenge each other to make digit changes. Each child chooses for her or his partner a number to enter on the calculator along with the changes to be made to the number. The children take turns challenging each other.

Children are often able to disguise their lack of understanding of place value by following directions, using the tens and ones pieces in prescribed ways, and using the language of place value.

The diagnostic tasks presented here are designed to help you look more closely at children's understanding of place value. Designed for one-on-one diagnostic interviews rather than for whole class activities, these tasks have been used by several researchers and are adapted primarily from Labinowicz (1985), Kamii (1985), and Ross (1986).

Write the number 342. Have the child read the number. Then, have the child write the number that is 1 more than 342. Next, ask for the number that is 10 more than the number. You may wish to explore further with models. One less and 10 less than the number can be checked in the same way.

The next task is referred to as the *Digit Correspondence Task* and has been used widely in the study of place-value development. Take out 36 blocks. Ask the child to count the blocks, then have the child write the number that tells how many there are. Circle the 6 in 36 and ask, "Does this part of your 36 have anything to do with how many blocks there are?" Then, circle the 3 and repeat the question exactly as before. Do not give clues. Based on responses to the task, Ross (1989, 2002) has identified five distinct levels of understanding of place value:

1. *Single numeral.* The child writes 36 but views it as a single numeral. The individual digits 3 and 6 have no meaning by themselves.
2. *Position names.* The child identifies correctly the tens and ones positions but still makes no connections between the individual digits and the blocks.
3. *Face value.* The child matches 6 blocks with the 6 and 3 blocks with the 3.
4. *Transition to place value.* The 6 is matched with 6 blocks and the 3 with the remaining 30 blocks but not as 3 groups of 10.
5. *Full understanding.* The 3 is correlated with 3 groups of 10 blocks and the 6 with 6 single blocks. ◆

Patterns and Relationships with Multi-Digit Numbers

In this section we want to move beyond this snapshot view of individual numbers toward an orientation that looks at the number as a whole, rather than at its digits. The focus here will be on the patterns in our number system and how numbers are related to one another. We are interested in the relationships of numbers to important special numbers—relationships that begin to overlap with computation or a readiness for it. In the standards-based curricula, ideas similar to those found in this section include nearly all of the place-value development, with lesser attention given to the ideas that were discussed earlier.

The Hundreds Chart

The hundreds chart (Figure 11.12) is such an important tool in the development of place-value concepts that it deserves special attention. K–2 classrooms should have a hundreds chart prominently displayed.

An extremely useful version of the chart is made of transparent pockets into which each of the 100 number

1	2	3	4	5	6	7	8	9	10
11	12	13	14	15	16	17	18	19	20
21	22	23	24	25	26	27	28	29	30
31	32	33	34	35	36	37	38	39	40
41	42	43	44	45	46	47	48	49	50
51	52	53	54	55	56	57	58	59	60
61	62	63	64	65	66	67	68	69	70
71	72	73	74	75	76	77	78	79	80
81	82	83	84	85	86	87	88	89	90
91	92	93	94	95	96	97	98	99	100

Figure 11.12 A hundreds chart.

cards can be inserted. You can hide a number by inserting a blank card in front of a number in the pocket. You can also insert coloured pieces of paper in the slots to highlight various number patterns. And you can remove the number cards and have students replace them in the correct positions.

An overhead transparency or representation on the interactive whiteboard of a hundreds chart is almost as flexible as the pocket chart version. Numbers can be hidden by placing opaque counters on them. Patterns can be marked with a pen or with transparent counters. A transparency of a blank 10 × 10 grid serves as an empty hundreds chart on which you can write numbers. These transparencies can be made from Blackline Master 22.

At the kindergarten and grade 1 levels, students can be helped to count and recognize two-digit numbers with the hundreds chart long before they develop a base-ten understanding of these numbers.

Activity 11.14

Patterns on the Hundreds Chart

Have children work in pairs to find patterns on the hundreds chart. Solicit ideas orally from the class. Have children explain patterns found by others to be sure that all understand the ideas that are being suggested.

There are many different patterns on the hundreds chart. In a discussion, different children will describe the same pattern in several ways. Accept all ideas. Here are some of the patterns they may point out:

- The numbers in a column all end with the same number, which is the same as the number at the top.
- In a row, one number (the ones digit) "counts," or goes up by ones (0, 1, 2, 3, ..., 9), or the "second" number goes up by ones, but the first number (tens digit) stays the same.
- In a column, the "first number" (tens digit) "counts" or goes up by ones.
- You can count by tens going down the right-hand column.
- The numbers under the 2 are all even numbers. (Every alternating number in the rows is even.)
- If you count by fives, you get two columns—the last column and the 5 column.

For children, these patterns are not at all obvious or trivial. For example, one child may notice the pattern in the column under the 4—every number ends in a 4. Two minutes later another child will "discover" the parallel pattern in the column under the 7. It may not be completely obvious that there is a pattern like this in every column.

Other patterns you might have students explore include numbers that have a 7 in them, numbers whose digits add up to four, numbers where both digits are the same (11, 22, etc.), and various skip-count patterns.

Activity 11.15

Skip-Count Patterns

As a full class activity, have students skip count by twos, threes, fours, and so on. After skip counting as a class, have students record a specific skip-count pattern on their own copy of the hundreds chart by colouring in each number they count. Every skip count produces an interesting pattern on the chart. You should also discuss the patterns in the numbers. For example, when you skip count by fours, you only land on numbers that you get when you count by twos. Which counts make columnar patterns and which make diagonal ones?

In the beginning, skip counting may be quite difficult for children. As they become more comfortable with skip counting, you can challenge students to skip-count without the aid of the hundreds chart. Skip-counting skills show a

Activity 11.16

Missing Numbers

Provide students with a hundreds chart on which some of the number cards have been removed. Use the classroom pocket chart or, for a whole class activity, you can use the overhead transparency. The students' task is to

replace the missing numbers or tell what they are. At first, remove only a random selection of individual numbers. Later, remove sequences of numbers from three or four different rows. Finally, remove all but one or two rows or columns. Eventually, challenge children to replace all the numbers in a blank chart.

readiness for multiplication combinations. They also help children begin to look for interesting and useful patterns in numbers.

Replacing the number cards or tiles from a blank chart is a good station activity on which two students can work together. By listening to how students go about finding the correct places for numbers, you can assess how well they have constructed an understanding of the 1-to-100 sequence.

Activity 11.17

More and Less on the Hundreds Chart

Begin with a blank or nearly blank chart (Blackline Master 21). Circle a particular missing number. Students are then required to fill in the designated number and its "neighbours," the numbers to the left, right, above, and below. This can be done on the overhead projector or the whiteboard with the whole class or worksheets can be prepared using a blank hundreds chart or 10 × 10 grid for students to work individually. After students become comfortable naming the neighbours of a number, ask what they notice about the neighbouring numbers. The numbers to the left and right are one more and one less than the given number. Those above and below are ten less and ten more, respectively. By discussing these relationships on the chart, students begin to see how the sequence of numbers is related to the numerical relationships in the numbers.

Notice that children will first use the hundreds chart to learn about the patterns in the sequence of numbers. Many students, especially at the kindergarten or grade 1 level, will not understand the corresponding numerical relationships such as those discussed in the last activity. In the following activity, number relationships on the chart are made more explicit by including the use of base-ten models.

Activity 11.18

Models with the Hundreds Chart

Use any physical model for two-digit numbers with which the students are familiar. The little ten-frame cards are recommended.

- Give children one or more numbers to first make with the models then find on the chart. Use groups

* of two or three numbers that are either in the same row or the same column.
* Indicate a number on the chart. What would you have to change to make the number the same as each of its neighbours (the numbers to the left, right, above, and below)?

The hundreds chart can extend even very young students' concepts of number. Children can use a hundreds chart to find combinations for any number with which they are familiar. Students use patterns on the chart to see how big numbers are related in a similar manner to the way little numbers are.

It is becoming more and more popular to have a chart that extends to 200, even in grade 1. Perhaps a more powerful idea is to extend the hundreds chart to 1000.

Activity 11.19

The Thousands Chart

Provide students with several sheets of blank hundreds charts from Blackline Master 21. Assign groups of three or four students the task of creating a 1-to-1000 chart. Make the chart by taping ten charts together in a long strip. Students should decide how they are going to divide up the task and who will work on the different parts of the chart.

The thousands chart should be discussed as a class to examine how numbers change as you count from one hundred to the next number, what the patterns are, and so on. In fact, the earlier hundreds chart activities can all be extended to the thousands chart.

 Several Web-based resources include hundreds charts that allow students to explore patterns. *Learning About Number Relationships* is an e-example from NCTM's *e-Standards* that has a calculator and a hundreds chart. It allows for a fairly open exploration. Patterns are coloured on the chart as students skip count with the calculator. Students can skip count by any number. They can also begin their counts at any number. Any two patterns can be overlapped using two colours. The chart also extends to 1000. The *Number Patterns* applet from the NLVM (http://nlvm.usu.edu/en/nav/vlibrary.html) presents students with number patterns to complete. ◆

Relationships with Landmark Numbers

One of the most valuable features of both the hundreds chart and the little ten-frame cards is how clearly they illus-

trate relationships with the next multiple of ten—the end of the row on the chart or the blank spaces on the ten-frame card. Multiples of 10, 100, and occasionally other special numbers, such as multiples of 25, are referred to in the *Investigations in Number, Data, and Space* program as *landmark numbers*. Students learn to use this term as they work with informal methods of computation. When finding the difference between 74 and 112, a child might say, "First I added 6 onto 74 to get to a landmark number. Then I added 2 more tens onto 80 to get to 100 because that's another landmark number...." Whatever terminology is used, understanding how numbers are related to these special numbers is an important step in students' number sense development.

In addition to the hundreds chart, the number line is an excellent way to get at these relationships. The next two activities are suggestions for using number lines.

Activity 11.20

Who Am I?

Draw a line labelled with 0 and 100 at opposite ends. Mark a point with a ? that corresponds to your secret number. (Estimate the position the best that you can.) Students try to guess your secret number. For each guess, place and label a mark on the line.

Continue marking each guess until your secret number is discovered. As a variation, the endpoints can be other than 0 and 100. For example, try 0 and 1000, 200 and 300, or 500 and 800.

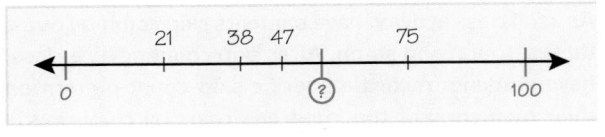

Activity 11.21

Who Could They Be?

Label two points on a number line (not necessarily the ends) with landmark numbers.

Show students different points labelled with letters. Ask what numbers they think the different points labelled might be, and why they think that. In the example shown here, B and C are less than 100 but probably more than 60. E could be about 180. You can also ask where 75 might be or where 400 is. About how far apart are A and D? Why do you think D is more than 107?

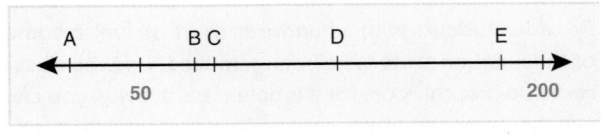

The next two activities are extensions of part–part–whole ideas that were explored in Chapter 8. In the first of these, one of the parts is a landmark number. In the second, the landmark number is the whole.

Activity 11.22

50 and Some More

Say or write a number between 50 and 100. Students respond with "50 and _____." For 63, the response is "50 and 13." Any landmark number can be used instead of 50. For example, you could use any number that ends in 50. You can also do this with numbers such as 70 or 230.

Accommodation

For students who are experiencing difficulty determining which number to add to the landmark number to get the target number, have them use a hundreds chart to help them.

Landmark numbers are often broken apart in computations. The next activity is aimed at what may be the most important landmark number, 100.

Activity 11.23

The Other Part of 100

Students work together in pairs with a set of little ten-frame cards. One student makes a two-digit number. Then both students work mentally to determine what goes with the ten-frame amount to make 100. They record their solutions on paper, then check by making the other part using the ten-frame cards to see if the total is 100. Students take turns making the original number. Figure 11.13 shows three different thought processes that students might use.

Being able to give the other part of 100 should become a focus in grades 2 to 4 because it is so useful for flexible methods of computation.

If your students are adept at being able to give the "other part of 100," you can change the whole from 100 to another number. At first, try other multiples of 10 such as 70 or 80. Then, extend the whole to any number less than 100.

❚❚ ———————— *Pause and Reflect*

Suppose the whole is 83. Sketch four little ten-frame cards showing 36. Looking at your "cards," what goes with 36 to make 83? How did you think about it?

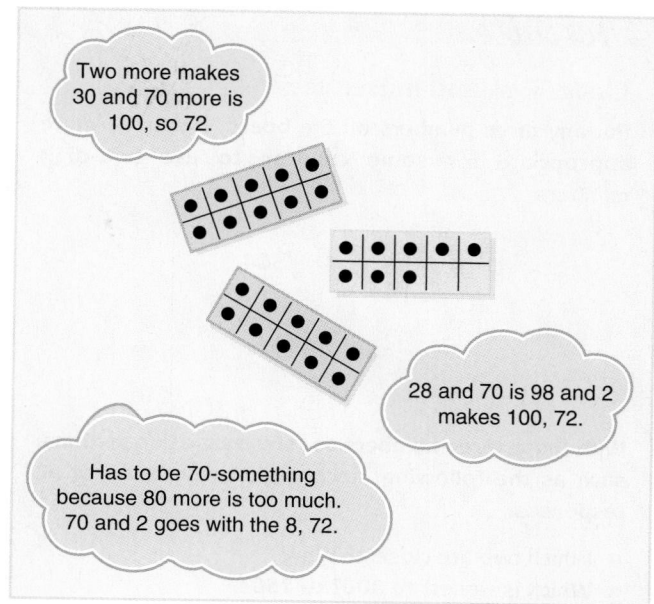

Figure 11.13 Using little ten-frames to help think about the "other part of 100."

What you just did to find the other part of 83 was to subtract 36 from 83. You did not borrow or regroup. Most likely you did it in your head. With more practice, you (and students as early as grade 3) can do this without the aid of the cards.

Compatible numbers for addition and subtraction are numbers that go together easily to make nice numbers. Numbers that make tens or hundreds are the most common examples. Compatible sums also include numbers that end in 5, 25, 50, or 75, since these numbers are easy to work with as well. The instructional task is to get students accustomed to looking for combinations that work together and then to looking for these combinations in computational situations.

Activity 11.24

Compatible Pairs

Searching for compatible pairs can be done as an individual activity using a worksheet format or with the whole class on the overhead projector. Prepare a transparency or use the whiteboard to duplicate a page with a search task. Four possible levels of difficulty are shown in Figure 11.14. Students call out or connect the compatible pairs as they see them.

The next activity has children apply some of the same ideas about landmark numbers we have been exploring.

Activity 11.25

Close, Far, and In Between

Put any three numbers on the board. It may be more appropriate for some children to use two-digit numbers.

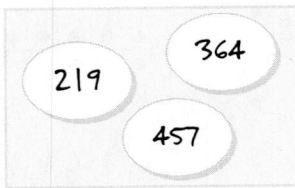

With these three numbers as referents, ask questions, such as the following, encouraging discussion of all responses.

- **Which two are closest? Why?**
- **Which is closest to 300? to 250?**
- **Name a number between 457 and 364.**
- **Name a multiple of 25 between 219 and 364.**
- **Name a number that is more than all of these.**
- **About how far apart are 219 and 500? 219 and 5000?**
- **If these are "big numbers," what are some small numbers? Numbers that are about the same? Numbers that make these seem small?**

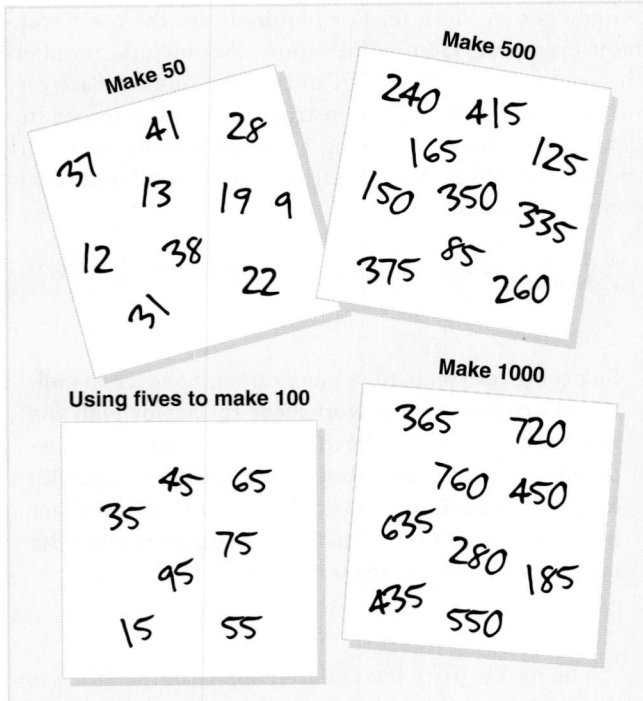

Figure 11.14 Compatible-pair searches.

Number Relationships for Addition and Subtraction

If you examine any conventional textbook for grades 1 to 5, you will find chapters on place value and chapters on computational strategies. The same, of course, is true of this book. However, evidence suggests that there is an interaction between learning about numeration and learning about computational techniques (NRC, 2001). That is, it is not necessary to complete the development of numeration concepts before exploring computation.

In January of grade 1, Jerrika solves a story problem for 10 + 13 + 22 using interlocking cubes. Her written work is shown in Figure 11.15. She is beginning to use one 10 but most likely counted on the remaining cubes by ones. Her classmate, Monica, solved the same problem but has clearly utilized more base-ten ideas (Figure 11.15). Ideas such as these continue to grow with additional problem solving and sharing of ideas during class discussion.

 The *Standards* authors also suggest a blending of numeration and computation. "It is not necessary to wait for students to fully develop place-value understandings before giving them opportunities to solve problems with two- and three-digit numbers. When such problems arise in interesting contexts, students can often invent ways to solve them that incorporate and deepen their understanding of place value, especially when students have the opportunities to discuss and explain their invented strategies and approaches" (p. 82).

The activities in this section are designed both to further students' understanding of base-ten concepts and to prepare them for computation—especially addition and subtraction. (Don't forget that simple story problems such as those shown in Figure 11.15 are also effective.) The first of these activities involves skip counting using the calculator. By adjusting the numbers, it can be made appropriate for almost any grade.

Activity 11.26

Calculator Challenge Counting

Students press any number on the calculator (e.g., 7) then ⊞ 4. They say the sum before they press ⊟. Then, they continue to add 4 mentally, challenging themselves to say the number before they press

The constant addend (⊞ 4) in "Calculator Challenge Counting" can be any number, even a two- or three-digit number. Generally, the starting number is less than ten but there is no reason that students cannot begin, for example, with 327 or any other number. Young students will even find jumps of five fairly challenging if the starting number

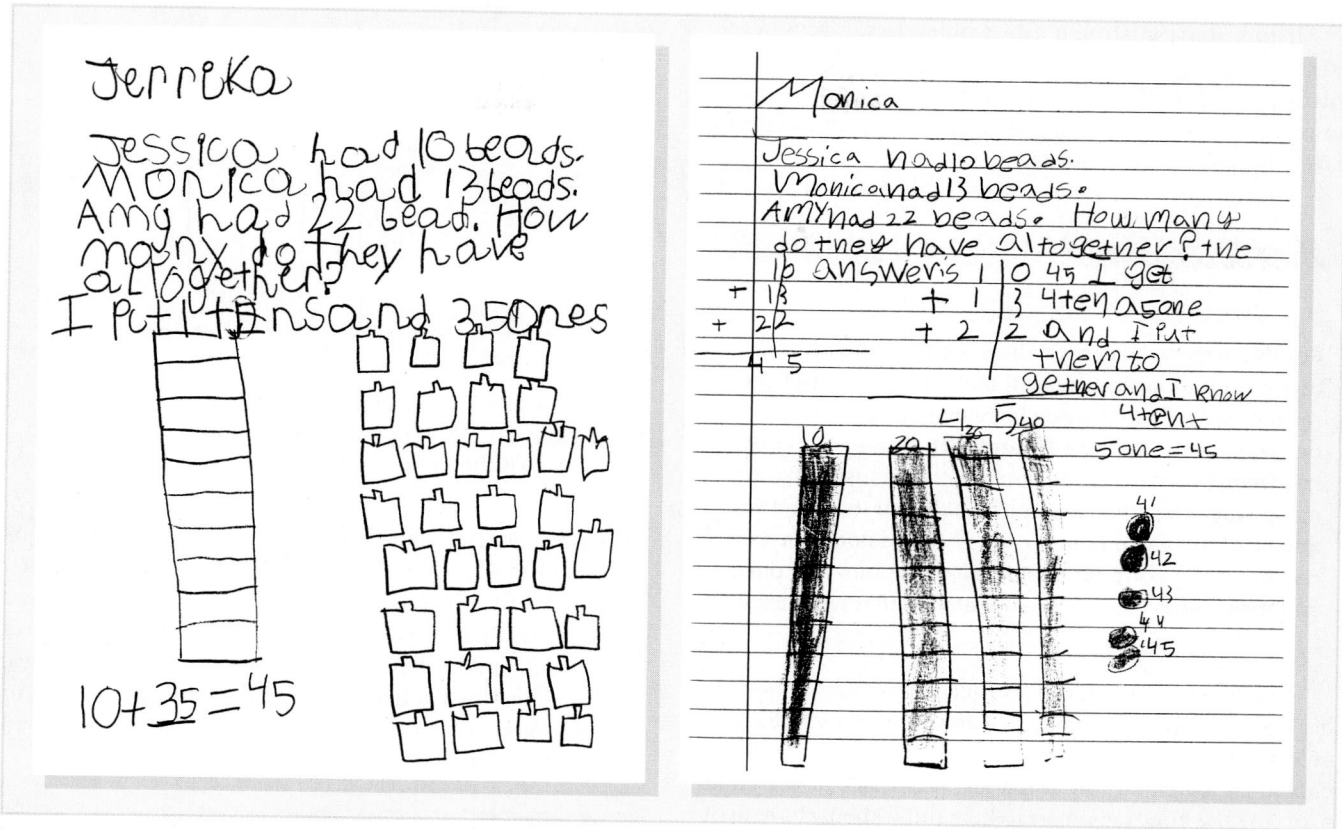

Figure 11.15 The work of two grade 1 children in January. They both solved the problem 10 + 13 + 22. Jerrika's work shows that she does not yet use tens in her computation, whereas Monica is clearly adding groups of ten.

is not a multiple of five. Skip counting by 20 or 25 will be easier than counting by 7 or 12 and will help to develop important patterns and relationships.

"Calculator Challenge Counting" can also be done in reverse. That is, enter a number such as 123 in the calculator and press minus 6. As before, students say the result before pressing ▣. Each successive press will subtract six or whatever constant was entered.

Two children can work together quite profitably on this activity. The flexibility of this activity allows for it to be used over and over at various skill levels, always challenging students and improving their mental skill with numbers.

The next activity combines symbolism with base-ten representations.

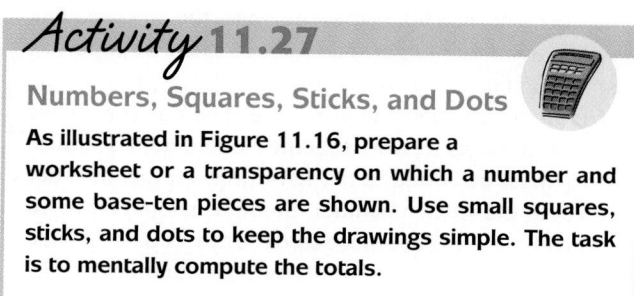

Numbers, Squares, Sticks, and Dots

As illustrated in Figure 11.16, prepare a worksheet or a transparency on which a number and some base-ten pieces are shown. Use small squares, sticks, and dots to keep the drawings simple. The task is to mentally compute the totals.

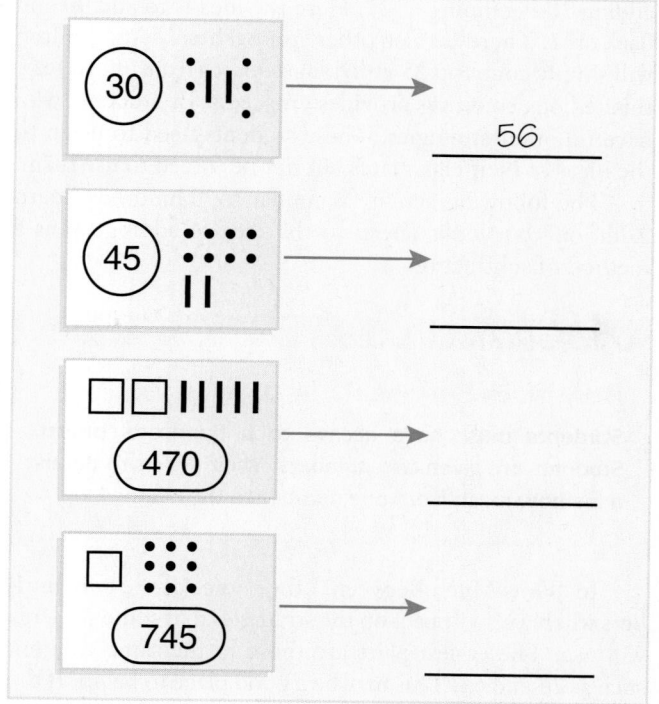

Figure 11.16 Flexible counting on or addition using both models and numbers.

If this activity is done as a whole class, discuss each exercise before going to the next one. If you use a worksheet format, include only a few examples and have students write how they went about solving them. It is still important to have a discussion with the class.

The next activity extends the use of the hundreds board.

Activity 11.28

Hundreds Board Addition

For this activity, it is best to have a classroom hundreds board (or a thousands board) that all students can see. An alternative is to provide individual hundreds boards on paper (see Blackline Master 22). Students use the hundreds board to add two numbers. Because there are many ways that the hundreds board can be used for addition, the value is in the class discussion. For this reason, it is a good idea to do only one sum at a time, and then discuss the different methods that were used.

The hundreds chart can also act as a number line—one that highlights the relationship of any number with the next multiple of ten. A move down a row is the same as adding ten and a move up a row is ten less. Consider how a child might use the hundreds chart to help think about the sum of 38 and 25. As illustrated in Figure 11.17(a), one approach is to begin at 38 and count over 2 to 40. From there a student might count down two rows to 60 for a total of 22, and then add 3 more in the next row. Figure 11.17(b) shows adding 38 beginning at 25. Here the idea is to add 40 and back off 2. There are also other approaches. Many children will simply count on 25 individual squares from 38. At least this tedious counting provides an access for students who have no other strategies. These students need to listen to the ideas of their classmates but not be forced to use them.

The following activity is similar to "Hundreds Board Addition" but looks ahead to the idea of adding up as a method of subtraction.

Activity 11.29

How Much Between?

Students must have access to a hundreds board. Students are given two numbers. Their task is to determine how much from one number to the next.

In "How Much Between?" the choice of the two numbers will have an impact on the strategies that some students will use. The easiest pairs are those in the same column, such as 24 and 64. This may be a good place to begin. If the larger number is to the right of the first number (e.g., 24 and 56), students will likely add on tens to get to the target number's row. They will then add ones. Of course, this is

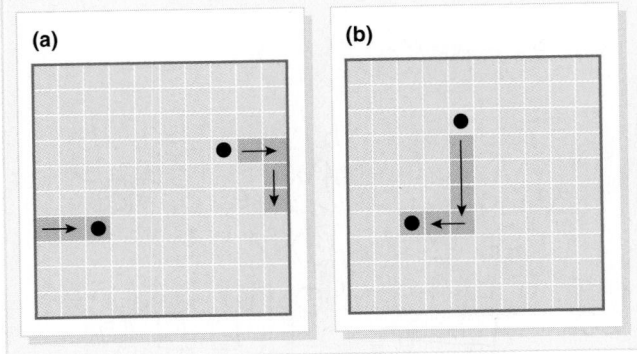

Figure 11.17 Two methods of adding 38 + 25 on the hundreds chart. It is important to stress the idea that moving down a row is the same as adding 10.

also a reasonable strategy for any two numbers. But consider 17 and 45, where 45 is to the left of 17 on the chart. With this pair, a reasonable strategy is to move down 3 rows (+30) to 47, then count back 2 (–2) to 45. The total count is now 30 – 2, or 28. There are also other possible approaches.

The next two activities are mathematically parallel to the previous two, but they use little ten-frame cards instead of the hundreds chart.

Activity 11.30

Little Ten-Frame Sums

Provide pairs of students with two sets of little ten-frame cards. Each child chooses a number and shows it using the cards. An example is shown in Figure 11.18(a). Students then work together to find the total number of dots. Each pair of numbers and the sum is written on paper with an agreed-upon answer.

The activity can also be done by showing the two numbers on the overhead projector, with students working in pairs at their desks.

Activity 11.31

How Far to My Number?

Students work in pairs with a single set of little ten-frame cards. One student uses the cards to make a number less than 50. In the meantime, the other student writes a number larger than 50 on a piece of paper, as shown in Figure 11.18(b). You may choose to limit the size of this number, but it is not necessary. The task is for the students to work together to find out how much more must be added to the ten-frame number in order to get to the written number. Students should try to do this without using any more cards. Once students decide upon an answer, they should make the number with the cards and see if the two match.

Accommodation

For those students who are experiencing difficulty finding out how much more must be added to the ten-frame number, you might limit the size of the number initially chosen. As well, students could use the ten-frame cards to help them figure out the difference.

Pause and Reflect

Try your hand at the two examples in Figure 11.18. How many ways can you imagine that two students might do these? Share your ideas with a colleague.

Chapter 12 will discuss a variety of solution strategies that students use to add and subtract numbers. Students should have ample opportunities to develop their ideas in activities like the ones in this section. Notice, however, that students may still be developing their ideas about numbers and the relationships between them. These ideas are as much about place-value understanding as about addition and subtraction. The little ten-frames and the hundreds chart are good models to help with the development of these relationships.

Students who are experiencing difficulty with any of these activities may also have difficulty with almost any type of invented computation. For example, how do students go about the exercises in Activity 11.27, "Numbers, Squares, Sticks, and Dots"? That activity requires that children have sufficient understanding of base-ten concepts in order to use them in meaningful counts. If students are counting by ones, perhaps on their fingers, then more practice with these activities may be misplaced. Instead, consider additional counting and grouping activities in which students have the opportunity to see the value of groups of ten. Using the little ten-frame cards may also help.

"How Far to My Number?" (Activity 11.31) is also a useful diagnostic task, for a diagnostic interview. As you listen to how children solve these problems, you will realize that there is a lot more you can learn about their thinking, beyond simply getting the correct answer. ◆

Connections to Real-World Ideas

We should not permit children to study place-value concepts without encouraging them to see numbers in the world about them. You do not need a prescribed activity to bring real numbers into the classroom.

Children in grade 2 should be thinking about numbers under 100 first, and soon after, numbers up to 1000. Quantities larger than that are difficult to think about. Where can you find numbers like this? Around your school: the number of children in each class, the numbers on the school buses, the number of minutes devoted to mathematics each day and each week, the numbers on the calendar (days in a week, month, year), the number of days since school has started. And then there are measurements, numbers at home, numbers on a field trip, numbers in the news, and so on.

What do you do with these numbers? Turn them into interesting graphs, write stories using them, make up problems, devise contests.

As children get a bit older, the interest in numbers can expand beyond the school and classroom. All sorts of things can and should be measured to create graphs, draw inferences, and make comparisons. For example, what numbers are associated with the "average" grade 5 student? Height, mass, arm span, age in months, number of siblings, number of grandparents, distance from home to school, length of standing broad jump, number of pets, hours spent watching TV in a week. How can you find the average for these or other numbers that may be of interest to the students in your room? Is anyone really average?

The particular way you bring number and the real world together in your class is up to you. But do not

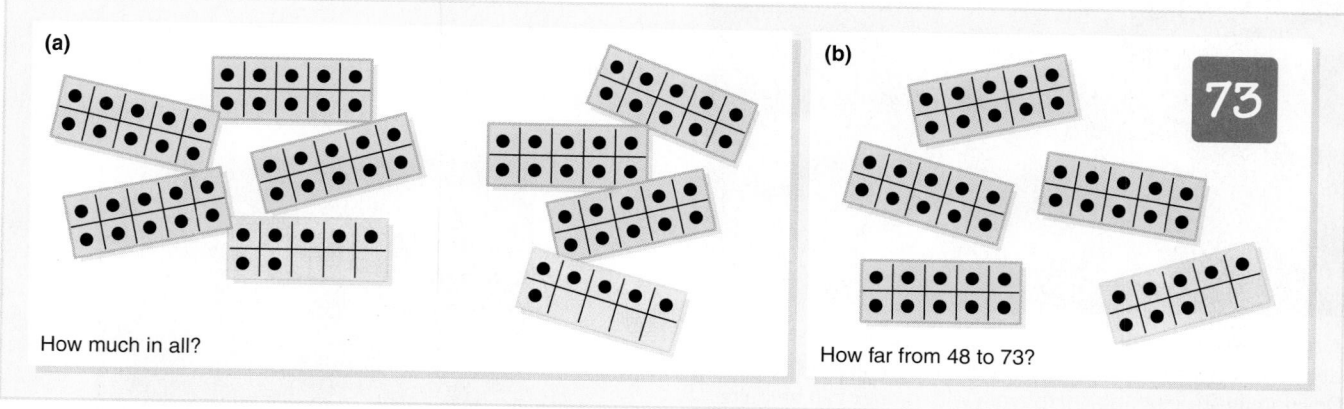

How much in all?

How far from 48 to 73?

Figure 11.18 Two tasks that can be done with little ten-frame cards.

underestimate the value of connecting the real world to the classroom.

Helping Children Work with Money

Developing children's ability to work with money can be quite challenging for primary teachers. The following concepts and skills are typically required for working with money:

- Coin recognition
- Values of coins
- Using the values of coins
- Counting sets of coins (including comparing two sets)
- Equivalent collections of coins (same amounts, different coins)
- Selecting coins for a given amount
- Making change

These concepts and skills will be discussed in the following sections.

Coin Recognition and Values

Students learn the names of coins in the same way that they learn the names of any physical objects in their daily environment—through exposure and repetition. However, the value of each coin is a convention that students must simply be told.

For these values to make sense, students must have an understanding of 5, 10, and 25. They also need to be able to think of these quantities without seeing countable objects. Nowhere else do we say, "This is five," while pointing to a single item. A child whose number concepts remain tied to counts of objects is not going to be able to understand the

A complete understanding of place value, which extends to decimal numeration, develops across the K–8 grade span. Developing students' ability to work with money can be quite challenging, but the real-world connections may be very satisfying!

values of coins. Instruction on the value of coins needs to focus on purchases—a dime can *buy the same thing* that 10 pennies can buy.

Using Coin Values

The remaining items in the list of skills are all a form of mental computation and/or compound skip counting. To name the total value of a group of coins is the same as mentally adding their values. Ironically, most provincial and territorial curricula require coin counting before they require students to do the symbolic sum mentally.

There is nothing wrong with asking grade 2 students to do the mental math required for counting a collection of coins. Fortunately, the numbers are restricted to multiples of five and ten, with some ones added at the end. The next activity is a preparation for counting money.

Activity 11.32

Money Skip Counts

Explain to students that they will skip count using these numbers: 100, 50, 25, 10, 5, 1. Begin with two different amounts, e.g., 25 and 10. Write these numbers on the board. Point to the larger number (25), and have students begin to skip count. After three or more counts, point to the smaller number (10). Children continue skip counting from where they left off, but now they count by 10s. Always start with the larger. Later, try three numbers, still in descending order.

Remember that working with coins requires not only adding up the values. It also requires first mentally giving each coin a value then ordering the coins. The following is a good readiness activity in which students add a mixed collection of numbers, each of which is the value of a coin.

Activity 11.33

Coin-Number Addition

On the board or overhead whiteboard, write a small collection of numbers that are the same as coin values, in random order.

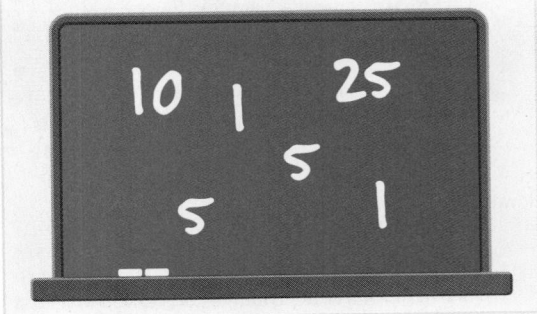

Begin with only 10s and 1s. Then add some 5s and eventually 25s (and 50s, if these are in your curriculum). The students' task is to add the numbers mentally. Do not suggest how they add the numbers or in what order. There is generally more than one way to do this. Discuss with students how they added the collection.

Accommodation

Those students who might have difficulty adding the numbers mentally should write the numbers down to aid them with their addition.

When discussing solutions to this last activity, be sure to value any approach that works. However, pay special attention to those students who begin with the larger values and those who put nice combinations together utilizing thinking with tens.

After students have gained experience working with coin-numbers, try the same activity with the coins. Simply spill some plastic coins on the overhead or draw "coins" on the board. (Draw circles with P (penny), N (nickel), D (dime), or Q (quarter) inside, but no numbers.)

Making Change

Making change is the only time that students are asked to add on to find a difference. Because adding on to find a difference is such a valuable skill—much easier than using the usual subtraction algorithm—it makes sense to give students a lot of experience with adding on to find differences before asking them to make change. As students become more skilled at adding on, they can see the process of making change as an extension of a skill already learned.

Numbers Beyond 1000

For children to have good number concepts beyond 1000, the conceptual ideas that have been carefully developed must be extended. This is sometimes difficult to do because physical models for thousands are not commonly available. At the same time, number sense ideas must also be developed. In many ways, it is these informal ideas about very large numbers that are the most important.

Extending the Place-Value System

Two important ideas developed for three-digit numbers should be extended to larger numbers. Firstly, the grouping idea should be generalized. That is, when you reach ten in any position, it makes a single group in the next position. The single group becomes ten again when you move the opposite way. Secondly, the oral and written patterns for numbers of three digits are duplicated for every three digits to the left of the decimal point. These two related

ideas are not as easy for children to understand, as adults seem to believe. Because models for large numbers are so difficult to have or picture, textbooks must deal with these ideas in a predominantly symbolic manner. Symbolism is not sufficient!

Activity 11.34

What Comes Next?

Have a "What Comes Next?" discussion using the base-ten strips and squares. The unit of the ones piece is a 1 centimetre square. The tens piece is a 10 × 1 strip. The hundreds piece is a square, 10 cm × 10 cm. What is next? Ten hundreds are called a thousand. What shape? It could be a strip made of 10 hundreds squares. Tape 10 hundreds together. What is next? (Reinforce the idea of "ten making one" that has progressed to this point.) Ten one-thousand strips would make a square measuring 1 metre on a side. Once the class has figured out the shape of the thousand piece, the problem-based task is "What comes next?" Let small groups work on the dimensions of a ten-thousand piece.

If your students become interested in seeing the big pieces from "What Comes Next?" engage them in measuring them on paper. Ten ten-thousand squares (100 000) go together to make a huge strip. Draw this strip on a long sheet of butcher paper, and mark off the ten squares that make it up. You will have to go out into the hall.

How far you want to extend this square, strip, square, strip sequence depends on your class. The idea that 10 in one place makes 1 in the next can be brought home dramatically. It is quite possible with older children to make the next 10 m × 10 m square using chalk lines on the playground. The next strip is 100 m × 10 m. This can be measured out on a large playground with children marking the corners. At this point, the payoff includes an appreciation of the increase in size of each successive amount as well as the ten-makes-one progression. The 100 m × 10 m strip is the model for 10 million, and the 10 m × 10 m square models 1 million. The difference between 1 million and 10 million is dramatic. Even the concept of 1 million tiny centimetre squares is dramatic.

Try the "What Comes Next?" discussion in the context of these three-dimensional models. The first three shapes are distinct: a *cube* (which is one unit), a *long* (which is ten), and a *flat* (which is a hundred). What comes next? Stack ten flats (which is a thousand) to make a cube. It is the same shape as the unit cube, only 1000 times larger. What comes next? (See Figure 11.19) Ten 1000 *cubes* make another *long*. What comes next? Ten big *longs* make a big *flat*. The first three shapes have now been repeated! Ten big flats will make an even bigger cube, and the triplet of shapes begins again.

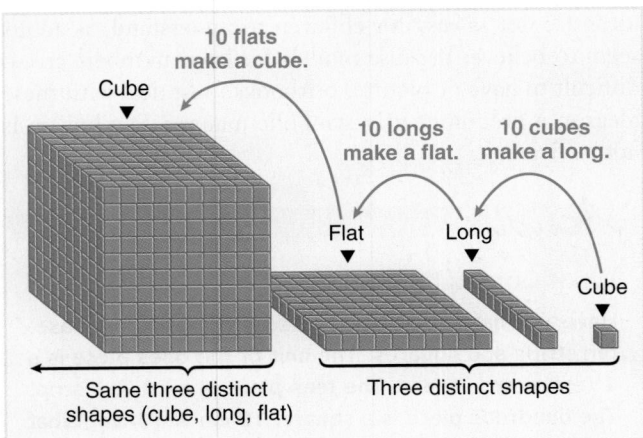

Figure 11.19 With every three places, the shapes repeat. Each cube represents a 1, each long represents a 10, and each flat represents a 100.

Each cube has a name. The first one is a *unit*, the next is a *thousand*, the next a *million*, then a *billion*, and so on. Each long is 10 cubes: 10 units, 10 thousands, 10 millions. Similarly, each flat is 100 cubes.

To read a large number, group the digits in threes starting from the right. Note that the last grouping on the left might have fewer than three digits. Beginning at the left, the groupings are then read, stopping at the end of each triple to name the unit (or cube shape) for that triple (see Figure 11.20). Leading zeros in each triple are ignored. If students can learn to read numbers like 059 (fifty-nine) or 009 (nine), they should be able to read any number. To write a number, use the same scheme. If first mastered orally, the system is quite easy. Remind students not to use the word "and" when reading a whole number. For example, 106 should be read as "one hundred six," not "one hundred *and* six." The word "and" will be needed to signify a decimal point. Please make sure you read numbers accurately.

It is important for children to realize that the system does have a logical structure, is not totally arbitrary, and can be understood.

Conceptualizing Large Numbers

The ideas just discussed are only partially helpful in thinking about the actual quantities involved in very large numbers. For example, in extending the square, strip, square, strip sequence, some appreciation for the quantities of 1000 or of 100 000 is included. But it is hard for anyone to translate quantities of small squares into quantities of other items, distances, or time.

Pause and Reflect

How do you think about 1000 or 100 000? Do you have any real concept of a million?

Creating References for Special Big Numbers In these activities, numbers like 1000, 10 000 (see Blackline Master 29), or even 1 million are translated literally or imaginatively into something that is easy or fun to think about. Interesting quantities become lasting reference points or benchmarks for large numbers, thereby adding meaning to numbers encountered in real life.

Activity 11.35

Collecting 10 000

Collections. As a class or grade-level project, collect some type of object with the goal of reaching some specific quantity—for example, 1000 or 10 000 buttons, walnuts, old pencils, jar lids, or pieces of junk mail. If you begin aiming for 100 000 or 1 million, be sure to think it through. One teacher spent nearly ten years with her classes before amassing a million bottle caps. It takes a small dump truck to hold that many!

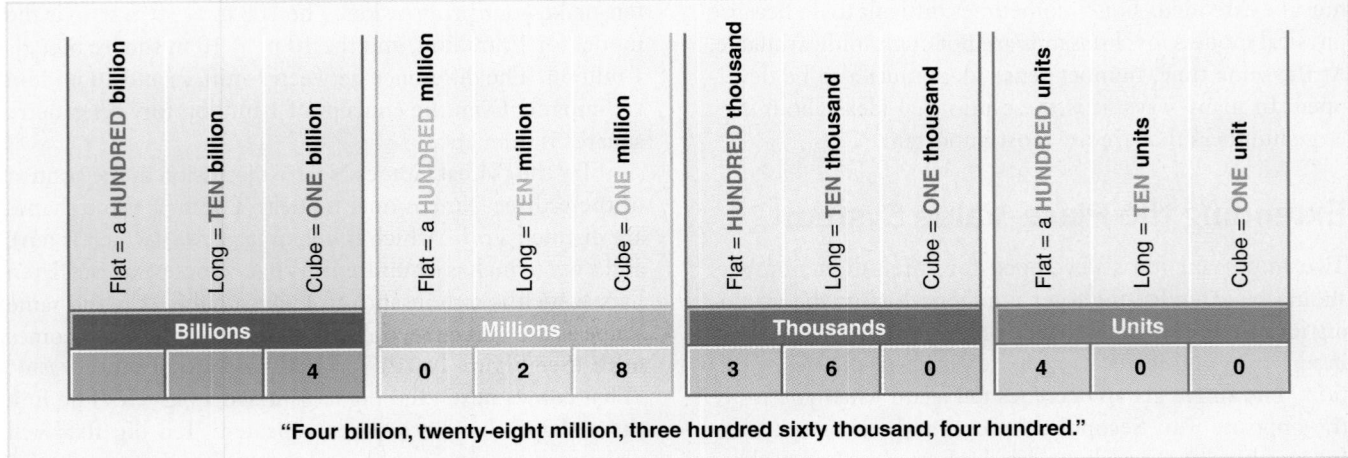

Billions			Millions			Thousands			Units		
Flat = a HUNDRED billion	Long = TEN billion	Cube = ONE billion	Flat = a HUNDRED million	Long = TEN million	Cube = ONE million	Flat = HUNDRED thousand	Long = TEN thousand	Cube = ONE thousand	Flat = a HUNDRED units	Long = TEN units	Cube = ONE unit
		4	0	2	8	3	6	0	4	0	0

"Four billion, twenty-eight million, three hundred sixty thousand, four hundred."

Figure 11.20 The triples system for naming large numbers.

Activity 11.36

Showing 10 000

Illustrations. Sometimes it is easier to create large amounts. For example, start a project where students draw 100 or 200 or even 500 dots on a sheet of paper. Each week, different students contribute a specified number. Another idea is to cut up newspaper into pieces the same size as dollar bills to see what a large quantity would look like. Paper chain links can be constructed over time and hung down the hallways with special numbers marked. Let the school be aware of the ultimate goal.

Activity 11.37

How Long? How Far?

Real and imagined distances. How long is a million baby steps? Other ideas that address length: toothpicks, dollar bills, or chocolate bars end to end; children holding hands in a line; blocks or bricks stacked up; children lying down head to toe. Real measures can also be used: centimetres, metres.

Activity 11.38

A Long Time

Time. How long is 1000 seconds? How long is a million seconds? A billion? How long would it take to count to 10 000 or 1 million? (To make the counts all the same, use your calculator to do the counting. Just press the ⊨.) How long would it take to do some task such as buttoning a button 1000 times?

Estimating Large Quantities Activities 11.35 through 11.38 focus on a specific number. The reverse idea is to select a large quantity and find some way to measure, count, or estimate how many.

Activity 11.39

Really Large Quantities

Ask how many
- **Chocolate bars would cover the floor of your room**
- **Steps an ant would take to walk around the school building**
- **Grains of rice would fill a cup or 25 litre jug**
- **Quarters could be stacked in one stack from floor to ceiling**
- **Pennies can be laid side by side down the entire hallway**
- **Pieces of notebook paper would cover the gym floor**
- **Seconds you have lived**

Big-number projects need not take up large amounts of class time. They can be explored over several weeks as take-home projects or group projects or, perhaps best of all, be translated into great school-wide estimation contests.

 The *Standards* document also recognizes the need for relating large numbers to the real world. "A third-grade class might explore the size of 1000 by skip-counting to 1000, building a model of 1000 using ten hundred charts, gathering 1000 items such as paper clips and developing efficient ways to count them, or using strips that are 10 or 100 centimetres long to show the length of 1000 centimetres" (p. 149).

Problem-Based Lesson:
Ancient Egyptian Number System

Grade Level: Grade 5

This problem-based lesson differentiates instruction to meet the varied abilities and needs of students. It offers students an opportunity to apply concepts of place value, addressed in this chapter, in a different context. The lesson demonstrates how a range of learner needs, from those students who require an extra challenge to those with other unique needs, can be accommodated. It does so by offering students a chance to work with concrete materials such as Dienes blocks, which are helpful when working with place value.

Mathematical Goals

- To reinforce students' knowledge of place value
- To demonstrate students' understanding that number systems are determined by the way in which the numbers are grouped
- To strengthen students' understanding of grouping, which underlies the concept of place value

To the Teacher—Background Information

Hieroglyphics is a form of writing in which pictures represent the letters of the Egyptian alphabet. Pictures were also used to represent numbers. The Ancient Egyptians used hieroglyphics for writing on monuments and for wall paintings.

The Ancient Egyptian number system is based on ten and its multiples. Numbers start at one and go up to a million. Unlike our number system, it does not make use of place value. Each multiple is represented by a different symbol. For example, the number ten, as shown below, is represented by a heel bone/arch. The number 1000 is represented by a lotus stalk, and so on. Although one is represented with a single stroke, there is no symbol for zero.

Number symbols have been found on pottery, limestone plaques, and on the fragile fibres of the papyrus. In the Egyptian number system, the number one is represented by a single stroke.

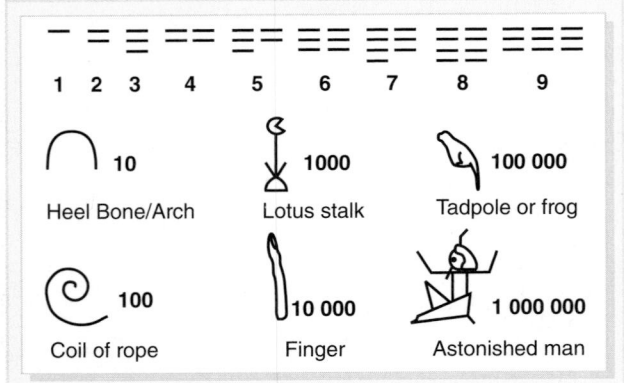

The convention for reading and writing numbers is quite simple. Like our number system, the number of greater value is always written in front of the number of lesser value. When there is more than one row of numbers, start at the top as you read the number. For example, the number 276 is made up of 15 symbols, two "hundred" symbols, seven "ten" symbols, and six "unit" symbols.

Thinking About the Students

- Students have been working on place value.
- They have worked with large numbers.
- Students have used a variety of graphic organizers to help them express and explain their thinking.
- It is recommended that this lesson be implemented after students have had a variety of opportunities to work with place value.
- Students work in pairs or groups of three, predetermined by the teacher. Doing so will ensure that children of different abilities have the opportunity to work together.

Materials and Preparation

- Poster-size picture of the Ancient Egyptian number system displayed in a prominent location in the classroom during the investigation. The poster could be pasted on the board or displayed on an easel.
- Cutouts of the different symbols for the Egyptian numbers to be used by students to show different numbers they will be required to make. Ensure that there are a sufficient number of the cutouts.
- Pictures and other information depicting Ancient Egyptian culture and life. One possible site for accessing material is http://shop.discoveringegypt.com/discoveringancientegypt.html.
- Venn diagram template. Venn diagrams are useful visual tools for showing the different ways in which concepts are related/connected. A Venn diagram can be used in the follow up during the whole-class discussion to illustrate the similarities and differences between the Ancient Egyptian number system and our number system that students have discovered.
- Dienes blocks (base-10 material)—The Dienes blocks could be made available to students who might still be experiencing difficulty understanding how to regroup numbers (that is, to carry out the trading process when adding/subtracting two-digit numbers).

Introduction

- Begin the lesson with a short discussion on Ancient Egypt. Use pictures or other media to illustrate the Egyptian culture and way of life.

- Show the class the Ancient Egyptian number system, displayed on the board.
- Initiate a discussion with the class about this system of counting. The following are some possible questions to include in the discussion.

  What are your thoughts about this system?
  Would it be easy to use on a day-to-day basis?
  Why or why not? What would the advantages be?
  What might the challenges be?
  How does it compare with our number system (that is, the way we count numbers)?

- Present the class with a two-digit number, for example, 25, and together figure out how it might be represented with symbols of the Ancient Egyptian number system.
- Try out some other examples. Include a three-digit number.
- You might wish to have a short discussion about the effectiveness of using this system to write numbers before assigning the task.

The Task

- Students will work in their assigned pairs or triads using the cutouts of the Ancient Egyptian numbers to represent a variety of two-, three-, four-, and five-digit numbers chosen by the teacher. The cutouts can be pasted onto a sheet of paper or the students could draw the symbols as they show the numbers. Note: Use two-digit numbers where the digit in the ones place is at least 5 or greater.
- Students will complete task cards once they have shown the two-, three-, four-, and five-digit numbers assigned by the teacher. Samples of task cards are shown.
- Task Card 1 requires the students to figure out how to show addition using the Ancient Egyptian number system. Note: It is important that some of the numbers that students choose to add have digits in the ones, tens, and hundreds place that are five or greater.
- Task Card 2 requires students to figure out how to show subtraction using the Ancient Egyptian number system. Note: It is important that some of the numbers that students choose to subtract have digits in the tens and hundreds or thousands place that are five or greater.

Task Card 1

Your task: You are an Egyptian scribe/priest and need to complete the following additions. Of course, you will use Ancient Egyptian number symbols.
1. Choose any of the two-digit numbers you represented.
2. Add the numbers. Be sure to show the sum with the number symbols.
3. Explain in writing how you arrived at your answer.
4. Include in your explanation the trading process you used.
5. Repeat using a two-digit and a three-digit number. You might wish to use 2 three-digit numbers.

Task Card 2

Your task: You are an Egyptian scribe/priest and need to complete the following subtractions. Of course, you will use Ancient Egyptian number symbols.
1. Choose any of the two-digit numbers you represented.
2. Subtract the numbers. Be sure to show the difference with the number symbols.
3. Explain in writing how you arrived at your answer.
4. Include in your explanation the trading process you used.
5. Repeat using a three-digit and a two-digit number. You might wish to use 2 three-digit numbers.

Establish Expectations

- Explain to the students that today they will be Ancient Egyptian scribes and priests keeping track of important information such as figuring out the number of animals people owned and/or traded or the amount of landowners' produce. They will use the numbers with which they have worked to complete the task cards and carry out their calculations.
- They can either paste the symbols onto paper or draw them as they work through each of the tasks.
- They are to explain in writing how they arrived at their answers, including an explanation of the trading process they used.
- They also need to think about how our number system compares with the Ancient Egyptian system.

Development

- Students work in their designated pairs/triads as Egyptian scribes/priests using the cutouts (or drawing the symbols, if they wish) to represent the numbers assigned by the teacher.
- They then complete the task cards requiring them to carry out the additions and subtractions. Students write about the task.
- The teacher walks around observing and talking with the students.
- Observing and talking with students should provide insight into students' understanding of the Egyptian number system and how it works. For example, are they aware that: (1) it is based on ten, (2) that it does not work on place value, and (3) that the process of trading does not work as our number system does?
- Students who might be experiencing difficulty with the additions and subtractions using the Ancient Egyptian symbols could work with the Dienes blocks (base-10 material) to carry out the operations.

Follow-up

- Students meet as a whole class to talk about the things they found out about how the Ancient Egyptian number system works; for example, whether the position/place-

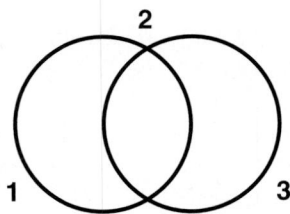

1: Ancient Egyptian Number System
2: Commonalities between the Ancient Egyptian
   Number System and Our Number System
3: Our Number System

ment of the symbols affects the value of the numbers, how addition and subtraction work, how the trading process works, whether it is necessary to read the numbers from left to right, whether it is easy or cumbersome to work with and why.

- As part of this discussion they could compare the Ancient Egyptian system with our number system, focusing on the previously suggested ideas. Some questions you might ask are:

    1. *Can you tell us what some of the similarities are between the two number systems? What are the differences?*
    2. *Does the placement of the symbols in the Ancient Egyptian number system affect the value of the number?*
    3. *Does the trading process work the same or differently for the two systems?*
    4. *Which system is easier to work with? Why?*
    5. *Will you still get the same answer if you change the order of the symbols? Why?*

- A Venn diagram labelled as shown above could be used as an organizer for looking at the differences and similarities between the two systems.
    (1) Ancient Egyptian Number System
    (3) Our Number System
    (2) Commonalities between (1) and (3)

- The Venn diagram will help students "see" the commonalities and the differences that exist between the two systems. The commonalities would appear in the sec-

tion where the two circles overlap. Have students write in their journals regarding what they learned about the Ancient Egyptian number system and how it compares with our number system.

Next Steps_____

Assessment Notes

- Does the student understand how numbers are grouped in the Ancient Egyptian number system?
- Does the student understand that the Ancient Egyptian number system does not rely on place value?
- Does the student understand that both systems group numbers by tens?
- Is the student aware of the similarities between the Ancient Egyptian number system and our number system?
- Does the student understand trading when adding and subtracting two-, three-, and four-digit numbers?
- Students who need an extra challenge can research how multiplication and division work in the Ancient Egyptian number system. For an explanation of how these operations work, go to the following Web site: www.forestpath.net/egypt/maths/egnosys.htm.
- Students who would benefit from additional work with grouping and trading of numbers could do further work with the Ancient Egyptian symbols or they might work with a different base-10 material other than the Dienes blocks.
- If times permits, students might also investigate other number systems to figure out how they work and compare them with the Ancient Egyptian system and our number system. *Note:* The following two Web sites are some of the many that can be used for researching new number systems: http://mathforum.org/alejandre/numerals.html or www.saxakali.com/hystorymam2.htm.
- Students might also design their own number system.
- Students who require an additional challenge or enrichment could investigate other number systems, such as the Mayan or Babylonian systems. They could also work with other bases, such as binary numbers.

Reflections on Chapter 11

Writing to Learn

1. Explain how a child who has not yet developed base-ten concepts understands quantities as large as, say, 85. Contrast this with a child who understands these same quantities in terms of base-ten groupings.
2. What is meant by *equivalent representations?*
3. Explain the three ways one can count a set of objects and how these methods of counting can be used to coordinate concepts and oral and written names for numbers.
4. Describe the three types of physical models for base-ten concepts. What is significant about the difference among these models?
5. How do children learn to write two- and three-digit numbers in a way that is connected to the base-ten meanings of ones and tens or ones, tens, and hundreds?
6. Describe some patterns that can be found on the hundreds chart. In addition to looking for patterns, describe another activity with the hundreds chart.

7. What are landmark numbers? Describe the relationships that you want children to develop with respect to landmark numbers. Describe an activity that addresses this relationship.
8. How can place-value concepts and computation skills be developed at the same time? Describe two activities that can be used to address these dual agendas.
9. Explain why determining the value of a collection of coins is essentially a mental addition skill. Why is this more difficult than doing the same addition with numbers?

For Discussion and Exploration

1. Based on the suggestions in this chapter, design a diagnostic interview for a child at a particular grade level and conduct the interview. It is a good idea to take a friend to act as an observer or to use a tape recorder or video recorder to keep track of how the interview went. Analyze the child's understanding of the comments and suggest your next instructional steps.

Resources for Chapter 11

Literature Connections

Books that emphasize groups of things, even simple counting books, are a good beginning to the notion of ten things in a single group. Many books have wonderful explorations of large quantities and how they can be combined and separated.

Moira's Birthday   *Munsch, 1987*

As Moira plans her birthday party, she invites more and more children until she has invited all the children in kindergarten and grades 1, 2, 3, 4, 5, and 6. Then she needs to order food. She orders 200 cakes and 200 pizzas. Bedlam ensues brilliantly as the food and the children all arrive at the party. A grade 2 teacher, Diane Oppedal (1995), used this story as a background for the question "How can you show 200 things in different ways?" As children work on this or similar projects, they can be encouraged to use some form of grouping to keep track of their collections.

The same book can also be used to motivate a variety of computation situations that could be used prior to structured computation instruction. "How many children are in three classrooms?" "What if everyone at the party got two pieces of pizza?" "If Moira gave 37 of her 94 presents back to the children who helped her clean up, how many presents did she have left?"

My Arctic   *Kusugak, 1996*

In this counting book, we meet and count some of the animals Kusugak and his Inuit family watch in the Arctic. Numbers 1 through 10, 20, 100, and 1 000 000 are presented in English and Inuktitut along with simple descriptions of the animals. The illustrations add a wealth of information about the habitat, the inhabitants, and the colours of the region.

100th Day Worries   *Cuyler, 2000*

100 Days of School   *Harris, 1999*

Both of these books focus on the 100th day of school, which is one way to recognize the landmark number of 100. Through a variety of ways to think about 100, either through collections of 100 items or 10 salty peanuts every minute for 10 minutes, student will be able to use these stories to think about the relative size of 100 or ways to make 100 using a variety of combinations.

How Much Is a Million?   *Schwartz, 1985*

If You Made a Million   *Schwartz, 1989*

On Beyond a Million: An Amazing Math Journey   *Schwartz, 1999*

Magic of a Million Activity Book— Grades 2–5   *Schwartz and Whitin, 1998*

David Schwartz has generated a series of entertaining and conceptually sound children's books about the powers of ten or what makes a million—from visual images of students standing on one another's shoulders in a formation that reaches the moon to various monetary collections. In addition, the activity book by Schwartz and Whitin provides a series of powerful activities to help students interpret large numbers.

The King's Commissioners   *Friedman, 1994*

The king has so many commissioners. He can't keep track of how many there are. In a hilarious tale, the commissioners are marched into the throne room to be counted. One person tries to count them by twos and another by fives. The princess convinces the king that there are many other excellent ways to count. The story is a natural background for place-value concepts, including grouping and different counting methods, large numbers, and informal early computation challenges.

A Million Fish ... More or Less　*McKissack, 1992*

This story, which takes place in lower Louisiana, is a tall tale of a boy who catches three fish ... and then a million more. The story is full of exaggerations such as a turkey that weighs 500 pounds (225 kg) and a jump-rope contest (using a snake) where the story's hero wins with 5553 jumps. "Could these things really be? How long would it take to jump 5553 times? Could Hugh put a million fish in his wagon? How do you write half of a million?"

Recommendations for Further Reading

Articles

Ellett, K. (2005). Making a million meaningful. *Mathematics Teaching in the Middle School, 10* (8), 416–423.
　This amazing collection of ideas for helping students think about large numbers, especially 1 million, is found in the MTMS focus issue on Mathematics and Literature. Ellett gives examples of student projects and ways for students to conceptualize a million, shows student work, and connects many of these ideas to literature. This is easily one of the best resources for working with large-number concepts.

Kari, A. R., & Anderson, C. B. (2003). Opportunities to develop place value through student dialogue. *Teaching Children Mathematics, 10* (2), 78–82.
　These two teachers describe a combined grade 1–2 classroom illustrating in vivid detail how children's understanding of two-digit numbers can at first be quite mistaken, then be developed conceptually with the aid of discussion. Much of the discussion revolves around one child's belief that any 1 in a number stands for ten. This student is convinced that 11 + 11 + 11 is 60. Reading this article emphasizes the wide rage of student ideas and the value of classroom discourse.

Books

Burns, M. (1994). *Math by all means: Place value, grade 2.* Sausalito, CA: Math Solutions Publications.
　Burns provides 25 days of very detailed lessons in place value. There are ample examples of children's written work and descriptions of interactions that took place in the classroom.

Richardson, K. (2003). *Assessing math concepts: Grouping tens.* Bellingham WA: Mathematical Perspectives Inc.
　This is one of a nine-part series on using diagnostic interviews and other assessment tools to understand children's grasp of a concept—in this case, grouping by tens. Tips are shared about conducting careful observations and suggestions for instruction. Blackline Masters are included to support assessment.

Online Resources

Base-Ten Blocks
http://nlvm.usu.edu/en/nav/topic_t_1.hhtml
　There are several variations of the basic base-ten blocks applet here. Blocks appear on a place-value chart and can be grouped or broken apart. The addition and subtraction versions pose problems and allow blocks in two colours to model two separate numbers.

Comparison Estimator and Estimator
www.shodor.org/interactive/activities/estim2/index.html
　Two sets of small objects are shown and the task is to decide which set has more. The actual counts are then given. The same applet also allows for comparisons of length and areas.

Hundreds Board and Calculator
http://standards.nctm.org/document/eexamples/chap4/4.5/index.htm
　A calculator is used to create skip-counting patterns on a hundreds chart. You can start the pattern at any number and skip by any number. The chart extends to 1000. A second pattern will appear with red dots on top of the first pattern.

Lots of Dots and a Million Dots on One Page
www.vendian.org/envelope/
　These explorations of big numbers are only a hint at the array of ideas found on this Web site. A lot is beyond elementary school, but anyone interested in big numbers and measures will certainly be intrigued. See a dot for every second of the day!

Place Value K–3
http://mathcentral.uregina.ca/RR/database/RR.09.96/mcleod1.html
　The games and activities on this site, maintained by the University of Regina, focus on place value for the primary level. The games and activities are designed to match with curriculum objectives.

Quandaries and Queries
http://mathcentral.uregina.ca/QandQ/topics/billion
　The focus here is on a billion. There are 23 items to investigate. This is also part of the University of Regina Math Central site.

The MegaPenny Project
www.kokogiak.com/megapenny/default.asp
　This site takes a fascinating look at large numbers in terms of stacks of pennies. Stacks from 1 penny to a trillion pennies are shown with visual referents, value, mass, height if stacked, and more. The site is great for large-number concepts.

The Place Value Game (Jefferson Lab)
http://education.jlab.org/placevalue/index.html
　The goal is to make the largest possible number from the digits the computer gives you. Digits are presented one at a time. The player must place the digit in the number without knowing what the next digits will be. It's fun and also good for understanding the ordering of numbers.

---

myeducationlab *will help you improve your understanding of the concepts taught in this textbook and in your course. This online tool includes videos of real classroom experiences, sample lesson plans, simulations, case studies, and links to important educational and teaching Web sites that will help you make the transition from student to teacher. As you study in your course and with this textbook, please follow along in* **MyEducationLab***. Use it! Explore it! And improve your knowledge and your grade!*

Chapter 12
Developing Strategies for Whole-Number Computation

Much of the Canadian public sees computational skill as the hallmark of what it means to know mathematics at the elementary school level. Although this is far from the truth, the issue of computational skills with whole numbers is, in fact, a very important part of the elementary curriculum, especially in grades 2 to 6.

Rather than a single method for performing subtraction, or any operation, the most appropriate method can and should be adaptable so it can change as the numbers and the context change. In the spirit of the *Standards*, the issue is no longer a matter of "knows how to subtract three-digit numbers"; rather, it is the development over time of an assortment of flexible skills, including the ability to compute mentally, that will best serve students in the real world.

It is quite possible that you do not have these skills, but you can acquire them. Work at them as you learn about them. Equip yourself with a flexible array of computational strategies.

Big Ideas

1. Flexible methods of computation involve taking apart and combining numbers in a wide variety of ways. Most of the partitioning of numbers is based on place value or "compatible" numbers—number pairs that easily work together, such as 25 and 75.

2. "Invented" strategies are flexible methods of computing that vary with the numbers and the situation. Successful use of these strategies requires that they are understood by the person using them—hence, the term *invented.*

3. Flexible methods for computation require a good understanding of the operations and their properties, especially the commutative property and the distributive property for multiplication. The way in which the operations are related—

addition to subtraction, addition to multiplication, and multiplication to division—is also an important ingredient.

4. The traditional algorithms are clever strategies for computing, that have been developed over time. Each is based on an operation being performed on one place value at a time with transitions to an adjacent position (trades or regrouping). Traditional algorithms tend to make us think in terms of digits rather than the composite number that the digits make up. These algorithms work for all numbers but are often far from the most efficient or useful methods of computing.

Mathematics Content Connections

Flexible computation is built on the ideas found in the preceding three chapters. Flexible methods for computing, especially mental methods, allow one to reason much more effectively in every area of mathematics involving numbers.

- **Operation Meanings and Fact Mastery** (Chapters 9 and 10): Children can and should explore contextual problems involving multi-digit numbers as they develop their understanding of the operations. Without basic facts, students will be severely disadvantaged in any computational endeavour. Furthermore, many strategies and number concepts used to master the basic facts can be extended to computation.

- **Place Value** (Chapter 11): Place value is not only a basis for computation; students can also develop an understanding of place value as a result of finding their own methods of computing.

- **Computational Estimation** (Chapter 13): Computational estimation involves substituting "nice" numbers in a computation so that the new computation can be done mentally or at least with minimal effort.

Toward Computational Fluency

With today's technology, the need for doing tedious computations by hand has essentially disappeared. A study done in 1957, well before the commonplace use of calculators, found that adults used pencil-and-paper computation methods for only 25 percent of their calculations (Wandt & Brown in McIntosh, 1998). We now know that there are numerous methods of computing that can be handled either mentally or with pencil-and-paper support. In most everyday instances, these alternative strategies for computing are easier and faster, can often be done mentally, and contribute to our overall number sense. The traditional algorithms (procedures for computing) do not have these benefits. Consider the following problem.

Talia's photo album can hold 114 photographs. So far she has 89 photos in the album. How many more photos can she put in before the album is full?

 *Pause and Reflect*

Try solving the photo album problem using some method other than the one you were taught in school. If you want to begin with the 9 and the 4, try a different approach. Can you do it mentally? Can you do it in more than one way? Work on this before reading further.

Here are just four of many methods that have been used by students in the primary grades to solve the computation in the photo album problem:

89 + 11 is 100. 11 + 14 is 25.

90 + 10 is 100 and 14 more is 24 plus 1 (for 89, not 90) is 25.

Take away 14, then take away 11 more. That is 25 in all.

89, 99, 109 (that's 20). 110, 111, 112, 113, 114 (keeping track on fingers) is 25.

Strategies such as these can be done mentally, are generally faster than the traditional algorithms, and make sense to the person using them. Every day, students and adults resort to traditional, often error-prone strategies when other, more meaningful methods would be faster and less susceptible to error. Flexibility with a variety of computational strategies is an important tool for successful daily living. It is time to broaden our perspective of what it means to compute.

Figure 12.1 lists three general types of computing. The initial, inefficient direct modelling methods can, with guidance, develop into an assortment of invented strategies that are flexible and useful. As noted in the diagram, many of

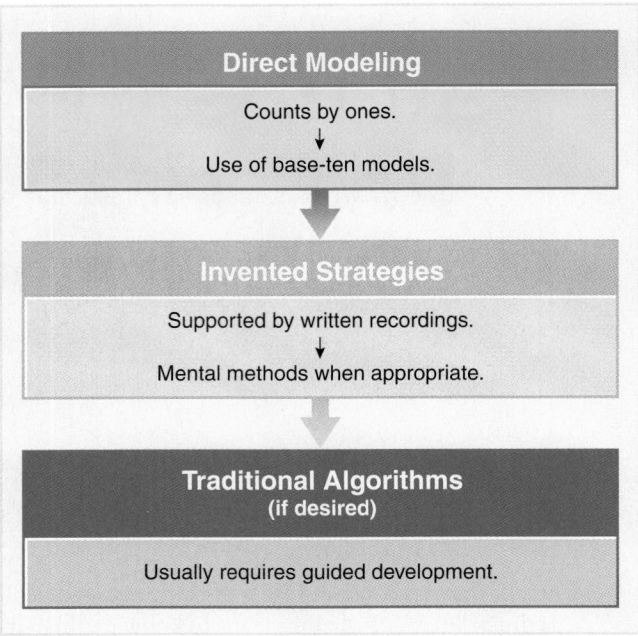

Figure 12.1 Three types of computational strategies.

these methods can be handled mentally, although no special methods are designed specifically for mental computation. The traditional pencil-and-paper algorithms remain in the mainstream curricula. However, the emphasis placed on them should, at the very least, be debated.

NCTM Standards "Equally essential [with basic facts] is computational fluency—having and using efficient and accurate methods for computing. Fluency might be manifested in using a combination of mental strategies and jottings on paper or using an algorithm with paper and pencil, particularly when the numbers are large, to produce accurate results quickly. Regardless of the particular methods used, students should be able to explain their method, understand that many methods exist, and see the usefulness of methods that are efficient, accurate, and general" (p. 32).

Direct Modelling

The developmental step that usually precedes invented strategies is called *direct modelling*: the use of manipulatives or drawings along with counting to represent directly the meaning of an operation or story problem. Figure 12.2 provides an example using base-ten materials, but often students use simple counters and count by ones.

Students who consistently count by ones most likely have not developed base-ten grouping concepts. That does not mean that they should not continue to solve problems involving two-digit numbers. As you work with these children, suggest (don't enforce) that they group counters by

Figure 12.2 A possible direct modelling of 36 × 7 using base-ten models.

tens as they count. Some students will use the ten-stick as a counting device to keep track of counts of ten, even though they are counting each segment of the stick by ones.

Students using direct modelling will soon transfer their ideas to methods that do not rely on materials or counting. The direct-modelling phase provides a necessary background of ideas. These developmental strategies are also important because they provide students who are not ready for more efficient methods with a way to explore the same problems as classmates who have progressed beyond this stage. It is important not to push students prematurely to abandon approaches where manipulatives are used.

Student-Invented Strategies

Carpenter, Franke, Jacobs, Fennema, and Empson (1998) refer to any strategy other than traditional algorithms, including any that do not involve the use of physical materials or counting by ones, as *invented strategies*. We will also use this term, even though *personal and flexible strategies* might be equally appropriate. At times, invented strategies become mental methods after the ideas have been explored, used, and understood. For example, 75 + 19 is not difficult to do mentally (75 + 20 is 95, less 1 is 94). For 847 + 256, some students may write down intermediate steps to aid recall, as they work through the problem. (Try that one yourself.) In the classroom, some written support is often encouraged as strategies develop. Written records of thinking are more easily shared and help students focus on the ideas. The distinction between written, partially written, and mental is not important, especially in the development period.

Over the past two decades, a number of research projects have focused attention on how children handle computational situations when they have not been taught a specific algorithm or strategy.[1] "There is mounting evidence that children both in and out of school can construct methods for adding and subtracting multi-digit numbers without explicit instruction" (Carpenter et al., 1998, p. 4). Data supporting students' construction of useful methods for multiplication and division have also been gathered (Baek, 2006; Fosnot & Dolk, 2001; Kamii & Dominick, 1997; Schifter, Bastable, & Russell, 1999b).

Not all students invent their own strategies. Strategies invented by class members are shared, explored, and tried out by others. However, no student should be permitted to use any strategy without understanding it (Campbell, Rowan, & Suarez, 1998).

Contrasts with Traditional Algorithms   There are significant differences between student-invented strategies and the traditional algorithms.

1. *Invented strategies are number oriented rather than digit oriented.* For example, an invented strategy for 68 × 7 begins 7 × 60 is 420 and 56 more is 476. The first product is 7 times *sixty*, not the digit 6, as would be the case in the traditional algorithm. Using the traditional algorithm for 45 + 32, children never think of 40 and 30 but rather 4 + 3. Kamii, long a crusader against standard algorithms, claims that they "unteach" place value (Kamii & Dominick, 1998).

2. *Invented strategies are left-handed rather than right-handed.* Invented strategies begin with the largest parts of numbers, those represented by the leftmost digits. For 26 × 47, invented strategies will begin with 20 × 40 is 800, providing some sense of the size of the eventual answer in just one step. The traditional algorithm begins with 7 × 6 is 42. By beginning on the right with a digit orientation, traditional methods may hide the result until the end. Long division is an exception.

3. *Invented strategies are flexible rather than rigid ("being the one right way").* Invented strategies tend to change with the numbers involved in order to make the computation easier. Try each of these mentally: 465 + 230 and 526 + 98. Did you use the same method? The traditional algorithm suggests using the same tool on all problems. The traditional algorithm for 7000 − 25 typically leads to student errors, yet a mental strategy is relatively simple.

Benefits of Student-Invented Strategies   The development of invented strategies delivers more than computational facility. Both the development of these strategies and their regular use have positive benefits that are difficult to ignore, as the following indicate.

- *Students make fewer errors.* Research indicates that students using methods they understand make many fewer errors than when strategies are learned without understanding (Gravemeijer & van Galen, 2003; Kamii & Dominick, 1997). After decades of good intentions with the standard algorithms, many students do not understand the concepts that support them. Not only do these students make errors, but also the errors are often systematic and difficult to remediate. Errors with invented strategies are less frequent and almost never systematic.

- *Less re-teaching is required.* Teachers often complain that students' early efforts with alternative strategies are slow and time consuming. The time-consuming struggle in these early stages, however, results in ideas that are meaningful and well integrated in a web of ideas that are robust and long lasting. An increase in development time is made up for with a significant decrease in the need for re-teaching and remediation.
- *Students develop number sense.* "More than just a means to produce answers, computation is increasingly seen as a window on the deep structure of the number system" (NRC, 2001, p. 182). Students' development and use of number-oriented, flexible algorithms offers them a rich understanding of the number system. In contrast, students frequently use traditional algorithms without being able to explain why they work (Carroll & Porter, 1997). Such rules without reasons have few benefits.
- *Invented strategies are the basis for mental computation and estimation.* When invented strategies are the norm for computation, there is no need to teach other methods or even to talk about mental computation as if it were a separate skill. Often, students who have been taught to record their thinking with invented strategies or to write down intermediate steps will ask if this writing is really required, since they find they can do the procedures more efficiently mentally. Computational estimation does involve a separate set of skills; the development of flexible, number-oriented strategies plays a significant role in most of these skills (NRC, 2001).
- *Flexible methods are often faster than the traditional algorithms.* Consider the product 64 × 8. A simple invented strategy might involve 60 × 8 = 480 and 8 × 4 = 32. The sum of 480 and 32 is 500 + 12 more—512. This is easily done mentally, or even with some recording, in much less time than the multiple steps of the traditional algorithm. Those who become adept with invented strategies will consistently perform addition and subtraction computations more quickly than those using a traditional algorithm.
- *Algorithm invention is itself a significantly important process of "doing mathematics."* Students who invent a strategy for computing, or who adopt a strategy from a classmate, are involved intimately in the process of making sense of mathematics. At the same time, they develop a confidence in their ability to do so. This

development of procedures is a process that traditionally has been hidden from elementary school students. By engaging in this aspect of mathematics, a significantly different and valuable view of "doing mathematics" is opened to young children.

In addition to these benefits, there is a growing body of evidence that students' computational skills do not suffer in contrast to those taught the traditional strategies. Data collected from school systems using standards-based programs reveal that those students consistently outperform their conventional program counterparts on measures of understanding and problem solving. In the area of multi-digit computation, most studies find that the standards-based students are either on a par with students in conventional programs or outperform them (Fuson, 2003). Students in the Netherlands are not taught to use traditional algorithms and they perform at least as well as U.S. students (Gravemeijer & van Galen, 2003; Torrence, 2003).

Mental Computation A mental computation strategy is simply any invented strategy that is done mentally. What may be a mental strategy for one student may require written support for another. Initially, students should not be asked to do computations mentally, as this may threaten students who have not yet developed a reasonable invented strategy or who are still at the direct-modelling stage. At the same time, you may be quite amazed at the ability of students (and at your own ability) to do computations mentally.

Try your own hand with this example:

$$342 + 153 + 481$$

❚❚ ———————— *Pause and Reflect*

For the addition task just shown, try this method: Begin by adding the hundreds, saying the totals as you go—*3 hundred, 4 hundred, 8 hundred.* Then add on the tens and finally the ones. Do it now.

When the computations are a bit more complicated, the challenge is more interesting and generally there are more alternatives. For 7 × 28, the *Standards* lists three paths to a solution, but there are at least two more (NCTM, 2000, p. 152). How many ways can you find?

As your students become more adept, they can and should be challenged from time to time to do appropriate computations mentally. Do not expect the same skills of all students.

Traditional Algorithms

Almost every commercial mathematics program teaches traditional algorithms. More than a century of tradition plus pressures from students' families are at least partly responsible for our unwillingness to abandon these approaches. Other arguments generally revolve around efficiency and the need for methods that will work with all numbers. For addition and subtraction, one can easily counter that well-understood and practised invented strategies are more than adequate. However, it is certainly true that a computation such as 486×372 is difficult with invented strategies. But shouldn't computations like that be done with technology?

No matter the growing interest in invented strategies, and no matter how compelling the arguments against the traditional algorithms may be, few classroom teachers will be able to independently abandon the traditional approaches.

Delay! Delay! Delay!   Students are not likely to invent the traditional algorithms. You will need to introduce and explain each algorithm to them and help them understand how and why they work. No matter how carefully you introduce these algorithms into your classroom as simply another alternative, students are likely to sense that "this is the real way" or the "right way" to compute. "This is the way the teacher taught us to do it and it is the way my mom and dad compute." Once having begun with traditional methods, it is extremely difficult to suggest to students that they learn other methods. Notice how difficult it is for you to begin computations by working from the left rather than the right and to think in terms of whole numbers rather than digits. These habits, once established, are difficult to change.

Can the traditional algorithms be taught meaningfully? Absolutely! Meaningful approaches for teaching each algorithm are discussed later in this chapter. If you plan to teach the traditional algorithms, you are well advised first to spend significant time with invented strategies—months, not weeks. Do not feel that you must rush to the traditional methods. Delay! Spend your effort on invented methods. The understanding children gain from working with invented strategies will make it much easier for you to teach the traditional algorithms.

Traditional Algorithms Will Happen   Children often pick up the traditional algorithms from older siblings, last year's teacher, and well-meaning parents ("My dad showed me an easy way"). Students who already know a traditional method often resist the invention of more flexible strategies. What do you do then?

First and foremost, apply the same rule to traditional algorithms as to all strategies: *If you use it, you must understand why it works and be able to explain it.* In an atmosphere that says, "Let's figure out why this works," students can profit from making sense of these algorithms just like any other. But the responsibility should be theirs, not yours.

Accept a traditional algorithm (once it is understood) as one more strategy to put in the class "tool box" of methods. But reinforce the idea that, like the other strategies, it may be more useful in some instances than in others. Pose problems where a mental strategy is much more useful, such as $504 - 498$ or 75×4. Discuss which method seemed best. Point out that for a problem such as $4568 + 12\,813$, the traditional algorithm has some advantages. But in the real world, most people do those computations on a calculator.

Cultural Differences in Algorithms   Although we may assume that mathematics is easier than other subjects for students who are English learners, the reality is that there are many differences in notation, conventions, and algorithms. Knowing more about the diverse algorithms students bring to the classroom and their ways of recording symbols for "doing mathematics" will assist you in supporting students and responding to families. Particularly, knowing that what we may call a "traditional algorithm" is not the tradition in other countries is helpful. Awareness of alternative algorithms will assist you with exploring the procedures and ways to record answers that your students know from prior experiences in schools in other countries or from approaches taught to them by their families.

The heavy emphasis on mental mathematics in other countries is another component in understanding differences in cultures regarding algorithms. This often surprises teachers, especially when a student writes down just an answer with no apparent partial products, intermediate calculations, or notations. Awkwardly, this is sometimes interpreted by teachers, unaware of this emphasis, as a student possibly copying another's work (Perkins & Flores, 2002). In fact, students are taught to pride themselves on their ability to do this work mentally.

Learning more about what your students, particularly those from other cultural backgrounds, are doing and thinking as they explore operations with numbers is often an opportunity to expand your own repertoire.

Development of Student-Invented Strategies

Students do not spontaneously invent wonderful computational methods while the teacher sits back and watches. Among different experimental programs students tended to develop or gravitate toward different strategies, suggesting that teachers and the programs do have an effect on what methods students develop (Fuson et al., 1997). The following section discusses general pedagogical methods for helping children develop invented strategies for all four operations that are appropriate at all grades.

Creating an Environment for Inventing Strategies

Invented strategies are developed out of a strong understanding of numbers. The standard development of place value often leaves students ill prepared for the challenges of inventing computational strategies. For example, some grade 3–4 students have difficulty naming a number that is ten more or ten less than a given two-digit number, without resorting to counting. Therefore, students need a classroom environment where they can act like mathematicians and feel comfortable doing so.

Students need to know, as they attempt to investigate new ideas, that their classroom is a safe place for expressing those naïve or rudimentary thoughts. Some of the very characteristics described earlier in this book regarding the development of a problem-solving environment, need to be reiterated here to establish the climate for testing conjectures and trying new approaches. Here are some factors to keep in mind:

- Expect and encourage student-to-student interactions, discussions, and conjectures
- Celebrate when students clarify previous knowledge and attempt to construct new ideas
- Encourage curiosity and an open mind to trying new things
- Talk about both right and wrong ideas in a non-evaluative or non-threatening way
- Move unsophisticated ideas to more sophisticated thinking through coaxing, coaching, and guided questioning
- Use contexts and story problems to capture student interest
- Consider carefully whether you should step in or step back when students are formulating new ideas (when in doubt—step back)

The three-part lesson format discussed in Chapter 3 is a good structure for an invented-strategy lesson. Whether the task is one or two story problems or even a mere computation, the method of solution should always be discussed. Sometimes you can meet individual needs by providing variations with different numbers to different groups.

Models to Support Invented Strategies

Activities that focus on the patterns in our number system and that explore addition and subtraction using the hundreds chart, the little ten-frame cards, or base-ten blocks can both prepare students for invented strategies and improve their number sense. A collection of appropriate activities focusing on number relationships and informal addition and subtraction strategies can be found in Chapter 11. (See pp. 208 to 211.)

Note also that many of the strategies for addition and subtraction are extensions of basic fact strategies, especially those that use 10 as a bridge. (See Chapter 10.) For example, as students are exploring methods for mastering facts with an 8 or 9, extend these ideas to 38 or 69. As another example, double 4 can be extended to double 40.

The notion of "splitting" a number into parts is a useful strategy for all operations. Both the word *split* and the use of a diagram, as shown, have been found to help students develop strategies (Sáenz-Ludlow, 2004). Try using arrows or lines to indicate how two computations are joined together as shown in Figure 12.3(a).

The *empty number line* (see Figure 12.3(b)) is a technique developed in the Netherlands that is increasingly being used as a model for representing children's mathematical thinking (Fosnot & Dolk, 2001; Gravemeijer & van Galen, 2003; Ineson, 2007; Varol & Farran, 2007). Initially, the empty number line is a good way for you to model a student's thinking for the class. Soon it will become a tool for students to use in creating their own thinking (Klein, Beishuizen, & Treffers, 1998). These researchers found that the empty number line is much more flexible than the usual number line because it can be used with any numbers and students are not confused with hash marks and the spaces between them. The hops on the line can be recorded as the students share or explain each step of their solution.

Student-Invented Strategies for Addition and Subtraction

Research has demonstrated that children will invent a lot of different strategies for addition and subtraction. Your goal might be that each of your children has at least one or two methods that are reasonably efficient, mathematically correct, and useful with a lot of different numbers. Expect different children to settle on different strategies.

There is no clear-cut progression to follow that will dictate what problems you should pose to your students. You must learn to listen to the kind of reasoning they are using and the strategies that are being suggested. The numbers involved in a computation and also the type of story problem used will tend to influence how students approach a problem. Even so, you will discover many variations in the thought processes of children in any classroom. The following sections suggest a variety of strategies that children often use. These are presented not as a curriculum but rather to give you some idea of the range of possibilities.

Adding and Subtracting Single Digits

When adding or subtracting small amounts, or finding the difference between two numbers that are reasonably close, many students will use counting to solve the problems. One

(a) How much is 86 and 47?

S: I know that 80 and 20 more is 100.

T: Where do the 80 and the 20 come from?

S: I split the 47 into 20 and 20 and 7 and the 86 into 80 and 6.

T: (illustrates the splitting with lines)
So then you added one of the 20s to 80?

S: Yes, 80 and 20 is 100. Then I added the other 20 and got 120.

T: (writes the equations on the board)

S: Then I added the 6 and the 7 and got 13.

T: (writes this equation)

S: Then I added the 120 to the 13 and got 133.

T: Indicates with joining lines.

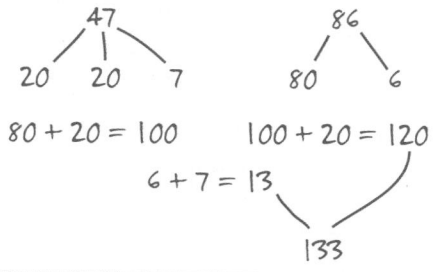

(b) How much is 4 times 68?

S: I used 70s because they were easier than 68s. First I did 70 and 70 is 140.

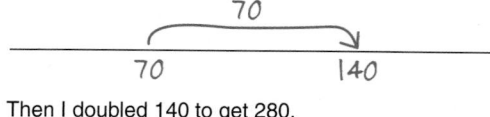

Then I doubled 140 to get 280.

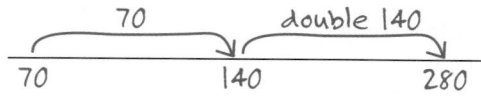

T: Why did you double 140?

S: Because that would make four 70s, and I already had two 70s. Then I had to take off four sets of 2 because I used 70 instead of only 68. That got me to 272.

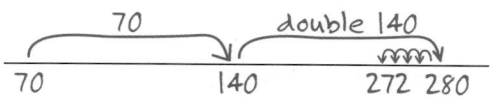

Figure 12.3 Two methods of recording students' thought processes on the board so that the class can see the strategy.

goal should be to extend students' knowledge of basic facts and the ten-structure of the number system so that counting is not required. When the difference crosses a ten (e.g.,

58 + 6), using the interval up to or down to the multiple of ten is extremely helpful.

Anthony was on page 47 of his book. Then he read 8 more pages. On what page did he end up?

How far is it from 68 to 75?

Yesenia had 52 cents. She bought a small toy for 8 cents. How much does she have left?

 Each of these problems crosses a multiple of ten and involves a change or a difference of less than ten. Listen for children who are counting on or counting back without paying attention to the ten. For these children, you might suggest using either the hundreds chart or the little ten-frames as shown in Figure 12.4. Also, find out how they solve fact combinations such as 8 + 6 or 13 – 5. The use of ten for these facts is essentially the same as for the higher-decade problems. Related activities are "Calculator Challenge Counting" (11.26), "How Much Between?" (11.29), or "Little Ten-Frame Sums" (11.30), which are all found in Chapter 11. ◆

As you move students from single-digit to two-digit numbers, adding and subtracting tens and hundreds is an important transition. Sums and differences involving multiples of 10 or 100 are easily computed mentally. Write a problem such as the following on the board:

$$300 + 500 + 20$$

Challenge children to solve it mentally. Ask students to share how they did it. Look for use of place-value words: "3 *hundred* and 5 *hundred* is 8 *hundred*, and 20 is 820."

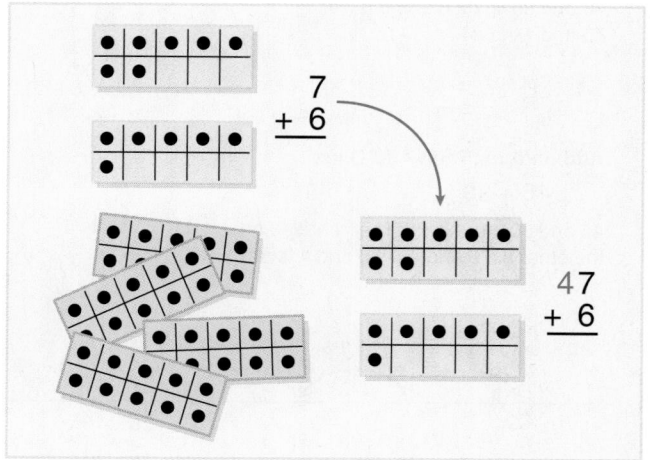

Figure 12.4 Little ten-frame cards can help children extend the make-ten idea to larger numbers (see Blackline Masters 15–16).

Use base-ten models to help children begin to think in terms of tens and hundreds. Early examples should not include any trades. The exercise 420 + 300 involves no trades, whereas 70 + 80 may be more difficult.

Adding Two-Digit Numbers

Problems involving the sum of 2 two-digit numbers will trigger a wide variety of strategies. Some of these will involve starting with one number or the other then working from that point, either by adding on to get to the next ten or by adding tens from one number to the other. That is, for 46 + 35, a student may add on 4 to the 46 to get to 50, and then add 31 more. Another may first add 30 to 46 then add 4 to get to 80 and 1 more. In either case there is a clear advantage to utilizing ten. At the same time, there are many children who will count past these multiples without stopping at ten.

Other approaches involve splitting the numbers into parts and adding the easier parts separately. Usually the split will involve tens and ones, or students may use other parts of numbers such as 50 or 25 as a "nice" part of a number with which to work.

Students will often use a counting-by-tens-and-ones technique. That is, instead of "46 + 30 is 76," they may count "46 → 56, 66, 76." These counts can be written down as they are said to help students keep track.

Figure 12.5 illustrates four different invented strategies for addition of 2 two-digit numbers. The ways that the solutions are recorded are suggestions. Note the use of the empty number line. The following story problem is a suggestion.

Summit Heights School's junior and senior choir went on a field trip to the National Arts Centre in Ottawa. There were 46 students in the junior choir and 39 in the senior choir. How many students went on the trip?

The *move to make ten* and *compensation* strategies are useful when one of the numbers ends in 8 or 9. To promote that strategy, present problems with addends like 39 or 58. Note that it is only necessary to adjust one of the two numbers.

‖ ———————————— *Pause and Reflect*

Try adding 367 + 155 in as many different ways as you can. How many of your ways are like those in Figure 12.5?

Subtracting by Counting Up

This is an amazingly powerful way to subtract. Students working on the *think-addition* strategy for their basic facts can also be solving problems with larger numbers. The concept is the same. For 38 – 19, the idea is to think, "How much do I add to 19 to get to 38?" Notice that this strategy is probably not efficient for 42 – 6. Using *join with change*

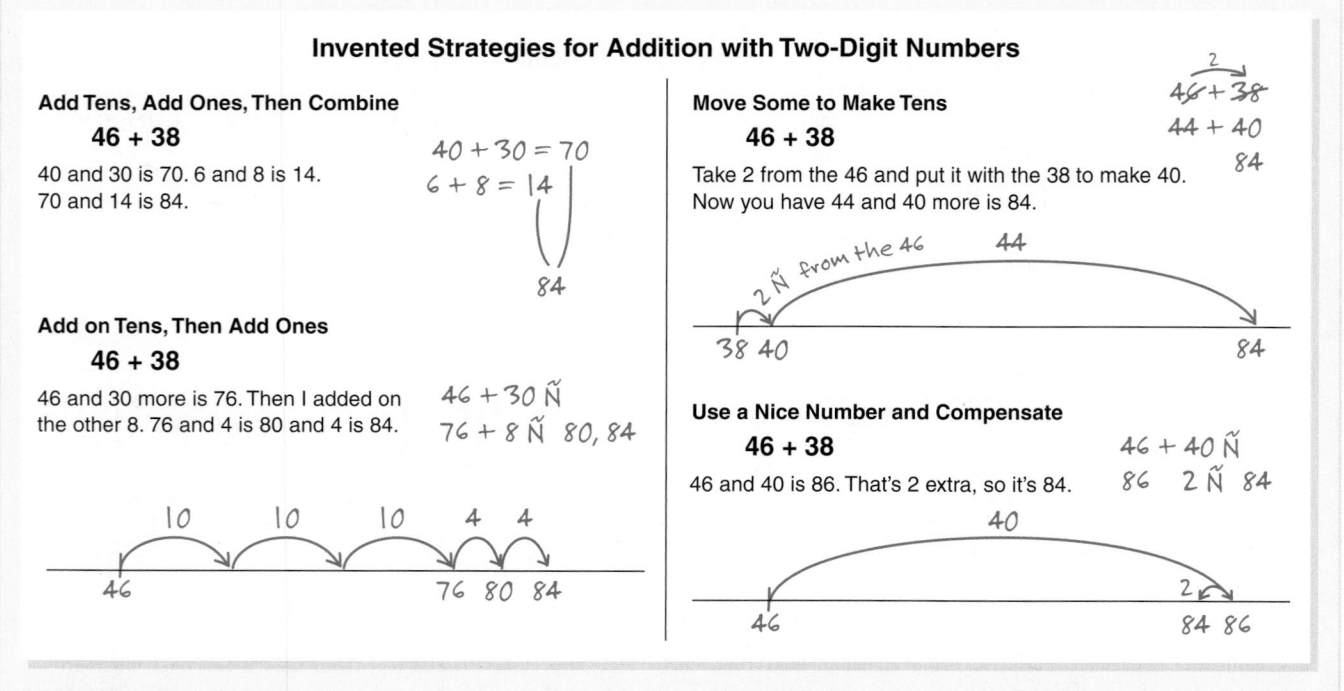

Figure 12.5 Four different invented strategies for adding 2 two-digit numbers.

unknown problems or *missing-part* problems will encourage the counting-up strategy. Here is an example of each.

Kira had 46 baseball cards. She went to a card show and bought some more cards for her collection. Now she has 73 cards. How many cards did Kira buy at the card show?

Somerset counted all her markers and found she had 73 in total. Some were dried up and not working. 46 were working. How many were not working?

The numbers in these problems are used in the strategies illustrated in Figure 12.6. Simply asking for the difference between two numbers may also prompt this strategy.

Take-Away Subtraction

Using take-away is considerably more difficult to do mentally. However, take-away strategies are common, probably because conventional textbooks emphasize take-away as the meaning of subtraction. When the number being subtracted is a multiple of ten or close to a multiple of ten, take-away can be an easy method to use. Four dif-

ferent strategies for the following problem are shown in Figure 12.7.

There were 73 children on the playground. After the bell rang, 46 grade 2 students came in. How many children were still outside?

The two methods that begin by taking tens from tens are reflective of what most students do with base-ten pieces. The other two methods leave one of the numbers intact and subtract from it. Try 83 – 29 in your head by first taking away 30 then adding 1 back. This is a good mental method when subtracting a number that is close to a multiple of ten.

Sometimes we need to be reminded of what comes naturally to children. Campbell (1997) tested over 2000 students in Baltimore who had not been taught the traditional algorithm for subtraction. Not one student began with the ones place!

Ⅱ ——————————— *Pause and Reflect*

Try computing 82 – 57. Use both take-away and counting-up methods. Can you use all the strategies in Figures 12.6 and 12.7 without looking?

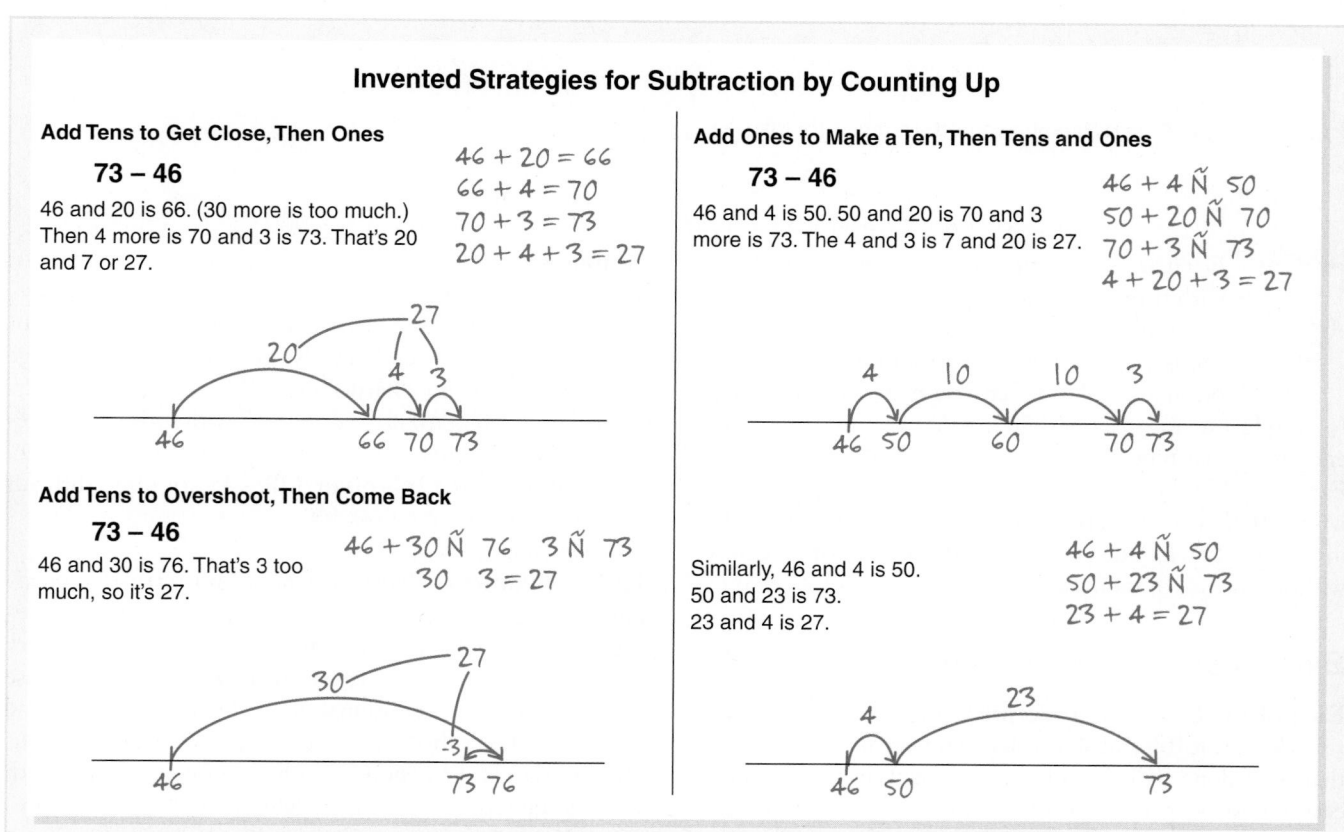

Invented Strategies for Subtraction by Counting Up

Add Tens to Get Close, Then Ones

73 – 46

46 and 20 is 66. (30 more is too much.) Then 4 more is 70 and 3 is 73. That's 20 and 7 or 27.

$$46 + 20 = 66$$
$$66 + 4 = 70$$
$$70 + 3 = 73$$
$$20 + 4 + 3 = 27$$

Add Tens to Overshoot, Then Come Back

73 – 46

46 and 30 is 76. That's 3 too much, so it's 27.

$$46 + 30 = 76 \quad 3 = 73$$
$$30 \quad 3 = 27$$

Add Ones to Make a Ten, Then Tens and Ones

73 – 46

46 and 4 is 50. 50 and 20 is 70 and 3 more is 73. The 4 and 3 is 7 and 20 is 27.

$$46 + 4 = 50$$
$$50 + 20 = 70$$
$$70 + 3 = 73$$
$$4 + 20 + 3 = 27$$

Similarly, 46 and 4 is 50. 50 and 23 is 73. 23 and 4 is 27.

$$46 + 4 = 50$$
$$50 + 23 = 73$$
$$23 + 4 = 27$$

Figure 12.6 Three different invented strategies for subtraction, by counting up.

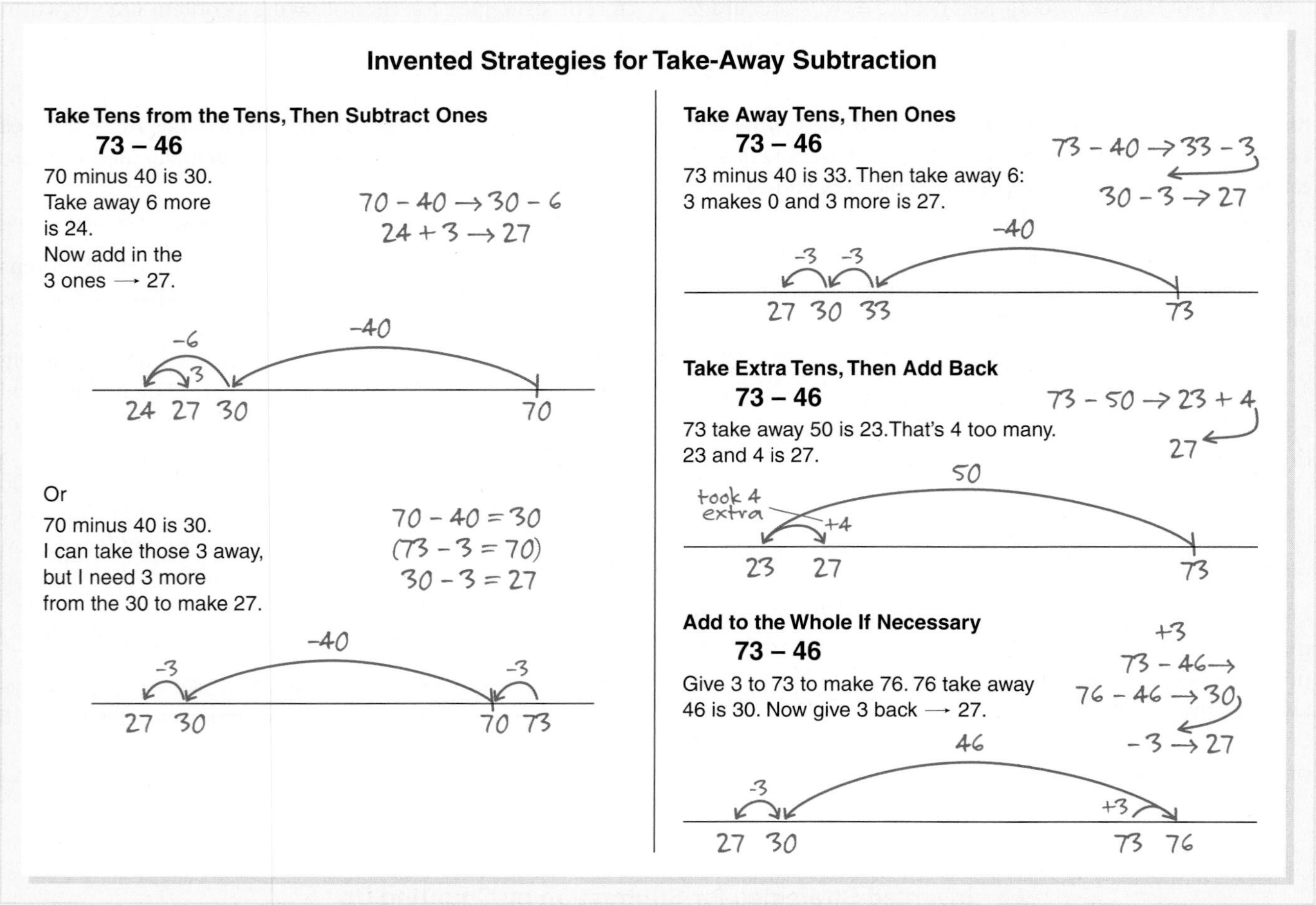

Invented Strategies for Take-Away Subtraction

Take Tens from the Tens, Then Subtract Ones

73 – 46

70 minus 40 is 30.
Take away 6 more
is 24.
Now add in the
3 ones → 27.

$70 - 40 \rightarrow 30 - 6$
$24 + 3 \rightarrow 27$

Or

70 minus 40 is 30.
I can take those 3 away,
but I need 3 more
from the 30 to make 27.

$70 - 40 = 30$
$(73 - 3 = 70)$
$30 - 3 = 27$

Take Away Tens, Then Ones

73 – 46

73 minus 40 is 33. Then take away 6:
3 makes 0 and 3 more is 27.

$73 - 40 \rightarrow 33 - 3$
$30 - 3 \rightarrow 27$

Take Extra Tens, Then Add Back

73 – 46

73 take away 50 is 23. That's 4 too many.
23 and 4 is 27.

$73 - 50 \rightarrow 23 + 4$
27

Add to the Whole If Necessary

73 – 46

Give 3 to 73 to make 76. 76 take away
46 is 30. Now give 3 back → 27.

$73 - 46 \rightarrow$
$76 - 46 \rightarrow 30$
$-3 \rightarrow 27$

Figure 12.7 Four different invented strategies for take-away subtraction.

For many subtraction problems, especially those with three digits, adding on is significantly easier than a take-away approach. Try not to force the issue for students who do not use an add-on method. However, you may want to return to simple missing-part activities that are more likely to encourage that type of thinking. Try Activity 11.31, "How Far to My Number?", or simply show a number such as 28 with little ten-frame cards and ask, "What goes with 28 to make 53?" You can do the same with three-digit numbers without the use of models. ◆

Extensions and Challenges

Each of the examples in the preceding sections involved sums less than 100 and all involved *bridging* or *crossing a ten*; that is, if done with a traditional algorithm, they require carrying or borrowing. Bridging, the size of the numbers, and the potential for doing problems mentally are all issues to consider.

Bridging   For most of the strategies, it is easier to add or subtract when bridging is not required. Try each strategy with 34 + 52 or 68 – 24 to see how it works. Easier problems instil confidence. They also permit you to challenge your students with a "harder one." There is also the issue of bridging 100 or 1000. Try 58 + 67 with different strategies. Bridging across 100 is also an issue for subtraction. Problems such as 128 – 50 or 128 – 45 are more difficult than ones that do not cross 100.

Larger Numbers   Most provincial and territorial curricula will expect grade 3 students to add and subtract three-digit numbers. Your curriculum may even require work with four-digit numbers. Try seeing how *you* would do these without using the traditional algorithms: 487 + 235 and 623 – 247. For subtraction, a counting-up strategy is usually the easiest. Occasionally, other strategies appear with larger numbers. For example, "chunking off" multiples of 50 or 25 is often a useful method. For 462 + 257, pull out 450 and 250 to make 700. That leaves 12 and 7 more = 719.

 The Number and Operation standard in both the pre-K–2 and 3–5 chapters will clearly demonstrate that the *Standards* are supportive of the approaches described in this chapter. For example, "When students compute with strategies they invent or choose because they are meaningful, their learning tends to be robust—they are able to remember and apply their knowledge. Children with specific learning disabilities can actively invent and transfer strategies if given well-designed tasks that are developmentally appropriate" (p. 86).

Traditional Algorithms for Addition and Subtraction

If you must teach traditional computational strategies for addition and subtraction, remember that several months' serious effort with invented strategies is still well worth it. Because your students will not be inventing the traditional algorithms, your instruction will be more directed. Students may infer from this approach that this "new" way of explaining computational strategies is preferred and many will abandon their invented strategies. Try to avoid this complete switch to the traditional algorithms by presenting them as another alternative and maintain practice with invented methods.

The traditional algorithms require an understanding of *regrouping*, exchanging 10 in one place value position for 1 in the position to the left—or the reverse, exchanging 1 for 10 in the position to the right. The corresponding terms *carrying* and *borrowing* are obsolete and conceptually misleading. The word *regroup* may have little meaning for young children. A preferable term is *trade*. Ten ones are *traded* for a ten. A hundred is *traded* for 10 tens. Notice that none of the invented strategies involves regrouping.

It is a serious error to work for mastery of problems that do not involve regrouping before tackling regrouping. Keeping these problems separate has been the documented source of many error patterns. Teaching problems that do not require grouping first causes bad habits that children must later unlearn.

Addition Algorithm

Explain to the students that they are going to learn a method of adding that most adults learned when they were in school. It is not the only way or even the best way; it is just a method you want them to learn.

Begin with Models Only In the beginning, avoid any written work except, possibly, for the recording of an answer. Provide children with place-value mats and base-ten models. The mat with two ten-frames in the ones place (Blackline Master 17) is suggested.

Have students make one number at the top of the mat and a second beneath it as shown in the top portion of Figure 12.8. If children are still developing base-ten concepts, a groupable model such as counters in cups is most helpful.

Explain this one rule: *You begin in the ones column.* "This is a way people came up with a long time ago, and it worked for them." Let students solve the problem on their own. Provide plenty of time, then have students explain what they did and why. Let students use overhead models or magnetic pieces to help with their explanations.

One or two problems in a lesson with much discussion is more productive than a lot of problems based on rules children don't understand.

Develop the Written Record Reproduce pages with simple place-value charts similar to those shown in Figure 12.9. The charts will help young children with the recording of numbers in columns. The general idea is to have children record on these pages each step of the procedure they do with the base-ten models *as it is done*. The first few

Figure 12.8 Working from right to left in addition.

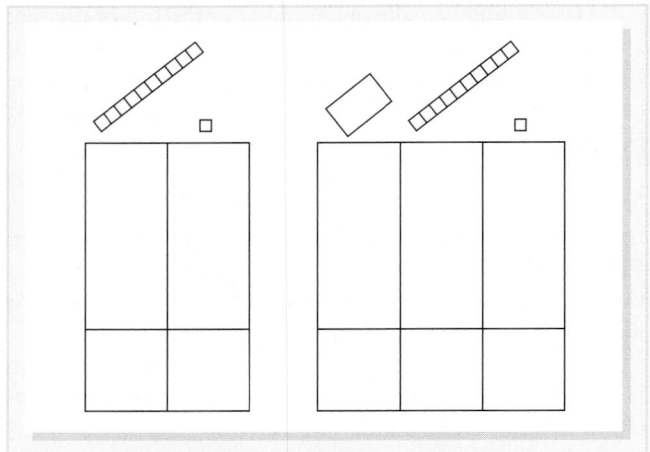

Figure 12.9 Blank recording charts are helpful (see Blackline Master 19.)

times you do this, guide each step carefully, as illustrated in Figure 12.10. A similar approach would be used for three-digit problems.

A suggestion is to have children work in pairs. One child is responsible for the models and the other for recording the steps. Children reverse roles with each problem.

Figure 12.11 shows a variation of the traditional recording scheme that is quite reasonable, at least for up to three digits. It avoids the little "carried ones" and focuses attention on the value of the digits. If students were permitted to start adding on the left as they are inclined to do, this recording procedure would be the same as that shown for the invented strategy "Add tens, add ones, then combine" (Figure 12.5).

Subtraction Algorithm

The general approach to developing the subtraction algorithm is the same as for addition. When the procedure is completely understood with models, a do-and-write approach connects it with a written form.

Begin with Models Only Start by having children model the top number in a subtraction problem on the top half of

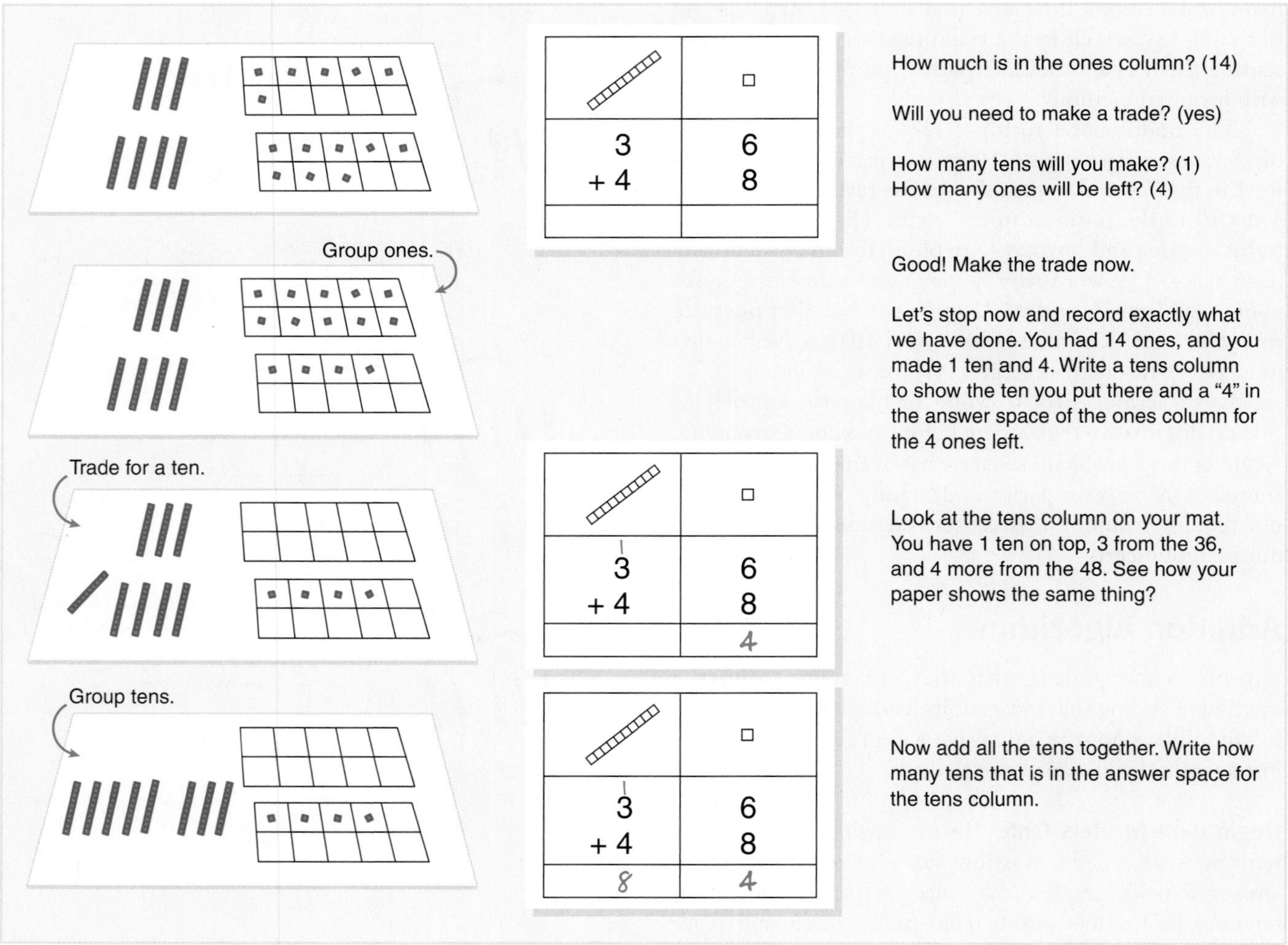

How much is in the ones column? (14)

Will you need to make a trade? (yes)

How many tens will you make? (1)
How many ones will be left? (4)

Good! Make the trade now.

Let's stop now and record exactly what we have done. You had 14 ones, and you made 1 ten and 4. Write a tens column to show the ten you put there and a "4" in the answer space of the ones column for the 4 ones left.

Look at the tens column on your mat. You have 1 ten on top, 3 from the 36, and 4 more from the 48. See how your paper shows the same thing?

Now add all the tens together. Write how many tens that is in the answer space for the tens column.

Figure 12.10 Help students record on paper each step as they do it on their place-value mats (see Blackline Masters 17 and 19).

Figure 12.11 An alternative recording scheme for addition. Notice that this can be used for working from left to right as well as from right to left.

their place-value mats. For the amount to be subtracted, have children write each digit on a small piece of paper and place these pieces near the bottom of their mats in the respective columns, as in Figure 12.12. To avoid inadvertent errors, suggest making all trades first. That way, the full amount on the paper slip can be taken off at once. Also explain to children that they are to begin working with the ones column first, as they did with addition.

Anticipate Difficulties with Zeros   Exercises in which zeros are involved anywhere in the problem tend to cause special difficulties. Give extra attention to these cases while still using models.

The very common error of "regrouping across zero" is best addressed at the modelling stage. For example, in 403 – 138, children must make a double trade, exchanging a hundreds piece for 10 tens and then one of the tens for 10 ones.

Develop the Written Record   The process of recording each step, as it is done, is the same as was suggested for addition. The same recording sheets (Figure 12.9) are also recommended.

When children can explain the use of symbols involved in the recording process, it is a signal to move them on to a completely symbolic level. Again, be attentive to problems with zeros.

If students are permitted to follow their natural instincts and begin with the big pieces (working from the left instead of the right), recording schemes similar to that shown in Figure 12.13 are possible. The trades are made from the pieces remaining *after* the subtraction in the column to the left has been done. However, a "regroup across zero" difficulty will still occur in problems like this: 462 – 168. Try it.

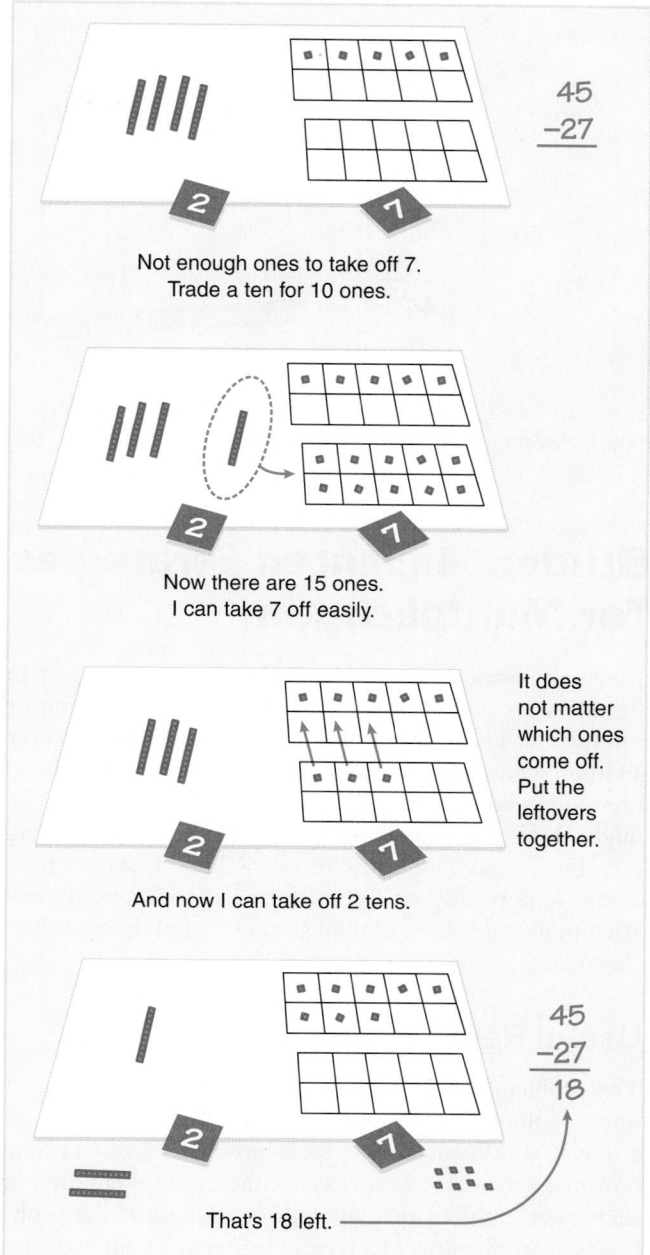

Not enough ones to take off 7.
Trade a ten for 10 ones.

Now there are 15 ones.
I can take 7 off easily.

It does not matter which ones come off. Put the leftovers together.

And now I can take off 2 tens.

That's 18 left.

Figure 12.12 Two-place subtraction with models.

II ———————— *Pause and Reflect*

Contrast the difficulties of teaching children to regroup in subtraction, especially regrouping across zero, with the ease of adding on. For example, try solving this: 428 and how much makes 703? Now think about teaching students to regroup across zero to solve 703 – 428.

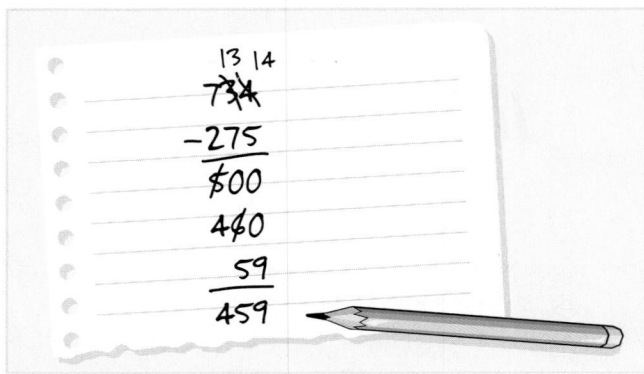

Figure 12.13 A left-hand recording scheme for subtraction. Other methods can also be devised.

Student-Invented Strategies for Multiplication

For multiplication, the ability to break numbers apart in flexible ways is even more important than in addition or subtraction. The distributive property of multiplication over addition is another concept that is important in multiplication computation. For example, to multiply 43 × 5, one might think about breaking 43 into 40 and 3, multiplying each by 5, then adding the results. Children should have ample opportunities to develop these concepts as they attempt to make sense of their own ideas and those of their classmates.

Useful Representations

The problem 6 × 34 may be represented in a number of ways, as illustrated in Figure 12.14. Often the choice of a model is influenced by a story problem. To determine how many apples 6 classes need if there are 34 children in each class, children may model 6 sets of 34. If the problem is about the area of a rectangle that is 34 cm by 6 cm, then some form of an array is likely. But each representation is appropriate for thinking about 34 × 6 regardless of the context, and students should get to a point where they select ways to think about multiplication that are meaningful to them.

How children represent a product interacts with their methods for determining answers. The groups of 34 might suggest repeated additions—perhaps taking the sets two at a time. Double 34 is 68 and there are three of those, so 68 + 68 + 68. From there various methods are possible.

The six sets of base-ten pieces might suggest breaking the numbers into tens and ones: 6 times 3 tens or 6 × 30 and 6 × 4. Some children might use the tens individually: 6 tens make 60. So that's 60 and 60 and 60 (180). Then, add on the 24 to make 204.

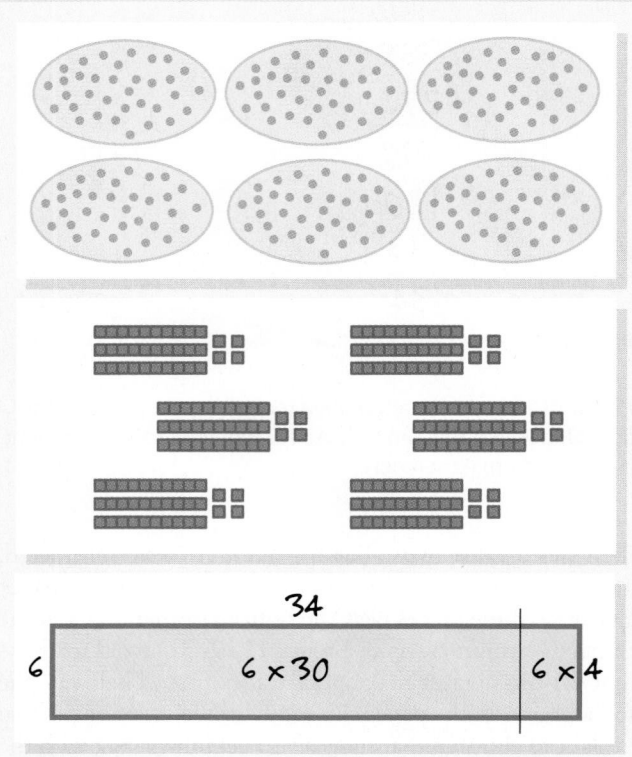

Figure 12.14 Different ways to model 6 × 34 may support different computational strategies.

All these ideas should be part of students' repertoire of models for multi-digit multiplication. Introduce different representations (one at a time) as ways to explore multiplication until you are comfortable that the class has a collection of useful ideas. At the same time, do not force students who reason very well without drawings to use models when they are not needed.

Multiplication by a Single-Digit Multiplier

As with addition and subtraction, it is helpful to place multiplication tasks in contextual story problems. Let students model the problems in ways that make sense to them. Do not be concerned about reversing factors (6 sets of 34 or 34 sets of 6). Nor should you be timid about the numbers you use. The problem 3 × 24 may be easier than 7 × 65, but the latter provides challenge. The types of strategies that students use for multiplication are much more varied than for addition and subtraction. However, the following three categories can be identified from the current research.

Complete-Number Strategies Children who are not yet comfortable breaking numbers into parts will approach the numbers in the sets as single groups. Most likely these early strategies will be based on repeated addition. Often students will list long columns of numbers and add them

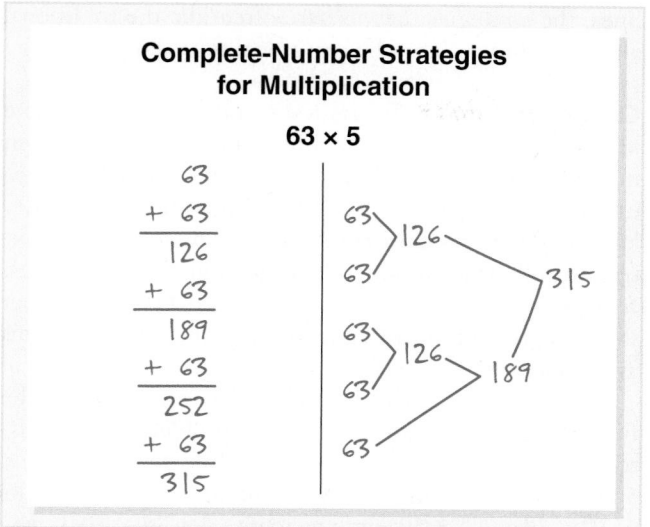

Figure 12.15 Children who use a complete-number strategy do not break numbers apart into decades or tens and ones.

up. In an attempt to shorten this tedious process, students soon realize that if they add two numbers, the next two will have the same sum and so on down the line. This doubling process can become the principal approach for many students, although it is certainly not very efficient (Ambrose, Baek, & Carpenter, 2003; Fosnot & Dolk, 2001). Figure 12.15 illustrates two methods they may use. These children will benefit from listening to children who use base-ten models. They may also need more work with base-ten grouping activities where they take numbers apart in different ways.

Partitioning Strategies Children break numbers up in a variety of ways that reflect an understanding of base-ten

concepts, at least four of which are illustrated in Figure 12.16. The "By Decades" approach is the same as the standard algorithm except that students always begin with the large values. It extends easily to three digits and is very powerful as a mental math strategy. Another valuable strategy for mental methods is found in the "Other Partitions" example. It is easy to compute mentally with multiples of 25 and 50 and then add or subtract a small adjustment. All partition strategies rely on the distributive property.

Compensation Strategies Children and adults look for ways to manipulate numbers so that the calculations are easy. In Figure 12.17, the problem 27 × 4 is changed to an easier one, and then an adjustment or compensation is made. In the second example, one factor is cut in half and the other doubled. This is often used when a 5 or a 50 is involved. Because these strategies are so dependent on the numbers involved, they can't be used for all computations. However, they are powerful strategies, especially for mental math and estimation.

Transitioning from Single-Digit to Two-Digit Factors As you move students from single-digit to two-digit factors, there is value in exposing students early to products involving multiples of 10 and 100.

> The Scout troop wanted to make up 400 first aid kits for a fundraising project. If each kit has 12 gauze bandages, how many gauze bandages will the Scouts need?

Children will use 4 × 12 = 48 to figure out that 400 × 12 is 4800. There will be discussion around how to say and write "forty-eight hundred." Be aware of students who simply tack on zeros without understanding why. Try problems

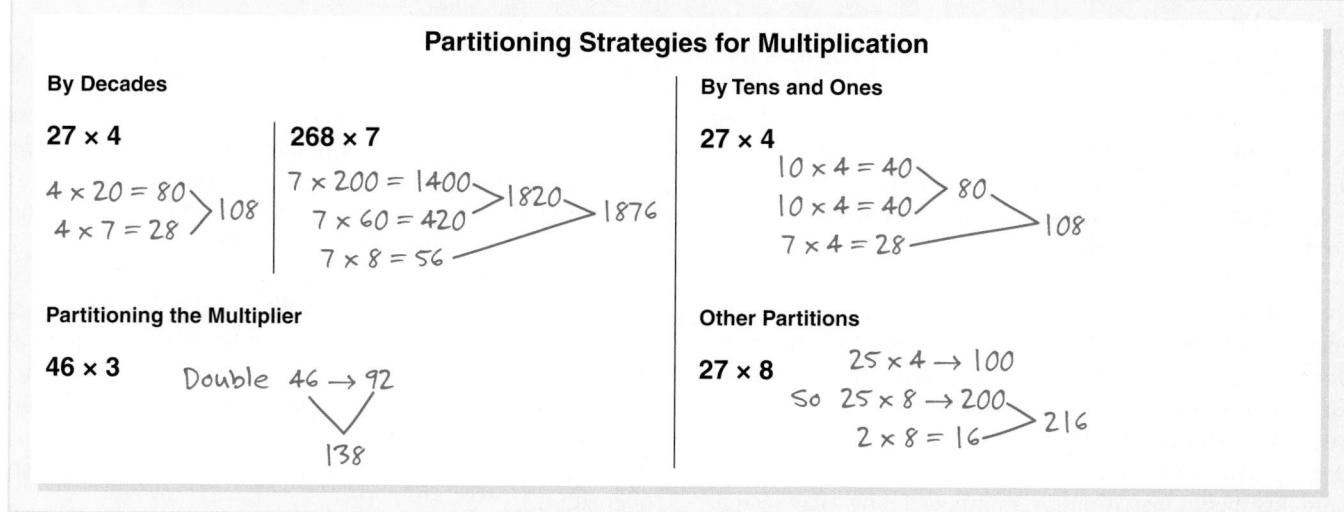

Figure 12.16 Four different ways to make easier partial products.

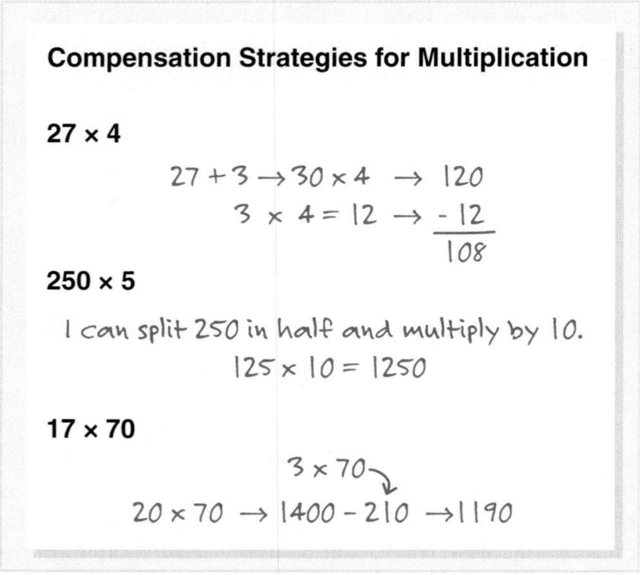

Compensation Strategies for Multiplication

27 × 4

$$27 + 3 \rightarrow 30 \times 4 \rightarrow 120$$
$$3 \times 4 = 12 \rightarrow -12$$
$$\overline{108}$$

250 × 5

I can split 250 in half and multiply by 10.
$$125 \times 10 = 1250$$

17 × 70

$$3 \times 70$$
$$20 \times 70 \rightarrow 1400 - 210 \rightarrow 1190$$

Figure 12.17 Compensation methods use a product related to the original. A compensation is made in the answer, or one factor is changed to compensate for a change in the other factor.

such as 30×60 or 210×40 where tens are multiplied by tens.

Multiplication of Larger Numbers

A problem such as this one can be solved in many different ways:

There were 23 clowns in the parade. Each clown carried 18 balloons. How many balloons were there altogether?

Some children look for smaller products such as 6×23 then add that result three times. Another method is to do 20×23 then subtract 2×23. Others will calculate four separate partial products: $10 \times 20 = 200$, $8 \times 20 = 160$, $10 \times 3 = 30$, and $8 \times 3 = 24$. And still others may add up a string of 23s. Two-digit multiplication is both complex and challenging. But students can solve these problems in a variety of interesting ways, many of which will contribute to the development of the traditional algorithm or one that is just as efficient. Figure 12.18 shows the work of three grade 4 students who had not been taught the traditional method for multiplication. Kenneth's "parting" refers to *partitioning*, a strategy label provided earlier by the teacher. Briannon is content with adding. She needs to see other strategies developed by her classmates. Nick's method is conceptually very similar to the traditional algorithm. As students begin partitioning numbers along place-value lines, the strategies they use are often like the traditional algorithm but without the traditional recording schemes.

Cluster Problems In grades 4 and 5 of *Investigations in Number, Data, and Space*, one approach to multi-digit multiplication is called "cluster problems." This approach encourages students to use facts and combinations they know to figure out more complex computations. For example, the following cluster could be used in a lesson: 7×6, 5×6, 10×6, 50×6, and 57×6. The goal is to figure out the final product (shown in bold) using the other problems as support.

It is useful to have students make an estimate of the final product before doing any of the problems in the cluster. For example, in a cluster for 34×50, 3×50 and 10×50 may be helpful in thinking about 30×50. The results of 30×50 and 4×50 combine to give you 34×50. It may seem that 34×25 is harder than 34×50. However, if you know 34×25, it need only be doubled to get the desired product. Students should be encouraged to add problems to the cluster if they need them. Think how you could use 10×34 (and some other related problems) to find 34×25.

The cluster problem approach begins with students being provided with the cluster problems. After they have become familiar with the approach, students should make up their own cluster of problems for a given product. At first, have students brainstorm clusters together as a class.

Pause and Reflect

Try your hand at making up a cluster of problems for 86×42. Include all possible problems that you think might be helpful, even if they are not all related to one approach for finding the product. Then use your cluster to find the product. Is there more than one way?

Here are some problems that might be in your cluster.

$$2 \times 80 \quad 4 \times 80 \quad 2 \times 86 \quad 40 \times 80$$
$$6 \times 40 \quad 10 \times 86 \quad 40 \times 86$$

Of course, your cluster may have included products not shown here. All that is required to begin the cluster problem approach is that your cluster eventually leads to a solution. Besides your own cluster, see if you can use the problems in this cluster to find 86×42.

Cluster problems help students think about ways they can break factors apart—or split numbers—into easier parts. The strategy of splitting numbers and multiplying the parts—the distributive property—is an extremely valuable technique for flexible computation. It is also fun to find different clever paths to the solution. For many problems, finding a workable cluster is actually faster than using an algorithm.

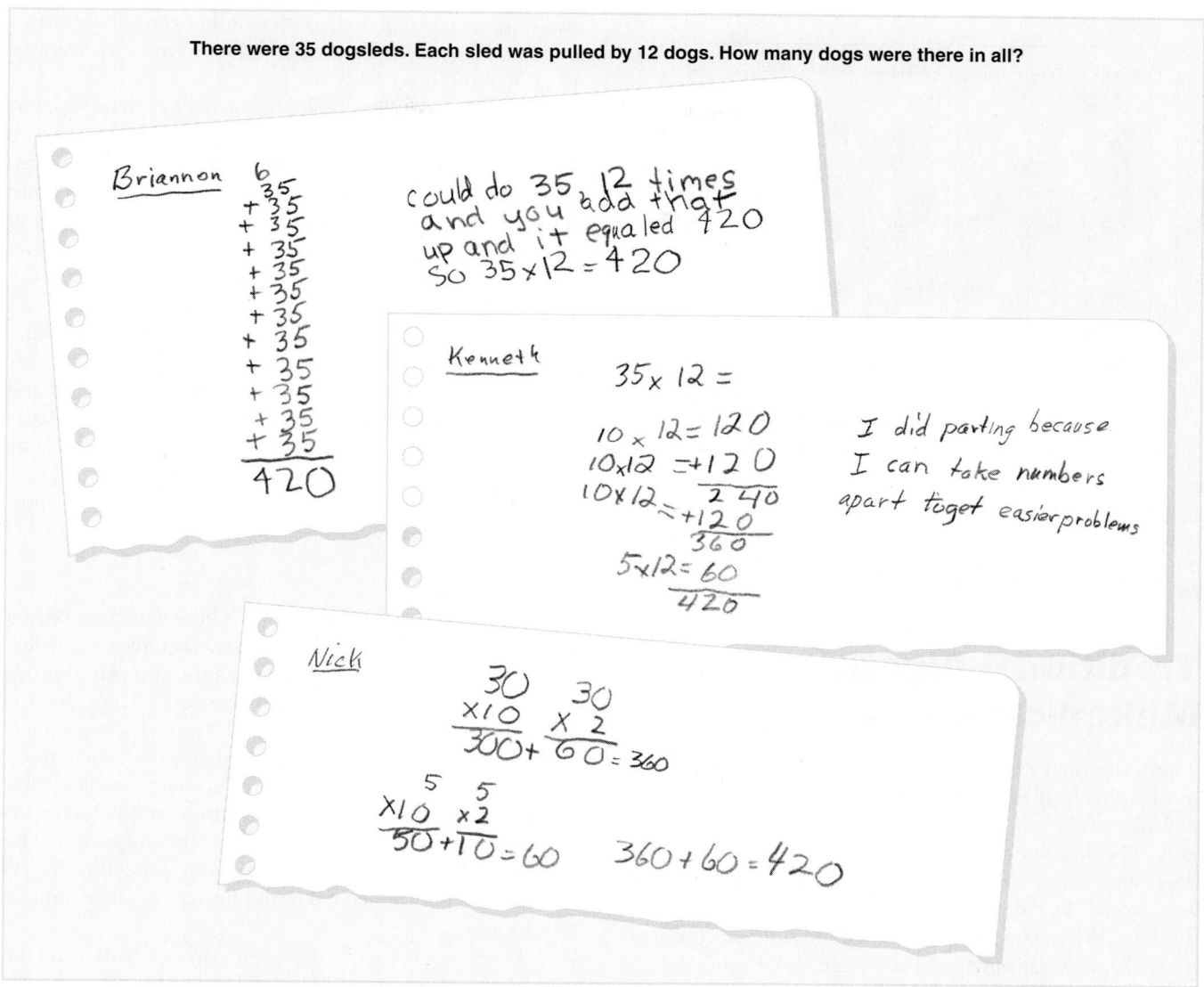

Figure 12.18 Three grade 4 students solve a multiplication problem using their own invented strategies. Each is at a different place in developing a reasonably efficient method for multiplication.

Area Models A valuable exploration is to prepare large rectangles for each group of two or three students. The rectangles should be measured carefully, with dimensions between 25 cm and 60 cm, and drawn accurately with square corners. The students' task is to determine how many of the small ones pieces (base-ten materials) will fit inside. Wooden or plastic base-ten pieces are best, but cardboard strips and squares are adequate. Alternatively, students can simply be given the task verbally: *What is the area of a rectangle that is 47 cm by 36 cm?*

Most children will fill the rectangle first with as many hundreds pieces as possible. One obvious approach is to put the 12 hundreds in one corner. This will leave narrow regions on two sides that can be filled with tens pieces and a final small rectangle that will hold ones. Especially if stu-

dents have had earlier experiences with finding products in arrays, figuring out the size of each sub-rectangle is not terribly difficult. The sketch in Figure 12.19 shows the four regions.

Pause and Reflect

If you did not already know the algorithm, how would you determine the size of the rectangle? Use your method (not the standard algorithm) on a rectangle measuring 68 cm × 24 cm. Make a sketch to show and explain your work.

As you will see in the discussion of the traditional algorithm, the area model leads to a fairly reasonable approach to multiplying numbers.

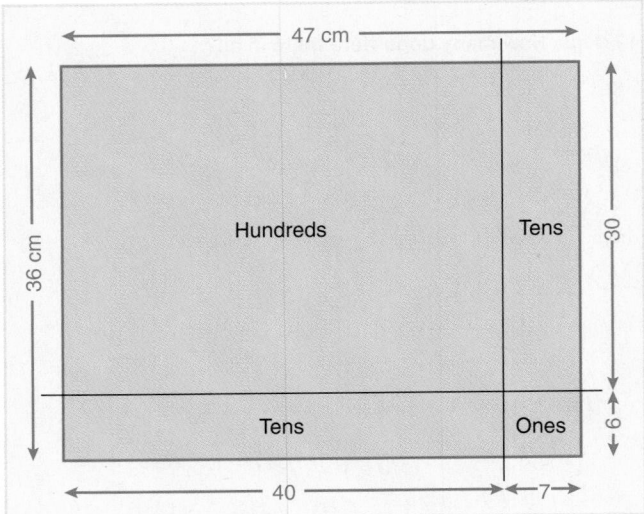

Figure 12.19 Ones, tens, and hundreds pieces fit exactly into the four sections of this 47 cm × 36 cm rectangle. Figure the size of each section to determine the size of the whole rectangle.

Traditional Algorithm for Multiplication

The traditional multiplication algorithm is probably the most difficult of the four algorithms if students have not had plenty of opportunities to explore their own strategies. The multiplication algorithm can be meaningfully developed using either a repeated addition model or an area model. For single-digit multipliers, the difference is minimal. When you move to two-digit multipliers, the area model has some advantages. For that reason, the discussion here will use the area model. Again, you are reminded of the need for a more directed approach than when developing invented strategies.

One-Digit Multipliers

As with other algorithms, as much time as is necessary should be devoted to the conceptual development of the algorithm, with the recording or the written part coming later. In contrast, most textbooks spend less time on development and more time on drill.

Begin with Models   Give students a drawing of a rectangle that is 47 cm by 6 cm. *How many small square centimetre pieces will fit in the rectangle?* (What is the area of the rectangle in square centimetres?) Let students solve the problem in groups before discussing it as a class. This simple task can be made into a good problem for students. Challenge them to find a way to determine the number of unit squares on the inside of the rectangle by slicing it into

two or more parts, in such a way that they can tell the size of each part. For example, it could be sliced into two sections of 20 × 6 and one of 7 × 6.

As shown in Figure 12.20, the rectangle can be sliced or separated into two parts so that one part will be 6 ones by 7 ones, or 42 ones, and the other will be 6 ones by 4 tens, or 24 tens. Notice that the base-ten language "6 ones times 4 tens is 24 tens" tells how many *pieces* (strips of ten) are in the big section. To say "6 times 40 is 240" is also correct and it tells how many units or square centimetres are in the section. Each section is referred to as a *partial product*. By adding the two partial products, you get the total product or area of the rectangle.

To avoid the tedium of drawing large rectangles and arranging base-ten pieces, use the base-ten grid paper found in Blackline Master 18. On the grid paper, students can easily draw accurate rectangles showing all the pieces. Do not force any recording technique on students until they understand how to use the two dimensions of a rectangle to get a product.

Develop the Written Record   To help with a recording scheme, provide sheets with base-ten columns on which students can record problems. When the two partial products are written separately as in Figure 12.21(a), there is little new to learn. Students simply record the products and add them together. As illustrated, it is possible to teach students how to write the first product with a carried digit so that the combined product is written on one line. This recording scheme is known to be a source of errors. The little carried digit is often the source of difficulty—it gets added in before the second multiplication is carried out or is forgotten.

There is no practical reason why students can't be allowed to record both partial products and avoid the errors related to the carried digit. When you accept that, it makes no difference in which order the products are written. Why not simply permit students to do written multiplication as shown in Figure 12.21(b)? When the factors are in a word

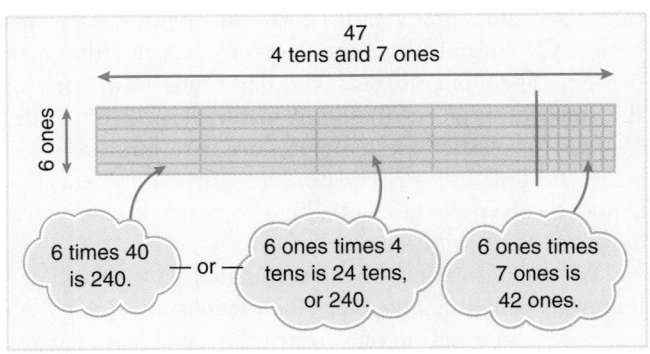

Figure 12.20   A rectangle filled with base-ten pieces is a useful model for two-digit-by-one-digit multiplication.

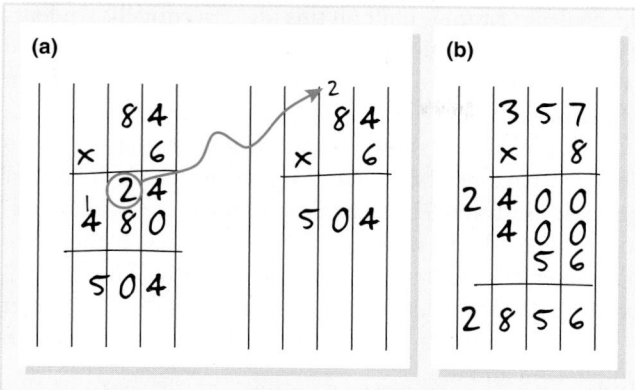

Figure 12.21 (a) In the standard form, the product of ones is recorded first. The tens digit of this first product can be written as a "carried" digit above the tens column. (b) It is quite reasonable to abandon the "carried" digit and permit the partial products to be recorded in any order.

problem, a chart, or some other format, all that is really necessary is to write down all the partial products and add. Furthermore, that is precisely how it is done mentally.

Most standard curricula progress from two digits to three digits with a single-digit multiplier. Students can make this progression easily. They still should be permitted to write all three partial products separately and not have to bother with carrying.

Two-Digit Multipliers

With the area model, the progression to a two-digit multiplier is relatively straightforward. Rectangles can be drawn on base-ten grid paper, or full-sized rectangles can be filled in with base-ten pieces. There will be four partial products, corresponding to four different sections of the rectangle.

Several variations in language might be used. Consider the product 47×36 as illustrated in Figure 12.22. In the partial product 40×30, if base-ten language is used—*4 tens times 3 tens is 12 hundreds*—the result tells how many hundreds pieces are in that section. In standard form, the product "forty times thirty" is formidable. Try to avoid "four times three," which promotes thinking about digits rather than numbers. It is well worth stressing the idea that in all cases, a product of *tens times tens is in the hundreds*.

Figure 12.22 also shows the recording of four partial products in the traditional order. It also shows how these can be collapsed to two lines if carried digits are used. Here the second "carry" technically belongs in the hundreds column, but is rarely written there. Often it gets confused with the first; thus it is an additional source of error. The lower left of the figure shows the same computation with all four products written in a different order. This is quite an acceptable algorithm. In the rare instance when someone multiplies numbers such as 538×29 with pencil and paper, there would be six partial products. But far fewer errors

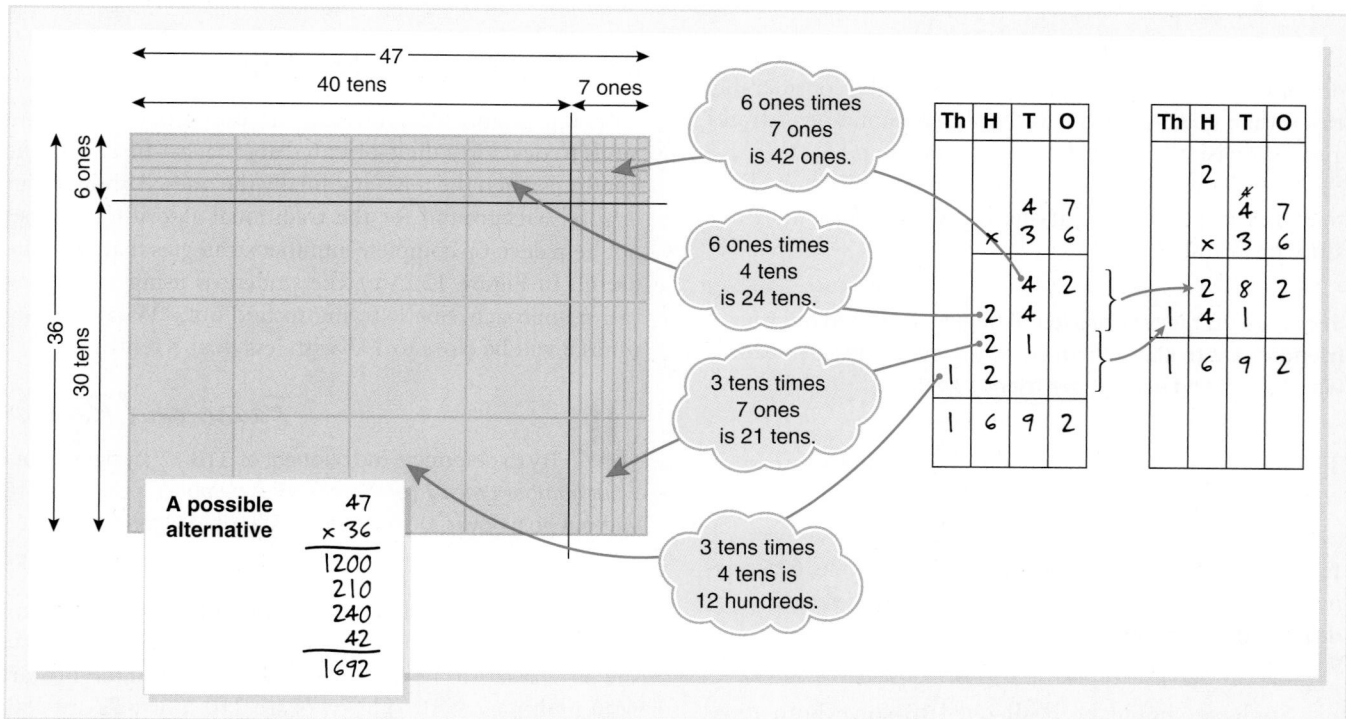

Figure 12.22 36 cm × 47 cm rectangle filled with base-ten pieces. Base-ten language connects the four partial products to the traditional written format. Note the possibility of recording the products in some other order.

would occur, requiring less instructional time and much less remediation.

 "As students move from third to fifth grade, they should consolidate and practice a small number of computational algorithms for addition, subtraction, multiplication and division that they understand well and can use routinely.... Having access to more than one method for each operation allows students to choose an approach that best fits the numbers in a particular problem. For example, 298 × 42 can be thought of as (300 × 42) – (2 × 42), whereas 41 × 16 can be computed by multiplying 41 × 8 to get 328 and then doubling 328 to get 656" (p. 155).

 Computer versions of the area model for multiplication can alleviate some of the difficulties of physically filling in place-value blocks into rectangles. On the NLVM Web site, (http://nlvm.usu.edu/en/nav/frames_asid_192_g_2_t_l.html), the Rectangle Multiplication applet will model any rectangle up to 30 × 30. The rectangle is split into two parts rather than four, corresponding to the tens and ones digits in the multiplier. The result is nicely correlated with the standard algorithm. ◆

Student-Invented Strategies for Division

Even though many adults think division is the most onerous of the computational operations, it can be considerably easier than multiplication. Typically, computational strategies for division are developed in grades 4 and 5.

Recall that there are two concepts of division. First there is the partition or fair-sharing idea, illustrated by this story problem:

There are 783 jelly beans in the bag. Mohani and her four friends want to share them equally. How many jelly beans will Mohani and each of her friends get?

Then there is the measurement or repeated subtraction concept:

Jumbo the elephant loves peanuts. His trainer has 625 peanuts. If he gives Jumbo 20 peanuts each day, how many days will the peanuts last?

Students should be challenged to solve both types of problems. However, the fair-share problems are often easier to solve with base-ten pieces. Furthermore, the tra-

ditional algorithm is built on this idea. Eventually, students will develop strategies that they will apply to both types of problems, even when the process does not match the action of the story.

Figure 12.23 shows some strategies that grade 4 children have used to solve division problems. The first example illustrates 92 ÷ 4 using base-ten pieces with a sharing process. A ten is traded for 10 ones when there are no longer enough tens to be shared equally. Then the 12 ones are distributed, resulting in 23 in each set. This direct modelling approach with base-ten pieces is quite easy to understand and use.

In the second example, the student sets out the base-ten pieces and draws a "bar graph" with six columns. After noting that there are not enough hundreds for each child, he splits the 3 hundreds in half, putting 50 in each column. That leaves him with 1 hundred, 5 tens, and 3 ones. After trading the hundred for 10 tens (now 15 tens), he gives 20 to each, recording 2 tens in each bar. Now he is left with 3 tens and 3 ones, or 33. He knows that 5 × 6 is 30, so he gives each child 5, leaving him with 3. He splits these in half and writes $\frac{1}{2}$ in each column.

The child in the third example is solving a sharing problem but tries to do it using a measurement process. She wants to find out how many eights are in 143. Initially she guesses. By multiplying 8 first by 10, then by 20 (work not shown), and then by 14, she knows the answer is more than 14 and less than 20. Then, she rethinks the problem as how many eights are in 100 and how many are in 40.

Missing-Factor Strategies

Notice in Figure 12.23(a) how the use of base-ten blocks tends to develop a digit-oriented approach—first share the hundreds, then the tens, and finally the ones. Although this is good background for the traditional algorithm, it does not help develop complete-number strategies that are quite useful. In Figure 12.23(c), the student is using a multiplicative approach. She is trying to find out, "What number times 8 will be close to 143 with less than 8 remaining?"

Ⅱ ———————— *Pause and Reflect*

Try to determine the quotient of 318 ÷ 7 by figuring out *what number times 7 (or 7 times what number)* is close to 318 without going over. Do not use the standard algorithm.

There are several places to begin solving this problem. For instance, since 10 × 7 is only 70 and 100 × 7 is 700, the answer has to be between 10 and 100. You might start with multiples of 10. Thirty 7s are 210. Forty 7s are 280. Fifty 7s are 350. So 40 is not enough and 50 is too much. It has to be forty-something. At this point you could guess at

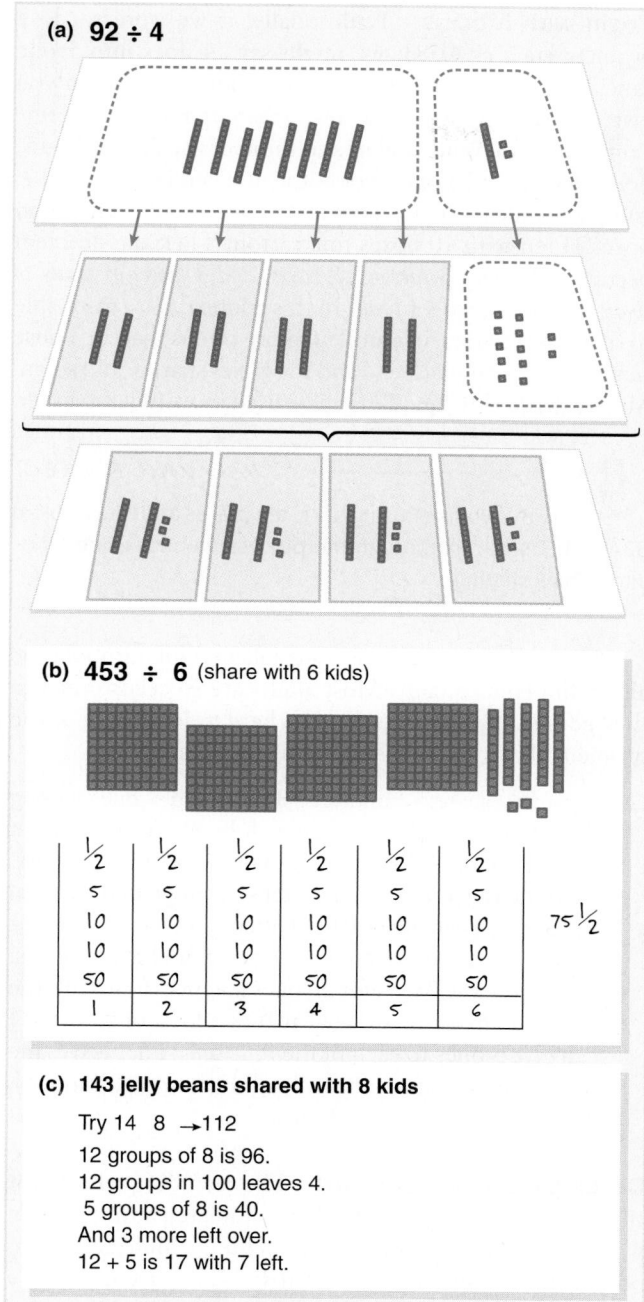

Figure 12.23 Students use both models and symbols to solve division tasks.

Source: Adapted from *Developing Mathematical Ideas: Numbers and Operations, Part I: Building a System of Tens—Casebook* by Deborah Schifter, Virginia Bastable, and Susan Jo Russell. © 2002 by Educational Development Center, Inc. Published by Dale Seymour Publications, an imprint of Pearson Learning Group, a division of Pearson Education, Inc. Used by permission.

numbers between 40 and 50. Or you might add on 7s. Or you could notice that forty 7s (280) leaves you with 20 plus 18 or 38. Five 7s will be 35 of the 38 with 3 left over. In all, that's 40 + 5 or 45 with a remainder of 3.

This missing-factor approach is likely to be invented by some students if they are solving measurement problems such as the following:

Amy can put 6 pictures on one page of her photo album. If she has 82 pictures, how many pages will she need?

Alternatively, you can simply pose a task such as 82 ÷ 6 and ask students, "What number times 6 would be close to 82?" and continue from there.

Cluster Problems

Another approach to developing missing-factor strategies is to use cluster problems as discussed for multiplication. Here are two examples:

100 × 4	10 × 72
500 × 4	5 × 70
4 × 25	2 × 72
6 × 4	4 × 72
527 ÷ 4	5 × 72
	381 ÷ 72

Notice that the missing-factor strategy works equally as well for one-digit divisors as for two-digit divisors. Also notice that it is okay to include division problems in the cluster. In the first example, 400 ÷ 4 could replace 100 × 4 and 125 × 4 could easily have replaced 500 ÷ 4. The idea is to keep multiplication and division as closely connected as possible.

Cluster problems accentuate a flexible approach to computation, helping students realize that there are many different good ways to compute. Another way to develop flexibility is to pose a division problem (or a multiplication problem) and have students solve the problem using two different approaches. Of course, neither of the methods should be the traditional algorithm or a calculator.

Cluster problems provide students with a sense that problems can be solved in different ways and with different starting points. Therefore, rather than cluster problems, you can provide students with a variety of first steps for solving a problem. Their task is to select one of the starting points and solve the problem from there. For example, here are four possible starting points for 514 × 8:

10 × 80	400 ÷ 8	60 × 8	80 ÷ 8

When students are first asked to solve problems using two methods, they often use a primitive or completely inefficient method for their second approach (or revert to a standard algorithm). For example, to solve 514 ÷ 8, a student might perform a very long string of subtractions (514 − 8 = 506, 506 − 8 = 498, 498 − 8 = 490, and so on) and count how many times he or she subtracted 8. Others will actually draw 514 tally marks and loop groups of 8. These students have not developed sufficient flexibility to think of other efficient methods. The idea just suggested of posing a variety of starting points can nudge students into other more profitable alternatives. Class discussions will also help students begin to see more flexible approaches. ◆

Traditional Algorithm for Division

Long division is the one traditional algorithm that starts with the left-hand or big pieces. The conceptual basis for the algorithm most often taught in textbooks is the partition or fair-share method, the method we will explore in detail. Another well-known algorithm is based on repeated subtraction. This method may be viewed as a good way to record the missing-factor approach with partial products recorded in a column to the right of the division computation. As shown by the two examples in Figure 12.24, one advantage is that there is total flexibility in the factors selected at each step of the way.

One-Digit Divisors

Typically, the division algorithm with one-digit divisors is introduced in grade 3. If done well, it should not have to be re-taught, and it should provide the basis for two-digit divisors. Students in the upper grades who are having difficulty with the division algorithm can also benefit from a conceptual development of division.

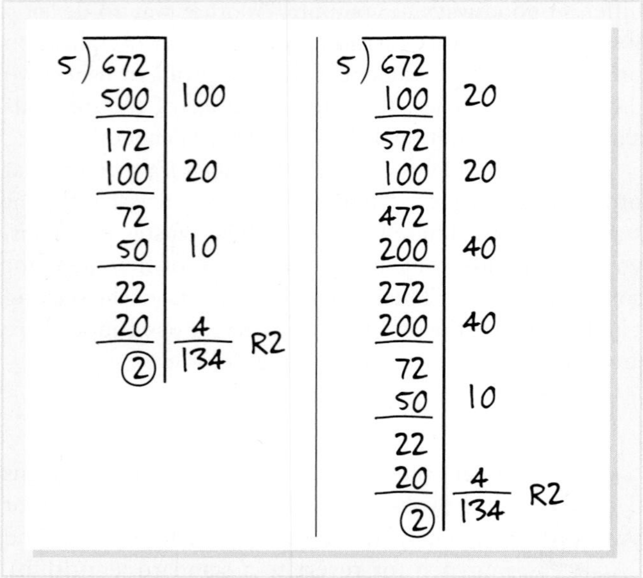

Figure 12.24 In the division algorithm shown, the numbers on the side indicate the quantity of the divisor being subtracted from the dividend. As the two examples indicate, the divisor can be subtracted from the dividend in any amount desired.

Begin with Models Traditionally, if we were to do a problem such as 4)583, we might say "4 goes into 5 one time." This is quite mysterious to children. How can you just ignore the "83" and keep changing the problem? Preferably, you want students to think of the 583 as 5 hundreds, 8 tens, and 3 ones, not as the independent digits 5, 8, and 3. One idea is to use a context such as candy bundled in boxes of ten with 10 boxes to a carton. Then the problem becomes *We have 5 cartons, 8 boxes, and 3 pieces of candy to share evenly amongst 4 schools.* In this context, it is reasonable to share the cartons first until no more can be shared. Those remaining are "unpacked," and the boxes shared, and so on. Money ($100, $10, and $1) can be used in a similar manner.

II —————————— *Pause and Reflect*

Try this yourself using base-ten pieces and the problem 524 ÷ 3. Try to talk through the process without using "goes into." Think sharing.

Language plays an enormous role in thinking about the algorithm conceptually. Most adults are so accustomed to the "goes into" language that it is hard to let it go. For the problem 583 ÷ 4, here is some suggested language:

- I want to share 5 hundreds, 8 tens, and 3 ones among these four sets. There are enough hundreds for each set to get 1 hundred. That leaves 1 hundred that I can't share.
- I'll trade the hundred for 10 tens. That gives me a total of 18 tens. I can give each set 4 tens and have 2 tens left over. Two tens is not enough to go around the four sets.
- I can trade the 2 tens for 20 ones and put those with the 3 ones I already had. That makes a total of 23 ones. I can give 5 ones to each of the four sets. That leaves me with 3 ones as a remainder. In all I gave out 1 hundred, 4 tens, and 5 ones with 3 left over.

Develop the Written Record The recording scheme for the long-division algorithm is not completely intuitive. You will need to be quite directive in helping children learn to record the fair sharing with models. There are essentially four steps:

1. *Share* and record the number of pieces put in each group.
2. *Record* the number of pieces shared in all. Multiply to find this number.
3. *Record* the number of pieces remaining. Subtract to find this number.
4. *Trade* (if necessary) for smaller pieces, and combine with any that are there already. Record the new total number in the next column.

When students model problems with a one-digit divisor, steps 2 and 3 seem unnecessary. Explain that these steps really help when you don't have the pieces there to count.

Record Explicit Trades Figure 12.25 details each step of the recording process just described. On the left, you see the traditional algorithm. To the right is a suggestion that matches the actual action with the models by explicitly

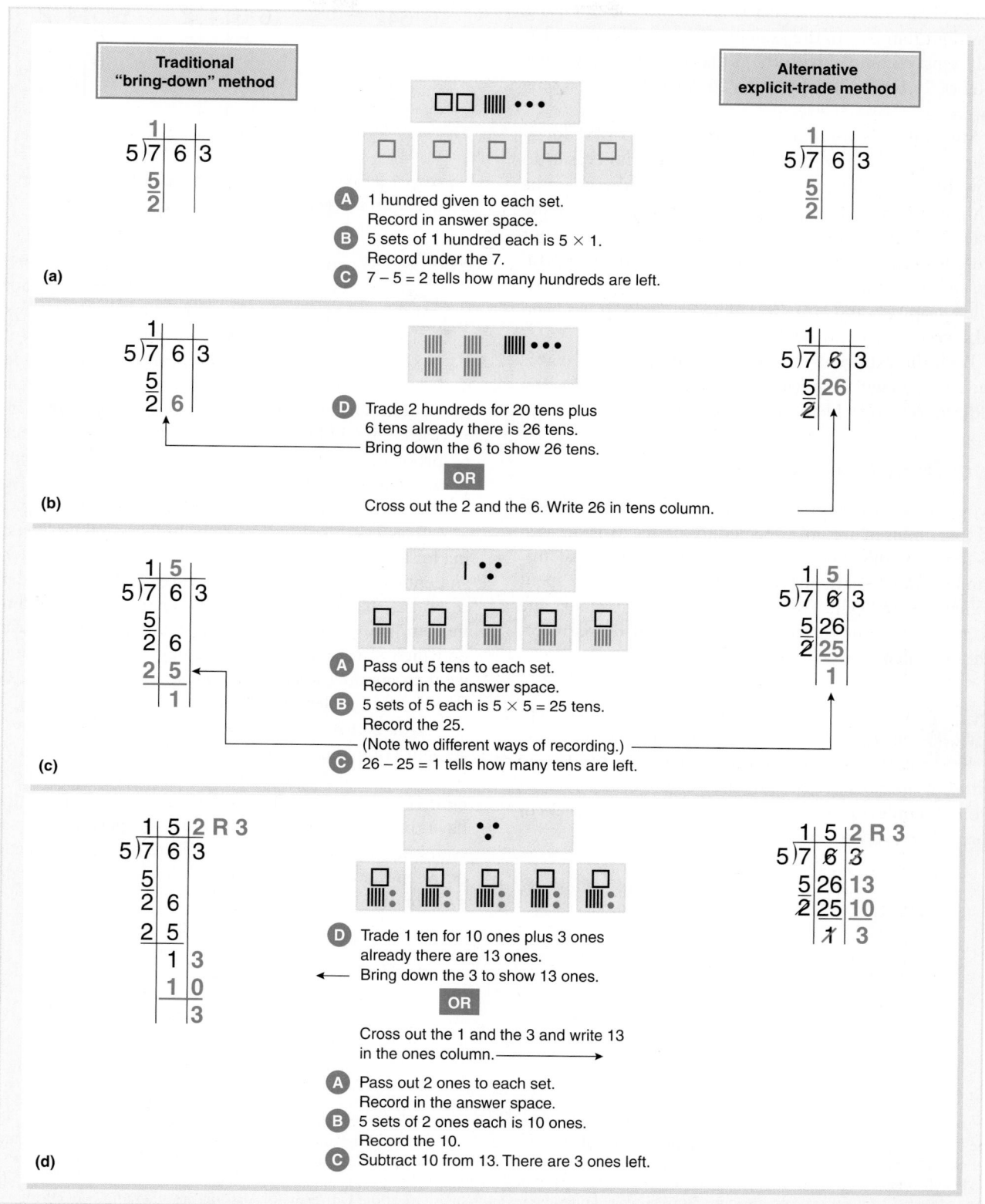

Figure 12.25 The traditional and explicit-trade methods are connected to each step of the division process. Every step can and should make sense.

recording the trades. Instead of the somewhat mysterious "bring-down" procedure, the traded pieces are crossed out, as is the number of existing pieces in the next column. The combined number of pieces is written in this column using a two-digit number. In the example, 2 hundreds are traded for 20 tens, combined with the 6 that were there, making a total of 26 tens. Therefore, the 26 is written in the tens column.

Students who are required to make sense of the long-division procedure find the explicit-trade method easier to follow. Blank division charts with wide place-value columns are highly recommended. These can be found in Blackline Master 20. Without the charts, it is important to spread out the digits in the dividend when writing down the problem. (*Authors' note:* The explicit-trade method is John Van de Walle's invention and is not found in textbooks. It has been used successfully in grades 3 to 8.)

Both the explicit-trade method and the use of place-value columns will help with the problem of leaving out a middle zero in a problem (see Figure 12.26).

Two-Digit Divisors

As you explore your regional curriculum document you will find that children are not expected to master division with two-digit divisors. The cost in terms of time and students' attitudes toward mathematics is too enormous to be spent on this outdated skill. Only a few times in any adult's life will an exact result for such a computation be required, without a calculator being available.

 The following comes from the grade 3–5 chapter of the *Standards:* "Although the expectation is that students develop fluency in computing with whole numbers, frequently they should use calculators to solve complex computations involving large numbers or as part of an extended problem" (p. 155).

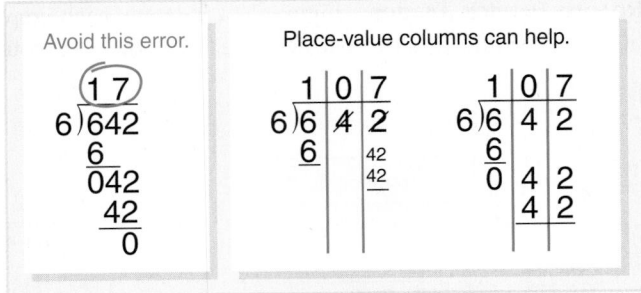

Figure 12.26 Using lines to mark place-value columns can help avoid forgetting to record zeros.

 When teaching a traditional algorithm for any operation, you may give quizzes or use chapter-end tests found in your textbook. Whether students do well or not so well, it is important to ask yourself if you really can assess what students understand or do not understand from a strictly computational test. When students make a systematic error in an algorithm, it will likely show up in the same way in repeated problems. What you do not know is what conceptual knowledge children are using—or not using. Don't mistake correct use of a standard algorithm for understanding.

To assess this very important background understanding for algorithms, during class discussions, call on different students to explain individual steps. Keep track of students' responses in a simple chart or other recording technique, indicating how well they seem to understand the algorithm on which you are working. For struggling students you may want to conduct a short diagonostic interview to explore their level of understanding in more detail.

A diagonostic interview might begin by having the student complete a computation. When it is finished, ask for explanations for specific steps in the process. If the student is having difficulty explaining the symbolic process, have the student use base-ten blocks to perform the same computation. Then ask the student to explain connections between what was done with the models and what was done symbolically. ◆

---

[1]The Cognitively Guided Instruction (CGI) project, directed by Carpenter, Fennema, and Franke at the University of Wisconsin; the Conceptually Based Instruction (CBI) project, directed by Hiebert and Wearne at the University of Delaware; the Problem Centered Mathematics Project (PCMP), directed by Human, Murray, and Olivier at the University of Stellenbosch, South Africa; the Supporting Ten-Structured Thinking (STST) project, directed by Fuson at Northwestern University; and ongoing research by Kamii at the University of Alabama are all examples of efforts that have informed thinking about invented strategies for computation.

Reflections on Chapter 12

Writing to Learn

1. What is the difference between solving a problem with direct modelling and solving a problem with an invented strategy? What is a traditional algorithm?
2. How are traditional algorithms different from invented strategies? Explain the benefits of invented strategies over traditional algorithms.
3. Illustrate three different strategies for adding 46 + 39. Which ones are easy to do mentally? Is there a strategy that is easier because 39 is close to 40? What strategies work well for sums such as 538 + 243? For each strategy you work with, think about how you could record it on the board so that other students will be able to follow what is being done.
4. Use two different adding-up strategies for 93 − 27 and for 545 − 267. Make up a story problem that would encourage an adding-up strategy.
5. Describe how you would go about developing the traditional algorithms for addition and subtraction. How would you deal with the issue of beginning on the right with the ones place when students' natural tendency is to begin on the left? Use 385 + 128 to illustrate a reasonable written algorithm that begins on the left instead of the right. Do the same for 453 − 278.
6. Draw pictures showing how 57 × 4 could be modelled: with counters, with base-ten pieces, with rectangles or arrays on base-ten grids.
7. What would you do if your students seemed to persist in using repeated addition for multiplication problems without really doing any multiplication?
8. Which division concept, measurement or partition, is easier for direct modelling and is also the one used to develop the usual long-division algorithm? Make up an appropriate word story with that concept to go with 735 ÷ 6.
9. Use the traditional algorithm for 735 ÷ 6, then repeat the process using our suggested method of recording trades explicitly. With the two algorithms side by side, explain every recorded number in terms of what it stands for when sharing base-ten pieces.
10. Why is some form of assessment that gets at student understanding so important when teaching traditional algorithms?

For Discussion and Exploration

1. Conduct a four-person panel discussion to debate whether or not traditional computational algorithms for whole numbers should continue to be taught. Have two people represent each view. Arguments should show the benefits of each approach, the efficiency of various methods, students' understanding of "doing mathematics," the issue of available technology in the real world, the need for computation of various types outside of the classroom, high-stakes testing, and the desires of parents (valid or not). Two intermediate views are also possible: including traditional algorithms only for multiplication and division, and withholding teaching of the traditional algorithms until grades 7–8, after flexible strategies and better number sense have been developed. Have separate panel members for these views.

Resources for Chapter 12

Literature Connections

Children's literature can play a very useful role in helping you develop problems for your invented strategies and mental computation lessons. There are many fascinating books that involve large numbers and opportunities to compute. Some are about real data, and others are fictional.

100 Canadian Heroines   *Forster, 2004*

The 100 Canadian heroines that students meet in this book are remarkable women in science, sport, politics, entertainment, arts, and other fields. The book is full of amazing facts and fascinating trivia that students can explore using number

operations. It is the kind of book that teachers could read to students and follow up with discussion and mathematical activities.

Crazy About Canada! Amazing Things Kids Want to Know   *Bowers, 2006*

This book delivers a wealth of information for students to learn about Canada and things Canadian. The book was shaped by real questions from real children. This book of jam-packed facts can be used as a basis for students to investigate and carry out a variety of calculations involving strategies for whole number computation.

Canadian Boys Who Rocked the World
Lloyd Kyi, 2007

This book also provides a wealth of information about 30 Canadians that achieved greatness before age 20. Students can use the information and quick facts to create questions that compare and contrast numbers as well as require performing whole number operations.

The Breakfast Cereal Gourmet   *Hoffman, 2005*

The History of Everyday Life   *Landau, 2006*

These non-fiction books include interesting facts and figures that can be used for a variety of calculations and investigations. Hoffman's book provided fun information about breakfast eating habits. For example, the average person eats 160 bowls of cereal in a year. Such facts can be used to find how many bowls are eaten in 5 years, or how many are consumed in a month.

In the *History of Everyday Life*, inventions are discussed, including facts and figures about the toilet. If the toilet uses 3 (12.5 litres) or 4 (18 litres) gallons of water for every flush, how much water are you using at home? *Note:* you will need to convert all Imperial measures to metric before presenting them to the students.

Look for other titles on your bookshelf or explore facts in your local newspaper to engage children in mathematical calculations that naturally emerge from real-life situations.

Is a Blue Whale the Biggest Thing There Is?
Wells, 2005

This is one of the most intriguing books you will find about large objects and large distances. Blue whales look small next to Mount Everest, which in turn looks small next to Earth. The data in the book allow children to make other comparisons, such as the number of grade 4 students that would have the same mass or volume as a blue whale or that would fill the gymnasium. These comparisons are the perfect place for estimations and discussions about how much precision is necessary to make a meaningful comparison.

Recommendations for Further Reading

Articles

National Council of Teachers of Mathematics. (2003). Computational fluency [Focus Issue]. *Teaching Children Mathematics, 9.*
How to help children achieve skills and understanding in the area of computation is the focus of this entire journal, which can be purchased separately from the NCTM. Each of the nine articles is well worth reading. These include a discussion of teaching computation to English language learners, an article on computational fluency written by an internationally prominent mathematician,
a reprint of a classic article on meaning and skill by William Brownell, plus other worthwhile papers by both classroom teachers and researchers in the area of computation.

O'Loughlin, T. A. (2007). Using research to develop computational fluency in young mathematicians. *Teaching Children Mathematics, 14* (3), 132–138.
Written by a second grade teacher, this article describes her journey to improve her students' computational fluency through research-based practice. Using Fosnot and Dolk (2001) books referred to in the "Books" section that follows, she encourages student-invented strategies to explore her students' thinking and understanding. The interesting collection of student work and thought-provoking associated debriefing will demonstrate various methods, such as place-value strategies and empty number line representations.

Russell, S. J. (2000). Developing computational fluency with whole numbers. *Teaching Children Mathematics, 7,* 155–158.
In just four pages, Russell provides a well-articulated view of what Principles and Standards *means by computational fluency. Russell accompanies each of her points with examples from children. She talks about connecting understanding with procedures and how to assess computational fluency. She ends this little article by explaining that teaching for fluency is a complex task that requires the teacher to understand the mathematics, how to select appropriate tasks, and how to recognize when to capitalize on students' ideas.*

Books

Bay-Williams, J. M. & Martinie, S. L. (2008). *Mathematics and Non-Fiction: Grades 6–8.* Sausalito, CA: Math Solutions Publications.
This resource book for middle school teachers uses nonfiction as a springboard to explore mathematical concepts.

Duncan, N., Geer, C., Huinker, D., Leutzinger, L., Rathnell, E., & Thompson, C. (2007). *Navigating through number operations in grades 3–5.* Reston, VA: NCTM.
This book (particularly Chapters 3 and 4) is a perfect companion to this chapter. It reflects on how to introduce and develop the four operations with the ultimate goal of developing computational fluency and mathematical proficiency. There is also a follow-up on how to assess and interpret student work. Part of the publication is a CD that includes blackline masters that correspond to a variety of activities in the book and a collection of related articles and chapters from NCTM publications.

Fosnot, C. T., & Dolk, M. (2001). *Young mathematicians at work: Constructing multiplication and division.* Portsmouth, NH: Heinemann.

Fosnot, C. T., & Dolk, M. (2001). Young mathematicians at work: Constructing number sense, addition, and subtraction. Portsmouth, NH: Heinemann.
These are two in a series of three books by Fosnot (a U.S. mathematics educator and expert in constructivism) and Dolk (a mathematics educator at the Freudenthal Institute in the Netherlands). The books are products of a collaborative effort of working with teachers to examine how children learn and how to support that learning. They show children constructing ideas about number, operations, and computation in ways not found elsewhere. (Their third book is on fractions and decimals.)

Online Resources

Base Blocks Addition
http://nlvm.usu.edu/en/nav/frames_asid_154_g_2_t_l.html

Base Blocks Subtraction
http://nlvm.usu.edu/en/nav/frames_asid_155_g_2_t_l.html

These two similar applets use base-ten blocks on a place-value chart. You can form any problem you wish up to four digits. The subtraction model shows the bottom number in red instead of blue. When the top blocks are dragged onto the red blocks, they disappear. Although you can begin in any column, the model forces a regrouping strategy as well as a take-away model for subtraction. It is good for reinforcing the traditional algorithms.

Multiplying with Base Ten Blocks
http://argyll.epsb.ca/jreed/

This applet, developed by Jim Reed for Alberta Education, offers a mini-lesson on two-digit by two-digit multiplication using an area model with the base-ten blocks. Drill-type practice follows.

Dividing with Base Ten Blocks
http://argyll.epsb.ca/jreed/

A similar approach to multiplication is employed here in a mini-lesson on division.

Rectangle Multiplication
http://nlvm.usu.edu/en/nav/frames_asid_192_g_l_t_l.html

This applet nicely models two-digit by two-digit products up to 30 × 30.

Rectangle Division
http://nlvm.usu.edu/en/nav/frames_asid_193_g_l_t_l.html

This applet uses an array model to represent any two-digit number as a product of two numbers. Remainders are included.

PEARSON
myeducationlab *will help you improve your understanding of the concepts taught in this textbook and in your course. This online tool includes videos of real classroom experiences, sample lesson plans, simulations, case studies, and links to important educational and teaching Web sites that will help you make the transition from student to teacher. As you study in your course and with this textbook, please follow along in* **MyEducationLab**. *Use it! Explore it! And improve your knowledge and your grade!*

Chapter 13
Using Computational Estimation with Whole Numbers

Recall that *Principles and Standards* defined computational fluency as "having and using efficient and accurate methods for computing" (NCTM, 2000, p. 32). Computational estimation skills more fully round out the development of flexible and fluent thinking with whole numbers. Moreover, whole-number estimation skills form the basis for most estimation skills with fractions, decimals, and percents.

Mental computation and computational estimation are decidedly related, yet they are quite different skills. Estimates are made using mental computations with numbers that are easier to work with than the actual numbers involved. Hence, estimation depends on students' mental computational skills. However, because of the importance of estimation—both in the real world and in much of mathematics—and because the strategies for computational estimation are quite different from those discussed in the preceding chapter, it makes sense to address this topic separately.

Big Ideas

1. Multi-digit numbers can be built or taken apart in a wide variety of ways. When the parts of numbers are easier to work with, these parts can be used to create estimates for calculations, rather than using the exact numbers involved. For example, 36 is 30 and 6 or 25 and 10 and 1. 483 can be thought of as 500 − 20 + 3.

2. Nearly all computational estimations involve using parts of numbers that are easier to work with, or substituting challenging numbers with close "nice" numbers so the resulting computations can be done mentally.

Mathematics Content Connections

Estimation skills, once developed, are a tool for everyday living as well as a tool for sense making in other areas of mathematics.

- **Operations, Place Value, and Whole-Number Computation** (Chapters 9, 11, and 12): Many estimating skills grow directly out of invented strategies for computation. For example, to estimate $708 \div 27$, you might compute 20×27 (540) and then 5×27 (135, for a total of 675). Thus, the quotient is a little more than 25. To compute these two products requires an understanding of place value. To understand how multiplication can help with a division estimate requires an understanding of how multiplication and division are related.

- **Estimation with Fractions, Decimals, and Percents** (Chapters 16 and 17): Once students have an understanding of what an estimate is and have developed strategies for whole-number estimation, few new strategies are required for estimation with other types of numbers. To estimate $3.45 + 24.6 − 0.0057$ requires no new estimation skill, only a good understanding of the decimal concepts involved. Similar statements are true of fractions and percents.

Introducing Computational Estimation

Whenever we are faced with a computation in real life or even in school, we have a variety of choices to make concerning how we will handle it. As pointed out in the 1989 *Standards* document, the first decision is: "Do we need an exact answer or will an approximate answer be okay?" If an exact answer is called for, we can use an invented or mental strategy, a pencil-and-paper algorithm, a calculator, or even a computer. A computer is called for when there are many repetitive computations that lend themselves to spreadsheet formats. Often, however, we do not need an exact answer and so we can use an estimate. How good an estimate—how close it must be to the actual computation—is a matter of context, as was the original decision to be satisfied with an estimate.

The goal of computational estimation is for a student to be able to flexibly and quickly produce an approximation for a computation that is appropriate for the situation. In everyday life, estimation skills are valuable time savers. Many situations do not require an exact answer, so reaching for a calculator or a pencil is not necessary if one has good estimation skills. However, computational estimation is a higher-level thinking skill as it requires many decisions by the estimator (Sowder, 1989). Students are not as good at computational estimation as they are at finding exact answers and find computational estimation uncomfortable (Hanson & Hogan, 2000; Reys, Reys, & Penafiel, 1991; Reys, Reys, Nohda, Ishida, Yoshikawa, & Shimizu, 1991).

Good estimators tend to employ a variety of computational strategies they have developed over time. Teaching these strategies to children has become a regular part of the curriculum. As early as grade 3, we can help children develop an understanding of what it means to estimate a computation and begin to develop some early strategies that may be useful. From then on, throughout elementary school, children should continue to develop and add to their estimation strategies and skills.

Understanding Computational Estimation

By itself, the noun *estimate* refers to a number that is a suitable approximation for an exact number, given the particular context. This concept of an estimate applies to measures and quantities as well as to computation.

Three Types of Estimation   In the K–8 mathematics curriculum, *estimation* refers to three quite different ideas:

- *Measurement estimation*—determining an approximate measure without making an exact measurement. For example, we can estimate the length of a room or the mass of a watermelon in the grocery store.

- *Quantity estimation (holistic estimation)*—approximating the number of items in a collection. For example, we might estimate the number of students in the auditorium or jelly beans in the "estimation jar."

- *Computational estimation*—determining a number that is an approximation of a computation that we cannot or do not wish to determine exactly. For example, we might want to know the approximate rate of litres per kilometre when we travelled 456 kilometres on 52 litres of gas ($456 \div 52$). In some instances, it is sufficient to know that a computation is either more or less than a given number. Do I have enough money to buy six boxes of doughnuts at $4.99 each? We have 28 dozen doughnuts. Are there enough for the 117 students to have two each?

Estimate or Guess   Many children confuse the idea of estimation with guessing. None of the three types of estimation involves outright guessing. Each involves some form of reasoning. Computational estimation, for example, involves some computation; it is not a guess at all. It is therefore important to (1) not use the word *guessing* when working on estimation, and (2) explicitly help students see the difference between a guess and an estimate.

In everyday life, estimation skills are valuable time savers for comparative shopping, and figuring total costs. The goal of computational estimation is for a student to be able to flexibly and quickly produce an approximation for a computation that is appropriate for the situation.

"Teachers should help students learn how to decide when an exact answer or an estimate would be more appropriate, how to choose the computational methods that would be best to use, and how to evaluate the reasonableness of answers to computations. Most calculations should arise as students solve problems in context" (p. 220).

Suggestions for Teaching Computational Estimation

Here are some general principles that are worth keeping in mind as you help your students develop estimation skills.

Use Real Examples of Estimation   Discuss situations in which computational estimations are used in real life. Some simple examples include dealing with grocery store situations (doing comparative shopping, determining if there is enough to pay the bill), adding up distances in planning a trip, determining approximate yearly or monthly totals of all sorts of things (school supplies, haircuts, lawn-mowing income, time watching TV), and figuring the cost of going to a sporting event or show including transportation, tickets, and snacks. Discuss why exact answers are not necessary in some instances but necessary in others. Look in a newspaper or magazine to find where numbers are the result of estimation and where they are the result of exact computations. Real examples are also a way to motivate students—for example, asking students in upper grades, "Are you a million seconds old? How can you find out?" Students enjoy exchanging information about birthdays and estimating how many seconds old they are (Martinie & Coates, 2007).

Use the Language of Estimation   Words and phrases such as *about*, *close*, *just about*, *a little more* (or *less*) *than*, and *between* are part of the language of estimation. Students should understand that they are trying to get as close as possible using quick and easy methods, but there is no correct estimate. Language can help convey that idea.

Use Context to Help with Estimates   A real-world number sense also plays a role in estimation. For example, for thirty 69-cent soft drinks, is $2.10, $21, or $210 most reasonable? It is much easier to focus on 7×3 and use a result that makes sense than to compute 0.69×30 and try to place the decimal correctly. Similar assists would come from knowing if the cost of a car would likely be $950 or $9500. Could attendance at the school play be 30 or 300 or 3000? A simple computation can provide the important digits, with number sense providing the rest.

Accept a Range of Estimates   Since they are based on computation, how can there be different answers to

estimates? The answer, of course, is that any particular estimate depends on the strategy used and the kinds of adjustments in the numbers that might be made. Estimates also tend to vary with the need for the estimate. Estimating litres of gas used per kilometre is quite different from trying to decide if your last $10 will cover the three items you need at the Fast Mart. These are new and difficult ideas for young students.

What estimate would you give for 27×325? If you use 20×300, you might say 6000. Or you might use 25 for the 27, noting that four 25s make 100. Since $325 \div 4$ is about 81, it would make 8100. If you use 30×300, your estimate is 9000, and 30×320 gives an estimate of 9600. Is one of these "right"?

By listing the estimates of many students and letting students discuss how and why different estimates resulted, they can begin to see that estimates generally fall in a range around the exact answer. Different approaches provide different results. And don't forget the context. Some situations call for more careful estimates than others. All results should be judged on how reasonable they are.

Focus on Flexible Methods, Not Answers   Remember that your primary concern is to help students develop strategies for making computational estimates quickly. Reflecting on the strategies will lead to strategy development. Class discussion of strategies for estimating is just as important as it was for the development of invented methods of computation. For any given estimation, there are often several very good but different methods. Students will learn strategies from each other.

Discussing different strategies will also help students understand that there is no "right" estimate.

> ⏸ ——————— *Pause and Reflect*
>
> Estimate this product: 438×62. Use the first idea that comes to your head and write down the result. Then, return to the task and try a different approach, perhaps using different numbers in your approach to the estimate.

Sometimes different strategies produce the same estimates. For 438×62, you might have thought about using 450×60 as a first step. Then, suppose you think 10×450 is 4500. Double 4500 is 9000 and 3×9000 is 27 000. You might also have thought 6×45 is $240 + 30$ or 270. But this is not 6×45 but 60 times 450 so you add two more zeros—27 000.

Alternatively, you could have used 400×60 and arrived at 24 000, conscious that you rounded both numbers down. You lost at least 38 sets of 62 or about 40×60. So add 2400 to the 24 000 to get 26 400.

If just a "ballpark" estimate was alright, you might have thought 500×60 is 30 000 and realized that it was a bit high. But the exact answer is also at least 400 × 60 or 24 000. So it's between 24 and 30 thousand.

You've just seen four of many possible estimation strategies for one computation. The more strategies you experience, the more you will learn. The more strategies you have, the better you can select one that best suits the situation at hand. Students will learn like this as well. In contrast, if you tell students to use a given strategy (e.g., round each number to one significant digit and multiply), they won't develop the skills to pick different strategies for different situations. Sometimes rounding is cumbersome and other strategies are quicker or more accurate.

Ask for Information, But No Answer   Consider the threat a grade 3 student perceives when you ask for an estimate of the sum $349.29 + $85.99 + $175.25. The requirement to come up with *a* number can result in students trying to quickly calculate an exact answer, then round it. This is a common strategy, especially amongst poor estimators (Hanson & Hogan, 2000). To counter this, ask questions that provide a possible result. Use prompts such as "Is it over or under 4000?" or "Will $50 be enough to pay for the tickets?" For the three prices, the question "About how much?" is quite different from "Is it more than $600? How would you answer each of those questions?

Each activity that follows suggests a format for estimation in which a specific numerical response is not required.

Activity 13.1

Over or Under?

Prepare several estimation exercises on a transparency. With each, provide an "over or under number." In Figure 13.1, each is either over or under $1.50, but the number need not be the same for each task.

The last activity need not be very elaborate. Here are some more "over/under" examples:

37 + 75	over/under 100
712 − 458	over/under 300
17 × 38	over/under 400
349 ÷ 45	over/under 10

A meaningful context can be added to the examples to make the task accessible to more learners. Simple, non-contextual tasks such as these can be prepared quickly. After presenting each, have students select their choice then discuss their reasoning. The next activity is similar. It is adapted from an activity in the *Investigations in Number, Data, and Space* grade 5 materials.

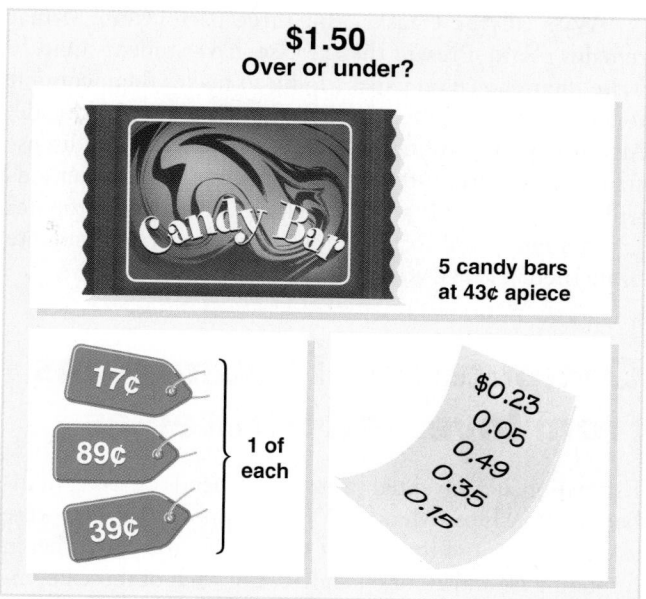

Figure 13.1   "Over or Under?" is a good beginning estimation activity.

Activity 13.2

High or Low?

Display a computation along with three or more computations that could be possible estimates for it. The students' task is to decide if the estimates will be higher or lower than the actual computation. For example, present the computation 736 × 18. For each of the following, decide if the result will be higher or lower than the exact amount and explain why you think so.

750 × 10	730 × 15
700 × 20	750 × 20

Activity 13.3

Best Choice

For any single estimation task, offer three or four possible estimates.

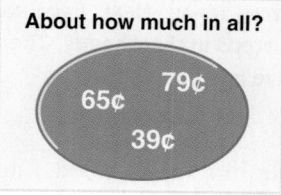

How close the choices are to each other will determine the difficulty of the task. Sometimes it is a good idea to use multiples of ten, such as $21, $210, and $2100.

With all these tasks, the three-part lesson format remains useful. Present the exercise, have students quickly write their choice on paper (doing so makes them commit to an answer), and then discuss why the choice was made. All three parts may take only 10 minutes. In the discussion, a wide variety of estimates and estimation methods will be shared. This will help students see that estimates fall in a range and that there is no single correct estimate or method.

Computational Estimations from Invented Strategies

Estimation, like invented strategies, depends on using number relationships (Menon, 2003). Suppose that you were asked to compute the sum of 64 and 28. You might begin by adding 60 and 20 or 64 and 30. For each of these beginnings, you would need to make one or two additional computations before arriving at the answer. However, each of these beginnings is actually a reasonable estimate.

Stop Before the Details

Often it is the first step or two in an invented computation that is good enough for the estimate. In the 64 × 28 example, even a grade 3 student would probably continue to the exact answer. But estimations are generally called for because an exact answer is too tedious or not necessary. When students have a good repertoire of invented strategies, one approach to an estimate is simply to begin to compute until you've gotten close enough to the exact answer.

Activity 13.4

That's Good Enough

Present students with a computation that is reasonably difficult for their skill level. For example: *T-shirts with the school logo cost $6 wholesale. The Pep Club has saved $257. How many shirts can they buy for their fundraiser?* The task is to describe the steps they would take to get an exact answer, but not to do them.

Share students' ideas. Next, have students actually do one or two steps in their heads. Then, stop and see if what they have is a good estimate.

The example in "That's Good Enough" may have seemed difficult to you. Try the same idea with a sum of four to six numbers: 47 + 79 + 74 + 55. Try it with a nasty difference: 7021 − 4583. Try it with a product: 86 × 29. The methods that students will come up with will be based on the ideas that they have learned for computing. In most instances, the beginnings of these computations are good estimates. By completing these first steps, students are also improving their understanding of invented strategies and computations. They are also enhancing their number sense.

Use Related Problem Sets

In Chapter 12, the use of related cluster problem sets or cluster problems was explained as a technique to help students develop invented strategies for multiplication and division (see p. 236). The cluster-problem approach, adapted from the *Investigations* curriculum, has students solve a collection of problems related to but easier than the target problem. These problems are then used to solve the harder problem. An important aspect of the cluster-problem approach is that students first make (and write down) an estimate of the target computation.

Pause and Reflect

What follows are some cluster problems for each of the operations. The last problem is the target problem. Give these a try. Remember to first make an estimate of the target. Then solve all the problems in the set. Use problems in the set to estimate the target. Which choices lead to good estimates?

4 + 5 + 6 400 + 500 + 600 400 + 600 60 + 30 + 100 60 + 20 + 90 **467 + 528 + 693**	600 − 300 600 − 400 85 + 15 15 + 13 85 − 13 **613 − 385**
10 ÷ 7 70 ÷ 7 7 × 11 7 × 12 **87 ÷ 7**	6 × 7 6 × 8 70 × 7 60 × 7 **68 × 7**
40 × 20 50 × 4 48 × 2 48 × 4 50 × 20 **48 × 24**	5 × 20 5 × 22 5 × 10 22 × 10 2 × 22 **147 ÷ 22**

There are many possible paths to the results. Notice, however, that some of the related problems (not the target) are actually good problems to use for making estimates. Once students are comfortable with sets of problems, try the following task.

Activity 13.5

Make a Little Cluster

Give students a target problem for a related problem set. It can be any operation on which you are working. The task is to create a set of two to three problems that will help produce a reasonable estimate. Once students have made the little cluster set, they should use their problems to estimate the target.

Computational Estimation Strategies

Estimation strategies are specific algorithms that produce approximate rather than exact results. As you work through the strategies in this section, you should recognize many of the same approaches that students are likely to have developed from their invented methods. It is also likely that some of the strategies in this section will not have been developed. You will need to introduce these to your students. Be very clear whenever you suggest a strategy; the intention is to create a "basketful" of good strategies. Those that you introduce are no more correct or important than ideas they have devised.

NCTM Standards "Instructional attention and frequent modeling by the teacher can help students develop a range of computational estimation strategies including flexible rounding, the use of benchmarks, and front-end strategies. Students should be encouraged to frequently explain their thinking as they estimate" (p. 156).

Front-End Methods

Front-end methods focus on the leading or leftmost digits in numbers, ignoring the rest. After an estimate is made on the basis of these front-end digits, an adjustment can then be made by checking the digits that have been ignored.

For students who have had a lot of experience with invented strategies, the front-end strategy will make a lot of sense since all invented strategies begin with the large part of the numbers involved. The front-end approach is an especially good place to begin the topic of estimation for students who use only traditional algorithms. They will have to work hard at the idea of only looking at digits in the left portion of numbers in a computation.

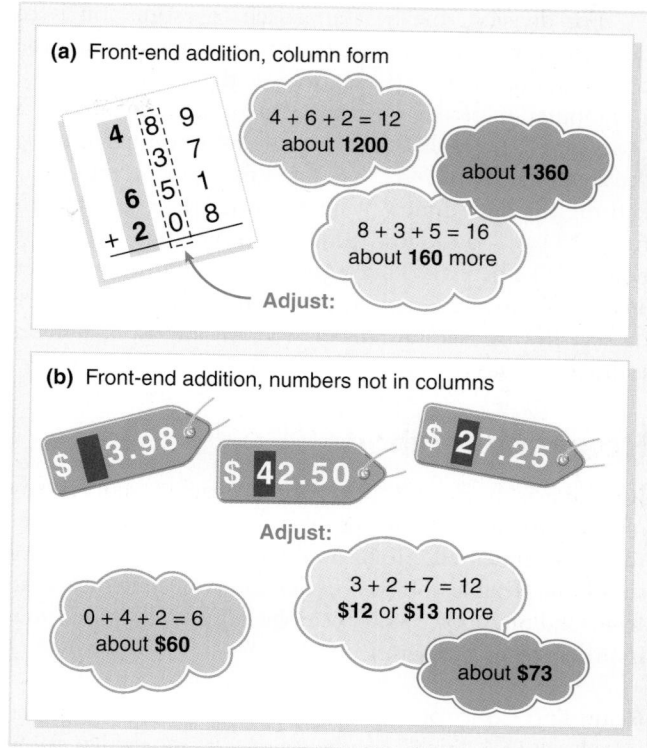
Figure 13.2 Front-end estimation in addition.

Front-End Addition and Subtraction A front-end approach is reasonable for addition or subtraction when all or most of the numbers have the same number of digits. Figure 13.2 illustrates the idea. Notice that when a number has fewer digits than the rest, that number is initially ignored.

After adding or subtracting the front digits, an adjustment is made to compensate for the digits or numbers that were ignored. Making an adjustment is actually a separate skill. For young children, first practise using just the front digits.

The leading-digit strategy is easy to use because it does not require rounding or changing numbers. The numbers used are visible, so children can estimate without changing the numbers. You do need to be sure that children pay close attention to place value and only consider digits in the largest place. This is especially important if the number of digits in each of the numbers varies.

Front-End Multiplication and Division For multiplication and division, the front-end method uses the first digit in each factor. The computation is then done using zeros in the other positions. For example, a front-end estimation of 48×7 is 40 times 7, or 280. When both numbers have more than one digit, the front ends of both are used. For 452×23, consider 400×20, or 8000. Because of the greater error that occurs in estimating with multiplication, it is important to adjust these estimates.

For division, the best approach to estimation is to think multiplication. Avoid presenting problems using the computational form ($7\overline{)3482}$) because this tends to suggest a computation rather than an estimate and encourages a "goes into" approach. Present problems in context or using the algebraic form: $3482 \div 7$. For this problem, the front-end digit is determined by first getting the correct position. (100×7 is too low. 1000×7 is too high. It's in the hundreds.) There are 34 hundreds in the dividend, so since $34 \div 7$ is between 4 and 5, the front-end estimate is 400 or 500. In this example, since $34 \div 7$ is almost 5, a closer estimate is 500.

Rounding Methods

Rounding is the most familiar form of estimation. It is a way of changing numbers in a problem to others that are easier to compute mentally. To be useful for estimating, rounding should be flexible and well understood conceptually. Like front-end methods, answers can be adjusted as a final step in order to get a closer estimate.

Rounding Concept   To round a number simply means to substitute a "nice" number that is close so that some computation can be done more easily. The close number can be any nice number and need not be a multiple of 10 or 100, as has been traditional. It should be whatever makes the computation or estimation easier or simplifies numbers sufficiently in a story, chart, or conversation. You might say, "Last night it took me 57 minutes to do my homework" or "Last night it took me about one hour to do my homework." The first expression is more precise; the second substitutes a rounded number for better communication.

A number line with nice numbers highlighted can be useful for helping children select near nice numbers. An unlabelled number line, like the one shown in Figure 13.3, can be made using three strips of poster board taped end to end. Labels are written above the line on the chalkboard. The ends can be labelled 0 and 100, 100 and 200, ..., 900, and 1000. The other markings then show multiples of 25, 10, and 5. Indicate a number above the line that you want to round. Discuss the marks (nice numbers) that are close. (*Author's note:* The term *nice number* is not found in textbooks. It refers to numbers that would make the problem easier to compute mentally.)

Rounding in Addition and Subtraction   When several numbers are to be added, it is usually a good idea to round them to the same place value. Keep a running sum as you round each number. Figure 13.4 shows an example of rounding.

For addition and subtraction problems involving only two terms, one strategy is to round only one of the two numbers. For example, you can round only the number

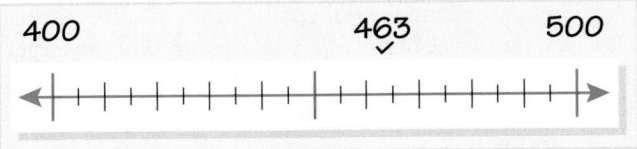

Figure 13.3 A blank number line can be labelled in different ways to help students with near and nice numbers.

being subtracted. (e.g., 6724 – 1863, becomes 6724 – 2000 and the result is 4724). You can stop here or you can adjust. Adjusting might go like this: You took away a bigger number, so the result must be too small. Adjust to about 4800.

Rounding to nice numbers depends on what you, the estimator, consider "nice." For example, in 627 + 385, you may want to round 385 to 375 or 400. The point is that there are no rigid rules. Choices depend on the relationships held by the estimator, on how quickly the estimate is needed, and on how accurate an estimate is required.

Rounding in Multiplication and Division   The rounding strategy for multiplication is no different from that for other operations. However, the error involved can be significant, especially when both factors are rounded. In Figure 13.5, several multiplication situations are illustrated, and rounding is used to estimate each.

If one number can be rounded to 10, 100, or 1000, the resulting product is easy to determine without adjusting the other factor. Figure 13.5 shows a similar process.

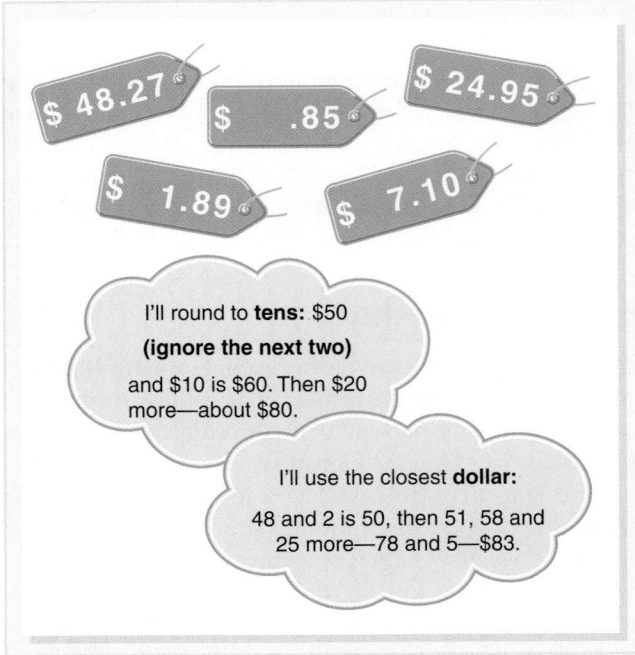

Figure 13.4 Rounding in addition.

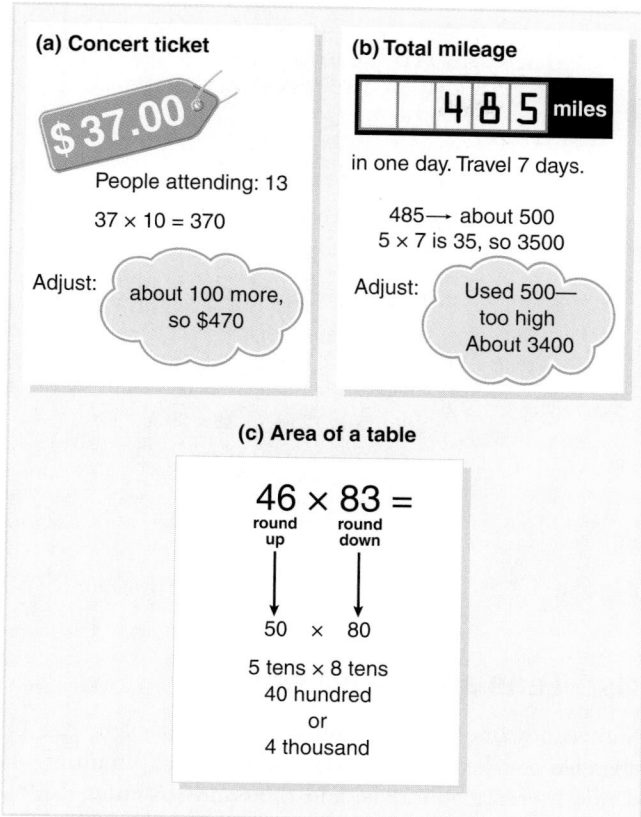

Figure 13.5 Rounding in multiplication.

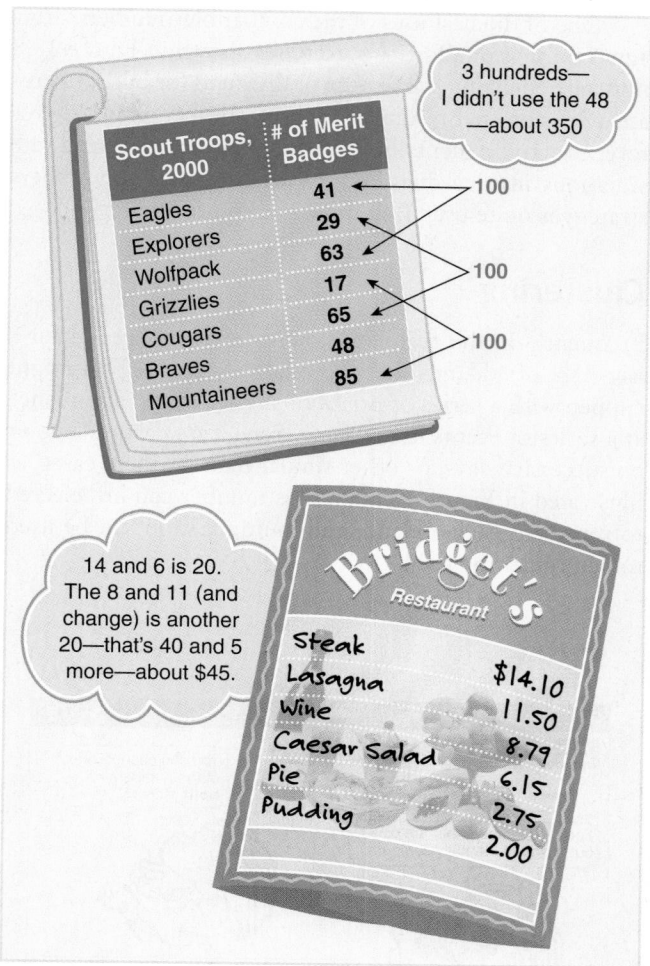

Figure 13.6 Compatibles used in addition.

When one factor is a single digit, examine the other factor. Consider the product 7×485. If 485 is rounded to 500, the estimate is relatively easy, but is too high by 7×15. If a more accurate result is required, subtract about 100 (an estimate of 7×15). See Figure 13.5(b).

Another good rule of thumb with multiplication is to round one factor up and the other down (even if it is not the closest rounded number). When estimating 86×28, 86 is between 80 and 90, but 28 is very close to 30. Try rounding 86 down to 80 and 28 up to 30. The actual product is 2408, only 8 off from the 80×30 estimate. If both numbers were rounded to the nearest 10, the estimate would be based on 90×30, with an error of nearly 300 (see Figure 13.5(c) for another example).

When rounding in division, the key is to find two nice numbers, rather than round to the nearest benchmark. For example, you can estimate $4325 \div 7$ by using the close compatible number 4200 to yield an estimate of 600. Rounding to the nearest hundred results in a dividend of 4300, which does not make the division easier to do.

Compatible Numbers

It is sometimes useful to look for two or three numbers that can be grouped to make benchmark values (e.g. 10, 100, 500).

If numbers in the list can be adjusted slightly to produce these groups, it will make finding an estimate easier. This approach is illustrated in Figure 13.6.

In subtraction, it is often possible to adjust only one number to produce an easily observed difference, as illustrated in Figure 13.7.

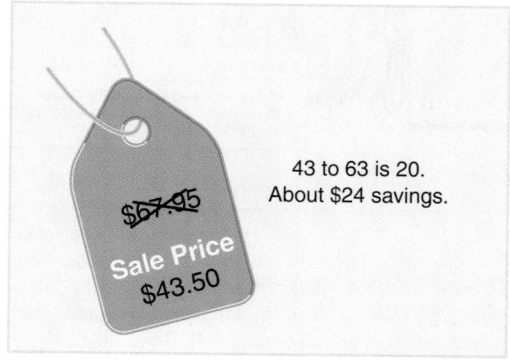

Figure 13.7 Compatibles can mean an adjustment that produces an easy difference.

One of the best uses of the compatible-numbers strategy is in division. The two exercises shown in Figure 13.8 illustrate adjusting the divisor or dividend (or both) to create a division that results in a whole number and is, therefore, easy to do mentally. Many percent, fraction, and rate situations involve division, and the compatible-numbers strategy is quite useful, as shown in Figure 13.9.

Clustering

Frequently in the real world, an estimate is needed for a large list of addends that are relatively close. This might happen with a series of prices of similar items, attendance at a series of events in the same arena, cars passing a point on successive days, or other similar data. In these cases, as illustrated in Figure 13.10, a nice number can be selected to represent each addend, and multiplication can be used to determine the total.

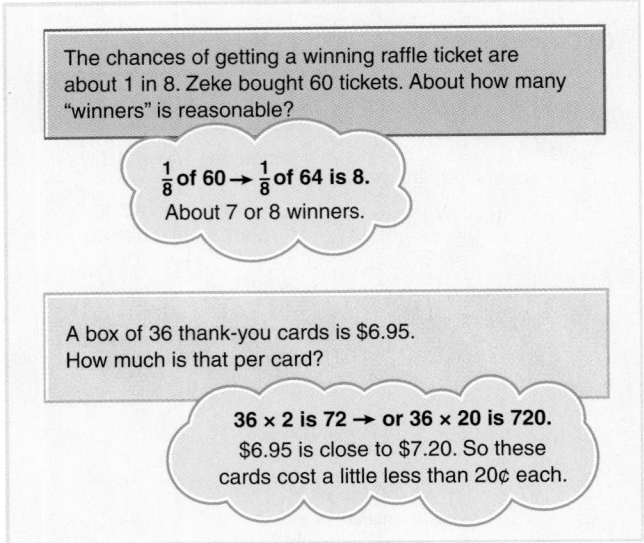

Figure **13.9** Using compatible numbers in division.

Figure **13.8** Adjusting to simplify division.
Source: From *GUESS (Guide to Using Estimation Skills and Strategies)* (box 1, cards 2 and 3), by B.J. Reys and R.E. Reys, 1983, White Plains, NY: Dale Seymour Publications. Copyright 1983 by Dale Seymour Publications. Reprinted by permission of Dale Seymour Publications.

Use Tens and Hundreds

Sometimes one of the numbers in the problem can be changed to take advantage of how easy it is to multiply or divide by tens, hundreds, and thousands (Menon, 2003). For example, take 456×5. Five is really 10/2 (so substitute $10 \div 2$ to solve mentally). Multiply 456 by 10 to get 4560, then estimate what half of that is—about 2300. See if you can apply this strategy to a larger problem: 786×48. You may have first thought that 48 is almost 50, which is the same as $100 \div 2$. Since 786 times 100 equals 78 600, which is about 80 000, half of that equals 40 000. Alternatively, you can divide by the two first, then multiply by 10 or 100.

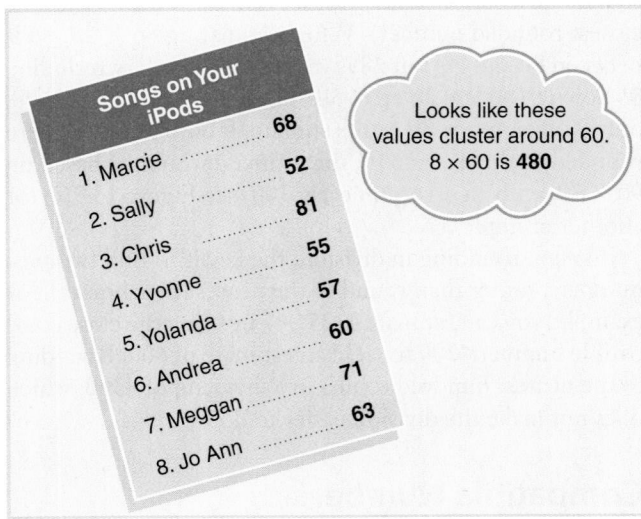

Figure **13.10** Estimating sums using clustering.

In the last example, it would mean taking half of 786, which is about 400, and multiplying by 100 to get 40 000.

This works with division, too. Consider 429 ÷ 5. Think: 429 ÷ 10 × 2 (or 429 × 2 ÷ 10). 429 ÷ 10 is about 42 and double that is 84. This can be a particularly useful strategy as the numbers get larger, like the following:

2309 ÷ 53

This strategy can also be extended to numbers close to 25 (which is 100/4). For example: 786 ÷ 23 can be thought of this way: 786 × 4 ÷ 100. So 786 is close to 800, times 4 is 3200, then divided by 100 is 32.

 Since computational estimation involves a certain element of speed, teachers often wonder how they can test it so that students are not computing on paper then rounding the answer to look like an estimate. One method is to prepare a short list of about three estimation exercises on a transparency. The cards in the GUESS boxes (Reys & Reys, 1983) are a ready source for these, or you can simply write some computations. Students have their paper ready to record their answer as you briefly show one exercise at a time on the overhead, perhaps for 20 seconds, depending on the task. Students immediately write their estimate and indicate if they think their estimate is "low" or "high"—that is, lower or higher than the exact computation. They do not do any written computation. Continue until you are finished. Then, show all the exercises and have students write down how they did each estimate. They should also indicate if they think the estimate was a good or not so good estimate and the reason why. By only doing a few estimates, and having students reflect on them, you actually gain more information than you would with just the answers to a longer list. ◆

Estimation Experiences

The examples presented here are not designed to teach estimation strategies, but only to offer useful formats to provide your students with practice using skills as they are being developed. These will be a good addition to any estimation program.

Because students are less comfortable (and have less ability) with estimation as opposed to calculation, it is important to include regular experiences and activities that help students improve their estimation skills. The following activity works well on the overhead projector, as do many full-class estimation activities. This activity is also good for engaging students in discussions of estimation strategies.

Activity 13.6

What Was Your Method?

Select a problem with an estimation given. For example, 139 × 43 might be estimated as 6000. Ask questions concerning this estimate: "How do you think that estimate was arrived at? Was that a good approach? How should it be adjusted? Why might someone select 150 instead of 140 as a substitute for 139?" Almost every estimate can involve different choices and methods. Alternatives make good discussions, helping students see different methods and learn that there is no single correct estimate.

Activity 13.7

Jump to It

This activity focuses on division concepts. Students begin with a start number and estimate how many times they will add that start number to reach the goal. Here are a few to get you started (the numbers can vary to meet the needs and experiences of your students):

Jump Number	Goal	Estimate of Jumps	Was Estimate Reasonable?
5	72		
11	97		
7	150		
14	135		
47	1200		

To check estimates on the calculator, students can enter 0 + [jump number] and key ⬓ for every estimated jump, or multiply ✕ [estimate of jumps].

Calculator Activities

The calculator is not only a good source for estimation activities; it is one of the reasons estimation is so important. In the real world, we frequently hit a wrong key, leave off a zero or a decimal, or simply enter numbers incorrectly. An estimate of the expected result alerts us to these errors. The calculator as a tool for teaching estimation provides students with an opportunity to work independently or in pairs in a challenging, fun way without fear of embarrassment.

Activity 13.8

The Range Game

This is an estimation game for any of the four operations. First pick a start number and an operation. The start number and operation are stored in the calculator. Students then take turns entering the start number, ⊠ a number of choice, and ⊜ to try to make the result land in the target range. The following example for multiplication illustrates the activity:

> Start number: 17
>
> Range: 800 to 830

If the first number tried is 25, pressing 17 ⊠ 25 gives 425. This is not in the range, so the calculator is passed to the partner, who clears the screen and picks a different number. For example, a number close to 50 is picked because the first product was about half of the target range.

A second guess might be 17 ⊠ 45, or 765. This is closer, but still not in the range. The calculator then goes back to the first person. Continue to clear each guess and start again until someone gets a product that lands in the range. Figure 13.11 gives examples of all four operations. Prepare a list of start numbers and target ranges. Let students play in pairs to see who can hit the most targets on the list (Wheatley & Hersberger, 1986).

"The Range Game" can also be played on an overhead calculator with the whole class. The extent of the range and the types of numbers used can all be adjusted to suit the level of the class.

Activity 13.9

The Range Game: Continuous Input

Select a target range as before. Next enter the starting number in the calculator, and hand it to the first player. For addition and subtraction, the first player then presses either ⊞ or ⊟ followed by a number, and then ⊜. If the result is not in the range, the calculator (with answer still on the screen) is handed to the next player, who begins his or her turn by entering ⊞ or ⊟ and an appropriate number. If the target is 423 to 425, a sequence of turns might go like this:

> Start with 119.
>
> ⊞ 350 ⊜ 469 (too high)
>
> ⊟ 42 ⊜ 427 (a little over)
>
> ⊟ 3 ⊜ 424 (success)

For multiplication or division, only one operation is used through the whole game. After the first or second turn, decimal factors are usually required. This variation allows students to develop an excellent understanding of multiplication or division by decimal numbers. A sequence for a target of 262 to 265 might be like this:

> Start with 63.
>
> ⊠ 5 ⊜ 315 (too high)
>
> ⊠ 0.7 ⊜ 220.5 (too low)
>
> ⊠ 1.3 ⊜ 286.65 (too high)
>
> ⊠ 0.9 ⊜ 257.985 (too low)
>
> ⊠ 1.03 ⊜ 265.72455 (very close)

(What would you press next?)

Try a target of 76 to 80, begin with 495, and use only division.

After entering the setup with the start # as shown, players take turns pressing a number, then ⊜ to try to get a result in the target range.

Addition:
Press: 0 ⊞ (start #) ⊜

START		TARGET
153	→	790 ⓡ 800
216	→	400 ⓡ 410
53	→	215 ⓡ 220

Subtraction:
Press: 0 ⊟ (start #) ⊜

START		TARGET
18	→	25 ⓡ 30
41	→	630 ⓡ 635
129	→	475 ⓡ 485

Multiplication:
Press: (start #) ⊠ 0 ⊜

START		TARGET
67	→	1100 ⓡ 1200
143	→	3500 ⓡ 3600
39	→	1600 ⓡ 1700

Division:
Press: 0 ÷ (start #) ⊜

START		TARGET
20	→	25 ⓡ 30
39	→	50 ⓡ 60
123	→	15 ⓡ 20

Figure 13.11 "The Range Game."

The following activity is a blend of mental computation and estimation. Figuring out where the numbers go to create the exact solution involves estimation.

Activity 13.10

Box Math

Give students three digits to use (e.g., 3, 5, 7) and two operations (+ and −), preferably on cut out cardstock so they can manipulate the numbers easily. Give students a set of equations with answers only and ask them to use only their digits (in the squares) and operations (in the circle) to get to the answer, as shown in the following display.

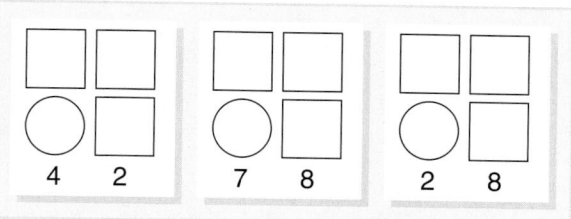

There are at least nine different possible answers. The same can be done with multiplication and division, though it must be written horizontally to account for both operations (adapted from Coates & Thompson, 2003).

 Estimation skills are often embedded in software drill-and-practice packages, although very few are designed for estimation skills alone. *Mathville* (Courseware Solutions, 2005) and *Math Trek* (Nectar Foundation, 2006) are two Canadian software programs that offer practice with estimation. *Mathville 1* and *Mathville Middle School* offer practice with estimation in a real-world setting. In *Mathville 1*, students must estimate the number of objects in a set and compare their estimate with the actual number. In *Mathville Middle School*, students must estimate and round the cost of items in a clothing or hardware store to make certain they have enough money, before making their purchases. The interactive tutorial in *Math Trek 4, 5, 6*, one of the components of the *Math Trek* program, teaches students about estimating and rounding. Rounding extends to large numbers, decimals, and extensions. The program also includes *Math Trek 1, 2, 3* and *Math Trek 7, 8* and *Math Strategies Understanding Arithmetic—Level 1*. ◆

Using Whole Numbers to Estimate Rational Numbers

It might be argued that much of the estimating we do in the real world involves fractions, decimals, and percents. A few examples are suggested here:

- SALE! Original price of a jacket is $58.00. It is marked one-fourth off. What is the sale price?
- About 62 percent of the 834 students bought their lunch last Wednesday. How many bought lunch?
- Tickets sold for $1.25. If attendance was 3124, about how much was the total take?
- I drove 245 kilometres on 26.34 litres of gas. How many kilometres per litre did my car get?

⏸ Pause and Reflect

Suppose you were to make estimates in each of the previous situations. Without actually getting an estimate, decide what numbers you would use in each case. For instance, in the first example you would not use 51.99 but perhaps 50 or 52. What about the fractions, decimal numbers, and percents in the other problems? Think about that now before reading on.

The first example asks for an estimate of $\frac{1}{4}$ off, or $\frac{3}{4}$ of $58.00. To get $\frac{3}{4}$ of a quantity requires dividing by 4 and multiplying by 3. Those are whole-number computations, but they require an understanding of fractional multiplication.

In the next example, the problem is finding a way to deal with 62 percent. Well, that's close to 60 percent, which is $\frac{3}{5}$ or, equivalently, 6 times 10 percent. In either case, the required computations involve whole numbers. The translation of 62 percent requires an understanding of percents.

In the third example, an understanding of decimals and fractions converts the problem to $1\frac{1}{4}$ of 3125. The computations involve dividing 3125 (perhaps 3200) by 4 and adding that to 3125—all whole-number computations. Similarly, the final example requires an understanding of decimals followed by whole-number computations.

The point is that when fractions, decimals, and percents are involved, an understanding of numeration is often the first thing required to make an estimate. That understanding often translates the situation into one involving only whole-number computations.

Of course, this is not always the case for fractions and decimals. Consider what is required to make estimates for the following:

$$2\frac{3}{8} + 4\frac{1}{9} - \frac{1}{12}$$

$$4.0178 + 73.4$$

A reasonable estimate in each case requires an understanding of rational numbers. Very few new estimation skills are required. These types of problems are discussed in Chapter 16.

Reflections on Chapter 13

Writing to Learn

1. How is computational estimation different from other types of estimation?
2. Why might computational estimation be strange to students?
3. What are some important considerations for teaching computational estimation?
4. What is the purpose of activities like "Over or Under" where students do not actually produce an answer?
5. Describe in general terms how estimation can grow out of the development of invented strategies.
6. Describe each of these estimation strategies. Make up a good example for each and use it in your explanation.

   a. Front-end
   b. Rounding
   c. Compatibles
   d. Clustering
   e. Adapting to use 10s, 100s, 1000s, and so forth.

For Discussion and Exploration

1. You notice a student is estimating by doing the computation and rounding the answer. Why might the student be using this strategy? What experiences might you plan to improve the student's ability to estimate?
2. Examine your regional mathematics curriculum document. Does the curriculum require that different computational estimation strategies and mental computation be taught? How do guidelines for computation influence what computation methods are taught in school? Do you agree with what is required?

Resources for Chapter 13

Literature Connections

Literature often provides excellent contexts for which estimates, not exact answers, are the goal, as in the following engaging examples.

Beware Pirates   *Wishinsky, 2007*

Transported back through time, as early as 1577, on the Canadian Flyer, an antique red sled, Emily and Matt experience the past firsthand. Thrilling adventures take them to different parts of the country at fascinating points in our rich Canadian history. Not only does this book provide opportunities for students to estimate time and distances, it allows for connections with history and geography.

Counting on Frank   *Clement, 1991*

This popular book has a narrator who uses his dog, Frank, as a counting reference. For example, he explains that 24 Franks would fit in his room. Since the book offers approximations, there are limitless opportunities to do computational estimation. For example, how many Franks would fit in five rooms? If there were 24 Franks, how many cans of dog food (discussed on a later page) might be needed? The back of the book offers a series of estimation questions to get you started.

"How Many, How Much" from *A Light in the Attic*   *Silverstein, 1981*

This very short poem is a nice lead in to lessons on estimation, especially as it asks some unanswerable estimates, like how many slices in a loaf of bread (depends on how you slice it!). No answers are given, but students can estimate how many eggs in a dozen, how many crayons in 70 boxes (boxes with 8, 16, or any amount) or how many weeks in their lifetime.

How Much, How Many, How Far, How Heavy, How Long, How Tall Is 1000   *Nolan, 1995*

Children will be intrigued by the comparisons—how 1000 of this seems a lot smaller than 1000 or that, in this playful look at the number 1000. An amusing twist on the traditional counting book, this book can be used for estimating numbers and amounts. A thousand freckles may seem like a lot, but a thousand hairs will make a very thin hairdo indeed!

Recommendations for Further Reading

Books

Bresser, R., & Holtzman, C. (1999). *Developing number sense: Grades 3–6.* Sausalito, CA: Math Solutions Publications.
This book includes 13 worthwhile number-sense activities covering a range of topics including estimation. Activities include extensions, practical suggestions, and examples of students' work.

Reys, B. (1991). *Developing Number Sense.* Addenda Series, Grades 5–8. Reston, VA: NCTM.
This is still a fabulous resource—providing a discussion about number sense and including a great collection of activities, some of which focus on computational estimation.

Online Resources

Count on Math (NCTMs *Illuminations—Lessons, Grades 6–8*)
http://illuminations.nctm.org/LessonsDetail.aspx?id=U96
The two lessons here provide activities for older students to estimate and develop number sense through data collection activities.

Estimation—Tens
www.quia.com/custom/292main.html

Estimation—Hundreds
www.quia.com/custom/293main.html
Both Estimation Tens and Hundreds provide students with an opportunity to engage in matching and concentration games to practise estimating and rounding.
The above two sites can be accessed under the topic "Number Extras" on Jim Reed's home site for Learn Alberta at http://argyll.epsb.ca/jreed/.

Estimate!
www.fi.uu.nl/toepassingen/00062/schatten/welcome_en.html
This is a fun fast-paced estimation applet for all four operations (go to "options" to select the one you want to do). You click on start and a timer records how long until you get your answer entered. After ten problems you get a score, based on speed and accuracy.

Estimate Sums
www.ixl.com/math/practice/grade-2-estimate-sums
This site has various applets for practising skills for pre-K–3 students. There is a range of rounding and estimating activities for grades 2 and 3.

Estimator Quiz (Shodor's Project Interactive)
www.shodor.org/interactive/activities/EstimatorQuiz
Similar to Estimate!, this applet allows a student to practise estimation for addition, multiplication, and percentage problems, getting instant feedback. But the site gives one problem at a time. A timer and instant feedback allow for independent practice and reinforcement.

myeducationlab *will help you improve your understanding of the concepts taught in this textbook and in your course. This online tool includes videos of real classroom experiences, sample lesson plans, simulations, case studies, and links to important educational and teaching Web sites that will help you make the transition from student to teacher. As you study in your course and with this textbook, please follow along in **MyEducationLab**. Use it! Explore it! And improve your knowledge and your grade!*

Chapter 14
Algebraic Thinking: Generalizations, Patterns, and Functions

lgebra is one of the five content standards in NCTM's *Principles and Standards* and an important component of K–12 provincial and territorial curricula. Even though algebra requirements may vary at the elementary level, one thing is certain: the algebra envisioned for this level—and for high school as well—is not the algebra that you most likely experienced. Typical senior elementary or high school algebra consisted primarily of symbol manipulation procedures and artificial applications with little connection to the real world. The focus now is on the type of thinking and reasoning that prepares students to think mathematically across all areas of mathematics.

Algebraic thinking or algebraic reasoning involves forming generalizations from experiences with number and computation, formalizing these ideas with the use of a meaningful symbol system, and exploring the concepts of pattern and functions. Far from a topic with little real-world use, algebraic thinking pervades all of mathematics and is essential for making mathematics useful in daily life.

Big Ideas

1. Algebra is a useful tool for generalizing arithmetic and representing patterns in our world.

2. Symbolism, especially involving equations and variables, must be well understood conceptually for students to be successful in mathematics, particularly algebra.

3. Methods we use to compute and the structures in our number system can and should be generalized. For example, the generalization that $a + b = b + a$ tells us that $83 + 27 = 27 + 83$ *without computing the sums on each side of the equal sign.*

4. Patterns, both repeating and growing, can be recognized, extended, and generalized.

5. Functions in K–8 mathematics describe in concrete ways the notion that for every input there is a unique output.

6. Understanding is strengthened with functions that are explored across representations, as each one provides a different view of the same relationship.

Mathematics Content Connections

As Kaput (1998) notes, it is difficult to find an area of mathematics that does not involve generalizing and formalizing in some central way. In fact, this type of reasoning is at the heart of mathematics as a science of pattern and order.

- **Number, Place Value, Basic Facts, and Computation** (Chapters 8, 10, 11, and 12): The most important generalizations at the core of algebraic thinking are those made about number and computation—arithmetic. Not only does algebraic thinking generalize from number and computation; the generalizations themselves add to the understanding and facility with computation. We can use our understanding of 10 to add $5 + 8$ ($5 + 8 = 3 + 2 + 8 = 3 + 10$), and $5 + 38$ ($5 + 38 = 3 + 2 + 38 = 3 + 40$). The generalization to be made here is that 2 can be taken from one addend and moved to the other: $a + b = (a - 2) + (b + 2)$. Although students may not conceptualize this general idea symbolically, seeing that it works is algebraic thinking.

- **Operation Concepts** (Chapter 9): As children learn about the operations, they also learn that there are regularities in the way that the operations work. Examples include the commutative properties ($a + b = b + a$ and $a \times b = b \times a$), as well as the way that operations are related to one another.

- **Proportional Reasoning** (Chapter 18): Exploring concepts of ratio and proportion in the elementary grades is important to students' development of proportional reasoning. Thus students need many opportunities to reason in multiplicative situations.

- **Measurement** (Chapter 19): Measures are a principal means of describing relationships in the physical world. These relationships are often algebraic in nature. Measurement formulas such as circumference of a circle are functions. You can say that the height of a building is a function of how many stories it has.

- **Geometry** (Chapter 20): Geometric patterns are some of the first that children experience. Growing patterns give rise to functional relationships. Coordinates are used to generalize distance concepts and to control transformations. And, of course, functions are graphed on the coordinate plane to visually show algebraic relationships.

- **Data Analysis** (Chapter 21): When data are gathered, the algebraic thinker is able to examine them for regularities and patterns. Functions are used to approximate trends or describe the relationships in mathematically useful ways.

Algebraic Thinking

Algebraic thinking begins in pre-kindergarten and continues through high school. As well, it continues to be included in every grade level, with the primary topics being the use of patterns leading to generalizations (especially with the operations), the study of change, and the concept of function. In examining algebraic thinking in the NCTM *Curriculum Focal Points*, Seeley & Schielack note:

> Underlying all these particular topics is the fundamental idea that, for students to be prepared to succeed in algebra, one of the best tools they can have is a deep understanding of the number system, its operations, and the properties related to those operations. (p. 266)

This chapter follows the chapters on these concepts so that you can see how closely related number concepts, operations, and algebraic thinking are.

Kaput (1999), a leader in crafting appropriate algebra curricula across the grades, talks about algebra that "involves generalizing and expressing that generality using increasingly formal languages, where the generalizing begins in arithmetic, in modelling situations, in geometry, and in virtually all the mathematics that can or should appear in the elementary grades" (pp. 134–135). Although many authors and researchers have written about algebraic thinking, Kaput's description is the most complete encompassing the ideas of many other contributors. He describes five different forms of algebraic reasoning:

1. Generalization from arithmetic and from patterns in all of mathematics.
2. Meaningful use of symbols.
3. Study of structure in the number system.
4. Study of patterns and functions.
5. Process of mathematical modelling, which integrates the first four items in this list.

Thus, algebraic thinking is not a singular idea but is composed of different forms of thought and an understanding of symbolism. It is a separate component of the curriculum but should also be embedded in all areas of mathematics. There is general agreement that we must begin the development of these forms of thinking from the very beginning of school so that students will learn to think productively with the powerful ideas of mathematics—so that they can think mathematically.

In this chapter, these five themes are used to discuss algebraic thinking. The categories themselves are not developmental, but within each category there are important developmental considerations. Therefore, in reading this chapter, you will find that each category offers considerations and effective instructional activities across the K–8 curriculum.

Generalization from Arithmetic and from Patterns

The process of creating generalizations from number and arithmetic begins as early as kindergarten and continues as students learn about all aspects of number and computation, including basic facts and meanings of the operations. Therefore, algebraic thinking is very much connected to the ideas in Chapters 9 through 13.

In order to make generalizations, it is helpful to use symbolism. Thus, both generalizations and an understanding of variables and symbolism are developed at the same time.

Generalizations with Addition

Young children explore addition families and in the process learn how to decompose and recompose numbers. The monkeys and trees problem illustrated in Figure 14.1 provides students a chance to not only consider ways to decompose 7, but also to see characteristics that are generalizable, such as increasing the number in the small tree by one means reducing the number in the large tree by one.

Students may be asked to find all the ways the monkeys can be in the two trees. The significant question is how to decide when all the solutions have been found. At one level, students will just not be able to think of any more and many will forget about using 0. Other children may try to use each number from 0 to 7 for one tree. The student who explains that for each number 0 to 7 there is one solution is no longer partitioning 7 into parts. Rather, the student is making a generalization that yields the number of solutions without even listing them (Yackel, 1997). That reasoning can be generalized to the number of ways that 376

Figure 14.1 Seven monkeys want to play in two trees, one big and one small. Show all the different ways that the seven monkeys could play in two trees.

Source: Adapted from Yackel, E. (1997). A foundation for algebraic reasoning in the early grades. *Teaching Childrem Mathematics, 3* (6), 276–280. A similar task was explored in Carpenter, T. P., Franke, M. L., and Levi, L. (2003). *Thinking mathematically: Integrating arithmetic and algebra in elementary school.* Portsmouth, NH: Heinemann.

monkeys occupy the two trees. Carpenter, Franke, and Levi (2003) found students at the grade 2 level who articulated that there is always one more solution than the number of monkeys. Notice how this is a generalization that no longer depends on the numbers involved.

Generalizing does not need to involve symbols. However, it is an important inclusion for older students (see the next major section). For example, grade 7 students doing a problem like the monkeys but with 8 mice in a green or a blue cage discovered three equations to describe the situation: $b + g = 8$, $8 - g = b$, and $8 - b = g$ (Stephens, 2005).

This is just one example of how algebraic thinking can and should be infused into work with number. To do so requires planning in advance—thinking of what questions you can ask to help students think about generalized characteristics within the problem they are working on (when the number of monkeys in one tree goes down, the number in the other goes up by one) and to other problems that have the same pattern (376 monkeys).

Generalizations in the Hundreds Chart

The hundreds chart is a rich field for exploring number relationships and should not be thought of solely as a device for teaching numeration. In Chapter 11, children coloured skip counts on the hundreds chart and looked for patterns (see Activities 11.14–11.19 and 11.28). Here are some additional tasks you might explore in a similar manner.

- Which numbers make diagonal patterns? Which make columnar patterns? Can you make up a rule to explain

when a number will have a diagonal or columnar pattern? (See Figure 14.2, noting that the patterns depend on how many columns the charts contain.)

- If you move down two and over the hundreds chart, what is the relationship between the original number and the new number?
- Can you find two skip-count patterns where one is "on top of" the other? That is, all the shaded squares for one pattern are part of the shaded squares for the other. How are these two skip-count numbers related? Is this true for any pair of numbers that have this relationship? Will this be true on hundreds charts with different widths? Why or why not?
- Find any value on the hundreds chart. Add it with the number to the left and the one to the right; then divide by 3. What did you get? Why?

These examples are just some of the many questions that extend number concepts to algebraic thinking concepts. "Can you find a rule?", "Why does this work?", and "When will this be true?" are questions that require justification and reasoning. They, in turn, strengthen students' understanding of number and of algebra.

Generalization Through Exploring a Pattern

One of the most interesting and perhaps most valuable methods for searching for a functional relationship is to find it in the growing physical pattern. One method of doing this is to examine only one step of a physical pattern

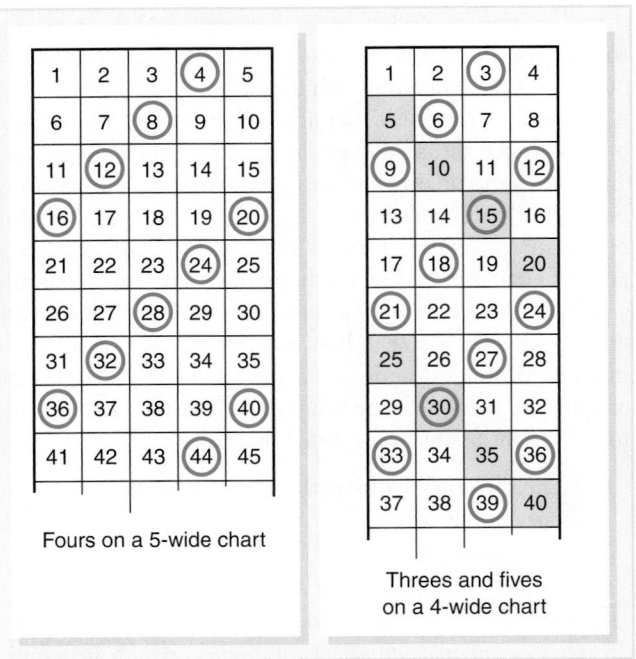

Figure 14.2 Patterns on hundreds charts of different widths.

and ask students to find a method of counting the elements without simply counting each one by one. The following problem is a classic example of such a task. It is described in many resources, including Burns and McLaughlin (1990) and Boaler and Humphreys (2005).

Activity 14.1

The Border Problem

On centimetre grid paper, have students draw an 8 × 8 square representing a swimming pool. Next, have them shade in the surrounding squares representing the tiles around the pool (see Figure 14.3). The task is to find a way to count the border tiles, without counting them one by one. Students should use their drawings, words, and number sentences to show how they counted the squares.

There are at least five different methods of counting the border tiles around a square, other than counting them one at a time.

❚❚ *Pause and Reflect*

Before reading further, see if you can find four or five different counting schemes for the border tiles problem. Apply your method to the same type of border for a square with other dimensions.

A very common solution is to notice that there are ten squares across the top and also across the bottom, leaving eight squares on either side. This might be written as:

$$10 + 10 + 8 + 8 = 36 \qquad \text{or} \qquad 2 \times 10 + 2 \times 8 = 36$$

Each of the following expressions can likewise be traced to looking at the squares in various groupings:

4×9

$4 \times 8 + 4$

$4 \times 10 - 4$

$100 - 64$

More expressions are possible, since students may use addition instead of multiplication in the expressions. In any case, once the generalizations are created, students need to justify how the elements in the expression map with the physical representation.

Another approach to the Border Problem is to have students build a series of pools in steps, each with one more tile on the side (3 × 3, 4 × 4, 5 × 5, etc.). They would then need to find a way, at each step, to count the elements using an algorithm that handles the step numbers in the same manner. For example, students can find number sentences that parallel what they wrote for the 8 × 8 to find a 6 × 6

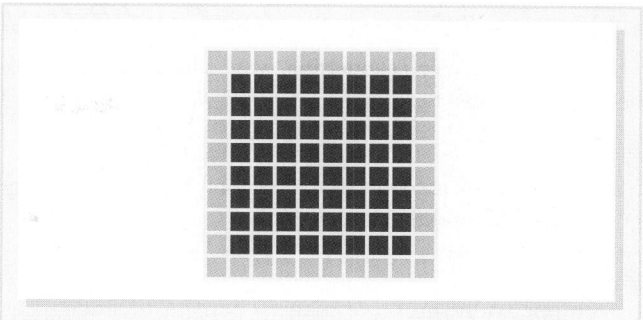

Figure 14.3 How many different ways can you find to count the border tiles of an 8 × 8 pool without counting them one at a time?

pool and a 7 × 7 pool. Eventually, this can result in a generalized statement. For example, take $2 \times 10 + 2 \times 8$ and generalize it to make $2 \times (n + 2) + 2 (n)$.

One important idea with generalizations is recognizing where a new situation can apply, then adapting it appropriately. For example, students may explore other perimeter-related growing patterns, such as a triangle with 3, 4, and 5 dots on each side. Students should reason that this is the same type of pattern, except that it has three sides, and be able to use their previous generalization for this specific problem (Steele, 2005).

Meaningful Use of Symbols

Perhaps one reason that students are unsuccessful in algebra is that they do not have a strong understanding of the symbols they are using. For many adults, the word *algebra* elicits memories of simplifying long equations with the goal of finding *x*. These experiences of manipulating symbols were often devoid of meaning and resulted in such a strong dislike for mathematics that algebra has become a favourite target of cartoonists. In reality, symbols represent real events and should be seen as useful tools for solving important problems that aid in decision making (e.g., calculating how many we need to sell to make *x* dollars or at what rate a given number of employees need to work to finish the project on time). Students cannot make sense of such questions without meaningful instruction on two very important (and poorly understood) topics: the equal sign and variables.

The Meaning of the Equal Sign

The equal sign is one of the most important symbols in elementary arithmetic, in algebra, and in all mathematics using numbers and operations. At the same time, research dating from 1975 to the present indicates clearly that "=" is a very poorly understood symbol. (RAND Mathematics Study panel, 2003).

Pause and Reflect

In the following expression, what number do you think belongs in the box?

$$8 + 4 = \square + 5$$

How do you think students in the early or middle elementary grades typically answer this question?

In one study, no more than 10 percent of students at any grade from 1 to 6 put the correct number (7) in the box. The common responses were 12 and 17. (How did students get the answers?) In grade 6, not one student out of 145 put a 7 in the box (Falkner, Levi, & Carpenter, 1999). Earlier studies found similar results (Behr, Erlwanger, & Nichols, 1975; Erlwanger & Berlanger, 1983).

Where do such misconceptions come from? Most, if not all, equations that students encounter in elementary school look like this: $5 + 7 = $ _____ or $8 \times 45 = $ _____ or $9(3 + 8) = $ _____. Naturally, students come to think that = signifies "and the answer is" rather than being a symbol to indicate equivalence (Carpenter, Franke, & Levi, 2003; McNeil & Alibali, 2005; Molina & Ambrose, 2006).

Why is it so important that students correctly understand the equal sign? First, it is important for students to see, understand, and symbolize the relationships in our number system. The equal sign is a principal method for representing these relationships. For example, $6 \times 7 = 5 \times 7 + 7$. Not only is this a fact strategy, it is also an application of the distributive property. The distributive property allows us to multiply each of the parts separately $(1 + 5) \times 7 = (1 \times 7) + (5 \times 7)$. Even further, other number properties are used to convert this last expression to $5 \times$

$7 + 7$. When these ideas, initially and informally developed through arithmetic, are generalized and expressed symbolically, powerful relationships become available for working with other numbers in a generalized manner.

A second reason is that when students fail to understand the equal sign, they typically have difficulty when it is encountered in algebraic expressions (Knuth et al., 2006). Even solving a simple equation such as $5x - 24 = 81$ requires students to see both sides of the equal sign as equivalent expressions. It is not possible to "do" the left-hand side. However, if both sides are the same, then they will remain the same when 24 is added to each side.

Conceptualizing the Equal Sign as a Balance Helping students understand the idea of equivalence can be developed concretely, beginning in the elementary grades. The next two activities illustrate how tactile objects and visualizations can reinforce the "balancing" notion of the equal sign (ideas adapted from Mann, 2004).

Activity 14.2

Seesaw Students

Ask students to raise their arms to look like a seesaw. Explain that you have big juicy oranges, all weighing the same, and tiny little apples, all weighing the same. Ask students to imagine that you have placed an orange in each of their left hands (students should bend to lower left side). Ask students to imagine that you place another orange on the right side (students level off). Next, with oranges still there, ask students to imagine an apple added to the left. Finally, say you are adding another apple, but tell students it is going on the left (again). Then ask them to imagine it moving over to the right. After acting out the seesaw several times, ask students to write Seesaw Findings (e.g., "If you have a balanced seesaw and add something to one side, it will tilt to that side," and "If you take away the same object from both sides of the seesaw, it will still be balanced").

Algebraic thinking is not a singular idea but is composed of different forms of thought and an understanding of symbolism. The need for understanding equality in equations cannot be overstated, and activities using a balance may help students make a symbolic connection to the equal sign in an equation

Activity 14.3

What Do You Know about the Shapes?

Present a scale with objects on both sides. Ask students what they know about the shapes. You can create your own, but here is one example:

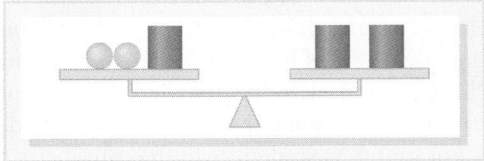

> The red cylinders have the same mass. The yellow spheres have the same mass. What do you know about the masses of the balls and cylinders? Figure 14.4 illustrates how one grade 3 student explained what she knew. (Notice how these tasks, appropriate for the early grades, serve as good beginnings for the more advanced balancing tasks later in this chapter.)

After students have experiences with shapes, they can then explore numbers, eventually going on to variables.

Figure 14.5 offers examples that connect the balance to the related equation. This two-pan-balance model also illustrates that the expressions on each side represent a number.

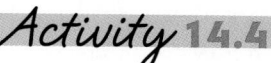

Tilt or Balance

On the board or overhead, draw a simple two-pan balance. In each pan, write a numerical expression and ask which pan will go down or whether the two will balance each other (see Figure 14.5). Challenge students to write expressions for each side of the scale to make it balance. For each, write a corresponding equation to illustrate the meaning of =. Note that when the scale "tilts," either a "greater than" or "less than" symbol (> or <) is used.

Accommodation

For children who are unsure or having difficulty determining what will happen, you might have them use concrete materials to represent the expressions on either side of the pan and compare the results.

After a short time, add variables to the expressions and allow students to solve them using whatever methods they wish (see Figure 14.5(b)). Do not make the task so easy that the solutions can be found by simple inspection.

The balance is a concrete tool that can help students understand that if you add or subtract a value from one side, you must add or subtract a like value from the other side to keep the equation balanced.

Figure 14.6 shows solutions for two equations, one in a balance and the other without. Even after you have stopped using the balance, it is a good idea to refer to the scale or balance-pan concept of equality and the idea of keeping the scales balanced.

As students begin to develop equations they wish to graph, the equations will often be in a form in which neither variable is isolated. For example, in the equation $3A - B = 2A$, they may want A in terms of B or B in terms of A. The

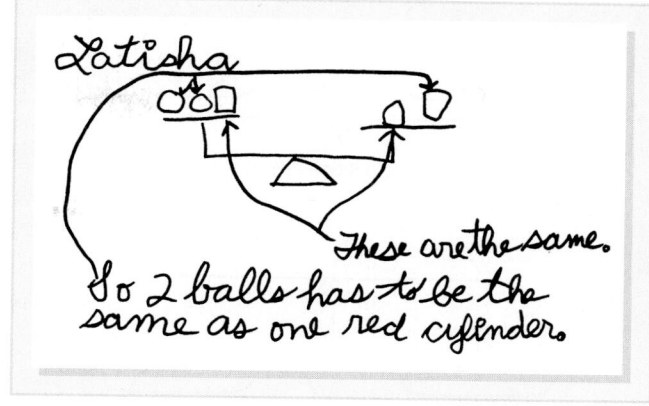

Figure 14.4 Latisha's work on the problem.

Source: Figure 4 from Mann, R. L. (2004). "Balancing Act: The Truth Behind the Equals Sign." *Teaching Children Mathematics,* 11 (2), p. 68.

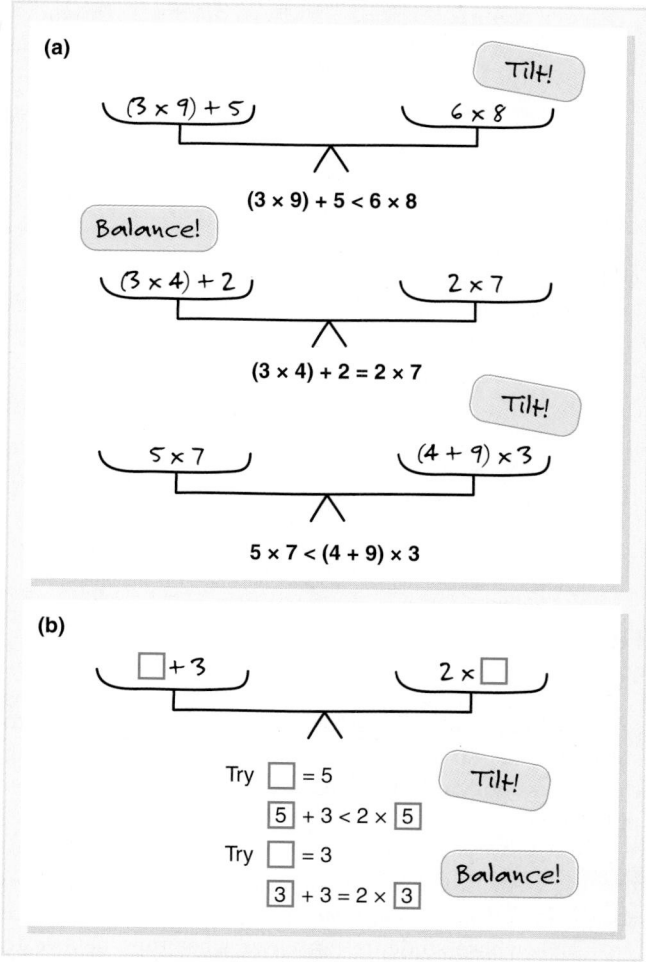

Figure 14.5 Using expressions and variables in equations and inequalities. The two-pan balance helps develop the meaning of =.

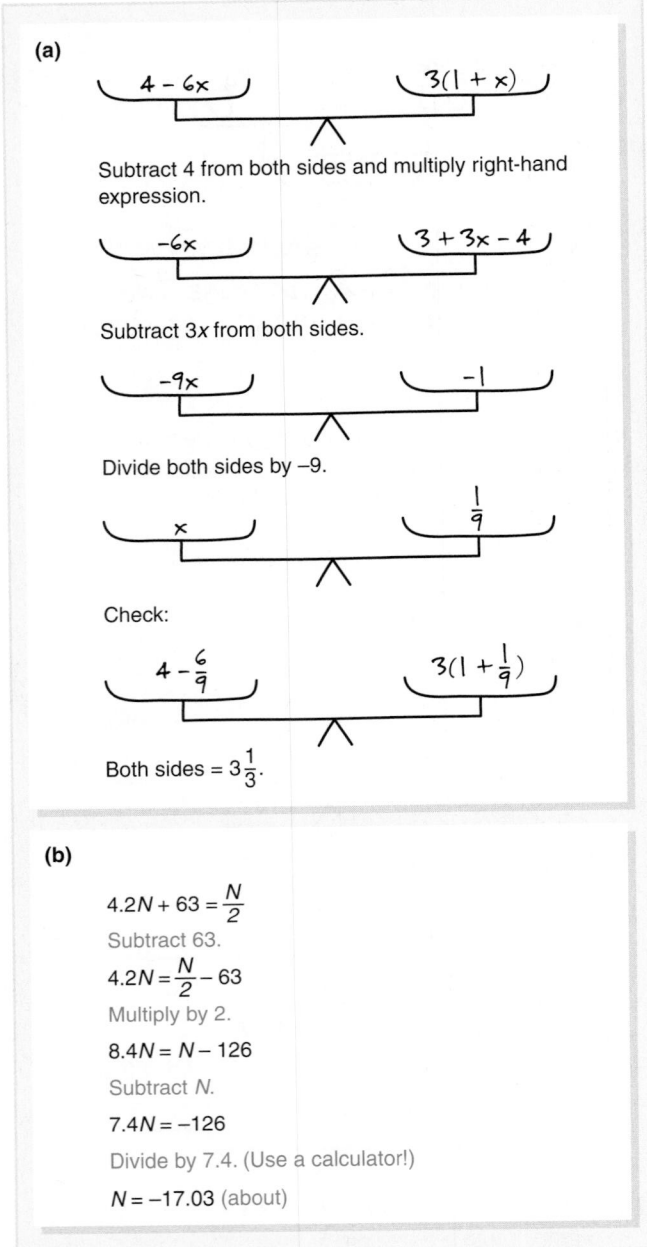

(a)

Subtract 4 from both sides and multiply right-hand expression.

Subtract 3x from both sides.

Divide both sides by –9.

Check:

Both sides = $3\frac{1}{3}$.

(b)

$4.2N + 63 = \frac{N}{2}$

Subtract 63.

$4.2N = \frac{N}{2} - 63$

Multiply by 2.

$8.4N = N - 126$

Subtract N.

$7.4N = -126$

Divide by 7.4. (Use a calculator!)

$N = -17.03$ (about)

Figure 14.6 Using a balance scale to think about solving equations.

same technique of solving for one variable can be used to solve for one variable in terms of the other by adjusting the expressions on both sides while keeping the equation in balance.

 An NCTM *Illuminations* applet titled *Pan Balance—Expressions* provides a virtual balance where students can enter what they believe to be equivalent expressions (with numbers or symbols) each in a separate pan to see if, in fact, the expressions balance. ◆

True/False and Open Sentences Carpenter, Franke, and Levi (2003) suggest that a good starting point for helping students with the equal sign is to explore equations as either true or false. Clarifying the meaning of the equal sign is just one of the outcomes of this type of exploration, as seen in the following activity.

Activity 14.5

True or False

Introduce true/false sentences or equations with simple examples to explain what is meant by a true equation and a false equation. Then put several simple equations on the board, some true and some false. The following are appropriate for primary grades:

$$5 + 2 = 7 \qquad 4 + 1 = 5$$
$$4 + 4 = 8 \qquad 8 = 10 - 1$$

Your collection might include other operations but keep the computations simple. The students' task is to decide which of the equations are true and which are not. For each response, they are to explain their reasoning.

After this initial exploration of true/false sentences, have students explore equations that are less traditional in form:

$$4 + 5 = 8 + 1 \quad 3 + 7 = 7 + 3 \quad 6 - 3 = 7 - 4 \quad 8 = 8$$
$$4 + 5 = 4 + 5 \quad 9 + 5 = 14 \qquad 9 + 5 = 14 + 0$$

Do not try to explore all variations in a single lesson. Listen to the types of reasons that students are using to justify their answers, then plan additional equations accordingly for subsequent days.

Accommodation

For those students who might be experiencing difficulty with the less traditional forms of equations, have them use concrete materials to represent the number expressions on either side of the equal sign and compare the results.

Students will generally agree on equations where there is an expression on one side and a single number on the other, although initially, the less familiar form of $7 = 2 + 5$ may cause some discussion. For an equation with no operation ($8 = 8$), the discussion may be heated. Students often believe that there must be an operation on one side. Equations with an operation on both sides of the equal sign can elicit powerful discussions and help clear up misunderstandings. Reinforce with the students that the equal sign means "is the same as." Their internalization of this idea will come from the discussions and their own justifications. Inequalities should be explored in a similar manner.

After students have experienced true/false sentences, introduce an open sentence—one with a box to be filled in or a letter to be replaced. To develop understanding of open sentences, encourage students to look at the number sentence holistically and to discuss in words what the equation represents.

Activity 14.6

Open Sentences

Write several open sentences on the board. To begin with, these can be similar to the true/false sentences that you have been exploring.

$5 + 2 = \square$	$4 + \square = 6$	$4 + 5 = \square - 1$
$3 + 7 = 7 + \square$	$\square + 4 = 8$	$\square = 10 - 1$
$6 - \square = 7 - 4$	$\square + 5 = 5 + 8$	

The task is to decide what number can be put into the box to make the sentence true. Of course, an explanation is also required.

Accommodation

For grade 3 and above, include multiplication as well as addition and subtraction.

Initially, some students will revert to doing computations and putting the answer in the box. This is a result of too many exercises where an answer is to be written as a single number following an equal sign. In fact, the box is a forerunner of a variable, not an answer holder.

Relational Thinking Once students understand that the equal sign means that quantities on both sides are the same, they can use relational thinking in solving problems. Relational thinking takes place when a student observes and uses numeric relationships between the two sides of the equal sign rather than actually computing the amounts. Relational thinking of this sort is a first step toward generalizing relationships found in arithmetic so that these same relationships can be used when variables are involved rather than numbers.

Consider two distinctly different explanations for why a 5 goes in the box for the open sentence $7 - \square = 6 - 4$.

a. Since $6 - 4$ is 2, you need to take away a number from 7 to get 2. $7 - 5$ is 2, so 5 goes in the box.

b. Seven is one more than the 6 on the other side. That means that you need to take one more away on the left side to get the same number. One more than 4 is 5 so 5 goes in the box.

⏸ —————— *Pause and Reflect*

How are these two correct responses actually quite different? How would each of these students solve this open sentence? $534 + 175 = 174 + \square$

The first student computes the result on one side and adjusts the result on the other to make the sentence true. The second student is using a relationship between the expressions on either side of the equal sign. This student does not need to compute the values on each side. When the numbers are large, the relationship approach is much more useful. Since 174 is one less than 175, the number in the box must be one more than 534 to make up the difference. The first student will need to do the computation and will perhaps have difficulty finding the correct addend.

In order to nurture relational thinking and the meaning of the equal sign, continue to explore an increasingly complex series of true/false and open sentences with your class. Select equations designed to elicit good thinking and challenges rather than computation. Use large numbers that make computation difficult (not impossible) to push the students toward relational thinking.

True/False

$674 - 389 = 664 - 379$	$5 \times 84 = 10 \times 42$
$37 + 54 = 38 + 53$	$64 \div 14 = 32 \div 28$

Open Sentences

$73 + 56 = 71 + \square$	$126 - 37 = \square - 40$
$20 \times 48 = \square \times 24$	$68 + 58 = 57 + 69 + \square$

⏸ —————— *Pause and Reflect*

In the preceding true/false equations, one is false. Try to explain why, using relational thinking.

Marta Molina and Rebecca Ambrose (2006), researchers in mathematics education, used the true/false and open-ended prompts with third graders, none of whom understood the equal sign in a relational way at the start of their study. For example, all 13 students answered $8 + 4 = \_\_\_ + 5$ with 12. They found that asking students to write their own open sentences was particularly effective in helping students solidify their understanding of the equal sign. The following forms were provided as guidance (though students could use multiplication and division if they wanted):

$$\_\_\_ + \_\_\_ = \_\_\_ + \_\_\_$$
$$\_\_\_ - \_\_\_ = \_\_\_ - \_\_\_$$
$$\_\_\_ + \_\_\_ = \_\_\_ - \_\_\_.$$

Activity 14.7

Writing True/False Sentences

After students have had ample time to discuss true/false and open sentences, have them make up their own true/false sentences that they can use to challenge their classmates. Each student should write a collection of three or four sentences with at least one that is true and one that is false. Encourage them to include one "tricky" one. Their equations can either be traded with a partner or can be used for a whole-class discussion. Repeat for open sentence problems.

When students write their own true/false sentences, they often are intrigued with the idea of using large numbers and a lot of numbers in their sentences. Doing so encourages them to create sentences that require relational thinking.

 As students explore true/false and open sentence activities, look for two developments. First, are students developing an appropriate understanding of the equal sign? Look to see if they are comfortable using operations on both sides of the equal sign and if they can use the meaning of *equal* as "is the same as" to solve open sentences.

Second, look for an emergence of relational thinking. Students who rely on relationships found in the operations on each side of the equal sign rather than on direct computation have moved up a step in their algebraic thinking. ◆

Variables in Equations

Expressions or equations with variables allow for the expression of generalizations. When students can work with expressions involving variables without even thinking about the specific number or numbers that the letters may stand for, they have achieved what Kaput (1999) refers to as manipulation of *opaque formalism*—they can look at and work with the symbols themselves. Variables can be used as unique unknown values or as quantities that vary. Unfortunately, students often think of variables as the former, rather than the latter. Experiences in elementary school should focus on building meaning for both uses, as delineated in the next two sections.

Variables Used as Unknown Values   Students first experiences tend to focus exclusively on variables used as symbols that stand for an unknown value. In the open sentence explorations, the use of the ☐ in this way is a precursor to the variable. Early on, you can begin using different letters instead of a box in your open sentences. Rather than asking students what number goes in the box, ask what number

the letter could stand for to make the sentence true. Initial work with finding the value of the variable that makes the sentence true—solving the equation—should rely on relational thinking. Later, students will develop specific techniques for solving equations when these relationships are insufficient.

The balancing ideas described in the previous section can also serve this purpose. NCTM *Illuminations*, for example, uses an applet titled "Pan Balance—Shapes," along with two excellent pre-K–2 lesson plans, for having students (virtually) find the mass of different shapes to figure out what number each shape represents.

Consider the following open sentence: ☐ + ☐ + 7 = ☐ + 17 (or equivalently, $n + n + 7 = n + 17$). Without a convention for the multiple use of a variable in an equation, there would be no unique solution. However, there is a convention stating that if the same symbol or letter appears more than once in an equation, then it must stand for the same number every place it occurs. Carpenter, Franke, and Levi (2003) refer to it as "the mathematician's rule." In the preceding example, the ☐ must stand for 10.

Many story problems involve a situation in which the variable is a specific unknown, as in the following basic example:

Devon ate 5 strawberries and Jess ate some. The container of 12 was gone! How many did Jess eat?

Although students can solve this problem without using algebra, they can begin to learn about variables by expressing the problem with symbols: $5 + s = 12$. These problems can grow in difficulty.

The same technique of solving for one variable can be used to explore three variables for an unknown value. This system of equations can be done through balancing, using scales with variables on the pans in the form of geometric shapes. This type of work is particularly appropriate for upper elementary students. It helps them build a foundation for working with systems of equations later on.

In Figure 14.7, a series of examples show scale problems in which each shape on the scales represents a different value. Two or more scales for a single problem provide different information about the shapes or variables. Building the concept of the equal sign is applied here to understanding and solving for variables. Problems of this type can be adjusted in difficulty for children across the grades. Greenes and Findell (1999a, b) have developed a whole collection of these and similar activities in books for grades 1–7.

When no numbers are involved, as in the top two examples of Figure 14.7, students can find combinations of numbers for the shapes that make all the scales balance. If an arbitrary value is given to one of the shapes, then values for the other shapes can be found accordingly.

In the second example, if the sphere equals 2, then the cylinder must be 4 and the cube equals 8. If a different value is given to the sphere, the other shapes will change accordingly.

The scale problems (with a number for each scale) are to be solved for a unique value for each shape. There are usually several paths to finding a solution.

⏸ ———————————— *Pause and Reflect*

How would you solve the last problem in Figure 14.7? Can you solve it in two ways?

You (and your students) can tell if you are correct by checking your solutions with the original scale positions. Believe it or not, you have just solved a series of simultaneous equations, a skill generally left to a formal algebra class.

Simplifying Expressions and Equations   As noted earlier, simplifying equations or solving for *x* have often been meaningless tasks, and students are unsure of when to perform what steps. Still, knowing how to simplify and what an equivalent expression is are essential skills for working algebraically.

Students need an understanding of how to apply mathematical properties and how to preserve equivalence as they simplify. One way to do this is to have students look at simplifications that have errors and explain how to fix the errors (Hawes, 2007). Figure 14.8 shows how three students have justified the correct simplification of $(2x + 1) - (x + 6)$.

Variables Used as Quantities That Vary   As noted earlier, the important concept that variables can represent more than one missing value is not well understood by students. When there are different variables in a single equation, each variable can represent many, even infinite, numbers. In the upper grades, variables that are used to describe functions (e.g., $y = 3x - 5$) are variables that have many possible numerical solutions. This shift from the variable as an unknown to a variable representing a relationship can be difficult for students. This difficulty can be alleviated if students have experiences with variables that vary in the elementary curriculum.

Recall the monkeys in two trees problem in Figure 14.1 of this chapter. Even very young students can represent the possible solutions using symbols. For example, they might draw the following illustration

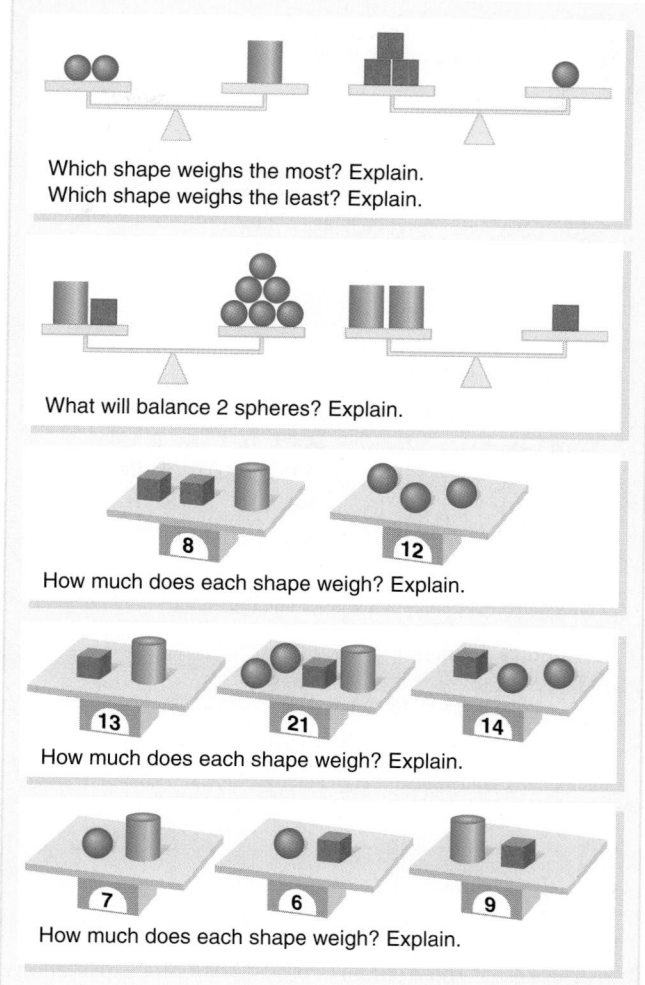

Figure 14.7 Examples of problems with multiple variables and multiple scales.

to represent the number of monkeys in the small tree plus the number of monkeys in the big tree equals 7. Or, you can use letters and help students make the connection from the context to the equation, for example writing: $b = 7 - s$ to communicate that the number of big monkeys is the number of total monkeys minus the number of small monkeys.

Context continues to be important in developing understanding of variables for students throughout the upper grades. The following problem, adapted from Hyde et al., (2006), provides a context for exploring how variables used as quantities can vary:

> If you have $10 to spend on $2 hamburgers and $1 frankfurters, how many different ways can you spend your money buying hamburgers and frankfurters for your friends, without receiving change?

This problem provides a familiar context for students and they could model it using circles and rectangles cut from construction paper to represent the hamburgers and

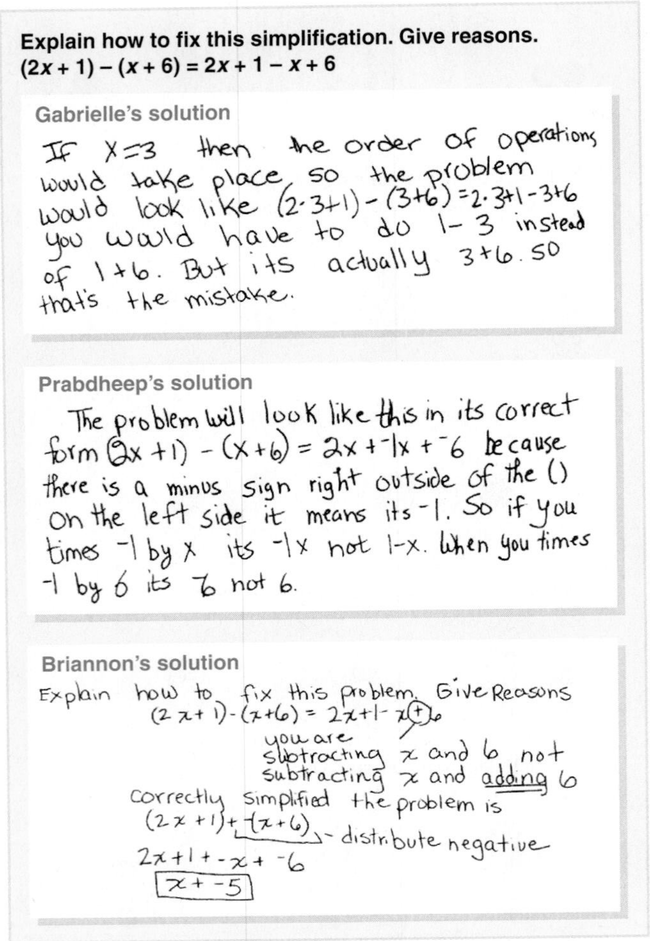

Explain how to fix this simplification. Give reasons.
$(2x + 1) - (x + 6) = 2x + 1 - x + 6$

Gabrielle's solution

IF X =3 then the order of operations would take place, so the problem would look like (2·3+1) - (3+6) = 2·3+1 - 3+6 you would have to do 1 - 3 instead of 1 + 6. But its actually 3+6. So that's the mistake.

Prabdheep's solution

The problem will look like this in its correct form (2x +1) - (x+6) = 2x + ⁻1x + ⁻6 because there is a minus sign right outside of the () on the left side it means its -1. So if you times -1 by x its -1x not 1-x. When you times -1 by 6 its ⁻6 not 6.

Briannon's solution

Explain how to fix this problem. Give Reasons
(2x + 1) - (x+6) = 2x+1- x(+6)
you are subtracting x and 6 not subtracting x and adding 6
Correctly simplified the problem is
(2x +1) + ⁻(x+6) ~ distribute negative
2x+1 + ⁻x + ⁻6
x + ⁻5

Figure 14.8 Three students provide different explanations for fixing the flawed simplification given.

Source: Figure 3 from Hawes, K. (2007). "Using Error Analysis to Teach Equation Solving." *Mathematics Teaching in the Middle School, 12* (5), p. 241. Reprinted with permission. Copyright Inc. www.nctm.org. All rights reserved.

franks. As noted in Chapter 2, you could use any context that you think is engaging, culturally relevant, and appropriate for the mathematics being taught.

To begin exploring this problem, students record data in a table and look for patterns. They will notice when the number of hamburgers changes by 1, the number of franks changes by 2. Symbolically, this representation is $2H + 1F = \$10$, where H is the number of hamburgers and F is the number of franks.

It is also important to include decimal and fractional values in the exploration of variables. Students struggle most with these numbers as a result of the paucity of earlier, more concrete experiences mixing fractions and decimal numbers with variables. For example, if you had $35.00 to spend on classroom supplies and you spent all of it on pens that cost $1.75 each, and pencils that cost $1.25 each, how many different combinations are possible? What equation represents this situation?

To accommodate students with special needs or those who might not be familiar with using a table, it is helpful to adapt the table to include both how many and how much, as shown in Figure 14.9 (Hyde et al., 2006). With each entry in the table, you could reinforce the two elements (how many and how much). Moreover, calculators can facilitate exploration of possible solutions. For students who require an extra challenge, ask them to graph the values or to consider more complex situations.

Once the expression is in symbolic form (in this case, $1.75x + 1.25y = \$35.00$), have students link each number and variable back to its context. Doing so helps them make sense of what is normally poorly understood. It also helps them to develop a strong foundation for the algebra they will study in high school.

Making Structure in the Number System Explicit

Chapter 9 discusses a few properties for each operation (pp. 152–153 and 160–161) that are important for students as they learn basic facts and strategies for computation. For example, the commutative or order property for both addition and multiplication substantially reduces the number of facts it is necessary to learn. These and other properties are likely to be used informally as students develop relational thinking while working with true/false and open sentences, as described in the previous sections.

A next step is to have students examine these structures or properties explicitly and express them in general terms without reference to specific numbers. For example, a student solving $394 + 176 = N + 394$ may say that N must be 176 because $394 + 176$ is the same as $176 + 394$. This is a specific instance of the commutative property. To articulate this (and other structural properties of our number system) in a form such as $a + b = b + a$, and to note that it is true for all numbers, is the goal of looking at structure. When made explicit and understood, these structures not only add to students' tools for computation, but also enrich their understanding of the number system and provide a base for even higher levels of abstraction (Carpenter et al., 2003).

Making Conjectures about Properties

Properties of the number system can be built into students' explorations with true/false and open-number sentences. For example, grade 3 students will generally agree that the true/false sentence $41 \times 3 = 3 \times 41$ is true. The pivotal question, however, is, "Is this true for any numbers?" Some students will argue that while it seems to be true all the time, there may be two numbers that haven't been tried yet for which it does not work.

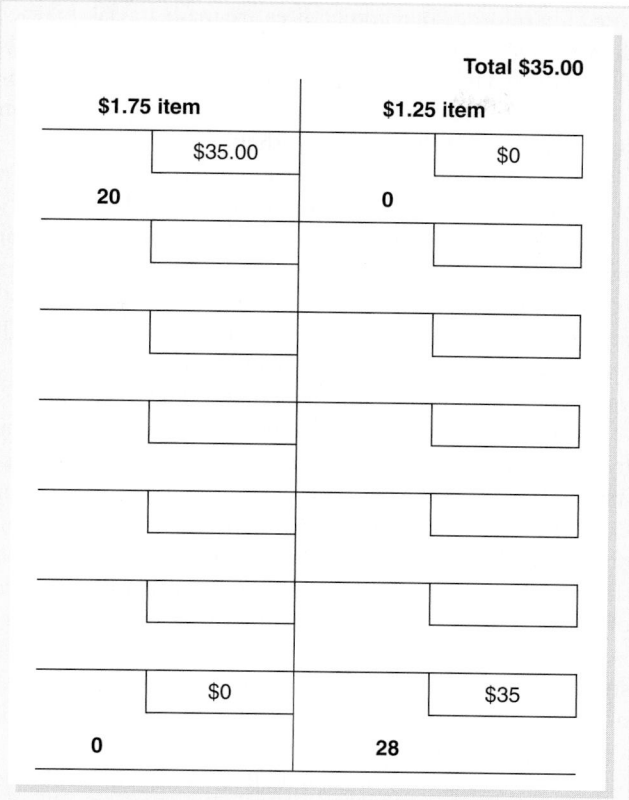

Figure 14.9 A table adapted to include how many and how much for each row.

Source: Hyde, A., George, K., Mynard, S., Hull, C., Watson, S., & Watson, P. (2006). "Creating Multiple Representations in Algebra: All chocolate, 0 change," *Mathematics Teaching in the Middle School,* 11 (6), 262–268. Reprinted with permission. Copyright © 2006 by the National Council of Teachers of Mathematics, Inc., www.nctm.org. All rights reserved.

The following classroom problem and discussion focused on investigating the distributive and associative properties, not on whether the equation was true or false (from Baek, 2008):

Ms. J: [*Pointing at* $(2 \times 8) + (2 \times 8) = 16 + 16$ *on the board*] Is it true or false?

LeJuan: True, because two 8 is 16 and two 8 is 16.

Lizett: $(2 \times 8) + (2 \times 8)$ is 32 and $16 + 16$ is 32.

Carlos: 8 plus 8 is 16, so 2 times 8 is 16, and 8 plus 8 is 16, and 2 times 8 is 16.

Ms. J: [*Writing* $4 \times 8 = (2 \times 8) + (2 \times 8)$ *on the board*] True or false?

Students: True.

Ms. J: What does the 2 stand for?

Reggie: Two boxes of eight.

Ms. J: So how many boxes are there?

Students: Four.

Ms. J: [*Writing* $32 + 16 = (4 \times 8) + (a \times 8)$ *on the board*] What is *a*?

Michael: Two, because 4 times 8 is 32, and 2 times 8 is 16.

Ms. J: [*Writing* $(4 \times 8) + (2 \times 8) = (b \times 8)$ *on the board*] What is *b*?

Students: 6 (pp. 151-152)

Notice how the teacher develops aspects of these properties in a conceptual manner. As this is their first experience (which could be meaningless and rote) she focuses on exemplars as she guides students to generalize, rather than presenting the properties as they appear in Table 14.1

You can follow specific examples, such as those used in the dialogue, by asking students to try to state the idea in words, without using a specific number. For example, when multiplying a number by a second number, you can split the first number and multiply each part by the second number, and you will get the same answer. If a generalization is not clear or entirely correct, have students discuss the wording until all agree that they understand what it means. Write this oral statement of the property on the board. Call it a conjecture and explain that it is not necessarily a true statement just because we think that it is true. Until someone either proves it or finds a counter example—an instance for which the conjecture is not true—it remains a conjecture.

Students can make conjectures about properties as early as first or second grade. By grade 3 or 4, students should be challenged to translate oral conjectures into open sentences. The preceding conjecture can be written using any two letters as follows: $a \times b = (c \times b) + (d \times b)$, where $c + d = a$. Ask students to state conjectures orally before moving to the symbolic statement of the same idea. Then have them explain what each variable in the symbolic form means.

Activity 14.8

Conjecture Creation

Once students have seen a couple of conjectures developed out of your explorations of true/false sentences, challenge students to make up conjectures on their own—to create statements about numbers and computation that they believe are always true. It is best to have them articulate their conjectures in words. The whole class should discuss the various conjectures. They should edit each conjecture for clarity or challenge the conjecture with a counter-example. Conjectures agreed upon by all should be added to a class list, written in words and in symbols.

Table 14.1 lists basic properties of the number system for which students may make conjectures.

Students are almost certainly not going to know or understand why division by zero is not possible. You will need to provide contexts for them to make sense of this property.

Table 14.1

Properties of the Number System	
Number Sentence	**Student Statement of Conjecture**
Addition and Subtraction	
$a + 0 = a$	When you add zero to a number, you get the same number you started with.
$a - 0 = a$	When you subtract zero from a number, you get the number you started with.
$a - a = 0$	When you subtract a number from itself, you get zero.
$a + b = b + a$	You can add numbers in one order and then change the order and you will get the same number.
Multiplication and Division	
$a \times 1 = a$	When you multiply a number by 1, you get the number you started with.
$a \div 1 = a$	When you divide a number by 1, you get the number you started with.
$a \div a = 1, a \neq 0$	When you divide a number that is not zero by itself, you get 1.
$a \times 0 = 0$	When you multiply a number times zero, you get zero.
$0 \div a = 0, a \neq 0$	When you divide zero by any number except zero, you get zero.
$a \times b = b \times a$	When you multiply two numbers, you can do it in any order and you will get the same number.
Conjectures Derived from Basic Properties	
$a + b - b = a$	When you add a number to another number and then subtract the number that you added, you will get the number that you started with.
$a \times b \div b = a, b \neq 0$	When you multiply a number by another number that is not zero and then divide by the same number, you get the number you started with.

Source: Adapted from Carpenter, T. P., Franke,, M. L., and Levi, L. (2003). *Thinking Mathematically: Integrating Arithmetic and Algebra in Elementary School.* Portsmouth, NH: Heinemann.

Justifying Conjectures

Attempting to justify that a conjecture is true is a significant form of algebraic reasoning and is at the heart of what it means to do mathematics. How young students attempt to prove that something is always true is a relatively new and interesting area of research (Ball & Bass, 2003; Carpenter, Franke, & Levi, 2003; Schifter, 1999; Schifter, Bastable, Russell, & Monk, 2007). These researchers all believe that there is real value in challenging students, even as early as grade 2, to justify that the conjectures they make are always

true. Therefore, when conjectures are made in class, rather than respond with an answer, ask, "Do you think that is always true? How can we find out?" Students need to reason through ideas based on their own thinking rather than simply relying on the words of others.

The most common form of justification, especially in elementary school, is the use of examples. Students will try a lot of specific numbers in a conjecture. "See, it works for any number you try." They may try very large numbers as substitutes for "any" number and they may try rational fractions or decimal values. There will be students who will not accept this approach as proof and will ask. "How do we know there aren't some numbers that it doesn't work for?"

It is less common for students to attempt to use some form of logic. Often these efforts include the use of physical materials to show the reasoning behind the conjecture. For example, a student attempting to prove that $a + b = b + a$ might show two bars of snap cubes, one with 8 cubes and the other with 6. The bars are used to show that the number of cubes does not change when the order of the two bars is reversed. What moves this beyond just an example is the student's statement or explanation that the number of cubes in the bars is not part of the argument: "It would work this way no matter how many cubes are in each bar."

At the elementary level, not all students will be able to create arguments. Some may not even follow those constructed by others (Carpenter et al., 2003). However, at all levels it is important to push students to reason using logic and not be content with appeals to authority or the use of examples. Remember that your goal is the students' thinking involved in these justifications. There is little value in making a good argument for your students.

Odd and Even Relationships

An interesting category of conjectures surrounds the concepts of odd and even numbers. Students will often observe that the sum of two even numbers is even, that the sum of two odd numbers is even, or that the sum of an even and an odd number is always odd. Similar statements can be made about multiplication.

❚❚ ———— *Pause and Reflect*

Before reading on, think for a moment about how you might prove that the sum of two odd numbers is always even.

Students will provide a variety of interesting proofs of odd/even conjectures. As with other conjectures, they typically begin by trying a lot of numbers. But here it is a bit easier to imagine that there just might be two numbers "out there" that don't work. Then, students turn to the definition or a model that illustrates the definition. For example, if a number is odd and you split it in two, there will be a leftover. If you do this with the second odd number, it will have a leftover also. So if you put these two numbers together, the two leftovers will go together so there won't be a leftover in the sum. Students frequently use models such as bars of snap cubes to strengthen their arguments.

The following calculator activity helps students explore properties of odd and even numbers.

Activity 14.9

Broken Calculator: Can You Fix It?

Explore these two challenges. Afterward, ask students for conjectures they might make about odds and evens.

1. **If you cannot use any of the even keys (0, 2, 4, 6, 8), can you created an even number in the calculator display? If so, how?**
2. **If you cannot use any of the odd keys (1, 3, 5, 7, 9), can you create an odd number in the calculator display? If so, how?**

It is not important that all students initiate conjectures. It is important that all students actively consider the validity of all conjectures made by classmates. When deciding if a conjecture is always true, have students write their ideas before sharing with the class. If you begin with a class discussion only a few students are likely to participate, with others content to listen whether or not they are following the arguments. You can then use what the students write as well as their input in discussions to assess their level of reasoning: authority, use of examples, or an appeal to logic. ◆

Study of Patterns and Functions

Patterns are found in all areas of mathematics. Learning to search for patterns and how to describe, translate, and extend them is part of doing mathematics and thinking algebraically.

Repeating Patterns

The concept of a repeating pattern and how a pattern is extended or continued can be introduced to the whole class in several ways. One possibility is to draw simple shape patterns on the board and extend them in a class discussion. Oral patterns can be recited. For example, "do, mi, mi, do, mi, mi, ..." is a simple pattern. Three different arm positions—up, down, and sideways—are another way to make a pattern. One example is up, side, side, down, up, side, side, down, ... Boy–girl patterns or stand–sit patterns are also good movement patterns.

Children's books often have repeating patterns. For example, a very long repeating pattern can be found in *If You Give a Mouse a Cookie* (Numeroff, 1985) in which each event eventually leads back to giving a mouse a cookie, with the implication that the sequence would be repeated.

Identifying and Extending Repeating Patterns An important concept in working with repeating patterns is for students to identify the core of the pattern (Warren & Cooper, 2008). The *core* of a repeating pattern is the string of elements that repeats. It is important to use knowledge of the core to extend the pattern.

Activity 14.10

Making Pattern Strips

Students can work independently or in groups of two or three to extend patterns made from simple materials: buttons, coloured blocks, connecting cubes, toothpicks, geometric shapes—items you can gather easily. For each set of materials, draw *three* complete repetitions of a pattern on strips of tag-board about 5 centimetres by 30 centimetres. The students' task is to copy the pattern shown, using actual materials, extending it as a far as they wish. Figure 14.10 illustrates one possible pattern for each of the variety of manipulatives. You can also select one manipulative and make ten different pattern strips so that students are able to work with partners. They then trade and work on identifying the core and extending the patterns.

Young children make a significant generalization when they see that two patterns constructed with different materials are actually the same pattern. For example, in creating a repeating pattern with cubes, as in Figure 14.10, you can ask students to find a pattern block pattern with the same pattern (as one of the strips), or have them build such a pattern.

"... students should recognize that the color pattern 'blue, blue, red, blue, blue, red, blue, blue, red' is the same in form as 'clap, clap, step, clap, clap, step, clap, clap, step.' This recognition lays the foundation for the idea that two very different situations can have the same mathematical features and thus are the same in some important ways. Knowing that each pattern above could be described as having the form AABAAB is for students an early introduction to the power of algebra" (pp. 91–92).

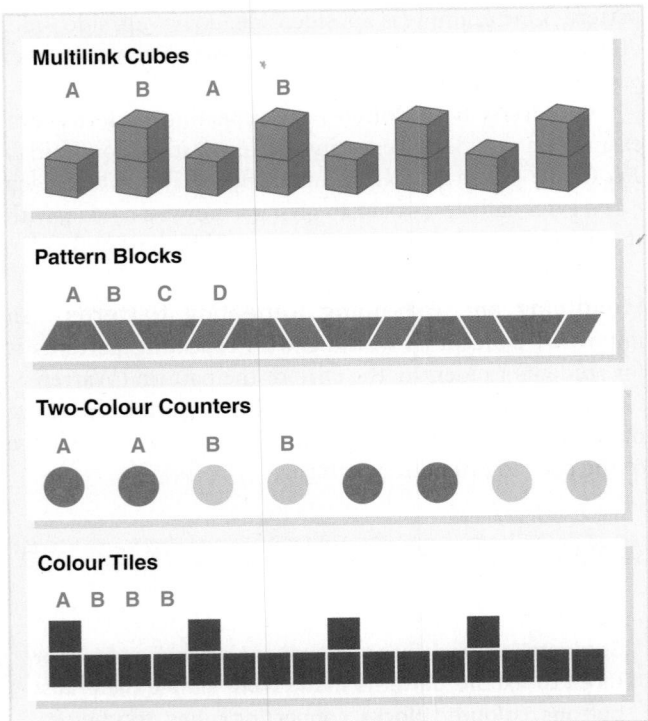

Figure 14.10 Examples of patterns using manipulatives.

The following activities reflect the powerful algebraic concept of repeating patterns just described in the quotation from *Principles and Standards*.

Activity 14.11

Pattern Match

Using the chalkboard or overhead projector, show students six or seven patterns (e.g., ABAB, ABCABC, etc.) with different materials or pictures (e.g., smiley faces, arrows pointing in different directions, etc.). Teach students to use an A, B, C scheme for reading a pattern. Have the students work in pairs. One student in each pair closes her or his eyes while the partner uses the A, B, C scheme to identify and read the core of a pattern he or she has selected.

After hearing the pattern, the students who had their eyes closed examine the patterns and try to decide which pattern was described. If two of the patterns in the list have the same structure, the discussion can be very interesting.

Conversely, give students the A, B, C form of the core of a pattern (e.g., ABCD or ABB) and ask them to create a pattern of this kind using two or three different models. Translation of a pattern from one medium to another is an alternative way to help students separate the relationship in a pattern from the material used to build it.

Predicting with Repeating Patterns: Linking to Divisibility Prediction is an important part of algebraic thinking. The next activity focuses on prediction as a forerunner to looking at functions.

Activity 14.12

Predict Down the Line

For most repeating patterns, the elements of the pattern can be numbered 1, 2, 3, and so on. Provide students with a pattern to extend. Before students begin to extend the pattern, have them predict exactly what element will be in, say, the 15th position. Students should be required to provide a reason for their prediction, preferably in writing.

Notice in an ABC pattern that the 3rd, 6th, 9th, and 12th terms are the C. Students can use concepts of multiplication and division they are developing to predict what the 18th and 25th items would be. Ask them to predict the 100th item. Since 100 ÷ 3 = 33 remainder 1, it would be the A item in the pattern. If predicting the 100th element, students will not be able to check the prediction by extending the pattern. Justification focuses on students' knowledge of multiplication and division (Warren & Cooper, 2008).

Using Real Contexts Though geometric patterns and motions, like clapping, are good ways to introduce patterns, it is important that students see patterns in the world around them. The seasons, days of the week, and months of the year are just a beginning. Students might be able to think of AB patterns in their daily activities, for example "to school, home from school" or "set table before eating, clear table after eating."

Predicting what happens down the line has some interesting real-world contexts appropriate for upper elementary and middle school students. One context is the Olympics (Bay-Williams & Martinie, 2004). The Summer Olympics are held in 2008, 2012, and every four years after that. The Winter Olympics are held in 2010, 2014, and so on. This makes the ABCD or ABAC pattern: No Olympics, Summer Olympics, No Olympics, Winter Olympics.

A second context is the names of hurricanes, which are in an ABCDEF repeating pattern by letter in the alphabet, meaning that for each letter of the alphabet, there are six names that are used and then repeated (except that a name is retired when a major hurricane is given that name, like Katrina) (Fernandez & Schoen, 2008). The A names, for example, are: 2006—Alberto, 2007—Andrea, 2008—Arthur, 2009—Ana, 2010—Alex, and 2011—Arlene. (Good for you if you noticed the ABAB pattern regarding gender!).

Assuming the names don't get retired, ask students questions such as:

- In what year will the first hurricane of that year be named Alex?
- What will be the first hurricane's name in the year 2020? 2050?
- Can you describe in words how to figure out the name of a hurricane, given the year?

Number Patterns   In the same way that contexts can be used to predict a number down the line, number patterns can be engaging for students. They can vary in complexity from simple repeating patterns such as 1, 2, 1, 2, 1, 2, ... to more advanced ones. In this way, they can provide an interesting challenge for gifted students or be part of a learning station and explored by those students who other work early. Here are a few numerical patterns:

2, 4, 6, 8, 10, ...	(even numbers; add 2 each time)
1, 4, 7, 10, 13, ...	(start with 1; add 3 each time)
1, 4, 9, 16, ...	(squares; 1^2, 2^2, 3^2, etc.)
0, 1, 5, 14, 30, ...	(add the next square number)
2, 5, 11, 23, ...	(double the number and add 1)
2, 6, 12, 20, 30, ...	(multiply pairs of counting numbers)
3, 3, 6, 9, 15, 24, ...	(add the two preceding numbers—an example of a Fibonacci sequence)

For each of these patterns, students predict the 30th number or the 100th number. They then work toward finding a general rule to produce any number in the sequence.

The calculator provides a powerful approach to patterns. For a good example, see the discussion of "Start and Jump Numbers" in Chapter 2 (p. 12).

Growing Patterns

Beginning at about grades 4–5 and extending through to grade 8, students can explore patterns that involve a progression from one step to the next. In technical terms, these are called sequences. We will simply call them growing patterns because the elements increase as you move from one step to the next. With these patterns, students not only extend a pattern, but they also look for a generalization or an algebraic relationship that will tell them what the pattern will be at any point along the way. Growing patterns can be functions and those used in school textbooks tend to be. Figure 14.11(a) is a growing pattern in which design 1 requires three triangles; design 2 requires six triangles; and so on. We can say that the number of triangles needed is a function of the particular design (in this case, it happens to be the number of triangles (the function) = 3 × the design number). The Border Problem, discussed earlier in

this chapter, can be adapted so it is a growing pattern, by simply having a swimming pool that is 5 by 5, then 6 by 6, then 7 by 7, and so on.

Geometric patterns make good exemplars because the pattern is easy to see and because students can manipulate the objects. Figure 14.11 shows one growing pattern for four different manipulatives, though the possibilities are endless.

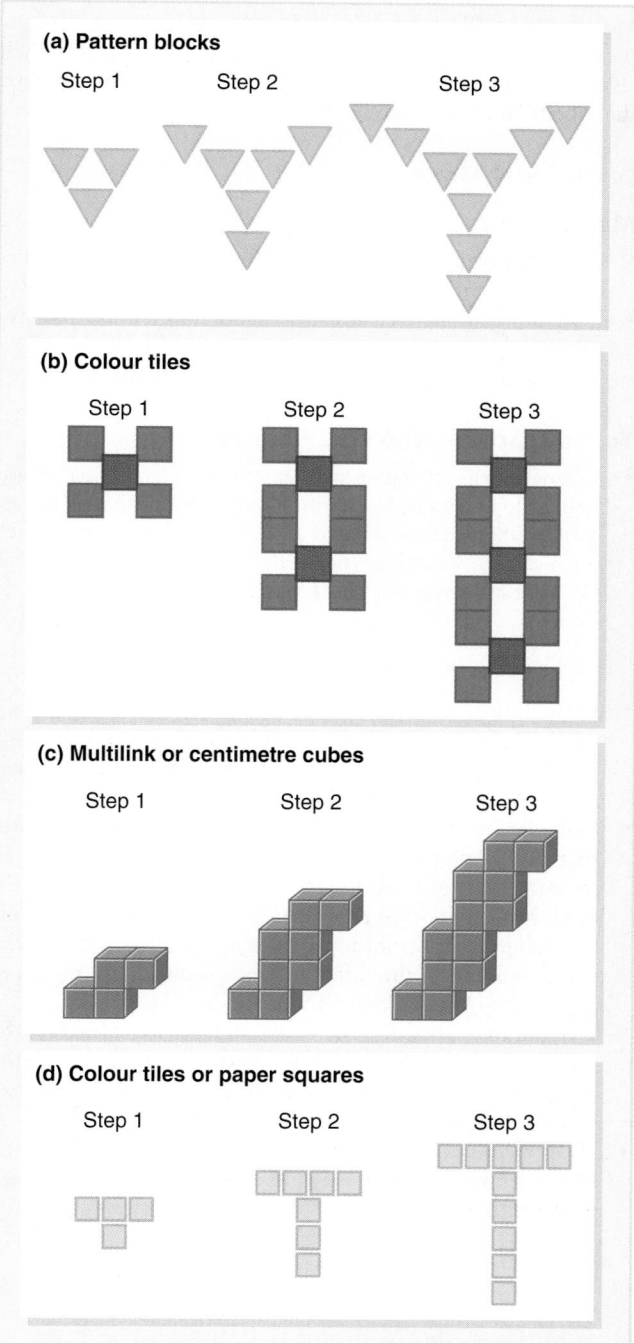

(a) Pattern blocks

Step 1   Step 2   Step 3

(b) Colour tiles

Step 1   Step 2   Step 3

(c) Multilink or centimetre cubes

Step 1   Step 2   Step 3

(d) Colour tiles or paper squares

Step 1   Step 2   Step 3

Figure 14.11 Geometric growing patterns using manipulatives.

Problem-Based Lesson:
Fun with Fibonacci

Differentiating the Learning

This lesson demonstrates how a range of learner needs, from those students who require an extra challenge to those with other unique needs, can be accommodated. It does so by offering students a chance to use manipulatives to represent number sequences they will be exploring. Also, the open-ended nature of the lesson allows students to work at a pace best suited to their level of ability as they investigate real-world patterns based on the Fibonacci number sequence.

Grade Level: Grades 6 and 7

Mathematical Goals

- To have students learn about the Fibonacci number sequence and its many real-life applications.
- To reinforce students' knowledge about how number patterns work.
- To have students identify, build, and extend number sequences.

To the Teacher—Who Was Fibonacci?

- Fibonacci was an Italian mathematician. His real name was Leonardo of Pisa or Leonardo Pisano. His nickname, or pen name, Fibonacci, originated from his father's name, which was Bonacci. Fibonacci means the son of (*figlio di*) Bonacci. He is best known for the Fibonacci number sequence, as shown:

    The Fibonacci Sequence: 0, 1, 1, 2, 3, 5, 8, 13, 21, 34, ...

- In the Fibonacci sequence, each term is the sum of the two preceding terms. For instance, $1 + 1 = 2$, $2 + 3 = 5$, $3 + 5 = 8$, ... This numerical series is found everywhere in nature, and has other real-life applications.
- Many of the materials, pictures, and explanations needed to successfully prepare for this investigation can be found at: www.mcs.surrey.ac.uk/Personal/R.Knott/Fibonacci/fibnat. html#bees. The Web site http://britton.disted.camosun.bc. ca/fibslide/jbfibslide.htm provides an excellent view of the patterns found in the different items shown (e.g., the pineapple, when you click on "Animation").
- It is best to use real-life objects so students are able to see the way in which the patterns found in nature connect with the Fibonacci numbers. However, pictures of real-life objects can be found at the above-noted and other Web sites.
- *Wild Fibonacci: Nature's Secret Code Revealed* by Joy Hulme and Carol Schwartz (ISBN: 1-58246-154-6) is an excellent book to use with the students.

Thinking About the Students

Students have already done some work with number sequences and patterns. They have identified and extended sequences and figured out rules/generalizations that explain how these sequences work. They have also created their own sequences using tables, *t*-charts, and pictures/drawings to represent them.

Materials and Preparation

- Students work in small heterogeneous groups so children with different abilities can work together. For this activity each student in a group will have a particular job/role, assigned before starting the activity.

    Student 1 = materials manager
    Student 2 = recorder for the group observation sheet
    Student 3 = presenter during share time
    Student 4 = time manager

- The following real-life objects all showing Fibonacci numbers can be used for this lesson: apples, which must be sliced horizontally to reveal the seeds and the particular design made by doing so; bananas, which are also sliced horizontally to reveal the seeds; pineapples; pine cones; flowers such as calla lilies, buttercups, black-eyed susans, sunflowers, shastas, and marigolds; pussy-willow, sneezewort, and other tree branches; the florets in the spiral of a cauliflower; and broccoli florets. There are many other objects found on the array of Web sites with Fibonacci's name that can be used. The different objects are laid out on group tables for students to examine.
- Ensure that all the different objects at the group tables have petals, leaves, seed arrangements, or spiral arrangements that represent the different numbers in the Fibonacci sequence. For example, a calla lily has 3 petals, a black-eyed susan has 21 petals, the pattern that results from cutting an apple horizontally has 5 sections to it, a banana cut horizontally has 3 sections, a pineapple has different spiral arrangements revealing different numbers such as 13, 5, 8. Note: It is important that the different objects placed at the group tables represent a broad cross-section of the numbers in the Fibonacci sequence. Also, it is important to provide a sufficient number of objects.
- Pictures of real-life objects downloaded from the aforementioned or other Fibonacci-related Web sites.
- Pattern observation sheets
- The following chart is included to help the teacher prepare materials needed for this lesson. The chart lists possible objects that reveal how Fibonacci numbers appear in nature. (Many more possibilities can be found at Fibonacci Web sites.)

Possible Objects that Could Be Used for the Lesson	Number of Petals, Seeds, Leaves, Flowers, etc. that Are Fibonacci Numbers
Banana cut in half	3 sections
Trillium	3 petals
Calla lily	3 petals
Apple cut in half	5 sections
Bloodroot flower	8 petals
Pine cones	13 spirals found
Pineapple	13 spirals
Marigolds	13 petals
Romanesque broccoli	13 spirals
Black-eyed susan	13 petals
Grapefruit cut in half	13 sections
Shasta daisy	21 petals

Introduction

- Begin the lesson by looking at some different number sequences that the class has previously explored. Include some that are new. Talk about significant features of the numbers in these sequences, how they are formed, and the rule or generalization on which the sequence is based that makes them a pattern.
- Tell the class that today they are going to investigate a very special number sequence called the Fibonacci number sequence. Talk about who Fibonacci was, his importance in the field of mathematics, and that the sequence he discovered, although mathematical, has many real-life applications. The numbers in the sequence appear in many different forms in real life. For example, the Fibonacci numbers can be seen everywhere in nature.

The Task

- The students will examine the many different real-life objects laid out at each group table. All the objects provide examples of where Fibonacci numbers are found in nature. The students are to consider the number of petals on the different flowers, the way in which seeds are arranged in each of the fruits, the arrangement of flowers and/or leaves on the branches, the arrangement of spirals on the cones, pineapples, cauliflowers, etc. They are to record the name of each object on the Pattern Observation Sheet, draw the object, and record the number of petals, the number of flowers and leaves, or the number of protrusions in a spiral.
- After the Pattern Observation Sheets are completed, students meet as a whole class to discuss their findings and attempt to figure out the Fibonacci sequence and how it works.

Patterns in Nature—Our Observations

Record your observations as you examine each of the different objects on your table.

Object	Illustration of the Object	Number of Petals, Sections, Spirals, Leaves or Petals Arranged on a Branch

Development

- Assuming the roles they have been assigned, students work in their groups examining the different items on their tables and discussing their findings.
- Each recorder fills in the group's Pattern Observation Sheet.
- The teacher circulates around the room observing and talking with the students as they work, noting the discussions and conversations.

Follow-up

Students meet as a whole class to discuss and share their findings. Ensure that students have their Pattern Observation Sheets in front of them. You might want to have them displayed so that students will see the similarities among the numbers within them. Some questions you might ask to stimulate discussion include:

1. *Can you tell us about some of the things you found out or noticed in the objects you examined?*
2. *What did you notice about the numbers that seemed to come up when you counted the number of petals, leaves, flowers, spirals, etc. in the different items you looked at?*
3. *Do you have any theories about why these particular numbers kept appearing? If so, what are they?*
4. *If these numbers are all part of the Fibonacci sequence, what do you think the sequence is?*
5. *What do you think is the pattern of the numbers in this sequence?*
6. *How are the numbers determined?*

Have students write in their journals about their reflections on the investigation.

Next Steps_____

Assessment Notes

- Is the student able to make the connection between his or her observations and subsequent findings with the Fibonacci sequence?
- Can the student identify and extend the Fibonacci sequence? For example, is the student able to figure out the next number, 3, 5, 8, 13, ___?
- What is the number that comes after 21? After 34? After 89? Note: Results of assessment can be used to determine the type of follow up that could be used for different students after this lesson. For example, students who need reinforcement can use materials such as snap cubes to build the numbers of the sequence. Doing so will provide them with an opportunity to see concretely how the sequence works and the pattern that emerges.
- Students who would benefit from an added challenge could do further research on the Fibonacci sequence to find out other places where it correlates with real life. Doing so will provide them with another opportunity to develop their research skills.
- One possible topic to examine is the connection of the Fibonacci sequence with our teeth.
- Other possible research topics include:
    The golden mean
    The golden ratio
    The connection of the Fibonacci sequence with art and/or the human body

The questions in Activity 14.13, mapped onto the pattern in Figure 14.11(a), are commonly used (and good ones to use!) to help students begin to think about the functional relationship.

Activity 14.13

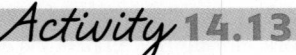

Predict How Many

Working in pairs or small groups, have students explore a pattern and respond to the following instructions.

- **Make a table that shows the number of triangles needed in each step or frame of the pattern.**

Step Number	1	2	3	4	5	6	7
Number of Triangles							

- **Predict how many triangles are needed for step 10? Step 20? Step 100? Explain your reasoning.**
- **Write a rule (in words or symbols) that indicates the total number of pieces needed to build the number (*n*) of items for any step.**

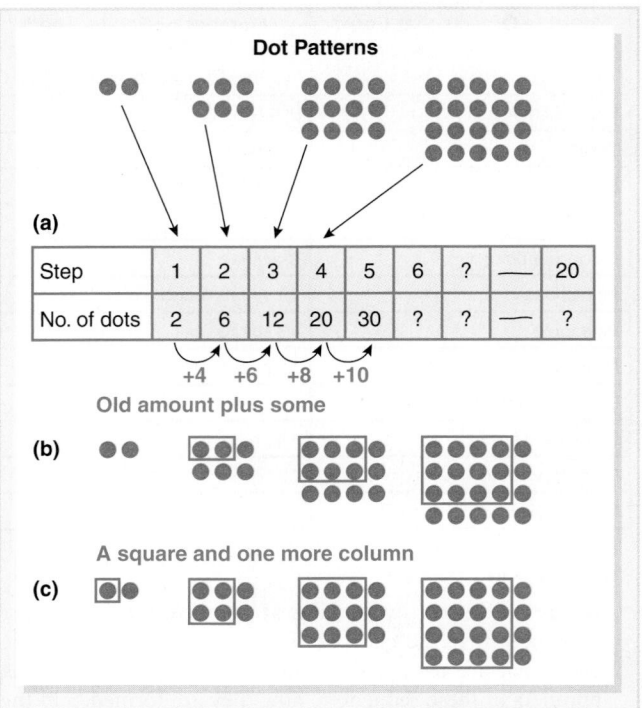

Figure 14.12 Two different ways to analyze relationships in the "dot" pattern.

Student experiences with growing patterns should start with fairly straightforward patterns (such as in Figure 14.11), move to somewhat more complicated ones (see Figure 14.12), then move to ones that are very difficult. It is also important to include fractions and decimals in working with growing patterns.

The following problem-based lesson provides students with an opportunity to practise working with growing patterns, using real contexts.

When looking for relationships, some students will focus on the table and others will focus on the physical pattern. It is important for students to see that whatever relationships they discover, they exist in both forms. So if a relationship is found in a table, challenge students to see how it plays out in the physical version.

Recursive Patterns and Formulas   For most students, it is easier to see the patterns developing from one frame or step to the next. In Figure 14.12(a) the number in each step can be determined by adding successive even numbers to the numbers in the previous step. The description that tells how a pattern changes from a given step to the next is known as a *recursive* pattern (Bezuszka & Kenney, 2008).

A recursive pattern can also be observed in the physical version of the pattern. In Figure 14.12(b), notice that in each step of the physical version, the dots have been outlined with a rectangle. Doing so lets you examine the amount added. It also lets you see how a pattern of adding on even numbers is created.

Recursive formulas are equations that show you how to get the next quantity, given the one you have. For example, in Figure 14.11, the first design grows by 3 triangles each

time, so the recursive formula can be written as NEXT = NOW + 3. If NOW is the quantity in step 5, then NEXT is the quantity in step 6. Try to write a recursive formula for the other three patterns in Figure 14.11.

Explicit Formulas   To find the table entry for the hundredth frame or step, the only way a recursive pattern can help is to find all of the prior 99 entries in the table. If a formula can be discovered that connects the number of objects in a step to the step or frame number, any entry in a table can be determined without building or calculating any previous entries. A rule that determines the number of elements in a step from the step (frame) number is called the *explicit formula*. Activities and textbooks in elementary textbooks often call the explicit formula the "rule" for the growing pattern.

▮▮ ──────────── Pause and Reflect

Can you determine the explicit formula for the pattern in Figure 14.12? How did you find the formula?

There is no single best method for finding the relationship between the step number and step. Some students will analyze the table and notice that if they multiply the step number by the next step number, they will get the number of dots for that step. This leads to the explicit formula: $d = n(n + 1)$, where d is the number of dots and n is the step number.

Some will examine the physical pattern to see what is changing. In Figure 14.12(c), a square array is outlined for each step. Each successive square increases by one dot on a side. In this example, the side of each square is the same as the step number. The column to the right of each square is also the same as the step (frame) number. At this point, writing a numerical expression for each step (frame) number can help students find the explicit formula. For example, the first four steps in Figure 14.12 are $1^2 + 1$, $2^2 + 2$, $3^2 + 3$, and $4^2 + 4$. The explicit formula is therefore $d = n^2 + n$.

Regardless of whether students use the table or the model, they will likely be able to describe the explicit formula in words before they can write it in symbols. If the goal of your lesson is to be able to find the rule, then stopping with the verbal formula is appropriate. In this case, you may have some students that are ready to represent the formula symbolically. As a way of differentiating your instruction, you may challenge them to do so. If your instructional goal is to write formulas using symbols, then ask students to first write the formula, or rule, in words. Then, think about how they can translate that statement to numbers and symbols.

 **NCTM Standards** "In grades 3–5, students should investigate numerical and geometric patterns and express them mathematically in words or symbols. They should analyze the structure of the pattern and how it grows or changes, organize this information systematically, and use their analysis to develop generalizations about the mathematical relationships in the pattern" (p. 159).

Graphs of Functions   So far, growing patterns have been represented by (1) the physical materials or drawings, (2) a chart, (3) words, and (4) symbols. A graph adds a fifth representation. Figure 14.13 shows the graph for the Border Problem and the Dot Pattern. Notice that the first is a straight-line (linear) relationship and the other is a curved line that would make half of a parabola if the points were joined. The horizontal axis is always used to represent the step numbers, the independent variable.

Graphs provide visuals that allow students to readily see relationships among growing patterns. Consider strings of a single colour of pattern blocks (Figure 14.14) and the corresponding perimeters. This is a good pattern to explore in the same manner as "The Border Problem." Begin with a string of seven or eight blocks and find ways to determine the perimeter without counting. Again, there are at least five different ways to find the perimeter, each resulting in a general formula that appears on the surface to be different from the others.

Having graphs of three related growing patterns offers the opportunity to compare and connect the graphs to the patterns and to the tables (see Figure 14.15). For example, ask students to discuss how to get from one coordinate to the next (up six, over one) and then ask how that informa-

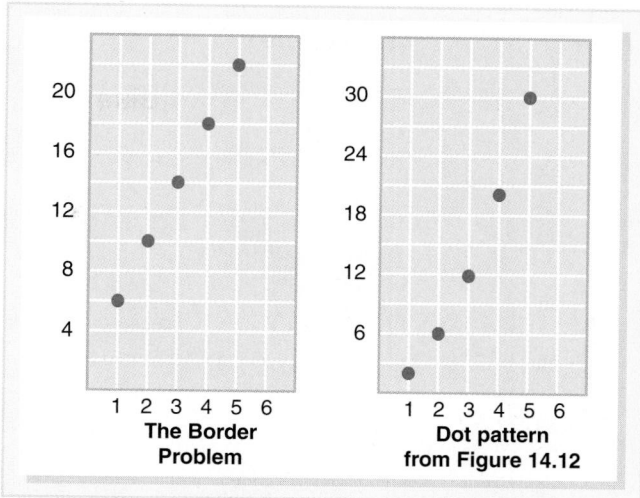

Figure 14.13 Graphs of two growing patterns.

tion can be found in the table. Second, you can point at a particular point on the graph and ask what it tells about the model.

See you if you answer the following questions, which you can also pose to students to help them understand the graphical representation of the function:

- How does each graph represent each of the string models?
- Why is there not a line connecting the dots?
- Why is one line steeper than the others?
- Why is there no dot on the y-axis?
- If the dots were plotted on the y-axis, what would they be for each string? Why?

 Being able to make connections across representations is important for understanding functions. When asking questions like the ones listed above. Look to see if students are able to link the graph to the context, to the table, and to the formula. ◆

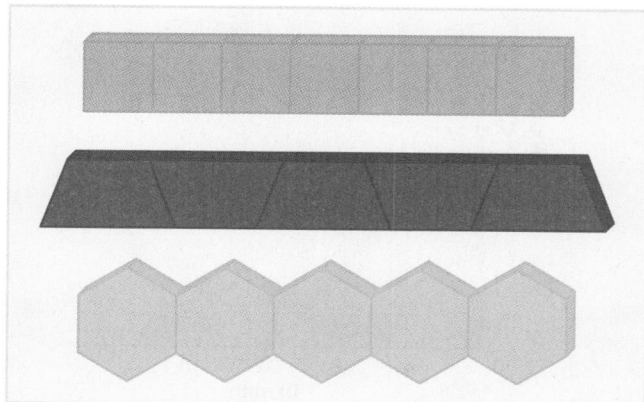

Figure 14.14 For each string of pattern blocks, can you termine the perimeter for *N* pattern blocks?

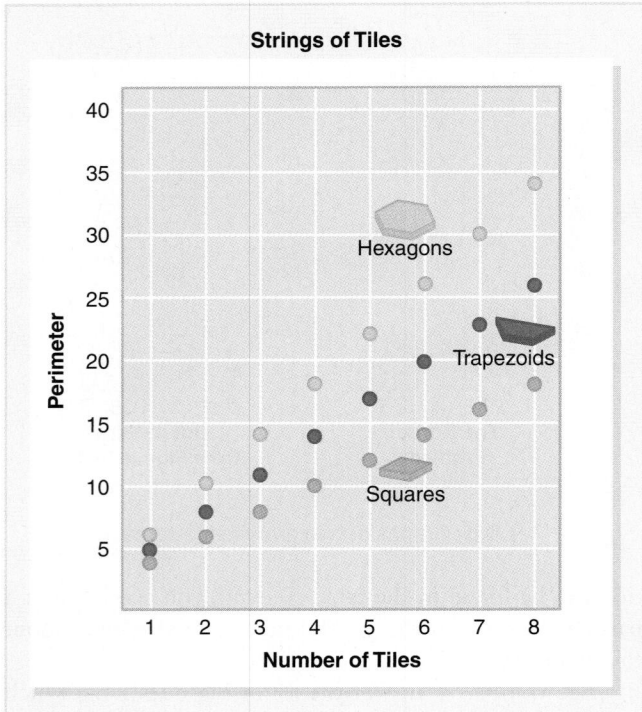

Figure 14.15 Graphs of the perimeters of three different pattern-block strings. The lines are not drawn because for this context, there are no solutions between the points.

Not all functions have straight-line graphs. For example, in building a rectangular pen with 24 metres of fence, if you increase the width, you will decrease the length. The area will vary accordingly (see Figure 14.16). An explicit formula for the width is $w = 12 - l$ (l is the length), which decreases at a constant rate, therefore looking like a line.

By contrast, the explicit formula for area of the pen is $a = l(12 - l)$. It rises in a curve, reaches a maximum value, and then goes back down.

Graphs and Contexts   It is important for students to be able to interpret and construct graphs related to real situations, including sketching the shape of a graph, without using any specific data, equations, or numbers. The advantage of activities such as these is the focus on how a graph can express the relationships involved.

Activity 14.14

Sketch a Graph

Sketch a graph for each of these situations. No numbers or formulas are to be used.

a. The temperature of a frozen dinner from 30 minutes before it is removed from the freezer until it is removed from the microwave and placed on the table. (Consider time 0 to be the moment the dinner is removed from the freezer.)
b. The value of a 1970 Volkswagen Beetle from the time it was purchased to the present. (It was kept by a loving owner and is in top condition.)
c. The level of water in the bathtub from the time you begin to fill it to the time it is completely empty after your bath.
d. Profit in terms of number of items sold.
e. The height of a baseball in terms of time from when it is thrown straight up to the time it hits the ground.
f. The speed of the baseball in the situation in (e).

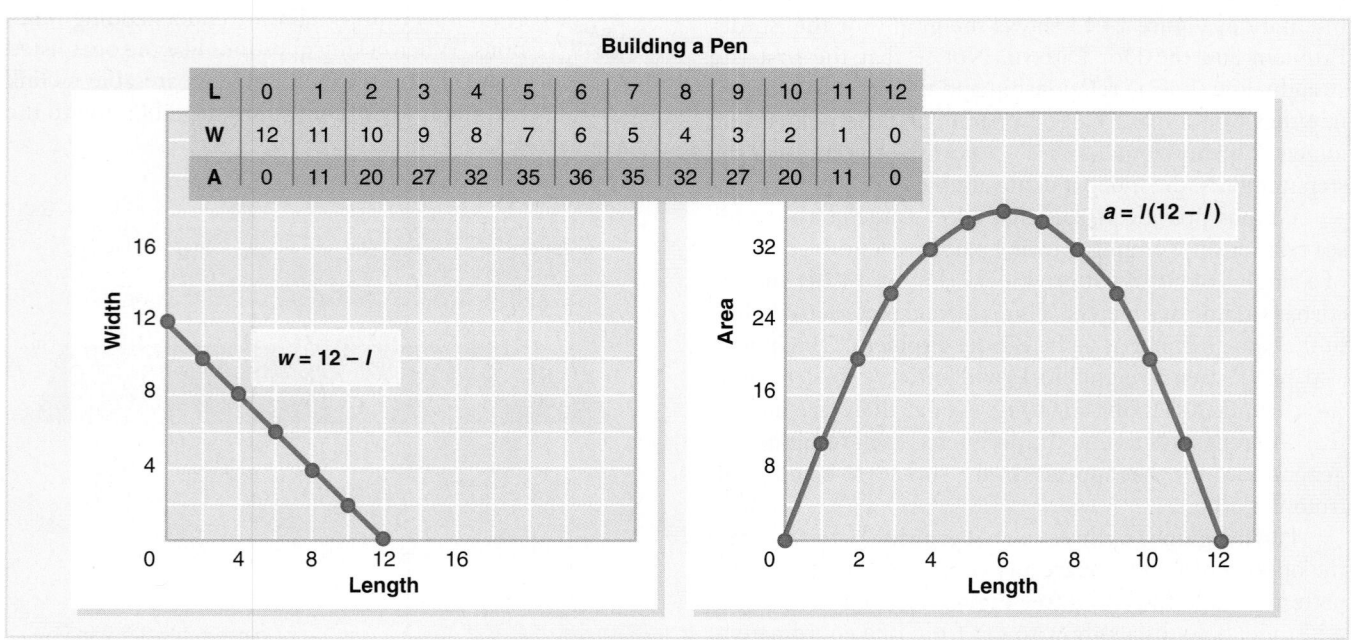

Figure 14.16 The width and area graphs as functions of the length of a rectangle with a fixed perimeter of 24 units.

Pause and Reflect

Ⅱ Stop for a moment and sketch graphs for each of the situations in the last activity.

In a classroom, it is fun to have students sketch their graphs on transparencies without identifying which situation they selected (no labels on the graphs). Let students examine the graphs to see if they can determine which situation goes with each graph that is presented. Figure 14.17 contains six graphs that match the six situations described in the "Sketch a Graph" activity. Can you match these graphs with the six situations?

Graphs and Rate of Change Notice that the analysis of the graphs focuses on how the graphs increase or decrease and how steeply or gradually. A graph is a picture of the rate of change of one variable in terms of the other. Essentially, graphs can have only one of the seven characteristics shown in Figure 14.18 or some combination of these. These types of change will be seen in the following activity.

Activity 14.15

Bottles and Volume Graphs

Figure 14.19 shows six bottles and six graphs. Assume that the bottles are filled at a constant rate. Because of their shapes, the height of the liquid in the bottles will increase either more slowly or more quickly as the bottle gets wider or narrower. Match the graphs with the bottles.

Find some bottles or glasses that have different shapes. Give each group or pair one bottle to use for the activity. Fill a small container (e.g., a medicine cup or test tube) with water and pour into the bottle. Measure the height of the water after each pouring. Record in a table the number of containers used and the height of the water after each pouring. After each group gathers the data, have them graph their findings. Graphs are collected. Then the students try to match graphs with bottles.

Linear Functions

Linear functions are a subset of growing patterns and functions, which can be linear or non-linear. Because linearity is an important component of middle- and upper-grade study of mathematics, and because growing patterns in elementary school tend to be linear situations, it deserves additional attention. Linear functions are defined quite simply as functions that grow in a linear or constant manner. In a graph, this can be easily established by seeing that the plotted points lie on one line.

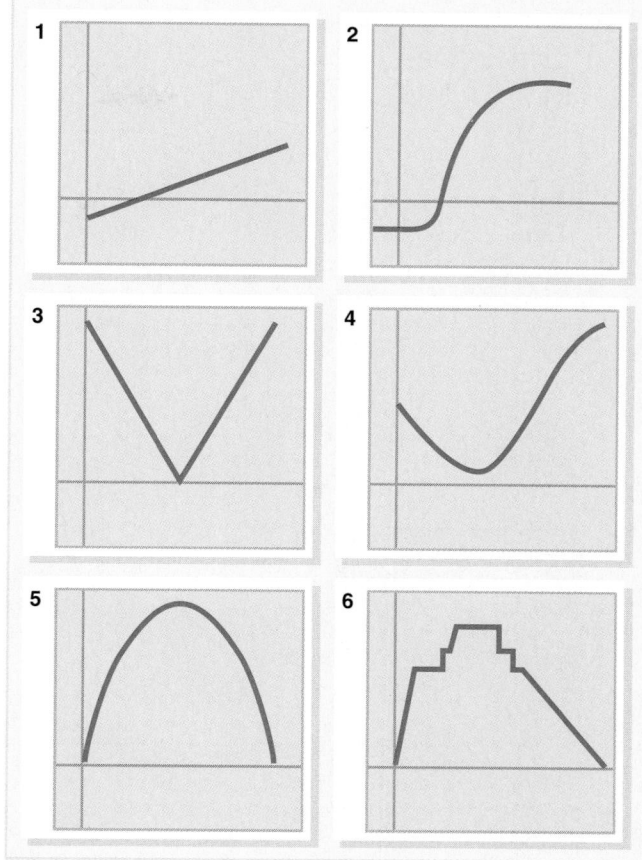

Figure 14.17 Match each graph with the situations described in Activity 14.14. Talk about what change is happening in each case.

Linearity can be viewed in several of the previous representations. If you make a table for the hexagon perimeter task in Figure 14.14, you will notice that the recursive pattern (the pattern from step to step) is a constant 4 (+4). The rate of change from one step to the next is constant. You can always look at the recursive relationship to determine if the function is growing at a constant rate and is therefore linear. Straight lines have a constant recursive pattern.

In the equation, linearity can be determined by looking at the part of the expression that changes. Compare the two formulas from the rectangular pen problem. One was $w = 12 - l$ and the other was $a = l(12 - l)$ or $a = 12l - l^2$. Notice that in the first case, the change is related to l and each time

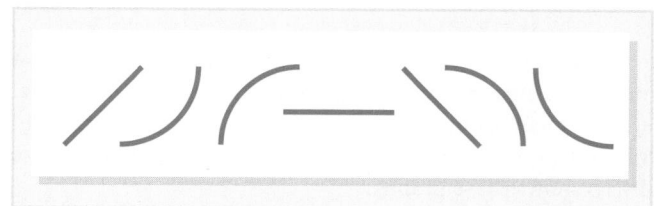

Figure 14.18 Seven ways that graphs can change. a graph often has combinations of these characteristics.

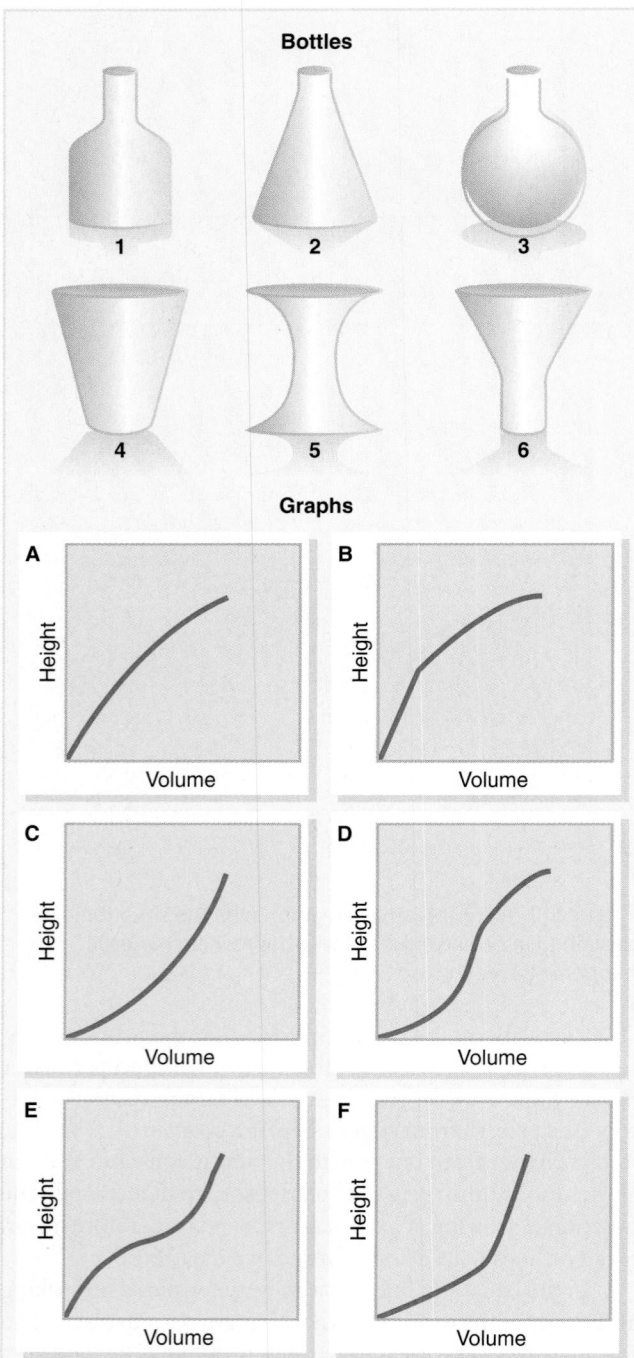

Figure 14.19 Assuming bottles are filled at a constant rate, match the graphs with the bottles.

l changes by 1, w changes by the same amount—a constant rate of change, as in linear situations. In the area formula, when l changes by the same amount, the area changes in varying amounts. In fact, this is a quadratic situation. Figure 14.16 shows these graphs.

Rate of Change and Slope Rate, whether constant or varying, is a type of change often associated with how fast

something is travelling. Rate is an excellent context for exploring linearity, because constant rates can be seen in a wide range of contexts, such as the geometric model of the pattern block perimeter pattern or the rate of growth of a plant. Other rate contexts in numerical situations include hourly wages, amount of gas per kilometre, profit, and even the cost of an item, such as a bus ticket.

 The NCTM e-examples has two applets that target rate, making the connection between a real-world context and graphs. In Applet 5.2 students can adjust the speed, direction, and starting position of two runners. As the runners are set in motion, a time–distance graph is generated dynamically for each runner (see Figure 14.20). ◆

The NCTM applet compares two rates by way of two representations (a visual model and a graph). Many real-world situations can be described in this way. For example, in the NCTM Applet 6.2, phone call rates are also explored through a graph and an equation. Figure 14.15 offers another example. The three graphs are increasing at different rates. Notice that each slant or slope is different. *Slope* is the numerical value that describes the rate of change for a linear function. The rate at which the function values increase or decrease is evident in how steep the line is, either up or down.

One of the explicit formulas for the hexagon growing pattern is $y = 4x + 2$. Note that the rate of change is 4 because the perimeter increases by 4 with each new piece. All linear functions can be written in this form: $y = mx + b$

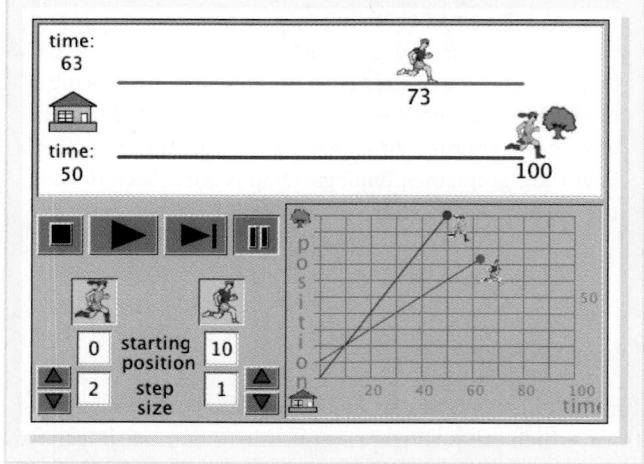

Figure 14.20 Applet 5.2, "Understanding Distance, Speed, and Time Relationships Using Simulation Software."
Used with permission from NCTM *e-Standards*. Copyright © 2003 by the National Council of Teachers of Mathematics, Inc. All rights reserved. The presence of the screenshot from NCTM e-Standards, http://standards.nctm.org/document/eexamples/chap5/5.2/index.htm, does not constitute or imply an endorsement by NCTM.

(including $y = mx$ when $b = 0$). The value m in this formula is the rate of change or the slope of the line.

Conceptually, then, slope signifies how much y changes when x increases by 1. If a line contains the points (2, 4) and (3, 5), then you can see that as x increases by 1, y decreases by 9. So the rate of change is –9. For the points (4, 3) and (7, 9), you can see that when x increases by 3, y increases by 6. Therefore, an increase of 1 in x results in a change of 2 in y. Upon further exploration and experiences, you (and your students) will begin to notice that you can find the rate of change or slope by finding the difference in the y-values and dividing by the difference in the x-values.

Sometimes, an equation may not look like the familiar form $y = mx + b$. For example, in the rectangular pen problem, if l and w represent the length and the width, and the perimeter is 24, then $2l + 2w = 24$ is an equation that relates the length to the width. If we solve this equation for w, we end up with $w = \frac{(24 - 2l)}{2}$ or $w = 12 - l$. This can also be written as $w = -1l + 12$, a linear equation with a slope of negative 1 and an initial value of 12.

Proportional Situations   Many relationships involving rates or proportions offer a valuable opportunity for examining functions. The following is a typical proportion problem.

Two out of every three students who eat in the cafeteria drink a 500 mL container of white milk each day. If 450 students eat in the cafeteria, how many litres of milk are consumed?

As the problem is stated, there are a fixed number of students (450) and a single answer to the problem. Students would be expected to set up a proportion and solve for the unknown. But if only the first sentence of the problem is provided, students can be asked to create a table showing the number of litres of milk consumed for four or five different numbers of students, plot the data on a graph, and create an equation that shows the relationship between students in the cafeteria and milk consumed. The number of litres of milk, m, consumed in the cafeteria *is a function of* the number of students who eat there. The graph can be used to answer the question about milk for 450 students. Students can be challenged to find an equation that gives the amount of milk in terms of the number of students, $m = \frac{2}{3}/2s$.

The following problem has been converted to a function investigation by asking for an answer in terms of an unknown instead of a specific number.

If each lemonade recipe will serve 20 people, how many recipes are needed to serve *n* people? If it takes three cans of concentrate to make one recipe, how many cans should be purchased to serve *n* people?

This example has two questions. One equation can be written to relate the number of recipes as a function of the number of people [$R = f(p)$], and a second equation to give the number of cans of concentrate as a function of the number of recipes [$C = g(R)$]. Using these equations you can find an equation that gives cans of concentrate as a function of the number of people.

All proportional situations can be represented by equations in the form of $y = mx$. As well, the graphs of all proportional situations are straight lines that pass through the origin. Students will find that the slope of these lines is also the rate of change between the two variables.

Parallel and Perpendicular Lines   Consider the situation of Larry and Mary, each earning $30 a week for the summer months. Mary starts the summer $50 in the hole and Larry already has $20. When will Mary and Larry have the same amount of money? In week 3, how much more money does Larry have? How much more does he have in week 7? In any week, what is the difference in their wealth? The rate for Larry's and Mary's earnings are the same—and the graphs of their wealth would go up at the same rate; that is, the slopes would be the same. We can tell that the graphs of $y = 3x + 2$ (Larry's money) and $y = 3x - 5$ (Mary's money) are parallel without even making the graphs. In general, if two lines have the same slope, it means that the lines are either increasing or decreasing at exactly the same rate and the two lines are parallel.

Slopes can also tell us when two lines are perpendicular, but it is less obvious. A little bit of analysis using similar triangles will show that for perpendicular lines, the slope of one is the negative reciprocal of the other.

Mathematical Modelling

Kaput (1999) defines *modelling* as the process of beginning with real phenomena and an attempt to mathematize them. Mathematical models, or equations, are used to predict other phenomena. Mathematical models are not be confused with the models that use manipulatives or visuals for building a pattern (such as a pattern block).

We have already seen many examples of mathematical models. How is modelling used to predict? Take the example of selling widgets marked up at some percentage over wholesale. Once a formula is derived for a given price and markup, it can be used to determine the profit at different sales levels. Furthermore, it is relatively easy to make adjustments in the price and the mark-up percentage, allowing for further predictions. That is, the equation, or mathematical model, allows us to find values that cannot be observed in the real phenomenon.

Consider creating a mathematical model to describe the depreciation of a car at 20 percent each year. Determining the model might progress in the following steps: If the car loses 20 percent of its value in 1 year, then it must be worth 80 percent of its value after a year. So after 1 year, a $15 000 car is worth $15 000 × 0.8. In the second year, it loses 20 percent of that value, so it will be worth only 80 percent of its value at the end of year one, which was $15 000 × 0.8. The value at the end of year 2 would be ($15 000 × 0.8) × 0.8, and so on. At the end of *y* years, the value of the car can be expressed in this equation: Value = $15 000 × 0.8^y. Figure 14.21 shows the graph and the table of values on a graphing calculator.

The next activity provides another context appropriate for developing a mathematical model.

Activity 14.16

How Many Litres Left?

A car gets 9.7 kilometres per litre of gas. Its gas tank holds 76 litres. Suppose that you were on a trip and had filled the tank at the outset. Determine a mathematical model that describes the number of litres left (*L*), given the number of kilometres travelled (*d*).

Notice that the word *rule* could replace "mathematical model." In this case, one possible equation is $L = 76 - \frac{m}{23}$. Use the model, or equation, to make predictions. For example, "How can you tell from the graph how much gas will be left after driving 450 kilometres?" "How many kilometres can you drive before the gas tank has only 10 litres left?"

Here are two other engaging contexts for similar exploration.

Mark is an avid cyclist. He can average 27 kilometres per hour for about 4 hours. He leaves home and travels for $2\frac{1}{2}$ hours at this rate. What is his distance from home at any given time? Create a formula to represent distance travelled (*d*) for any given time (*t*).

Mercier's Hardware buys widgets for $4.17 each, marks them up 35 percent over wholesale, and sells them at that price. Create a mathematical model to relate widgets sold (*w*) to profit (*p*). Suppose the manager puts the widgets on sale at 25% off the regular price and asked you to determine a formula for the sale. What is your formula or mathematical model, comparing widgets sold (*s*) to profit (*p*)?

Teaching Considerations

It is important to emphasize some key considerations that will lead students to feel empowered to do algebra. Some of these ideas have already been implied in the previous discussions of algebraic concepts.

Emphasize Appropriate Algebra Vocabulary

A large part of understanding mathematics is the ability to communicate mathematically, so it is important to use appropriate terminology in teaching algebra. This is far more than a vocabulary list; it is the practice of consistently using, and having students use, appropriate words for situations. Creating word walls and keeping a journal of terms are ways to help all students, especially English language learners (ELLs). Having graphs, models, or tables to illustrate the words is essential. Here we briefly share some important vocabulary terms.

Independent and Dependent Variables   Although the meanings of "independent" and "dependent" variables are implied by the words themselves, they can still be challenging for students. The independent variable is the step number, or the input, or whatever value is being used to find another value. For example, in the case of the strings of pattern blocks, the independent variable is the number of blocks in the string. The dependent variable is the number of objects needed, the output, or whatever value you get from using the independent variable. In the pattern block problem, it is the perimeter. You can say that the perimeter of the block structure depends on the number of blocks. Recall the two equations and graphs representing a pen of 24 meters in Figure 14.16. In this case, the length has been selected as the independent variable (though it could have as easily been the width) and the dependent variable is width.

Discrete and Continuous   A discussion of functions, especially graphical representation, in the elementary grades, could include a discussion of whether the points

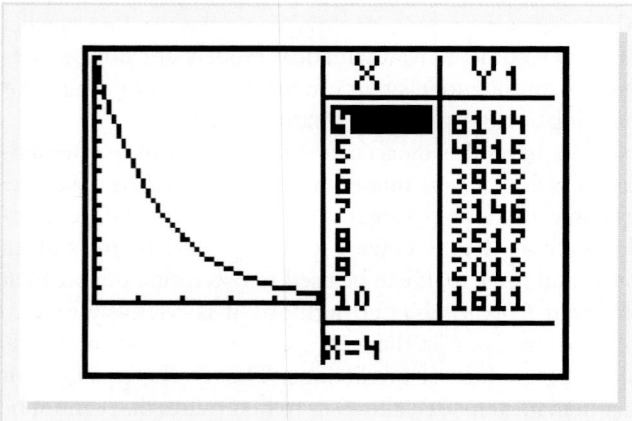

Figure 14.21 The graph and table for $V = 15,000 \times 0.8^y$. Years, the independent variable, are shown under *X* and value, the dependent variable, is shown under Y1.

plotted on the graph should be connected or not and why. In the pattern block perimeter problem, the answer is no because you will only have whole number values. When isolated or selected values are the only ones appropriate for a context, the function is *discrete*. If all values along a line or curve are solutions to the function, then it is *continuous*. The pen example is continuous—the length can be any value up to a certain maximum and the width (area) would change accordingly.

Domain and Range   The *domain* of a function comprises the possible values for the independent variable. If it is discrete, like the pattern block perimeter problem, it may include all positive whole numbers. For the rectangular pen that is 24 metres, the domain is all real numbers between 0 and 12. The *range* is the corresponding possible values for the dependent variable. In the pattern block perimeter problem, the range is the positive whole numbers; in the rectangular pen, the range for the length is the same as the domain—real numbers between 0 and 12.

Multiple Representations

Functions can be represented in any of five ways: (1) the pattern itself, which we can refer to as the context; (2) the chart or table; (3) the symbolic equation; (4) the graph; and (5) the verbal description, the language. In both the repeating and the growing patterns section each example has at least two representations included (e.g., context and a table) and as many as all five (e.g., the dot pattern in Figure 14.12). It is important to see that each representation is a way of looking at the function, yet each provides a different way of looking at or thinking about the function. The value of each representation is the way that it helps us see and understand the function in a different manner than the others do. To illustrate this point, we will use the context of a hot dog vendor.

Brian is trying to make money to help pay for university by selling hot dogs from a hot dog cart at the coliseum during major performances and ball games. He pays the cart owner $35 per night for the use of the cart. He sells hot dogs for $1.25 each. His costs for the hot dogs, condiments, napkins, and other paper products are about 60 cents per hot dog on average. The profit from a single hot dog is, therefore, 65 cents.

Context   This function begins with a context: selling hot dogs and the resulting profit. We are interested in Brian's profit in terms of the number of hot dogs sold: The more hot dogs Brian sells, the more profit he will make. Brian does not begin to make a profit immediately because he must pay the $35 rent on the vending cart. Nonetheless, Brian's profit is dependent on—*is a function of*—the number of hot dogs he sells.

The context helps students make sense of what changes (number of hot dogs sold) and what stays the same ($35 rental), which can help them figure out the explicit formula. The context supports students' conceptual understanding of the other more abstract representations and illustrates that algebra is a tool for describing real-world phenomena. The context alone, though, is not sufficient—carefully selected prompts to connect the context to other representations are needed to support students' algebraic thinking (Earnest & Balti, 2008).

Table   Brian, the hot dog vendor, might well sit down and calculate some possible income figures based on anticipated sales. This will give him some idea of how many hot dogs he must sell to break even and what his profit might be for an evening. A table of values might resemble Table 14.2.

The number of hot dogs shown in the table is purely a matter of choice. One could calculate the profit for 10 000 hot dogs (10 000 × 0.65 − 35), even though it is not reasonable in this context. One of the values of contexts in thinking about functions is to see how mathematical representations can ignore reality. The person who interprets the table must take the context into consideration.

Verbal Description (Language)   In the hot dog vendor situation, Brian's profit depends on the number of hot dogs that are sold. In functional language, we can say, "Profit *is a function of* the number of hot dogs sold." The phrase "is a function of" expresses the dependent relationship. The profit *depends on*—is a function of—the hot dog sales. The verbal description (language) of the explicit formula for the hot dog stand might be stated by students as, "You multiply each hot dog sold by $0.65; then you subtract the $35 for the cart."

The verbal explanation of the explicit formula provides a connection from the context to the symbolic representation. Students may struggle with using variables and being able to first describe the formula in words is an important stepping-stone for being able to use symbols (Lannin, Townsend, Armer, Green, & Schneider, 2008).

Symbols   Suppose that we pick a letter—say, *h*—to represent the number of hot dogs Brian sells. Brian's profit is

Table 14.2

Number of Hot Dogs Sold (Independent Variable) and the Profit (Dependent Variable)	
Hot Dogs Sold	**Profit**
0	−35.00
50	−2.50
100	30.00
150	62.50

represented by the equation $p = (0.65 \times h) - 35$, where p is the letter selected to stand for profit. This equation defines a mathematical relationship between two values or two variables, profit and hot dogs.

By expressing a function as an equation, it is possible to find the profit for any number of hot dogs. Conversely, if Brian wants to make $100, he can figure out how many hot dogs he needs to sell. Because it is abstract, it is particularly important that students explain what each number and each variable represents.

 The equation can be entered into a graphing calculator, and the calculator can do the calculations to produce a table or draw a graph. Doing so enables students to make connections across representations without having the tedious work of creating each one by hand.

Graphs In Figure 14.22, four different values of hot dog sales are plotted on a graph. The horizontal axis represents the number of hot dogs sold, and the vertical axis, the profit. As we have already established, the profit goes up as the sales go up. There is, in this situation, a very clear pattern to the six values. In this context, it means that the profit is going up at a constant rate, namely at 0.65 per hot dog.

The graphical representation allows one to see "at a glance" that the relationship between sales and profits is linear—a straight line—and is increasing. It also can be used to get quick approximate answers to questions about Brian's profits. For example: "How many hot dogs must be sold to break even?" "How many will need to be sold to earn $100.00?" (It looks to be near 210 or 215.). The

context gives meaning to the graph, and the graph adds understanding to the context.

The graph indicates the pattern in the data, but in terms of the context, all values may not make sense for the context. In this case, it would not make sense to extend the line to the left of the vertical axis. Doing so would mean selling a negative quantity of hot dogs. Neither is it reasonable to talk about sales of millions of hot dogs (unless he develops a national chain!).

 In the past, when students had to plot points and do by hand all the computations that were involved, functions were limited to examples using whole numbers. Doing so would avoid the tedium of computing and plotting fractions. Thanks to technology, we can now explore realistic contexts involving more precise and "messy" numbers. ◆

Connect Representations

Figure 14.23 illustrates the five representations of functions for the hot dog context. The most important idea is to see that each of these representations illustrates the same relationship, for a given function. It is important for students to be able to explain the connections across these representations, in a conceptual manner. This experience might be different from the one you had with algebra where the textbook instructed, along with a set of steps to follow, "Graph the function, given the equation." The difference lies in whether the instruction/learning is about following a rote procedure or about making sense of the function. The latter is your goal as a teacher.

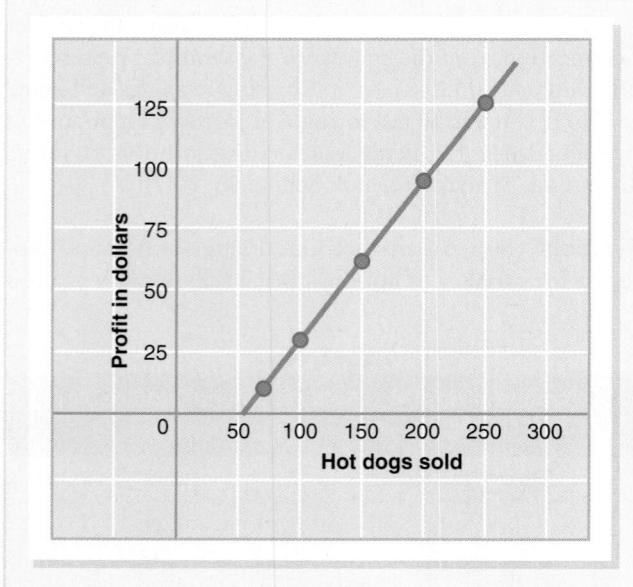

Figure 14.22 A graph showing profit as a function of hot dogs sold.

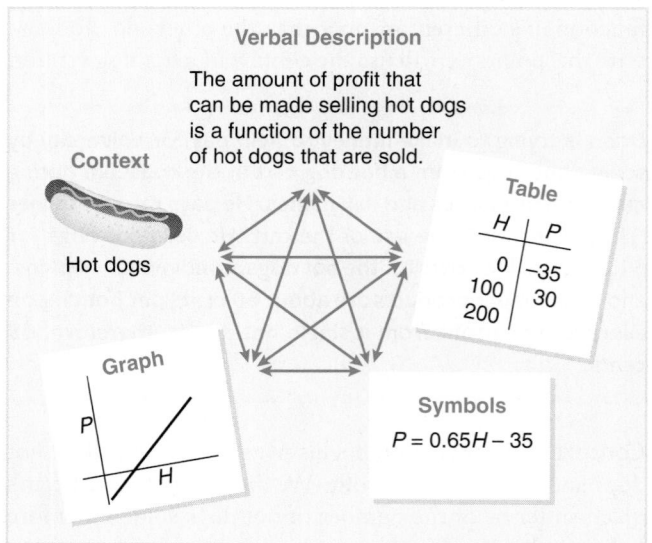

Figure 14.23 Five different representations of a function. For any given function, students should see that all these representations are connected and illustrate the same relationship.

The grade 7 *Connected Mathematics Project* has an entire unit titled, "Variables and Patterns" in which students explore and use different representations of functions found in real contexts. The excerpt that follows is a lesson that focuses on tables and graphs.

"By the middle grades, students should be able to understand the relationships among tables, graphs, and symbols and to judge the advantages and disadvantages of each way of representing relationships for practical purposes. As they work with multiple representations of functions—including numeric, graphic, and symbolic—they will develop a more comprehensive understanding of functions" (p. 38).

A good formative or summative assessment prompt for the hot dog problem (which can be adapted to any task) is: "Can you show me how to use each representation to find the profit for selling 225 hot dogs?" ◆

Algebraic Thinking Across the Curriculum

One reason the phrase "algebraic thinking" is used instead of "algebra" is that the practice of looking for patterns and generalizations goes beyond curriculum topics that are usually categorized as algebra topics. You have already experienced some of this integration—looking at geometric growing patterns and working with perimeter and area. In the sections that follow, the emphasis of the content moves to other content areas, with algebraic thinking used as a tool for discovery. This brief discussion will be developed more fully in later chapters.

Measurement and Algebra   Soares, Blanton, and Kaput (2006) describe how to "algebrafy" the elementary curriculum. One measurement example they give uses *Spaghetti and Meatballs for All*, looking at the increasing number of chairs needed, given the number of tables put together.

Geometric formulas relate various dimensions, areas, and volumes of shapes. Each of these formulas involves at least one functional relationship. Consider any familiar formula for measuring a geometric shape. For example, the circumference of a circle is $c = 2\pi r$. The radius is the independent variable and circumference is the dependent variable. We can say that the circumference is dependent on the radius. Even non-linear formulas like volume of a cone ($V = 1/3\pi r^2 h$) is a function. Here the volume is a function of both the height of the cone and the radius. If the radius is held constant, the volume is a function of the height. Similarly, for a fixed height, the volume is a function of the radius.

The following activity explores how the volume of a box varies as a result of changing the dimensions.

Activity 14.17

Designing the Largest Box

Begin with a rectangle sheet of cardboard, and from each corner, cut a square. Fold up the four resulting flaps, and tape them together to form an open box. The volume of the box will vary, depending on the size of the squares (see Figure 14.24, the sheet measures 9 units by 12 units). Write a formula that gives the volume of the box as a function of the size of the cut-out squares. Use the function to determine what size the squares should be to create the box with the largest volume.

Data and Algebra   Data can also be obtained from sports records, census reports, the business section of the newspaper, and many other sources. Students can gather data such as measurement examples or survey data. As noted toward the end of Chapter 7, the Internet has many sites where data can be found.

"When doing experiments or dealing with real data, students may encounter 'messy data,' for which a line or a curve may not be an exact fit. They will need experience with such situations and assistance from the teacher to develop their ability to find a function that fits the data well enough to be useful as a prediction tool" (p. 228).

Experiments.   There are many experiments that students can explore to see the functional relationships, if any, that exist between two variables. Gathering real data is an excellent way to engage a range of learners and to see how mathematics can be used to describe real phenomena.

Data should be collected, then represented in a table or on a graph. The goal is to determine if there is a functional

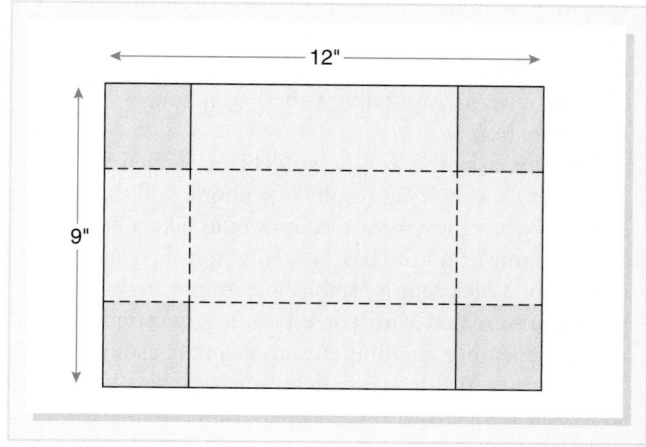

Figure 14.24 If squares are cut from a 9 unit by 12 unit piece of cardboard so that the four flaps can be folded up, what size squares should be cut so that the volume of the box is the largest possible?

Connected Mathematics

Middle Grades

Grade 7, Variables and Patterns
Investigation 3: Analyzing Graphs and Tables

Context

Much of this unit is built on the context of a group of students who take a multi-day bike trip from Philadelphia to Williamsburg, Virginia, then decide to set up a bike tour business of their own. Students explore a variety of functional relationships between time, distance, speed, expenses, profits, and so on. When data are plotted as discrete points, students consider what the graph might look like between points. For example, what interpretations could be given to each of these five graphs showing speed change from 0 to 15 mph (24 km/h) in the first 10 minutes of a trip?

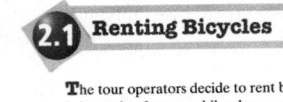

Task Description

In this investigation, the fictional students in the unit are gathering data in preparation for setting up their tour business. For the first task, data are given from two different bike rental companies as shown here—from one company in the form of a table, and from the other in the form of a graph. The task is interesting because of the firsthand way in which students experience the value of one representation over another, depending on the need of the situation. In this unit, students are frequently asked whether a graph or a table is the better source of information.

In the tasks that follow, students are given a table of data showing results of a phone poll that asked at which price former tour riders would take a bike tour. Students must find the best way to graph this data. After a price for a bike tour is established, graphs for estimated profits are created with corresponding questions about profits depending on different numbers of customers.

The investigations use no formulas to this point. The subsequent investigation is called "Patterns and Rules" and begins the exploration of connecting equations or

2.1 Renting Bicycles

The tour operators decide to rent bicycles for their customers. They get information from two bike shops.

Rocky's Cycle Center sends a table of weekly rental fees for bikes.

Rocky's Weekly Rental Rates for Bikes

Number of Bikes	5	10	15	20	25	30	35	40	45	50
Rental Fee	$400	$535	$655	$770	$875	$975	$1,070	$1,140	$1,180	$1,200

Adrian's Bike Shop sends a graph of their weekly rental fees. Because the rental fee depends on the number of bikes, they put the number of bikes on the *x*-axis.

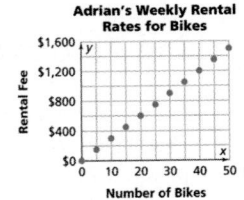

Adrian's Weekly Rental Rates for Bikes

Problem 2.1 Analyzing a Table and a Graph

A. Which bike shop should Ocean Bike Tours use? Explain.

B. Suppose you make a graph from the table for Rocky's Cycle Center. Would it make sense to connect the points? Explain.

C. How much do you think each company charges to rent 32 bikes?

D. 1. What patterns do you find in the table and in the graph?

    2. Based on the patterns you found in part (1), how can you predict values that are not included in the table or graph?

E. 1. Describe a way to find the costs for renting any number of bikes from Adrian's Bike Shop.

    2. Describe a way to find the costs for renting any number of bikes from Rocky's Cycle Center.

ACE Homework starts on page 35.

Investigation 2 Analyzing Graphs and Tables **31**

rules to the representations of graphs and tables. In the final investigation, students use graphing calculators to explore how graphs change in appearance when the rules that produce the graphs change.

relationship between the independent and dependent variable, and if so, whether it is linear or non-linear, as in the following engaging experiments:

◆ **How long would it take for 100 students standing in a row to complete a wave like the ones done at football games? Experiment with different numbers of students from 5 to 25. Can the relationship predict how many students it would take for a given wave time?**

◆ **How far will a Matchbox car roll off of a ramp, based on the height to which the ramp is raised?**

◆ **How is the flight time of a paper airplane affected by the number of paper clips attached to the nose of the plane?**

◆ **What is the relationship between the number of dominoes in a row and the time required for them to fall over? (Use multiples of 100 dominoes.)**

◆ **Make wadded newspaper balls using different numbers of sheets of newspaper. Rubber bands help hold the paper in a ball. What is the relationship between the number of sheets and the distance the ball can be thrown?**

◆ **What is the relationship between the number of drops of coloured water dropped on a paper towel and the diameter of the spot? Does the relationship vary for different brands of towels?**

◆ **What is the largest mass that a toothpick bridge can hold? Lay toothpicks in a bunch to span a 5 centimetre gap between two boards. From the toothpicks, hang a bag or other container into which weights can be added until the toothpicks break. Begin with only one toothpick.**

Experiments like these are fun and accessible to a wide range of learners. They also provide an opportunity for students to engage in experimental design. Students need practice in identifying independent and dependent variables, controlling experiments for other variables, measuring and recording results, and analyzing data. This is a perfect blend of mathematics and science.

Scatter Plots. Often in the real world, phenomena are observed that seem to suggest a functional relationship but not necessarily one as clean or as well defined as the situations we have observed so far. Certainly this would be true of the experiments just described. However, even in the case of measuring the increasing height of a stack of identical books, as each new one is added, a linear situation, measuring error will lead to values that are not exactly on a line. In these cases, the data are generally plotted on a graph to produce a scatter plot of points.

A visual inspection of the graphed data may suggest what kind of relationship, if any, exists. For example, if a linear relationship seems to exist, students can approximate a line of best fit or use graphing technology to do a linear regression to find the line of best fit (along with the equation). They do not need to understand what linear regression is to use this function on the graphing calculator. They just need to know that is a statistical method for finding the line of best fit.

Not all scatter plots will show a straight-line relationship. Suppose students were to figure out the time it takes for balloons of various diameters to deflate (another engaging experiment!). A parabolic or cubic function, rather than a straight line, might better approximate the shape of the data. Graphing calculators can also find best-fitting curves. These brief examples of algebraic thinking in other content areas illustrate the importance of algebra in the K–8 curriculum.

Reflections on Chapter 14

Writing to Learn

1. Kaput lists five types of algebraic thinking. Rather than list each of these, describe algebraic thinking in no more than three sentences in a manner that encompasses Kaput's main ideas and the spirit of this chapter.
2. What misconceptions do students have about the equal sign? What causes these misconceptions and how can instruction clear these up?
3. What misconceptions do students have regarding variables? What causes these misconceptions and how can instruction clear these up?
4. Explain how to solve the equation $4x + 3 = x + 12$ using the pan-balance approach.
5. What is a recursive relationship? Where in a table for a growing pattern would you look for the recursive relationship? What would it mean in terms of the pattern itself?
6. How can you tell from the recursive relationship whether the graph of the growing pattern will be straight or curved?
7. Describe in your own words the five different representations of a function and how they actually all represent the same functional relationship.

For Discussion and Exploration

1. The idea of having students make connections from arithmetic to algebra is a relatively new idea for the elementary curriculum. What examples for taking an algorithm and presenting it in a way that it becomes a process for generalizing a rule can you find in the number strand?
2. Explore some of the online applets that focus on functions (see "Online Resources" at the end of the chapter). For each consider what the technology provides in terms of learning opportunities. How might the technology be used to support diversity in a classroom?

Resources for Chapter 14

Literature Connections

Many teachers find pattern explorations sufficiently interesting that they may not think of using literature to provide a springboard for student explorations. However, the following three examples of books are excellent beginnings for patterns and chart building.

Anno's Magic Seeds   *Anno, 1994*

Anno's Magic Seeds has several patterns. A wise man gives Jack two magic seeds, one to eat and one to plant. The seed he eats will keep him from hunger for a whole year, and the planted seed will produce two new seeds by the following year. Several years later, Jack decides to plant both seeds rather than eat one. This new pattern continues until he marries, has a child, and starts to sell seeds.

At each stage of the story, there is an opportunity to develop a chart and extend the current pattern into the future. Austin and Thompson (1997) describe how they used the story to develop patterns and charts with grade 6–7 students.

Bats on Parade   *Appelt, 1999*

This story includes the pattern of bats walking 1 by 1, then 2 by 2, and so on. One activity from this enjoyable book is determining the growing pattern of the number of bats given the array length (e.g., 3 for the 3 by 3 array). There is also one mouse, so this can be included in a second investigation. Activity sheets for these two ideas and two others can be found in Roy and Beckmann, 2007.

In My Backyard   *Ruurs, 2007*

This lavishly illustrated book by Canadian author Margriet Ruurs celebrates nature and backyard animals through the seasons. From the singing of little wrens in spring to paper wasps building their nests in summer to baby bats drinking mother's milk in fall to baby possums climbing into mother's pouch in winter, students are presented with a variety of animals and insects. Patterns in nature, such as seasonal patterns, weather patterns, and animal and plant patterns, can be connected to patterns in mathematics.

Pattern   *Pluckrose, 1988*

This book brings pattern from the real world to the classroom in the form of brilliantly coloured photographs. Pattern is seen in the soles of running shoes, dishes, butterflies, leaves, and flowers. The book provides a jumping-off point for an exploration of pattern in the world around us.

Two by Two   *Reid, 1992*

This book by Canadian author Barbara Reid tells the story of Noah's Ark. Students can work with the pattern of animals coming in two by two, three by three, and so forth, to extend it, illustrate it, and create new ones using other content. They could also write their own stories. The three-dimensional art work done with plasticine makes the book particularly extraordinary.

Two of Everything: A Chinese Folktale
Hong, 1993

The magic pot discovered by Mr. Haktak doubles whatever goes in it, including his wife! This idea of input–output is great for exploring functions from grades 2 through 8; just vary the rule of the magic pot from doubling to something more complex. For more details and handouts, see Suh (2007) and Wickett, Kharas, and Burns (2002).

Recommendations for Further Reading

Articles

Joram, E., Hartman, C., & Trafton, P. R. (2004). "As people get older, they get taller": An integrated unit on measurement, linear relationships, and data analysis. *Teaching Children Mathematics, 10,* 344–351.
This is a wonderful unit for second grade showing students using real data to answer the question of how much taller students in the fourth grade were compared to students in the second grade. They used a best-fit line to create a function from the scatter plot data.

Kalman, R. (2008). Teaching algebra without algebra. *Mathematics Teaching in the Middle School, 13* (6), 334–339.
This article includes three contexts that involve simplifying equations and effectively explains how to make sense of the simplification by relating it to the context. An excellent resource for helping middle school students make sense of symbols and properties.

Molina, M., & Ambrose, R. C. (2006). Fostering relational thinking while negotiating the meaning of the equals sign. *Teaching Children Mathematics, 13* (2), 111–117.
This article helps us understand the conceptual considerations related to the equal sign while simultaneously illustrating the value of errors and misconceptions in creating opportunities for learning.

Proulx, J. (2006). Making the transition to algebraic thinking: taking students' arithmetic modes of reasoning into account. *delta-K, 44* (1) 8–16.
This article, which appeared in the Alberta Teacher's Association publication, discusses strategies for teaching students how to transition from arithmetic to algebraic problem solving. Examples of how to do so are provided.

Books

Carpenter, T. P., Franke, M. L., & Levi, L. (2003). *Thinking mathematically: Integrating arithmetic & algebra in elementary school.* Portsmouth, NH: Heinemann.
This book takes a detailed look at helping children in the primary grades develop their thinking and create the generalizations of algebra. The CD that is included shows classroom-based examples

of the ideas discussed. Many of the ideas about equality, true/false sentences, and generalizations discussed in this chapter were influenced by this book.

Driscol, M. (1999). *Fostering algebraic thinking: A guide for teachers, grades 6–10.* Portsmouth, NH: Heinemann.

Driscol's book is one of the most popular algebra resources—full of rich problems to use and helpful for expanding the reader's understanding of algebra.

Greenes, C. E., & Rubinstein, R. (Eds.). (2008). *Algebra and algebraic thinking in school mathematics.* NCTM 70th Yearbook. Reston, VA: NCTM.

NCTM Yearbooks are always excellent collections of articles for grades pre-K–12. This one is no exception, offering a wealth of thought-provoking and helpful articles about algebraic thinking.

NCTM's *Navigations* Series

Cuevas, G. J., & Yeatts, K. (2001). *Navigating through algebra in grades 3–5.* Reston, VA: National Council of Teachers of Mathematics.

Friel, S., Rachlin, S., & Doyle, D. (2001). *Navigating through algebra in grades 6–8.* Reston, VA: National Council of Teachers of Mathematics.

Greenes, C., Cavanagh, M., Dacey, L., Findell, C., & Small, M. (2001). *Navigating through algebra in prekindergarten–grade 2.* Reston, VA: National Council of Teachers of Mathematics.

These books offer high-quality algebra activities that reflect the Principles and Standards. Each book includes a CD-ROM with blackline masters for the activities, applets, and selected articles.

Online Resources

Math Frog Fun Resources and Online Games
http://cemc2.math.uwaterloo.ca/mathfrog/ english/kidz/index.shtml

This site, maintained by the University of Waterloo, provides games and resources appropriate for grades 4, 5, and 6. Along with the games and activities for patterns, there are others that fit with other strands of these grade-level curricula.

Patterns Variables and Equations
http://argyll.epsb.ca/jreed/math7/

A series of lessons on patterns, variables, and equations for grades 7, 8, and 9 are offered by Jim Reed of the Argyll Centre in Alberta. The lessons are designed to match curriculum expectations.

Algebra Balance Scales and Algebra Balance Scales–Negative
http://nlvm.usu.edu/en/nav/frames_asid _324_g_3_t_2.html

Linear equations are presented on a two-pan balance with variables on each side. The user can solve equations in the same way as described in the text. The negative version uses balloons for negative values and negative variables.

Graph Sketcher
www.shodor.org/interactiv/activities/GraphSketcher

Works very much like a graphing calculator for graphing functions of any type. A good demonstration tool for making graphs of equations.

Learning about Rate of Change (e-Examples)
http://standards.nctm.org/document/eexamples/chap6/6.2/index.htm

A nice interactive lesson in which the cost per minute to make a phone call (the slope) can be adjusted and then the graph of the cost can be displayed. A slider helps connect points on the two graphs.

Pan Balance—Shapes
http://illuminations.nctm.org/ActivityDetail.aspx?id=33

With each problem, four shapes are assigned unknown values. By stacking shapes on the two balance pans, the user attempts to balance the scale and then create additional balances. A numbers version and an expressions version are extensions of this applet.

Patterns, Relations and Functions (eNLVM module)
http://enlvm.usu.edu/ma/nav/toc.jsp?sid=__ shared&cid=emready@patterns_ relations_ functions&bb=published

This site encourages students to generate rules and functions for geometric sequences, describing relationships between the pattern number and characteristics of the pattern.

Slope Slider
www.shodor.org/interactivate/activities/slopeslider

This is a good interactive tool for illustrating the meaning of slope and the *y*-intercept for a linear equation of the form $y = mx + b$. The user can employ a slider to change the value of *m* or *b* and see the graph change dynamically.

Function Machine Applets

Function Machine (NLVM)
http://nlvm.usu.edu/en/nav/frames_asid_191_g_3_t_1.html

Function Machine (Math Playground)
www.mathplayground.com/functionmachine.html

This is a nice, Flash-based tool.

Stop That Creature! (PBS Kids' CyberChase)
http://pbskids.org/cyberchase/games/functions/functions.html

In this fun game, figure out the rule that runs the game to shut down the creature cloning machine.

Function Machine (Shodor Project Interactivate)
www.shodor.org/interactivate/activities/FunctionMachine

The functions on this site have one of the following forms: $y = x x \_\_, y = x + \_\_, y = x$, where the underline can be any integer between −10 and 10.

Linear Function Machine (Shodor Project Interactivate)
www.shodor.org/interactivate/activities/ LinearFunctMachine

Chapter 15
Developing Fraction Concepts

Fractions have always represented a considerable challenge for students, even into the upper grades. Results have shown that students have a very weak understanding of fraction concepts (Sowder & Wearne, 2006; Wearne & Kouba, 2000). This lack of understanding is then translated into difficulties with fraction computation, decimal and percent concepts, and the use of fractions in other content areas, particularly algebra.

For the most part, students have limited exposure to fractions in the primary grades, with most of the work on fraction development occurring in the junior grades. Elementary school programs must provide students with the necessary time and experiences to develop a deep understanding of this important area of the curriculum. This chapter explores a conceptual development of fraction concepts that can help students construct a firm foundation for further exploration.

Big Ideas

1. For students to really understand fractions, they must experience fractions across many constructs, including part of a whole, ratios, and division.

2. Three categories of models exist for working with fractions—area (e.g., $\frac{1}{3}$ of a garden), length (e.g., $\frac{3}{4}$ of a metre), and set or quantity (e.g., $\frac{1}{2}$ of the class).

3. Partitioning and iterating are ways for students to understand the meaning of fractions, especially numerator and denominator.

4. Students need many experiences estimating fractions.

5. Understanding equivalent fractions is critical. Two equivalent fractions represent two ways of describing the same amount, using different-sized fraction parts. For example, in the fraction $\frac{6}{8}$, if the whole was divided into four equal parts, instead of eight, then $\frac{6}{8}$ could be seen as $\frac{3}{4}$. One fourth would then take up the same space as two eighths.

Mathematics Content Connections

Students bring their early understanding of fair sharing to the topic of fractions. Other whole-number ideas they have acquired actually interfere with early concept development of fractions. However, fraction concepts are intimately connected with other curriculum areas. In addition to the clear content connections that are listed, fractions are frequently used in measurement (Chapter 19) and in probability (Chapter 22).

:• **Fraction Computation** (Chapter 16): Without a firm conceptual understanding of fractions and the principle of equivalent fractions, computation with fractions is relegated to rules without reason.

:• **Decimals and Percents** (Chapter 17): A key idea for students is that decimal notation and percent notation are simply two other representations of fraction ideas. Connecting these three representations reduces the number of ideas students need to learn. It also aids in building understanding.

:• **Ratio and Proportion** (Chapter 18): The part-to-whole concept of a fraction is just one form of a ratio. The same fraction notation can be used for part-to-part ratios (e.g., the ratio of boys to girls in the room is 3 to 5 or $\frac{3}{5}$).

:• **Algebra** (Chapter 14): As described in Chapter 14, fractions are a part of algebra. Equations with variables often involve fractions or can be solved using fractions. For example, $\frac{x}{4} = \frac{5}{16}$.

Meanings of Fractions

Fractions are a critical foundation for students, as they are used in measurement across various professions, and they are essential to the study of algebra and more advanced mathematics. This understanding must go well beyond recognizing that $\frac{3}{5}$ of a region is shaded. This chapter begins with a look at the multiple concepts related to fractions and how these relate to students' knowledge of whole numbers.

Fraction Constructs

Understanding fractions means understanding all the possible concepts that fractions can represent. One of the commonly used meanings of fraction is part–whole, including examples when part of a whole is shaded. In fact, part–whole is so ingrained in elementary textbooks as the way to represent fractions, it may be difficult for you to think about what else fractions might represent. Although the part–whole model is the most used in textbooks, many who research fraction understanding believe students would understand fractions better with more emphasis across other meanings of fractions (Clarke, Roche, & Mitchell, 2008; Siebert & Gaskin, 2006).

❚❚ ─────────── *Pause and Reflect*

Beyond shading a region of a shape, how else are fractions modelled? Try to name these three ideas.

Part–Whole Part–whole is one meaning of fractions and goes beyond shading a region. For example, it could be part of a group of people ($\frac{3}{5}$ of the class went on the field trip) or it could be part of a length (we walked $8\frac{1}{4}$ kilometres). Cramer, Wyberg, and Leavitt (2008), who conducted research on rational numbers, note that the circle model is particularly effective in illustrating the part–whole relationship. Perhaps these were among the ideas you listed in responding to the Pause and Reflect. The following paragraphs present some other meanings that are important for students to experience in order to achieve a deep understanding with many connections among ideas, as discussed in Chapter 2.

Measurement Measurement involves identifying a unit of length then using that unit to determine the length of an object. For example, in the fraction $\frac{5}{8}$, you can use the unit fraction $\frac{1}{8}$ as the selected length then count or measure to show that it takes five of those eighths to reach $\frac{5}{8}$. This concept focuses on how much rather than how many parts, which is the case in part–whole situations (Behr, Lesh, Post, & Silver, 1983; Martinie, 2007).

Division Consider the idea of sharing $10 with 4 people. This is not a part–whole scenario, but it still means that each person will receive one-fourth ($\frac{1}{4}$) of the money, or $2\frac{1}{2}$ dollars. Division is often not connected to fractions, which is unfortunate. Students should understand and feel comfortable with the example here written as $\frac{10}{4}$, $4\overline{)10}$, $10 \div 4$, $2\frac{2}{4}$, and $2\frac{1}{2}$ (Flores, Samson, & Yanik, 2006). Division of fractions is addressed in detail in the next chapter.

Operator Fractions can be used to indicate an operation, as in $\frac{4}{5}$ of 20 square metres or $\frac{2}{3}$ of the audience were students from our school. These situations indicate a fraction of a whole number, and students may be able to use mental math to determine the answer. Researchers note that this construct is not emphasized enough in school curricula (Usiskin, 2007) and that just knowing how to represent fractions doesn't mean students will know how to operate with fractions, such as when working in other areas of the curriculum where fractions occur (Johanning, 2008).

Ratio Discussed at length in Chapter 18, the concept of ratio is yet another context in which fractions are used. The fraction $\frac{1}{4}$ means that the probability of an event is one in four.

Ratios can be part–part or part–whole. For example, the ratio 3:4 could be the ratio of those wearing jackets (part) to those not wearing jackets (part); or it could be part–whole, meaning those wearing jackets (part) in the class (whole). When working with ratios, students have to attend to part–part and part–whole, which requires attention to the context.

Building on Whole-Number Concepts

As described in Chapter 2, students build on their prior knowledge. In other words, when they encounter situations with fractions, they naturally use what they know about whole numbers to solve the problems. Their prior knowledge of whole numbers both supports and inhibits their work with fractions. It is important for a teacher to help students see how fractions are like and different from whole numbers. The following list shows some common misapplications of whole numbers to fractions:

1. Students think that the numerator and denominator are separate values. It is hard for them to see that $\frac{3}{4}$ is one number. Finding fractional values on a number line or ruler can help students develop this notion. Also, avoid the phrase "three *out of* four" (unless talking about ratios or probability) or "three over four"; instead, say "three *fourths*" (Siebert & Gaskin, 2006).
2. In thinking of the numbers separately, students may think that $\frac{2}{3}$ means any two parts, not two equal-size parts. For example, students may think that the shape below shows $\frac{3}{4}$ green, rather than $\frac{1}{2}$ green.

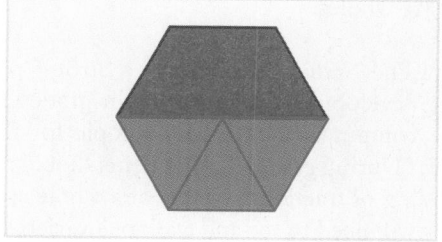

3. Students think that a fraction such as $\frac{1}{5}$ is smaller than a fraction such as $\frac{1}{10}$ because 5 is less than 10. Many visuals showing parts of the whole and contexts are necessary for helping students build their understanding. For example, ask students if they would rather go outside for $\frac{1}{2}$ of an hour, $\frac{1}{4}$ of an hour, or $\frac{1}{3}$ of an hour.

4. Students mistakenly use "rules" for whole numbers operations to compute fractions, for example, $\frac{1}{2} + \frac{1}{2} = \frac{2}{4}$. The explorations in the estimation section of this chapter can help students understand that this answer is not reasonable. See Chapter 16 for more on helping students understand the operations of fractions.

Only One Size for the Whole   A key idea about fractions that students must come to understand is that a fraction does not say anything about the size of the whole or the relationship of the parts. A fraction tells us only about the *relationship between* the part and the whole. Consider the following situation.

Krishana is offered the choice of a third of a pizza or a half of a pizza. Because she is hungry and likes pizza, she chooses the half. Her friend Yvonne gets a third of a pizza but ends up with more than Krishana. How can that be?

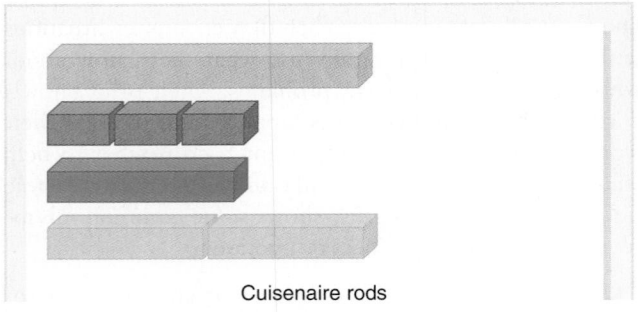

Cuisenaire rods

The visual illustrates how Krishana erred in her choice. The "pizza fallacy" here is: It cannot be assumed (as Krishana did in choosing a half of a pizza) that, when two or more fractions are discussed in the same context, the fractions being compared are each part of the same size whole.

Comparisons with any model can be made only if both fractions are parts of the same size whole. For example, when using Cuisenaire Rods, $\frac{2}{3}$ of a light green strip cannot be compared to $\frac{2}{3}$ of an orange strip, if the strips represent different size wholes.

NCTM Standards   The *Standards* supports a strong conceptual development of fractions in grades 3–5, with computation primarily a topic for the grades that follow. "During grades 3–5, students should build their understanding of fractions as parts of a whole and as division. They will need to see and explore a variety of models

Models should be used at all grade levels as they can help students clarify ideas that are often confused when working symbolically. Sometimes it is useful to do the same activity with two quite different models as this provides students with a different perspective.

of fractions, focusing primarily on fractions such as halves, thirds, fourths, fifths, sixths, eighths, and tenths" (p. 150).

Models for Fractions

There is substantial evidence to suggest that the use of models in fraction tasks is important (Cramer & Henry, 2002; Siebert & Gaskin, 2006). Unfortunately, even teachers who use models do not always employ manipulatives or spend adequate time so that students can make sense of fractions. When models are properly used, they can help students clarify ideas that are often confused when only working symbolically. Sometimes, it is useful to do the same activity with two quite different models as it provides students with a different perspective. It also helps to build understanding.

Different models offer different opportunities to learn. For example, an area model helps students visualize parts of the whole. A linear model shows that there is always another fraction to be found between any two fractions—an important concept that is underemphasized in the teaching of fractions. Also, some students are able to make sense of one model, but not another. Using appropriate models and using models of each type broaden and deepen students' (and teachers') understanding of fractions. This section focuses on three categories of models: region/area, length, and set.

Region or Area Models

Tasks that involve sharing often show something that is cut into smaller parts. The fractions, in this case, are based on parts of an area or a region. This is a good place to begin when doing these sharing tasks. There are many good region models, as shown in Figure 15.1, that are effective when working concretely with fractions.

Circular fraction piece models are commonly used area models. (See Blackline Masters 24–26.) Yet, rectangular regions help children see that shapes other than circles can represent fractions. Like circular regions, they emphasize the part–whole concept of fractions and the meaning of the relative size of a part to the whole (Cramer, Wyberg, & Leavitt, 2008). The other models in Figure 15.1 also demonstrate how different shapes can represent the whole. Grid and dot paper, found in the Blackline Masters, are easy to use and do not require management of materials. However, they do not provide the same level of concreteness as the other models. The commercial versions of area models,

shown in Figure 15.1, are widely available and offered in different versions.

The following activity is an example of how area models can be used to help students develop concepts of equal shares. The activity below is an example of how area models can be used to help students develop concepts of equal shares.

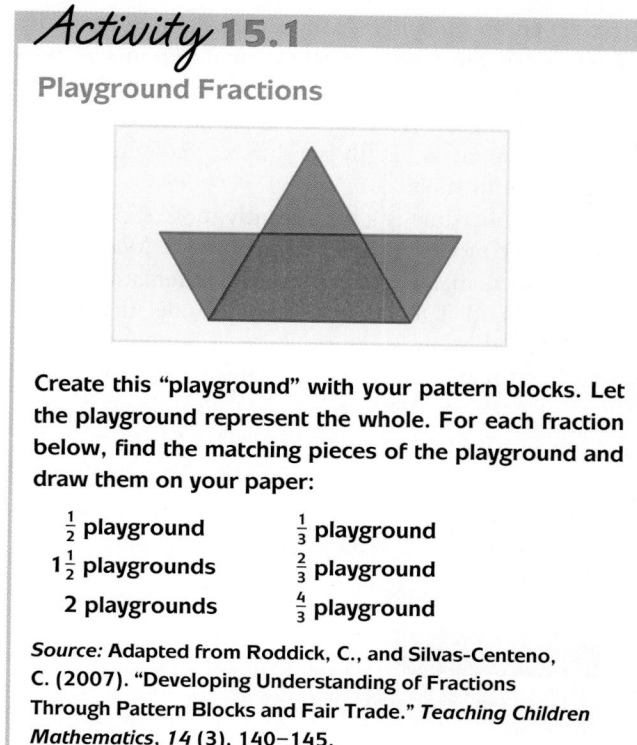

Activity 15.1

Playground Fractions

Create this "playground" with your pattern blocks. Let the playground represent the whole. For each fraction below, find the matching pieces of the playground and draw them on your paper:

$\frac{1}{2}$ playground	$\frac{1}{3}$ playground
$1\frac{1}{2}$ playgrounds	$\frac{2}{3}$ playground
2 playgrounds	$\frac{4}{3}$ playground

Source: Adapted from Roddick, C., and Silvas-Centeno, C. (2007). "Developing Understanding of Fractions Through Pattern Blocks and Fair Trade." *Teaching Children Mathematics, 14* (3), 140–145.

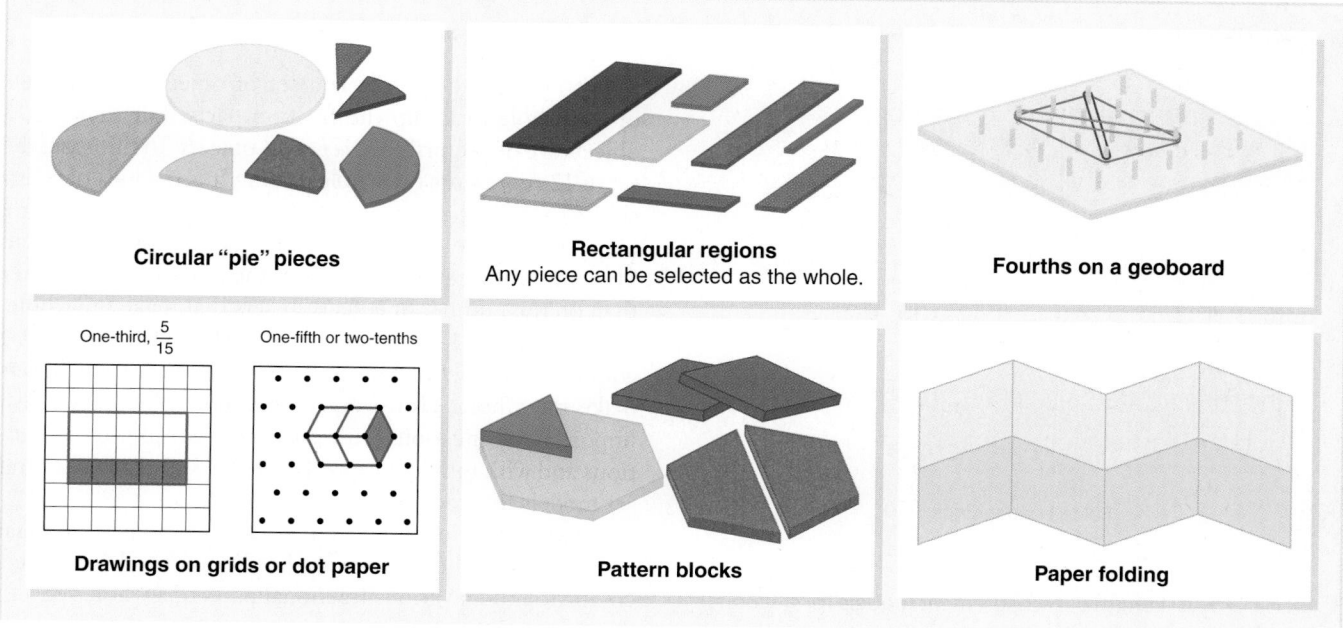

Circular "pie" pieces

Rectangular regions
Any piece can be selected as the whole.

Fourths on a geoboard

One-third, $\frac{5}{15}$ One-fifth or two-tenths

Drawings on grids or dot paper

Pattern blocks

Paper folding

Figure 15.1 Area or region models for fractions.

Length Models

With length models, lengths or measurements are compared instead of areas. Either lines are drawn and subdivided, or physical materials are compared on the basis of length, as shown in Figure 15.2.

Cuisenaire rods, paper fraction strips, or adding machine tape folded to produce student-made fractions are effective length models that offer considerable flexibility. Any strip can represent the whole or different-size fraction values. Cuisenaire rods, which vary in length from 1 to 10 units, can be used to compare different fraction values. Each Cuisenaire rod length is a different colour, allowing for easy identification.

The number line is a significantly more sophisticated measurement model (Bright, Behr, Post, & Wachsmuth, 1988). In fact, many researchers in mathematics education have found it to be an essential model that should be emphasized more in the teaching of fractions (Clarke, Roche, & Mitchell, 2008; Flores, Samson, & Yanik, 2006;

Middleton, van den Heuvel-Panhuizen, & Shew, 1998; Usiskin, 2007; Watanabe, 2006). Linear models are closely connected to the real-world contexts in which fractions are commonly used—measuring. Music, for example, is an excellent opportunity to explore $\frac{1}{2}$s, $\frac{1}{4}$s, $\frac{1}{8}$s, and $\frac{1}{16}$s (Goral & Wiest, 2007).

The number line also highlights that a fraction is just one number. It also helps students see how a fraction is related in size to other numbers, which is not as clear when using area models. The number line importantly reinforces that there is always one more fraction to be found between two fractions. The following activity is a fun way to use a real-world context to engage students in thinking about fractions through a linear model.

Activity 15.2

Who Is Winning?

The friends below are playing red light–green light. Who is winning? The fractions tell how much of the distance they have already moved.

Margot—$\frac{3}{4}$	Micah—$\frac{1}{2}$	Leah—$\frac{5}{6}$
Han—$\frac{5}{8}$	Miguel—$\frac{5}{9}$	Angel—$\frac{2}{3}$

Can you place these friends on a line to show where they are between the start and finish?

Source: Adapted from Bay-Williams, J. M., and Martinie, S. L. (2003). "Thinking Rationally about Number in the Middle School." *Mathematics Teaching in the Middle School, 8* (6), 282–287.

Set Models

In set models, the whole is a set of objects, and subsets of the whole make up the fraction parts. For example, 3 objects are one-fourth of a set of 12 objects. In this case, the set of 12 represents the whole or one. It is the idea of referring to a collection of objects (e.g., counters), as a single entity that makes set models difficult for some children. Students will frequently focus on the size of the set rather than on the number of equal sub-sets that make the whole. For example, if 12 counters make a whole, then a set of 4 counters is *one-third*, not one-fourth, since three equal sets make the whole. However, the set model helps establish important connections with many real-world uses of fractions and with ratio concepts. Figure 15.3 illustrates several set models for fractions.

Two-colour counters can be used to model fractional parts of sets. They can easily be flipped to change their colour to model various fractional parts of a whole set.

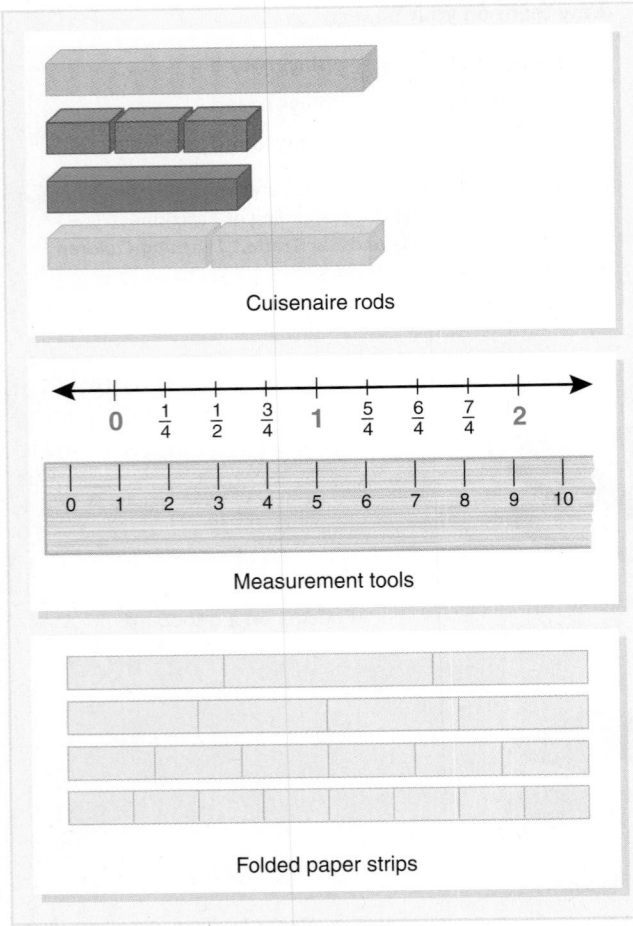

Cuisenaire rods

Measurement tools

Folded paper strips

Figure 15.2 Length or measurement models for fractions.

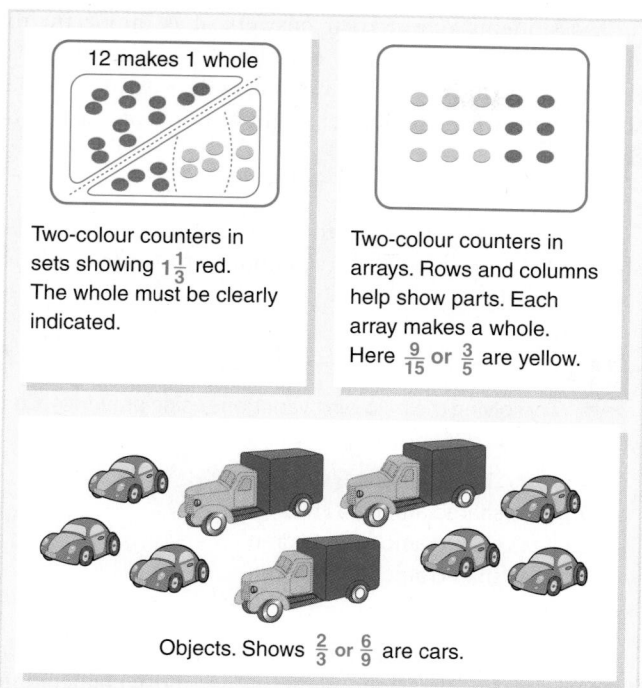

Two-colour counters in sets showing $1\frac{1}{3}$ red. The whole must be clearly indicated.

Two-colour counters in arrays. Rows and columns help show parts. Each array makes a whole. Here $\frac{9}{15}$ or $\frac{3}{5}$ are yellow.

Objects. Shows $\frac{2}{3}$ or $\frac{6}{9}$ are cars.

Figure 15.3 Set models for fractions.

The activity below can be done as an energizer or as a quick activity when you find you have five minutes.

Activity 15.3

Class Fractions

Use a group of students as the whole. For example, if you want to work on thirds, halves, and sixths, start with six students. Ask the class, "what fraction of the group [is wearing basketball shoes, has brown hair, etc.]? Change the number of people over time and repeat with different attributes.

It is important to remember that students must be able to explore fractions using different models. If they never see fractions represented as a length, they will struggle to solve any problem or context that is linear. As a teacher, you will not know if students really understand the meaning of a fraction such as $\frac{1}{4}$ unless you have seen them model one-fourth with different contexts and models.

A straightforward way to assess students' knowledge of a fractional amount is to give them a piece of paper, fold it into thirds, and at the top of each section write area, length, and set. Have the students show you a picture and write a sentence for the fraction (e.g., $\frac{3}{4}$) in all three ways (NCTM, 2007, p. 32). This can be done for commonly used fractions

or it can be done as an estimation activity with fractions like $\frac{31}{58}$.

Concept of Fractional Parts

The first goal in the development of fractions should be to help children construct the idea of *fractional parts of the whole*—the parts that result when the whole or unit has been partitioned into *equal-sized portions* or *fair shares*.

Children seem to understand the idea of separating a quantity into two or more parts to be shared fairly among friends. They eventually make connections between the idea of fair shares and fractional parts. Therefore, sharing tasks are good places to begin the development of fractions.

Sharing Tasks

Considerable research has been done with children in grades 1–8 to determine how they go about the process of forming fair shares and how the tasks posed to them influence their responses (Empson, 2002; Lamon, 1996; Mack, 2001; Pothier & Sawada, 1983).

Sharing tasks are generally posed in the form of a simple story problem. *Suppose there are four brownie squares to be shared among three children so that each child gets the same amount. How much will each child get (or, show how much each child will get)?* The difficulty of the task changes with the numbers involved, the types of things to be shared (regions such as brownies; discrete objects such as pieces of chewing gum), and the presence or use of a model.

Students initially perform sharing tasks (division) by distributing items one at a time. When this process leaves leftover pieces, students must think about how to subdivide the items so that each group (or person) gets a fair share. Typical "regions" to share include brownies (rectangles), sandwiches, pizzas, crackers, cake, candy bars, and so on. The problems and variations that follow are adapted from Empson (2002).

Four children are sharing 10 brownies so that each child will get the same amount. How much will each child get?

Problem difficulty is determined by the relationship between the number of things to be shared and the number of people who are sharing. Because children's initial strategies for sharing involve halving, a good place to begin is with two, four, or even eight people sharing. For 10 brownies and 4 people sharing, many children will deal out 2 to each child, then halve each of the remaining brownies (see Figure 15.4).

Consider these variations in numbers:

- 5 brownies shared between 2 children
- 2 brownies shared among 4 children
- 5 brownies shared among 4 children
- 7 brownies shared among 4 children
- 4 brownies shared among 8 children
- 3 brownies shared among 4 children

Pause and Reflect

Try drawing pictures for each of the preceding sharing tasks. Which do you think is most difficult? Which of these represent essentially the same degree of difficulty?

The last example, 3 brownies shared among 4 children, was significantly more challenging. Figure 15.5 shows how one grade 3 student, who easily solved the first three, worked hard to solve this problem. Her guess and check strategy involved first subdividing each cookie in two parts, five parts, six parts, seven parts, and then dropping back to four parts.

When the number of items to be shared can be distributed whole (5 brownies shared between 2 children), some students will first share them whole, then cut up the leftovers. Others will slice every piece in half, then distribute the halves. When there are more people sharing than items being shared, some partitioning must happen at the beginning of the solution process.

When students who are still using a halving strategy try to share 5 things among 4 children, they will eventually be left with 2 halves to give to 4 children. For some, the solution will be to cut each half in half; that is, "each child gets a whole (or two halves) and a half of a half."

As always, it is important to meet the needs of the range of learners in your classroom. The level of difficulty of these tasks varies. Thus, a tiered lesson can be implemented to provide appropriate tasks for different students, while still enabling all students to learn the important mathematics of the lesson (fair sharing as a meaning of fractions). Figure 15.6 shows how one teacher offers these three tiers for her lesson on sharing brownies (Williams, 2008, p. 326).

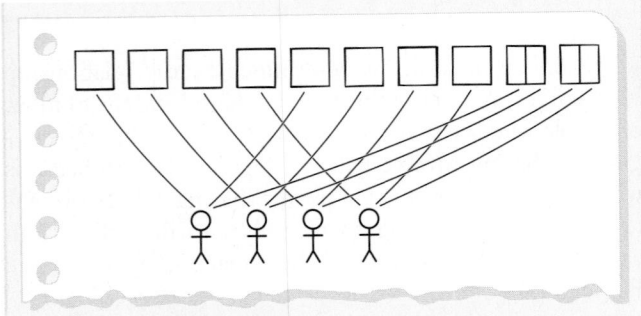

Figure 15.4 Ten brownies shared among four children.

As students report their answers, it is important to emphasize the equivalence of different representations (Flores & Klein, 2005). For example, in the case of 3 people sharing 4 brownies the answer might be noted on the board this way:

$$\frac{4}{3} = 1\frac{1}{3} = 1 + \frac{1}{3}$$

It is a progression then to move to three or six people sharing because this will force children to confront their halving strategies.

Pause and Reflect

Try solving the following variations using drawings. Can you do them in different ways?

4 pizzas shared among 6 children
7 pizzas shared among 6 children
5 pizzas shared among 3 children
5 pizzas shared among 4 children

Subdividing a region into a number of parts other than a power of two (four, eight, etc.) is more challenging for students. Figure 15.7 shows a student's partitioning to solve the third pizza problem. This took much guessing and checking at which point the teacher asked, "Can you see a pattern in how you have divided the pizza and how many people are eating?" At this point, the student noticed a pattern: if there are three people, the remaining pizzas need to

Each child gets 3/4 of a brownie. I figured it out by making 3 squares and 4 heads and I split them up into different ways until I figured it out.

Figure 15.5 Liza partitions to find the fair shares for 3 brownies shared among 4 people.

Tier 1 task: for students who still need experience with halving	Tier 2 task: for students comfortable with halving and ready to try other strategies.	Tier 3 task: for students ready to solve tasks where students combine halving with new strategies
How can 2 people share 3 brownies? How can 2 people share 5 brownies? How can 4 people share 3 brownies? How can 3 people share 4 brownies?	How can 4 people share 3 brownies? How can 3 people share 4 brownies? How can 3 people share 5 brownies? How can 6 people share 4 brownies?	How can 3 people share 5 brownies? How can 3 people share 2 brownies? How can 6 people share 4 brownies? How can 5 people share 4 brownies?

Figure 15.6 Example of a tiered lesson for the sharing brownies problem.

be partitioned into thirds. She used this fact to quickly solve the fourth problem. This emphasizes the importance of not telling students what to think; rather, asking questions that lead students to pause and analyze their work. Notice that the context and the model match—both are circles. It is important to use a range of contexts and to encourage a range of representations across the different types of models (area, length, and set).

Fraction pieces, Cuisenaire rods, and fraction circles can be subdivided. Another possibility is to cut out circles or squares from construction paper. Some students may need to cut and physically distribute the pieces. Students can use connecting cubes to make bars that they can separate into pieces. Or they can use more traditional fraction models such as circular "pie" pieces.

Figure 15.7 Student explains a pattern for finding equal shares of a pizza.

Fraction Language

During the discussions of students' solutions (and discussions are essential!) is a good time to introduce the vocabulary of fractional parts. When a brownie or other region has been broken into equal shares, simply say, "We call these *fourths*. The whole is cut into four parts and all the parts are the same size—fourths."

In addition to helping children use the words *halves*, *thirds*, *fourths*, *fifths*, and so on, be sure to make regular comparison of fractional parts to the whole. Make it a point to use the terms *whole*, or *one whole*, or simply *one* so that students have a language they can use regardless of the model involved.

A physical model, like colour tiles, can mislead students into believing that fractional parts must be the same *shape* as well as the same size. For example:

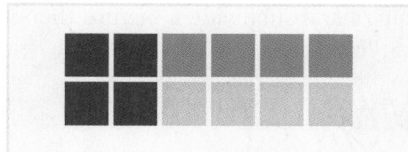

Class discussions that challenge students' thinking and expose their ideas are the best ways to help students develop accurate concepts and to find out what they understand.

Equivalent Size of Fraction Pieces

Too often, when students are asked questions about fractions they see a representation where the parts are all the same shape and size. The result is that students think that equal shares might need to be the same shape, which is not the case. Young children, in particular, tend to focus on shape, when the focus should be on equal-*sized* parts.

The following activity focuses on having examples that are (1) same shape, same size; (2) different shape, same size; (3) different shape, different size; and (4) same shape, different size. The first two categories are then examples of fair shares, or equivalent shares. The activity is a simple extension of the sharing tasks. It is important that students be able to tell when a region has been separated into a particular type of fractional part.

Activity 15.4

Correct Shares

Draw regions like the ones in Figure 15.8 showing examples and non-examples of fractional parts. Have students identify the wholes that are correctly divided into the specified fractional parts and those that are not. For each response, have students explain their reasoning. The activity should be done with a variety of models, including length and set models.

In the "Correct Shares" activity, the most important part is to have students explain why they do or do not think the shape is partitioned correctly. The diagrams in the task fall into each of the following categories:

1. Same shape, same size: (a) and (f) [equivalent]
2. Different shape, same size: (e) and (g) [equivalent]
3. Different shape, different size: (b) and (c) [not equivalent]
4. Same shape, different size: (d) [not equivalent]

 The "Correct Shares" task is a good formative assessment to see whether students understand that it is the *size* that matters, not the shape. If students only miss (d) and (f), they do not have this concept and you need to plan future tasks that focus on equivalence—for example, asking students to take a square and subdivide a picture themselves, as in Activity 15.5. ◆

Activity 15.5

Finding Fair Shares

Give students dot paper and have them find halves, fourths, or other fractional parts of an enclosed region. The activity is especially interesting when the whole is represented by different fractional parts.

Partitioning

Dividing a shape into equal-sized pieces is called *partitioning*, a major part of developing fraction concepts with young children. In the previous section you were partitioning regions or shapes, which fall under area models. It is also important to partition lengths and quantities. The number line with only 0 and 1 can be used, as well as paper strips. Students can partition sets of objects such as coins, counters, or baseball cards.

Notice when partitioning sets that children may confuse the number of counters in a share with the name of the share. In the example in Figure 15.9 the 12 counters

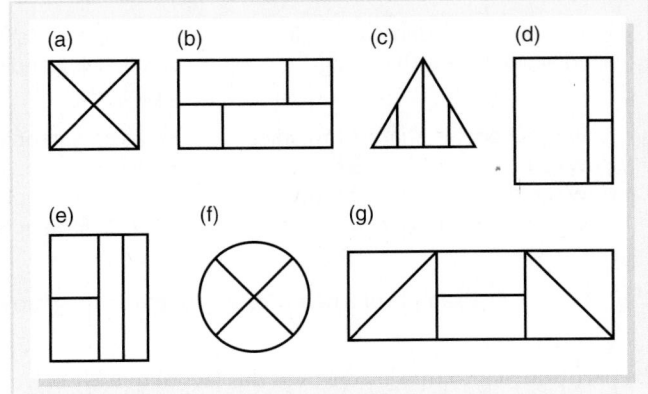

Figure 15.8 Students learning about fractional parts should be able to tell which of these figures are correctly partitioned in fourths. They should also be able to explain why the other figures are not showing fourths.

are partitioned into 6 sets—*sixths*. Each share or part has two counters, but it is the number of shares that makes the partition show *sixths*.

Using Fraction Language and Symbols

Fractional symbolism can be a fairly complex convention that is often misleading. It is well worth spending time to help students develop a strong understanding of what the numerator and the denominator of a fraction represent.

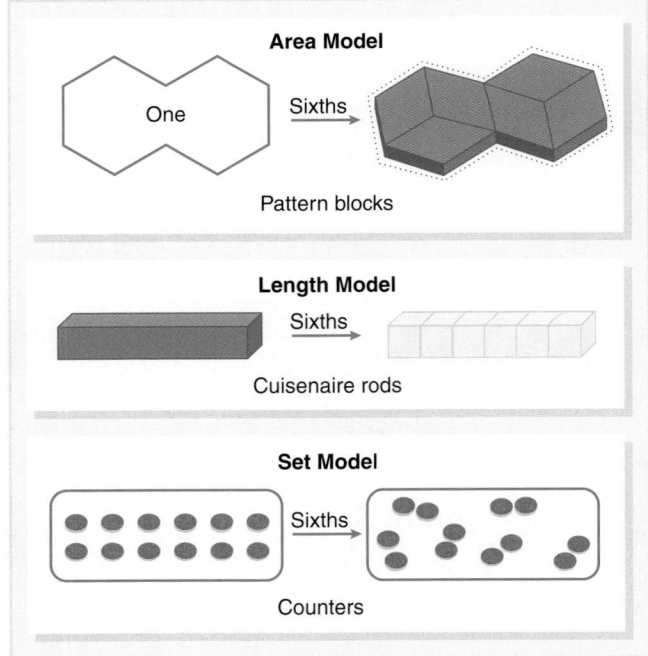

Figure 15.9 Given a whole, find fractional parts.

Counting Fractional Parts: Iteration

Counting fractional parts to see how multiple parts compare to the whole creates a foundation for the two parts of a fraction. Students should come to think of counting fractional parts in much the same way that they might count apples or any other objects. If you know the kind of part you are counting, you can tell when you get to one, when you get to two, and so on.

This counting or repeating a piece is called *iterating*. Like partitioning, iterating is an important part of being able to understand and use fractions. There is evidence that an iterative notion of fractions, one that views a fraction such as $\frac{3}{4}$ as a count of three parts called *fourths*, is an important idea for children to develop (Post, Wachsmuth, Lesh, & Behr, 1985; Siebert & Gaskin, 2006; Tzur, 1999). The iterative concept is most clear when focusing on these two ideas about fraction symbols:

- The top number *counts*.
- The bottom number tells *what is being counted*.

The *what* of fractions are the fractional parts. They can be counted. Fractional symbols are just a shorthand for saying *how many* and *what*.

Iterating makes sense with length models because iteration is much like measuring. Consider that you have $2\frac{1}{2}$ metres of string and are trying to figure out how many fourths you have. You can draw a strip and start counting (iterating) the fourths:

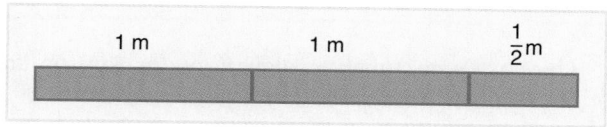

Using string that is $\frac{1}{4}$ of a metre long as a unit of measure, students mark off 10 fourths:

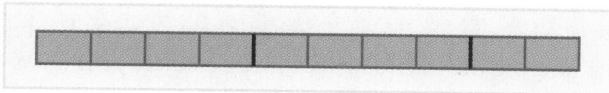

Students can participate in many tasks involving iterating lengths, that progressively increase in difficulty. For example, give the students a strip of paper and tell them that it is $\frac{3}{4}$ of the whole. Ask them to find: $\frac{1}{2}$, $1\frac{1}{2}$, $2\frac{1}{4}$, 3 and so on. To find these, students should partition the piece into three sections to find $\frac{1}{4}$ then iterate $\frac{1}{4}$ to find the fractions listed.

Iterating can be done with area models as well. Display several collections of circular fraction pieces as shown in Figure 15.10. Have students count the parts in each collection using the type of piece of being shown. Simply count: "*one*-fourth, *two*-fourths, *three*-fourths, *four*-fourths, *five*-fourths." Ask, "If we have five-fourths, is that more than one whole, less than one whole, or the same as one whole?"

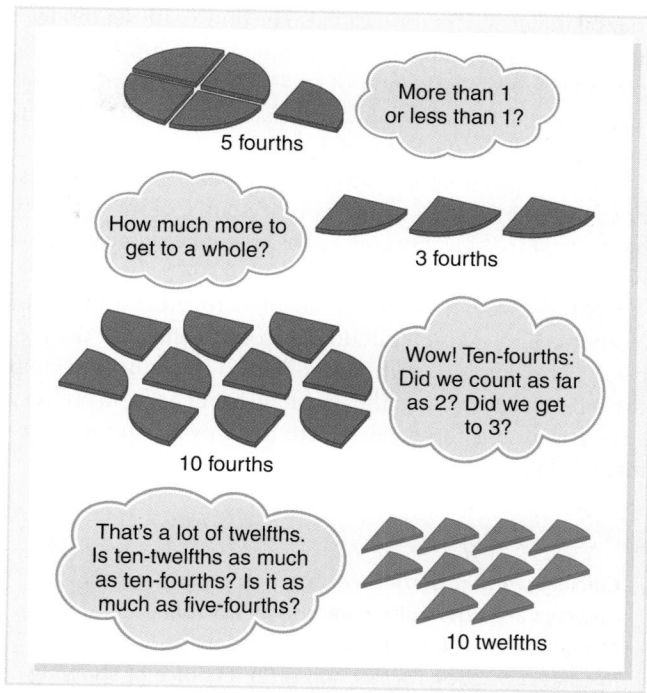

Figure 15.10 Iterating fractional parts in an area model. (See Blackline Masters 24–26.)

As students count each collection of parts, discuss their relationship to one whole (more than one whole, less than one whole, how much more than one whole). Make informal comparisons between different collections. "Why did we get almost two wholes with seven fourths, yet we don't even have one whole with ten twelfths?"

Also take this opportunity to lay the groundwork for mixed fractions. Ask, "What is another way that we could say seven-thirds?" (Two wholes and one more third or one whole and four-thirds)

With this introduction, students are ready for the following task.

Activity 15.6

More, Less, or Equal to One Whole

Give students a collection of fractional parts (all the same type) and indicate the kind of fractional part they have. Parts can be drawn on a worksheet or physical models can be placed in plastic baggies with an identifying card. For example, if done with fraction pieces (rectangular regions), the collection might have seven brown pieces with a caption or note indicating "These are eighths." The task is to decide if the collection is less than one whole, equal to one whole, or more than one whole. Have students draw pictures and/or use numbers to explain their answer.

Try Activity 15.6 with several different fraction models (pattern blocks work well). Then, try with no model, using mental imagery. Iteration can also be done with set models; however, it may cause students some initial difficulty. For example, show a collection of two-colour counters and ask questions such as, "If 5 counters is one-fourth of the set, how much of the set is 15 counters?"

Other questions can be engaging puzzles for students. For example: "Three counters represent $\frac{1}{8}$ of my set; how big is my set?" "Twenty counters represent $\frac{2}{3}$ of my set; how big is my set?"

Similar activities can be adapted to meet a range of learners. For example, adding a context such as people, candy, crayons, or an item familiar to students will help them better understand the problem. Students who are very strong at doing these can create their own "puzzle statements" and pose them to the class.

Activity 15.7

Calculators that permit fraction entries and displays are now quite common in schools. Many, like the TI-15, now display fractions in correct fraction format and offer a choice of showing results as mixed numbers or simple fractions. Counting by fourths with the TI-15 is done by first storing $\frac{1}{4}$ in one of the two operation keys: Op1 + 1 n 4 d Op1. To count, press 0 Op1 Op1 Op1, repeating to get the desired number of fourths. The display will show the counts by fourths; also the number of times that the Op1 key has been pressed. Ask students questions such as: "How many fourths are needed to get to 3?" "How many fifths are needed to get to 5?" These can become increasingly more challenging. "How many fourths to get to $4\frac{1}{2}$?" "How many $\frac{2}{3}$s to get to 6?" Estimate, then count by $\frac{2}{3}$ on the calculator. Students should coordinate their counts with fraction models, adding a new fourths piece to the pile with each count. At any time, the display can be shifted from mixed number form to simple fractions with a press of a key. The TI-15 can be set so that it will not simplify fractions automatically, which is the appropriate setting prior to the introduction of equivalent fractions.

Calculators with fraction functions provide a powerful way to help children develop fractional symbolism. A variation on Activity 15.7 is to show children a mixed number such as $3\frac{1}{8}$ and ask how many counts of $\frac{1}{8}$ on the calculator it would take to count that high. The students should try to stop at the correct number ($\frac{25}{8}$) before pressing the mixed number key.

Fraction Notation

After experiences with partitioning and iterating, students are ready to learn the symbolic notations for fractions.

The way that we write fractions, with a top and a bottom number and a bar between, is a convention—an arbitrary agreement for how to represent fractions. As a convention, it is one of those concepts that you simply tell students. By way of demonstration, the convention can be made so clear that students will tell *you* what the top and bottom numbers stand for. The following procedure is recommended even if your students have been "using" the symbolic form of fractions for years.

Display several collections of fractional parts in a manner similar to those in Figure 15.10. Have students count the parts in each set. After each count, write the correct fraction, indicating that this is how it is written in the symbolic form. Include sets that are more than 1, but write them as simple or "improper" fractions rather than as mixed numbers. Include at least two pairs of sets with the same numerator, such as $\frac{4}{8}$ and $\frac{4}{5}$. Likewise, include sets with the same denominators. After the class has counted and you have written the fraction for at least six sets, pose the following questions:

- What does the bottom number in a fraction tell us?
- What does the top number in a fraction tell us?

Pause and Reflect

Imagine counting a set of 5 eighths and a set of 5 fourths and writing the fractions for these sets. Use children's language in your formulations and try to come up with a way to explain what the numbers on the top and on the bottom mean.

Here are some likely explanations for the top and bottom numbers from grade 2 or 3 students.

- *Top number:* This is the counting number. It tells how many shares or parts we have. It tells how many have been counted. It tells how many parts we are talking about. It counts the parts or shares.
- *Bottom number:* This tells what is being counted. It tells how big the fractional part being counted is. If it is a 4, it means we are counting *fourths*; if it is a 6, we are counting *sixths*; and so on.

This formulation of the meanings of the numerator and denominator may seem unusual to you. It is often said that the top number tells "how many." (This phrase seems unfinished. How many *what*?) The bottom number, it is said, tells "how many parts it takes to make a whole." This may be correct, but can also be misleading. For example, $\frac{1}{6}$ of a piece of cake can be cut without cutting any slices from the remaining $\frac{5}{6}$ of the cake. That the cake has been divided into only two pieces does not change the fact that the piece taken is $\frac{1}{6}$. Or if a pizza is cut into 12 pieces, two pieces still make $\frac{1}{6}$ of the pizza. In neither of these instances does the bottom number tell how many pieces make a whole.

Fractions Greater Than 1

In the previous section, fractions less than and greater than 1 were mixed together. This was done intentionally and should similarly be done with students as they learn fractions. Too often students aren't exposed to numbers greater than one (e.g., $\frac{5}{2}$ or $4\frac{1}{4}$); then when they are added into the mix (no pun intended!), students find them confusing.

The term *improper fraction* is used to describe fractions such as $\frac{5}{2}$ that are greater than one. This term can be a source of confusion as the word *improper* implies that this representation is not acceptable, which is not the case at all—in fact, in algebra it is often the preferred representation. Instead, try not to use this phrase and instead use "fractions" or "fractions greater than 1." If you do use the term, then be sure to share with students that it is really not improper to write fractions greater than one as a single fraction.

In the fourth National Assessment of Educational Progress in the United States, about 80 percent of grade 7 students could change a mixed number to an improper fraction, but fewer than half knew that $5\frac{1}{4}$ was the same as $5 + \frac{1}{4}$ (Kouba et al., 1988a). The result suggests that many children are using procedures without understanding them.

If you have been counting fractional parts beyond a whole, as in the previous section, your students already know how to write $\frac{13}{6}$ or $\frac{11}{3}$. Ask students to use a model to illustrate and find equivalent representations. Neumer (2007), a grade 5 teacher, found that using Unifix cubes was the most effective way to help students see both forms for recording fractions greater than 1. Figure 15.11 illustrates how to use the connecting cubes. Students identify one cube as the unit fraction ($\frac{1}{5}$) for the problem ($\frac{12}{5}$). They count out 12 fifths and build wholes. Conversely, they could start with the mixed number, build it, and find out how many total cubes (or fifths) were used. This procedure is an example of a length model. Repeated experiences in building and solving these tasks will lead students to see a pattern of multiplication and division that closely resembles the algorithm for moving between these two forms.

Context can help students understand the equivalency of these two ways to record fractions, which is the focus of Activity 15.8.

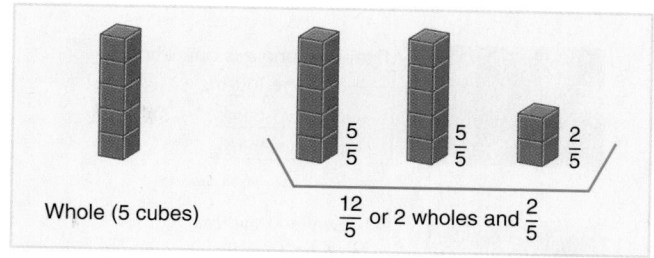

Figure 15.11 Unifix cubes are used to represent the equivalence of $\frac{12}{5}$ and $2\frac{2}{5}$.

Later, challenge students to figure out the two equivalent forms for a fraction, without using models. A good explanation for $3\frac{1}{4}$ might be that there are 4 fourths in one whole, so there are 8 fourths in two wholes and 12 fourths in three wholes. The extra fourth makes 13 fourths in all, or $\frac{13}{4}$. (Note how iteration plays a role here.)

For those students who are experiencing difficulty with finding mixed numbers and fractions greater than 1, have them use the materials and go back to finding how many thirds, fourths, fifths, and sixths make one whole. Repeat the process for two wholes, etc. Once this idea is established, have them lay down two wholes using sixths (the blue rhombuses in the pattern blocks work well here), remove some of the parts from the set, and have them count to say how many there are altogether. Once the fraction greater than 1 has been named, have the student name the mixed number. Repeat this task several times with different fractions.

Do not push the traditional algorithm (multiply the bottom by the whole number and add the top) as it can interfere with students ability to make sense of the relationship between the two forms of the fraction and their equivalency. Students will readily develop their understanding of this procedure from looking at the patterns in their work, using their own words.

Assessing Understanding

Preset students with exercises that require them to demonstrate their understanding of fractional parts as well as the meanings of the top and bottom numbers in a fraction. Models can be used to represent wholes and parts of wholes. Examples of these types of exercise are provided in Figures 15.12 and 15.13. Each figure includes examples with a regions model (freely drawn rectangles), a length model (fraction strips), and set model (counters).

Pause and Reflect

Work through the exercises in Figure 15.12 and Figure 15.13. If you do not have access to fraction pieces or counters, draw rectangles or circles. What can you learn about students' understanding of fractions, if they are able to solve problems in Figure 15.12 but not in Figure 15.13? What if students are able

Activity **15.8**

Pitchers and Cups

Show students a pitcher that can hold enough to fill six cups with juice. You can even use an actual pitcher and cups for sharing with the class. Ask questions such as the following: "If I have $3\frac{1}{2}$ pitchers, how many cups will I be able to fill?" "If we have 16 students in our class, how many pitchers will I need?" Alter the amount the pitcher can hold so other fractions are used.

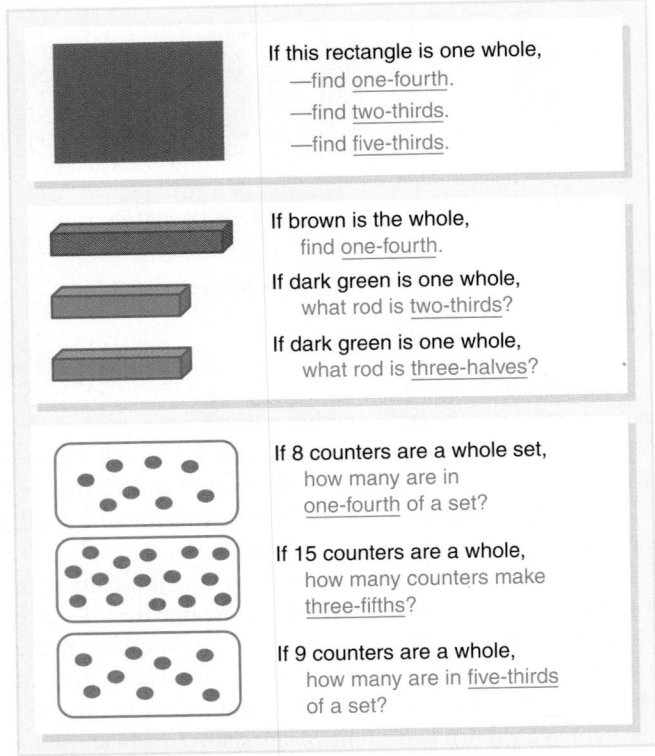

Figure 15.12 Given the whole and the fraction, find the part.

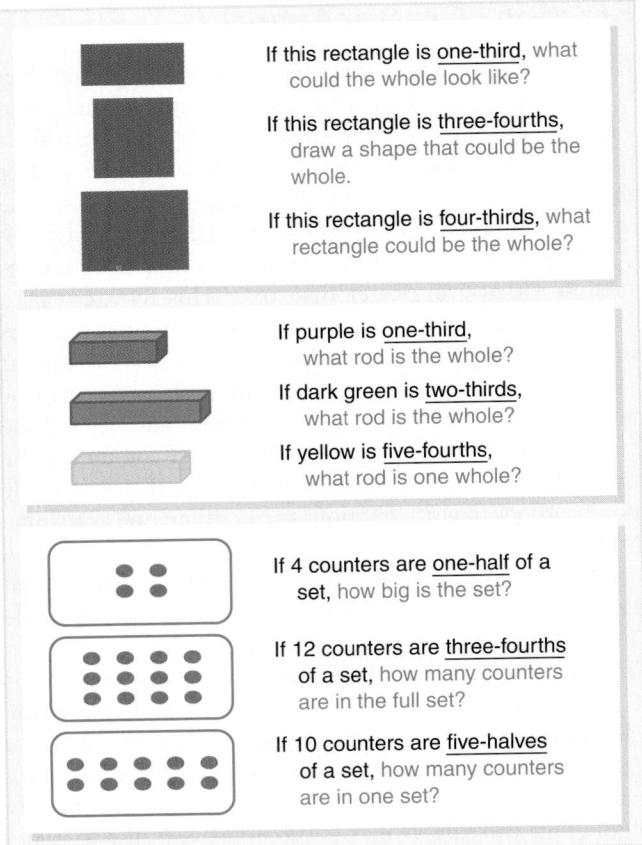

Figure 15.13 Given the part and the fraction, find the whole.

to use fraction pieces but not paper? If students are confused, what contexts for each model can be used to support their thinking?

Two or three challenging parts-and-whole questions can serve as an excellent performance assessment. The tasks should be presented to the class in the same form as in the figures. Physical models are often the best way to present the tasks so students can use a trial-and-error approach to determine their results. As with all tasks, it should be clear that an explanation is required to justify each answer. As students develop their solutions, you can walk around observing and asking questions to assess students' understanding.

As noted throughout this book, it is a good idea to create simple story problems that ask the same questions.

Mr. Samuels has finished $\frac{3}{4}$ of his patio. It looks like this:

Draw a picture that might be the shape of the finished patio.

The parts-and-whole questions are challenging yet very effective at helping students reflect on the meanings of the numerator and denominator. They also act as a good diagnostic assessment to see if students really understand the meanings of the numerator and denominator, as the tasks require students to *use* those meanings, not simply recite a definition.

Math Trek 4, 5, 6 (Nectar Foundation, 2000) is Canadian software that offers a range of challenges for the development of fractions. *In Search of Reptiles*, one of the interactive activities in the Number Sense and Numeration component, offers students an opportunity to apply their knowledge of fractions. There are four levels of difficulty from which students may choose to work as they order and compare simple fractions, mixed numbers, and fractions greater than 1. Tasks are designed so that students work at a symbolic level without the aid of visual representations.

In the *Math Trek* tutorials, ideas and concepts about fractions are presented using a variety of models. Students are able to work independently through a series of tasks to reinforce learning. Using a pizza model, students explore fractions by slicing the whole into equal parts. Strip models are employed for comparing unit fractions, and sets models for introducing improper fractions.

The *Mathville* series (Courseware Solutions, 2000) is also Canadian software that provides students with an opportunity to engage in activities to reinforce their knowledge of fractions. Activities, which are presented in a visually appealing context at levels as early as grade 2 (*Mathville Jungleway*), are fast-paced, highly motivating, and creative, allowing students to work in a non-linear, non-hierarchical manner. However, this environment can also be quite challenging for those students who require the benefit of the models discussed earlier. ◆

Estimating with Fractions

The focus on fractional parts is an important beginning in developing students' number sense. But number sense with fractions demands more—it requires that students have some intuitive feel for fractions. They should know "about" how big a particular fraction is and be able to tell easily which of two fractions is larger.

As with whole numbers, students are less confident and less capable of estimating than they are at computing exact answers. Therefore, you need to provide many opportunities for students to estimate. Even in daily classroom conversations, you can work on estimation with fractions. You can ask questions such as, "About what fraction of our class are wearing sweaters?" Or, after tallying survey data about a topic like favourite dinner, ask, "About what fraction of our class picked spaghetti?" Activity 15.9 offers some examples of visual estimating activities.

Activity 15.9

About How Much?

Draw a picture like one of those in Figure 15.14 (or prepare some ahead of time for the overhead). Have each student write down a fraction that he or she thinks is a good estimate of the amount shown (or show with an indicated mark on a number line, as shown in Figure 15.14). Listen, without judgment, to the ideas of several students, and discuss with them whether a particular estimate is a good one.

There is no single correct answer, but estimates should be "in the ballpark." If children have difficulty coming up with an estimate, ask if they think the amount is closer to 0, $\frac{1}{2}$, or 1.

Benchmarks of Zero, One-Half, and One

As suggested in Activity 15.9, the most important reference points or benchmarks for fractions are 0, $\frac{1}{2}$, and 1. For

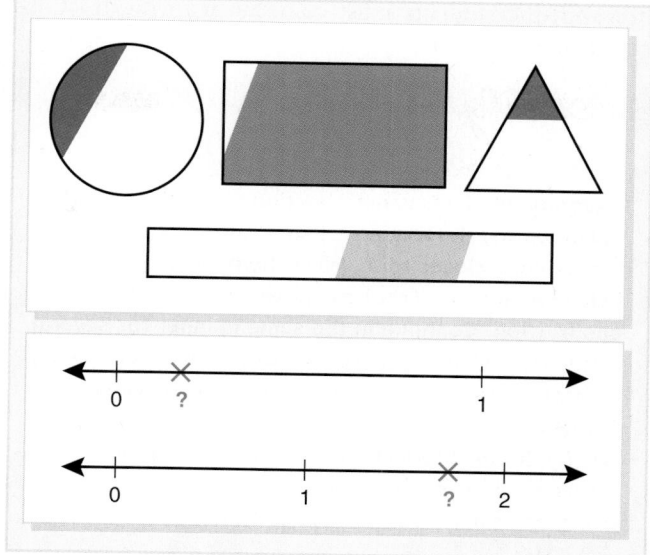

Figure 15.14 About how much? Name a fraction for each drawing, and explain why you chose that fraction.

fractions less than 1, simply comparing them to these three numbers gives quite a lot of information. For example, $\frac{3}{20}$ is small, close to 0, whereas $\frac{3}{4}$ is between $\frac{1}{2}$ and 1. The fraction $\frac{9}{10}$ is quite close to 1. Since any fraction greater than 1 is a whole number plus an amount less than 1, the same reference points are just as helpful: $3\frac{3}{7}$ is almost $3\frac{1}{2}$.

Activity 15.10

Zero, One-Half, or One

On a set of cards, write a collection of 10 to 15 fractions. A few should be greater than 1 ($\frac{9}{8}$ or $\frac{11}{10}$), with the others ranging from 0 to 1. Let students sort the fractions into three groups: those close to 0, close to $\frac{1}{2}$, and close to 1. For those close to $\frac{1}{2}$, have them decide if each fraction is more or less than $\frac{1}{2}$. The difficulty of this task depends largely on the fractions selected. The first time you try this activity, use fractions, such as $\frac{1}{20}$, $\frac{53}{100}$, or $\frac{9}{10}$, that are very close to the three benchmarks. On subsequent days, use fractions mostly with the denominators less than 20. You might include one or two fractions, such as $\frac{2}{8}$ or $\frac{3}{4}$, that are exactly between the benchmarks. Ask students to explain their choice for each fraction.

For those children who are experiencing difficulty with this activity, use materials to represent the fractions. Grid paper could also be used to represent the fractions, especially for fractions whose denominators are 20 or greater.

As an added challenge for those students who have easily mastered the activity, have them arrange the fractions in order from least to greatest or vice versa.

The next activity is also aimed at developing the same three reference points for fractions. In "Close Fractions," however, the students must come up with the fractions rather than sort them.

Activity 15.11

Close Fractions

Have your students name a fraction that is close to 1 but not more than 1. Next, have them name another fraction that is even closer to 1. Have them explain why they believe their second choice is closer to 1 than their previous fraction. Continue in the same manner for several fractions, each one being closer to 1 than the preceding fraction. Similarly, try using close to 0 or close to $\frac{1}{2}$ (either under or over). The first several times you try this activity, let the students use models to help with their thinking. Later, see how well their explanations work when they cannot use models or drawings.

Focus discussions on the important idea that number of fractions between fractions is infinite, so they can always find one in between.

Using Number Sense to Compare

The ability to tell which of two fractions is greater is another aspect of number sense with fractions. This ability is built around a conceptual understanding of fractions, not on an algorithmic skill or on symbolic tricks. In the 2000 NAEP test, only 21 percent of grade 4 students could explain why one unit fraction was larger or smaller than another—for example $\frac{1}{5}$ and $\frac{1}{4}$ (Kloosterman et al., 2004). At grade 8, only 41 percent of students were able to correctly order three fractions given in simplified form (Sowder, Wearne, Martin, & Struchens, 2004). As these researchers note, "How students can work meaningfully with fractions if they do not have a sense of the relative size of the fractions is difficult to imagine" (p. 116).

Comparing Unit Fractions   Children have a tremendously strong mind-set about numbers that can cause difficulties with the relative size of fractions. In their experience, larger numbers mean "more," which can translate to: Seven is more than four, so sevenths should be bigger than fourths (Mack, 1995). The inverse relationship between the number of parts and size of the parts cannot be told but must be a creation of each student's own thought process.

Activity 15.12

Ordering Unit Fractions

List a set of unit fractions such as $\frac{1}{3}$, $\frac{1}{8}$, $\frac{1}{5}$, and $\frac{1}{10}$. Ask children to put the fractions in order from least to greatest. Challenge children to defend the way they ordered the fractions. The first few times you do this activity, have them illustrate their ideas using models.

Students may notice that larger bottom numbers means smaller fractions. However, this is not a rule to be memorized. Revisit this basic idea periodically. Children will seem to understand one day and revert to their more comfortable ideas about big numbers a day or two later. Repeat Activity 15.12 with all numerators equal to numbers other than 1. You may be surprised to see that this is much harder for students.

Comparing Any Fraction   You have probably learned rules or algorithms for comparing two fractions. The usual approaches are finding common denominators and using cross-multiplication. These rules can be effective in getting correct answers but require no thought about the size of the fractions. This is especially true of the cross-multiplication procedure. If children are taught these rules before they have had the opportunity to think about the relative size of various fractions, there is little chance that they will develop any familiarity with, or number sense about, the size of fractions. Comparison activities (Which fraction is more?) can play a significant role in helping children develop concepts about the relative size of fractions. Keep in mind that reflective thought is the goal, not an algorithmic method of choosing the correct answer.

❚❚ ———————— Pause and Reflect

Assume for a moment that you know nothing about common denominators or cross-multiplication techniques. Now examine the pairs of fractions in Figure 15.15 and select the larger of each pair using a reasoning approach that a grade 4 or 5 student might use.

The following numbered list shows ways that the fractions in Figure 15.15 might have been compared:

1. *More of the same-size parts* (same denominators). To compare $\frac{3}{8}$ and $\frac{5}{8}$, think about having 3 of something and also 5 of the same thing. (B, G)
2. *Same number of parts, but parts are different sizes* (same numerators). Consider the case of $\frac{3}{4}$ and $\frac{3}{7}$. If a whole is divided into 7 equal parts, the parts will certainly be smaller than if the same whole is divided into only 4 equal parts. Children may select $\frac{3}{7}$ as larger because 7 is more than 4 and the top numbers are the same. (A, D, H)
3. *More and less than one-half or one whole.* The fractional pairs $\frac{3}{7}$ versus $\frac{5}{8}$ and $\frac{5}{4}$ versus $\frac{7}{8}$ do not lend themselves to either of the previous thought processes. In the first pair, $\frac{3}{7}$ is less than half of the number of sevenths needed to make a whole, so $\frac{3}{7}$ is less than a half. Similarly, $\frac{5}{8}$ is more than a half. Therefore, $\frac{5}{8}$ is the larger fraction. The second pair is determined by noting that one fraction is less than 1 and the other is greater than 1. (A, D, F, G, H)

Which fraction in each pair is greater?
Give one or more reasons. Try not to use drawings or models.
<u>Do</u> <u>not</u> <u>use</u> common denominators or cross-multiplication.
Rely on concepts.

A.	$\frac{4}{5}$ or $\frac{4}{9}$	G. $\frac{7}{12}$ or $\frac{5}{12}$
B.	$\frac{4}{7}$ or $\frac{5}{7}$	H. $\frac{3}{5}$ or $\frac{3}{7}$
C.	$\frac{3}{8}$ or $\frac{4}{10}$	I. $\frac{5}{8}$ or $\frac{6}{10}$
D.	$\frac{5}{3}$ or $\frac{5}{8}$	J. $\frac{9}{8}$ or $\frac{4}{3}$
E.	$\frac{3}{4}$ or $\frac{9}{10}$	K. $\frac{4}{6}$ or $\frac{7}{12}$
F.	$\frac{3}{8}$ or $\frac{4}{7}$	L. $\frac{8}{9}$ or $\frac{7}{8}$

Figure 15.15 Comparing fractions using concepts.

4. *Distance from one-half or one whole.* Why is $\frac{9}{10}$ greater than $\frac{3}{4}$? Not because the 9 and 10 are big numbers. Each is one fractional part away from one whole, and tenths are smaller than fourths. Similarly, notice that $\frac{5}{8}$ is smaller than $\frac{4}{6}$ because it is only one-eighth more than a half, while $\frac{4}{6}$ is a sixth more than a half. Can you use this basic idea to compare $\frac{3}{5}$ and $\frac{5}{9}$? (*Hint:* Each fraction is half of a fractional part more than $\frac{1}{2}$.) Also try $\frac{5}{7}$ and $\frac{7}{9}$. (C, E, I, J, K, L)

How did your reasons for choosing fractions in Figure 15.15 compare with these ideas? It is important that you are comfortable with these informal comparison strategies as a major component of your own number sense, as well as for helping children develop theirs. Notice that some of the comparisons, such as D and H, could have been solved using more than one of the strategies listed.

Tasks you design for your students should assist them in developing these and possibly other methods of comparing two fractions. It is important that the ideas come from your students and their discussions. To teach "the four ways to compare fractions" would be adding four more mysterious rules. It defeats the purpose of encouraging students to use their number sense.

To develop these methods for comparing fractions, select pairs of fractions that are likely to elicit desired strategies for doing so. For example, on one day you might have students compare two pairs with the same denominator and one with the same numerator. On another day, you might pick fraction pairs in which each fraction is exactly one part less than a whole. Try to develop different strategies over several days. Be strategic in your choice of fraction pairs.

The use of a region or number line model is important for helping students develop their mental reasoning. However, it is useful to change the activity after several experiences so that testing with a model is omitted and greater emphasis is placed on students' reasoning. The next activity extends the comparison task a bit more.

Activity **15.13**

Line 'Em Up

Select four or five fractions for students to place in order from least to greatest on a number line. Have them indicate approximately where each fraction belongs on the number line, which is labelled with the points 0, $\frac{1}{2}$, and 1. Adding machine tape can be used as the number line. Students can compare their number lines with others and explain how they decided where to place the fractions.

In order to place fractions on the number line, students must also estimate the size of the fractions, in addition to ordering them.

Including Equivalent Fractions   The discussion to this point has somewhat artificially ignored the idea that students might use equivalent fraction concepts in making comparisons. Equivalent fraction concepts are such an important idea that the entire following section is devoted to the development of that idea. However, equivalent fraction concepts need not be put off until last and certainly should be allowed in the discussions of which fraction is more.

Smith (2002) suggests that the comparison question to ask is: "Which of the following two (or more) fractions is greater, *or are they equal*?" (p. 9). He points out that this question leaves open the possibility that two fractions that may look different can, in fact, be equal.

In addition to this point with equivalent fraction concepts, students can adjust how a fraction looks so that they can use ideas that make sense to them. Burns (1999) tells of grade 5 students who were comparing $\frac{6}{8}$ to $\frac{4}{5}$. (You might want to stop for a moment and think how you would compare these two fractions.) One child changed the $\frac{4}{5}$ to $\frac{8}{10}$ so that both fractions would be two parts away from a whole and reasoned: since tenths are smaller than eighths, $\frac{4}{5}$ is larger. Another child changed both fractions to a common *numerator* of 12.

Be absolutely certain to revisit the comparison activities and include pairs such as $\frac{8}{12}$ and $\frac{2}{3}$, where fractions are equal but do not appear to be so.

Equivalent-Fraction Concepts

As discussed in Chapter 14, equivalence is a critical but often poorly understood concept. This is particularly true with fraction equivalence.

Conceptual Focus on Equivalence

Pause and Reflect

How do you know that $\frac{4}{6} = \frac{2}{3}$? Before reading further, think of at least two different explanations.

Here are some possible answers to the question just posed:

1. They are the same because you can reduce $\frac{4}{6}$ and get $\frac{2}{3}$.
2. If you have a set of 6 things and you take 4 of them, it would be $\frac{4}{6}$. But you can make the 6 into groups of 2. Then there would be 3 groups, and the 4 would be 2 groups out of the 3 groups. That means it is $\frac{2}{3}$.

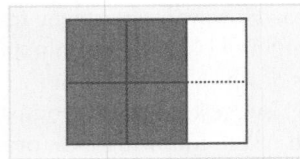

3. If you start with $\frac{2}{3}$, you can multiply the top and the bottom numbers by 2, which will give you $\frac{4}{6}$, so they are equal.
4. If you cut a rectangle into 3 parts and you shaded 2 parts, $\frac{2}{3}$ would be shaded. If you cut all 3 of these parts in half, it would be 4 parts shaded and 6 parts in all. That's $\frac{4}{6}$, and it would be the same amount.

All of these answers are correct. But let's think about what they tell us. Responses 2 and 4 are conceptual in their explanation, though not as efficient. The procedural responses 1 and 3 are quite efficient but indicate no conceptual knowledge. All students should eventually be able to write an equivalent fraction for a given fraction. At the same time, the procedures should never be taught or used until the students understand what the result means. Consider how different the procedure and the concept appear to be.

> *Concept:* Two fractions are equivalent if they are representations for the same amount or quantity—if they represent the same number.
>
> *Algorithm:* To make an equivalent fraction, multiply (or divide) the top and bottom numbers by the same non-zero number.

In a problem-based classroom, students can develop an understanding of equivalent fractions and from that understanding develop a conceptually based algorithm. As with most algorithms, a serious instructional error is to rush too quickly to the rule. Be patient! Intuitive methods are always best at first.

Equivalent-Fraction Models

The general approach to helping students create a conceptual understanding of equivalent fractions is to have them use a variety of models to generate different names for fractions. Consider that this is the first time in their experience that a fixed quantity can have multiple names (actually an infinite number). The following activities are possible starting places.

Activity 15.14

Different Fillers

Using an area model for fractions that is familiar to your students, prepare a worksheet with two or, at most, three outlines of different fractions, as in Figure 15.16. Do not limit yourself to unit fractions. For example, if the model is circular, you might draw an outline for $\frac{2}{3}$, $\frac{1}{2}$, and $\frac{3}{4}$. The students' task is to use their own fraction pieces to find as many equivalent fractions as possible for the region. After completing the three examples, have students write about the ideas or patterns they may have noticed while finding the names. Follow the activity with a class discussion.

In the class discussion following the "Different Fillers" activity, a good question involves asking what equivalent

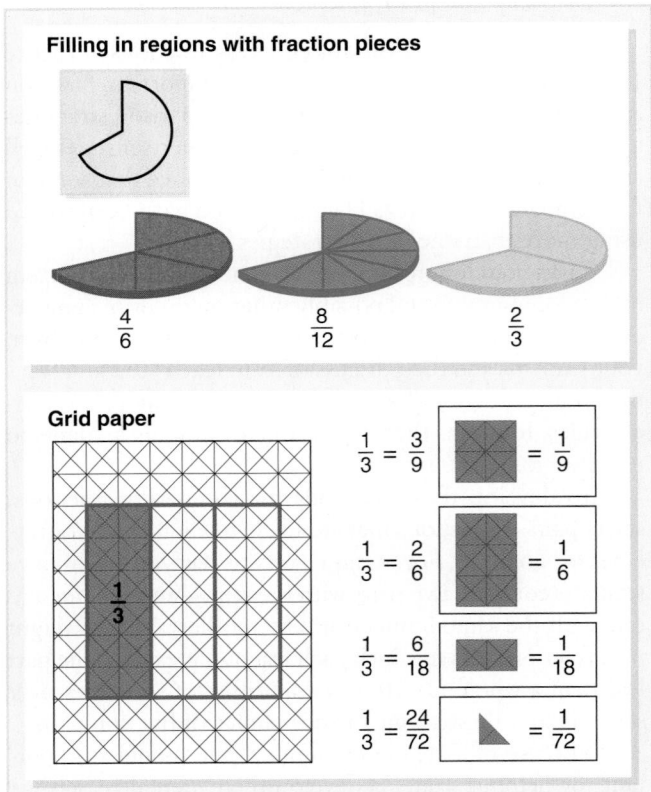

Figure 15.16 Area models for equivalent fractions.

fractions could be found if students had any-size fraction pieces. For example, ask students, "What fractions could you find if we had sixteenths in our fraction kit? What fractions could you find if you had pieces of any size?"

The following activity is just a variation of "Different Fillers." Instead of using a manipulative, the task is carried out using dot paper.

Activity 15.15

Dot Paper Equivalencies

Create a worksheet using a portion of either isometric or rectangular dot grid paper (see Blackline Masters). Draw an outline of a region on the grid paper and designate it as one whole. Draw a part of the region within the whole. The task is to use the grid to figure out the fractional name for the different parts within the whole. See Figure 15.16, which includes an example drawn on an isometric grid. Students should draw a picture of the unit fractional part that they use to name each fraction. The larger the size of the whole, the greater the number of names generated.

The "Dot Paper Equivalencies" activity is a form of what Lamon (2002) calls "unitizing," which is finding different ways to chunk a given quantity into parts in order to name it. She points out that this is a key ability related not only to equivalent fractions, but also to proportional reasoning, especially in the comparison of ratios. (See also Lamon 1999a b.)

Length models can be used to create activities similar to the "Different Fillers" task. For example, as shown in Figure 15.17, fraction strips can be used to designate both a whole and a part. Students use the strips to find the fractional names for the given parts. Different strips can be used to name the same fraction. Folding paper strips is another method for creating different fractions that name the same number. In the example shown in Figure 15.17, one half is subdivided by successive folding in half. The additional folds would produce fractions with different names for $\frac{1}{2}$. These possibilities should be discussed if no one tries to fold the strip to produce an odd number of parts.

The following activity is also a unitizing activity in which students look for different units or chunks of the whole in order to name a part of the whole in different ways. This activity is significant because it utilizes a set model.

Activity 15.16

Apples and Bananas

Have students set out a specific number of counters in two colours—for example, 24 counters, 16 of them red (apples) and 8 yellow (bananas). These 24 counters make up the whole. The task is to group the counters into different fractional parts of the whole, according to colour, and find as many fractional names as they can for the fractions that represent the apples and those that represent the bananas. In Figure 15.18, 24 counters are arranged in different array patterns. You might also suggest some possible arrays or allow students to make their own (see Figure 15.19).

In Lamon's version of the last activity, she prompts students with questions such as, "If we make groups of four, what part of the set is red?" With these prompts you can suggest fraction names that students are unlikely to think of.

In the activities so far, there has been only a hint of a rule for finding equivalent fractions. The following activity moves a bit closer to doing so, but should still be done before developing a algorithm.

Activity 15.17

Missing-Number Equivalencies

Give students an equation expressing equivalence between two fractions, but leave out one of the numbers. Have them draw a picture as part of the solution. Here are four different examples:

$$\frac{5}{3} = \frac{\square}{6} \qquad \frac{2}{3} = \frac{6}{\square} \qquad \frac{8}{12} = \frac{\square}{3} \qquad \frac{9}{12} = \frac{3}{\square}$$

The missing number can be either a numerator or a denominator. Furthermore, the missing number can be either larger or smaller than the corresponding part of the equivalent fraction. (All four possibilities are represented in the examples.) The examples shown involve simple whole-number multiples between equivalent fractions. Next consider pairs such as $\frac{6}{8} = \frac{\square}{12}$ or $\frac{6}{12} = \frac{8}{\square}$. In these pairs, neither fraction is in lowest terms.

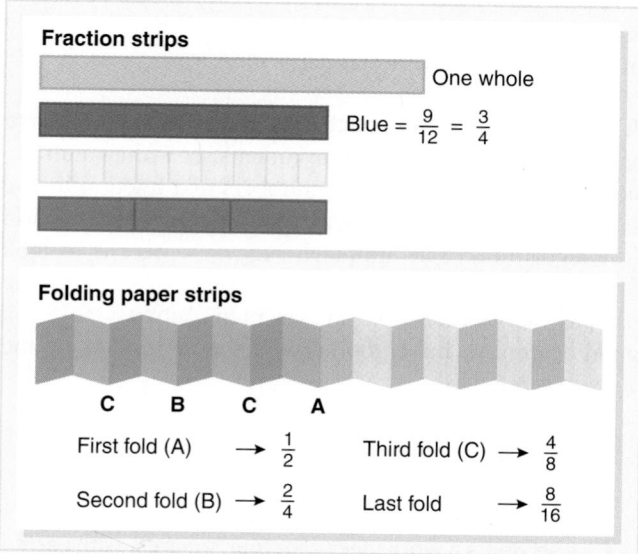

Figure 15.17 Length models for equivalent fractions.

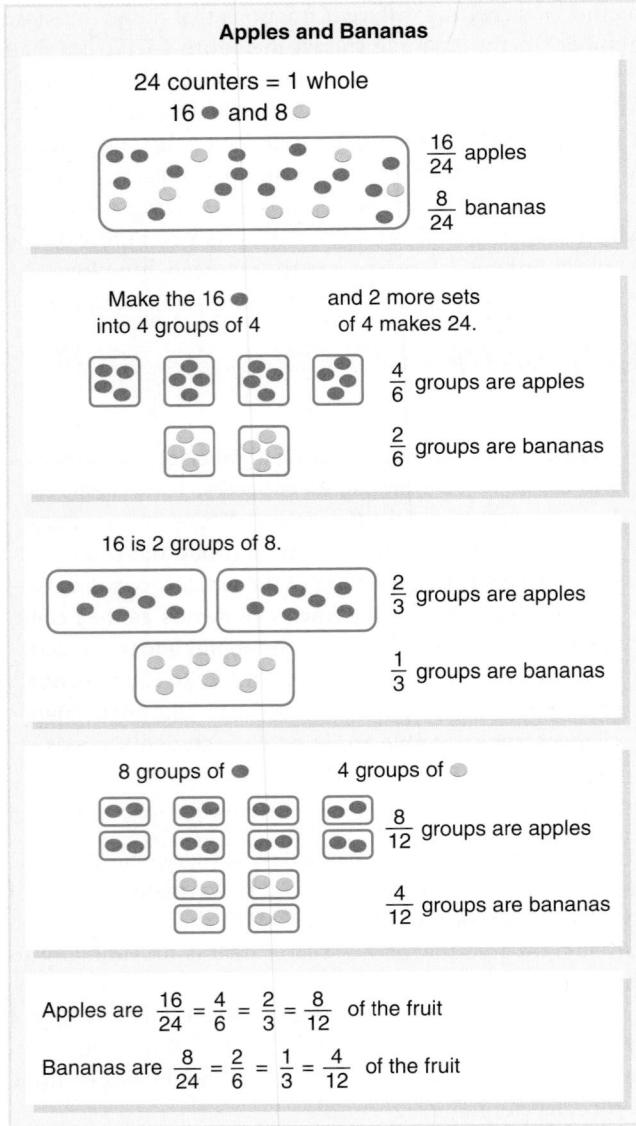

Figure 15.18 Set models for illustrating equivalent fractions.

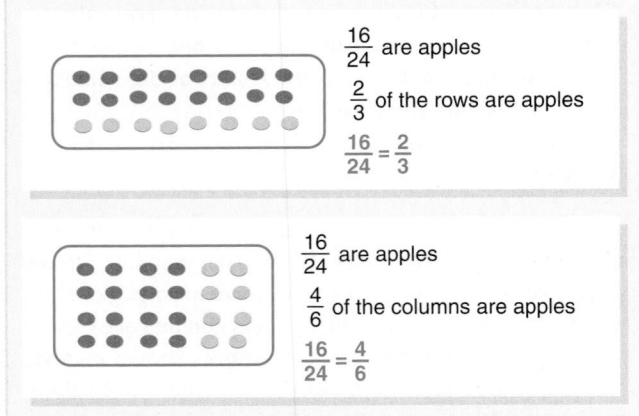

Figure 15.19 Arrays for illustrating equivalent fractions.

When doing "Missing-Number Equivalencies" you may want to specify a particular model, such as sets or pie pieces. Alternatively, you can allow students to select whatever methods they wish to solve these problems. To accommodate students who find these challenging, you might want to use clocks to figure out equivalence. Chick, Tierney, and Storegard (2007) found that clocks were very helpful when working with students in highly diverse classrooms. The students were able to use the clocks to find equivalent fractions for $\frac{10}{12}$, $\frac{3}{4}$, $\frac{4}{6}$ and so on.

 NCTM's *Illuminations* Web site offers an excellent set of three lesson units, Fun with Fractions. Each unit uses one of the model types (set, region, length) and focuses on comparing and ordering fractions and equivalency. The five or six lessons in each unit incorporate a range of manipulatives and engaging activities to support student learning.

Set Model Unit: http://illuminations.nctm.org/LessonDetail.aspx?id=U112

Region Model Unit: http://illuminations.nctm.org/LessonDetail.aspx?id=U113

Length Model Unit: http://illuminations.nctm.org/LessonDetail.aspx?id=U152 ◆

Developing an Equivalent-Fraction Algorithm

Kamii and Clark (1995) argue that undue reliance on physical models does not help children construct equivalence schemes. When children understand that fractions can have different names, they should be challenged to develop a method for finding these names. It might also be argued that students who are experienced at looking for patterns and developing schemes for doing things can invent an algorithm for equivalent fractions without further assistance. However, the following approach will certainly improve the chances of that happening.

A Region Model Approach Rectangular regions serve as a good visual and they help students see if they multiply both the top and the bottom numbers of a fraction by the same number, they will always get an equivalent fraction (the algorithm). The approach suggested here is to look for a pattern in the way that the fractional parts in both the part, as well as the whole, are counted. Activity 15.18 is a good beginning, but a good class discussion following the activity is required.

Activity 15.18

Slicing Squares

Give students a worksheet with four squares, with each side approximately 3 cm long. Have the students draw

vertical lines in each square and shade them in to show the same fraction. For example, slice each square into fourths and shade three-fourths, as in Figure 15.20. You can use the context of a garden or a farm. Next, tell students to slice each square horizontally, so that there are equal size sections, in each square. The number of horizontal slices should vary from one to eight, so each square will have a different number of sections. Have students record an equation, which shows an equivalent fraction, to represent the area shaded, in each square. Have students examine their equations and drawings to find any patterns. You many want to repeat this activity with four more squares and a different fraction.

Following this activity, write on the board four or five equations that name the same fraction found by the students. Discuss any patterns they discovered. To focus the discussion, show on the overhead a square illustrating $\frac{4}{5}$ made with vertical slices, as in Figure 15.21. Turn off the overhead and slice the square into six parts in the opposite direction. Cover all but two edges of the square as shown in the figure. Ask, "What is the new name for my $\frac{4}{5}$?"

The reason for this exercise is that many students simply count the small regions and never think to use multiplication. With the square covered, students can see that there

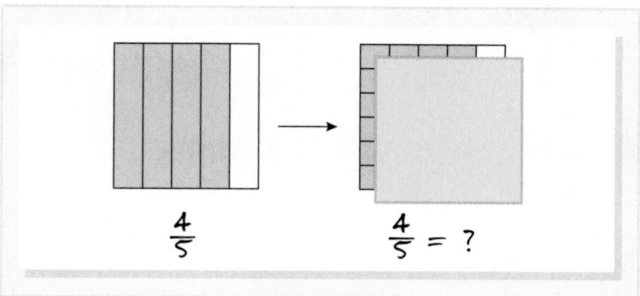

Figure 15.21 How can you count the fractional parts if you cannot see them all?

are four columns and six rows to the shaded part, so there must be 4×6 parts shaded. Similarly, there must be 5×6 parts in the whole. Therefore, the new name for $\frac{4}{5}$ is $\frac{4 \times 6}{5 \times 6}$.

Using this idea, have students return to the fractions on their worksheet to see if the pattern works for other fractions.

Examine examples of equivalent fractions that have been generated with other models and see if the rule of multiplying top and bottom numbers by the same number holds there also. If the rule is correct, how can $\frac{6}{8}$ and $\frac{9}{12}$ be equivalent?

Writing Fractions in Simplest Terms The multiplication scheme for equivalent fractions produces fractions with larger denominators. To write a fraction in *simplest terms* means to write it so that the numerator and the denominator have no common whole number factors, other than 1. (Some texts use the name *lowest terms* instead of *simplest terms*.) One meaningful approach to this task of finding simplest terms is to reverse the earlier process, as illustrated in Figure 15.22.

The search for a common factor or finding a simplified fraction should be connected to the concept of grouping in multiplication.

Two additional notes should be made:

1. Notice that the phrase *reducing fractions* was not used. This terminology implies making a fraction smaller and is rarely used any longer in textbooks. Fractions are simplified, not reduced.

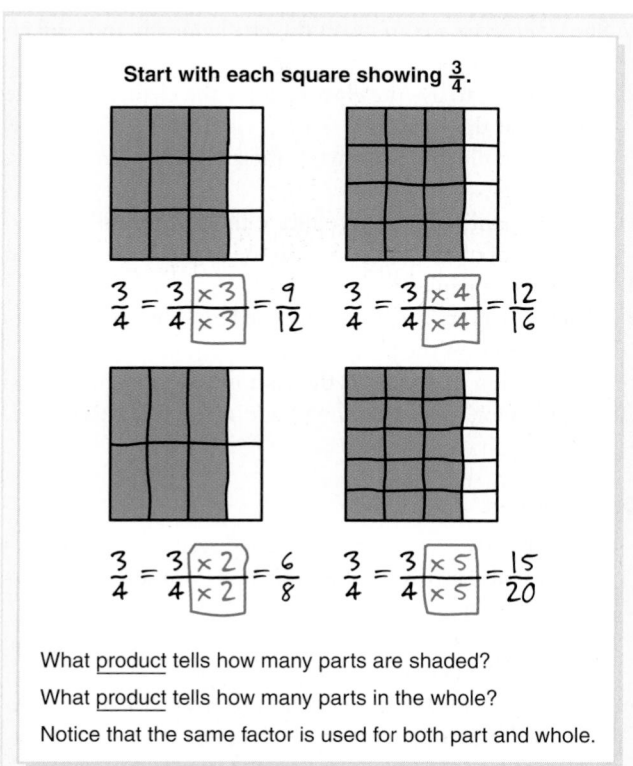

Start with each square showing $\frac{3}{4}$.

$\frac{3}{4} = \frac{3 \times 3}{4 \times 3} = \frac{9}{12}$ $\frac{3}{4} = \frac{3 \times 4}{4 \times 4} = \frac{12}{16}$

$\frac{3}{4} = \frac{3 \times 2}{4 \times 2} = \frac{6}{8}$ $\frac{3}{4} = \frac{3 \times 5}{4 \times 5} = \frac{15}{20}$

What <u>product</u> tells how many parts are shaded?

What <u>product</u> tells how many parts in the whole?

Notice that the same factor is used for both part and whole.

Figure 15.20 A model for developing the equivalent fraction algorithm.

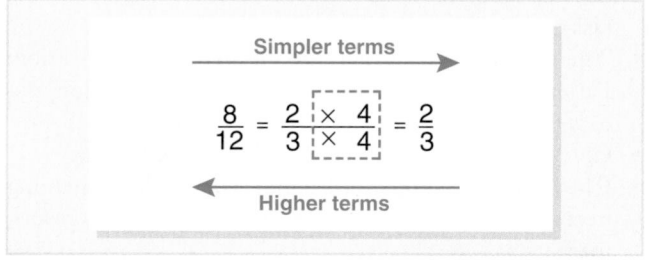

Simpler terms →

$\frac{8}{12} = \frac{2}{3} \frac{\times 4}{\times 4} = \frac{2}{3}$

← Higher terms

Figure 15.22 Using the equivalent-fraction algorithm to write fractions in simplest terms.

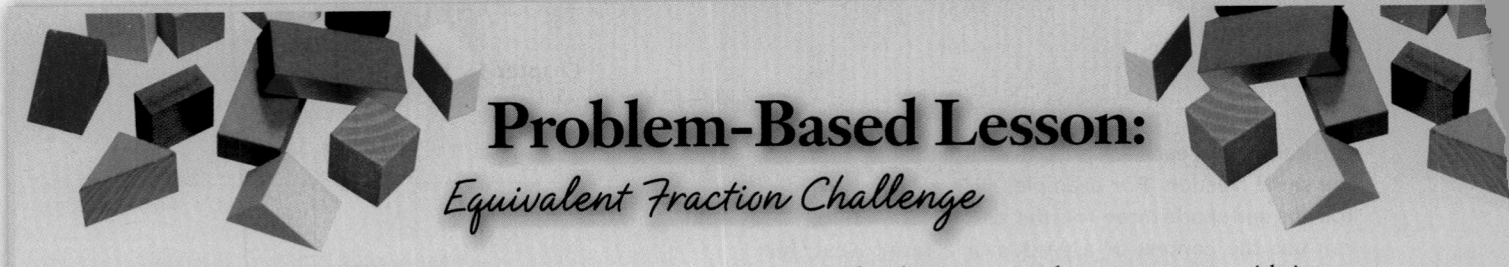

Problem-Based Lesson:
Equivalent Fraction Challenge

Differentiating the Learning

The following problem-based lesson provides students with an opportunity to apply their knowledge of equivalent fractions. This lesson demonstrates how the range of learner needs in a class can be accommodated. There are two parts to this lesson, requiring that it extend over two days. The open-ended nature of the lesson allows students to work at a pace best suited to their level of ability as they work through the tasks, collaborating with their peers. Students also have the opportunity to use manipulatives to represent their ideas as they work through the lesson. *Note:* in anticipation of the possible needs that could arise on day one, the task cards for day two have been designed so that there are three paths for students to follow. Doing so offers another opportunity for students to work at their level of ability.

Grade Level: Grades 5 and 6

Mathematical Goals

- To reinforce students' understanding of equivalent fractions
- To strengthen students' mathematical language of fractions
- To ensure students understand that equivalent fractions are merely different ways of representing the same amount

Thinking About the Students

Students have done some work on equivalent fractions using the materials suggested for this activity. However, they require further opportunities to work on the concept in order to strengthen their understanding of this important mathematical principle. As part of this understanding, it is important that students realize equivalent fractions are merely different names (symbolic representations) for the same fractional amount.

Materials and Preparation

- For this activity, students of different abilities work in pairs at stations (3 or 4 stations is an optimal number to provide students with sufficient space to carry out the task)
- The following materials are needed at each station: Pattern blocks, geoboards, fraction circles, fraction factory pieces, and cubes
- Clues, which need to be prepared for each day's task
- Challenge kits (zippered baggies work well) containing necessary instructions, clues, pencils, rulers, erasers, markers
- Grid chart paper, geoboards, dot paper

- An overhead projector and a transparency with instructions on how to carry out the different tasks.

Lesson: Day One
Introduction

- Read the book *The Hershey's Milk Chocolate Fraction Book* (if this one is not available, other books that can be used are *Fraction Fun*, *Apple Fractions*, and *Eating Fractions*) together with the class. As you read the book talk about the different ways that the fractions presented in the book can be represented for example using equivalent fractions.
- Explain the purpose of the activity.

The Task

- Students will work with their partners, using the clues in their kits to solve each challenge.
- Solutions for each challenge are to be illustrated and justifications for them written on the grid chart paper.
- The materials can be used as a template for the illustrations.

Establish Expectations

- Read the instructions on the overhead projector for the activity.
- Show the class the items in the challenge kit and explain how each will be used.
- Students are to use the clues to solve the challenges while working at the stations.
- They then illustrate and write their solutions on the grid chart paper.
- The dot paper is used to replicate the fractions illustrated on the geoboards (the paper can be stapled onto the grid paper accompanied by a solution).
- Pencils, markers, and rulers are used for drawing and writing solutions to the challenges.
- The fraction materials at the stations can also be used as templates for any illustrations made on the grid chart paper.
- Student pairs are identified.

Development

- Student pairs work at their assigned stations reading and solving clues, justifying their thinking with solutions written on the grid chart paper.
- The teacher circulates around the room observing and noting students working.
- The teacher looks for students who may be having difficulty with the instructions on the clues.
- The teacher looks for students who may be experiencing difficulty showing equivalent fractions and justifying their thinking.

Follow-up

- Students meet as a whole class to discuss the activity.
- Students show and talk about their solutions to the challenges, explaining how they solved them.
- Students share with a partner their definitions and conclusions about finding equivalent fractions.

Next Steps＿＿＿＿＿＿＿＿＿＿＿＿＿＿＿＿＿

Assessment Notes

- Are some students still confused about what equivalent fractions are and how to find them?
- Which ones are still experiencing difficulty with the concept?
- Which ones require an added challenge?
- Which ones have "got it"?

Fraction Challenge

Clue List ＿＿＿＿＿＿＿＿＿＿＿＿＿＿＿＿ **Day One**

Clue #1

To answer clue #1, you will need to write each fractional number on the grid paper. Use the material of your choice to represent each of these numbers and illustrate them on the grid paper. Then choose one fractional number and explain in writing why you represented it in this way.

(a) $\frac{3}{12}$　　(b) $\frac{9}{15}$　　(c) $\frac{1}{2}$

Clue #2

To answer clue #2, use the material of your choice to show $\frac{1}{2}$ in three different ways. Use a different material than you did for clue #1. Explain in writing why you showed $\frac{1}{2}$ in these three ways.

Clue #3

There are 5 blue cubes and 6 red cubes in the bag. Write a fractional number that will represent the relationship between the number of red and blue cubes. Write two other fractional numbers that represent this relationship. Explain in writing why you think your choice for the other two numbers is correct.

Note to the Teacher: For those students who are experiencing difficulty with clue #3, omit clue #4.

Clue #4

Does $\frac{1}{3} = \frac{3}{15}$? Use the material of your choice to justify your answer; then explain in writing how you solved this problem. You may also use diagrams to accompany your explanation.

Lesson ＿＿＿＿＿＿＿＿＿＿＿＿＿＿＿＿＿**Day Two**

The purpose of this lesson is to accommodate the particular needs of students in the class, based on the previous day's assessment of their work. There will be 3 different paths for students to follow.

1. Path One is for students who are still experiencing difficulty with the concept.

2. Path Two is for students who require an added challenge.
3. Path Three is for students who have achieved the goals of the previous day's lesson.

- Students are grouped in pairs according to the path they will follow for the lesson.
- Path One students are given a set of challenge clues to answer at an assigned station.
- Path Two students are given a set of challenge clues to answer at an assigned station.
- Path Three students will work at a station to design their own equivalent fraction booklets.

The same format for the development and follow-up phases is used for lesson two. In the introduction phase directions for following assigned paths are given.

Fraction Challenge

Clue List for Day Two＿＿＿＿＿＿＿＿＿ **Path One**

Clue A

Are $\frac{1}{2}$ and $\frac{5}{10}$ equal to each other, or is one greater than the other? Use the materials of your choice to prove your selection, then write about how you solved this problem.

Clue B

There are 4 red cubes and 7 blue cubes in the bag. Write a fraction that represents the relationship between the number of red and blue cubes. Write one other fractional number that represents this relationship. Explain in writing why you think your second choice is correct.

Clue C

Use the fraction pieces of your choice to show that $\frac{1}{2}$ and $\frac{2}{4}$ are equal to each other. Explain in writing how you figured out this problem.

Fraction Challenge

Clue List for Day Two ＿＿＿＿＿＿＿＿＿ **Path Two**

Clue A1

Cooking Cube Soup. It's your turn to make a soup. Follow the recipe. This recipe serves 2 people. $\frac{1}{2}$ of the cubes are red; yellow cubes make up $\frac{1}{4}$ of the soup, and there are 12 cubes in all. How many blue cubes are there? Now make this cube soup to serve 4 people.

Clue B1

Put $\frac{2}{5}$, $\frac{3}{10}$, and $\frac{2}{10}$ in order from least to greatest. Explain in writing how you figured out this problem. You may use diagrams.

Clue C1

Write $\frac{9}{4}$ as a whole number and a fraction in two different ways. Explain your thinking in writing. You may use illustrations and/or diagrams to accompany your answer.

2. Teachers may tell students that their fraction answers are incorrect if not in simplest or lowest terms. This belief also misinforms students about the equivalency of fractions. When students add $\frac{1}{6}+\frac{1}{2}$, both $\frac{2}{3}$ and $\frac{4}{6}$ are correct. As well, they are equivalent.

Multiplying by One Many elementary school textbooks use a strictly symbolic approach to equivalent fractions. It is based on the multiplicative property that says any number multiplied by 1 remains unchanged. Any fraction of the form *n/n* can be used as the identity element. Therefore, $\frac{3}{4}=\frac{3}{4}\times 1=\frac{3}{4}\times\frac{2}{2}=\frac{6}{8}$. Furthermore, the numerator and the denominator of the identity element can also be fractions.

In this way, $\frac{6}{12}=\frac{6}{12}\times\frac{\frac{1}{6}}{\frac{1}{6}}=\frac{1}{2}$.

This explanation relies on an understanding of the multiplicative identity property, which most students in grades 4–6 do not fully appreciate. It also relies on the procedure for multiplying two fractions. Finally, the argument uses solely deductive reasoning based on an axiom of the rational number system. It does not lend itself to intuitive modelling. A reasonable conclusion is to delay this important explanation until at least grades 7–8 in an appropriate pre-algebra context, and not as a method or a rationale for producing equivalent fractions.

 *Math Trek* (Nectar Foundation, 2000) tutorials offer students an opportunity to reinforce learning about equivalent fractions and related concepts. Models such as pizza pies, rectangles, and circles are used effectively, but terms such as "reducing fractions" do appear. There also seems to be an emphasis on employing the multiplication and division rule for making fractions equivalent rather than on promoting the development of understanding. In the tutorials for the upper elementary grades, cross-multiplication is also employed as a strategy for making fractions equivalent.

In the NCTM *e-Examples* (http://standards.nctm.org/document/eexamples/index.htm), there is a motivating fraction game for two players (Applet 5.1, Communicating about Mathematics Using Games). The game uses a number-line model and knowledge of equivalent fractions plays a significant role.

The NLVM Web site (http://nlvm.usu.edu) has a limited applet tool for exploring equivalent fractions, *Fraction—Equivalent*. Proper fractions are presented randomly in either square or circular formats. Students can slice the model in as many parts as they wish to see which slices create equivalent fractions. For squares, the new slices go in the same direction as the original slices. For circles,

it is a bit harder to distinguish new slices from old ones. Students enter an equivalent fraction, then click a button to check their response. ◆

Teaching Considerations for Fraction Concepts

Because the teaching of fractions is so important, and because fractions are often not well understood, even by adults, a recap of the big ideas is needed. Hopefully, you have recognized that one reason fractions are not well understood is that there is a lot to know about them—from part–whole relationships to division. In addition, building understanding means representing across area, length, and set models—and including contexts that fit these models. Using estimation activities can support student understanding of fractions. It is an important skill in and of itself.

Equivalence is a central idea for which students must have sound understanding and skill. Connecting visuals with the procedure and not rushing the algorithm too soon is important.

Clarke, Roche, and Mitchell (2008), well-known researchers of fraction teaching and learning, offer "10 Practical Tips for Making Fractions Come Alive and Make Sense." These tips are listed here as an effective summary of this chapter:

1. Give a greater emphasis to the meaning of fractions than to the procedures for manipulating them.
2. Develop a generalizable rule for explaining the numerator and denominator of a fraction.
3. Emphasize that fractions are numbers, making extensive use of number lines for representing fractions and decimal numbers.
4. Take opportunities early to focus on improper fractions and equivalencies.
5. Provide a variety of models to represent fractions.
6. Link fractions to key benchmarks and encourage estimation.
7. Give emphasis to fractions as division.
8. Link fractions, decimals, and percents, wherever possible.
9. Take the opportunity to interview several students one on one ... to gain awareness of their thinking strategies.
10. Look for examples and activities that can engage students in thinking about fractions in particular and rational number ideas in general (pp. 374-378).

Reflections on Chapter **15**

Writing to Learn

1. Describe what is meant by "sharing activities." What is the goal of these activities? When would you implement them?
2. Give examples of manipulatives within each of the three categories of fractional models.
3. What does partitioning mean? Explain and illustrate.
4. What does iteration mean? Explain and illustrate.
5. Describe how a student might explain what the numerator and the denominator mean.
6. What are two ways you can support students' development of estimating fractions?
7. Describe two ways to compare $\frac{5}{12}$ and $\frac{5}{8}$ (not common denominator or cross-product methods).
8. What are two ways to build the conceptual relationship between $1\frac{1}{4}$ and $2\frac{3}{4}$?
9. What contexts might you use to develop the concept of equivalence within each of the models—area, length, and set?
10. How could you help children develop the algorithm for equivalent fractions?

For Discussion and Exploration

1. A common error that children make is to write $\frac{3}{5}$ for the fraction represented here:

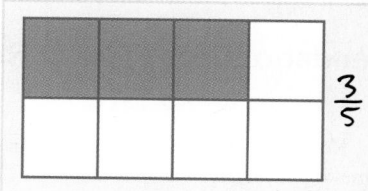

   Why do you think they do this? What activity or strategy would you use to try to address this common error?
2. Fractions are often named by adults in cartoons as a dreaded topic of mathematics. Why do you think this is true? How might your instruction of fractions alter this perception for your students?

Resources for Chapter **15**

Literature Connections

Context takes children away from rules and encourages them to explore ideas in a more open and informal manner. The way that children approach fraction concepts in these contexts may surprise you.

How the Moon Regained Her Shape   *Heller, 2006*

This metaphorical story, influenced by North American folktales, emphasizes dealing with adversity, building self-confidence, and understanding the phases of the moon. As students explore the phases of the moon, a connection can easily be made to fractional concepts. The book can also serve as an excellent resource for discussions about the topic of bullying. The special section, For Creative Minds, at the back of the book provides diagrams of moon phases, a project, and a glossary of Native American terms for the moon. Worksheets can also be downloaded from the Web site.

How Many Snails? A Counting Book   *Giganti, 1988*

Each page of this book has a similar pattern of questions. For example, "I went walking and I wondered: How many clouds were there? How many clouds were big and fluffy? How

many were big and fluffy and gray?" Students can look at the pictures and find the fraction of the objects (e.g., clouds) that have the particular characteristic (big and fluffy). Whitin and Whitin (2006) describe how a class used this book to write their own stories in this pattern and record the fractions for each subset of the objects.

The Doorbell Rang   *Hutchins, 1986*

Often used to investigate whole-number operations of multiplication and division, this book is also an excellent early introduction to fractions. The story is a simple tale of two children preparing to share a plate of 12 cookies. Just as they have figured out how to share the cookies, the doorbell rings and more children arrive. You can change the number of children to create a sharing situation that requires fractions (e.g., 5 children).

The Man Who Counted: A Collection of Mathematical Adventures   *Tahan, 1993*

This book contains a story, "Beasts of Burden," about a wise mathematician, Beremiz, and the narrator who are travelling together on one camel. They are asked by three brothers to solve an argument. Their father has left them 35 camels to divide among them: $\frac{1}{2}$ to one brother, $\frac{1}{3}$ to another, and $\frac{1}{9}$ to the third. The story provides an excellent context for discussing fractional parts of sets and how fractional parts change as the whole changes. However, if the whole is changed from 35 to, say, 36 or 34, the problem of the indicated shares remains unresolved. The sum of $\frac{1}{2}$, $\frac{1}{3}$, and $\frac{1}{9}$ will never be 1, no matter how many camels are involved. Bresser (1995) describes three days of discussion and activities with his grade 5 students, who proposed a wide range of solutions.

Recommendations for Further Reading

Articles

Clarke, D. M., Roche, A., & Mitchell, A. (2008). Ten practical tips for making fractions come alive and make sense. *Mathematics Teaching in the Middle School, 13* (7), 373–380.
This article has the ten suggestions listed in the summary of this chapter. Each is discussed and favourite activities are shared. This is an excellent overview of teaching fractions.

Flores, A., & Klein, E. (2005). From students' problem-solving strategies to connections in fractions. *Teaching Children Mathematics, 11,* 452–457.
This article offers a very realistic view (complete with photos of student work) of how children develop initial fraction concepts and an understanding of notation as they engage in sharing tasks like those described in this chapter. The information here is significant for anyone wishing to help students make this important connection.

Pirie, S., & Kieren, T. (1992). Creating constructivist environments and constructing creative classrooms. *Educational Studies in Mathematics, 23,* 505–528.
This article focuses on the constructivist nature of teaching and learning mathematics in the elementary classroom, and also describes children's work with fractions. A series of episodes shows how teachers attempt to teach fractional concepts for understanding. Both the narrative and the accompanying illustrations reinforce the concept development in this chapter in a unique manner.

Reys, B. J., Kim, O., & Bay, J. M. (1999). Establishing fraction benchmarks. *Mathematics Teaching in the Middle School, 4,* 530–532.
This short article describes a simple three-question interview administered to 20 grade 5 students. The results are both sad and surprising. A significant conclusion is that the teaching of benchmarks for fractions, specifically 0, $\frac{1}{2}$, and 1, is generally neglected in the standard curriculum. The questions used in the interview can profitably be used with children in grades 4–7.

Stump, S. (2003). Designing fraction counting books. *Teaching Children Mathematics, 9,* 546–549.
This little article describes the work of several pre-service teachers whose students created counting books in which they count by unit fractions as described in this chapter. Some nice examples are shared, and the author describes difficulties and insights gained from this simple activity.

Books

Burns, M. (2001). *Teaching arithmetic: Lessons for introducing fractions, grades 4–5.* Sausalito, CA: Math Solutions Publications. *Typical of Marilyn Burns, this book offers well-designed lessons with a lot of detail, sample student dialogue, and Blackline Masters. These are introductory ideas for fractional concepts. Five lessons cover one-half as a benchmark. Assessments are also included.*

Online Resources

Cyberchase (PBS)
www.pbs.org/teachers/search/results.
html?q=fractions&x=0&y=0&num=100&loggedin=0&logg
edin=0&active=audiovideo
Cyberchase is a very popular television series targeting important mathematics. The site offers videos that model fractions with real-world connections. Also offered are activities such as "Make a Match" (http://pbskids.org/cyberchase/games/equivalentfractions/index.html), in which students examine the concept of equivalent fractions and match a fraction with a graphic representation of that fraction. Another activity is Thirteen Ways of Looking at a Half (http://pbskids.org/cyberchase/games/fractions/index.html) Students explore fractions of geometric shapes—in particular, the 13 ways half of an eight- piece square can be arranged.

Drag and Drop Fraction Matching, Fraction Frenzy Wordsearch
http://olc.spsd.sk.ca/DE/math1-3/fraction.html
These activities are just two of the five found at this site that provide practice with fractions. The site is maintained by Saskatoon Public Schools.

Exploring Fractions
http://www.learnalberta.ca/content/mejhm/index.
html?l=0&ID1=AB.MATH.JR.NUMB&ID2=AB.MATH.
JR.NUMB.FRA&lesson=html/video_interactives/
fractions/fractionsSmall.html
This interactive video about real-life application of fractions is accompanied by an interactive resource, which includes print activities solutions and learning strategies.

Fraction Bars (Math Playground)
http://mathplayground.com/Fractions_bars.html
Here the user sets the total parts, and the shaded parts for each part. Fractional parts, the concept of numerator and denominator, and equivalency are explored. The user can turn the numbers on or off.

Fraction Concepts (eNLVM Module)
http://enlvm.usu.edu/ma/nav/toc.jsp?sid=_
shared&cid=emready@fractions_concepts&bb=published
These part–whole activities provide practice in writing and comparing fractions. A full lesson plan with NCTM standards correlations and worksheets is provided, and the teacher can log in to see how students performed.

Fraction Track
http://standards.nctm.org/document/eexamples/chap5/5.1/index.htm

Players position fractions with different denominators on number lines. Fractions can be split into parts. This is a challenging game involving equivalent-fraction concepts.

Fraction Pointer
www.shodor.org/interactivate/activities/FractionPointer

This is a good applet for connecting an area model with the number line. After creating area models for two fractions, the user must then create a new fraction between the first two. It is similar to the *Illumination* applet, Equivalent Fractions.

National Library of Virtual Manipulatives
http://nlvm.usu.edu

This site offers numerous models for exploring fractions, including fraction bars and fraction pieces. Also there is an applet for comparing and visualizing fractions.

The Learning Equation Math, Fraction Conversion
http://argyll.epsb.ca/jreed/math7/strand1/1105.htm

This Canadian fraction applet, developed by Jim Reed for The Argyll Centre, is appropriate for grade 7. There is also material for grades 8 and 9. Students have the opportunity to demonstrate and describe equivalent mixed numbers and improper fractions pictorially and symbolically. Cuisenaire rods and pattern blocks are used to help visualize equivalent fractions.

PEARSON
myeducationlab *will help you improve your understanding of the concepts taught in this textbook and in your course. This online tool includes videos of real classroom experiences, sample lesson plans, simulations, case studies, and links to important educational and teaching Web sites that will help you make the transition from student to teacher. As you study in your course and with this textbook, please follow along in* **MyEducationLab**. *Use it! Explore it! And improve your knowledge and your grade!*

Chapter 16
Developing Strategies for Computation with Fractions

A grade 5 student asks, "Why is it when we times 29 times two-ninths that the answer goes down?" (Taber, 2002, p. 67). Although generalizations from whole numbers can confuse students, you should realize that their ideas about the operations were developed with whole numbers. Students need to build on their ideas of whole-number operations. We can use their prior understanding of the whole number operations to give meaning to fractional computation. This, combined with a firm understanding of fractions, provides the foundation for understanding fractional computation. Without this foundation, your students will almost certainly be learning rules without reasons—an unacceptable goal.

Big Ideas

1. The meaning of each operation on fractions is the same as the meaning for each operation with whole numbers. Operations with fractions should begin by applying these same meanings to fractional parts.
   - For addition and subtraction, it is critical to understand that the numerator tells the number of parts and the denominator the type of part. It is the parts that are added or subtracted.
   - For multiplication by a fraction, repeated addition and area models support the development of the algorithm for multiplication of fractions.
   - For division by a fraction, the two ways of thinking about the operation—partition and measurement—will lead to two different thought processes for division. Both are important.

2. Estimation of fractional computation is tied almost entirely to the concepts of fractions and to the operations with fractions. A computational algorithm is not required for making esti-

mates. Estimation should be an integral part of computational development in order to keep students' attention focused on the meaning of the operations and the expected size of the results.

Mathematics Content Connections

As just noted, computation with fractions is built on an understanding of the operations for whole numbers and on fraction sense (Chapters 12 and 15). Understanding fractional computation has connections in these areas, as well.

- **Algebraic Thinking** (Chapter 14): Equations with variables often involve fractions or can be solved using fractions. For example $\frac{3}{4}x = 15$ could be solved mentally, if fractional multiplication is understood and the procedure for solving it requires multiplication (or division) of fractions.

- **Decimals and Percents** (Chapter 17): Because decimals and percents are alternative representations for fractions, they can often help with computational fluency, especially in the area of estimation. For example, 2.452×0.513 is about $2\frac{1}{2} \times \frac{1}{2}$ or $1\frac{1}{4} = 1.25$. Twenty-five percent off the list price of $132 is easily computed as $\frac{1}{4}$ of 132.

- **Proportional Reasoning** (Chapter 18): Fractional multiplication helps us to think about fractions as operators. This in turn is connected to the concepts of ratio and proportion, especially the ideas of scaling and scale factors.

- **Measurement** (Chapter 19): Not only does measuring often involve adding, subtracting, multiplying, and dividing with fractions, but the models for understanding the operations include a measurement interpretation. (How many $\frac{1}{2}$ metre lengths are there in 15 metres?)

Number Sense and Fraction Algorithms

Today it is important to be able to compute with fractions, primarily for the purpose of making estimates, and for understanding computations in algebra, measurement, and other strands of mathematics.

Conceptual Development Takes Time

It is important to give students ample opportunity to develop fractional number sense prior to and during instruction about common denominators and other procedures for computation. Even in grade 7 or 8, it makes sense to delay computation and work on concepts if students are not ready conceptually.

Premature attention to rules for fractional computation has a number of serious drawbacks. First, none of the algorithms help students think about the operations and what they mean. When students follow a procedure they do not understand, they do not have the means to assess their results to see if they make sense. Second, mastery of a poorly understood algorithm, in the short term, is quickly lost. When mixed together, the varying procedures for fractional operations soon become a meaningless jumble. Students ask, "Do I need a common denominator, or do you just add the bottom numbers like in multiplication?" "Which one do you invert, the first number or the second one?" When the numbers in a problem are altered slightly, such as for mixed numbers, students think that the algorithm doesn't apply.

 *Principles and Standards* suggests that the main focus on fractions and decimals in grades 3–5 should be on the development of number sense and informal approaches to addition and subtraction. In grades 6–8, students should expand their skills to include all operations with fractions, decimals, and percents.

A Problem-Based, Number Sense Approach

Even if your curriculum guidelines call for teaching all four of the operations with fractions, you must still delay a rush to algorithmic procedures until it becomes clear that students are ready. Students can become adequately proficient using informal, student-invented methods that they understand.

The following guidelines should be kept in mind when developing computational strategies for fractions:

1. *Begin with simple contextual tasks.* This recommendation applies to nearly every topic. Huiniker (1998) makes an excellent case for using contextual problems and letting students develop their own methods of computation with fractions. Problems or contexts need not be elaborate. What you want is a context for both the meaning of the operation and the fractions involved.

2. *Connect the meaning of fractional computation with whole-number computation.* When considering what $2\frac{1}{2} \times \frac{3}{4}$ might mean, we should think, "What does 2×3 mean?" The concepts in each situation are the same, and benefits can be had by connecting to whole number operations, explicitly discussing what is similar and what is different.

3. *Let estimation and informal methods play a big role in the development of strategies.* "Should $2\frac{1}{2} \times \frac{1}{4}$ be more or less than 1? More or less than 2?" Estimation keeps the focus on the meanings of the numbers and the operations, encouraging reflective thinking, and helps build informal number sense with fractions.

4. *Explore each of the operations using models.* Use a variety of models. Have students defend their solutions using the models including simple student drawings. You will find that sometimes it is possible to get answers with models that do not seem to work as effectively as approaches with pencil and paper. That's fine! The ideas will help children learn to think about the fractions and the operations, contribute to mental methods, and provide a useful background when you eventually do get to the standard algorithms.

These four steps are embedded in each of the sections of this chapter.

Computational Estimation

A frequently quoted result from the Second National Assessment (Post, 1981) concerns the following item:

Estimate the answer to $\frac{12}{13} + \frac{7}{8}$. You will not have time to solve the problem using paper and pencil.

Here is how 13-year-olds answered:

Responses	Percent of 13-Year-Olds
1	7
2	19
19	28
21	27
Don't know	14

A more recent study of grade 6 and 8 Taiwanese students included the same item. The results were nearly identical to those in the NAEP study (Reys, 1998). However, in the Taiwanese study, a significantly higher percentage of students (61 percent and 63 percent) were able to correctly compute the sum, a process that requires finding the common denominator of thirteenths and eighths! Notice that to estimate this sum does not require computational skill whatsoever—only a feeling for the size of the two fractions.

Addition and Subtraction The development of fraction number sense should most certainly include estimation of fraction sums and differences—even before computational strategies are introduced. The following activity can be done regularly as a short whole class warm-up for any fraction lesson.

Activity 16.1

First Estimates

Tell students that they are going to estimate a sum or difference of two fractions. They are to decide only if the exact answer is more or less than 1. On the overhead projector show, for no more than about 10 seconds, an addition or subtraction problem involving two fractions. Students write down, on paper or on mini whiteboard, their choice of more or less than one. Do several problems in a row. Then return to each problem and discuss how students decided on their estimate.

Activity 16.1, which requires estimating over or under 1, is the beginning of related tasks that are more complicated. When students are ready for a tougher challenge, choose from the following variations:

- Use a target answer that is different than 1. For example, estimate more or less than $\frac{1}{2}$, $1\frac{1}{2}$, 2, or 3.
- Choose fractions both less than and greater than 1. Estimate to the nearest half.

In the discussions following these estimation exercises, ask students if they think that the exact answer is more or less than the estimate that they gave.

Figure 16.1 shows six sample sums and differences that might be used in a "First Estimates" activity.

 *Pause and Reflect*

Test you own estimation skills with the sample problems in Figure 16.1. Look at each computation for about 10 seconds, then record an estimate. After recording all six of your estimates, look at the problems and decide whether your estimate is higher or lower than the actual computation. Don't guess! Have a good reason.

In most cases students' estimates should not be much more than $\frac{1}{2}$ away from the exact sum or difference.

NCTM Standards "The development of rational number concepts is a major goal for grades 3–5, which should lead to informal methods for calculating with fractions. For example, a problem such as $\frac{1}{4} + \frac{1}{2}$ should be solved mentally with ease because students can picture $\frac{1}{2}$ and $\frac{1}{4}$ or can use decomposition strategies, such as $\frac{1}{4} + \frac{1}{2} = \frac{1}{4} + (\frac{1}{4} + \frac{1}{4})$" (p. 35).

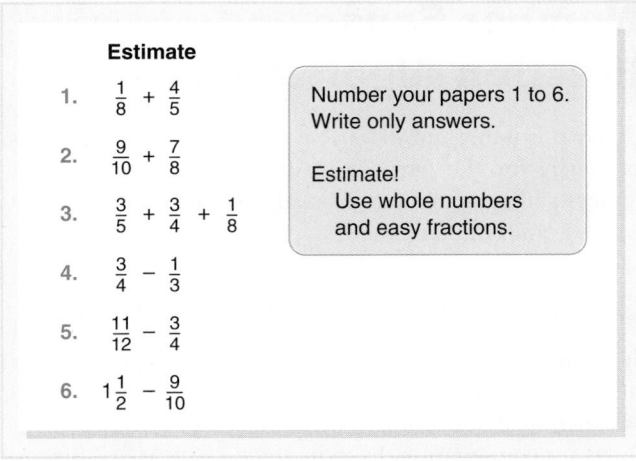

Figure 16.1 Example of fractional estimation expressions.

Multiplication and Division How would you estimate the answer to $3\frac{2}{3} \times 2\frac{1}{4}$? Using the estimation technique of rounding one factor up and the other down, this product might be estimated as 4×2. That simple estimation may be all that is required in a real setting. It is also good enough to help students know if their actual answer is in the right ballpark.

In the real world, there are many instances when the product of whole numbers multiplied by fractions occurs, and mental estimates or even exact answers are quite useful. For example, sale items are frequently listed as "$\frac{1}{4}$ off," or we read, "a $\frac{1}{3}$ increase" in the number of registered voters. Fractions are excellent substitutes for percents, as you will see in the next chapter. To get an estimate of 60 percent of $36.69, it is useful to think of 60 percent as $\frac{3}{5}$ or as a little less than $\frac{2}{3}$.

These products of fractions with large whole numbers can be calculated mentally by thinking of the meanings of the top and bottom numbers. For example, $\frac{3}{5}$ is 3 *one*-fifths. So if you want $\frac{3}{5}$ of 350, for example, first think about *one* fifth of 350, or 70. If *one*-fifth is 70, then *three*-fifths is 3×70, or 210. Although this example has very compatible numbers, it illustrates a process for mentally multiplying a large number by a fraction: First determine the unit fractional part, then multiply by the number of parts you want.

When numbers are not so nice, encourage students to use compatible numbers. To estimate $\frac{3}{5}$ of $36.69, a useful compatible is $35. One-fifth of 35 is 7, so three-fifths is 3×7, or 21. Now adjust a bit—perhaps add an additional 50 cents, for an estimate of $21.50.

Understanding division can be greatly supported by using estimation. Consider the problem $12 \div 4$. This can mean "How many fours in 12?" Similarly, $12 \div \frac{1}{4}$ means "How many fourths in 12?" There are 48 fourths in 12. With this basic idea in mind, students should be able to estimate problems like $4 \div \frac{1}{8}$ and $2\frac{1}{4} \div \frac{1}{2}$. Asking students to first use words to describe what these equations are asking (e.g., how many halves are in $2\frac{1}{4}$) can help them think about the meaning of division and then estimate.

As with other operations, using context is important in estimating with division. An example is: "There are 5 submarine sandwiches. A full serving for one person is $\frac{2}{5}$ of a sandwich. About how many people will get a full serving?"

Addition and Subtraction

Students usually learn addition and subtraction of fractions in grades 5 or 6. It is important that they are able to model and represent, estimate, and have fluency with these fractional operations.

As with whole-number computation, provide computational tasks without giving rules or procedures for completing them. Expect that students will use a variety of methods and that the methods will vary widely with the fractions encountered in the problems.

Students should find a variety of ways to solve problems with fractions, and their invented approaches will contribute to the development of the standard algorithms (Huinker, 1998; Lappan & Mouck, 1998; Schifter, Bastable, & Russell, 1999c).

Invented Strategies

Invented strategies are critical for developing an understanding of fractions, as they require students to use their number sense. Besides, most of the fractions people add in their adult lives involve halves, fourths, eighths—fractions that can be added mentally in whatever ways people find most comfortable. Apply the same strategies discussed in Chapter 12, encouraging students to model the problem or solve it in a way that makes sense to them.

Consider the following problem.

Mark's mother bought $4\frac{1}{4}$ kilograms of apples for baking cakes for the school bake sale. She used $\frac{7}{8}$ of a kilogram for a new recipe she was trying out. How much did she have left for the other cakes?

A grade 5 class was asked to solve this problem in two ways. Many students attempted or correctly used a standard subtraction algorithm for mixed numbers as one method. However, not a single drawing or other explanation for the algorithm could be found in the class. As shown in Figure 16.2, Christian makes an error with the algorithm but draws a correct picture showing $4\frac{1}{4} = \frac{34}{8}$ and gets a correct answer of $\frac{27}{8}$. However, he is not confident in his drawing and crosses it out. Although many students do not understand their procedural methods, those who are not used to justifying their methods will believe in the algorithm more than their own reasoning.

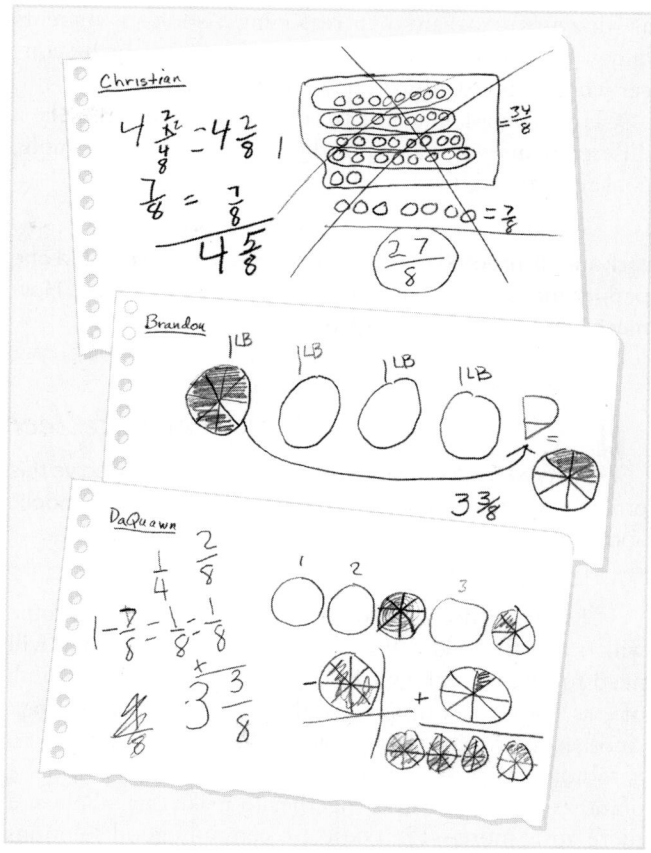

Figure 16.2 Grade 5 students show how they solved the problem $4\frac{1}{4} - \frac{7}{8}$. For most students, their methods, based on drawings, have little to do with their symbolic algorithms. The work of DaQuawn, a student who struggles, is an exception.

Another method, using drawing, employed by many in the class involved taking the $\frac{1}{8}$ left from the $\frac{7}{8}$ and adding it onto the $\frac{1}{4}$, as shown in Brandon's drawing. Only DaQuawn does it first symbolically. His "second method," a drawing, is used to support his work. When DaQuawn shares with the class he says, "I took this from eighths so I could minus it from $\frac{7}{8}$. That leaves $\frac{1}{8}$. Then change [points to quarter-circle] to $\frac{1}{8}$. Minus $\frac{1}{8}$ from ... no, add it to $\frac{1}{8}$ equals $\frac{2}{8}$ plus $\frac{1}{8}$ equals $\frac{3}{8}$." DaQuawn's teacher notes that he "struggles with reading and writing although he has good number sense." This teacher values students' thinking and carefully distinguishes mathematics learning from their ability to express ideas.

These examples illustrate how written work can provide insight into students' thinking—in this case, showing that students have difficulty connecting symbols and pictures.

Fraction Circles   Students seem to have a preference for drawing circles to represent fractions. Perhaps it says something about an overuse of that model. The drawings in Figure 16.2 are not accurate. The partitioning does not show equal parts. However, the students are not making conclusions based on the size of the pieces, rather they are drawing to explain their reasoning. As long as students know that sections should be equivalent, do not be concerned with poorly drawn fraction models.

How you ask students to solve a problem can make a difference in what occurs in the classroom. For example, consider this problem:

Jack and Jill ordered two medium pizzas, one cheese and one pepperoni. Jack ate $\frac{5}{6}$ of a pizza and Jill ate $\frac{1}{2}$ of a pizza. How much pizza did they eat together?

Pause and Reflect

Try to think of two ways that students might solve this problem without using a common denominator symbolic approach.

If students draw circles as in the earlier example, some will try to fill in the $\frac{1}{6}$ gap in the pizza. Then they will need to figure out how to get $\frac{1}{6}$ from $\frac{1}{2}$. If they can think of $\frac{1}{2}$ as $\frac{3}{6}$, they can use one of the sixths to fill in the gap. Another approach, after drawing the two circular pizzas, is to notice that there is a half plus 2 more sixths in the $\frac{5}{6}$ pizza. Put the two halves together to make one whole and there are $\frac{2}{6}$ more—$1\frac{2}{6}$. These are certainly good solutions that represent the type of informal thinking that you want to encourage.

Number Lines   Another helpful model for using invented strategies to add or subtract fractions is the number line. One advantage of the number line is that it can be connected to the ruler, which is a familiar context for exploring addition and subtraction with fractions. The number line is also a more challenging model than the circle model, because it requires a student to not only understand $\frac{3}{4}$ as 3 out of 4, but as a value between 0 and 1 (Izsak, Tillema, & Tunc-Pekkam, 2008). Using the number line in addition to area representations, like the circle, can strengthen student understanding (Clarke, Roche, & Mitchell, 2008; Cramer, Wyberg, & Leavitt, 2008, Usiskin, 2007).

Pause and Reflect

Use the ruler as a visual and find the result of these three problems without applying the common denominator algorithm:

$$\frac{3}{4} + \frac{1}{2} \qquad 2\frac{1}{2} - 1\frac{1}{4} \qquad 1\frac{1}{8} + 1\frac{1}{2}$$

Think about how you solved the problems in Pause and Reflect. Do you think there are other ways? In the first problem, students might use 1 as a benchmark (in the way that 10 or 100 is used as a benchmark with whole numbers). They use $\frac{1}{4}$ from the $\frac{1}{2}$ to get to one whole, then have $\frac{1}{4}$ more to add on—so they now have $1\frac{1}{4}$. Similarly, they could take $\frac{1}{2}$ from $\frac{3}{4}$ to make a whole with the $\frac{1}{2}$ and then add on the $\frac{1}{4}$ or, they might just know that $\frac{1}{2}$ is $\frac{2}{4}$ and then count to get $\frac{5}{4}$ (or $1\frac{1}{4}$).

Adding a context (that fits a linear situation) can also support students' use of invented strategies. For example, in the second problem posed in the Pause and Reflect, one context might be: Jeremy runs $5\frac{1}{2}$ kilometres a day. If he has just passed the $2\frac{1}{4}$ kilometre marker, how far does he still need to go? Students may first subtract the whole numbers to get $3\frac{1}{2} - \frac{1}{4}$; then know that $\frac{1}{2} - \frac{1}{4}$ is $\frac{1}{4}$, or they might prefer to change $\frac{1}{2}$ to $\frac{2}{4}$.

Students can share their strategies and illustrate them on a number line. The more opportunities they have to do so, the more flexible they will become with adding and subtracting fractions. As with whole numbers, sometimes invented strategies offer the best and most efficient way to solve a problem. Yet, there are times when the numbers don't lend themselves to a mental strategy, in which case, an algorithm can be very useful.

Now suppose that you had asked the students to solve the Jack and Jill pizza problem but changed the context to submarine sandwiches. You also had the students use fraction pieces to model the problem. The first decision is which piece to use as the whole. The whole must be the same for both fractions in order to allow both fractions to be modelled. The tendency is to use the most obvious piece, which in this case, is the black piece. Figure 16.3(a) illustrates a solution. The thinking required in this task helps pave the way for a common-denominator approach.

What if you asked students instead to compare the quantities that Jack and Jill ate. Figure 16.3(b) illustrates lining up the "sandwiches" to compare their lengths. Recall that subtraction can be thought of as "separate" where the total is known and a part is "removed." It can also be thought of as a "comparison" where two amounts are being compared to find the difference. Another way of looking at subtraction is to ask, "how many more are needed?" Start with a smaller value then ask how much more is needed to get to the higher value. This sandwich example is a comparison. Be sure to include more than and "take away" examples in the stories and examples you create.

As we saw in the very first example (Figure 16.2), students can and do use invented methods for subtraction as well as addition. This reasoning is extremely important. Students should become comfortable with different methods of taking simple fractions apart and combining them in ways that make sense. Keep the fractions in your problems "friendly," with denominators no greater than 12. There is rarely a need to add fifths and sevenths or even fifths and

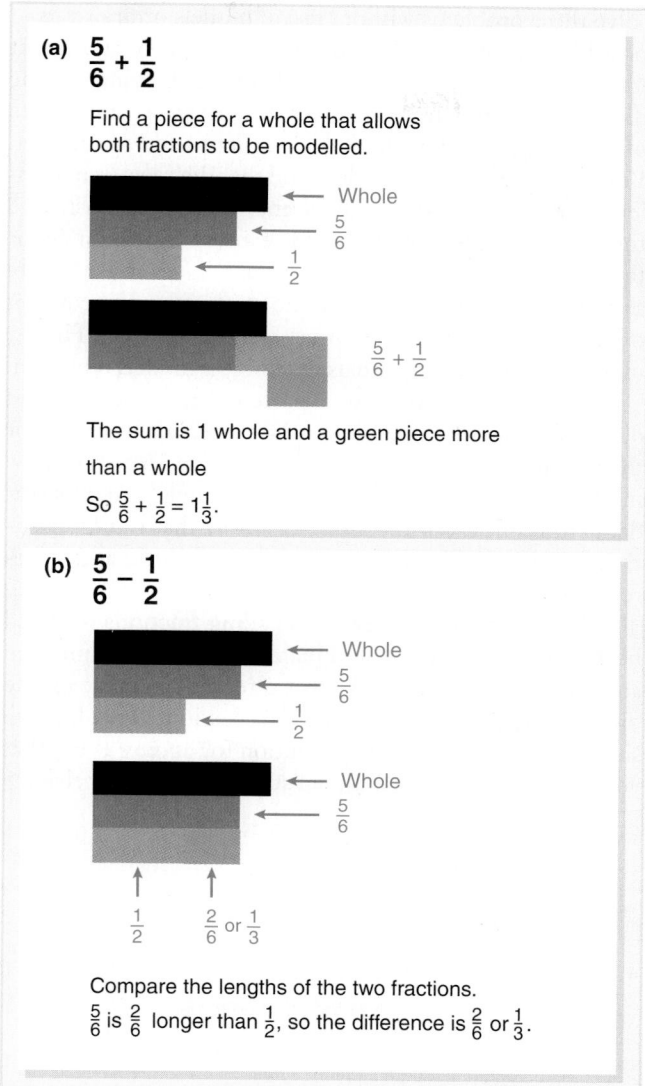

(a) $\frac{5}{6} + \frac{1}{2}$

Find a piece for a whole that allows both fractions to be modelled.

Whole
$\frac{5}{6}$
$\frac{1}{2}$

$\frac{5}{6} + \frac{1}{2}$

The sum is 1 whole and a green piece more than a whole

So $\frac{5}{6} + \frac{1}{2} = 1\frac{1}{3}$.

(b) $\frac{5}{6} - \frac{1}{2}$

Whole
$\frac{5}{6}$
$\frac{1}{2}$

Whole
$\frac{5}{6}$

$\frac{1}{2}$ $\frac{2}{6}$ or $\frac{1}{3}$

Compare the lengths of the two fractions.
$\frac{5}{6}$ is $\frac{2}{6}$ longer than $\frac{1}{2}$, so the difference is $\frac{2}{6}$ or $\frac{1}{3}$.

Figure 16.3 Using fraction pieces to add and subtract fractions.

twelfths. With numbers like that, drawings are difficult as the common denominators are quite large. Although forcing the use of a model such as fraction pieces or sets can cause students to prepare for common denominators, it is best to delay that emphasis in the beginning.

Why Are Common Denominators "Required?" Teachers commonly tell students, "In order to add or subtract fractions, you must first get common denominators." The explanation usually goes something like, "After all, you can't add apples and oranges." This well-intentioned statement is essentially false. A correct statement might be, "In order *to use the standard algorithm* to add or subtract fractions, you must first get common denominators." And the explanation is then, "The algorithm is designed to work only with common denominators because it is based on the idea of adding parts that are the same size."

Using their own invented strategies, students will see that many correct solutions are found without ever getting a common denominator. Consider these sums and differences:

$$\frac{3}{4} + \frac{1}{8} \qquad \frac{1}{2} - \frac{1}{8} \qquad \frac{2}{3} + \frac{1}{2} \qquad 1\frac{1}{2} - \frac{3}{4} \qquad 1\frac{2}{3} + \frac{3}{4}$$

Working with the ways different fractional parts are related one to another often provides solutions without common denominators. For example, halves, fourths, and eighths are easily related because $\frac{1}{8}$ is half of $\frac{1}{4}$ and $\frac{1}{4}$ is half of $\frac{1}{2}$. Also, picture three-thirds making up a whole in a circle as in Figure 16.4. Have you ever noticed that one-half of the whole is a third plus a half of a third or a sixth? Similarly, the difference between a third and a fourth is a twelfth.

As noted, the number line is also a tool that can be used mentally to solve addition and subtraction without finding a common denominator. Students instead may start with finding one fraction on the number line then "jump" the value of the other fraction. For example, in $3\frac{1}{4} - 1\frac{1}{2}$, student can find $3\frac{1}{4}$, jump down one to $2\frac{1}{4}$, and then jump $\frac{1}{2}$, which takes them to $1\frac{3}{4}$.

Developing an Algorithm

Students can build on their invented strategies and knowledge of equivalence to develop the common-denominator approach for adding and subtracting fractions. As discussed in Chapter 15, in the section on equivalent fractions, having a strong conceptual foundation of equivalence is important in many other mathematics topics, one of which is computation of fractions. Students that have a level of fluency in moving among $\frac{1}{2}$, $\frac{2}{4}$, $\frac{4}{8}$, and $\frac{8}{16}$, or $\frac{3}{4}$, $\frac{6}{8}$, and $\frac{12}{16}$ can adjust the fractions as needed to combine or subtract fractions. Whether using an area, length, or set model, establishing

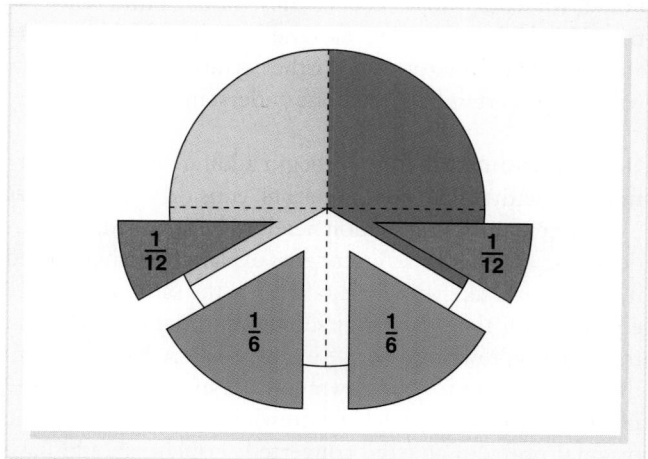

Figure 16.4 There are lots of fractional relationships that can be observed simply by looking at how halves, thirds, fourths, sixths, and twelfths fit into a partitioned circle.

equivalence is foundational and needs continued reinforcement during instruction on addition and subtraction of fractions. For example, have students complete a sum such as $\frac{3}{8} + \frac{4}{8}$ and write the finished equation on the board. Then, beneath this equation, write a second sum composed of easily seen equivalents for each fraction as shown here:

$$\frac{3}{8} + \frac{4}{8} = \frac{7}{8}$$

$$\frac{6}{16} + \frac{1}{2} = ?$$

Discuss briefly the fact that $\frac{3}{8}$ is equivalent to $\frac{6}{16}$ just as $\frac{4}{8}$ is to $\frac{1}{2}$. Now have students write the answer to the second equation and give a reason for their answer. Students should see that the answer is $\frac{7}{8}$. The second sum is the same as the first. The reason is, although the fractions look different, they actually are the same numbers; they represent the same amount.

Like Denominators   Most lists of objectives first specify addition and subtraction with like denominators. If students have a good foundation with fractional concepts, they should be able to add or subtract like fractions immediately. Students who are not confident solving problems such as $\frac{3}{4} + \frac{2}{4}$ or $3\frac{7}{8} - 1\frac{3}{8}$ may not have good fraction concepts and will need more further experience manipulating models. The idea that the top number counts and the bottom number tells what is counted makes addition and subtraction of like fractions the same as adding and subtracting whole numbers. When working on adding denominators, it is important to be sure that students are focusing on the key idea—the units are the same, so they can be combined (Mack, 2004).

 The ease with which students can or cannot add like-denominator fractions should be viewed as an important concept assessment before pushing students forward to an algorithm. As just noted, students who do not see these sums or differences as trivial likely do not understand the meanings of the numerator and denominator. Any further symbolic development will almost certainly be without understanding. ◆

Unlike Denominators   To begin adding and subtracting fractions with unlike denominators, consider a task such as $\frac{5}{8} + \frac{1}{4}$ where only one fraction needs to be changed. Let students use any method. As students explain how they solved it, someone is likely to explain that $\frac{1}{4}$ is the same as $\frac{2}{8}$. Write equations on the board that show the initial equation and the equation rewritten with $\frac{2}{8}$ in place of $\frac{1}{4}$. Ask, "Is this still the same equation?" "Why would we want to change the $\frac{1}{4}$?" Have students use models or drawings to explain why the original problem and the converted problem should have the same answer.

Next try some examples where both fractions need to be changed—for example, $\frac{2}{3} + \frac{1}{4}$. Encourage students to

solve these problems without use of models or drawings, if possible. Suggest (don't require) that the use of equivalent fractions might be an easier tool than a drawing. In the discussion of student solutions, focus attention on the idea of *rewriting the problem* to make it easier to add or subtract. Be certain that students understand that the rewritten problem is the same as the original and, therefore, must have the same answer. If your students express any doubt about the equivalence of the two problems ("Is $\frac{8}{12}$ and $\frac{3}{12}$ really the answer to $\frac{2}{3} + \frac{1}{4}$?"), it should be a clue that the concept of equivalent fractions is not yet well understood. Hence, more experience using visuals or concrete models is needed.

As students continue to explore solutions to sums and differences of fractions, models should remain available for them to use. The three examples in Figure 16.5 show how models might be used. Note that each model requires students to think about the size of a whole that can be partitioned into the units of both fractions (e.g., fifths and halves require tenths).

The most common error in adding fractions is to add both numerators and denominators. Rather than jump in and attempt to correct this error directly, capitalize on the opportunity for a wonderful class discussion. One idea is to show students the following solution for adding $\frac{1}{2} + \frac{1}{3}$ that you "saw" offered by a fictional student in another class:

$$\frac{1}{2} \bullet\bullet \qquad\qquad \frac{1}{3} \circ\bullet\bullet$$

add $\circ\circ\bullet\bullet\bullet$

Therefore, $\frac{1}{2} + \frac{1}{3} = \frac{2}{5}$.

Add tops and bottoms.

Ask students to decide if the student could be right. If not, what is wrong with the solution?

⏸ ——————— *Pause and Reflect*

Why can't the answer be $\frac{2}{5}$ and what is wrong with the student's reasoning?

Focus first on the answer. The sum of $\frac{2}{5}$ is smaller than $\frac{1}{2}$ when, in fact, $\frac{1}{2} + \frac{1}{3}$ must be more than $\frac{1}{2}$. When students are convinced that the sum cannot be $\frac{2}{5}$, there is real value in letting them decide what is wrong with the reasoning. You must first see where students are in their understanding. Nancy Mack, a researcher and teacher, asked her grade 5 class if the following was correct: $\frac{3}{8} + \frac{2}{8} = \frac{5}{16}$. A student correctly replied, "No because they are eighths (*holds up one-eighth of a fraction circle*). If you put them together, you still see eighths (*shows this with the fraction circles*). See, you didn't make them into sixteenths when you put them together. They're still eighths." (Mack, 2004, p. 229)

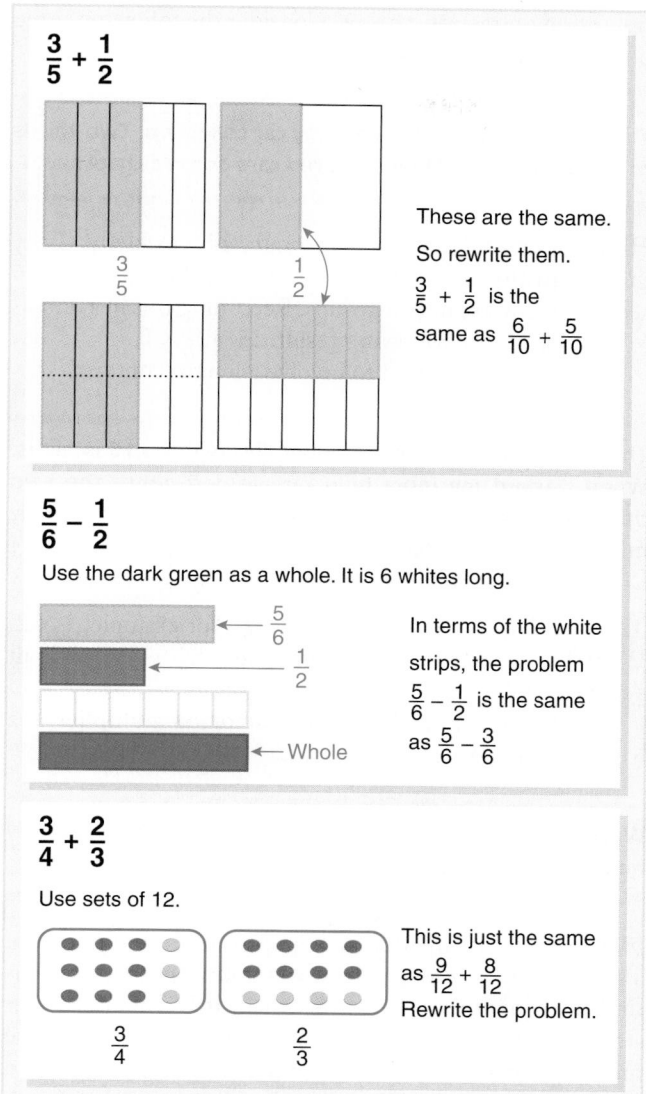

Figure 16.5 Rewriting addition and subtraction problems involving fractions so they have a common denominator.

Activity 16.2

LCM Flash Cards

Make flash cards with pairs of numbers that are potential denominators. Most should be less than 16. For each card, students try to give the least common multiple, or LCM (see Figure 16.6). Be sure to include pairs that are prime, such as 9 and 5; pairs in which one is a multiple of the other, such as 2 and 8; and pairs that have a common divisor, such as 8 and 12.

Mixed Numbers and Improper Fractions

A separate algorithm for mixed numbers in addition and subtraction is not necessary, even though mixed numbers are often treated as separate topics in traditional textbooks and in some lists of objectives. Include mixed numbers in all your activities with addition and subtraction, and let students solve these problems in ways that make sense to them. Students will tend naturally to add the whole numbers first then deal with the fractions. Sometimes this is all that needs to be done. However, in other cases regrouping across the whole number and the fraction is needed. In subtraction, this happens when the second fraction is larger than the first, and it occurs in addition when the answer of the fractional sum is over 1.

Dealing with the whole numbers first still makes sense. Consider this problem: $5\frac{1}{8} - 3\frac{5}{8}$. After subtracting 3 from 5, students will need to deal with the $\frac{5}{8}$. Some will take $\frac{5}{8}$ from the whole part, 2, leaving $1\frac{3}{8}$, then $\frac{1}{8}$ more is $1\frac{4}{8}$. Others may take away the $\frac{1}{8}$ that is there and then take $\frac{4}{8}$ from the remaining 2. A third, but unlikely method, is to trade one of the wholes for $\frac{8}{8}$, add it to the $\frac{1}{8}$, then take $\frac{5}{8}$ from the resulting $\frac{9}{8}$. This last method is the same as the traditional algorithm.

Common Multiples Many students have trouble with finding common denominators because they are not able to come up with common multiples of the denominators quickly. It is a skill that you may wish to drill. But it also depends on having a good command of the basic facts for multiplication. Activity 16.2 is aimed at the skill of finding least common multiples or common denominators. Least common denominators are preferred because the computation is more manageable with smaller numbers, and there is less simplifying to do after adding and subtracting. But *any* common denominator will work, whether it is the smallest or not. Do not require least common multiples. Support all common denominators and in discussion students will see that finding the smallest multiple is more efficient.

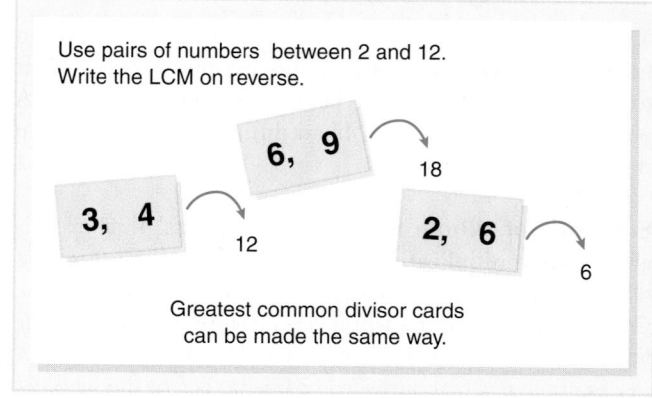

Figure 16.6 Least common multiple (LCM) flash cards.

One underemphasized technique, that is nevertheless a great strategy, is to change the mixed numbers to single, or improper, fractions. You may have been taught that this was the process used for multiplication, but that is part of the "rules without reason" approach of having one way to do one procedure. Let's revisit $5\frac{1}{8} - 3\frac{5}{8}$. This can be rewritten as $\frac{41}{8} - \frac{29}{8}$. (See Chapter 15 for conceptual ways for helping students do this.) Because $41 - 29$ is 12, the solution is $\frac{12}{8}$ or $1\frac{1}{2}$. This is certainly efficient and will always work. The message here is to provide options to students and you will find that more students understand and are able to solve these problems successfully.

Multiplication

Multiplication of fractions is usually taught in the upper elementary grades, though informal fraction activities that reflect multiplication such as, "What is $\frac{2}{3}$ of 30?" are introduced earlier. Students, at this level, need to develop fluency with multiplication and division of fractions. Developing fluency means that students cannot only do the algorithm, they can also understand it and can model problems. As well, they can solve situations that involve multiplication and division of fractions and estimate.

It is important to emphasize the application component of fluency, as very few people have learned multiplication and division of fractions so that they are able to do much more than the basic procedure. If you fall in this category, then carefully read the examples in this section and try to solve the problems—many figures are provided to help illustrate the meaning of multiplication of fractions.

When working with whole numbers, we would say that 3×5 means "3 sets of 5" (repeated addition) to "3 rows of 5" (area or array). The first factor tells how much of the second factor you have or want. This is a good place to begin. Using contexts and simple story problems are a significant help in this development.

Developing the Concept

The story problems that you use to pose multiplication tasks to children need not be elaborate, but it is important to think about the numbers that you use in the problems. A possible progression of problem difficulty is developed in the sections that follow.

Fractions of Whole Numbers　Students' first experiences with multiplication should involve finding fractions of whole numbers. In Chapter 15, several examples of finding fractions of the whole are provided, such as "If the whole is 45, how much is $\frac{1}{5}$ of the whole?" A more challenging example is, "If the whole is 24, what is $\frac{3}{8}$ of the whole?" These reasoning tasks can lead to discussions of what mul-

tiplication of fractions means. Consider the following three problems as good starting tasks:

There are 15 cars in Michael's toy car collection. Two-thirds of the cars are red. How many red cars does Michael have?

How might students think through this problem? They might partition 15 into 3 groups, five in each group, then see how many are in two groups. Recording this in symbols ($\frac{2}{3}$ of 15) gives the following result: $15 \div 3 \times 2$.

This can be adapted to involve a length context:

The walk from school to the public library takes 15 minutes. When I asked my mom how far we had gone, she said that we had gone $\frac{2}{3}$ of the way. Can you tell me how many minutes we have walked?

Tasks can have lower whole numbers—for example, $\frac{1}{4} \times 2$. What does this mean? How might you solve it? What about $\frac{1}{4}$ of 5? $\frac{3}{4}$ of 5?

Problems in which the first factor or multiplier is a whole number are also important.

Wayne filled 5 glasses with $\frac{2}{3}$ litre of juice in each glass. How much juice did Wayne use?

Notice that this situation is "5 groups of $\frac{2}{3}$" and not "$\frac{2}{3}$ of a group of 5." Although the commutative property means that these numbers can be switched, it is important that students understand each type as representations whose meanings are different. The problem might be solved in a counting-up strategy. It may be solved by repeated addition: $\frac{2}{3} + \frac{2}{3} + \frac{2}{3} + \frac{2}{3} + \frac{2}{3} = \frac{10}{3}$. Students may notice that what they did was multiply the numerator by 5, so $5 \times \frac{2}{3} = \frac{5 \times 2}{3} = \frac{10}{3}$.

This problem may be solved in different ways. Some children will put the thirds together, making wholes as they go. Others will count all the thirds then find out how many whole litres are in 10 thirds.

Unit Parts Without Subdivisions　To expand on the ideas just presented, consider these three problems:

You have $\frac{3}{4}$ of a pizza left. If you give $\frac{1}{3}$ of the leftover pizza to your brother, how much of a whole pizza will your brother get?

Simone ate $\frac{1}{10}$ of a loaf of bread, leaving only $\frac{9}{10}$. If you use $\frac{2}{3}$ of what is left to make French toast, how much of a whole loaf will you have used?

Kate made $2\frac{1}{2}$ pitchers of punch for the family picnic. If she used $\frac{4}{5}$ litre of grape juice for each pitcher, how many litres of grape juice did she need?

Intentionally, the units or fractional parts in these problems do not need to be subdivided further. The first problem is $\frac{1}{3}$ of three things, the second is $\frac{2}{3}$ of nine things, and the last is $2\frac{1}{2}$ of four things. The focus remains on the number of unit parts in all then the size of the parts determines the number of wholes. Figure 16.7 shows how problems of this type might be modelled. However, it is very important to let students model and solve these problems in their own way, using whatever models or drawings they choose. Require only that they are able to explain their reasoning.

Subdividing the Unit Parts   When the pieces must be subdivided into smaller unit parts, the problems become more challenging.

Zack had $\frac{2}{3}$ of the lawn left to cut. After lunch, he cut $\frac{3}{4}$ of the part that was left. How much of the whole lawn did Zack cut after lunch?

The zookeeper had a huge bottle of Zoo Cola, the animals' favourite liquid treat. The monkey drank $\frac{1}{5}$ of the bottle. The zebra drank $\frac{2}{3}$ of what was left. How much of the bottle of Zoo Cola did the zebra drink?

Pause and Reflect

Pause for a moment and figure out how you would solve each of these problems. Draw pictures to help you, but do not use a computational algorithm.

In Zack's lawn problem, it is necessary to find fourths of two things, the 2 *thirds* of the grass left to cut. In the Zoo Cola problem, you need thirds of four things, the 4 *fifths* of the cola that remain. Again, the concepts of the top number counting and the bottom number naming what is counted play an important role. Figure 16.8 shows a possible solution for Zack's lawn problem. A similar approach can be used for the Zoo Cola problem. You may have used different drawings, but the ideas should be the same.

Using paper strips and partitioning is an effective way to solve multiplication problems, especially when they require additional partitioning (Siebert & Gaskin, 2006). Figure 16.8 illustrates how to use paper strips for solving the problem $\frac{3}{5} \times \frac{2}{3}$. (*Three-fifths of $\frac{2}{3}$ of a whole is how much of a whole?*). Here the representation of a whole must be changed so that the thirds can be subdivided.

Multiplication of fractions can be modelled with counters (see Figure 16.9). Do not discourage students from using counters, but be prepared to help them find ways to determine the whole.

Task	Finding the starting amount	Showing the fraction of the starting amount	Solution
Pizza Find $\frac{1}{3}$ of $\frac{3}{4}$ (of a pizza) or $\frac{1}{3} \times \frac{3}{4}$	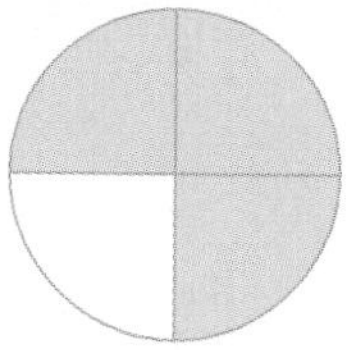	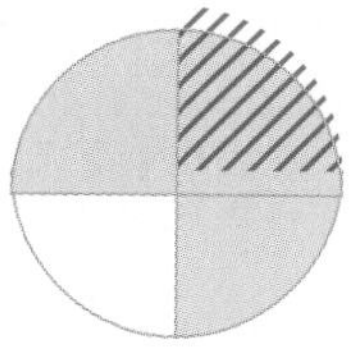	$\frac{1}{3}$ of the $\frac{3}{4}$ is $\frac{1}{4}$ of the original pizza. $\frac{1}{3} \times \frac{3}{4} = \frac{1}{4}$
Bread Find $\frac{2}{3}$ of $\frac{9}{10}$ (of a loaf of bread) or $\frac{2}{3} \times \frac{9}{10}$	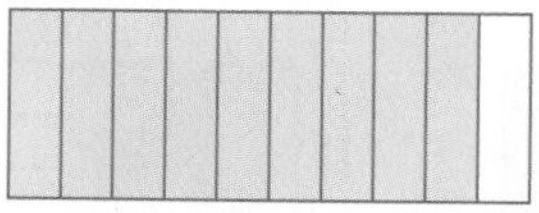	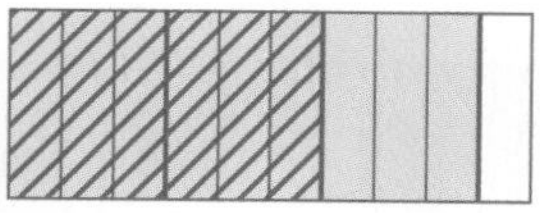	$\frac{2}{3}$ of the $\frac{9}{10}$ is 6 slices of the loaf or $\frac{6}{10}$ of the whole. $\frac{2}{3} \times \frac{9}{10} = \frac{6}{10}$
Grape Juice Find $2\frac{1}{2}$ of $\frac{4}{5}$ (ounces of grape juice) or $2\frac{1}{2} \times \frac{4}{5}$		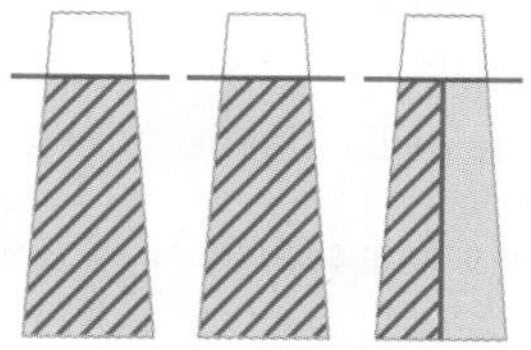	$2\frac{1}{2}$ of the $\frac{4}{5}$ is $\frac{4}{5} + \frac{4}{5} + \frac{2}{5} = \frac{10}{5}$

Figure 16.7 Models that illustrate three problems involving multiplication.

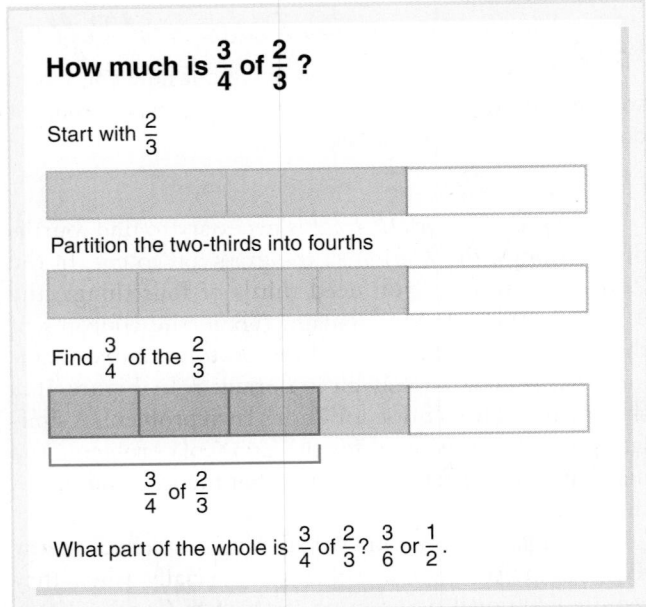

Figure16.8 Solutions to a multiplication problem when the parts must be subdivided.

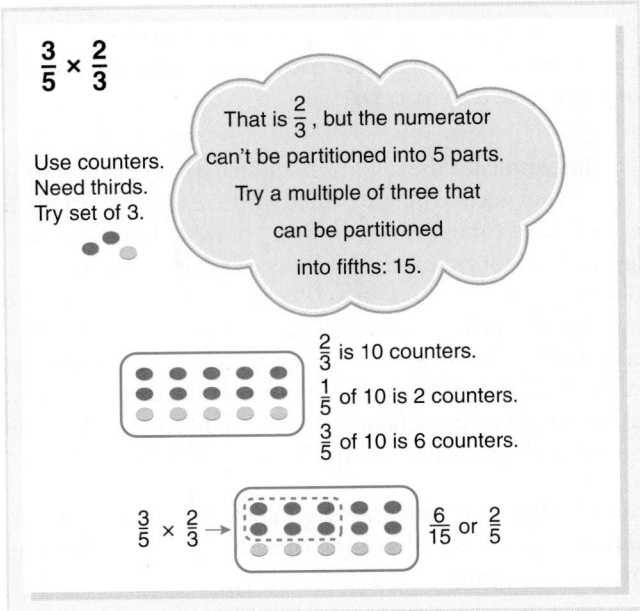

Figure 16.9 Modelling multiplication of fractions with counters.

Area Model The area model for demonstrating multiplication of fractions has several advantages. First, it works for problems where partitioning a length can be tedious. Second, it provides a nice visual to show that a result can be quite a bit smaller than either of the fractions used. If the fractions are both close to 1, then the result is also close to one. Third, it is a good model for connecting to the standard algorithm for multiplying fractions.

Provide students with a square as in Figure 16.10 and have them illustrate the first fraction. For example, in $\frac{3}{5} \times \frac{3}{4}$, you are finding $\frac{3}{5}$ of $\frac{3}{4}$, so you must first show $\frac{3}{4}$ (see Figure 16.10(a)). To find fifths of $\frac{3}{4}$, draw five horizontal lines through the $\frac{3}{4}$ (see Figure 16.10(b)) or all the way across the square so that the whole is partitioned into the same size sections (see Figure 16.10(c)).

Developing the Algorithm

With enough experiences using the area model (or the linear model), students will start to notice a pattern. Remember that "enough" is probably a lot more than is

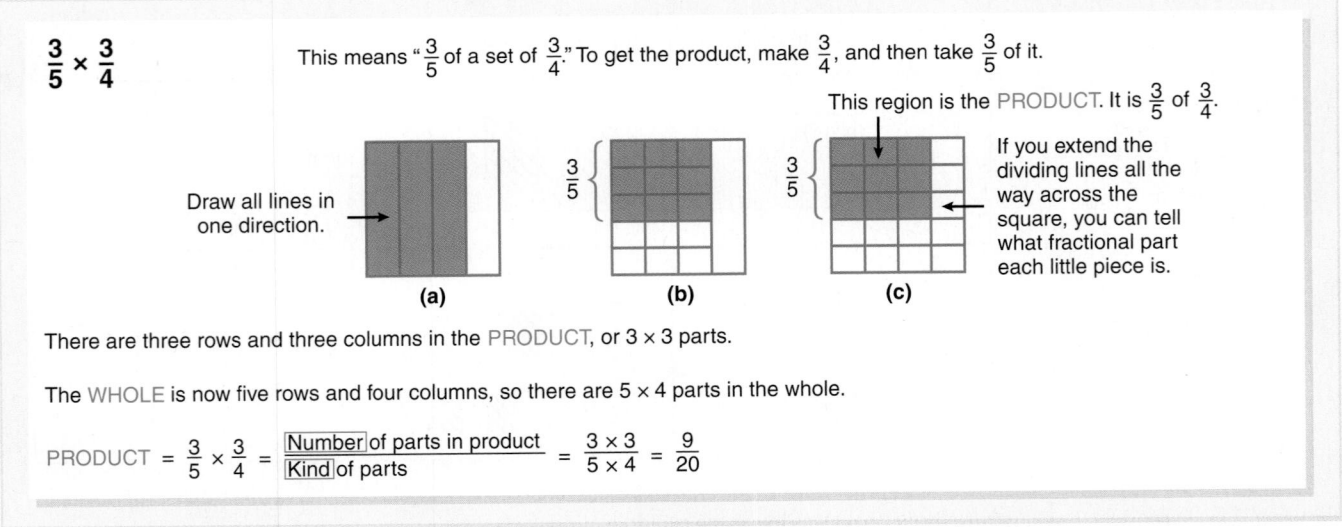

Figure 16.10 Development of the algorithm for multiplication of fractions.

usually provided. This does not mean three examples, but several days, even weeks, working with different examples and problems. These exercises will lead students to focus on how the denominators relate to how the grid (or line) is partitioned and how the numerator affects the solution to the problem.

When students are ready to start using the algorithm, have them solve three examples such as the following:

$$\frac{5}{6} \times \frac{1}{2} \qquad \frac{3}{4} \times \frac{1}{5} \qquad \frac{1}{3} \times \frac{9}{10}$$

For each one, use a square and partition it vertically and horizontally to model the problems. Ask, "How did you figure out what the unit for the fraction [the denominator] would be?" Or more specifically, on the first problem, you can ask, "How did you figure out that the denominator would be twelfths? Is this a pattern that is true for the other examples?" Then, ask students to see if they can find a similar pattern for how the number of parts is determined (the numerator).

As you are helping students focus on the pattern and learn to use the algorithm, do not forget to focus on the meaning of what they are doing. Ask questions that require them to estimate how big they think the answer will be and why. In the first example here, a student might note that the answer will be slightly less than $\frac{1}{2}$ since $\frac{5}{6}$ is close to, but less than, 1.

Factors Greater Than One

As students are exploring multiplication, begin to include tasks where one of the factors is a mixed number, for example, $\frac{3}{4} \times 2\frac{1}{2}$. Many textbooks have students change mixed numbers to improper fractions in order to multiply them. In fact, students can make improper fractions or used mixed numbers. Either way, area representations can be used to model the problem, as illustrated in Figure 16.11. This is an efficient way to solve these types of problems, but it is not the only way. Students who understand that $2\frac{1}{2}$ means $2 + \frac{1}{2}$ might multiply $\frac{3}{4} \times 2$ and $\frac{3}{4} \times \frac{1}{2}$, then add the results—the distributive property.

When both factors are mixed numbers, there are four partial products, just as there are when multiplying 2 two-digit numbers.

Pause and Reflect

Find the four partial products in this multiplication: $3\frac{2}{3} \times 2\frac{1}{4}$.

Figure 16.12 shows how this product might be calculated, by multiplying the individual parts. In most cases, the resulting fractions are not likely to be difficult to work with. More importantly, the process is more conceptual and lends itself to estimation—either before the partial products

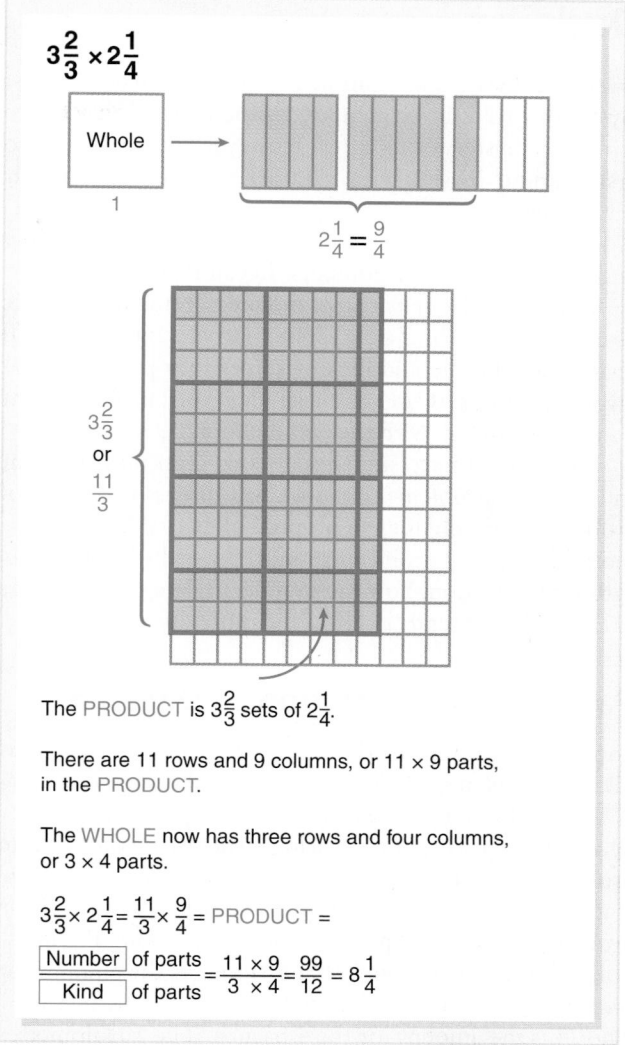

The PRODUCT is $3\frac{2}{3}$ sets of $2\frac{1}{4}$.

There are 11 rows and 9 columns, or 11 × 9 parts, in the PRODUCT.

The WHOLE now has three rows and four columns, or 3 × 4 parts.

$$3\frac{2}{3} \times 2\frac{1}{4} = \frac{11}{3} \times \frac{9}{4} = \text{PRODUCT} =$$

$$\frac{\boxed{\text{Number}} \text{ of parts}}{\boxed{\text{Kind}} \text{ of parts}} = \frac{11 \times 9}{3 \times 4} = \frac{99}{12} = 8\frac{1}{4}$$

Figure 16.11 The same approach used to develop the algorithm for fractions less than 1 can be expanded to mixed numbers.

are determined or after. Notice that the same four partial products of Figure 16.12 can be found in the rectangle in Figure 16.11.

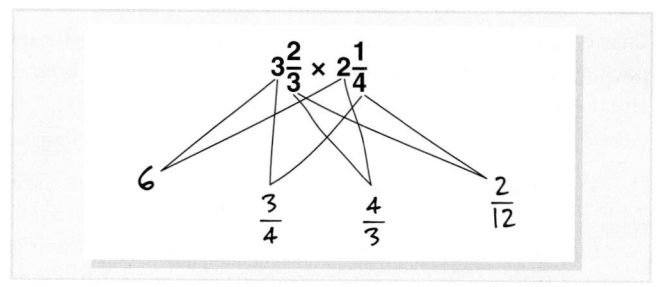

Figure 16.12 When multiplying two mixed numbers, there will be four partial products. These can be added up to get the total product or an estimate may be enough. Here the answer is about 8.

Division

Invert the divisor and multiply is probably one of the most mysterious rules in elementary mathematics. We want to avoid this mystery at all costs. However, it makes sense to first examine division with fractions from a more familiar perspective.

As with the other operations, go back to the meaning of division with whole numbers. Recall that there are two meanings of division: partitive and measurement (Gregg & Gregg, 2007; Kribs Zaleta, 2008; Tirosh, 2000). We will review each briefly and look at some story problems that involve fractions. (Can you make up a word problem right now that would go with the computation $2\frac{1}{2} \div \frac{1}{4}$?)

You should have students explore both measurement and partitive problems. Here we will discuss each type of problem separately for the purpose of clarity. In the classroom, the types of problems should eventually be mixed. As with multiplication, how the numbers relate to each other in the problems tends to affect the difficulty.

Partitive Interpretation of Division

Too often we think of the partition problems strictly as sharing problems: 24 hockey cards to be shared among 4 friends. How many will each friend get? Recall from Chapter 9 that this same sharing structure applies to rate problems: If you run 10 kilometres in 48 minutes, how many kilometres per minute can you run? Both of these problems, in fact, are partition problems asking the questions, "How much is one?" "How much is the amount for *one* friend?" "How many kilometres are run in *one* minute?" The 24 is the amount for the 4 friends. The 10 kilometres is the amount for the 48 minutes.

Whole-Number Divisors Having the total amount as a fraction with the divisor a whole number is not really a big leap. These problems can still be considered to be sharing situations. As you work through these questions, notice that you are answering the question, "How much is the whole?" or "How much for one?"

Cassie has $4\frac{4}{5}$ metres of ribbon to make 3 bows for birthday packages. How much ribbon should she use for each bow if she wants to use the same length of ribbon for each?

When the $4\frac{4}{5}$ is thought of as fractional parts, there are 24 fifths to share, or 8 fifths for each ribbon. Alternatively, one might think of first allotting 1 metre per bow, leaving $1\frac{4}{5}$, or 9 fifths. These 9 fifths are then shared, 3 fifths per bow, for a total of $1\frac{3}{5}$ metres for each bow. Regardless of the particular process, the unit parts required no further

partitioning in order to do the division. In the following problem, the parts must be split into smaller parts.

Srdjan has $1\frac{1}{4}$ hours to complete his 3 household chores. If he divides his time evenly, how many hours can he devote to each?

Note that the question is, "How many hours for one chore?" The 5 fourths of an hour that Srdjan has do not split neatly into three parts. So some or all of the parts must be partitioned. Figure 16.13 shows three different models for figuring this out. In each case, all the fourths are subdivided into three equal parts, producing twelfths. There are a total of 15 twelfths, or $\frac{5}{12}$ hour for each chore. (Test this answer against the solution in minutes: $1\frac{1}{4}$ hours is 75 minutes, which divided among 3 chores is 25 minutes per chore.)

Fractional Divisors The sharing concept appears to break down when the divisor is a fraction. However, it is enormously helpful to keep in mind that for partition and rate problems the fundamental question is, "How much is one?" Interestingly, this is exactly the second type of question in the parts-and-whole tasks from Chapter 15: Given the part, find the whole—how much is one? For example, if a set of 18 counters represents $2\frac{1}{4}$, how many counters are in a whole set? (See Figure 16.13 for more examples.) In solving these problems, the first task is to find the number in one-fourth then multiply by 4 to get four-fourths or *one*. Let's see if we can see the same process in the following problem:

Elizabeth bought $3\frac{1}{3}$ kilograms of tomatoes for $12.50. How much did she pay per kilogram?

❚❚ ———————————— *Pause and Reflect*

The given amount of $12.50 is distributed across $3\frac{1}{3}$ kilograms. How much is distributed to 1 kilogram? Solve the problem the same way as you would a parts-and-whole problem. Try it now before reading on.

In $3\frac{1}{3}$ there are 10 thirds. Since the $12.50 covers (or is distributed across) 10 thirds, the first step is to partition and find out how much for 1 third. If 10 thirds is $12.50 then 1 third is $1.25. There are 3 thirds in 1 whole. Therefore, $3.75 must cover 1 kilogram, or 1 kilogram costs $3.75.

Try the following problems using a similar strategy.

Dan paid $5.40 for a $\frac{3}{4}$ kilogram container of candy. How much is that per kilogram?

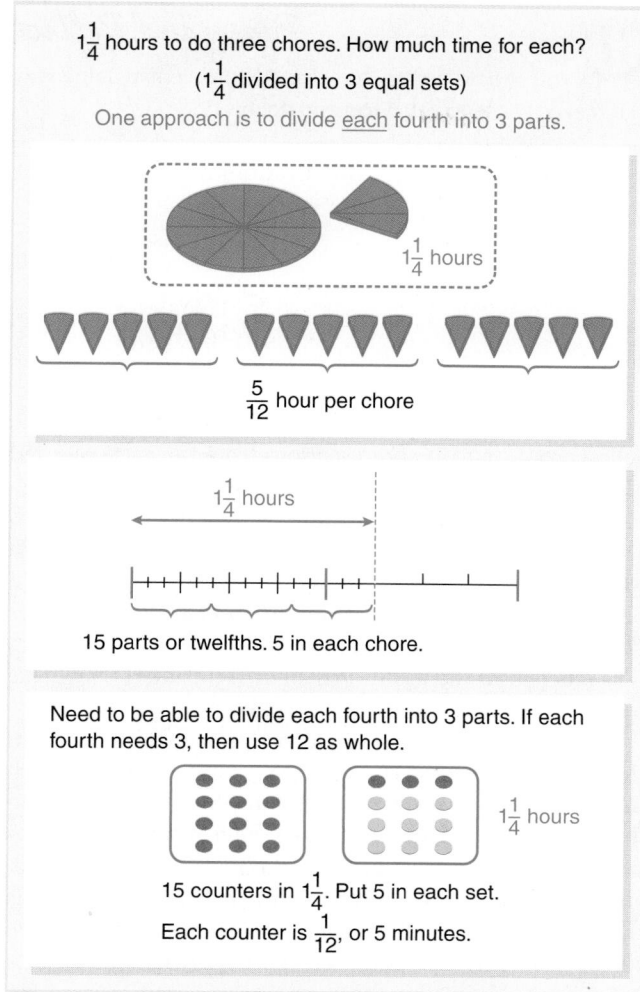

$1\frac{1}{4}$ hours to do three chores. How much time for each?
($1\frac{1}{4}$ divided into 3 equal sets)

One approach is to divide <u>each</u> fourth into 3 parts.

$1\frac{1}{4}$ hours

$\frac{5}{12}$ hour per chore

$1\frac{1}{4}$ hours

15 parts or twelfths. 5 in each chore.

Need to be able to divide each fourth into 3 parts. If each fourth needs 3, then use 12 as whole.

$1\frac{1}{4}$ hours

15 counters in $1\frac{1}{4}$. Put 5 in each set.

Each counter is $\frac{1}{12}$, or 5 minutes.

Figure 16.13 Three models of partition division with a whole-number divisor.

Aidan found out that if she walks really fast during her morning exercise, she can cover $4\frac{1}{4}$ kilometres in $\frac{3}{4}$ hour. She wonders how fast she is walking in kilometres per hour.

With both problems, first find the amount of one-fourth (partitioning) and then the value of one whole (iterating). Aidan's walking problem is a bit harder because the $4\frac{1}{4}$ kilometres, or 17 quarter-kilometres, do not neatly divide into three parts. If this was difficult for you, try dividing each quarter into three parts. Draw pictures or use models if that will help.

Measurement Interpretation of Division

The measurement interpretation of division is also called repeated subtraction of equal groups (NCTM, 2006). In

these situations, an equal group is taken away from the total repeatedly. For example, *If you have 13 litres of lemonade, how many pitchers holding 3 litres each can you fill?* Notice that this is not a sharing situation; rather, it is an equal subtraction situation.

Since this is the concept of division that is almost always seen in textbooks and is used to develop an algorithm for dividing fractions, it is important for students to explore this idea in contextual situations.

Students readily understand problems such as the following:

Marilena is hosting a birthday party. She bought 6 litres of ice cream. If she serves $\frac{1}{5}$ litre of ice cream to each guest, how many guests can be served?

Students typically draw pictures of 6 things divided into fifths and count out how many sets of $\frac{1}{5}$ can be found. The difficulty is in seeing this as $6 \div \frac{1}{5}$, and that part will require some direct guidance on your part. One idea is to compare the problem to one involving whole numbers (6 litres, 1 per guest) and make a comparison.

Gregg and Gregg (2007) produced a method for developing the concept of division of fractions through servings, also a measurement context. They pose problems along with visuals of the size of the pieces, for tasks that progress in difficulty. Figure 16.14 includes a subset of these tasks.

As the figure shows, moving very slowly to more complex examples will enable students to use their whole number concepts to build an understanding of division with fractions. Over time students will be able to take on problems that are more complex in context and in the numbers involved, as in the following example.

Farmer Brown found that he had $5\frac{1}{4}$ litres of liquid fertilizer concentrate. It takes $\frac{2}{3}$ litre of concentrate to make a tank of mixed fertilizer. How many tanks of mixed fertilizer can he make?

Try solving this problem yourself. Use any model or drawing you wish to help explain what you are doing. Notice that you are trying to find out *How many sets of $\frac{2}{3}$ are in a set of 21 fourths?* Your answer should be 7 tanks (not 7 thirds).

Answers That Are Not Whole Numbers

If Linda had 5 metres of material to make baby dresses that each require $1\frac{1}{6}$ metres of material, she could make only four dresses because a part of a dress does not make sense. However, Farmer Brown still has enough concentrate

1. A serving is $\frac{1}{2}$ cookie. How many servings can I make from 2 cookies?

2. A serving is $\frac{1}{2}$ cookie. How many servings can I make from 1 cookie?

3. A serving is $\frac{1}{2}$ cookie. How many servings can I make from $\frac{3}{4}$ cookie?

4. A serving is $\frac{1}{2}$ cookie. How many servings can I make from $\frac{3}{8}$ cookie?

5. A serving is $\frac{1}{2}$ cookie. How many servings can I make from $\frac{5}{8}$ cookie?

Figure 16.14 Tasks that use the measurement interpretation of "How many servings?" to develop the concept of division.

Source: Gregg, J., & Gregg, D. W. (2007). "Measurement and Fair-Sharing Models for Dividing Fractions. "*Mathematics Teaching in the Middle School*, 12 (9), 491. Reprinted with permission. Copyright © 2008 by The National Council of Teachers of Mathematics, Inc. www.nctm.org. All rights reserved.

to make $\frac{7}{8}$ of a tank of mixed fertilizer from the original $5\frac{1}{4}$ litres of concentrate. He could use this toward making another tank of mixed fertilizer.

Here is another problem to try:

John is building a patio. Each section requires $\frac{1}{2}$ cubic metre of concrete. The concrete truck holds $1\frac{3}{4}$ cubic metres of concrete. If there is not enough for a full section at the end, John can put in a divider and make a partial section. How many patio sections can John make with the concrete in the truck?

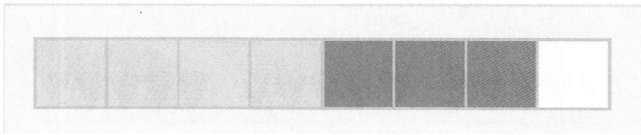

Pause and Reflect

You should first try to solve this problem in some way that makes sense to *you*. Stop and do this now.

One way to do this is by counting how many halves are in $1\frac{3}{4}$.

Here you can see that you get 2 patio sections from the yellow whole, and $1\frac{1}{2}$ more sections from the part coloured orange in the second rectangle. The answer is $3\frac{1}{2}$ sections.

Will common denominators work for division? Let's see. In the problem you just solved, $1\frac{3}{4} \div \frac{1}{2}$, the problem would become $1\frac{3}{4} \div \frac{2}{4}$, or it could be $\frac{7}{4} \div \frac{2}{4}$. The question becomes: *How many sets of 2 quarters are in a set of 7 quarters? Or, How many 2s are in 7?* The answer is $3\frac{1}{2}$. This approach is as efficient as the traditional algorithm, and it may make more sense to students to do it this way.

Figure 16.15 shows two division problems solved in this same way, each with a different model. That is, both the dividend or given quantity and the divisor are expressed in the same type of fractional parts. This results in a whole-number division problem. Similar to the concrete problem, after changing the denominators to twelfths, the answer is the same as $15 \div 8$. In the classroom, after students have solved problems such as this using their own methods, suggest this common-unit approach.

Developing the Algorithms

There are two different algorithms for division of fractions. Methods of teaching both algorithms are discussed here.

Common-Denominator Algorithm The common-denominator algorithm relies on the measurement or repeated subtraction concept of division. Consider the problem $\frac{5}{3} \div \frac{1}{2}$. As shown in Figure 16.16, once each number is expressed in terms of the same fractional part, the answer is exactly the same as the whole-number problem $10 \div 3$. The name of the fractional part (the denominator) is no longer important, and the problem is one of dividing the numerators. The resulting algorithm, therefore, is as follows: *To divide fractions, first get common denominators, and then divide numerators.* For example,

$$\frac{5}{3} \div \frac{1}{4} = \frac{20}{12} \div \frac{3}{12} = 20 \div 3 = \frac{20}{3} = 6\frac{2}{3}$$

Try using circular fraction pieces, fraction strips, then sets of counters to model $1\frac{2}{3} \div \frac{3}{4}$ using a common denominator approach.

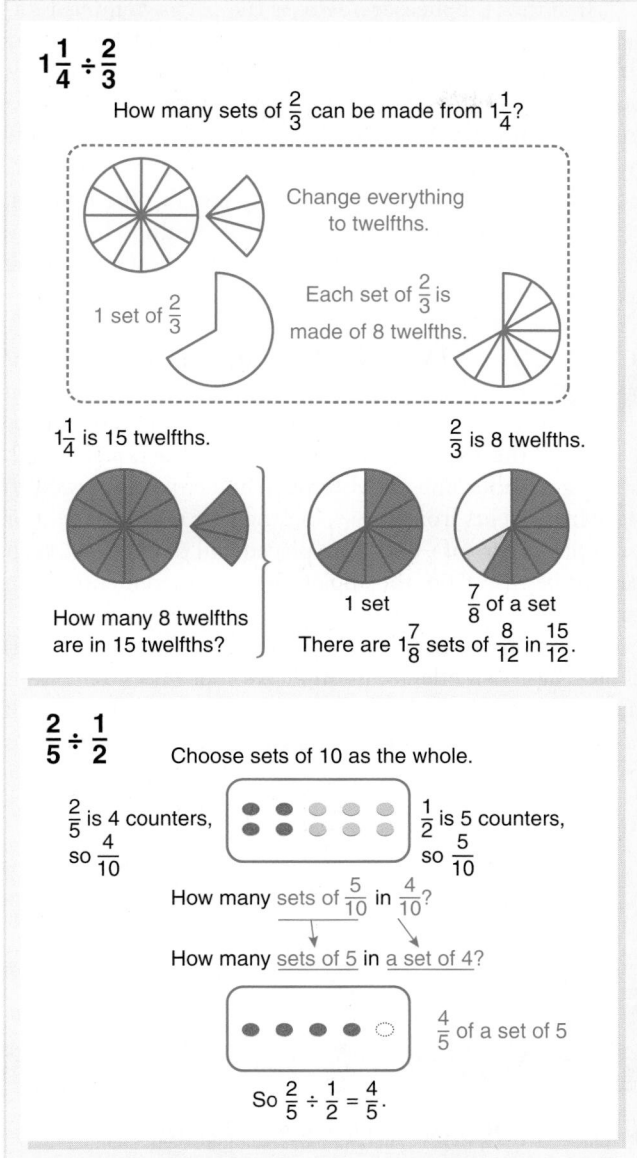

Figure 16.15 Common denominators can be used to solve division of fraction problems.

The Invert-and-Multiply Algorithm

To invert the divisor and multiply may be one of the most poorly understood procedures in the K–8 curriculum. (Do you know why invert-and-multiply works?) Interestingly, in a much discussed study of Chinese and U.S. teachers, Liping Ma (1999) found that most Chinese teachers not only use and teach this algorithm, but they also understand why it works. U.S. teachers were found to be sadly lacking in their understanding of fractional division.

Providing a series of tasks and having students look for patterns in how they are finding the answers can help students discover the algorithm. For example, consider this first set, in which the divisor is a unit fraction. Remember

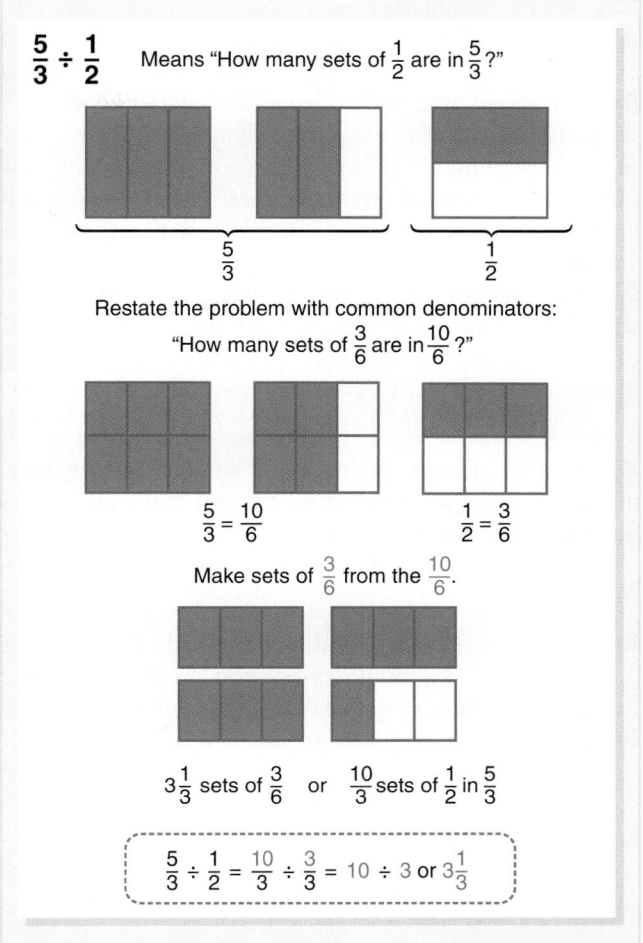

Figure 16.16 Models for the common-denominator method for fraction division.

to pose the related question that goes with each equation. Servings of food can be the context.

$$3 \div \tfrac{1}{2} = \text{(How many servings of } \tfrac{1}{2} \text{ in 3 containers?)}$$
$$5 \div \tfrac{1}{4} = \text{(How many servings of } \tfrac{1}{4} \text{ in 5 containers?)}$$
$$3\tfrac{3}{4} \div \tfrac{1}{2} = \text{(How many servings of } \tfrac{1}{2} \text{ in } 3\tfrac{3}{4} \text{ containers?)}$$
$$6 \div \tfrac{1}{3} = \text{(How many servings of } \tfrac{1}{3} \text{ in 6 containers?)}$$
$$8 \div \tfrac{1}{5} = \text{(How many servings of } \tfrac{1}{5} \text{ in 8 containers?)}$$

In looking across these problems (and more if you are working with students) and looking for a pattern, students will notice they are multiplying by the denominator of the second fraction. For example, in the last example, a student might say, "You get five for every whole container, so 5×8 is 40."

Then take similar problems, but with a second fraction that is not a unit fraction:

$$5 \div \tfrac{3}{4} =$$
$$6 \div \tfrac{2}{3} =$$
$$8 \div \tfrac{2}{5} =$$

Have students compare these responses to the corresponding problems in the first set. Notice that if there are 40 one-fifths in 8, then when you group the fifths in pairs (two-fifths), you will have half as many—20. Stated in servings, if the serving is twice as big, you will have half the number of servings. Similarly, if the fraction is $\frac{3}{4}$, after finding how many fourths, you will group in threes. This means you will get $\frac{1}{3}$ the number of servings. You can see that this means you must divide by 3.

The examples given were measurements because the size of the group (serving) was known, but not the number of groups. Using partitioning, or sharing, examples nicely illustrates the standard algorithm. Consider this example:

You have $1\frac{1}{2}$ oranges, which is $\frac{3}{5}$ of an adult serving. How many oranges (and parts of an orange) make up 1 adult serving? (Kribs Zaleta, 2008).

You may be thinking that you first need to find what one fifth would be—which would be one-third of the oranges you have—or $\frac{1}{2}$ an orange (notice you are dividing by the numerator). Then, to get the whole serving you multiply by 5 (the denominator) to get $2\frac{1}{2}$ oranges in one adult serving.

In either the measurement or the partitive interpretations, the denominator leads you to find out how many fifths, eighths, or sixths you have. The numerator tells you the size of the serving, so you group according to how many are in the serving. So the process means to multiply by the denominator and divide by the numerator. At some point someone thought, well, if they just flip the fraction, then it would be more straightforward—multiplying by the top and dividing by the bottom—-and that is why we have learned to "invert and multiply."

The NLVM Web site (http://nlvm.usu.edu/en/nav/vlibrary.html) has a nice collection of fraction applets. Number Line Bars—Fractions allows the user to place bars of any fractional length along a number line. The number line can be adjusted to have increments from $\frac{1}{2}$ to $\frac{1}{15}$, but the user must decide. For example, if bars of $\frac{1}{4}$ and $\frac{1}{3}$ are placed end to end, the result cannot be read from the applet until the increments are in twelfths.

Fractions—Rectangle Multiplication (also at NLVM) shows the area model for multiplication of any two fractions up to 2×2. Although the applet does an excellent job of connecting the model to the equation, the thinking comes from the user. ◆

Reflections on Chapter **16**

Writing to Learn

1. When should estimation of fractional computation be taught to students? Why is it important to teach computational estimation with fractions?

2. A student adds $\frac{4}{5} + \frac{2}{3}$ and gets $\frac{6}{8}$. How will you help the student understand that this answer is incorrect? How will you redirect her or him to do it correctly?

3. For the fraction sentence $3\frac{1}{4} - 1\frac{1}{2}$, create a story problem that would be a "take away" situation and one that would be a "comparison situation."

4. Explain at least one mental method (estimation or mental computation) for each of these:

$$\frac{3}{4} \times 5\frac{1}{2} \qquad 1\frac{1}{8} \text{ of } 40$$

5. Make up a word problem with a fraction as a divisor. Is your problem a measurement problem or a partition problem? Make up a second word problem with fractions of the other type (measurement or partition).

For Discussion and Exploration

1. Imagine teaching fractional computation, a subject required by your curriculum, in grade 6 or 7. You quickly find that your students have a very weak understanding of fractions. Your textbook primarily targets algorithms. Some teachers argue that there is no time to re-teach the concepts of fractions. Others would argue that it is necessary to teach the meanings of numerators and denominators and equivalent fractions or else all the computation will be meaningless rules. How will you plan for instruction? Justify your approach.

2. Draw pictures using a measurement approach to explain each of these divisions:

$$\frac{2}{4} \div \frac{1}{4} \qquad 2\frac{1}{3} \div \frac{2}{3} \qquad \frac{3}{4} \div \frac{1}{8} \qquad 2\frac{3}{4} \div \frac{2}{3}$$

In the second and fourth examples, the answer is not a whole number. To help you explain the fractional part of the answer, use a set of counters to explain why $13 \div 5 = 2\frac{3}{5}$.

Use a measurement approach. (That is, how many sets of 5 are in 13?) Use the same problems and explain a common denominator algorithm for division. Use the same rationale to explain why $\frac{13}{79} \div \frac{5}{79} = 13 \div 5 = \frac{13}{5}$.

3. Several calculators are now available that do computations in fractional form as well as in decimal form. Some of these automatically give results in simplest terms. If you have access to such a calculator, discuss how it might be used in teaching fractions and especially fractional computation. If such calculators become commonplace, should we continue to teach fractional computation?

Resources for Chapter 16

Literature Connections

Alice's Adventures in Wonderland
Carroll, 1865/1982

This well-known children's story needs no introduction. Because Alice shrinks in the story, there is an opportunity to explore multiplication by fractions. S. B. Taber (2007) describes how she used the meaning of multiplication of fractions. She begins by asking if Alice was originally 135 centimetres (54 inches) tall, but was shrunk to $\frac{1}{9}$ of her height, how tall would she be?

What if later she was restored to only $\frac{5}{6}$ of her original height, how tall would she be? The students were then asked to write down their own Alice explanations for multiplication equations.

The Man Who Made Parks   *Wishinsky, 1999*

This non-fiction novel explains the remarkable story of Frederick Olmsted, who decided he was going to design a park for New York City—what became Central Park. Creating a park design, students can be given fractional amounts for what needs to be included in the park—for example, $\frac{2}{5}$ gardens, $\frac{1}{10}$ playgrounds, $\frac{1}{2}$ natural habitat (streams and forest), and the rest special features (like a baseball arena). Students can build the plan for their park on a rectangular grid. To incorporate multiplication of fractions, include guidelines such as $\frac{3}{4}$ of the park is natural habitat, $\frac{1}{3}$ of it is wooded, and $\frac{1}{6}$ is water features, and so on.

Recommendations for Further Reading

Articles

Cramer, K., Wyberg, T., & Leavitt, S. (2008). The role of representations in fraction addition and subtraction. *Mathematics Teaching in the Middle School, 13* (8), 490–496.
This article provides illustrations and student work to show how to teach addition using the fraction circle. Essential considerations of effective instruction are emphasized.

Gregg, J., & Gregg, D. U. (2007). Measurement and fair-sharing models for dividing fractions. *Mathematics Teaching in the Middle School, 12* (9), 490–496.
These authors provide specific series of tasks to develop the concept of division of fractions—a must read for a teacher needing more experiences exploring division or trying to plan a good sequence for her students.

Huinker, D. (1998). Letting fraction algorithms emerge through problem solving. In L. J. Morrow (Ed.), *The teaching and learning of algorithms in school mathematics* (pp. 170–182). Reston, VA: NCTM.
Huinker takes the idea of students inventing algorithms as described for whole numbers in Chapter 12 and applies it to problems involving fractions. With examples of children's work, this article makes a good case for avoiding rules and letting students work with ideas that make sense.

Imm, K. L., Stylianou, D. A., & Chae, N. (2008). Students representations at the center: Promoting classroom equity. *Mathematics Teaching in the Middle School, 13* (8), 458–463.
These authors explain how to use a park context to teach multiplication of fractions. Equity and a culture for learning are at the centre of their discussions of the lessons.

Kieren, T., Davis, B., & Mason, R. (1996). Fraction flags: Learning from children to help children learn. *Mathematics Teaching in the Middle School, 2,* 14–19.
The authors began with a simple area model involving rectangular pieces cut from a standard sheet of paper. When smaller pieces were placed on larger pieces with spaces in between, the results looked like flags and presented interesting problem-based tasks for the students. These researchers have a long history of work with fractions and this article offers useful insights as well as a suggestion for an easily made model.

Perlwitz, M. D. (2005). Dividing fractions: Reconciling self-generated solutions with algorithmic answers. *Mathematics Teaching in the Middle School, 10,* 278–282.
On the surface, this article is about dealing with the remainder in fraction division. The discussion gets at the deeper question of understanding algorithms, wrestling with the minimal knowledge that many teachers bring to this subject, and the value of classroom discourse.

Online Resources

Diffy

http://nlvm.usu.edu/en/nav/frames_asid_326_g_3_t_1.
html?from=category_g_3_t_1.html

The goal in a Diffy puzzle is to find differences between the numbers on the corners of the square, working to a desired difference in the centre. When working with fractions, the difference of two fractions is a fraction that can be written in many different ways and students must recognize equivalent forms.

Fraction Bars

http://nlvm.usu.edu/en/nav/frames_asid_203_g_2_t_1.html

Much like Cuisenaire rods, this applet places bars over a number line on which the step size can be adjusted. This is a flexible model that can be used for all four operations.

Fractions—Adding

http://nlvm.usu.edu/en/nav/frames_asid_106_g_2_t_1.html

Two fractions and an area model for each are given. The user must find a common denominator to rename and add the fractions.

---

myeducationlab *will help you improve your understanding of the concepts taught in this textbook and in your course. This online tool includes videos of real classroom experiences, sample lesson plans, simulations, case studies, and links to important educational and teaching Web sites that will help you make the transition from student to teacher. As you study in your course and with this textbook, please follow along in* **MyEducationLab**. *Use it! Explore it! And improve your knowledge and your grade!*

Chapter 17
Decimal and Percent Concepts and Decimal Computation

In most Canadian mathematics curricula, decimal numbers are typically introduced in grade 4 and most of the computation work with decimals occurs in grade 5 and is repeated later in grades 6 and 7. This fractions-first, decimals-later sequence is arguably the best approach. However, the unfortunate fact is that the topics of fractions and decimal numbers are too often developed separately. Linking the ideas of fractions to decimals can be extremely useful, from a pedagogical perspective as well as from a practical view. Most of this chapter focuses on the connection between these two topics.

Big Ideas

1. Decimal numbers are simply another way of writing fractions. Both notations have value. Maximum flexibility is gained by understanding how the two symbol systems are related.

2. The base-ten place-value system extends infinitely in two directions: to tiny values as well as to large values. Between any two place values, the ten-to-one ratio remains the same.

3. The decimal point is a convention that has been developed to indicate the position of the units. The position to the left of the decimal point is the unit that is counted as singles or ones.

4. Percents are simply hundredths and as such are a third way of writing both fractions and decimals.

5. Addition and subtraction with decimal numbers are based on the fundamental concept of adding and subtracting the numbers in like positional values—a simple extension from whole numbers.

6. Multiplication and division of two numbers (whether whole or decimal numbers) will produce the same digits, regardless of the position of the decimal point. Thus, for most practical purposes, it is not necessary to develop new rules for decimal multiplication and division. Rather, the computations can be performed as whole numbers with the decimal placed afterward, by way of estimation.

Mathematics Content Connections

The most important connections for decimals are built within this chapter—between decimal numbers and the concepts of fractions.

- **Fractional Concepts** (Chapter 15): Both decimal and fraction symbolism represent the same ideas—the rational numbers.

- **Measurement** (Chapter 19): The metric system is modelled after the base-ten system, and all metric measures are expressed in decimals rather than in fractions. Conversion from one metric measure to another is quite simple, given an understanding of the decimal system.

- **Real Number System** (Chapter 23): Decimal numeration is helpful in characterizing and understanding the density of the rational numbers and also for approximating irrational numbers.

Connecting Two Different Representational Systems

In a world where almost everything can be measured, people need to be able to interpret decimal numbers for calculating distances, understanding sports statistics such as those at the Olympics where winners and losers are separated by hundredths of a second, and in baseball where hitters (and fans) evaluate performance to the thousandths of points. Decimal numbers are important in many occupations ranging from nurses and pharmacists to workers building airplanes, where the level of precision affects safety of the general public. Because children tend to have greater difficulty understanding decimal numbers than fractions (Martinie, 2007), conceptual understanding of decimal numbers and their connections to fractions must be developed.

The symbols 3.75 and $3\frac{3}{4}$ represent the same quantity, yet on the surface the two appear quite different. For children especially, the world of fractions and the world of decimals are very distinct. Even adults tend to think of fractions as sets or regions (three-fourths *of* something), whereas we think of decimals as being more like numbers. When we tell children that 0.75 is the same as $\frac{3}{4}$, it can be especially confusing. Even though different ways of writing the numbers have been invented, the numbers themselves are not different. A significant goal of instruction with decimal and fraction numeration should be to help students see that both systems represent the same concepts.

There are at least three ways to help students see the connection between fractions and decimal numbers. First, we can use familiar fractional concepts and models to explore rational numbers that are easily represented by decimal numbers: tenths, hundredths, and thousandths. Second, we can help them see how the base-ten system can be extended to include numbers less than 1, as well as large numbers. Third, we can help children use models to make meaningful translations between fractions and decimal numbers. These three components are discussed in turn.

Base-Ten Fractions

Fractions that have denominators of 10, 100, 1000, and so on will be referred to as *base-ten fractions* in this chapter. This is simply a convenient label and is not one commonly found in the literature. Fractions such as $\frac{7}{10}$ or $\frac{63}{100}$ are examples of base-ten fractions.

A significant goal of instruction with decimal and fraction numeration should be to help students see that both systems represent the same concepts.

Base-Ten Fraction Models   Most of the common models for fractions are somewhat limited for the purpose of depicting base-ten fractions. Generally, the familiar fractional models cannot show hundredths or thousandths. It is important to provide models for these fractions using the same conceptual approaches that were used for fractions such as thirds and fourths.

Two very important region models can be used to model base-ten fractions. First, to model tenths and hundredths, circular disks such as the one shown in Figure 17.1 can be printed on cardstock (see Blackline Master 28). Each disk is marked with 100 equal intervals around the edge and is cut along one radius. Two disks of different colours, slipped together as shown, can be used to model any fraction less than 1. Fractions modelled on this hundredths disk, still reminiscent of the traditional pie model, can be read as base-ten fractions by noting the spaces around the edge.

The most common model for base-ten fractions is a 10×10 square. These squares, representing one whole, can be run off on paper for students to shade in various fractions (see Figure 17.2 and Blackline Master 27). Another important model, fashioned after the Dienes blocks, is the base-ten place-value model using strips and squares. As a fractional model, the 10 cm square used earlier with whole numbers to represent one hundred is now the whole or 1. Each strip is then 1 tenth, and each small

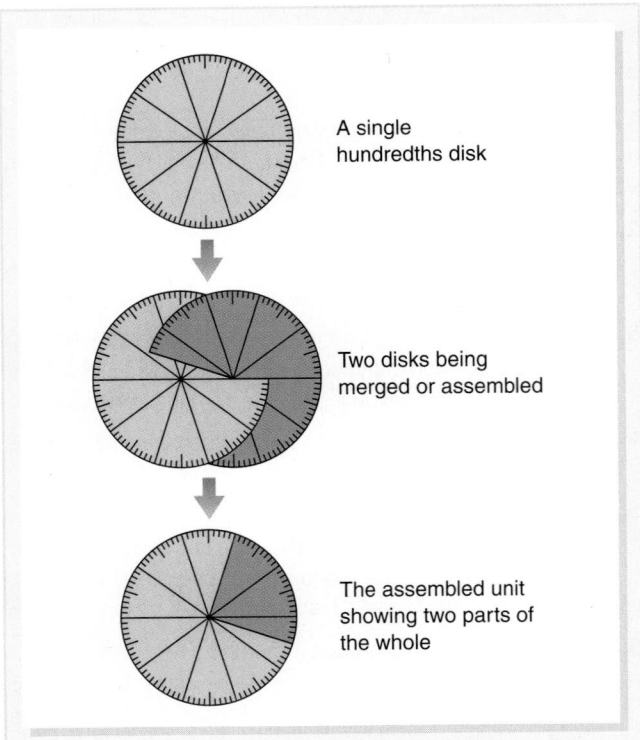

Figure 17.1 A hundredths disk for modelling base-ten fractions.

square is 1 hundredth. Blackline Master 29 provides a large square that is subdivided into 10 000 tiny squares. When shown on an overhead projector, individual squares or ten-thousandths can easily be identified and shaded with a pen on the transparency.

One of the best length models is a metre stick. Each decimetre is one-tenth of the whole stick, each centimetre is one-hundredth, and each millimetre is one-thousandth. Any number-line model broken into 100 subparts is likewise a useful model for hundredths.

Blank number lines are also very useful in helping students compare decimal numbers and think about scale and place value (Martinie & Bay-Williams, 2003). Given two or more decimal numbers, students can use the blank number line to position the values, revealing what they know about the size of these decimal numbers using zero, one, other whole numbers, or other decimal values as benchmarks. Again, the use of multiple representations will broaden students' understanding, as well as your understanding of their level of performance.

Many teachers use money as a model for decimals, and to some extent this is helpful. However, for children, money is almost exclusively a two-place system: Numbers like 3.2 or 12.1389 do not relate to money. Children's initial contact with decimal numbers should be more flexible, so money is not recommended as a decimal model, at least not at the introductory level. Money is certainly an important *application* of decimal numeration.

Multiple Names and Formats   Early work with base-ten fractions is designed primarily to acquaint students with the models, to help them begin to think of quantities in terms of tenths and hundredths, and to learn to read and write base-ten fractions in different ways.

Have students show a base-ten fraction using any base-ten fractional model. Once a fraction, say $\frac{65}{100}$, is modelled, the following things can be explored:

- Is this fraction more or less than $\frac{1}{2}$? than $\frac{2}{3}$? than $\frac{3}{4}$? Some familiarity with these base-ten fractions can be developed by comparison with fractions that are easy to think about.
- What are some different ways to say this fraction using tenths and hundredths ("6 tenths and 5 hundredths," "65 hundredths")? Include thousandths when appropriate.
- Show two ways to write this fraction ($\frac{65}{100}$ or $\frac{6}{10} + \frac{5}{100}$).

The last two questions are very important. When base-ten fractions are later written as decimals, they are usually read as a single fraction. That is, 0.65 is read "sixty-five hundredths." But to understand them in terms of place value, the same number must be thought of as 6 tenths and 5 hundredths. A mixed number such as $5\frac{13}{100}$ is usually read the same way as a decimal: 5.13 is "five and thirteen-hundredths." For purposes of place value, it should also be understood as $5 + \frac{1}{10} + \frac{3}{100}$.

The expanded forms will be helpful in translating these fractions to decimals. Given a model or a written or an oral fraction, students should be able to give the other two forms of the fraction, including equivalent forms where appropriate.

Extending the Place-Value System

Before considering decimal numbers with students, it is advisable to review some whole-number place-value ideas. One of the most basic ideas is the 10-to-1 relationship between the digits in any two adjacent positions in a number. In terms of a base-ten model such as strips and squares, 10 of any one piece is equal to 1 of the next larger piece, and vice versa.

A Two-Way Relationship   The 10-makes-1 rule extends indefinitely to larger and larger pieces or positional values. As you learned in Chapter 11, if you are using the strips-and-squares model, for example, the strip and square shapes alternate in an infinite progression as they become larger and larger. Once you have established the progression to larger pieces, focus on the idea that each piece to the right in this string decreases by one-tenth. The critical question then becomes "Is there ever a smallest piece?" In the students' experience, the smallest piece is the centimetre square or unit piece. But couldn't that piece be divided into 10 small strips? And couldn't these small strips be divided into 10 very small squares, and so on? In the mind's eye, there is no smallest strip or smallest square.

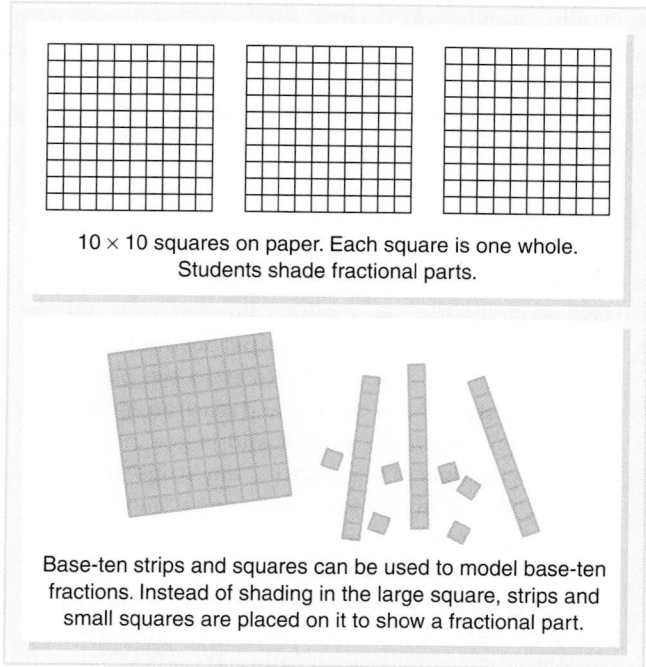

10 × 10 squares on paper. Each square is one whole. Students shade fractional parts.

Base-ten strips and squares can be used to model base-ten fractions. Instead of shading in the large square, strips and small squares are placed on it to show a fractional part.

Figure 17.2   10 × 10 squares model base-ten fractions.

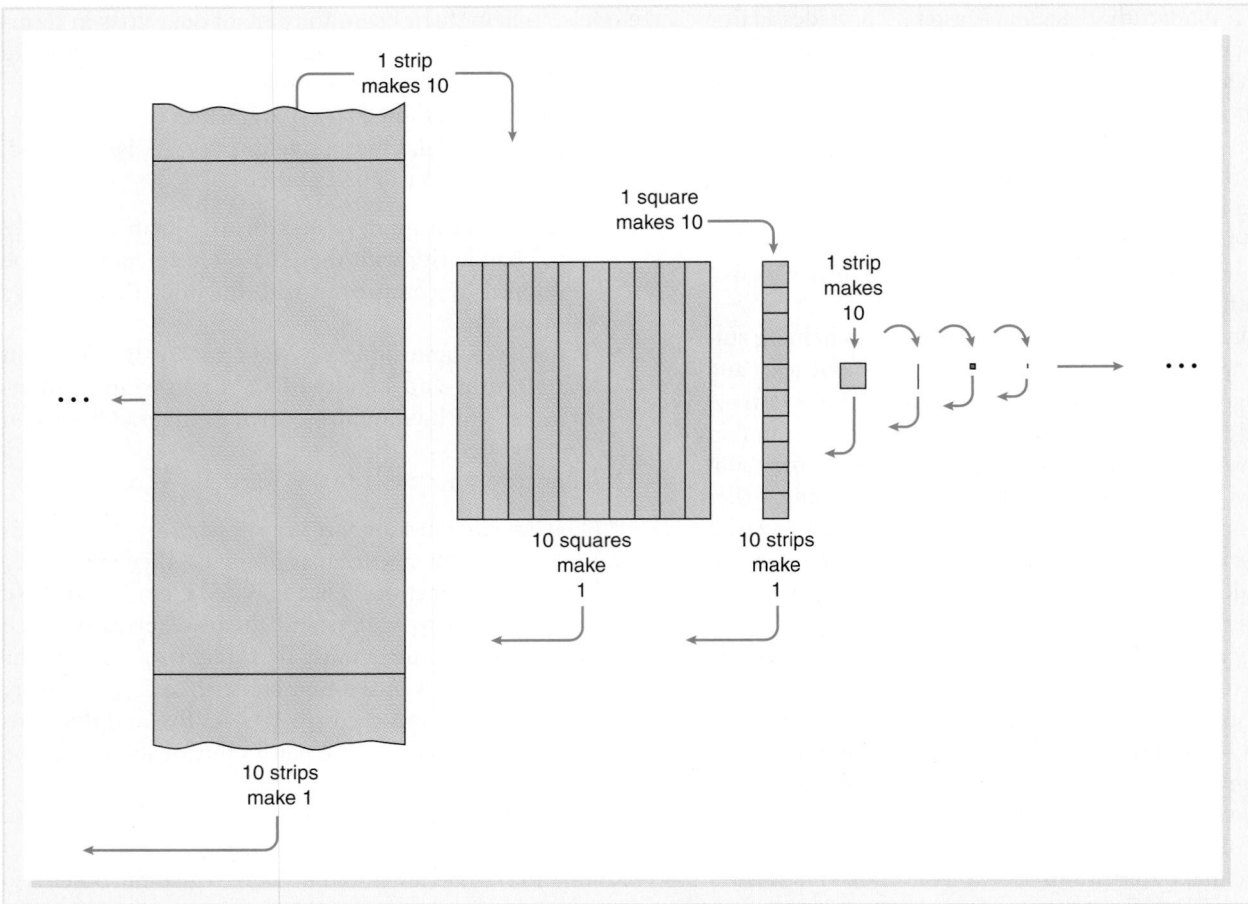

Figure 17.3 Theoretically, the strips and squares extend infinitely in both directions.

The goal of this discussion is to help students see that a 10-to-1 relationship can extend *infinitely in two directions.* There is no smallest piece and no largest piece. The relationship between adjacent pieces is the same regardless of which two adjacent pieces are being considered. Figure 17.3 illustrates this idea.

The Role of the Decimal Point   An important idea to realize in this discussion is that there is no built-in reason why any one position (or base-ten piece) should naturally be chosen to be the unit or ones position. In terms of strips and squares, for example, which piece is the ones piece? The small centimetre square? Why? Why not a larger or a smaller square? Why not a strip? *Any piece could effectively be chosen as the ones piece.*

As shown in Figure 17.4, a given quantity can be written in different ways, depending on the choice of the unit or what piece is used to count the entire collection. The decimal point is situated between two positions with the convention that the place to the left of the decimal point is the units or ones place. Thus, the role of the decimal point is *to designate the units place*, and it does so by sitting just to the right of that position.

A fitting caricature for the decimal is shown in Figure 17.5. The "eyes" of the decimal always focus up toward the name of the units or ones. If the "smiling" decimal point was placed between the squares and strips in Figure 17.4, the squares would then be designated as the units, and 16.24 would be the correct written form for the model.

Activity **17.1**

The Decimal Names the Unit

Have students display a certain number of base-ten pieces on their desks. For example, put out three squares, seven strips, and four tinies. Refer to the pieces as "squares," "strips," and "tinies," and reach an agreement on names for both the smaller and larger theoretical pieces. To the right of tinies can be "tiny strips" and "tiny squares." To the left of the squares can be "super strips" and "super squares." Each student should also have a smiley decimal point. Now ask students to write and say how many squares they have, how many super strips, and so on, as in Figure 17.4. The students position their decimal point accordingly and write and say the amounts.

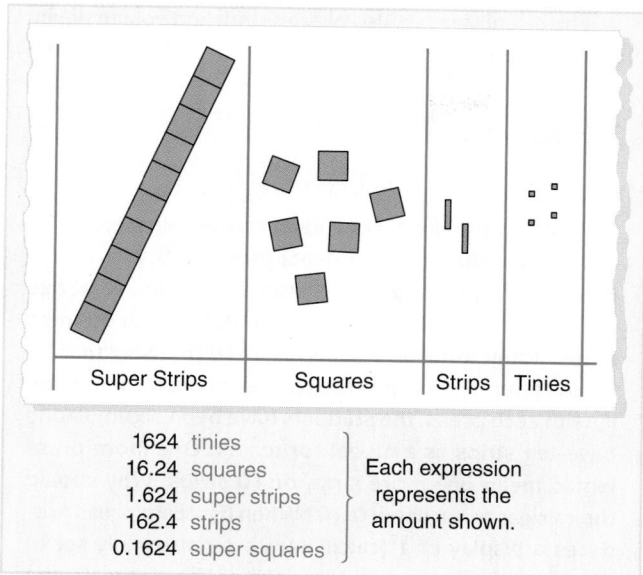

1624	tinies
16.24	squares
1.624	super strips
162.4	strips
0.1624	super squares

Each expression represents the amount shown.

Figure 17.4 The placement of the decimal point indicates which position is the units.

Activity 17.1 illustrates vividly the convention that the decimal indicates the named unit and that the unit can change without changing the quantity.

The Decimal with Measurement and Monetary Units   The notion that the decimal "looks at the units place" is useful in a variety of contexts. For example, in Figure 17.6, as shown with linear measure, the decimal point can be used to designate any of the seven places as the unit without changing the actual measure. Our monetary system is also a decimal system. For the amount $172.95, the decimal point designates the dollars position as the unit. There are 1 hundred (of dollars), 7 tens, 2 singles, 9 dimes, and 5 pennies or cents regardless of how it is written. If pennies were the designated unit, the same amount would

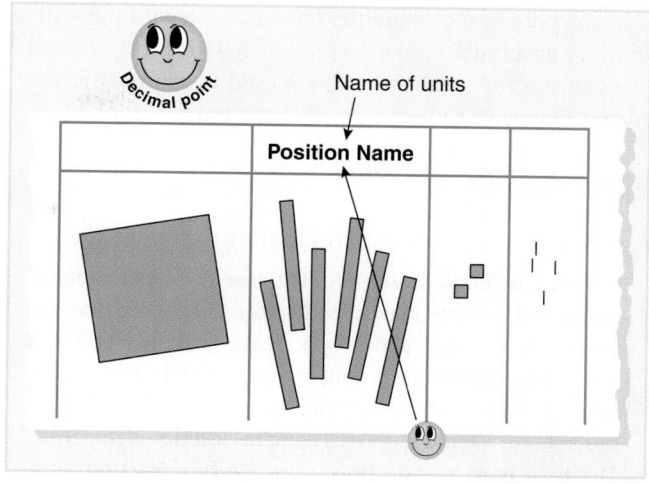

Figure 17.5 The decimal point always "looks up at" the name of the units position. In this case we have 16.24.

be written as 17 295 cents or 17 295.0 cents. It could just as correctly be 0.172 95 thousands of dollars or 1729.5 dimes.

In the case of actual measures for length, area, capacity, or mass, or for money, the name of the unit is written after the number rather than above the digit as on a place-value chart. You may be 1.62 metres tall, but it does not make sense to say you are "1.62 tall." In the paper, we may read about government spending $7.3 billion. Here the units are billions of dollars, not dollars. A city may have a population of 2.4 million people. That is the same as 2 400 000 individuals.

The Fraction–Decimal Connection

To connect fractions and decimal numbers, students need to make concept-oriented translations; that is, translations based on understanding rather than a rule or algorithm.

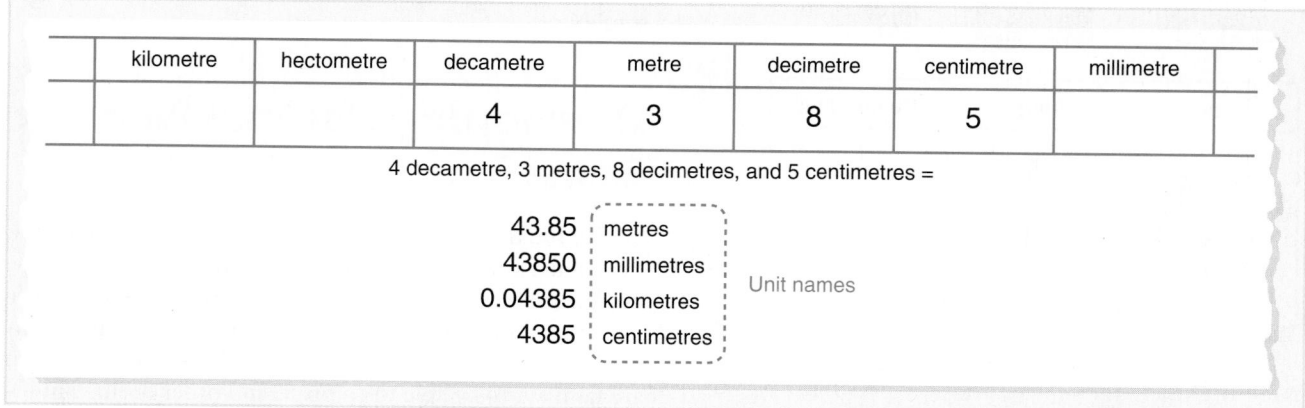

kilometre	hectometre	decametre	metre	decimetre	centimetre	millimetre
		4	3	8	5	

4 decametre, 3 metres, 8 decimetres, and 5 centimetres =

43.85	metres
43850	millimetres
0.04385	kilometres
4385	centimetres

Unit names

Figure 17.6 Each place-value position for metric measure has a name. The decimal point designates which length is the unit length.

The purpose of such activities has less to do with the skill of converting a fraction to a decimal than with construction of the concept that both systems are used to express the same ideas. The place to begin is with base-ten fractions.

Activity 17.2

Base-Ten Fractions to Decimals

For this activity, have students use their place-value strips and squares (Blackline Master 14). Agree that the large square represents one. Have students cover a base-ten fractional amount of the square using their strips and tinies. For example, have them cover $2\frac{35}{100}$ of the square. Whole numbers require additional squares. The task is to decide how to write this fraction as a decimal number and demonstrate the connection using their physical models.

For the last activity, a typical (and correct) reason why $2\frac{35}{100}$ is the same as 2.35 is that there are 2 wholes, 3 tenths, and 5 hundredths. It is important to see this physically. The exact same materials that are used to represent $2\frac{35}{100}$ of the square can be rearranged or placed on an imaginary place-value chart with a paper decimal point used to designate the units position as shown in Figure 17.7.

The reverse of this activity is also worthwhile. Give students a decimal number such as 1.68 and have them show it with base-ten pieces. Their task is to write it as a fraction and show it as a fractional part of a square.

Although these translations between decimal numbers and base-ten fractions are rather simple, the main agenda is for students to learn from the beginning that decimal numbers are simply another way to represent fractions.

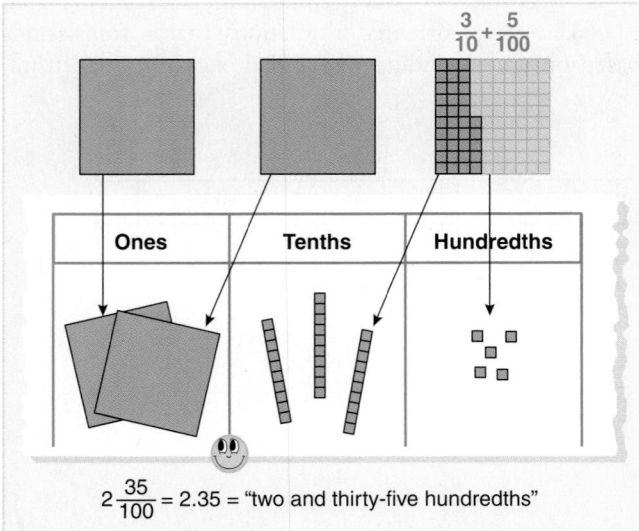

$2\frac{35}{100} = 2.35 =$ "two and thirty-five hundredths"

Figure 17.7 Translation of a base-ten fraction to a decimal number.

The calculator can also play a significant role in decimal concept development.

Activity 17.3

Calculator Decimal Counting

Recall how to make the calculator "count" by pressing ⊞ 1 ⊜ ⊜ .... Now have students press ⊞ 0.1 ⊜ ⊜ .... When the display shows 0.9, stop and discuss what this means and what the display will look like with the next press. Many students will predict 0.10 (thinking that 10 comes after 9). This prediction is even more interesting if, with each press, the students have been accumulating base-ten strips as a model for tenths. One more press would mean one more strip, or 10 strips. Why should the calculator not show 0.10? When the tenth press produces a display of 1 (calculators are not usually set to display trailing zeros to the right of the decimal), the discussion should revolve around trading 10 strips for a square. Continue to count to 4 or 5 by tenths. How many presses to get from one whole number to the next? Try counting by 0.01 or by 0.001. These counts illustrate dramatically how small one-hundredth and one-thousandth really are. It requires 10 counts by 0.001 to get to 0.01 and 1000 counts to reach 1.

The fact that the calculator counts 0.8, 0.9, 1, 1.1 instead of 0.8, 0.9, 0.10, 0.11 should give rise to the question "Does this make sense? If so, why?"

Calculators that permit entry of fractions also have a fraction–decimal conversion key. On some calculators a decimal such as 0.25 will convert to the base-ten fraction $\frac{25}{100}$ and allow for either manual or automatic simplification. Graphing calculators can be set so that the conversion is either with or without simplification. The ability of calculators with fraction functions to go back and forth between fractions and decimal numbers makes them a valuable tool as students begin to connect fraction and decimal symbolism.

Developing Decimal Number Sense

So far, the discussion has revolved around the connection of decimal numbers with base-ten fractions. Number sense implies more. It means having intuition about or a friendly understanding of numbers. To this end, it is useful to connect decimal numbers to the fractions with which children are familiar, to be able to compare and order decimal numbers readily, and to approximate decimal numbers with useful familiar numbers.

Familiar Fractions Connected to Decimals

Chapter 15 showed how to help students develop a conceptual familiarity with simple fractions, especially halves, thirds, fourths, fifths, and eighths. We should extend this familiarity to the same concepts expressed as decimal numbers. One way to do this is to have students translate familiar fractions to decimal numbers by means of a base-ten model.

The following two activities have the same purpose— to help students think of decimal numbers in terms of familiar fraction equivalents and to make this connection in a conceptual manner.

Activity 17.4

Friendly Fractions to Decimals

Students are given a "friendly" fraction to convert to a decimal number. They first model the fraction using either a 10 × 10 grid or the base-ten strips and squares. With the model as a guide, they draw and write an explanation for the decimal number equivalent. If strips and squares are used, be sure that students draw pictures as part of their explanations.

A good sequence is to work with halves, fifths, and fourths. For those children who require an added challenge, have them work with eighths. The fraction $\frac{3}{8}$ in particular represents a wonderful challenge. A hint might be to find $\frac{1}{4}$ first, then notice that $\frac{1}{8}$ is half of a fourth. Remember that the next smaller pieces are tenths of the little squares. Therefore, a half of a square is $\frac{5}{1000}$. Thirds can then be done as a special activity.

Figure 17.8 shows how translations in the last activity might go with a 10 × 10 grid. For fourths, students will often shade a 5 × 5 section (half of a half). The question then becomes how to translate this to decimal numbers. Ask these students how they would cover $\frac{1}{4}$ with strips and squares if they were only permitted to use nine or fewer tinies.

Because the circular model carries such a strong mental link to fractions, it is well worth the time to do some fraction-to-decimal conversions with the hundredths disk shown in Figure 17.1.

Activity 17.5

Estimate, Then Verify

With the blank side of the disk facing them, have students adjust the disk to show a particular friendly fraction, for example, $\frac{3}{4}$. Next they turn the disk over and record how many hundredths were in the section they estimated (note that the colour reverses when the disk is turned over). Finally, they should make an argument for the correct number of hundredths and the corresponding decimal equivalent.

The estimation component of the last activity adds the visual "feeling" for fractions. In one grade 5 class that was having difficulty finding a decimal equivalent for their hundredths disk fraction, the teacher cut up some extra disks into tenths and hundredths so that these parts of the fraction could be placed on a chart. (See Figure 17.9.)

The exploration of modelling $\frac{1}{3}$ as a decimal number is a good introduction to the concept of an infinitely repeating

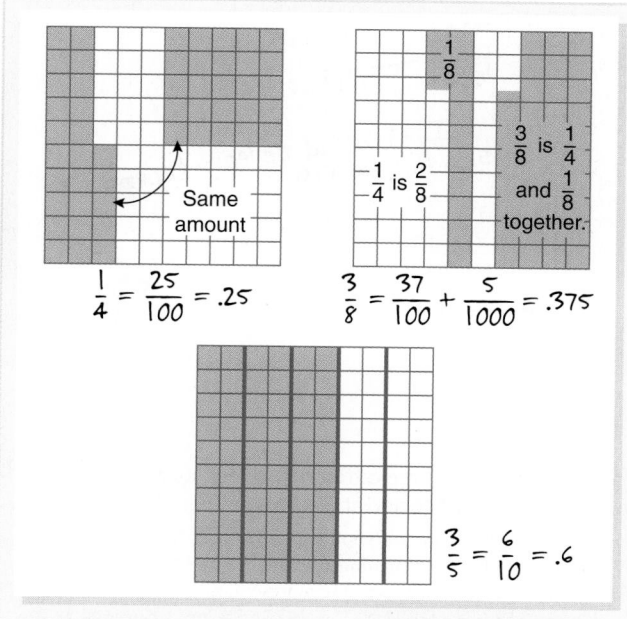

Figure 17.8 Familiar fractions converted to decimals using a 10 × 10 square.

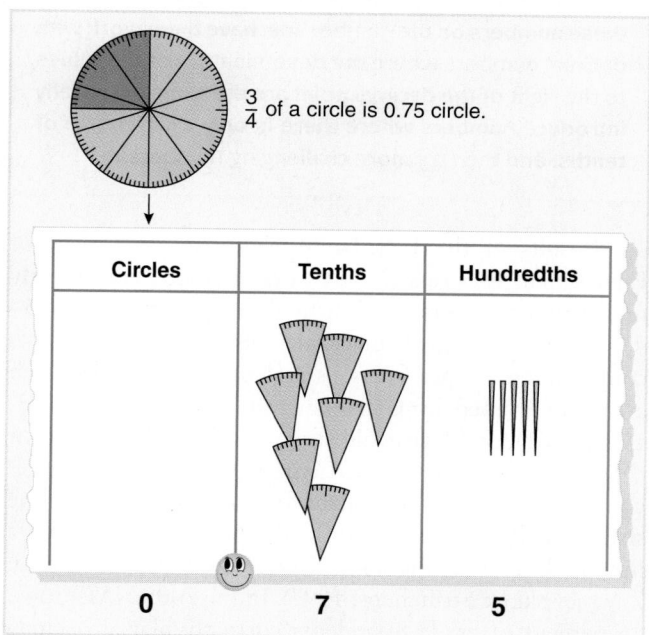

Figure 17.9 Fraction models could be decimal models.

decimal number. Try to partition the whole 10×10 square into 3 parts using strips and squares. Each part receives 3 strips with 1 left over. To divide the leftover strip, each part gets 3 small squares with 1 left over. To divide the small square, each part gets 3 tiny strips with 1 left over. (Recall that with base-ten pieces, each smaller piece must be $\frac{1}{10}$ of the preceding size piece.) It becomes obvious that this process is never-ending. As a result, $\frac{1}{3}$ is the same as 0.333 333... or $0.\overline{3}$. For practical purposes, $\frac{1}{3}$ is about 0.333. Similarly, $\frac{2}{3}$ is a repeating string of sixes, or about 0.667. Later, students will discover that many fractions cannot be represented by a finite decimal.

The number line is another good connecting model. Students are more apt to think of decimal numbers as numbers that appear on the number line than they are to think of fractions in that way. The following activity continues the development of fraction–decimal equivalences.

Activity 17.6

Decimals on a Friendly Fraction Line

Give students five decimal numbers that have friendly fractional equivalents. Keep the numbers between two consecutive whole numbers. For example, use 3.5, 3.125, 3.4, 3.75, and 3.66. On a worksheet, show a number line encompassing the same whole numbers. The subdivisions on the number line should be only fourths, only thirds, or only fifths, but without labels. The students' task is to locate each of the decimal numbers on the number line and to provide the fraction equivalent for each.

Accommodation

For those students who are having difficulty locating these numbers on the number line, have them work with decimal numbers where the denominators of the values to the right of the decimal point are the same. Gradually introduce numbers where there is only a difference of tenths, and then try more challenging numbers.

Results of the U.S.-based National Assessment of Educational Progress (NAEP) examinations consistently reveal that students have difficulties with the fraction–decimal relationship. Kouba et al. (1988a) note that students could express proper fractions as decimals, findings which are substantiated by Canadian test results (SAIP, 1993, 1997, 2001) for 13-year-old students. Yet, only 40 percent of grade 7 students who participated in the fourth NAEP could give a decimal equivalent for a mixed number. In the sixth NAEP, students had difficulty placing decimals on a number line where the subdivisions were fractions (Kouba, Zawojewski, & Strutchens, 1997). In the 2005 NAEP, only 56 percent of grade 8 students correctly placed decimal numbers on a number line when the increments were mul-

tiples of 0.2—not even in fractional increments). Division of the numerator by the denominator may be a means of converting fractions to decimal numbers, but it contributes nothing to understanding its equivalent result. Note that this method has not been and will not be suggested in this chapter.

A simple yet powerful assessment of decimal understanding has students represent two related decimal numbers, such as 0.6 and 0.06, using each of three or four different representations: a number line (not provided but student-drawn), a 10×10 grid, money, and base-ten materials (Martinie & Bay-Williams, 2003). For additional information, have students give reasons for their representations. If students have significantly more difficulty with one model than others, this may mean that they have learned how to use certain models but have not necessarily developed true understanding of decimal numbers. Placement of decimal numbers on a blank number line is perhaps the most interesting—and the most telling. (See Figure 17.10.) ◆

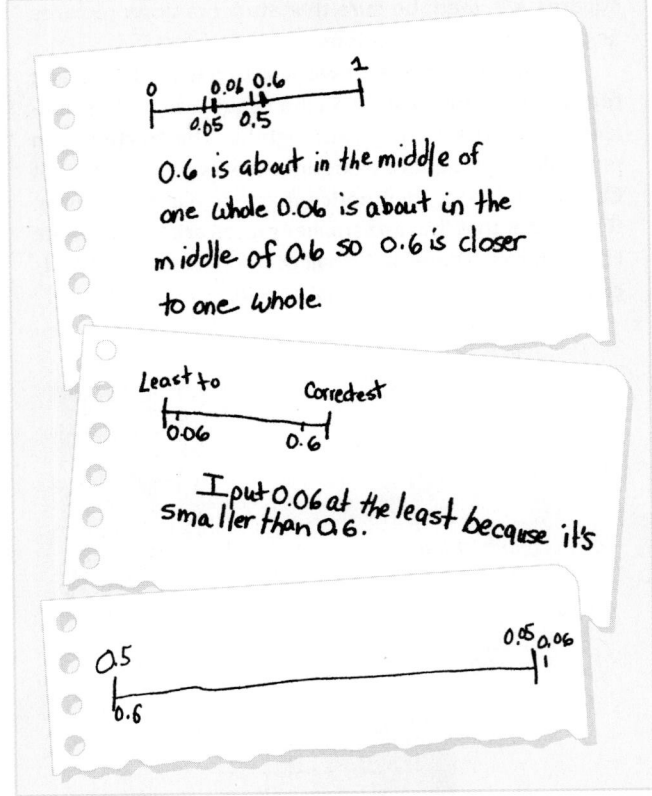

Figure 17.10 Three different grade 6 students attempt to draw a number line and show the numbers 0.6 and 0.06.

Source: Reprinted with permission from Martinie, S.L., & Bay-Williams, J. (2003). Investigating students' conceptual understanding of decimal fractions using multiple representations. *Mathematics Teaching in the Middle School, 8,* 244–247 at p.Â246. Copyright © 2003 by the National Council of Teachers of Mathematics. All rights reserved.

Approximation with a Nice Fraction

In the real world, decimal numbers rarely have exact equivalents of nice fractions. What fraction would you say approximates the decimal 0.52? In the sixth NAEP exam in the United States, only 51 percent of grade 8s selected $\frac{1}{2}$. The other choices were $\frac{1}{50}$ (29 percent), $\frac{1}{5}$ (11 percent), $\frac{1}{4}$ (6 percent), and $\frac{1}{3}$ (4 percent) (Kouba et al., 1997). Again, the most plausible explanation for this performance is a reliance on rules. The less-than-satisfactory results of Canadian (as well as international) students on the Third International Science and Mathematics Study (TIMSS) underscores the need for more time to be spent developing conceptual understanding of decimals, rather than relying on rules (Robitaille, Taylor, & Orpwood, 1996). Students need to wrestle with the size of decimal numbers and begin to develop a sense of familiarity with them.

As with fractions, the first benchmarks that should be developed are 0, $\frac{1}{2}$, and 1. For example, is 7.396 closer to 7 or 8? Why? (Would you accept this response: "Closer to 7 because 3 is less than 5"?) Is it closer to 7 or $7\frac{1}{2}$? Often, the 0, $\frac{1}{2}$, or 1 benchmarks are good enough to make sense of a situation. If a closer approximation is required, students should be encouraged to consider the other friendly fractions (thirds, fourths, fifths, and eighths). In this example, 7.396 is close to 7.4, which is $7\frac{2}{5}$. A good number sense with decimal numbers would imply the ability to think quickly of a meaningful fraction that is a close substitute for almost any number.

To develop this type of familiarity with decimal numbers, children do not need new concepts or skills. They do need the opportunity to apply and discuss the related concepts of fractions, place value, and decimals in activities such as the following.

Activity 17.7

Close to a Friendly Fraction

Make a list of about five decimal numbers that are close to but not exactly equal to a nice or friendly fraction equivalent. For example, use 24.802, 6.59, 0.9003, 124.356, and 7.7.

The students' task is to decide on a decimal number that is close to each of these numbers that also has a friendly fraction equivalent that they know. For example, 6.59 is close to 6.6, which is 6 $\frac{3}{5}$. They should write an explanation for their choices. Different students may select different equivalent fractions, providing for a discussion of which is closer.

Activity 17.8

Best Match

On the chalk board or white board, list a scattered arrangement of five familiar fractions and at least five decimal numbers that are close to the fractions but not exact. Students are to pair each fraction with the decimal number that best matches it. The difficulty is determined by how close the various fractions are to one another.

In Activities 17.7 and 17.8, students will have a variety of reasons for their answers. Sharing their thinking with the class provides a valuable opportunity for all to learn. Do not focus on the answers but on the rationales.

The connections between models and the two symbol systems for rational numbers—fractions and decimals—provide a good task for a diagnostic interview. Provide students with a number represented in any one of these three ways and have them provide the other two along with an explanation. Here are a few examples:

- Write the fraction $\frac{5}{8}$ as a decimal number. Use a drawing or a physical model (metre stick or 10×10 grid) and explain why your decimal equivalent is correct.
- What fraction is also represented by the decimal number 2.6? Use words, pictures, and numbers to explain your answer.
- Use both a fraction and a decimal number to tell what point might be indicated on this number line. Explain your reasoning.

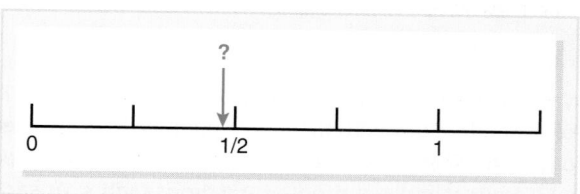

In the last example, it is especially interesting to see which representation students select first—fraction or decimal. Furthermore, do they then translate this number to the other representation or make a second independent estimate? ◆

Ordering Decimal Numbers

Putting a list of decimal numbers in order from least to greatest is a skill closely related to the one just discussed. Consider the following list: 0.36, 0.058, 0.375, and 0.4. The most common error is to select the number with more digits as largest, an incorrect application of whole-number ideas. Another common error is to think that longer numbers are smaller because digits far to the right represent very small numbers (Steinle & Stacey, 2004). Both errors reflect a lack of conceptual understanding of how decimal numbers are constructed. The following activities can help promote discussion about the relative size of decimal numbers.

Activity 17.9

Line 'Em Up

Prepare a list of four or five decimal numbers that students might have difficulty putting in order. They should all be between the same two consecutive whole numbers. Have students first predict the order of the numbers, from least to greatest. Require students to use a model of their choice to defend their ordering. As students wrestle with representing the numbers with a model (perhaps a number line with 100 subdivisions or the 10 000 grid), it will quickly become obvious which digits contribute the most to the size of a decimal number.

In the world outside of classrooms, we almost never have to think about the order of "ragged" decimal numbers—decimal numbers with different numbers of digits after the decimal point. The real purpose of exercises such as "Line 'Em Up" is not to develop a skill—but rather to create a better understanding of decimal numeration. Tasks such as this will, however, continue to be on standardized tests because they are good assessments of decimal understanding.

Activity 17.10

Close "Nice" Numbers

Write a four-digit decimal number on the board—3.0917, for example. Start with the whole numbers: "Is it closer to 3 or 4? Then go to the tenths: "Is it closer to 3.0 or 3.1?" Repeat with hundredths and thousandths. At each answer, challenge students to defend their choices with the use of a model or other conceptual explanation. A large number line without numbers, shown in Figure 17.11, is useful.

Other Fraction–Decimal Equivalents

Recall that in any fraction the denominator is a divisor and the numerator is a multiplier. For example, therefore, $\frac{3}{4}$ means the same as $3 \times (1 \div 4)$ or $3 \div 4$. So how would you express $\frac{3}{4}$ on a simple four-function calculator? Simply enter $3 \div 4$. The display will read 0.75.

Too often students think that dividing the denominator into the numerator is simply an algorithm for converting fractions to decimal numbers, and they have no understanding of why this might work. Use the opportunity to help students develop the idea that in general $\frac{a}{b} = a \div b$. (See Chapter 15, p. 295.)

The calculator is an important tool when developing familiarity with decimal concepts. Finding the decimal number equivalents with a calculator can produce some interesting patterns and observations. For example, here are some questions to explore:

- Which fractions have decimal equivalents that terminate? Is the answer based on the numerator, the denominator, or both?
- For a given fraction, how can you tell the maximum length of the repeating part of the decimal number? Try dividing by 7 and 11 and 13 to reach an answer.
- Explore all of the ninths: $\frac{1}{9}, \frac{2}{9}, \frac{3}{9}, \ldots \frac{8}{9}$. Remember that $\frac{1}{3}$ is $\frac{3}{9}$ and $\frac{2}{3}$ is $\frac{6}{9}$. Use only the pattern you discover to predict what $\frac{9}{9}$ should be. But doesn't $\frac{9}{9} = 1$?
- How can you find what fraction produces this repeating decimal number: 3.454 545...?

The final task in this list can be generalized for any repeating decimal number, illustrating that every repeating decimal number is a rational number. It is not at all useful for students to become skilled at this.

 Much of what was discussed in this section is recommended by the *Standards*. "Students in [grades 3 to 5] should use models and other strategies to represent and study decimal numbers. For example, they should count by tenths (one-tenth, two-tenths, three-tenths, ...) verbally or use a calculator to link and relate whole numbers with decimal numbers.... They

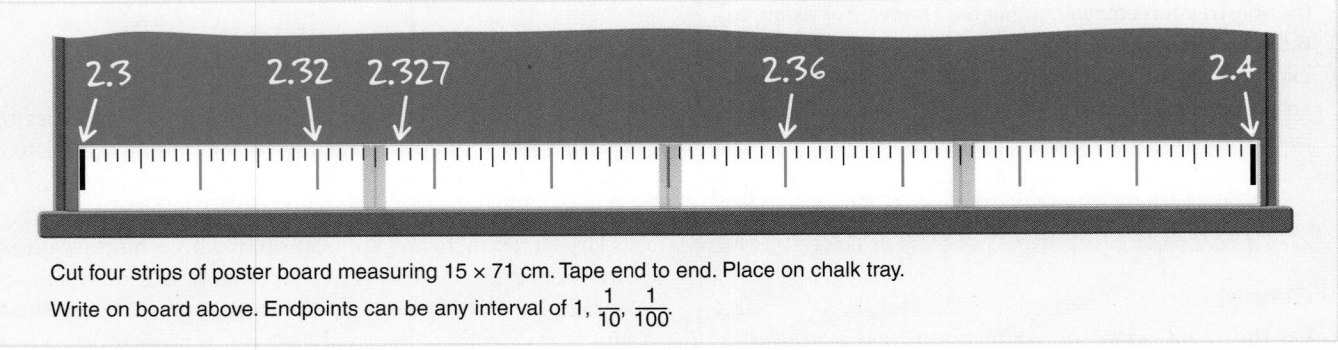

Cut four strips of poster board measuring 15 × 71 cm. Tape end to end. Place on chalk tray.

Write on board above. Endpoints can be any interval of $1, \frac{1}{10}, \frac{1}{100}$.

Figure 17.11 A decimal number line.

should also investigate the relationship between fractions and decimals, focusing on equivalence" (p. 150).

Introducing Percents

The term *percent* is simply another name for *hundredths*. As such, it is a standardized ratio with a denominator of 100. If students can express common fractions and simple decimal numbers as hundredths, the term *percent* can be substituted for the term *hundredth*. Consider the fraction $\frac{3}{4}$. As a fraction expressed in hundredths, it $\frac{75}{100}$. When $\frac{3}{4}$ is written as a decimal number, it 0.75. Both 0.75 and $\frac{75}{100}$ are read in exactly the same way "seventy-five hundredths." When used as operators, $\frac{3}{4}$ of something is the same as 0.75 or 75 percent of the same thing. Thus percent is merely a new notation and terminology, not a new concept.

The results of the NAEP tests and numerous other studies have consistently shown that students have difficulty with problems involving percents (Wearne & Kouba, 2000). For example, on the eighth NAEP, only 37 percent of grade 8 students could determine an amount following a given percent increase. Most are likely to select the answer obtained by adding the percent itself to the original amount. That is, for a 10 percent increase, they selected the answer that was 10 more than the original amount. Only 37 percent of students could accurately calculate what percent the tip represented, when given the cost of the meal and the amount of the tip left by diners. A reason for this continued dismal performance is a failure to develop percent concepts meaningfully. In this book we explore percent twice. Here we will connect them to fractions and decimal numbers. In Chapter 18, we will revisit percent as a ratio as part of the study of proportional reasoning.

Models and Terminology

Models provide the main link among fractions, decimals, and percents, as shown in Figure 17.12 (see Blackline Masters 27 and 28). Base-ten fraction models are suitable for fractions, decimals, and percents, since they all represent the same idea. Students should use base-ten models for percents in much the same way as they would for decimals. The disk (Figure 17.1) with 100 markings around the edge is now a model for percents as well as a fractional model for hundredths. The same is true of a 10 × 10 square. Each tiny square inside is 1 percent of the square. Each row or strip of 10 squares is not only a tenth but also 10 percent of the square.

Zambo (2008) suggests linking fractions to percent using the 10 × 10 blank hundreds chart. By marking one out of every four squares on the chart students can discover the link between $\frac{1}{4}$ and $\frac{25}{100}$ or 25 percent. He goes on to suggest that even more complex representations such as $\frac{1}{8}$ can lead to interesting discussions about the remaining

squares left at the end that result in $12\frac{1}{2}$ out of 100 squares or $12\frac{1}{2}$ percent.

Similarly, the familiar fractions (halves, thirds, fourths, fifths, and eighths) should become familiar in terms of percents as well as decimals. Three-fifths, for example, is 60 percent as well as 0.6. One-third of an amount is frequently expressed as $33\frac{1}{3}$ percent instead of 33.3333... percent. Likewise, $\frac{1}{8}$ of a quantity is $12\frac{1}{2}$ percent or 12.5 percent of the quantity. These ideas should be explored with base-ten models and not as rules about moving decimal points.

One representation that can be used to link percents with data collection is a percent necklace. Using fishing cord or other sturdy string, link 100 beads and knot them in a tight, circular necklace. Any time a circle graph is created or observed in class, the percent necklace can provide an estimation tool to help think about the percent that falls in any given category. Given any circle graph, even one of humans as shown on page 460 in Figure 21.7, place the necklace in a circle so that its centre coincides with the centre of the circle, rather than trying to align with the outside edge of the circle graph. If the necklace makes a wider concentric circle, the students can use a ruler to extend the lines distinguishing the different categories straight out to meet the necklace. If the circle is larger than the necklace, as it would be in Figure 21.7, you will use the actual radial lines marking off the categories. Have students explore the number of beads between any two given lines that represent a wedge of the circle. For example, they might find that 24 beads are in the section of the circle graph that shows how many students like blue as their favourite colour. That is an estimate that approximately 24 percent of the students favour blue. Such counting of beads gives students an informal approach to estimating percent, while investigating a meaningful model for thinking about the per one hundred concept.

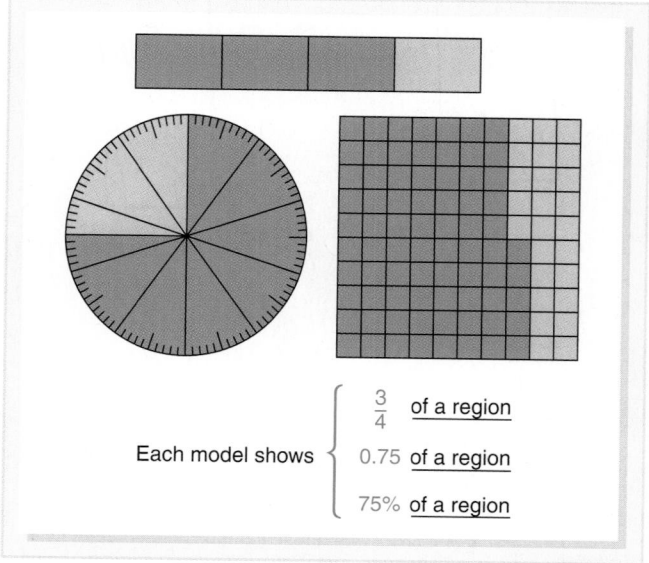

Figure 17.12 Models connect three different notations.

Percent concepts can be developed through other powerful visual representations that link to proportional thinking. One option is the use of a three-part model to represent the original amount, the decrease/increase and the final amount (Parker, 2004). Using three rectangles that can be positioned and divided, students can analyze components and consider each piece of the model. The rectangles can be a particularly useful representation for the oft confusing problems, that include a percentage increase to find an amount greater than the original. Using Parker's suggested model, you can see in Figure 17.13 how a student used this proportional model to come up with a correct solution. The use of the proportional model to think about percents will be revisited in the next chapter on proportional reasoning.

Another helpful approach to the terminology of percent is through the role of the decimal point. Recall that the decimal identifies the units. When the unit is ones, a number such as 0.659 means a little more than 6 tenths of 1. The word *ones* is understood (6 tenths of 1 *one* or one *whole*). But 0.659 is also 6.59 tenths and 65.9 hundredths and 659 thousandths. The name of the unit must be explicitly identified, or else the unit would change with each position of the decimal. Since *percent* is another name for *hundredths*, when the decimal identifies the hundredths position as the unit, the word *percent* can be specified as a synonym for *hundredths*. Thus, 0.659 (of some whole or 1) is 65.9 hundredths or 65.9 percent of that same whole. As illustrated

in Figure 17.14, the notion of placing the decimal point *to identify the percent position* is conceptually more meaningful than the apparently arbitrary rule: "To change a decimal to a percent, move the decimal two places to the right." A more conceptually focused idea is to equate hundredths with percent both orally and in notation.

Realistic Percent Problems

Some senior grade teachers may talk about "the three percent problems." The sentence " _____ is _____ percent of _____ " has three spaces for numbers; for example, "20 is 25 percent of 80." The classic three percent problems come from this sterile expression; two of the numbers are given, and the students are asked to produce the third. Students learn very quickly that you either multiply or divide the two given numbers, and sometimes you have to move a decimal point. But they have no way of determining when to do what, which numbers to divide, or which way to shift the decimal point. As a result, performance on percentage problems is very poor. Furthermore, commonly encountered expressions using percent terminology—such as sales figures, taxes, census data, political information, and trends in economics—are almost never in the " _____ is _____ percent of _____ " format. So when asked to solve a realistic percent problem, students are frequently at a loss.

Chapter 15 explored exercises with fractions, in which one element—part, whole, or fraction—was unknown. Students used models and simple fractional relationships in those exercises. Those three types of exercises are precisely the same as the three percent problems. Developmentally, then, it makes sense to help students make the connection between the exercises done with fractions and those done with percents. How? Use the same types of models and the same terminology of parts, wholes, and fractions. The only thing that is different is that the word *percent* is used instead of *fraction*. In Figure 17.15, the three part–whole–fraction exercises demonstrate the link between fractions and percents.

Teaching Percents Though students must have some experience with the non-contextual situations in

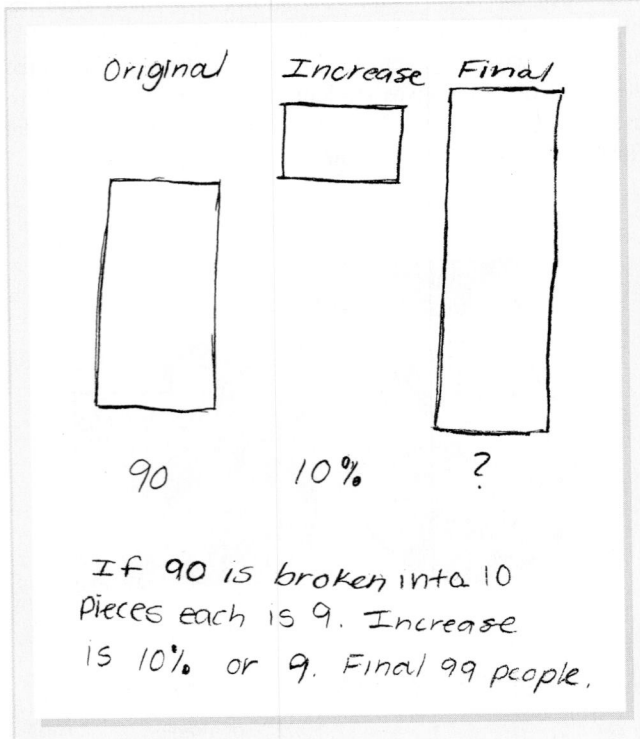

If 90 is broken into 10
pieces each is 9. Increase
is 10% or 9. Final 99 people.

Figure 17.13 A proportional model for reasoning about percent.

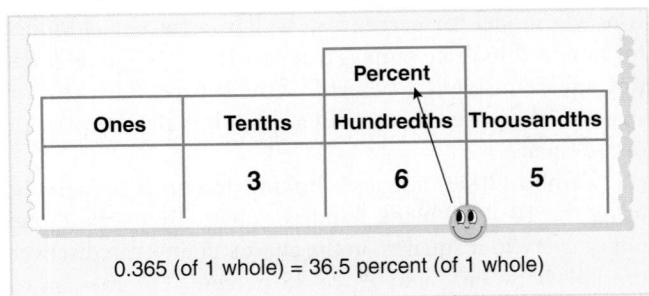

0.365 (of 1 whole) = 36.5 percent (of 1 whole)

Figure 17.14 Hundredths are also known as percents.

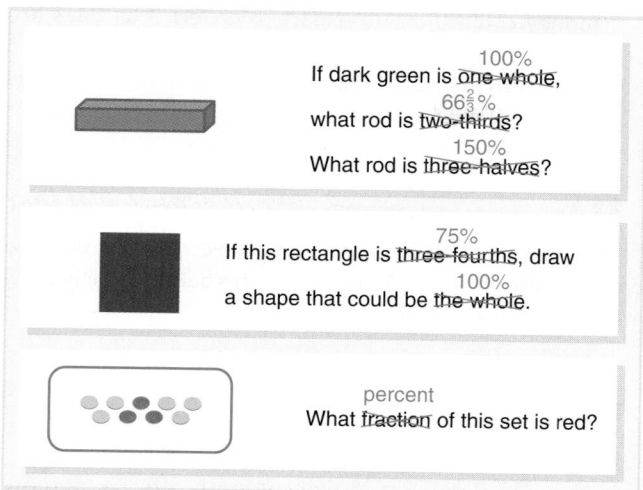

Figure 17.15 Part-whole fraction exercises can be translated into percent exercises.

Figure 17.15, it is important to have them explore percent relationships in real contexts. Find or make up percent problems, and present them in the same way that they appear in newspapers, on television, and in other real contexts. In addition to realistic problems and formats, follow these maxims for your unit on percents:

- Limit the percents to familiar fractions (halves, thirds, fourths, fifths, and eighths) or easy percents ($\frac{1}{10}$, $\frac{1}{100}$), and use numbers compatible with these fractions. The focus of these exercises is the relationships involved, not complex computational skills.
- Do not suggest any rules or procedures for different types of problems. Do not categorize or label problem types.
- Use the terms *part*, *whole*, and *percent* (or *fraction*). *Fraction* and *percent* are interchangeable. Help students see these percent exercises as the same types of exercises they did with simple fractions.
- Require students to use models or drawings to explain their solutions. It is wiser to assign three problems requiring a drawing and an explanation than to give 15 problems requiring only computation and answers. Remember that the purpose is the exploration of relationships, not computational skill.
- Encourage mental computation.

The following sample problems meet these criteria for familiar fractions and compatible numbers. Try working each problem, identifying each number as a part, a whole, or a fraction. Draw length or area models to explain or work through your thought process. Examples of this informal reasoning are illustrated with additional problems in Figure 17.16.

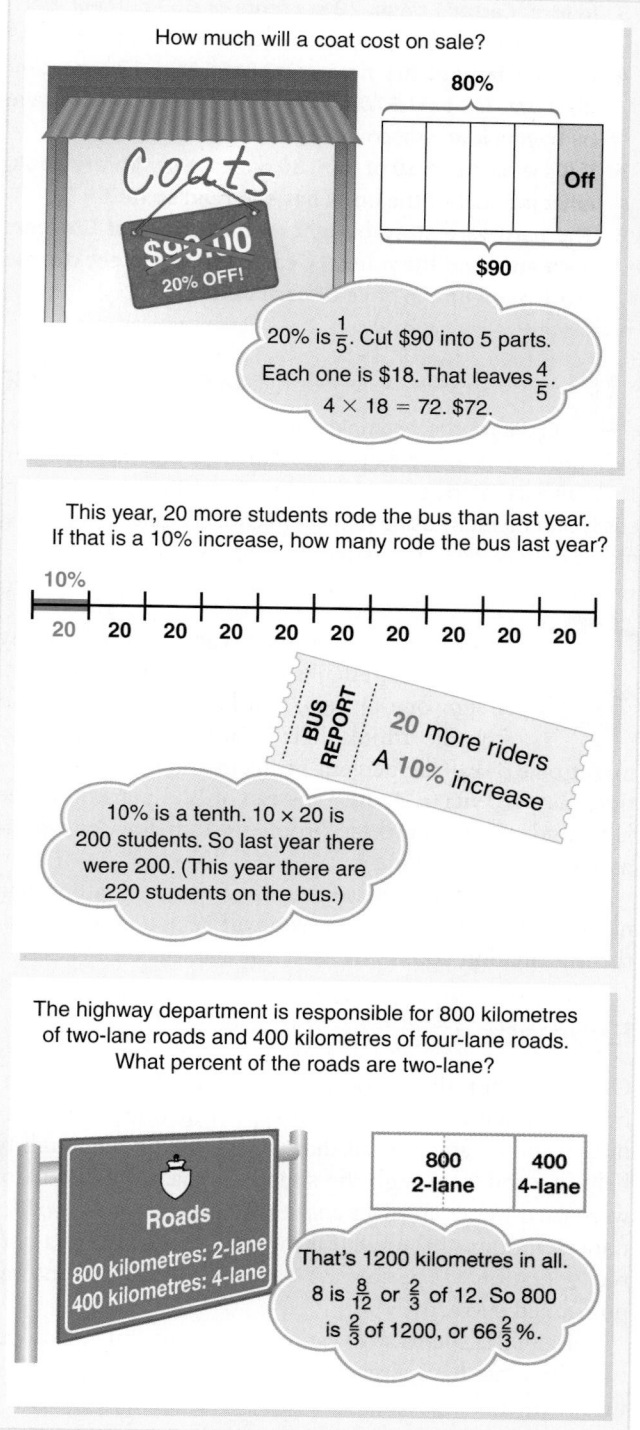

Figure 17.16 Part-whole fraction exercises can be translated into percent exercises.

1. The Parent–Teacher Association reported that 75 percent of the total number of families were represented at the meeting last night. If children from 320 families go to the school, how many were represented at the meeting?

2. The baseball team won 80 percent of the 25 games it played this year. How many games were lost?

3. In Mrs. Carter's class, 20 students or $66\frac{2}{3}$ percent were on the honour roll. How many students are in her class?

4. George bought his new computer at a $12\frac{1}{2}$ percent discount. He paid $700. How many dollars did he save by buying it at a discount?

5. If Alicia has read 60 of the 180 pages in her library book, what percent of the book has she read so far?

6. The hardware store bought machine bolts at 80 cents each and sold them for $1 each. What percent did the store mark up the price of each bolt?

Pause and Reflect

Examine the examples in Figure 17.16. Notice how each problem is solved with simple fractions and mental math. Then try each of the six problems just listed. Each can be done easily and mentally using familiar fractional equivalents. Use a model or drawing that you think your students might use.

Realistic percent problems are still the best way to assess a student's understanding of percent. Assign one or two, and have students explain why they think their answer makes sense. You might take a realistic percent problem and substitute fractions for percents (e.g., use $\frac{1}{8}$ instead of 12.5 percent) to see how students handle these problems with fractions compared to decimal numbers.

If your focus is on reasons and justifications rather than number of problems correct, you will be able to collect all the information you need. ◆

Estimation

Of course, not all real percent problems have nice numbers. Frequently in real life an approximation or estimate in percent situations is all that is required or is enough to help one think through the situation. Even if a calculator were used to get an exact answer, an estimate based on an understanding of the relationship can confirm that a correct operation was performed or that the decimal point was positioned correctly.

To help students with estimation in percent situations, two ideas that have already been discussed can be applied. First, when the percent is not a "nice" one, substitute a close percent that is easy to work with. Second, select numbers that are compatible with the percent involved to make the calculation easy to do mentally. In essence, convert the not-nice percent problem to one that is nice. Here are some examples.

1. The 43 000-seat stadium was 73 percent full. How many people were at the game?

2. The treasurer reported that 68.3 percent of the dues, for a total of $385, had been collected. How much more money could the club expect to collect if all dues are paid?

3. Max McStrike had 217 hits in 842 turns at bat. What was his batting average?

Pause and Reflect

Use nice fractions and compatible numbers to solve each of these last three problems. Do this before reading on.

Possible Estimates

1. (Use $\frac{3}{4}$ and 80 000) → about 60 000

2. (Use $\frac{2}{3}$ and $380; will collect $\frac{1}{3}$ more) → about $190

3. ($4 \times 217 > 842$; $\frac{1}{4}$ is 25 percent, or 0.250) → a bit more than 0.250

Here are three more percent problems with two sets of numbers. The first number in the set is a nice number that allows the problem to be worked mentally using fractional equivalents. The second number requires that the number be substituted with an approximation allowing for an estimate, as in the last activity.

1. The school has {480, 547} students. Yesterday {$12\frac{1}{2}$ percent, 13 percent} of the students were absent. How many came to school?

2. Mr. Carver sold his lawn mower for {$45, $89}. This was {60 percent, 62 percent} of the price he paid for it new. What did the mower cost when it was new?

3. When the box fell off the shelf {90, 63} of the {720, 500} widgets broke. What percent were lost in the breakage?

The first problem asks for a part (whole and fraction given), the second asks for a whole (part and fraction given), and the third asks for a fraction (part and whole given).

It is also convenient at times to use simple base-ten equivalents: 1 percent and 10 percent and multiples of these (including halves). For example, we often use 10 percent plus half of that much to compute a 15 percent tip at a restaurant. To find 0.5 percent we can think of half of 1 percent.

There are several rules of thumb for estimating percents in real-world situations. As students gain full conceptual understanding and flexibility, there are ways to think about percents that are useful when you are shopping or in situations that bring thinking about percents to the forefront. As mentioned previously, to calculate a tip you can find 10 percent of the amount and then half of that again to make 15 percent. The same approach is used for adding on sales tax. Depending on your amount, you can find 10 percent, take half of that, then find 1 percent and add on or subtract that as needed. You can encourage other approaches as well.

Students should realize that finding percents is a process of multiplication. Therefore, finding 50 percent of 16 will generate the same result as finding 16 percent of 50. This is an important estimation tool when you are "on the go." Also, a 30 percent decrease is the same as 70 percent of the original amount. Sometimes, depending on the original amount, using percent in this way is easier in mental calculations than the other. Again, this is nothing more than using the full understanding of percent concepts to your advantage.

Computation with Decimals

Certainly, students should develop some computational fluency with decimal numbers. In the past, decimal computation was dominated by the following rules: Line up the decimal points (addition and subtraction), count the decimal places (multiplication), and shift the decimal point in the divisor and dividend so that the divisor is a whole number (division). Some textbooks continue to emphasize these rules. The position taken in this book is that specific rules for decimal computation are not really necessary, especially if computation is built on a firm understanding of place value and a connection between decimals and fractions.

 At the grade 3–5 level, the *Standards* says that students should "develop and use strategies to estimate computations involving fractions and decimals in situations relevant to students' experience" (p. 148). At the grade 6–8 level, students are to "select appropriate methods and tools for computing with fractions and decimals from among mental computation, estimation, calculators or computers, and paper and pencil, depending on the situation" (p. 214).

The Role of Estimation

Students should become adept at estimating decimal computations well before they learn to compute with pencil and paper. For many decimal computations, rough estimates can be made easily by rounding the numbers to nice whole numbers or simple base-ten fractions. A minimum goal for your students should be to have the estimate contain the correct number of digits to the left of the decimal—the whole-number part. Select problems for which estimates are not terribly difficult.

⏸ ───────────── *Pause and Reflect*

Before going on, try making easy whole-number estimates of the following computations. Do not spend time with fine adjustments in your estimates.

1. 4.907 + 123.01 + 56.1234
2. 459.8 − 12.345
3. 24.67 × 1.84
4. 514.67 ÷ 3.59

Your estimates might be similar to the following:

1. Between 175 and 200
2. More than 400, or about 425 to 450
3. More than 25, closer to 50 (1.84 is more than 1 and close to 2)
4. More than 125, less than 200 (500 ÷ 4 = 125 and 600 ÷ 3 = 200)

In these examples, an understanding of decimal numeration and some simple whole-number estimation skills can produce rough estimates. When estimating, focus on the meanings of the numbers and the operations and not on counting decimal places. However, students who are taught to focus on the pencil-and-paper rules for decimal computation do not even consider the actual values of the number, much less estimate.

Therefore, a good *place* to begin decimal computation is with estimation. Not only is it a highly practical skill, but it also helps children look at answers in "ballpark" terms, a reasonable range, and can form a check on calculator computation.

A good *time* to begin computation with decimal numbers is as soon as a conceptual background in decimal numeration has been developed. An emphasis on estimation is very important, even for students in grades 7–8 who have been exposed to and have used rules for decimal computation, especially for multiplication and division. Many students who are totally reliant on rules for decimal numbers make mistakes without being aware.

Addition and Subtraction

Consider this problem:

Jaimie and McKenna each timed their own half-kilometre run with a stopwatch. Jaimie says that she ran the half kilometre in 135.5 seconds. McKenna was more accurate. She reported her run as 141.34 seconds. How many seconds faster did Jaimie run than McKenna?

Students who understand decimal numeration should first of all be able to tell approximately what the difference is—close to 6 seconds. With an estimate as a beginning, students should then be challenged to figure out the exact difference. The estimate will help them avoid the typical error of lining up the 5 under the 4. A variety of student strategies are possible. For example, students might note that 135.4 and 6 is 141.4, then figure out how much extra that is. Others may count on from 135.5 by adding 0.5 then 5 more seconds to get 141 seconds then add on the remaining 0.34 second. These and other strategies will eventually confront the difference between 0.5 and 0.34. Students can resolve this issue by drawing on their understanding of place value. Similar story problems for addition and subtraction, some involving different numbers of decimal places, will help develop students' understanding of these two operations. Always request an estimate prior to computation.

After students have had several opportunities to solve addition and subtraction story problems, the following activity is reasonable.

Activity **17.11**

Exact Sums and Differences

Give students a computation involving different numbers of decimal places. For example, 73.46 + 6.2 + 0.582. The first task is to make an estimate and explain the way the estimate was made. The second task is to compute the exact answer and explain how that was done (no calculators). In the third and final task, students devise a method for adding and subtracting decimal numbers that they can use with any two numbers.

When students have completed these three tasks, have them share their strategies for computation, then test them on a new computation that you provide.

The same task can be repeated for subtraction.

The earlier estimation practice will focus students' attention on the meanings of the numbers. Remember, students can also think about rewriting decimal numbers in fraction form, with the appropriate denominator, to make connections. It is reasonable to expect that students will develop an algorithm that is essentially the same as aligning the decimal points.

If students have difficulty with Activity 17.11, it is an indication that they have a weak understanding of decimal concepts and the role of the decimal point. This is true even for students who get a correct sum, using a rule they learned in an earlier grade, but have difficulty with their explanations. Rather than focusing on how to add or subtract decimal numbers, return or shift your focus to decimal concepts as discussed earlier in the chapter. ◆

Multiplication

Estimation should play a significant role in developing an algorithm for multiplication. As a beginning point, consider this problem:

Farmer Daniela sells apple cider in plastic jugs. She fills each jug with 3.7 litres of cider. If you buy 4 jugs when you visit her apple orchard, how many litres of cider is that?

Begin with an estimate. It is more than 12 litres. What is the most it could be? Could it be 16 litres? Once an esti-mate of the result is decided on, let students use their own methods for determining an exact answer. Many will use repeated addition: 3.7 + 3.7 + 3.7 + 3.7. Others may begin by multiplying 3 × 4 then add up 0.7 four times. Eventually, students will agree on the exact result of 14.8 litres. Explore other problems involving whole-number multipliers. Multipliers such as 3.5 or 8.25 that involve nice fractional parts—here, one-half and one-fourth—are also reasonable.

As a next step, have students compare a decimal product with one involving the same digits but no decimal. For example, how are 23.4 × 6.5 and 234 × 65 alike? Interestingly, both products will have exactly the same digits: 15210. (The zero may be missing from the decimal product.) Using a calculator, have students explore other products that are alike except for the decimals involved. The digits in the answer are always alike. After seeing how the digits remain the same for these related products, do the following activity.

Activity **17.12**

Where Does the Decimal Point Go?— Multiplication

Have students compute the following product: 24 × 63. Using only the result of this computation and estimation, have them give the exact answer to each of the following:

0.24 × 6.3   24 × 0.63   2.4 × 63   0.24 × 0.63

For each computation they should write a rationale for the placement of the decimal point in the answer. They can check their results with a calculator. Any errors must be acknowledged, and the rationale that produced the error adjusted.

❚❚ ——————— *Pause and Reflect*

The product of 24 × 63 is 1512. Use this information to give the answer to each of the products in the previous activity. Do not count decimal places. Remember your fractional equivalents.

The method of placing the decimal point in a product by estimating is more difficult as the product gets smaller. For example, knowing that 54 × 83 is 4482 does not make it easy to place the decimal point in the product of 0.0054 × 0.00083. Even the product of 0.054 × 0.83 is hard. A reasonable algorithm for multiplication is: *Ignore the decimal points, and do the computation as if all numbers were whole numbers. When finished, place the decimal by estimation.* Even if students have already learned the traditional algorithm, they need to understand the rationale underlying place value and how to count the powers of ten for shifting the decimal places. By focusing on rote applications of rules algorithm, they need to know the conceptual rationale centred on place value and the powers of ten for "counting" and shifting the decimal places. By focusing on rote applications of rules, students lose out on approaches that emphasize opportunities to understand the meaning and effects of operations and are more prone to inappropriately apply procedures (Martinie & Bay-Williams, 2003).

Questions such as the following keep the focus on number sense and provide useful information about your students' understanding.

1. Consider these computations: $3\frac{1}{2} \times 2\frac{1}{4}$ and 2.276×3.18. Without doing the calculations, which do you think is larger? Provide a reason for your answer that can be understood by someone else in this class.
2. How much larger is 0.76×5 than 0.75×5? How can you tell without doing the computation (Kulm, 1994)?

Students' discussions and explanations as they work on these or similar questions can provide insights into their decimal and fraction number sense, and their understanding of the connections between the two representations. ◆

Division

Division can be approached in a manner exactly parallel to multiplication. In fact, the best approach to a division estimate generally comes from thinking about multiplication rather than division. Consider the following problem:

The trip to Moncton was 452.5 kilometres. It took exactly $5\frac{1}{2}$ hours or 5.5 hours to drive. What was the average rate of kilometres per hour?

To estimate this quotient, think about what times 4 or 5 is close to 452. You might think $80 \times 5.5 = 440 + 10 = 450$. So maybe about 82 or 83 kilometres per hour.

Here is a second example without context. Make an estimate of $45.7 \div 1.83$. Think only of what times $1\frac{8}{10}$ is close to 45.

❚❚ ———————————— *Pause and Reflect*

Will the answer be more or less than 45? Why? Will it be more or less than 20? Now think about 1.8 being close to 2. What times 2 is close to 46? Use this to produce an estimate.

Since 1.83 is close to 2, the estimate is near 22. And since 1.83 is less than 2, the answer must be greater than 22—say 25 or 26. (The actual answer is 24.972677.)

Okay, so estimation can produce a reasonable result, but you may still require a pencil-and-paper algorithm to

produce the digits the way it was done for multiplication. Figure 17.17 shows division by a whole number and how that can be carried out to as many places as you wish. (The explicit-trade method described in Chapter 12 is shown on the right.) It is not necessary to move the decimal point up into the quotient. Leave that to estimation.

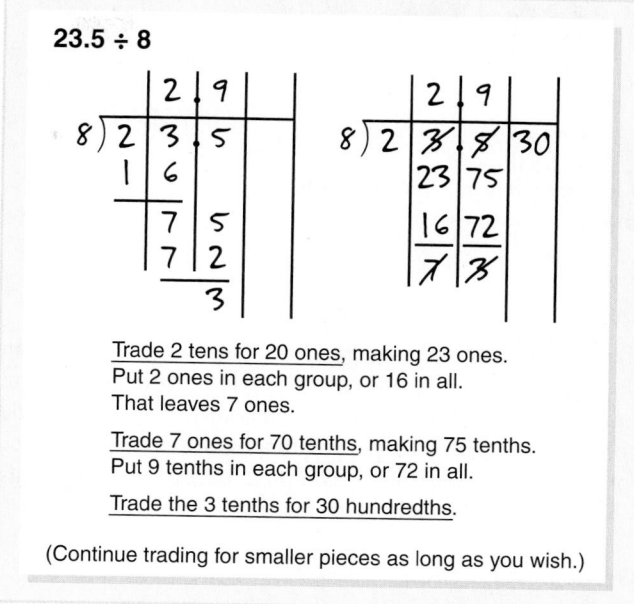

23.5 ÷ 8

Trade 2 tens for 20 ones, making 23 ones.
Put 2 ones in each group, or 16 in all.
That leaves 7 ones.

Trade 7 ones for 70 tenths, making 75 tenths.
Put 9 tenths in each group, or 72 in all.

Trade the 3 tenths for 30 hundredths.

(Continue trading for smaller pieces as long as you wish.)

Figure 17.17 Extension of the division algorithm.

Activity **17.13**

Where Does the Decimal Point Go?— Division

Provide a quotient such as 146 ÷ 7 = 20857 correct to five digits but without the decimal point. The task is to use only this information and estimation to give a fairly precise answer to each of the following:

   146 ÷ 0.7   1.46 ÷ 7   14.6 ÷ 0.7   1460 ÷ 70

For each computation students should write a rationale for their answers then check their results with a calculator. Any errors should be acknowledged, and the rationale that produced the error adjusted.

A reasonable algorithm for division is parallel to that for multiplication: *Ignore the decimal points, and do the computation as if all numbers were whole numbers. When finished, place the decimal point by estimating.* This is reasonable for divisors greater than 1 or close to a familiar value (e.g., 0.1, 0.5, 0.01). If students have a method for dividing by 45, they can divide by 0.45 and 4.5 and even 0.045.

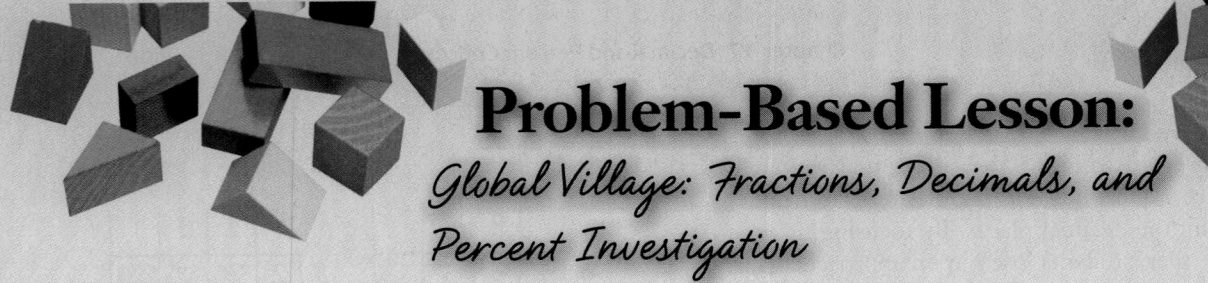

Problem-Based Lesson:
Global Village: Fractions, Decimals, and Percent Investigation

The following problem-based lesson provides learners with an opportunity to make the fraction–decimal–percent connection.

Differentiating the Learning:

This lesson demonstrates how a range of learner needs can be accommodated. It does so by providing students with an opportunity to work at their level of ability on the task, while collaborating with their peers. Students also have the chance to work with calculators to complete necessary calculations while working through the task.

Grade Level: Grades 6 and 7
Mathematical Goals

- To reinforce students' knowledge of fractions
- To develop students' understanding of the fraction–decimal–percent relationship
- To help students see that decimal numbers and percents are alternate ways of representing fractional concepts
- To ensure that students are able to move easily from fractions to decimal numbers to percents and the reverse.

To the Teacher

This lesson illustrates how other areas of the curriculum can be effectively integrated with mathematics. It gives students the chance to learn about and appreciate other cultures and ethnic groups and the location of their countries of origin. It also helps students identify and locate the continents of the world.

Thinking About the Students

Students have already worked on the meaning of fractions and operations with fractions. At this level students have been exposed to, and done some work with, decimal numbers and percents.

Materials and Preparation

- Students work in small groups according to the particular task to which they have been assigned. Tasks have been designed to meet the varied needs and ability levels of the students.
- David Smith's *If The World Were a Village* (ISBN: 550747797) serves as the starting point for the lesson. Reading the book to the class gives them a chance to learn about the diverseness of the world's population.

- A map of the world is used to locate the continents and the countries identified in the book, as well as the countries of origin of the students in the class (and other classes) and/or their family members.
- Chart paper is used to record information regarding the different countries of origin of classmates or of students in other classes, as well as the numbers for each group. Data regarding the different groups of people cited in the book *If The World Were a Village* are also recorded on the chart paper.
- Calculators will be used to calculate fractional numbers representing the different groups and their decimal and percent equivalents.
- 2 square centimetre grid paper is used for graphing the data.

Introduction

- Begin the lesson by reading the book to the students.
- Display on the board the chart paper with the following information:

  Out of 100 people in the global village:

  > 61 are from Asia
  >
  > 13 are from Africa
  >
  > 12 are from Europe
  >
  > 8 are from South America, Central America, and the Caribbean
  >
  > 5 are from Canada and the U.S.A.
  >
  > 1 is from Oceania

- Look at the data together with the students and talk about what they see.
- Some possible things to consider in the discussion are what David Smith means when he talks about the world as a global village, why he used the number 100 to represent the people in the global village, and whether these numbers will match with data they will collect for the class, for other classes in the school, or with the entire school population.
- Possible questions to ask are: Why did David Smith choose these numbers to represent the population of the world? Where in the world are these places? Can you find these continents and countries on the map? What do these numbers tell us about the world's population? Why do you think so many people live in some areas, and very few people live in other areas? What kinds of things might we learn as a result of reading this book?

- Have the students locate and indicate the different continents on the map with some type of marker (for example, small flags with pins made from paper).
- Work as a class to label the continents.

The Task

- Students will work in their assigned groups, designated by the teacher, to collect necessary data about the population of the class or other classes in the school; that is, the different countries students or their parents come from and the numbers for each of these, which they will use to compare with the information about the different groups in David Smith's global village.
- Students will need to express the data in fraction, decimal, and percent form.
- Students will compare their calculations with the figures for the different groups in the book. Note: students will need to combine results for countries on the same continent in order to be able to compare their findings with the numbers for the book's populations.
- Students will also use their data to make predictions about figures representing the school's population.

Establish Expectations

- Explain to the students that their job today is to conduct a survey to find out the different countries of origin of their classmates or those of the students of the class to which they have been assigned. They will need to use this information (a) to compare their data with the information in the book, and (b) to predict figures for the school's population.
- They are to record the names of these countries, as well as the number of students from each of these places.
- They will also need to figure out on what continent these countries are found so they can match these with the places (continents or countries) listed in the book.

Development

- Students work in their assigned groups, designated by the teacher, collecting and recording the necessary data about the population of the class or other classes in the school.
- Those students who are experiencing difficulty with the fraction–decimal–percent connection and who are not able to convert fractions whose denominators are not ten or multiples of ten may work with the book's populations, as they are all based on 100.
- Students calculate the fraction, decimal, and percent equivalents for the different groups to which they have been assigned.

- They use these numbers to calculate the figures for the continents and compare these with the figures for the different groups in David Smith's global village.
- They can also use their calculations for the different groups within each class to predict and record their numbers for the school's population.
- If time permits, or as a follow up to the lesson, students can also graph their findings and use these as a way of comparing the information.

Note: Provide a sufficient number of calculators for students to carry out their calculations, particularly for those students who find working with the concepts challenging.

Follow-up

- On completion of the task students meet as a class to share their findings, which they have calculated in fraction, decimal, and percent form.
- As part of the discussion student groups talk about the figures for the class they surveyed, comparing them with each others' findings as well as with the figures calculated for the groups in the book.
- Suggested questions for discussion include:

  Did collecting data about our class and the other classes in the school help you better understand why David Smith chose the figures he did to represent the world's population?

  How do the figures we have compiled for our class, other classes, or our school compare with those in the book?

  Are these numbers a realistic representation of our world?

  How do your figures match with those for the whole school?

  How did your prediction for the whole school match with the actual figures?

- Talking about why some areas of the world are more populated than others and the reasons for this occurrence should stimulate much discussion and serve as a catalyst for further research and information-gathering activities, integrating mathematics with other curriculum areas.

Next Steps

Assessment Notes

- Which students still are having difficulty with the fraction–decimal–percent connection?
- What strategies do I need to consider in order to help these students?
- Which students do not have the percent concept clear?
- Which students need additional enrichment? Where can I find suitable activities?

Reflections on Chapter 17

Writing to Learn

1. Describe three different base-ten models for fractions and decimals, and use each to illustrate how base-ten fractions can easily be represented.
2. How can we help students think about very small place values such as thousandths and millionths in the same way we get students to think about very large place values such as million and billion?
3. Use an example involving base-ten blocks to explain the role of the decimal point in identifying the units position. Relate this idea to changing units of measurement with money or with linear measure.
4. For addition and subtraction of decimal numbers, the line-up-the decimals rule can be reasonably developed through practice with estimation. Explain.
5. Give an example explaining how, in most problems, multiplication and division with decimal numbers can be replaced with estimation and whole-number methods.

For Discussion and Exploration

1. One way to order a series of decimal numbers is to annex zeros to each number so that all numbers have the same number of decimal places. For example, rewrite

0.34	as	0.3400
0.3004	as	0.3004
0.059	as	0.0590

   Now ignore the decimal points and any leading zeros, and order the resulting whole numbers. Discuss the merits of teaching this approach to children. If taught this procedure, what would students learn about decimal numeration? How will you ensure that this process is not just a "rule."

Resources for Chapter 17

Literature Connections

In the daily paper and weekly magazines, you will find decimal and percent situations with endless real-world connections. One issue with percents in news stories is the frequent omission of the base amount or the whole on which the percent is determined. "March sales of video games were reported to be up 3.6 percent." Does that mean an increase over February or over March of the previous year? Increases and decreases by percents are interesting to project over several years. If the consumer price index rises 3 percent a year, how much will a $100.00 basket of groceries cost by the time your students are 21 years old?

The Phantom Tollbooth   *Juster, 1961*

References to mathematical ideas about Milo's adventures in Digitopolis, where everything is number oriented, abound throughout this book. There, Milo meets a boy who is only half of a boy, appearing in the drawing to be the left half of a boy, cut top to bottom. As it turns out, the boy is actually 0.58 since he is a member of the average family: a mother, father, and 2.58 children. The boy is the 0.58. One advantage, he explains, is that he is the only one who can drive the 3/10 or 0.3 of a car, with the average family owning 1.3 cars. This section of the tale involves a great discussion of averages that come out in decimal numbers.

An obvious extension of the story is to explore averages of things that are interesting to the students (average number of siblings, average arm span, etc.) and see where these odd decimal parts come from. In the case of measures of length, for example, an average length can be a real length even if no one has it. But an average number of something like pets can be very humorous as discussed in the story. Where else are fractions and decimals used in this way?

Piece = Part = Portion: Fraction = Decimal = Percent   *Gifford & Thaler, 2008*

Illustrated with vivid photos, this is a beginning look at how fractions relate to corresponding decimals and percents. Written by an elementary classroom teacher, the links between the concepts are drawn through common representations, such as one sneaker representing $\frac{1}{2}$ a pair of shoes, 0.50 in decimal form, or 50 percent. Real-world links such as one-seventh of a week and one-eleventh of a soccer team will connect with students. Note that some decimals and percents are rounded.

Recommendations for Further Reading

Articles

Irwin, K. C. (2001). Using everyday knowledge of decimals to enhance understanding. *Journal for Research in Mathematics Education, 4*, 399–420.

Irwin's article describes her work with 16 children, aged 11 and 12. The students worked in eight pairs, half of whom solved problems given in contexts. The other four pairs solved the same problems but without contexts. The article is enlightening on a number of fronts, particularly the transcriptions that clearly indicate the students' misconceptions of decimal numeration.

Martinie, S. L., & Bay-Williams, J. M. (2003). Investigating students' conceptual understanding of decimal fractions using multiple representations. *Mathematics Teaching in the Middle School, 8*, 244–247.

This article describes the results of 43 grade 6 students who were asked to represent 0.6 and 0.06 with four different representations: a number line, a 10 × 10 grid, money, and base-ten materials. The results indicate that students may appear to understand decimal numbers with one model but not with another. The authors make an argument for using multiple models in teaching decimals.

Books

Albert, L., & McAdam, J. (2007). Making sense of decimal fraction algorithms using base-ten blocks. In W. Gary Martin, Marilyn Strutchens, and Portia Elliott (Eds.), *The learning of mathematics: Sixty-ninth yearbook of the National Council of Teachers of Mathematics* (pp. 303–315). Reston, VA: National Council of Teachers of Mathematics.

This chapter emphasizes the critical need for precise mathematical language in the development of algorithms for multiplying decimal fractions. A classroom example details how teachers can use place-value knowledge and arrays of base-ten blocks to build students' conceptual understanding of decimals. Since the article is about prospective teachers' learning of this material, it is easy to relate to the challenges and connections readers may be experiencing.

Online Resources

100-Grid
http://Argyll.epsb.ca/jreed/math7/strand1/1207.htm

This applet has users select squares on a hundred grid. The proportion of highlighted squares is then displayed in fraction, decimal, and percent form.

Base Blocks—Decimals
http://nlvm.usu.edu/en/nav/frames_asid_264_g_3_t_1.html

Base-ten blocks can be placed on a place-value chart in the same way as for whole numbers. The number of decimal places can be selected, thus designating any of the four blocks as the unit. Addition and subtraction problems can be created or can be generated randomly.

Circle 3
http://nlvm.usu.edu/en/nav/frames_asid_187_g_3_t_1.html

This game challenges students to use logic as they combine decimals to add to 3. Not as easy as it sounds.

Concentration
http://illuminations.nctm.org/Activities.aspx?grade=1&grade=2&grade=3

This is an engaging matching game using representations of percents, fractions, and a regional model.

Fractions Bar Applet
www.arcytech.org/java/fractions/fractions.html

This is a very nice applet for developing the relationships among fractions, decimals, and percents. Bars for one whole are displayed and can be partitioned according to selected fraction, decimal, or percent values and then labelled in any of these representations. This makes equivalencies easy to explore without being too leading.

Fraction Model—Version 3
http://illuminations.nctm.org/ActivityDetail.aspx?ID=45

The equivalence of fraction, decimal, and percent representations in a circle, set, or rectangle model is demonstrated. Versions 1 and 2 are the same but the numerators and denominators are restricted to 20.

Exploring Combined Percentages
www.learnalberta.ca/content/mejhm/index.html?l=0&ID1=AB.MATH.JR.NUMB&ID2=AB.MATH.JR.NUMB.PERC&lesson=html/video_interactives/percentages/percentagesSmall.html

This interactive video illustrates how mathematics is used to analyze plays within a football game. Students can explore combined percentages representing the number of completed passes for two games of a football season. A print activity is included.

Percentages
http://nlvm.usu.edu/en/nav/frames_asid_160_g_3_t_1.html?open=activities

The user enters any two of the values—whole, part, and percent—and clicks on Compute. Although the computer does the work, the applet nicely models percent problems.

Railroad Repair
http://pbskids.org/cyberchase/games/decimals/decimals.html

This fun activity has students repairing a railroad by choosing and combining different sized decimal pieces of railroad tracks to help get Cybertrain back to the station.

Sock
www.interactivestuff.org/sums4fun/sock.html

Click on directional arrows to guide the sphere into pushing the green cubes into holes that contain the decimals that will make the target number.

---

myeducationlab *will help you improve your understanding of the concepts taught in this textbook and in your course. This online tool includes videos of real classroom experiences, sample lesson plans, simulations, case studies, and links to important educational and teaching Web sites that will help you make the transition from student to teacher. As you study in your course and with this textbook, please follow along in* **MyEducationLab**. *Use it! Explore it! And improve your knowledge and your grade!*

Chapter 18
Proportional Reasoning

Proportional reasoning has been referred to as the capstone of the elementary curriculum and the cornerstone of algebra and beyond (Lesh, Post, & Behr, 1987).

Proportional reasoning begins with the ability to understand multiplicative relationships, distinguishing them from relationships that are additive in nature. The development of proportional reasoning is one of the most important goals of the grade 5–8 curriculum.

Proportional reasoning goes well beyond the notion of setting up a proportion to solve a problem. It is a way of reasoning about multiplicative situations. In fact, proportional reasoning, like equivalence, is considered to be a unifying theme in mathematics. You will see evidence of this in the many content connections listed on this page.

Big Ideas

1. A ratio is a multiplicative comparison of two quantities or measures. A key developmental milestone is the ability of a student to begin to think of a ratio as a distinct entity, different from the two measures from which it is composed.

2. Ratios and proportions involve multiplicative rather than additive comparisons. Equal ratios result from multiplication or division, not from addition or subtraction.

3. Proportional thinking is developed through activities involving comparing and determining the equivalence of ratios and solving proportions in a wide variety of problem-based contexts and situations without recourse to rules or formulas.

Mathematics Content Connections

Proportional reasoning is indeed the cornerstone of a wide variety of topics in the elementary and high school curriculum.

- **Algebra** (Chapter 14): Much of algebra concerns a study of change. Hence, rates of change (ratios) are particularly impor-

tant. In this chapter you will see that the graphs of equivalent ratios are straight lines passing through the origin. The slope of the line is the unit ratio.

- **Fractions** (Chapter 15): Equivalent fractions are found through a multiplicative process; numerators and denominators are multiplied or divided by the same number. Equivalent ratios can be found in the same manner. In fact, part–whole relationships (fractions) are an example of ratio. Fractions are also one of the principal methods of representing ratios.

- **Percents** (Chapter 17): Percents are a way of describing an amount as if it were out of 100. This is a part–whole ratio. For example, a 65 percent approval rating means the ratio of those who approved to those asked is 65 to 100.

- **Geometry** (Chapter 20): When two figures are the same shape but different sizes (i.e., similar), they constitute a visual example of a proportion. The ratios of linear measures in one figure will be equal to the corresponding ratios in the other.

- **Data Graphs** (Chapter 21): A relative frequency histogram shows the frequencies of different related events compared to all outcomes (visual part-to-whole ratios). A box-and-whisker plot shows the relative distribution of data along a number line and can be used to compare distributions of populations of very different sizes.

- **Probability** (Chapter 22): A probability is a ratio that compares the number of outcomes in an event to the total possible outcomes. Proportional reasoning helps students understand these ratios, especially in comparing large and small sample sizes.

Ratios

Regardless of how the objectives are stated in your curriculum regarding the ability to solve proportions or percent problems, the ultimate goal for your students should be to develop proportional reasoning, rather than to build a collection of skills. To this end it is useful to have a good idea of what constitutes a ratio and a proportion and in what contexts these mathematical ideas appear. With this information, we can then examine what it means to reason proportionally and begin to work toward helping students achieve that goal.

Types of Ratios

A *ratio* is a number that relates two quantities or measures within a given situation in a multiplicative relationship (in contrast to a difference or additive relationship). A ratio can be applied to another situation where the relative amounts of the quantities or measures are the same as in the first situation (Smith, 2002). Ratios appear in a variety of different contexts. Part of proportional reasoning is the ability to recognize ratios in these various settings. To the student just beginning to develop an understanding of ratio, different settings or contexts may well seem like different ideas even though they are essentially the same from a mathematical viewpoint.

Research shows that Chinese teachers spend a considered amount of time making sense of the subtle differences among fractions, ratios, and division (Cai and Wang, 2006). Table 18.1 offers comparisons among fractions, ratios, and division similar to those used in Chinese lessons, as prompts for students to discuss the relationships among these ideas.

Part-to-Whole Ratios   Ratios can express comparisons of a part to a whole. For example, the ratio of the number of girls to the number of students in the class is a part-to-whole ratio. Because fractions are also part–whole ratios, it follows that every fraction is also a ratio. In the same way, percentages are ratios. In fact, percentages are sometimes used to express ratios. Probabilities are also ratios because a part of a sample space is being compared to the whole sample space.

Part-to-Part Ratios   A ratio can also relate one part of a whole to another part of the same whole. For example, the number of girls in the class can be compared to the number of boys. The ratio of the length to the width of a rectangle

The toy-car to real-car ratio is an example of comparisons students could be encouraged to explore across a range of ratio and proportion tasks, including situations involving measurements, prices, geometric and other visual contexts, and rates of all sorts. Students may need as much as three years' worth of opportunities to reason in multiplicative situations to adequately develop proportional reasoning skills.

is a part-to-part relationship. Although the probability of an event is a part-to-whole ratio, the *odds* of an event happening is a ratio of the number of ways an event can happen to the number of ways it cannot happen—a part-to-part ratio.

Rates as Ratios   Both part-to-whole and part-to-part ratios compare two measures of the same type of thing. A ratio can also be a *rate*. A rate is a comparison of the measures

Table 18.1

Comparison of Fractions, Ratios, and Division				
Concept	**First Value**	**Symbol**	**Second Value**	**Result**
Ratio	First term	: Colon	Second term	Value of ratio
Fraction	Numerator	— Fraction line	Denominator	Value of fraction
Division	Dividend	÷ Division sign	Divisor	Quotient

Source: Adapted from Cai and Wang, 2006.

of two different things or quantities; the measuring unit is different for each value.

For example, if 4 similar boats carry 36 passengers, then the comparison of 4 boats to 36 passengers is a ratio. Boats and passengers are different types of things. The rate would be the passengers per boat: $\frac{p}{b} = \frac{36}{4} = \frac{9}{1}$. The ratio of passengers to boats is 36:4, which can also be written as $\frac{36}{4}$ or 36 to 4. The rate is 9 passengers per boat. Similarly, all rates of speed are ratios that compare distance to time: for example, driving at 90 kilometres per hour or jogging at 4.8 minutes per kilometre.

Kilometres per litre, square metres of coverage per litre of paint, passengers per busload, and roses per bouquet are all rates. Relationships between two units of measure are also rates or ratios—for example, millilitres per litre and grams per kilogram.

Examples of Ratio In geometry, the ratios of corresponding parts of similar geometric figures are always the same. The diagonal of a square is always $\sqrt{2}$ times a side; that is, the ratio of the diagonal of a square to its side is $\sqrt{2}$. The value π (pi) is the ratio of the circumference of a circle to the diameter.

The slope of a line or of a roof is a ratio of rise for each unit of horizontal distance or run. Slope is an extremely important ratio in algebra. Not only does it describe the steepness of a line, it also tells us the rate of change of one variable in terms of another.

In nature, the ratio known as the *golden ratio* is found in many spirals, from nautilus shells to the swirls of a pine-cone or a pineapple. Artists and architects have used the same ratio in creating shapes that are naturally pleasing to the eye. (See the problem-based lesson in this chapter for further information about the golden ratio.)

Recall that a ratio is a number that expresses a multiplicative relationship that can be applied to a second situation where the relative quantities or measures are the same as in the first situation.

Proportional Reasoning

Proportional reasoning is difficult to define in a simple sentence or two. It is not something that you either can or cannot do. It is both a qualitative and quantitative process. According to Lamon (1999), the following are a few of the characteristics of proportional thinkers:

- Proportional thinkers have a sense of co-variation. That is, they understand relationships in which two quantities vary and they are able to see how the variation in one coincides with the variation in another.
- Proportional thinkers recognize proportional relationships as distinct from non-proportional relationships, in real-world contexts.

- Proportional thinkers develop a wide variety of strategies for solving proportions or comparing ratios, most of which are based on informal strategies rather than prescribed algorithms.
- Proportional thinkers understand ratios as distinct entities representing a relationship different from the quantities they compare.

It is estimated that more than half of the adult population cannot be viewed as proportional thinkers (Lamon, 1999). That means that we do not acquire the habits and skills of proportional reasoning simply by getting older. On the other hand, Lamon's research and that of others indicate that instruction that focuses on reasoning (rather than a formula) can have an effect on students' ability to reason proportionally, which begins early with multiplicative reasoning. Chinese students begin their formal exploration of ratio and proportion in the elementary grades (Cai & Sun, 2002). In Canada, these concepts are generally taught in grades 6–9. It is important to keep in mind that merely focusing on the procedure of finding the missing value in a proportion encourages students to apply rules without thinking. Hence, the ability to reason proportionally often does not develop.

Considerable research has been conducted to determine how children reason in various proportionality tasks and to determine if developmental or instructional factors are related to proportional reasoning (for example, see Bright, Joyner, & Wallis, 2003; Karplus, Pulos, & Stage, 1983; Lamon, 1993, 2002; Lo & Watanabe, 1997; Noelting, 1980; and Post, Behr, & Lesh, 1988).

The research provides direction for how to help children develop proportional thought processes. Some of these ideas are outlined here.

1. Provide ratio and proportion tasks in a wide range of contexts. These might include situations involving measurements, prices, geometric and other visual contexts, and rates of all sorts.
2. Encourage discussion and experimentation in predicting and comparing ratios. Help children distinguish between proportional and non-proportional comparisons by providing examples of each and discussing the differences.
3. Help children relate proportional reasoning to existing processes. The concept of unit fractions is very similar to unit rates. Research indicates that the use of a unit rate for comparing ratios and solving proportions is the most common approach among junior high students even when cross-product methods have been taught. (This approach is explained later.)
4. Recognize that symbolic or mechanical methods, such as the cross-product algorithm, for solving proportions do not develop proportional reasoning and should not be introduced until students have had many experi-

ences with intuitive and conceptual methods. "The cross-product algorithm is efficient but often has little meaning" (Saskatchewan Education, 1996).

No one method for solving proportions should be favoured over another, and none should be taught in a rote manner. In the beginning, activities should focus on the development of understanding rather than on efficient strategies (Saskatchewan Education, 1996). Activities and guided discussion should help students learn to think proportionally in a variety of ways and contexts.

 In 1989, the *Curriculum Standards* noted that proportional reasoning "was of such great importance that it merits whatever time and effort must be expended to assure its careful development" (NCTM, 1989, p. 82). The emphasis on proportional reasoning is similarly reflected in the 2000 *Standards*. The *Principles and Standards* authors have focused on the need for an integrative approach, one that involves "percent, similarity, scaling, linear equations, slope, relative frequency histograms, and probability" (NCTM, 2000, p. 212).

Additive Versus Multiplicative Situations

Consider the following problem adapted from the book *Adding It Up* (National Research Council, 2001).

Two weeks ago, two flowers were measured at 20 centimetres and 30 centimetres, respectively. Today they are 28 centimetres and 38 centimetres tall. Did the 20 centimetre or 30 centimetre flower grow more?

❚❚ ———————— *Pause and Reflect*

Before reading further, find and defend two different answers to this problem.

One answer is that they both grew the same amount—8 centimetres. This correct response is based on additive reasoning. That is, a single quantity was added to each measure to result in the two new measures. A second way to look at the problem is to compare the amount of growth to the original height of the flower. The first flower grew $\frac{8}{20}$ or $\frac{4}{10}$ of its height while the second grew $\frac{8}{30}$ or $\frac{4}{15}$. Based on this multiplicative view (growing $\frac{8}{20}$ or $\frac{4}{10}$ *times as much* more), the first flower grew more. This is a proportional view of this change situation. Here, both the additive reasoning and multiplicative reasoning produce valid, albeit different, answers. Discussions should focus on the nature of the comparison, thus highlighting the distinction between additive and multiplicative comparisons. An ability to understand

the difference between these situations is an indication of proportional reasoning.

 As a further aid to help you understand the complexities of proportional reasoning, consider the following three items, adapted from Bright, Joyner, and Walls (2003), to assess students' appropriate use of additive or multiplicative reasoning. Notice the way that each item addresses the possibility of using additive versus multiplicative reasoning. These questions could be used in the classroom for pre-assessment or possibly for summative assessment. You might want to add one or two more questions.

1. Christina and Marielena were running equally fast around a track. Christina started first. When Christina had run 9 laps, Marielena had run 3 laps. When Marielena had completed 15 laps, how many laps had Christina run?

    a. 45 laps
    b. 24 laps
    c. 21 laps
    d. 6 laps

2. At the midway point of the basketball season, you must recommend the best free-throw shooter for the all-star game. Here are the statistics for four players.

    Novak: 8 of 11 shots Peterson: 22 of 29 shots
    Williams: 15 of 19 shots Reynolds: 33 of 41 shots

    Which player is the best free-throw shooter?

3. Write your answer to this problem.

    A farmer had three orchards. One is 56 metres × 75 metres, one is 23 metres × 35 metres, and one is 139 metres × 155 metres. If you were flying over these orchards, which one would seem to be most square? Which one would seem least square? Explain your answers. ◆

Identifying Multiplicative Relationships

As noted earlier, students may confuse additive situations for multiplicative situations. Making explicit the type of relationships that exist between two values can greatly support students' understanding of ratios and proportions. Consider the following situation suggested by Cai and Sun in their discussion of how Chinese teachers introduce the concept of ratio (2002, p. 196):

> Miller Middle School has 16 grade 6 students, and 12 of them say that they are basketball fans. The remaining students are not basketball fans.

Students are asked to describe whatever relationships they can between students who are basketball fans and those who are not. Once it is determined that there are four non-fans, there are now several different possibilities including these:

- There are eight more fans than non-fans.
- There are three times as many fans as non-fans.
- For every three students who like basketball, there is one who does not.

Of these, the first is an additive relationship—focusing on the difference between the two numbers. The other two are variations of the multiplicative relationship, each expressing the 3-to-1 ratio of fans to non-fans in a slightly different way. A discussion helps to contrast the multiplicative relationship with the additive one.

In the following activities, two ratios are compared. As with the earlier flower-growing problem, the choices can be made using either additive or multiplicative reasoning, providing your class with a helpful distinction between the two types of relationships without your attempting to define ratio for them.

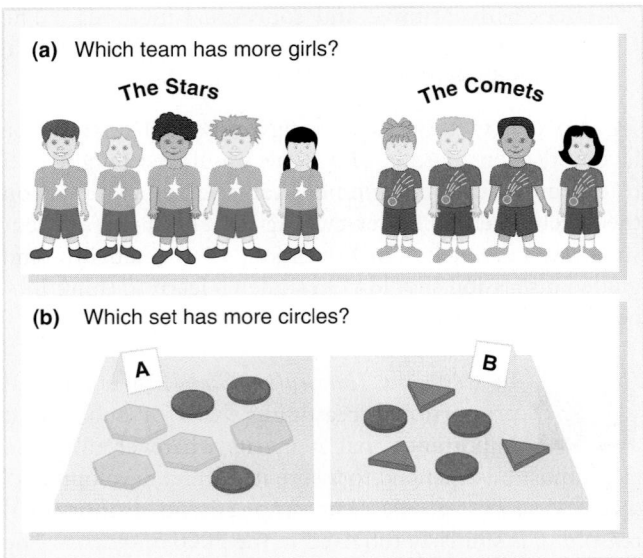

Figure 18.1 Two pictorial situations that can be interpreted with either additive or multiplicative comparisons.

Activity 18.1

Which Has More?

Provide students with two or three situations similar to those in Figure 18.1. Whether students work individually or in groups, a follow-up class discussion is imperative. This discussion can provide you with insights into how students are thinking and can also provide opportunities for students to help others see the situations from different perspectives.

Do not prompt students by telling them to look for a multiplicative relationship, but wait to see what sorts of answers the students offer.

The situations in Figure 18.1 can be interpreted either additively or multiplicatively. The ambiguity is the key: If students recognize and understand the difference between the additive and multiplicative approaches, this is a start to being able to reason proportionally. As with the flower problem, both interpretations are correct. You are looking for awareness that there is a different way of looking at the situation. If at first they do not voluntarily suggest another way, ask a different question: for example, "Rianna says it is the second group. Can you explain why she made that choice?" or "Which class team has a larger proportion of girls?"

Return for a moment to the earlier lap running question on p. 363. This item has been used in other studies that showed students tried to solve it as a proportion problem when it is strictly an additive situation.

The two runners will end up six laps apart, which is how they began. Watson and Shaughnessy (2004) note that, often, the way we word problems is a dead giveaway

that a proportion is involved. Students have learned how to arrange four quantities in a proportion, but they don't pay attention to whether there is a multiplicative relationship between the numbers. They are focused on the structure of the proportion, not the concept of the proportion (Heinz & Boatwright, 2008).

The next problem is similar in nature to the flower problem discussed earlier. It allows for an additive or multiplicative interpretation.

Activity 18.2

Weight Loss

Show students the data in the following chart:

Week	Max	Moe	Minnie
0	95	71	51
2	91	69	49
4	88	67	45

Max, Moe, and Minnie are each on a diet and have recorded their weight in kilograms at the start of their diet and at two-week intervals. After four weeks, which person is the most successful dieter?

The task is to make three different arguments—one that would favour each of the three dieters.

The way that the task in "Weight Loss" is presented, the students are forewarned that there are differing arguments and the results will ensure a good discussion. (The argument for Moe is that he is the most steady in his loss.)

Equivalent Ratios

In selection activities, a ratio is presented and students select an equivalent ratio from a range of others presented. The focus should be on an intuitive rationale for why the pairs selected are in the same ratio. Sometimes numerical values will play a part to help students develop numerical methods to explain their reasoning. In later activities, students will be asked to construct an equivalent ratio without choices being provided.

It is extremely useful in these activities to include pairs of ratios that are not proportional but have a common difference. For example, $\frac{5}{8}$ and $\frac{9}{12}$ are not equivalent ratios, but the corresponding differences are the same: $8 - 5 = 12 - 9$. Students who focus on this additive relationship are not seeing the multiplicative relationship of proportionality. Using contexts in comparing ratios helps students articulate their multiplicative or proportional thinking. Activity 18.3 uses sides of a rectangle as the context (linking to the important concepts of similarity and scale drawings).

Activity 18.3

Look-Alike Rectangles

Provide groups of students with a copy of Blackline Masters 30 and 31, shown in Figure 18.2, and have them cut out the 10 rectangles. Three of the rectangles (A, I, and D) have sides in the ratio of 3 to 4. Rectangles C, F, and H have sides in the ratio of 5 to 8. Rectangles J, E, and G have sides in the ratio of 1 to 3. Rectangle B is a square, so its sides are in the ratio of 1 to 1.

The task is to group the rectangles into three sets of three rectangles that "look alike" with one "oddball." If your students know the word *similar* from geometry, you can use that instead of "look alike." To explain what "look alike" means, draw three rectangles on the board with two that are similar and one that is clearly dissimilar to the other two, as in the following example. Have students use their language to explain why rectangles 1 and 3 are alike.

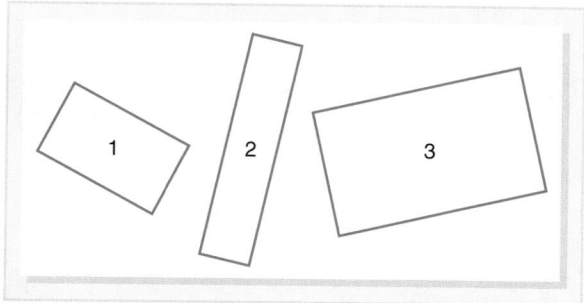

When students have decided on their groupings, stop and discuss the reasons they classified the rectangles as they did. Be prepared for some students to try to match

sides or look for rectangles that have the same amount of difference between them. Next have the students measure and record the sides of each rectangle to the nearest half-centimetre. They should then calculate the ratios of the short to long sides for each. Blackline Master 31 can be used to record the data. Discuss these results and ask students to offer explanations regarding how the ratios and groupings are related. If the groups are made up of proportional (similar) rectangles, the ratios within each group will all be the same.

From a geometric standpoint, "Look-Alike Rectangles" is an activity about similarity. The two concepts—proportionality and similarity—are closely connected.

Another characteristic of proportional rectangles can be observed by stacking like rectangles aligned at one corner, as in Figure 18.3. Place a straight-edge across the diagonals, and you will see that opposite corners also line up. If the rectangles are placed on a coordinate axis with the common corner at the origin, the slope of the line joining the corners is the ratio of the sides. Here is a connection between proportional reasoning and algebra.

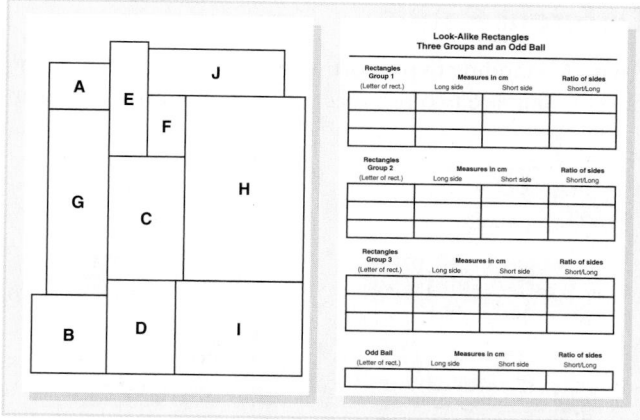

Figure 18.2 Blackline Masters 30 and 31 for use with Activity 18.3.

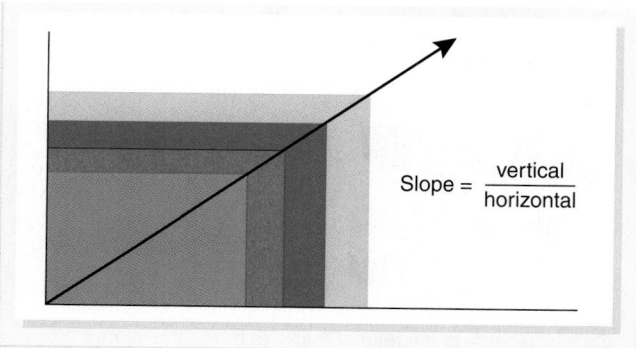

Figure 18.3 The slope of a line through a stack of proportional rectangles is equal to the ratio of the two sides.

Activity 18.4

Different Objects, Same Ratios

Prepare cards with distinctly different objects, as shown in Figure 18.4. Given one card, students then select another card on which the ratio of the two types of objects is the same. This task moves students to a numerical approach rather than a visual one and introduces the notion of ratios as rates. In this context, it makes the most sense to find the boxes per truck as the rate (rather than trucks per box). Finding the rate (the amount for 1 unit) for pairs of quantities facilitates comparisons (like the unit prices provided in supermarkets that allow you to compare the cost of different items).

Accommodation

For those students who might be experiencing difficulty with the concept of ratios as rates and unit rates, reviewing equivalent fractions and concentrating on the connection between the concepts would be helpful.

Different Ratios

An understanding of proportional situations includes being able to compare two ratios as well as to identify equivalent ratios. The following activity has been used in various studies of proportional reasoning.

Activity 18.5

Grape Punch

Show students a picture of two bowls of grape punch as in Figure 18.5. The bowls both have the same amount of grape punch. The little squares indicate the recipes used in each bowl. A purple square is a litre of grape juice and a yellow square is a litre of ginger ale. The task is to decide which bowl will have the stronger grape flavour or if they will both taste the same. Have students justify their answers.

⏸ —————————— *Pause and Reflect*

Solve the "Grape Punch" problem and jot down your reasoning. Can you think of more than one argument to support your conclusion?

The task in the "Grape Punch" problem is challenging for many students. It is interesting because of how many ways there are to make the comparison. A common method is to figure out how much ginger ale goes with each litre of grape juice. As we will see later, this is using a unit rate: litres of ginger ale per litre of grape juice ($1\frac{1}{2}$ vs. $1\frac{1}{3}$). Other approaches use fractions instead of unit rates and attempt to compare the fractions: grape juice compared to ginger ale ($\frac{2}{3}$ vs. $\frac{3}{4}$) or the reverse, also grape juice as a fraction of the total ($\frac{2}{5}$ vs. $\frac{3}{7}$). This can also be done with ginger ale as a fraction of the total. Some students may also use percentages instead of fractions, creating the same arguments. Another argument involves considering duplicates of one or both of the bowls until either the ginger ale or the grape juice is equal in both. (Make sure that you can both create and justify each of these various solutions.)

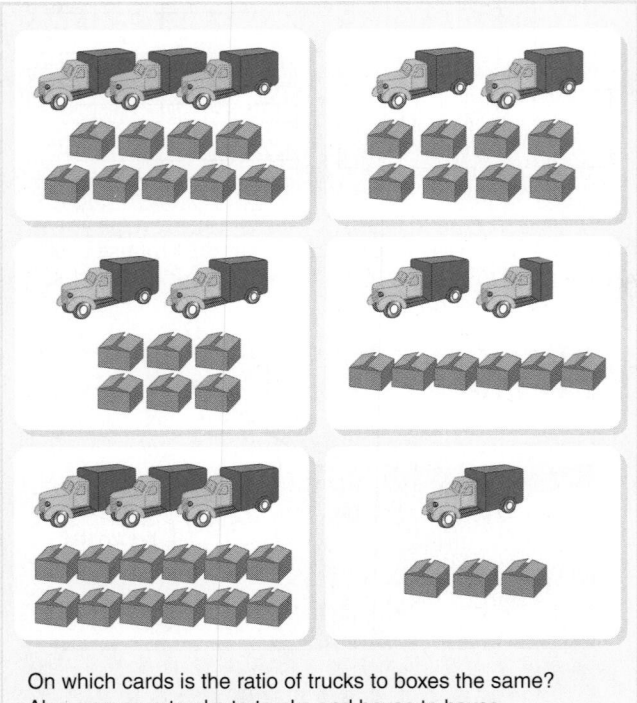

On which cards is the ratio of trucks to boxes the same? Also, compare trucks to trucks and boxes to boxes.

Figure 18.4 Ratio cards for exploring ratios and rates.

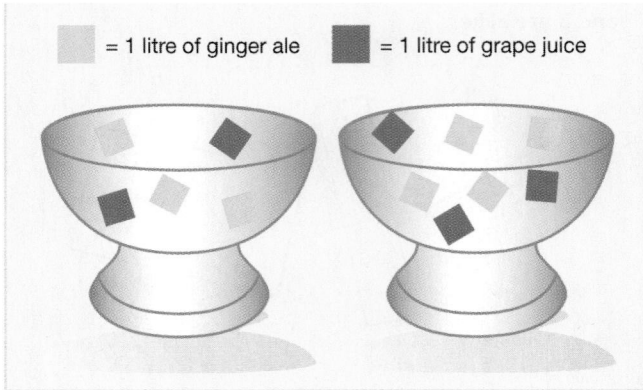

☐ = 1 litre of ginger ale   ■ = 1 litre of grape juice

Figure 18.5 Assume that both bowls are filled with the same amount of grape punch. The little squares indicate the recipe flavour. Will they taste the same?

One of the most interesting arguments is that the bowls will taste the same: If the grape juice and the ginger ale are matched up in each bowl, then there will be one litre of ginger ale left in each recipe. Although incorrect (can you tell why?), your class will likely have a spirited discussion about these ideas.

The grape punch problem can be adjusted for difficulty. As given, the two mixtures are reasonably close and there are no simple relationships between the two bowls of punch. If the solutions are 3 to 6 and 4 to 8 (equal flavours), the task is much simpler. For a 2-to-5 recipe versus a 4-to-9 recipe, it is easy to double the first and compare it to the second. When a 3-to-6 recipe is compared to a 2-to-5 recipe, the unit rates are perhaps more obvious (1 to 2 vs. 1 to $2\frac{1}{2}$).

The following problem also is adapted from the research literature.

Two groups of children, the Bear Scouts and the Raccoon Scouts, are having pizza parties. The Bear Scouts' leader ordered enough pizza so that every 3 scouts will have 2 pizzas. The Raccoon Scouts' leader ordered 3 pizzas for every 5 scouts. Did the Bear Scouts or the Raccoon Scouts have more pizza to eat?

Figure 18.6 shows two different reasoning strategies. When the pizzas are sliced into fractional parts (Figure 18.6(a)), the approach is to look for a unit rate—pizzas per scout. A sharing approach has been used for each ratio just as described for fractions in Chapter 15. But notice that this problem does not say that the troops have only 3 and 5 scouts, respectively. Any multiples of 2 to 3 and 3 to 5 can be used to make the appropriate comparison, the same as making multiple bowls of grape punch. This is the approach used in Figure 18.6(b). Three "clones" of the 2-to-3 ratio

and two clones of the 3-to-5 ratio are made so that a like number of scouts getting pizzas can be compared. From a fractions perspective, this is like getting common numerators. Because there are more scouts in the Raccoon troop ratio (larger denominator), there is less pizza for each scout.

Ratio Tables

Ratio tables or charts that show how two variable quantities are related are often good ways to organize information. Consider the following table:

Hectares	5	10	15	20	25		
Pine trees	75	150	225				

If the task is to find the number of trees for 35 hectares of land or the number of hectares needed for 825 trees, students can easily proceed by using addition. That is, they can add 5s along the top row until they reach 35. As discussed in Chapter 14, this is a recursive pattern, or repeated addition strategy. The pattern that connects hectares to pine trees is the generative pattern and the multiplicative relationship between the values. The equation for this situation is $y = 15x$, a proportional situation, discussed in Chapter 14 as a subset of linear equations.

Ratio tables may not always be in organized lists where a pattern can be found. In fact, ratio tables can be used when only one ratio is known and you are trying to find a specific equivalent ratio. Then the ratio table can be used as a strategy for solving a proportion. The following activity provides examples and Figure 18.7 illustrates this use of a ratio table.

Activity **18.6**

Using Ratio Tables

Given a situation like one of the following, build a ratio table and use it to answer the question. Tasks are adapted from Lamon (1999, p. 183).

a. **A person whose mass is 80 kilograms on Earth will have a mass of 208 kilograms on the planet Jupiter. Suppose a person's mass is 60 kilograms on Earth. What will it be on Jupiter?**

b. **At the local college, 5 out of every 8 graduating year students live in apartments. How many of the 30 graduating year math majors are likely to live in an apartment?**

c. **The tax on a purchase of $20 is $1.12. How much tax will there be on a purchase of $45.50?**

d. **When in Australia you can exchange $4.50 Canadian for $5.25 Australian. How much is $17.50 Australian in Canadian dollars?**

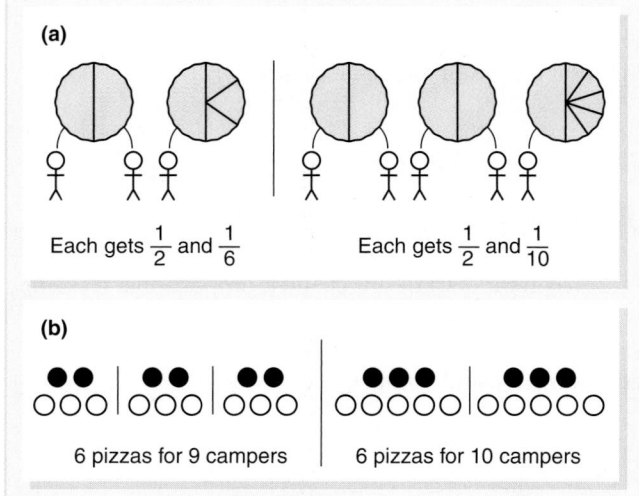

(a)

Each gets $\frac{1}{2}$ and $\frac{1}{6}$ Each gets $\frac{1}{2}$ and $\frac{1}{10}$

(b)

6 pizzas for 9 campers   6 pizzas for 10 campers

Figure 18.6 Two reasoning methods for comparing two ratios.

The tasks in this activity are typical "solve the proportion" tasks. One ratio and part of a second are given with the task being to find the fourth number. However, tasks such as these should come long before any formal approach is suggested. Note further, in no case is it easy to simply add or subtract to get to the desired entry. Rather, the student should use a ratio table to solve the problem. Figure 18.7 shows three different ways to solve the Jupiter problem using ratio tables.

The format of these ratio tables is not essential to solving the problem. Some students may not use a table format at all and simply draw arrows and explain in words how they got from one ratio to another. You may find value in a more structured format.

Pause and Reflect

Use a ratio table strategy to solve the last three problems from Activity 18.6. Describe any advantages this approach has over a cross-product algorithm.

The following problem and the table in Figure 18.8 are adapted from Lamon (1999, p. 233). Notice that the numbers are not "nice" at all.

Cheese is on sale for $4.25 per kilogram. How much will 12.13 kilograms cost?

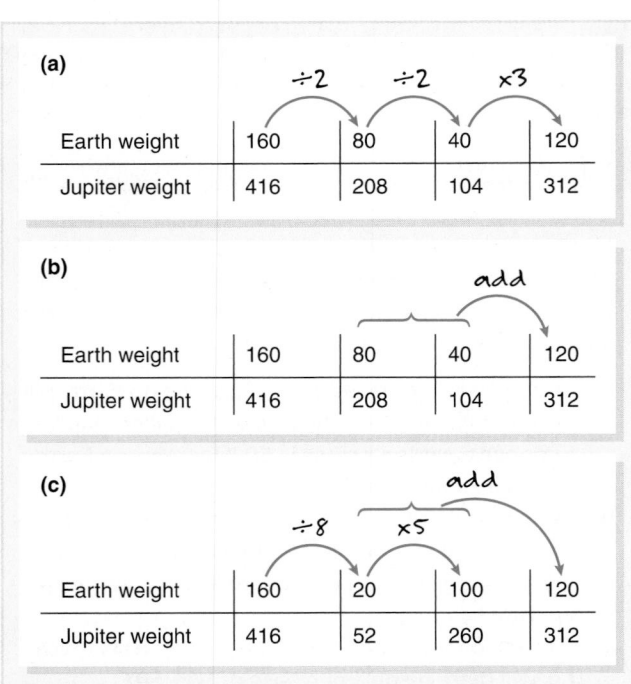

(a)

	÷2	÷2	×3
Earth weight	160	80	40	120
Jupiter weight	416	208	104	312

(b)

			add
Earth weight	160	80	40	120
Jupiter weight	416	208	104	312

(c)

	÷8	×5	add
Earth weight	160	20	100	120
Jupiter weight	416	52	260	312

Figure 18.7 80 kilograms on Earth is 208 kilograms on Jupiter. If the mass of something is 60 kilograms on Earth, how many kilograms will it weigh on Jupiter? Here are three solutions using ratio tables.

	Kilograms	Cost	Notes
A	1	4.25	Given
B	10	42.50	A × 10
C	2	8.50	A × 2
D	0.1	0.425	A ÷ 10
E	12.1	51.425	B + C + D
F	0.01	0.0425	D ÷ 10
G	0.03	0.1275	F × 3
H	12.13	51.5525	E + G

Figure 18.8 A more structured ratio table. The Notes column shows what was done in each step. The task is to find the cost of 12.13 kilograms.

The format in Figure 18.8 allows for easier tracing of what was done at each step. The format is just that—a format. It is not the same as an algorithm. For any problem there are likely to be several different reasonable ratio tables. In applying this technique, students are using multiplicative relationships to transform a given ratio into an equivalent ratio. As Lamon points out, the process is not at all random. Students should mentally devise a plan for getting from one number to another.

The tasks suggested in Activity 18.6 had quite reasonable numbers. However, as you can see from the cheese example, it is quite possible to use this technique with almost any numbers. By using easy multiples and divisors, often the arithmetic can be done mentally.

 It should be clear to students why the same factor must be used on both entries in a ratio table. For example, in row A of Figure 18.8, both the 1 and the 4.25 are multiplied by 10. In row G, both entries are multiplied by 3. Each pair of entries comprises a ratio. An equivalent ratio is found by multiplying both entries by the same number. ◆

Proportional Reasoning Across the Curriculum

As noted at the start of this chapter, proportional reasoning is essential to many concepts in the curriculum. Here are some brief examples in algebra, measurement and geometry, statistics, and number.

Algebra

Graphing ratios provides a powerful connection to algebra. As discussed earlier in this chapter and in Chapter 14, proportional situations are linear situations. In fact, ratios are a special case of linear situations that will always go through the origin, since they are multiplicative relationships. The ratio or rate is the slope of the graph.

Any ratio table provides data that can be graphed. Make each axis correspond to one of the quantities in the table. This idea is developed in the next activity.

Activity 18.7

Rectangle Ratios—Revisited

Have students make a graph of the data from a collection of equal ratios that they have scaled or discussed. The graph in Figure 18.9 represents the ratios of two sides of similar rectangles. If only a few ratios have actually been plotted, the graph can be drawn carefully, then used to determine other equivalent ratios. This is especially interesting when there is a physical model to coincide with the ratio. In the rectangle example, students can draw rectangles with sides determined by the graphs and compare them to the original rectangles. A unit ratio can be found by locating the point on the line at *x* = 1 or at *y* = 1. Ask students to see if they can find a rectangle that has a non-integer side (e.g., $4\frac{1}{2}$ units). Ask students how, if they knew the short side, they could find the long side (and vice versa).

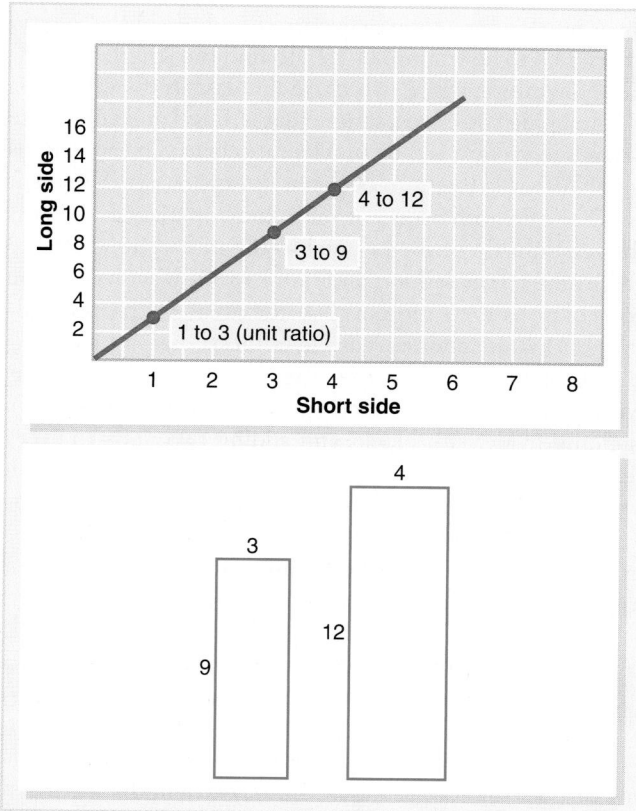

Figure 18.9 Graphs show ratios of sides in similar rectangles.

Graphs provide another way of thinking about proportions, and they connect proportional thought to algebraic interpretations. All graphs of equivalent ratios fall along straight lines that pass through the origin. If the equation of one of these lines is written in the form $y = mx$, the slope *m* is always one of the equivalent ratios. Note that the slope of any line through the origin is the ratio of the *y*-coordinate at any point with the *x*-coordinate of the same point.

Measurement and Geometry

In these activities, students make measurements or construct physical or visual models of equivalent ratios in order to provide a tangible example of a proportion as well as to look at numerical relationships.

Activity 18.8

Different Units, Equal Ratios

Cut strips of adding machine tape all the same length, and give one strip to each group in your class. Each group is to measure the strip using a different non-standard unit. Possible units include interlocking cubes, a piece of chalk, a pencil, the edge of a book, or index card. When every group has measured their strip, ask for one of the group's measurements. At the same time, display the unit of measure the group used. Next, hold up the unit of measure used by another group, and have the class compare it with the first one. See if the class can estimate the measurement that the second group found. The ratio of the measuring units should be the inverse of the measurements made with those units. For example, if two measuring units are in the ratio of 2 to 3, the respective measurements will be in a ratio of 3 to 2. Examine measurements made with other units. Finally, present a unit that no group has used, and see if the class can predict what the measurement will be when made with that unit.

Activity 18.8 can be extended by providing each group with an identical set of four strips of quite different lengths. Good lengths might be 20, 50, 80, and 120 centimetres. As before, each group is given a different unit for measuring the strips.

This time, have each group enter data into a common spreadsheet. (Alternatively, share group data so that all groups can enter data on their own spreadsheets.) Figure 18.10 shows what a spreadsheet might look like for three groups. A template can be prepared ahead of time, or students can create their own spreadsheets. Almost all spreadsheets will offer a variety of graphing options. In this activity, bar graphs show the actual measurements for each group and circle graphs show each measure in ratio to the sum of the measures (i.e., a percentage of total measures).

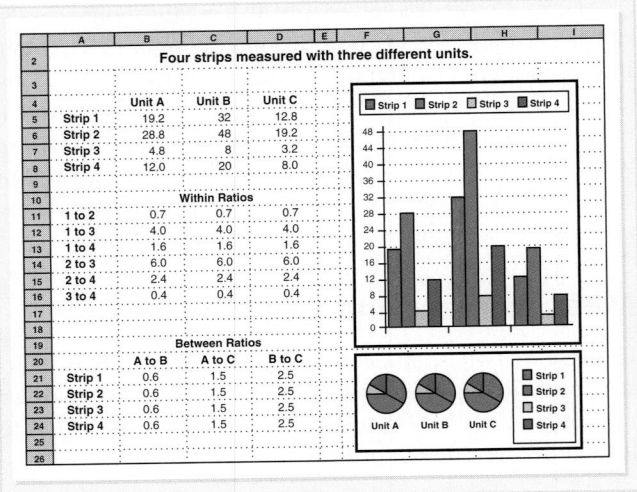

Figure 18.10 A spreadsheet can be used to record data, create tables of interesting ratios, and produce bar and circle graphs.

Source: Screen reprinted with permission from Apple Computer, Inc.

Once the graphs are completed, there are numerous opportunities to observe and explore multiplicative relationships within and between ratios. The bar graphs, though different in size, all look "alike." Since the circle graphs illustrate the ratios rather than the actual measurements, they will be identical or nearly so. Within ratios (for a set of strips) and between ratios (one unit to another) are easily calculated with the spreadsheet. (Within and between ratios are discussed later in the chapter.)

Continue the exploration by introducing a new strip. If you know its measurement with any one of the units, what will its measurement be with the other units? Similarly, if a new unit of measure is introduced, how can the measurements of the strips be determined? Can this be done by comparing the new unit with an old one? If a known strip is measured with the new unit, can all other measurements and ratios be determined?

The task just described may take several days to complete, but the time is well spent. Students will be able to solidify the different multiplicative relationships through the numerical and graphical representations.

Scale Drawings

The connection between proportional reasoning and the geometric concept of similarity is very important. Similar figures provide a visual representation of proportions, and proportional thinking enhances the understanding of similarity. Discussion of the similar figures should focus on the ratios between and within the figures. The next two activities are aimed at this connection.

Part three of Activity 18.9 involves area as well as length. Comparisons of corresponding lengths, areas, and volumes in proportional figures lead to some interesting patterns. If two figures are proportional (similar), any two linear dimensions you measure on each figure will be in the same ratio, say, for example, 1 to k (the variable k is often used with proportions, whereas m is used with equations to describe slope; both refer to the rate or ratio between two values). This means if a similar figure is twice the length of the original figure, then each corresponding side has a ratio of original to new figure of 1:2. To find the length of a new side, you multiply by 2, which, in this case, is the value of k.

Imagine you have a square that is 3 by 3 and you create a new square that is 6 by 6. The ratio between the lengths is 1:2. What is the ratio between the two areas? Why is it × 4? Try the same concept for volume of a cube—what is the relationship of the original to the new volume? Why? Returning to the sailboat in Figure 18.11, what would you conjecture is the ratio between the areas of the two sailboats? Measure and test your hypothesis.

As a means of contrasting proportional situations with additive ones, try starting with a figure on a grid or a building made with blocks and adding two units to every dimension in the figure. The result will be larger but will be a similar shape. Try this with a simple rectangle that is 1 centimetre by 15 centimetre. The new rectangle is twice as "thick" (2 centimetres) but only a bit longer. It will not appear to be the same shape as the original.

Dynamic geometry software such as as *GeoGebra* (a free download from www.geogebra.org) or *The Geometer's Sketchpad* (Key Curriculum Press) offers a very effective method of exploring the idea of ratio. In Figure 18.12, two lengths are drawn on a grid using the "snap-to-grid" option. The lengths are measured, and two ratios are computed. As the length of

Are the Measurements Proportional?

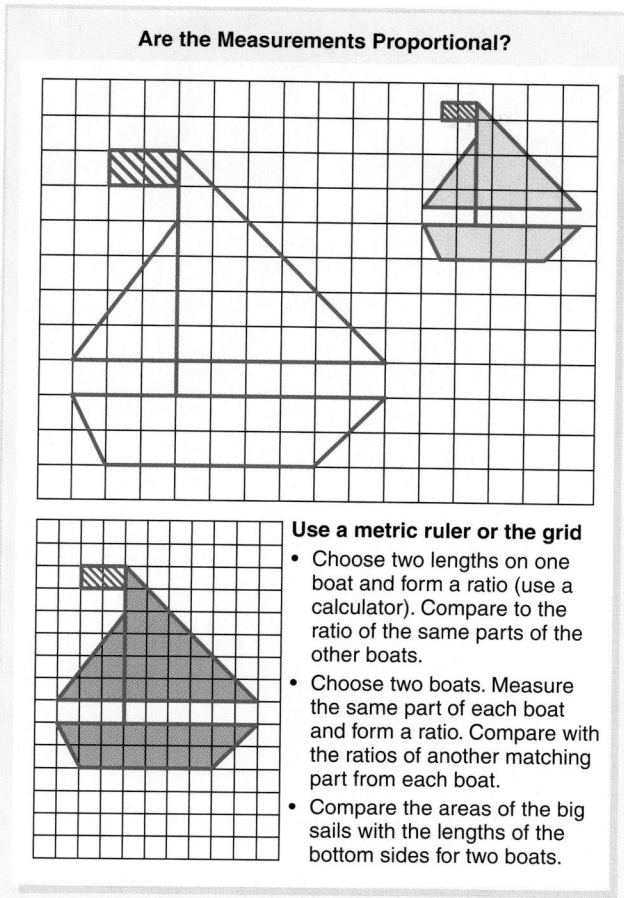

Use a metric ruler or the grid

- Choose two lengths on one boat and form a ratio (use a calculator). Compare to the ratio of the same parts of the other boats.
- Choose two boats. Measure the same part of each boat and form a ratio. Compare with the ratios of another matching part from each boat.
- Compare the areas of the big sails with the lengths of the bottom sides for two boats.

Figure 18.11 Comparing similar figures drawn on grids.

Are AB and CD in the same ratio as EF and GH?

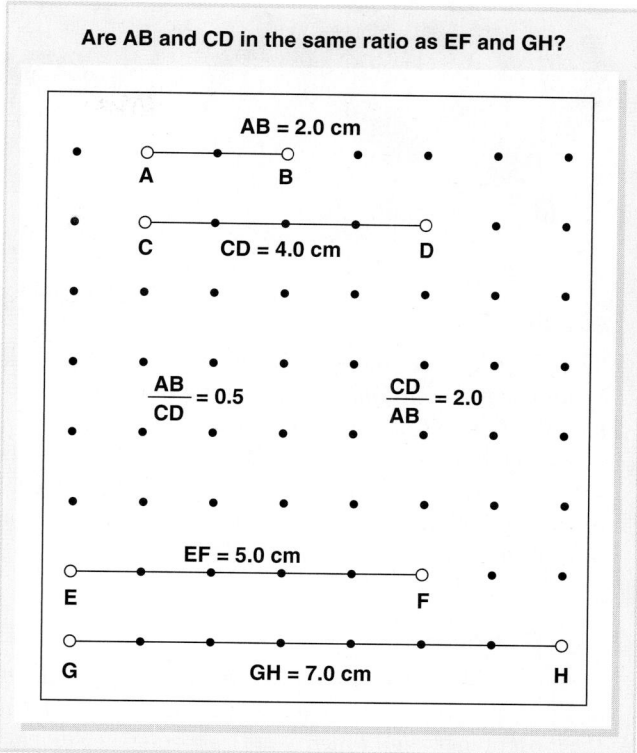

Figure 18.12 Dynamic geometry software or just a centimetre grid can be used to discuss ratios of two lengths.

Source: From *The Geometer's Sketchpad*, Key Curriculum Press, 1150 65th Street, Emeryville, CA 94608, 1-800-995-MATH, www.keypress.com. Reprinted by permission.

either line is changed, the measures and ratios are updated instantly. A screen similar to this could be used to discuss ratios of lengths as well as inverse ratios with your class. Notice that in this example the difference between the second pair of lines is the same as the first, but the ratios are not. A similar drawing could be prepared for the overhead on a transparency of a centimetre dot grid, if software was not available.

You can explore similar figures and corresponding measures. Using the Dilate feature, a figure can be drawn and then dilated (reduced or enlarged proportionally) according to any scale factor of your choice. The ratios of beginning and ending measures (lengths and areas) can then be compared to the scale factor. All the computations can be done within the software program. ◆

More interesting situations to consider for scale drawings are shown in the following list:

- If you wanted to make a scale model of the solar system and use a ping-pong ball for the earth, how far away should the sun be? How large a ball would you need?

- What scale should be used to draw a scale map of your city (or some interesting region) so that it will nicely fit onto a standard piece of poster board?
- Use the scale on a map to estimate the distance and travel time between two points of interest.
- Roll a toy car down a ramp, timing the trip with a stopwatch. How fast was the car travelling in kilometres per hour? If the speed is proportional to the size of the car, how fast would this have been for a real car?
- Your little sister wants a table and chair for her doll. Her doll is 135 centimetres tall. How big should you make the table?
- Determine the various distances that a ten-speed bike travels in one turn of the pedals. You will need to count the sprocket teeth on the front and back gears.

Statistics

Have you ever wondered how scientists estimate wildlife counts such as the number of bass in a lake or the number of monarch butterflies that migrate each year to Mexico? One method often used is a capture–recapture technique modelled in the next activity.

Connected Mathematics

Grade 7, *Comparing and Scaling*
Investigation 3: Comparing and Using Ratios

Context

This investigation occurs in the second week of the unit on ratio and proportions. In earlier activities, students explored ratios and percents to compare survey data from large populations with similar data gathered from their own class. Students used fractions, decimals, and percents to express ratios, and they compared ratios using their own strategies.

Task Description

In the juice problem shown (2.1: Mixing Juice), students apply proportional reasoning to figure out which recipe is the most orangey and which is the least orangey. Students are to apply their knowledge of ratios to reason to a solution. Students have solved this task in a variety of ways, including:

1. Make equal amounts of each recipe to compare (e.g., make 120 cups of each).

2. Make the cups of concentrate the same and look at how much water goes with each (e.g., for 30 cups of concentrate, how much water is needed for each recipe?).

3. Find part-to-whole fractions, find common denominators, and compare.

4. Find part-to-whole fractions, convert to percents, and compare.

5. Draw pictures to show how much water per cup of concentrate. For example, for Mix D:

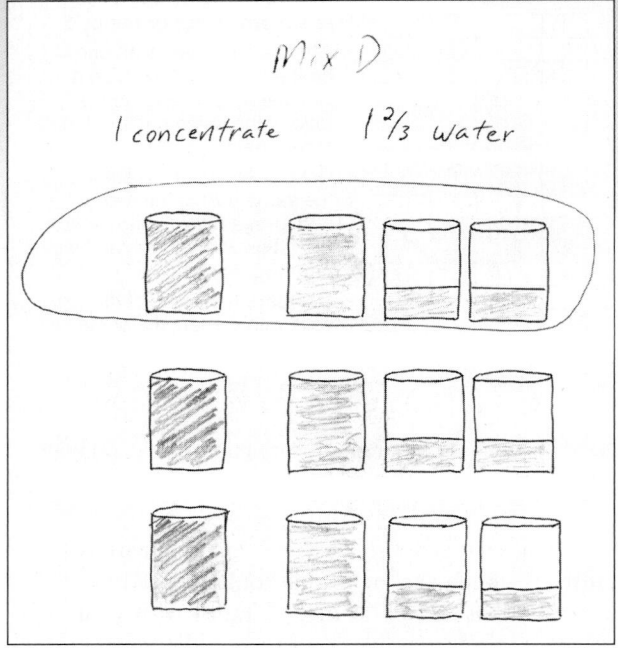

Capture–Recapture

Prepare a shoebox full of some uniform small objects such as centi-cubes or plastic chips. You could also use a larger box filled with Styrofoam™ packing "peanuts." If the box is your lake and the objects are the fish you want to count, how can you estimate the number without actually counting them? Remember, if they were fish, you couldn't even see them! Have a student reach into the box and "capture" a representative sample of the "fish." For a larger box, you may want to capture more than a handful. "Tag" each fish by marking it in some way—marking pen or sticky dot. Count and record the number tagged, then return them to the box. The assumption of the scientist is that tagged animals will mix uniformly with the larger population, so mix them thoroughly. Next, have five to ten students carry out a recapture of fish from the box. Each student counts the total captured and notes how many of these are tagged. The data are accumulated.

The task now is to use all the information to estimate the number of fish in the lake. The recapture data provide an estimate of the ratio of tagged to untagged fish. The number tagged to the total population should be in the same ratio. After solving the proportion, have students count the actual items in the box to see how close their estimate is.

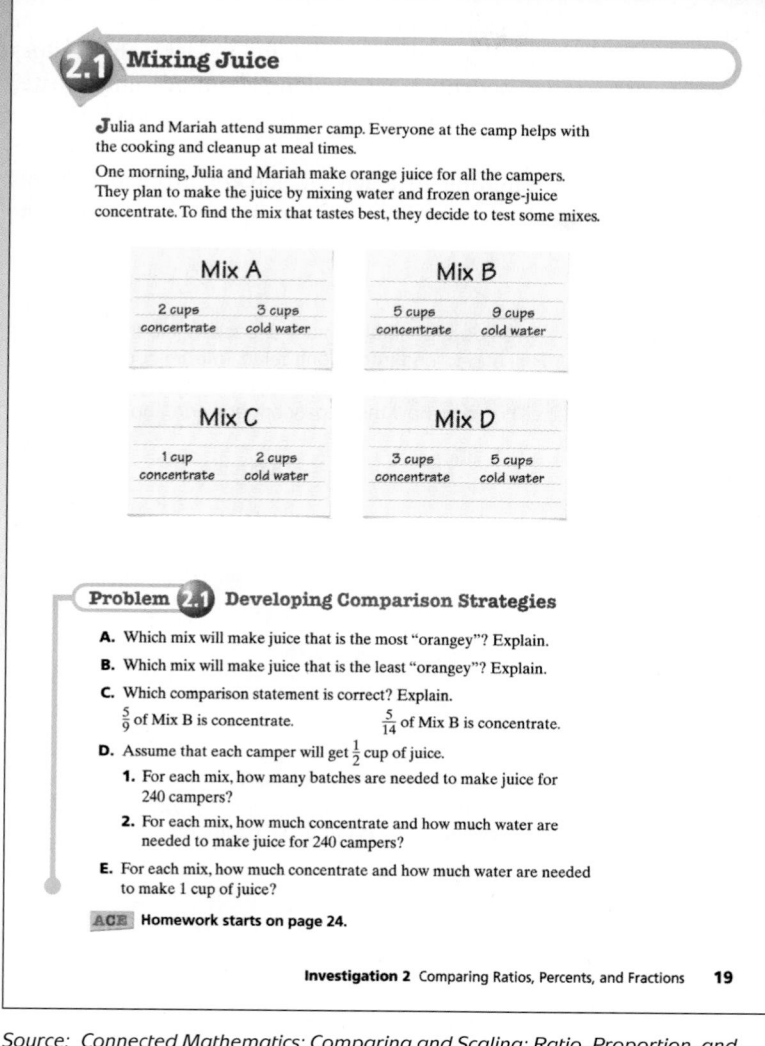

2.1 Mixing Juice

Julia and Mariah attend summer camp. Everyone at the camp helps with the cooking and cleanup at meal times.

One morning, Julia and Mariah make orange juice for all the campers. They plan to make the juice by mixing water and frozen orange-juice concentrate. To find the mix that tastes best, they decide to test some mixes.

Mix A

2 cups concentrate   3 cups cold water

Mix B

5 cups concentrate   9 cups cold water

Mix C

1 cup concentrate   2 cups cold water

Mix D

3 cups concentrate   5 cups cold water

Problem 2.1 Developing Comparison Strategies

A. Which mix will make juice that is the most "orangey"? Explain.

B. Which mix will make juice that is the least "orangey"? Explain.

C. Which comparison statement is correct? Explain.

$\frac{5}{9}$ of Mix B is concentrate. $\frac{5}{14}$ of Mix B is concentrate.

D. Assume that each camper will get $\frac{1}{2}$ cup of juice.

1. For each mix, how many batches are needed to make juice for 240 campers?

2. For each mix, how much concentrate and how much water are needed to make juice for 240 campers?

E. For each mix, how much concentrate and how much water are needed to make 1 cup of juice?

ACE Homework starts on page 24.

Investigation 2 Comparing Ratios, Percents, and Fractions   **19**

Source: Connected Mathematics: Comparing and Scaling: Ratio, Proportion, and Percent by Glenda Lappan, James T. Fey, William M. Fitzgerald, Susan N. Friel, & Elizabeth Difanis Phillips. Copyright © 2006 by Michigan State University. Used by permission of Pearson Education, Inc. All rights reserved.

For a more detailed description of the "Capture–Recapture" activity, see the NCTM Addenda Series book *Understanding Rational Numbers and Proportions* (Curcio & Bezuk, 1994).

Number: Fractions and Percent

Percent has traditionally been included as a topic with ratio and proportion because percent is one form of ratio, a part-to-whole ratio. In Chapter 17, it was shown that percent problems can be connected to fraction concepts. Here the same part-to-whole fraction concept of percent will be extended to ratio and proportion concepts. Ideally, all these ideas (fractions, decimals, ratio, proportion, and percent)

should be conceptually integrated. The better that students get at connecting these ideas, the more flexible and useful their reasoning and problem-solving skills will be.

Equivalent Fractions   First consider how equivalent fractions can be interpreted as a proportion using the same simple models already used. In Figure 18.13, a line segment is partitioned in two different ways: in fourths on one side and in twelfths on the other. In the previous examples, proportions were established based on two amounts of pizzas, two different distances or runs, and two different sizes of drawings. Here only one thing is measured—the part of a whole—but it is measured or partitioned two ways: in fourths and in twelfths.

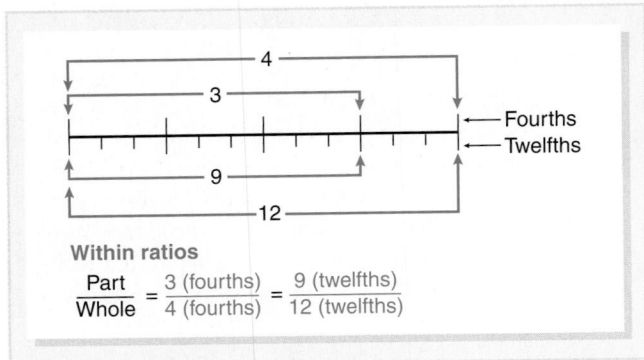

Figure 18.13 Equivalent fractions as proportions.

A simple line segment drawing similar to the one in Figure 18.13 could be drawn to set up a proportion to solve any equivalent-fraction problem, even ones that do not result in whole-number numerators or denominators. An example is shown in Figure 18.14.

Percents   All percent problems are exactly the same as the equivalent-fraction examples. They involve a part and a whole measured in some unit and the same part and whole measured in hundredths—that is, in percents. A simple line segment drawing can be used for each of the three types of percent problems. Let the measures on one side of the line correspond to the numbers or measures in the problem. On the opposite side of the line, indicate the corresponding values in terms of percents. Label the segments of the line rather than endpoints. Examples of each type of problem are shown in Figure 18.15.

Notice how flexible this simple line model is for every type of percent problem. It allows modelling of not only

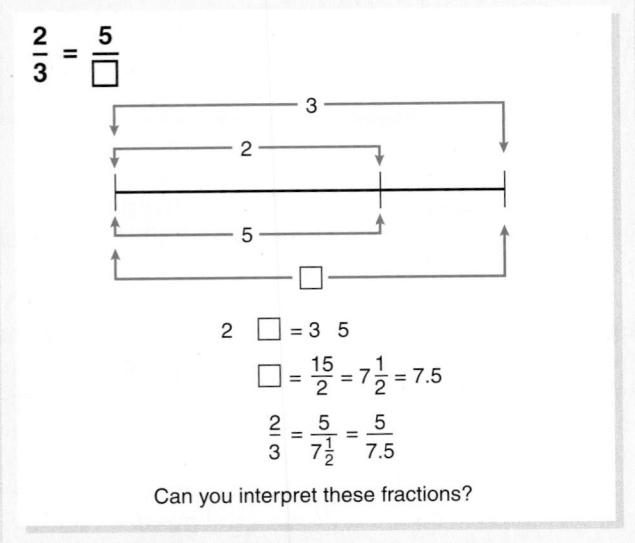

Figure 18.14 Solving equivalent-fraction problems as equivalent ratios using cross-products.

part–whole scenarios but also increase–decrease situations and those in which there is a comparison between two distinct quantities. One of each of these is included in Figure 18.15. Another advantage of the line model is that it does not restrict students from thinking about percents greater than 100, as does a circle graph or a 10 × 10 grid (Parker, 2004).

It is tempting to teach all percent problems in this one way. Developmentally, such an approach is not recom-

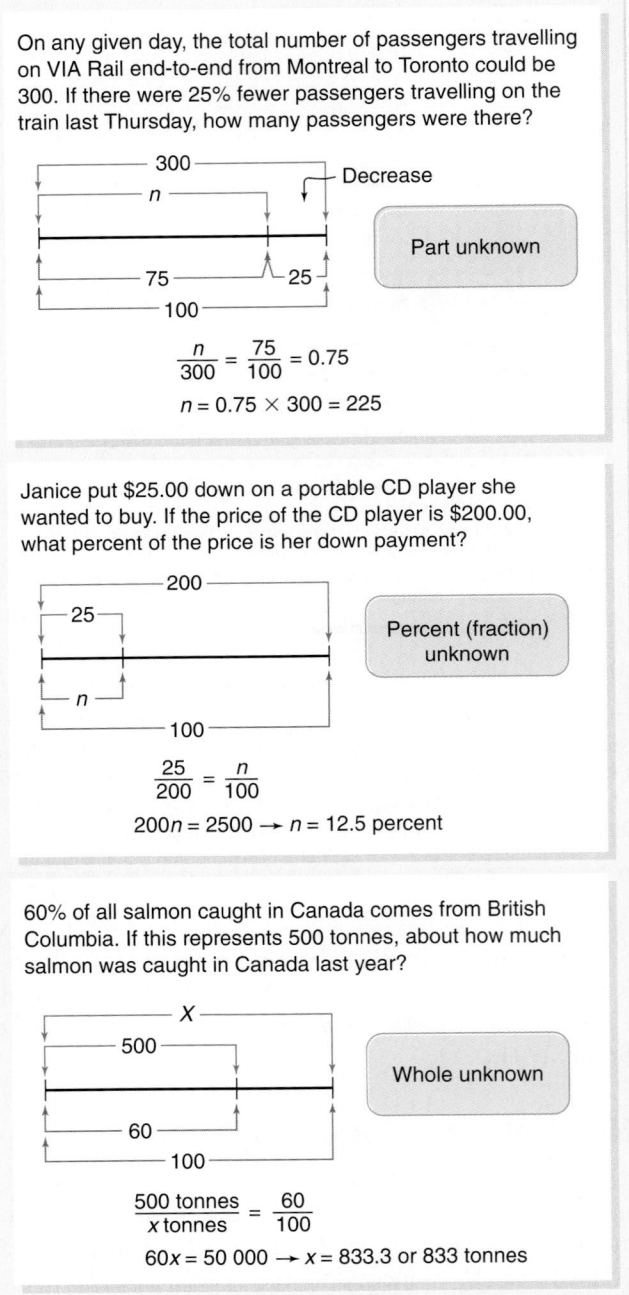

Figure 18.15 The three percentage problems solved by setting up a proportion using a simple line segment model.

mended. Even though the approach is conceptual, it does not translate easily to intuitive ideas, mental arithmetic, or estimation as discussed in Chapter 17. The modelling and proportion approach of Figure 18.15 is suggested only as a way to help students analyze problems that may verbally present some difficulty. The approach of Chapter 17, which relates percent to part–whole fraction concepts, should probably receive more emphasis.

Proportions

The activities to this point have been designed to lead students to an intuitive concept of ratio and proportion to help in the development of proportional reasoning.

One practical value of proportional reasoning is to use observed proportions to find unknown values. Knowledge of one ratio can often be used to find a value in the other. Comparison pricing, using scales on maps, and solving percentage problems are just a few everyday instances where solving proportions is required. Students need to learn to set up proportions symbolically and to solve them.

 "Attention to developing flexibility in working with rational numbers contributes to students' understanding of, and facility with, proportionality. Facility with proportionality involves much more than setting two ratios equal and solving for a missing term. It involves recognizing quantities that are related proportionally and using numbers, tables, graphs, and equations to think about the quantities and their relationship" (p. 217).

A *proportion* is a statement of equality between two ratios. If 4 boats carry 36 passengers, then 2 boats of the same size will carry 18 passengers, 3 boats will carry 27 passengers, and 20 boats will carry 180 passengers. The ratio of 4 to 36 can be applied to each of these situations even though the measures are different in each case.

Within and Between Ratios

When examining two ratios, it is sometimes useful to think of them as being either *within* ratios or *between* ratios. A ratio of two measures in the same setting is a *within* ratio. For example, in the case of similar rectangles, the ratio of length to width for any one rectangle is a within ratio, that is, it is "within" the context of that rectangle. For all similar rectangles, corresponding within ratios will be equal.

A *between* ratio is a ratio of two corresponding measures in different situations. In the case of similar rectangles, the ratio of the length of one rectangle to the length of another is a between ratio; that is, it is "between" the two rectangles. For two similar rectangles, all of the between ratios will be equal. However, the between ratios for each pair of similar rectangles will be different.

Pause and Reflect

Consider three rectangles A, B, and C. A measures 2 × 6, B measures 3 × 9, and C measures 8 × 24. Find the within ratio for each rectangle. This should convince you that the rectangles are similar. Now examine the between ratios for A and B and for A and C. Why are these ratios different?

As another example, Figure 18.4 (p. 366) shows six pictures of trucks and boxes. The within ratios are trucks to boxes (within one picture). The between ratios are from trucks to trucks and boxes to boxes.

The simple drawing in Figure 18.16 is an effective way of looking at two ratios and determining if a ratio is between or within. A drawing similar to this will be very helpful to students in setting up proportions, especially students who struggle with abstract representatives. Pick any two equivalent truck and box pictures and place the numbers in this figure.

Reasoning Approaches

There are textbooks that show students how to set up an equation with two ratios involving an unknown, to "cross-multiply," then to solve for the unknown. Doing so can be a very mechanical approach and will almost certainly lead to confusion and error. Although you may wish eventually to cover the cross-product algorithm, it is well worth the time to allow students to find ways to solve proportions using their own ideas. If you have been exploring proportions and discussing between and within relationships, students will have a good foundation on which to build their own approaches.

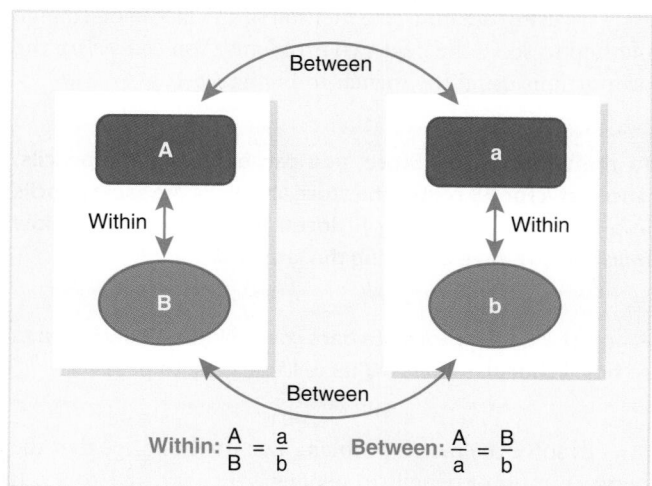

Figure 18.16 Given a proportional situation, the two between ratios and the two within ratios will be the same.

To illustrate some intuitive approaches for solving proportional tasks, consider the following:

Tammy bought 3 widgets for $2.40. At the same price, how much would 10 widgets cost?

Tammy bought 4 widgets for $3.75. How much would a dozen widgets cost?

ⅠⅠ ———————— *Pause and Reflect*
Before reading further, solve these two problems using an approach other than the cross-product algorithm.

In the first situation, it is perhaps easiest to determine the cost of one widget—the unit rate or unit price. This can be found by dividing the price of three widgets by 3. Multiplying this unit rate of $0.80 per widget by 10 will produce the answer. This approach is referred to as a *unit-rate* method of solving proportions. Notice that the unit rate is a within ratio.

In the second problem, a unit-rate approach could be used, but the division does not appear to be easy. Since 12 is a multiple of 4, it is easier to notice that the cost of a dozen is 3 times the cost of 4. This is called a *factor-of-change* method. It could have been used on the first problem but would have been awkward. The factor of change between 3 and 10 is $3\frac{1}{3}$. Multiplying $2.40 by $3\frac{1}{3}$ will produce the correct answer. (When you multiply entries in a ratio table, you are using a factor of change.) Although the factor-of-change method is a useful way of thinking about proportions, it is most frequently used when the numbers are compatible. Students should be given problems in which the numbers lend themselves to both approaches so that they will explore both methods. The factor of change is a between ratio.

Try using the unit-rate method or the factor-of-change method to solve the next two problems. You can set up the proportions using the format in Figure 18.16.

At the Office Super Store, you can buy plain #2 pencils, priced at 4 for 59 cents. The store also sells the same pencils in a large box containing 5 dozen pencils for $7.79. How much do you save by buying the large box?

A box of 2 dozen chocolate bars costs $4.80. Yonette wants to buy 5 chocolate bars. What will she have to pay?

To solve the pencil problem, you might notice that the between ratio of pencils to pencils is 4 to 60, or 1 to 15. If you multiply the 59 cents by 15, the factor of change, you will get the price of the box of 60 if the pencils were sold

at the same price. In the chocolate bar problem, the within ratio of 24 to $4.80 is easy to use to get the unit rate of 20 cents per chocolate bar.

It is important to follow these tasks, especially for students who are not challenged by problems where the numbers work out "nicely," with problems that have more difficult numbers. Have students still apply the same reasoning strategies.

For example, try to apply both strategies to the following problem.

Brian can run 5 kilometres in 18.4 minutes. If he keeps on running at the same speed, how far can he run in 23 minutes?

The Cross-Product Algorithm

"The central challenge of developing students' capacity to think with ratios (to reason proportionally) is to teach ideas and restrain the quick path to computation" (Smith, 2002, p. 15).

The methods just described come close to being well-defined algorithms, though they are a bit more flexible than cross-product methods. The reality is that the computations involved are exactly the same as in cross-multiplication. Grade 6–7 students rarely use cross-multiplication to solve proportion problems, even when that method has been taught (Smith, 2002). A possible reason is that, although the method is relatively efficient, it does not appear on the surface to look like the earlier conceptual approaches. If you are teaching cross-products, connect the unit-rate and/or factor-of-change approaches to this procedure.

Draw a Simple Model Given a ratio word problem, the greatest difficulty students have is setting up a correct proportion or equation of two ratios, one of which includes the missing value. "Which fractions do I make? Where does the *x* go?"

Rather than drill and drill in the hope that they will somehow eventually get it, show students how to sketch a simple picture that will help them determine what parts are related. In Figure 18.17, a simple model is drawn for a typical rate or price problem. The two equations in the figure come from setting up within and between ratios.

Solve the Proportion Examine the left (within) ratios. Find out what to multiply the left fraction by to get the right. You may see that can you divide 5 by 3 (5 ÷ 3) to find the factor-of-change. Then multiply $1.90 by the same factor-of-change.

$$\tfrac{5}{3} \times \$1.90$$

Looking at the same left equation in Figure 18.17, we could also determine the unit price or the price for 1 kilogram

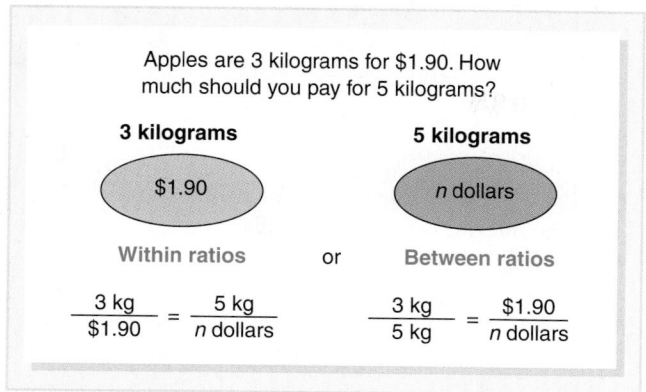

Figure 18.17 A simple drawing helps to establish correct proportion equations.

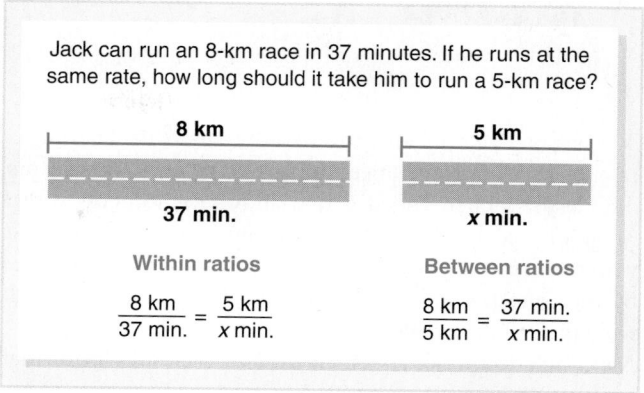

Figure 18.18 Line segments can be used to model both time and distance.

of apples by dividing the $1.90 by 3, then multiplying this result by 5 to determine the price of 5 kilograms:

$$\frac{\$1.90}{3} \times 5$$

Now look what happens if we cross-multiply in the original equation:

$$3n = 5 \times \$1.90$$

$$n = 5 \times \frac{\$1.90}{3}$$

This equation can be solved by dividing the 5 by 3, then multiplying by $1.90, or by dividing $1.90 by 3 and multiplying by 5. These are exactly the two devices we employed in the other approaches. If you cross-multiply the between ratios, you get exactly the same result. Furthermore, you would get the same result if you had written the two ratios inverted, that is, with the reciprocals of each fraction. Try it!

So if you want to develop a cross-product algorithm, it is not unreasonable to do problems like these while encouraging students to use their own methods. If the

cross-product approach is understood and presented as one strategy, rather than the only or the best approach, students will be more likely to continue to reason and choose the strategy that makes sense, given the context and the numbers involved in the problem.

Providing visual cues to set up proportions is a very effective way to support a wide range of learners. In Figure 18.18, the visual of the road is used to help students consider the quantities involved and to set up appropriate ratios. Notice how the visual is much like the ratio table and much like the picture in Figure 18.17. Different students will find different strategies more logical—encourage students to select a strategy that makes sense to them.

The activities in this chapter were intended to develop students' understanding of the concepts of ratio and proportion, as well as their proportional reasoning. The following activity offers students an opportunity to see the real-life application of these concepts and to explore other common uses of proportional reasoning.

Problem-Based Lesson:
Golden Mean

This lesson demonstrates how to differentiate the learning of ratio and proportion to meet the individual needs of students. The lesson's open-ended nature allows for students with a range of student abilities to be accommodated, from those who require an extra challenge to those who are challenged by the concepts addressed in this problem-based lesson. It will take 2–3 days to complete this lesson.

Note: Included in this lesson are sample Web sites for further exploration.

Grade Level: Grades 7 and 8

Mathematical Goals

- To further develop students' understanding of ratio and proportion
- To have students investigate the connection between math and art
- To have students learn about the mathematical properties of the golden mean
- To have students learn how the golden mean is used to create artistic and architectural masterpieces that are pleasing to the eye
- To have students investigate the relationship between fractions and decimals

To the Teacher

Golden mean, golden ratio, and golden section are popular names for a mathematical concept that expresses the relationship of the two parts of a whole with each other and of the larger part with the whole. It is represented by a decimal number (a quotient) that is approximately 1.618 033 989. This number is an irrational mathematical constant, which means that it is a non-terminating decimal.

www.mathsisfun.com/numbers/golden-ratio.html

In mathematics and in art, two quantities are in the golden ratio if the ratio between the sum of those quantities and the larger quantity is the same as the ratio between the larger quantity and the smaller one.

The golden section is a line segment divided in two according to the golden ratio. Thus the total length of the segment, $a + b$, is to the longer segment, a, as a is to the shorter segment, b (as shown in the illustration that follows).

http://goldennumber.net/goldsect.htm

You could also say:

- The division of a line segment AB (as shown below) by an interior point P is such that
- $\frac{AB}{AP} = \frac{AP}{PB}$. It follows then that $\frac{AP}{PB} = \frac{1}{2}(1 + \sqrt{5})$.
  $= 1.618033$
- Such a division of a line segment is often used, since it is considered pleasing to the eye.

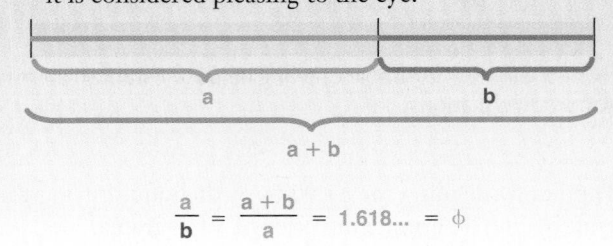

$$\frac{a}{b} = \frac{a + b}{a} = 1.618\ldots = \phi$$

- The golden ratio, shortened to 1.618 for our purposes, is often represented by the Greek letter ϕ (lowercase phi). Phi was named after the Greek sculptor Phidias because he employed the ratio in making the Parthenon sculptures, which perfectly exhibit the proportions of the golden ratio. The exterior dimensions of the Parthenon in Athens, built in about 440 BC, form a perfect golden rectangle. Many artists who lived after Phidias have used this proportion.

- The golden rectangle has side lengths that are in the golden ratio, 1:1.618. In other words, the ratio of the longer side to the shorter side is the golden ratio. www.mathopenref.com/rectanglegolden.html

Many artists and architects have proportioned their work to approximate the golden ratio, especially using the form of the golden rectangle.

The Golden Mean and Art

The following list provides information about some of the artists whose masterpieces emplify the golden ratio:

1. **Leonardo da Vinci—*Mona Lisa*:** Da Vinci called the golden ratio the "divine proportion" and featured it in many of his paintings, including his most famous one, the *Mona Lisa*. If you measure the length and the width of the painting, the ratio of the side lengths is golden. Draw a rectangle around the Mona Lisa's face (from the top of the forehead to the base of the chin, and from outside of the left cheek to outside of the right cheek). This is a golden rectangle. It is not known for sure if da Vinci deliberately employed this proportion in his works or if the proportion that he used simply happened to match the golden ratio.

The following Web site is one of many that discuss da Vinci's use of the golden ratio in the painting:

http://mathcentral.uregina.ca/beyond/articles/Art/DaVinci.html

2. **Leonardo da Vinci**—*The Last Supper:* All the key dimensions of the room and the table are based on the golden section.

3. **Georges Pierre Seurat**—*Bathing at Asnières:* The horizon in this painting falls right at the golden section of the height of the painting.

4. **Michelangelo**—*David:* This sculptor used proportions from the location of the navel with respect to the height, as well as the placement of the joints in the fingers, conforming to the golden ratio.

   Many artists used this visually pleasing technique in which the navel divides the height of the body in a golden section, including da Vinci in his *Study of Human Proportions According to Vitruvius.*

5. **Piet Mondrian**—*Composition in Red, Yellow, and Blue:* There are many golden rectangles in this work of art. The class will explore the ratio of length to width for various rectangles.

The following Web site has a set of slides "Golden Section in Art and Architecture" that may be useful: http://britton.disted.camosun.bc.ca/goldslide/jbgoldslide.htm

Thinking About the Students

The students have had already done some work on ratio and proportion. They also have some knowledge of percent and its relationship with fractions and decimal numbers. The students would have opportunities to see how geometry and art are closely related.

Materials and Preparation

The materials needed for Day 1 and Day 2.

- Overhead projector or computer with LCD projector to exhibit artists' works
- Grid paper (1-centimetre) for imprinting on transparencies
- Overhead transparencies of 1-centimetre grid (1 per student) on which students will construct their own golden rectangles. Transparencies will allow students to actually see how the concept of the golden ratio works in art.
- Fine-tip overhead markers
- Compasses
- Rulers (straightedge)
- Pictures of paintings such as: *Mona Lisa, The Last Supper, Bathing at Asnières, Composition in Red, Yellow, and Blue,* other Mondrian art, or any pieces of art that use the golden ratio
- Math dictionary: James, R. C., & James, G. (Eds.). (1992). *Mathematics Dictionary,* 5th edition. New York: Van Nostrand Rheinhold.

- Resource book: Theoni, Pappas. (1991). *Math Talk: Mathematical Ideas in Poems for Two Voices.* California: Wide World Publishing. ISBN: 0933174748

Lesson

Day One—Understanding the Golden Mean

Students will learn about the golden mean and engage in activities that will help them understand its relationship with art.

Introduction

- Begin the lesson with a discussion. Ask whether the students think artists use principles of mathematics when they create their works of art. Then ask if they have any idea what the math connection might be.
- Using the available projector, show works from the above list or any other works you may prefer.
- Have a brief discussion about the works and the artists who created them. Ask questions such as: "Are these works pleasing to the eye? If so, why? If not, why not?" "Do you know the names of any other famous artists whose work we could examine that are pleasing to look at?"
- Explain that many artists and architects employ the principle of the golden rectangle in their works because it makes the most pleasing and beautiful shape. The sides of the golden rectangle are in the golden ratio. Introduce this concept briefly.
- Artists have used proportions in their works and mathematicians have studied the golden ratio because of its unique and interesting properties.
- Review with the students the concepts of ratios and proportions along with some examples. Then, discuss in further detail and demonstrate the golden ratio using the illustration in the To The Teacher section on the previous page.

The Golden Rectangle

The rectangle in the diagram that follows is a representation of a golden rectangle. It is divided into a square and a small rectangle. The small rectangle and the larger rectangle (the whole rectangle) have the same shape, so they are similar figures. In other words, their sides are proportional. The proportions give us: $\frac{a}{b} = \frac{a+b}{a}$

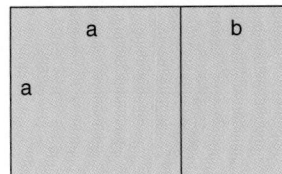

This fraction, $\frac{a+b}{a}$, is called the golden ratio (or golden section or golden mean).

A golden rectangle is any rectangle that exhibits this ratio. See Jim Loy. (1997). http://www.jimloy.com/geometry/golden.htm

The Task

The students work, either in pairs or independently, to construct golden rectangles (based on the principle of the golden ratio/mean). The teacher constructs on the overhead projector, while students follow along.

Development

Constructing the Golden Rectangle

A golden rectangle can be constructed with only straight-edge and compass.

Together with the students, complete the following steps on the transparencies.

On completion, check students' constructions.

Note: When the transparency is placed on top of a painting, it will allow students to see how the artist applied the principle of the golden rectangle.

1. To construct a golden rectangle, first construct a square ABCD with side length 5 cm.

2. Now construct the midpoint E of DC.

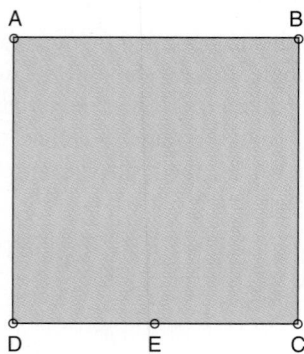

3. Extend DC. With centre E and radius EB, draw an arc crossing EC extended at F.

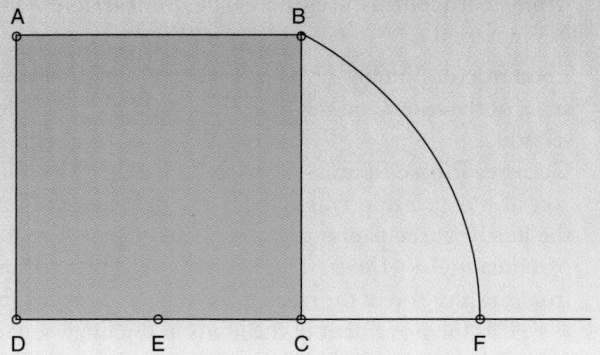

4. Construct a line perpendicular to DF at F.

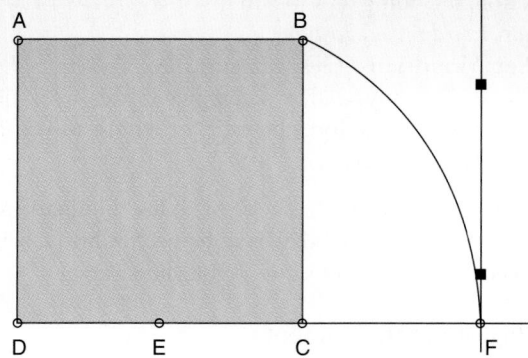

5. Extend AB to intersect the perpendicular at G.

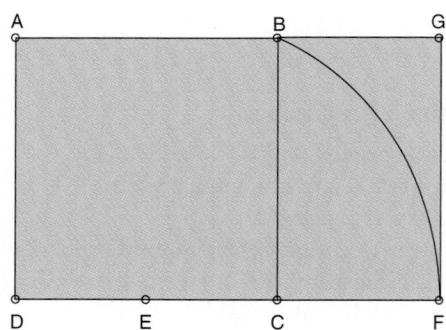

AGFD is a golden rectangle.

6. Now measure the length and width of the rectangle. Then find the ratio of the length to the width. This should be close to the golden ratio (approximately 1.618).

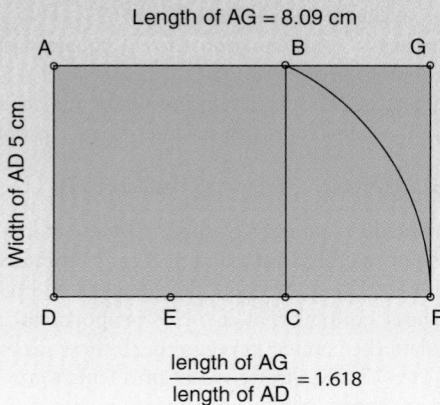

Length of AG = 8.09 cm

Width of AD 5 cm

$$\frac{\text{length of AG}}{\text{length of AD}} = 1.618$$

Follow-up

- Discuss with the students whether the sides of their rectangles are proportionate to the golden ratio.
- Have students describe in writing in their math journals their definition/understanding of the golden ratio.

Next Steps

Assessment Notes

- Is the student able to construct a golden rectangle?
- Is the student able to carry out the necessary calculation to find the golden ratio (mean)?
- Is the student able to connect prior knowledge of the concept of ratio to understand the concept of the golden ratio (mean)?

Challenges and Extensions

Students who would benefit from an added challenge could further investigate why the golden ratio works out to 1.618 034. What is it that makes this proportion so pleasing to the eye?

Students could investigate why the Greek letter φ (phi) represents the golden ratio. They might also learn more about Phidias.

Lesson

Day Two—Testing the Golden Rectangles on Actual Paintings

Introduction Review the concept of the golden ratio (mean) with the students and the decimal number that represents this ratio.

Development

- Provide students with a copy of Seurat's *Bathing at Asnieres*. Have students experiment with placing their transparencies on the painting to see how the golden ratio works. In this painting, for example, the ratio of the length of the light purple line to the length of the dark purple line is the same as the ratio of the length of the dark purple line to the length of entire line.
- Have students illustrate their findings on the overhead projector and discuss these with the class.
- Students can repeat the task with da Vinci's *Mona Lisa*.

http://goldennumber.net/art.htm
www.geom.uiuc.edu/~demo5337/s97b/art.htm

Follow-up

- Students share their findings in a class discussion.
- Students, as the artist, write a letter to a friend or family member explaining the golden mean and its connection to the masterpiece.

Next Steps

Assessment Notes

- Are some students still confused about the concepts of the golden ratio (mean) and the golden rectangle?
- Which students are experiencing difficulty with the concepts and the constructions?
- Which students require an added challenge?
- Which students have "got it?"

Challenges/Extensions

- Students create their own artistic masterpieces and test them with their golden rectangles.
- Students can investigate the connection between the golden ratio and the Fibonacci numbers.
- Students can investigate other areas where the golden ratio appears (e.g., the human body, architecture, music, and so on).

Reflections on Chapter 18

Writing to Learn

1. Describe the idea of a ratio in your own words. Explain how your idea fits with each of the following statements:

   a. A fraction is a ratio.
   b. Ratios can compare things that are not at all alike.
   c. Ratios can compare two parts of the same whole.
   d. Rates such as prices or speeds are ratios.

2. Describe a situation in which the comparison involved could be interpreted both in an additive sense as well as multiplicatively. Why might you want to explore a situation such as this early on in your discussion of ratio and proportion?

3. What can you say about the graph of a collection of equivalent ratios?

4. Make up a realistic proportional situation that can be solved by a factor-of-change approach and another that can be solved by a unit-rate approach.

5. Consider this problem: If 12 metres of material cost $56.95, how much can be purchased for $100? Draw a sketch to illustrate the proportion, and set up the equation in two different ways. One equation should equate within ratios and the other between ratios.

6. Make up a realistic percentage problem and set up a line-segment model to represent it. Then write a proportion.

For Discussion and Exploration

1. Proportional reasoning is a unifying theme in mathematics. For each of the following content strands (number, algebra, measurement, geometry, and data analysis and probability) think about content that involves proportional reasoning and explain the connections among all these ideas.

2. In Chapter 17, the three percent problems were developed around the theme of which element was missing—the part, the whole, or the fraction that related the two. In this chapter, percent is related to proportion, an equality of two ratios with one of the ratios a comparison to 100. How are these two approaches alike? How are they different? Explain how 100 percent could, in some problems, be a part rather than a whole.

Resources for Chapter 18

Literature Connections

Literature brings an exciting dimension to the exploration of proportional reasoning. Many books and stories discuss comparative sizes; concepts of scale as in maps; giants and miniature people who are proportional to regular people; comparative rates, especially rates of speed; and so on. For example, Beckman, Thompson, and Austin (2004) explore the popular *Harry Potter* stories, *The Lord of the Rings*, and *The Perfect Storm* for exciting contexts for proportional reasoning activities.

If You Hopped Like a Frog   *Schwartz, 1999*

David Schwartz, the author of *How Much Is a Million?* and *If You Made a Million*, uses proportional reasoning to determine what it would be like if we possessed the powers or dimensions of familiar animals. "If you hopped like a frog, you could jump from home plate to first base in one mighty leap." This short picture book contains 12 of these fascinating proportions: if you were as strong as an ant ..., if you flicked your tongue like a chameleon ..., and so on. At the end of the book, Schwartz provides some factual data on which the proportions are based. Students could figure out how strong or tall they would be if they were one of the featured animals.

Counting on Frank   *Clement, 1991*

We referred to this book in Chapter 13. Three spreads of the book are wonderful fantasies of proportions that could easily inspire an entire unit of proportional reasoning projects.

- If I had grown at the same speed as the gum tree—about two metres per year—I'd now be almost 16 metres tall! How fast do we grow? What if we kept growing at the same rate? How old is the narrator? How old would he be when he is 23 metres tall? Is this a multiplicative situation?

- If the mosquito that bothers him were 4 million times bigger.... What would any common object be like if it were a million times bigger?

- If the toaster that shoots toast about a metre in the air were as big as the house....

Frank also notes that the average ballpoint pen can produce a line that is 2060 metres long. The ratio of a line drawn by a ballpoint pen compared to a pencil is about 1:18 (Saskatchewan Ministry of Education, 1996).

As another activity, students could figure out how many kilometres long the pencil line would be. They could then use this information as the basis for figuring out other interesting data.

Holes *Sachar, 2000*

A popular book and movie, this novel tells the story of boys in a "camp" digging holes every day, which provides an opportunity to look at daily rates of dirt removal. Pugalee et al. (2008) describe an excellent activity with this book that not only involves proportional reasoning, but also measurement and algebra.

Literature with Large and/or Small People

There is a plethora of literature involving very little or very big people (or animals). With any of these books, body parts can be compared as a way to explore within and between ratios. The following list of some great literature can lead to wonderful lessons on proportional reasoning:

Alice's Adventures in Wonderland
Carroll, 1865/1982

In this classic, Alice becomes very small and very tall, opening doors to many ratio and proportion investigations.

The Borrowers *Norton, 1953*

This is the classic tale of little folk living in the walls of a house. The furnishings and implements are created from odds and ends from the full-size human world. The potential to make scale comparisons is endless.

Jim and the Beanstalk *Briggs, 1970*

What happened to the giant after Jack? Jim comes along. Jim wants to help the poor, pessimistic giant. This heartwarming story is great for multiplicative or proportional reasoning across grades K–8.

Kate and the Beanstalk *Osborne, 2000*

This version of *Jack and the Beanstalk* includes a giantess. The giantess falls to earth and Kate finds out the castle belongs to her family.

One Well; The Story of Water on Earth
Strauss, 2007

This beautifully illustrated Canadian award-winning book, suitable for grades 3–8, brings awareness of the life-giving importance of water not only for today, but also for future generations. The many facts it presents makes it ideal for connecting with proportions, fractions, and percent. Its focus on the environment and global issues allows for cross-curricular connections with science and social studies. Learning resource materials can be accessed on the KidsCan Press Web site.

Swamp Angel *Isaacs, 1999*

A swamp angel named Angelica is born very tiny but grows into a giant. Students can explore birth height to current height or compare Angelica's measurements to their own.

Recommendations for Further Reading

Articles

Langrall, C. W., & Swafford, J. (2000). Three balloons for two dollars. *Mathematics Teaching in the Middle School, 6,* 254–261.
The authors describe and give examples of four levels of proportional reasoning using examples from the classroom. This is a good article on a difficult topic.

Lo, J., Watanabe, T., & Cai, J. (2004). Developing ratio concepts: An Asian perspective. *Mathematics Teaching in the Middle School, 9,* 362–367.
These well-known researchers discuss the way that the concepts of ratio and proportion are developed in Asian countries. They share a sequence of activities adapted from textbooks used in China, Taiwan, and Japan. The series of examples will certainly be useful in your classroom.

Books

Lamon, S. J. (1999). *Teaching fractions and ratios for understanding: Essential content knowledge and instructional strategies for teachers.* Mahwah, NJ: Lawrence Erlbaum.
Lamon is one of the most prolific researchers and writers on the subject of fractions, ratios, and proportional reasoning. This book is full of specific practical examples of activities and is freely illustrated with children's work. At the same time this is a serious, research-based, thought-provoking book. Many of the ideas found in this chapter are adapted from this book and other works by Lamon.

Litwiller, B. (Ed.). (2002). *Making sense of fractions, ratios, and proportions: 2002 yearbook.* Reston, VA: National Council of Teachers of Mathematics.
Eleven of the 26 short chapters in this NCTM yearbook explicitly discuss the issue of multiplicative relationships and/or proportional reasoning. The remaining chapters are on various aspects of fractional concepts and fractional computation, many illustrating the connection with proportional thinking. Accompanying the yearbook is a book of Classroom Activities *complete with Blackline Masters.*

Online Resources

Exploring Rate, Ratio and Proportion
www.learnalberta.ca/content/mejhm/index.html?l=0&ID1=AB.MATH.JR.NUMB&ID2=AB.MATH.JR.NUMB.RATE&lesson=html/video_interactives/rateRatioProportions/rateRatioProportionsSmall.html
This multimedia mathematics resource examines how rate, ratio, and proportion play a role in photography. Students explore ratio equivalencies by enlarging and reducing images to compare an original ratio and a target ratio. A print activity is included.

Fibonacci Sequence
http://nlvm.usu.edu/en/nav/frames_asid_315_g_3_t_1.html
The applet simply computes successive terms of the Fibonacci sequence and shows in both fraction and decimal forms the ratio of successive terms of the sequence. This ratio converges to the *golden ratio.*

For what may be the most information assembled anywhere on the Fibonacci sequence, go to www.mcs.surrey.ac.uk/Personal/R.Knott/Fibonacci.

Fish Simulation Applet I
http://mathforum.org/escotpow/puzzles/fish/applet.html

A collection of two colours of fish is to be placed into three ponds to create specified ratios within each pond. Students should find out if there is more than one solution and then make up similar problems for their classmates.

Learning about Length, Area, Volume, Surface Area of Similar Objects (e-Example 6.3)
http://standards.nctm.org/document/eexamples

This is a two-part exploration complete with extensive teacher notes. The applets compare two rectangles or two prisms showing ratios of measures in both numerical and graphical form.

Percentage PI Game
http://cemc2.math.uwaterloo.ca/wired_math/english/grade7.shtml

Although the game provides practice with percentages, the follow up exercises link percents with ratios, decimals, and fractions.

Understanding Ratios of Inscribed Figures (e-Example 7.3)
http://standards.nctm.org/document/eexamples

A nice geometry/measurement link to ratio. The user explores the ratio of figures inscribed in polygons formed by joining midpoints of sides. These points can also be adjusted. The supporting lesson and activity suggestions are quite good.

Ameba (The Math Forum's Teacher Exchange)
http://mathforum.org/te/exchange/hosted/ameba

In this game, students select a total number of pellets to eat that is equal to the target ratio given at the top of the board, then return to the start/finish location.

---

myeducationlab *will help you improve your understanding of the concepts taught in this textbook and in your course. This online tool includes videos of real classroom experiences, sample lesson plans, simulations, case studies, and links to important educational and teaching Web sites that will help you make the transition from student to teacher. As you study in your course and with this textbook, please follow along in* **MyEducationLab***. Use it! Explore it! And improve your knowledge and your grade!*

Chapter 19
Developing Measurement Concepts

Measurement is one of the most useful content areas in mathematics. It is an important component of all we do from occupational tasks to life skills. From gigabytes that measure amounts of information to font size on computers, from the amount of litres per kilometre travelled to recipes for a meal, we are surrounded daily with measurement concepts. However, measurement is a challenging topic for students. Data from international studies (TIMSS) and American studies (NAEP) consistently indicate that students are weaker in this area than any other in the curriculum (Thompson & Preston, 2004). Although learning the customary measurement system may be a contributing factor, poor performance is more likely a function of how the subject is taught—too much reliance on pictures and worksheets rather than on hands-on experiences and a focus on skills with less attention to the concepts of measurement.

In this chapter you will learn how to help students develop a conceptual understanding of the measurement process and the tools of measurement. You will also learn about non-standard and standard units of measurement, estimation in measurement including the use of benchmarks, and the development of measurement formulas for area and volume.

Big Ideas

1. Measurement involves a comparison of an attribute of an item or situation with a unit that has the same attribute. Lengths are compared to units of length, areas are compared to units of area, time to units of time, and so on.

2. Meaningful measurement and estimation of measurements depend on a personal familiarity with the unit of measure being used.

3. Estimation of measures and the development of benchmarks for frequently used units of measure help students increase their familiarity with units, prevent errors in measurement, and aid in the meaningful use of measurement.

4. Measurement instruments are devices that replace the need for actual measurement units. It is important to understand how measurement instruments work.

5. Area and volume formulas provide a method for measuring these attributes, using only measures of length.

6. The relationship between area, perimeter, and volume can be demonstrated in different ways. For example, as the shapes of regions or three-dimensional objects change, while maintaining the same areas or volumes, there is a predictable effect on the perimeters and surface areas.

Mathematics Content Connections

In order to provide more time for students to engage in meaningful measurement activities, measurement should be integrated across the mathematics curriculum, as well as with the science curriculum.

- **Number** (Chapter 8): Early measurement activities provide a very meaningful context for counting. Measurement of important objects in the familiar environment connects ideas of number to the real world, enhancing number sense.

- **Place Value** (Chapter 11): Multiples of ten are profitably used by young children in counting non-standard measures. Also, the metric system of measurement is built on the base-ten system of numeration.

- **Algebra** (Chapter 14): Measurement formulas are themselves functions. Measurement provides data from which generalizations and functional relationships can be derived.

- **Fractions** (Chapter 15): The need for increased precision in measuring leads to fractional parts of units.

- **Proportional Reasoning** (Chapter 18): The use of benchmarks in estimating measures promotes multiplicative thinking.

Measures are used in scale drawings. Proportions are used to find unknown measures of similar figures.

- **Geometry** (Chapter 20): The development and understanding of perimeter, area, and volume formulas require an understanding of the shapes and relationships involved. Measures help to describe shapes and angular measures play a significant role in the properties of shapes.

- **Data** (Chapter 21): Statistics and graphs are used to describe our world and to help us answer questions about it. These descriptions are often carried out in terms of measures.

The Meaning and Process of Measuring

Suppose that you asked your students to measure an empty bucket. The first thing they would need to know is *what* attributes of the bucket are to be measured. They might measure the height or depth, the diameter (distance across), or the circumference (distance around). All these are length measures. The surface area of the side could also be determined. A bucket has volume and mass too. Each of these aspects that can be measured is an *attribute* of the bucket.

Once students determine the attribute to be measured, they need to choose a unit of measure. The unit must have the attribute that is being measured. Length is measured with linear units (units that have length), volume with cubic units (units that have volume), and so on.

Technically, a *measurement* is a number that indicates a comparison between the attribute of the object (or situation) being measured and the same attribute of a given unit of measure. We commonly use small units of measure to determine in some way a numerical relationship (the measurement) between what is measured and the unit. For example, to measure a length, the comparison can be done by lining up copies of the unit directly against the length being measured. To measure the mass of an object, you would first attach the object to a spring scale. Then a comparison is made between the mass of the object and the number of units of mass required to produce the effect on the spring. In either case, the number of units is the measure of the object.

For most of the attributes that students explore in school, we can say that *to measure* means that the attribute being measured is "filled," "covered," or "matched" with a unit of measure with that same attribute (as illustrated in Figure 19.1).

In summary, to measure something, one must perform three steps:

1. Decide on the attribute to be measured.
2. Select a unit that has that attribute.
3. Compare the units with the attribute of the object being measured, by filling, covering, matching the object, or using some other method.

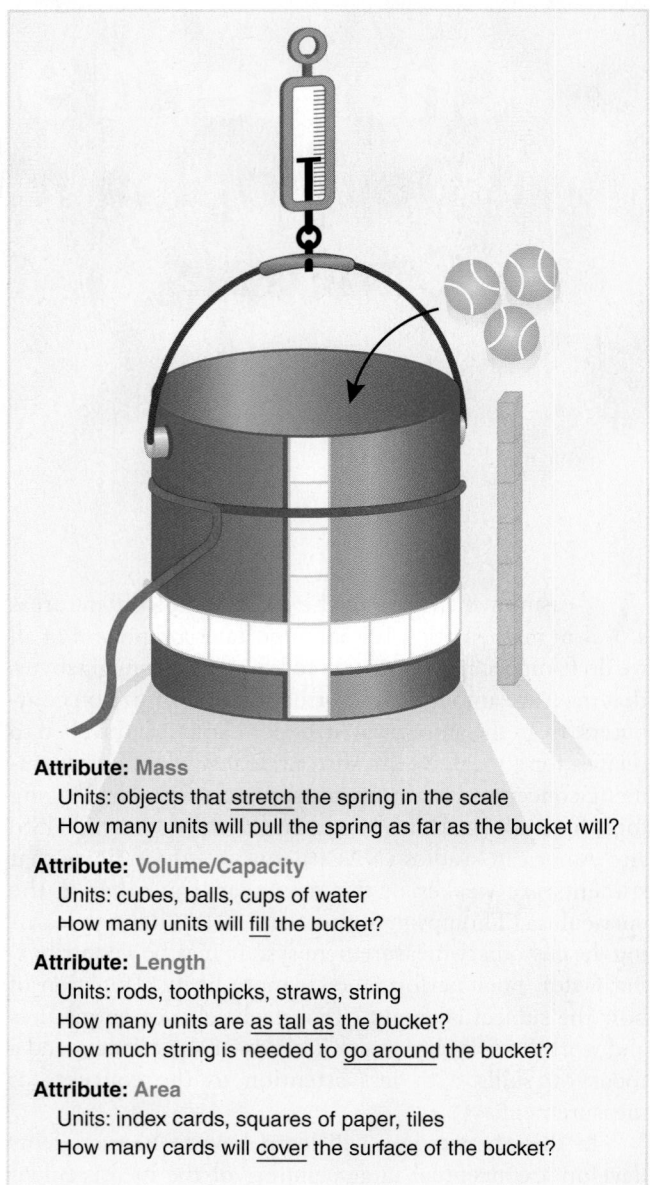

Attribute: Mass
Units: objects that <u>stretch</u> the spring in the scale
How many units will pull the spring as far as the bucket will?

Attribute: Volume/Capacity
Units: cubes, balls, cups of water
How many units will <u>fill</u> the bucket?

Attribute: Length
Units: rods, toothpicks, straws, string
How many units are <u>as tall as</u> the bucket?
How much string is needed to <u>go around</u> the bucket?

Attribute: Area
Units: index cards, squares of paper, tiles
How many cards will <u>cover</u> the surface of the bucket?

Figure 19.1 Measuring different attributes of a bucket.

Standard measuring instruments such as rulers, scales, protractors, and clocks are devices that make the filling, covering, or matching process easier.

Concepts and Skills

A typical group of grade 1 children attempt to measure the length of their classroom by laying paper strips of equal size (informal, non-standard units) end to end. But sometimes, the strips overlap, and the line can weave in a snakelike fashion. Do they understand the concept of length as an attribute of the classroom? Do they understand that each strip has this attribute of length? Do they understand that their task is to fill the longer unit of length with smaller ones? What they most likely understand is that they are

Whether they are considering length, area, volume, mass, or time, measurement is a challenging topic for students that may be best taught through hands-on experiences with a focus on measurement concepts. Integrating measurement across the mathematics curriculum and with the science curriculum will maximize opportunities for students to engage in meaningful measurement activities.

Table 19.1

Measurement Instructiion—A Sequence of Experiences

Step One—Making Comparisons

Goal: Students will understand the attribute to be measured.

Type of Activity: Make comparisons based on the attribute. For example, longer/shorter, heavier/lighter. Use direct comparisons whenever possible.

Notes: When it is clear that the attribute is understood, there is no further need for comparison activities.

Step Two—Using Physical Models of Measuring Units

Goal: Students will understand how filling, covering, matching, or making other comparisons of an attribute with measuring units produces a number called a measure.

Type of Activity: Use physical models of measuring units to fill, cover, match, or make the desired comparison of the attribute with the unit.

Notes: Begin with non-standard units. Progress to the direct use of standard units when appropriate and certainly before using formulas or measuring tools.

Step Three—Using Measuring Instruments

Goal: Students will use common measuring tools with understanding and flexibility.

Type of Activity: Make measuring instruments and use them in comparison with the actual unit models to see how the measurement tool is performing the same function as the individual units. Be certain to make direct comparisons between the student-made tools and the standard tools.

Notes: Student-made tools are usually best made with non-standard units. Without a careful comparison with the standard tools, much of the value in making the tools can be lost.

supposed to be making a line of strips stretching from wall to wall (and from their vantage point, they are doing quite well). They are performing a procedure instrumentally, without a conceptual basis. The skill of measuring with a unit must be explicitly linked to the concept of measuring as a process of comparing attributes, using measuring units and using measuring instruments. A sequence of experiences for measurement instruction is summarized in Table 19.1. The discussion that follows suggests the type of activities that will develop these skills.

Making Comparisons The first and most critical goal is for students to understand the attribute they are going to measure. When students compare objects on the basis of some measurable attribute, that attribute becomes the focus of the activity. For example, is the capacity of one box more than, less than, or about the same as the capacity of another? No measurement is required, but some manner of comparing one volume to the other must be devised. The attribute of "capacity" (how much a container can hold) is inescapable.

Many attributes can be compared directly, such as placing one length directly in line with another. In the case of volume or capacity, some indirect method is probably required, such as filling one box with beans, then pouring the beans into the other box. Using a string to compare the height of a wastebasket to the distance around it (its circumference) is another example of an indirect comparison. The string is the intermediary. It is impossible to compare these two lengths directly.

Constructing or making something that is the same in terms of a measurable attribute is another type of comparison activity—for example, "Cut the straw to be just as long as this piece of chalk" or "Draw a rectangle that is about the same size (has the same area) as this triangle."

Using Physical Models of Measuring Units The second goal is for students to understand what units of measure are appropriate for the particular attribute in question and how these units are used to produce a measurement. Regardless of grade level, you should not make assumptions that students have an understanding of measuring units for the attribute being considered. For most attributes that are measured in elementary school, it is possible to have physical models of the units of measure. Time and temperature are exceptions. (Many other attributes not commonly measured in school also do not have physical units of measure. Light intensity, speed, loudness, viscosity, and radioactivity are just a few examples.) Unit models can be found for both non-standard (sometimes referred to as informal) units and standard units. For length, drinking straws (non-standard) or paper strips 10 centimetres long (standard) may be used as units.

The most easily understood use of a unit model is to use as many copies of a unit as are needed to fill or match the attribute being measured. For example, to measure the area of the desktop with an index card as the unit of measure, you can literally cover the entire desktop with index cards. Somewhat more difficult, especially for younger children, is to use a single copy of the unit with an iteration process. It would mean that the same desktop area can be measured by moving a single index card from one position to another, keeping track of the number of times the card has been moved in order to cover the area.

It is useful to measure the same object with different size units. Results should be estimated in advance and discussed afterwards. Doing so will help students understand that the unit used is as important as the attribute being measured. The fact that smaller units produce larger numerical measures, and vice versa, is hard for young children to understand. This inverse relationship can only be constructed mentally by predicting, then experimenting, and finally reflecting on measurements with varying size units.

Using Measuring Instruments   An understanding of the devices we use to measure is the third goal. In the 2003 National Assessment of Educational Progress (Blume, Galindo, & Walcott, 2007), only 20 percent of grade 4 students could give the correct measure of an object that was not aligned with the end of a ruler, as in Figure 19.2. These results point to the difference between using a measuring device and understanding how it works. Students also experienced difficulty when the increments on a measuring device were other than one unit.

If students actually make simple measuring instruments using unit models with which they are familiar, it is more likely that they will understand how an instrument works. A ruler is a good example. If students line up individual physical units along a strip of tag-board and mark them off, they can see that it is the *spaces* (*the distance between two units*) on the ruler and not the marks or numbers that are impor-

tant. It is essential that students discuss how measurement with units compares with measurement using an instrument. Without this comparison and discussion, students may not understand that these two methods are essentially the same.

A discussion of student-made measuring instruments for each attribute is provided in the text that follows. Of course, children should also use standard, ready-made instruments, such as rulers and scales, and should compare the use of these devices with the use of the models they constructed.

Non-Standard Units and Standard Units: Reasons for Using Each

It is common in primary grades to use non-standard units to measure length and sometimes area. Unfortunately, measurement activities in the upper grades, where additional attributes are measured, often do not begin with non-standard units. The use of non-standard units for beginning measurement activities is beneficial at all grades for the following reasons:

- Non-standard units make it easier to focus directly on the attribute being measured. For example, in a discussion of how to measure the area of an irregular shape, units such as lima beans, square tiles, or circular counters may be suggested. Each unit covers area and each will give a different result. The discussion should then focus on what it means to measure area.
- The use of non-standard units can avoid a conflict of objectives in a beginning lesson. Is your lesson about what it means to measure area or about understanding square centimetres?
- Non-standard units provide a good rationale for using standard units. A discussion regarding the need for a standard unit can have more meaning after groups in your class have measured the same objects with their own units and arrived at different and some times confusing answers.
- Using informal units can be motivating.
- Knowledge of standard units is an essential objective of any measurement program. Not only must students develop a familiarity with standard units, but they must also understand the appropriate relationships between them.
- Once a measuring concept is fairly well developed, standard units can be introduced effectively. If there is no good instructional reason for using non-standard units, use standard units to increase students' familiarity with them.

The amount of time that should be spent using non-standard units varies with the age of the children and the attributes being measured. Grade 1 children need a lot of

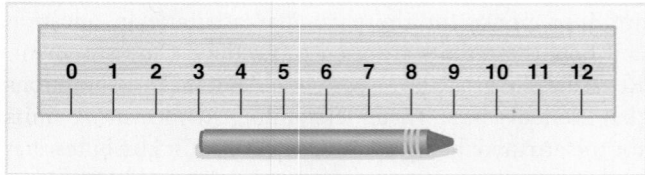

Figure 19.2 "How long is this crayon?"

experience with a variety of non-standard units of length, mass, and capacity. Conversely, the benefits of non-standard measuring units may last only a day or two for measurements of angles at the junior grade levels. When non-standard units have served their purpose, it is time to move on.

The Role of Estimation and Approximation

It is very important to have students estimate a measurement before actually making it. This applies to both non-standard and standard units. There are at least four good reasons for including estimation in measurement activities:

- Estimation helps students focus on the attribute being measured and the measuring process. Think how you would estimate the area of the front of this book with standard playing cards as the unit. To do so, you have to think about what area is and how the units might be placed to fit on the cover.
- Estimation provides intrinsic motivation for measuring activities. It is interesting to see how close you can come in your estimate.
- When standard units are used, estimation helps develop familiarity with the unit. If you estimate the height of the door in metres before measuring, you have to think about the size of a metre.
- The use of a benchmark to make an estimate promotes multiplicative reasoning. The width of my bedroom is about one-fourth the width of my house.

In all measuring activities, emphasize the use of approximate language. The desk is *about* 15 orange strips of paper long. The chair is *a little less than* 4 straws high. The use of approximate language is very useful for younger children because many measurements do not result in whole numbers. Older children will begin to search for smaller units or will use fractional units to try to measure exactly. Here is an opportunity to develop the idea that all measurements include some error. First acknowledge that each smaller unit or subdivision produces a greater degree of *precision*. For example, a length measure can never be more than one-half unit in error. And yet, since there is mathematically no "smallest unit," there is always some error involved.

 The Measurement Standard in *Principles and Standards* for grades 3–5 states that "students should understand that measurements are approximations and understand how differences in units affect precision" (NCTM, 2000, p. 398). In grades 6–8, NCTM states that "middle school students should select and apply techniques and tools to accurately find length, area, volume, and angle measure to appropriate levels of precision" (p. 300).

Length

Length is usually the first attribute students learn to measure. Be aware, though, that young children do not immediately understand length measurement.

Comparison Activities

At the pre-K to kindergarten level, children should begin with direct comparisons of two or more lengths.

Activity 19.1

Longer, Shorter, Same

Make several sort-by-length learning stations at which students sort objects as longer than, shorter than, or about the same as a specified object. The reference object can be changed to produce different sorts. A similar task is to put objects in order from shortest to longest.

Activity 19.2

Length (or Unit) Hunt

Give pairs of students a strip of tag-board, a stick, a length of rope, or some other object in which length is an obvious dimension. The task on one day might be to find five things in the room that are shorter than, longer than, or about the same length as their object of choice. They can draw pictures or write the names of the things they find.

By making the target length a standard unit (e.g., a metre stick or 1-metre length of rope), the activity can be repeated to prove familiarity with important standard units.

It is important to compare lengths that are not straight lines. One way to do this is with string or rope. Students can wrap string around objects in a search for things that are as long around as the distance from the floor to their belly button or as long as the distance around one's head or waist. Body measures are always fun.

Indirect comparisons are used in the next activity.

Activity 19.3

Crooked Paths

Make some crooked or curvy paths on the floor with masking tape (or outside with chalk). The task is to determine which path is the longest, next longest, and so on. The students should suggest ways to measure

the crooked paths so that they can be compared easily. If you wish to offer a hint, provide each pair of students with a long piece of rope. The task is easier if the rope is longer than the crooked paths. Have students explain how they solved the problem.

Units of Length

Students can use a variety of non-standard units to begin measuring length, for example:

- *Giant footprints:* Make about 20 copies of a large footprint about 50 to 60 centimetres long, cut out of poster board.
- *Measuring ropes:* Cut cotton clothesline into lengths of 1 metre. These can be used for measuring the perimeter and the circumference of objects such as the teacher's desk, a tree trunk, or the class pumpkin.
- *Plastic straws:* Drinking straws provide large quantities of a useful unit. Straws are easily cut into smaller units or linked together with a long string. A string of straws is an excellent bridge to a ruler or measuring tape.
- *Short units:* Toothpicks, interlocking cubes, wooden cubes, and paper clips are all useful non-standard units for measuring shorter lengths. Paper clips can readily be made into chains. Plastic chain links (available from suppliers of manipulatives) can also be used.

The temptation is to carefully explain to students how to use these units to measure before sending them off to practise measuring. Doing so will shift students' attention to the procedure (following instructions) and away from developing an understanding of measuring. In the following activity students are provided with a measuring task but are required to develop their own approach.

Activity 19.4

How Long Is the Teacher?

Explain that you have just received an important request from the principal. She needs to know how tall each teacher is. The students are to decide how to measure the teachers. They then write a note to the principal explaining how tall their teacher is and the process they used. If you wish to give a hint, have students make marks on the paper at your feet and head and draw a straight line between these marks.

Explain that the principal says you can choose any **ONE** of several non-standard units with which to measure. (Offer several choices.) Ensure that there is enough of each unit to more than cover your length. Have students work in pairs, allowing them to select one unit with which to measure.

The value of the last activity will come from the discussion. Good questions include "How did you get your measurement?" "Did students who measured with the same unit get the same answers? Why not?" "How could the principal make a line that was just as long as the teacher?" In your discussion, focus on the value of lining units up carefully, end to end. Discuss what happens if you overlap units, have a gap in the units, or don't stay in a straight line.

Activity 19.5

Estimate and Measure

Make lists of things in the room to measure (see Figure 19.3). For younger children, run a piece of masking tape along the dimension of each object to be measured. On the list, designate the units to be used. Remember to include distances that are curved or are not straight lines. Include estimating before actually measuring. Young children will not be very good at estimating distances at first.

For students beginning to learn about estimation, add the following component to the "Estimate and Measure" activity: Have students make a row or chain of exactly ten units to use in helping them with their estimates. First, they lay the ten units against the object; then they make their estimate.

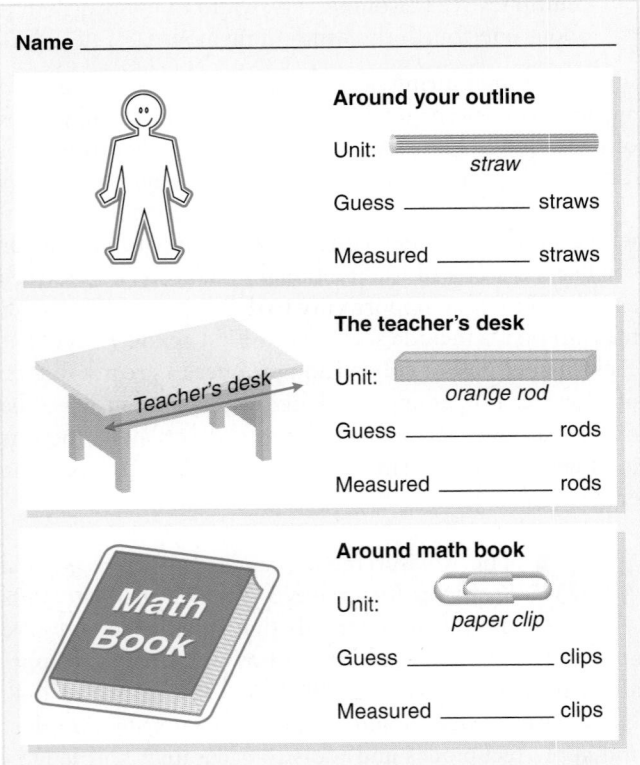

Figure 19.3 Example recording sheet for measuring with non-standard units of length.

It is a challenge to explain to students that larger units will produce a smaller measure and vice versa. Instead, engage students in an activity like the following where this issue is the focus.

Activity 19.6

Changing Units

Have students measure a length with a specified unit. Then, provide them with a different unit that is either twice as long or half as long as the original unit. The students' task is to predict the measure of the length using the new unit. Students should record their estimates and explain how they were made. A discussion about their estimates should follow. Then, have them make the actual measurement. Older students can be challenged with units that are more difficult multiples of the original unit.

In "Changing Units," you are looking first for the basic idea that, when the unit is longer, the measure is smaller and vice versa. This is a good activity to do just before you discuss unit conversion with standard units. For example, if an Olympic relay race is 1600 metres long, how many kilometres is this? Changing measurement units is an excellent proportional reasoning task for older students.

 Observation and discussion during activities such as those just described will tell you a lot about how well your students understand length measurement. Here are a few additional tasks that can be used in a diagnostic interview format:

- Provide a box with assorted different size linear units (e.g., Cuisenaire rods). Have the students use the material to measure a given length. Observe if students understand that the units used must be of equal size. If different size units are used to measure the same length, have them explain their measurement.
- Ask students to draw a line or mark off a distance of a prescribed number of units. Observe whether the students know how to align the units in a straight line so there is no overlapping or gaps.
- Have students measure two different objects. Then ask how much longer the longer object is. Observe if the students can use the measurements to answer, or if a third measurement must be made of the difference.
- Provide a length of string. Tell students that the string is 6 units long. Ask how they could they use the string to make a length of 3 units. How could they make a length of 9 units? In this task, you are looking to see if students can mentally subdivide the given length (string) based on an understanding of its measure. That is, can students visualize that 6 units are matched to the string length and half of this is 3 units? ◆

Fractional Parts of Units Children are perplexed sometimes when their measurements do not result in a whole number. One suggestion you might make to younger students is to use a smaller unit to fill in the remaining gap, as in Figure 19.4. Another idea is to suggest that they use fractions. Both ideas are used when measuring with standard units. With metric measure, units are rarely mixed and fractional units are expressed in decimal form (e.g., 3.2 metres). The use of fractional units can help students with understanding subdivision marks on a ruler.

Making and Using Rulers

The jump from measuring with non-standard units to using standard rulers is challenging. One of the best methods for helping students understand rulers is to have them make their own rulers using actual units.

Activity 19.7

Make Your Own Ruler

Pre-cut narrow strips of construction paper 5 centimetres long and approximately 2 centimetres wide. Use two different colours of paper. Discuss how the strips could be used as units for measuring by laying them end-to-end. Then, provide students with long strips of tag-board that are about 3 centimetres wide. Without explicit guided direction, have students make their own ruler by gluing the two colour strips onto the tag-board. Have a list of a few things to measure ready for them. Students use their new rulers to measure the items on the list. On completion, discuss their results. It is possible that there will be discrepancies because some rulers were not properly made or students did not understand how a ruler works.

The same activity can be done with larger non-standard units such as tracings of students' footprints glued onto strips of adding machine tape. Older children can use a standard unit such as a centimetre to mark the strips and colour in the spaces between the marks by alternating two colours.

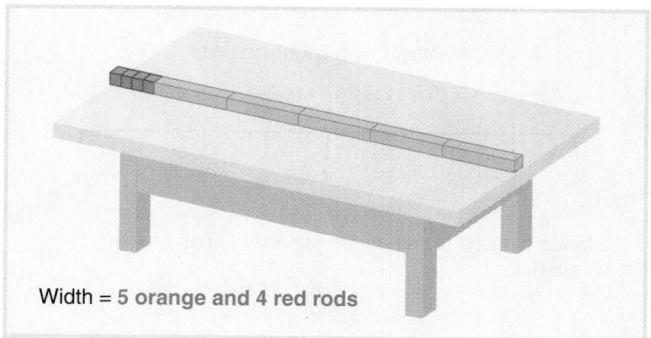

Width = 5 orange and 4 red rods

Figure 19.4 Using two units to measure length.

This activity makes the construction of a ruler a problem-based experience. Moreover, it will provide you with formative assessment information regarding students' understanding of the measurement process, if you are not overly detailed in your instructions about how to make the ruler. On completion of this process, all students should have made a ruler that measures correctly. The multiple unit copies on these student-made rulers (rather than markings and numbers) maximize the connection between the spaces on the ruler and the actual units. Students should use their rulers to measure lengths that are longer than their rulers and discuss how that can be done. Another important challenge is to find more than one way to measure a length with a ruler. Do you have to begin at the end? What if you begin at the centre?

Students should eventually put numbers on their rulers, as shown in Figure 19.5. For young children, numbers can be written in the centre of each unit to make it clear that the numbers are a way of pre-counting the units. When numbers are written at the end of the units, in the standard way, the ruler becomes a number line. This format is more sophisticated and should be carefully discussed with the children.

Much of the value of student-made rulers can be lost if you do not transfer this knowledge to standard rulers. Give children a standard ruler, and discuss how it is like and how it differs from the ones they have made. What are the units? Could you make a ruler with paper units the same as this? What do the numbers mean? What are the other marks for? Where do the units begin?

For children who are still having difficulty understanding how the ruler works, it might be helpful to create a number line on the floor with masking tape. Together with the children, mark off equal units by making hash marks at intervals that are equidistant from each other. Then, number the units. Play a "Simon Says" game by having children step along the number line to show the number of steps "Simon" has instructed them to take.

 Research indicates that, when students see standard rulers with the numbers on the hash marks, they often believe that the numbers are counting the marks, rather than indicating the units or spaces between the marks. This understanding is faulty and can lead to incorrect measurements. As an assessment, provide students with a ruler with hash marks but no numbers. Have students use the ruler to measure an item that is shorter than the ruler. Students who count the spaces between the hash marks demonstrate a correct understanding of the ruler.

Another good assessment of students' understanding of the ruler is to have students measure with a "broken" ruler—that is, one with the first two units broken off. Some students will say that it is impossible to measure with such a ruler because there is no starting point. Those who understand how to use rulers will be able to match and count the units meaningfully when they measure. (See Barrett, Jones, Thorton, & Dickson, 2003, for a complete discussion of student development of length measurement, which includes the use of rulers.)

Observing how children use a ruler to measure an object that is longer than the ruler is also informative. Children who simply read the last mark on the ruler may struggle because they do not understand that a ruler is a representation of a series of units. ◆

Area

Area is the two-dimensional space inside a region. As with other attributes, students must first understand the attribute of area before measuring. Results from the Third International Mathematics and Science Study (TIMSS) suggest that grade 4 and particularly grade 8 Canadian students have an incomplete understanding of area (Robitaille, Taylor, & Orpwood, 1996). Data from the 2003 National Assessment of Educational Progress (NAEP) reveal similar findings for grade 4 and grade 8 U.S. students (Blume, Galindo, & Walcott, 2007).

Comparison Activities

One of the purposes of comparison activities with areas is to help students distinguish among size (or area) and shape, length, and other dimensions. A long, skinny rectangle may have a smaller area than a triangle with shorter sides. This is an especially difficult concept for young children to understand. Many 8- or 9-year-olds (even older children) do not

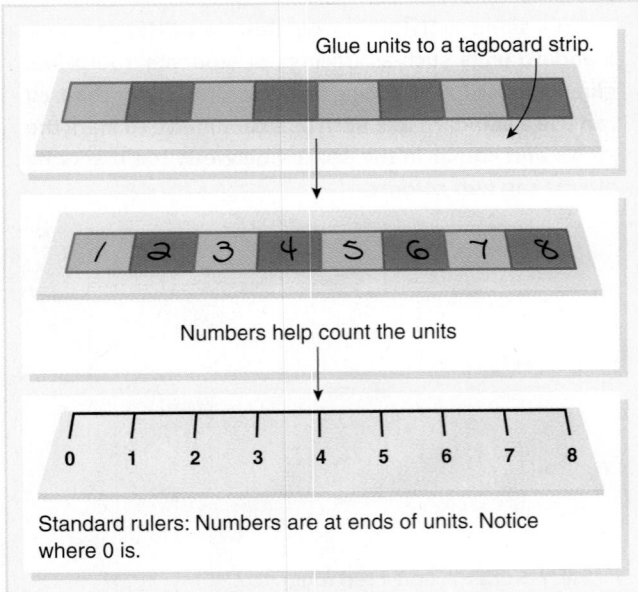

Glue units to a tagboard strip.

Numbers help count the units

0 1 2 3 4 5 6 7 8

Standard rulers: Numbers are at ends of units. Notice where 0 is.

Figure 19.5 Give meaning to numbers on rulers.

understand that rearranging areas into different shapes does not affect the area.

Direct comparison of two areas is almost always impossible, except when the shapes involved have some common dimension or property. For example, two rectangles with the same width can be compared directly, as can any two circles. But comparison of these special shapes fails to deal with the attribute of area. Instead, activities in which one area is rearranged are suggested. Cutting a shape into two parts and reassembling it into a different shape can show that the before and after shapes, even though they are different, have the same area. This idea is not at all obvious to children in kindergarten to grade 2.

Activity 19.8

Two-Piece Shapes

Cut a large number of rectangles that are the same size, approximately 8 centimetres by 12 centimetres. Provide pairs of students with six rectangles. Have the students fold and cut the rectangles on the diagonal, making two identical triangles. Next, have them rearrange the triangles into different shapes, including the original rectangle. The rule is that only sides with the same length can be matched up and they must match exactly. Have each group find all the shapes that can be made this way. Then have them glue the triangles on paper as a record of the shapes they made (see Figure 19.6). Discuss the size (area) and shape of the different results. Is one shape bigger than the rest? How is it bigger? Did one take more paper to make? Help children come to the understanding that although each figure has a different shape, all of them have the same *area*. (In this context, with very young children, *size* is a useful substitute for *area*, even though it does not mean exactly the same thing.)

Tangrams, a very old and popular set of puzzle shapes, can be used for the same purpose. The standard set of seven tangram pieces is cut from a square, as shown in Figure 19.7. The two small triangles can be used to make the parallelogram, the square, and the medium triangle. This feature of tangrams allows for a similar discussion about the pieces having the same size (area) but different shapes. (Tangram pieces can be found in the Blackline Master 51.)

Activity 19.9

Tangram Areas

Using the tangram pieces as a template, draw the outline of several shapes on a piece of paper, as shown in Figure 19.8. Then, let students use their tangram pieces to figure out which shapes are the same size, which are larger than the others, and which are smaller. The shapes can be duplicated on paper and children can work in groups. Let students explain how they came to their conclusions. You can use the animal shapes from *Grandfather Tang's Story* (Tompert, 1997) for additional investigations.

⏸ ——————————— *Pause and Reflect*

You might pause here to get a set of tangram pieces and make the area comparisons suggested in Figure 19.8.

Units of Area

Although squares are the most common units of area (and the most commonly used), any tile that conveniently fills up a plane region can be used. It is important that children under-

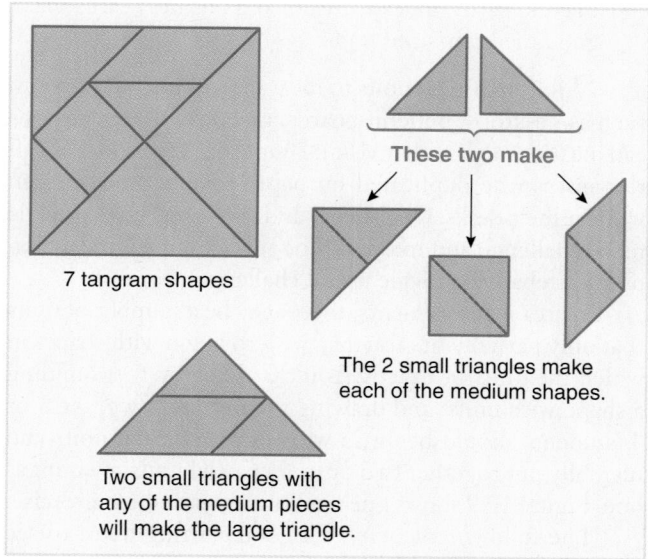

Figure 19.7 Tangrams provide an opportunity to investigate concepts of size (area) and shape.

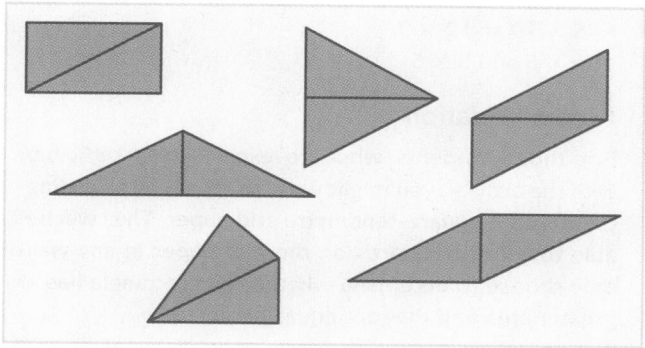

Figure 19.6 Different shapes, same size.

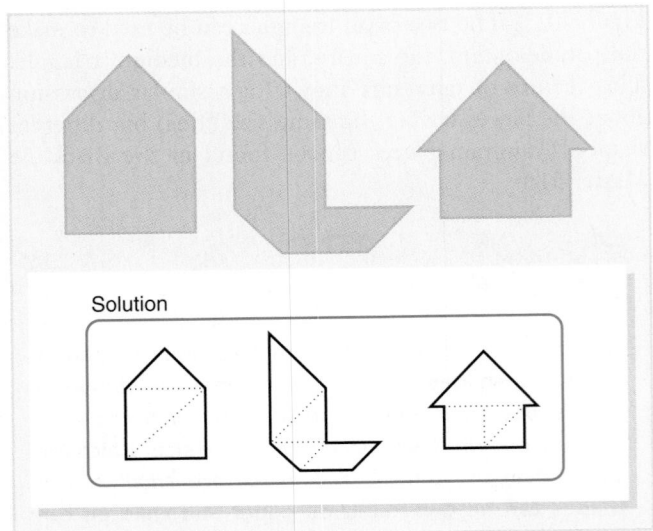

Solution

Figure 19.8 Compare shapes made of tangram pieces.

stand that finding area is all about filling a region with a particular area unit of measure. Even covering a region with lima beans provides a useful idea of what it means to measure area. Here are some suggestions for area units that are easy to gather or make in the large quantities you will need.

- Plastic chips, pennies, or lima beans can be used. It is not necessary at a beginning stage that the area units fit without any gaps.
- Commercial colour tiles.
- Squares cut from cardboard. Large squares (about 20 centimetres on a side) work well for large areas. Smaller units should be about 5–10 centimetres on a side.
- Sheets of newspaper make excellent units for very large areas.
- Playing cards, index cards, or old business cards make good medium-sized units.

Children can use units to measure surfaces in the room such as desktops, bulletin boards, or books. Large regions can be outlined with masking tape on the floor. Small regions can be duplicated on paper so that students can work at their desks. Odd shapes and curved surfaces provide more challenge and interest. The surfaces of a watermelon or a wastebasket provide useful challenges.

In area measurements, there may be a number of units that only partially fit. You may wish to begin with shapes in which the units fit exactly. You can do so by first building a shape with units, and drawing the outline. By grade 3 or 4, students should begin to wrestle with partial units and mentally put together two or more partial units to count as one. Figure 19.9 shows one possible measurement exercise.

The following activity is a good starting point to see what ideas your students bring to their understanding of area measurement.

Activity 19.10

Fill and Compare

Draw two rectangles and a blob shape on a sheet of paper. Ensure that the three areas are not the same, and no area is clearly the largest or smallest. The students' first task is to estimate which of the three shapes is the smallest and which is the largest. After recording their estimate, they should fill the shapes with a material of their choice to verify it. Students should explain their findings in writing.

Your objective in the beginning is to develop the idea that area is a *measure of finding how many units will cover a particular surface.* Do not introduce formulas. Groups are very likely to come up with different measures for the same region. Discuss these differences with the children, and point to the difficulties involved in making estimates around the edges. Avoid the idea that there is a "right" answer.

By grade 4, students should begin to relate the concept of multiplication to the area of rectangles, using arrays. The following activity is a good first step.

Activity 19.11

Rectangle Comparison—Square Units

Students are given a pair of rectangles that are either the same or very close in area. They are also given a model or drawing of a single square unit and an appropriate ruler. Students must be familiar with rulers in order to do this activity. (The ruler should clearly measure the appropriate unit.) The task is for students to use their rulers to determine, in any way they can, which rectangle is larger or if they are both the same. Students are not permitted to cut out the rectangles. However, they may draw on them if they wish. Students should use words, drawings, and numbers to explain their conclusions. Some suggested pairs of rectangles are as follows:

- **4 × 10 and 5 × 8**
- **5 × 10 and 7 × 7**
- **4 × 6 and 5 × 5**

Accommodation

For those students who are experiencing difficulty with the activity, you might want to repeat it, providing them with 2-square-centimetre grid paper. They will be able to use the squares on the grid paper in any way they choose to determine whether one rectangle has a greater area or if they are equal in size.

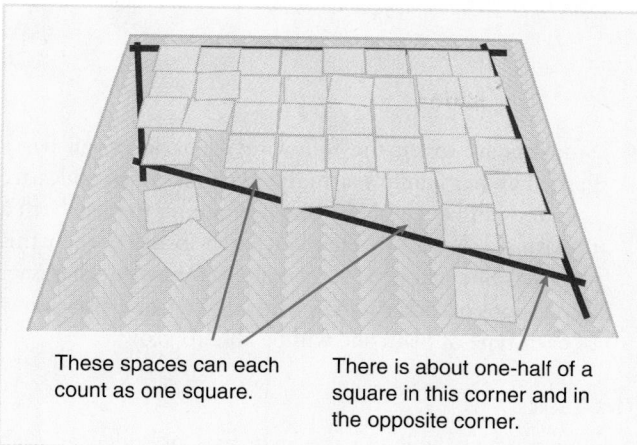

These spaces can each count as one square.

There is about one-half of a square in this corner and in the opposite corner.

Figure 19.9 Measuring the area of a large shape drawn with tape on the floor. Units are pieces of tag-board, all cut to squares of the same size.

The goal of this activity is not necessarily to develop an area formula but to apply students' developing conceptual knowledge of multiplication to the area of rectangles. Not all students will use a multiplicative approach. In order to count a single row of squares along one edge, and then multiply by the length of the other edge, the first row must be thought of as a unit that is then replicated to fill in the rectangle (Outbred & Mitchelmore, 2004). Many students will attempt to draw in all the squares. However, some may use their rulers to determine the number of squares that will fit along each side. From that, they will use multiplication to determine the total area (see Figure 19.10). By having students share their strategies, more students can be exposed to the use of multiplication in this context.

Grids Grids of various types can be thought of as a kind of "area ruler." A grid of squares does exactly what a ruler does for length—it lays out the units for you. Square grids to make transparencies are available in Blackline Masters 34–36. Have students place the grid over a region to be measured and count the units inside. An alternative method is to trace around a region on a paper grid.

The Relationship Between Area and Perimeter

Area and perimeter (the distance around a region) are continually a source of confusion for students. Perhaps it is because both involve regions to be measured or because students are taught formulas for each of these concepts at about the same time, and tend to get the formulas confused. Whatever the reason, expect that students (even in grades 5–6) will confuse these two ideas. An interesting approach to alleviating this confusion is to contrast the two ideas as in the next activities.

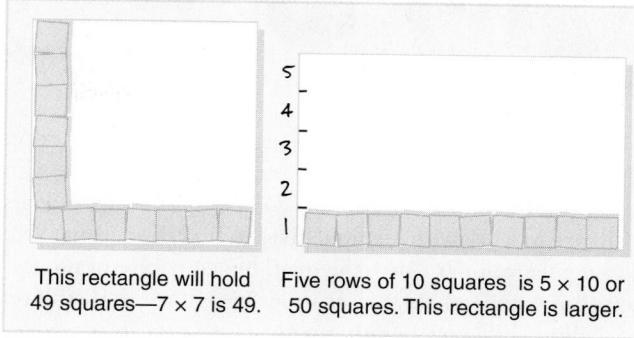

This rectangle will hold 49 squares—7 × 7 is 49.

Five rows of 10 squares is 5 × 10 or 50 squares. This rectangle is larger.

Figure 19.10 Some students use multiplication to tell the total number of square units.

Activity 19.12

Fixed Perimeters

Provide students with 2-square-centimetre grid paper. The task is for students to draw on the paper all possible rectangles with a perimeter of 24 centimetres. Students record the dimensions of each rectangle in a table, also noting the area for each.

Activity 19.13

Fixed Areas

Provide students with 36 square tiles (if you do not have commercial tiles, make squares from construction paper). The task is to see how many rectangles can be made with an area of 36, using all 36 tiles to make filled-in rectangles, not just borders. A copy of each new rectangle should be recorded, with the dimensions, on grid paper. For each rectangle, students should determine and record the dimensions and the perimeter in a table.

Accommodation

For students experiencing difficulty with the activity, use fewer tiles—such as 12 or 16.

For those students who require an added challenge, have them figure out other possibilities where the length and width of one of the rectangles are the same (squares).

Challenge them with the question: Are these rectangles? Are they squares? Or are they both?

Pause and Reflect

Before reading further, think about the two previous activities. For "Fixed Areas," will all of the perimeters be the same? If not, what can you say about the shapes with longer or shorter perimeters? For "Fixed Perimeters," will the areas remain the same? Why or why not?

Problem-Based Lesson:
Eden's Garden

This lesson demonstrates a range of learner needs, from those students who require an extra challenge to those who are challenged by the concepts. It does so by offering students a chance to work with manipulatives to find the perimeter of rectangular regions. Also, the open-ended nature of the lesson allows students to work at a pace best suited to their level of ability while collaborating with their peers in heterogeneous groupings.

Grade Level: Grades 3, 4, and 5

Mathematical Goals

- To reinforce students' understanding of the concept of perimeter.
- To build students' understanding of the idea that different-shaped rectangles could still have the same perimeter.
- To develop students' understanding of the difference between the concepts of perimeter and area.
- To develop students' problem-solving skills.

Thinking About the Students

Students have done some work on estimating, measuring, and recording the perimeter of two-dimensional shapes through investigation, using standard units. They still need practice with this process. They also need to develop their understanding of ideas embedded in the concept of perimeter. Students are grouped in pairs with children of different abilities working together.

Materials and Preparation

- An overhead projector and a transparency with the instructions for the activity.
- Geoboards and elastics, interlocking cubes, 2-square-centimetre grid paper. *Note:* For this activity, each metre of perimeter of the actual garden will be represented by the distance between pegs on the geoboard or the length of a cube.

Introduction

- Begin the lesson with a short discussion about students' favourite fruits and vegetables and the importance of eating fruits and vegetables to stay healthy. Then, introduce the idea of planting a garden to grow your favourite fruits and vegetables.

- Students are given the following scenario. Eden has a garden on her family's farm. Her favourite vegetables are tomatoes and cucumbers. She is planning to have both a tomato patch and a cucumber patch in her garden this summer. She will need some help to figure out the exact dimensions of each patch so she can determine how many of each type of plant she will be able to grow.

The Task

- The students will use the materials provided at each group table to figure out the possible dimensions for a rectangular-shaped tomato patch with a perimeter of 12 metres, and a rectangular-shaped cucumber patch with a perimeter of 14 metres.
- The different possibilities for each patch are to be constructed (with a ruler) and the dimensions for each recorded on the grid paper.
- Each square on the grid paper will represent one square metre of garden.

Establish Expectations

- Read the instructions shown on the overhead projector together with the students.
- Explain to the students that today, together with their partner, they will help Eden figure out the possible dimensions for each vegetable patch in her garden.
- To help them do so they are to use the material of their choice, either the geoboards or the interlocking cubes, to lay out the garden.
- Discuss with the students whether they think there is only one possible outcome for the dimensions of a vegetable patch or whether there could be more.
- Remind the students that each unit on the geoboard (the distance between two pegs) or one cube length represents one metre.
- Find the dimensions of each patch and show them on the grid paper. Again, remind them that each square on the grid paper also represents one metre by one metre.

Development

- Students work in small heterogeneous groups or pairs using the material of their choice to solve the problem.

- The teacher circulates around the room observing and talking with the students as they work, discussing the possibilities for the dimensions of each vegetable patch.
- Students illustrate their solutions on the grid paper.

Follow -up

- Students meet as a whole class to discuss the activity.
- Students show and talk about their solutions to the problem, explaining how they figured them out.
- Students share their understanding about finding the perimeter of two-dimensional shapes.
- Students will also have the opportunity to write about their findings in their mathematics journals. Possible sentence starters, if necessary, are:

> *The most challenging part of solving the Garden of Eden problem was ...*
>
> *I figured out the problem by ...*
>
> *The most important thing I learned about finding the perimeter of two-dimensional shapes was ...*

- A possible follow-up to this lesson is to look at factoring, given the factors generated by finding the dimensions of the garden patches. Students could explore other numbers that represent the perimeters of garden patches where they planted their favourite fruits and vegetables.

Next Steps_____

Assessment Notes

- Are some students still confused about how to find perimeter?
- Are some students confused about the idea that different-shaped two-dimensional rectangular figures could have the same perimeter?
- Which ones require additional assistance?
- Which ones require an added challenge?
- Which ones have "got it"?

As students complete Activities 19.12 and 19.13 in small groups, make sure that they record the areas and perimeters right on the rectangles (area = 12 square centimetres). They should also cut out these figures, keeping the fixed perimeters in one pile and the fixed areas in another. Labelling either two charts or locations on the board with "Perimeter" and "Area," the groups should come up and place their figures (left to right) from smallest perimeter to largest perimeter on the Perimeter Chart and from smallest area to largest area on the Area Chart. Have students state what they observed, make conjectures, and see if any conclusions can be drawn. They are often surprised to find out that two or more rectangles having the same areas do not necessarily have the same perimeters. Similarly two shapes with the same perimeters do not always have the same areas. And, of course, this fact is not restricted to rectangles.

Students will notice a fairly interesting relationship, that is, when the area is fixed, the shape with the smallest perimeter is a square or is "square-like." For a fixed perimeter, the rectangle with the largest area is also a square. If you allowed for any shapes whatsoever, the shape with the smallest perimeter and a fixed area is a circle. Assuming the areas are the same, the "fatter" a shape, the smaller its perimeter, and the skinnier a shape, the larger its perimeter. (A corresponding result is true in three dimensions. Replace perimeter with surface area and area with volume.)

Volume and Capacity

Volume and *capacity* are both terms for measures of the "size" of three-dimensional regions. The term *capacity* is generally used to refer to the amount that a container will hold. Standard units of capacity include litres and millilitres—units used for liquids, as well as the containers that hold them. The term *volume* can be used to refer to the capacity of a container but is also used when talking about the size of solid objects. Standard units of volume are expressed in terms of their linear measure such as cubic centimetres, cubic metres, etc. Capacity units are generally used for measuring liquids or the containers that hold those liquids.

Comparison Activities

Comparing the volumes of solid objects is very difficult. Therefore, for children at the primary level, it is appropriate to focus on capacity. A simple method for comparing capacity is to fill a container with some substance, then pour the substance into the comparison container to see if the first container holds more or less than the second one. By grade 3 most students will understand the concept of "holds more," in reference to containers. The concept of volume for solid objects may not be as readily understood.

Young children in pre-K to kindergarten should have many experiences directly comparing the capacities of different containers. Collect a large assortment of cans, small boxes, and plastic containers. Gather as many different shapes as possible. Also gather some plastic scoops. Cut a plastic 2-litre bottle in half, and use the top portion as a funnel. Rice or dried beans are good fillers to use. Sand and water are both possible, particularly if there is a water table available.

Activity **19.14**

Capacity Sort

Provide a collection of labelled containers, with one marked as the "target." The students' task is to sort the collection into those that hold more than, less than, or about the same amount as the target container. Provide a recording sheet that has two identical tables with four columns in each one. The first column has each container listed. The other three columns are labelled "Holds More," "Holds Less," and "Holds about the Same." The table in the top half of the sheet is where students first record their estimate made by observation. The second table is where they record "what was found." Provide a filler material (such as beans or rice), scoops, and funnels. Avoid explicit directions, but later discuss students' ideas for solving the task.

Do not expect students to be able to accurately predict which of two containers holds more. Even adults have difficulty making this judgment. Try the following task yourself; then do it with your students. Take two sheets of construction paper. Use one sheet to make a tube shape (cylinder) by taping the two long edges together. Then, tape the two short edges of the second sheet together to make a shorter, fatter cylinder. Place the two cylinders upright and decide which holds more (or less) or if they have the same capacity.

Before doing this with your class, survey them to see how many select which option. Most groups split roughly in thirds with one-third saying the short and fat cylinder holds the most; one-third saying the tall and skinny cylinder holds the most; and the last group saying that the two hold the same amount.

Try using fillers such as foam packing peanuts or lima beans. Place the tall, skinny cylinder inside the fatter one, and fill the inside one. Then, lift it up, allowing the filler to empty into the short, fatter cylinder.

The apparent volumes of solid objects are sometimes misleading and methods of comparison are also difficult. To compare volumes of solids such as a ball or an apple, some method of displacement must be used. Provide students with two or three containers that will each hold the objects being compared and fillers such as rice or beans. With this equipment some students may be able to devise their own comparison method. One approach is to first fill a container completely with the material; then pour it into an empty holding container. Next, place an object (a ball or apple) in the first container and fill it to the top, again using filler from the holding container. The volume of the filler remaining in the holding container is equal to the volume of the object. Mark the level of the leftover filler in the holding container; then repeat the experiment with other objects. By evaluating the level of the leftover filler for two or more objects, the volumes of the objects can be compared.

The following activity is a three-dimensional version of the "Fixed Areas" activity. Here the volume is fixed and students look for changes in surface area.

Activity 19.15

Fixed Volume: Comparing Prisms

Give each pair of students a supply of multilink cubes. Using a fixed number of cubes, the task is to build different rectangular prisms and record the dimensions and surface area for each in a table. Sixty-four is a good number to use since a lot of prisms can be made with this amount and a minimal surface area will occur with a 4 × 4 × 4 cube. If you are short of cubes, 24 and 36 are good choices. Students should be able to detect patterns that occur in their tables. In particular, they should notice what happens to the surface area as the prism becomes less like a tall, skinny box and more like a cube.

The goal in this activity is for students to realize that volume does not dictate surface area. They should also recognize that the pattern between surface area and volume is similar to the one found between area and perimeter. That is, prisms that are more cube-like in shape have less surface area than prisms with the same volume that are long and narrow.

Once students have developed formulas for computing area and volume, they can continue to explore the relationships between surface area and volume without actually building prisms.

Using Units of Volume and Capacity

Two types of units can be used to measure volume and capacity: solid units and containers. Solid units, such as wooden cubes or old tennis balls, can be used to fill a container being measured. The other type of unit model is a small container that is filled and emptied repeatedly into a container being measured. The following are a few examples of units you might want to collect.

- Plastic caps and liquid medicine cups.
- Plastic jars and containers of almost any size.
- Wooden cubes or blocks of any shape (which still produce conceptual measures of volume as long as you have enough of the same size).

- Styrofoam packing peanuts (which provide a conceptual measure of volume, even though they do not pack perfectly), can still be used.

The following activity is similar to Activity 19.11, "Rectangle Comparison—Square Units."

Activity 19.16

Box Comparison—Cubic Units

Provide students with two small boxes made from poster board (see Figure 19.11), one plastic or wooden block (such as an interlocking cube), and an appropriate ruler. The unit of measure for the boxes and the ruler should match the size of the block. (If 2-centimetre cubes are used, then the units of measure for the boxes and the rulers should be equal to 2 centimetres.) The students' task is to figure out which box has the greater volume or if they are both the same. The following are some suggested box dimensions (*l* × *w* × *h*).

    6 × 3 × 4   5 × 4 × 4   3 × 9 × 3   5 × 5 × 3

Students should explain their conclusions using words, drawings, and numbers.

A useful hint in the last activity is to first figure out how many cubes will fit on the bottom of the box. Some students, although certainly not all, will discover a multiplicative rule for the volume. The boxes can be filled with cubes to confirm conclusions. No formulas should be used unless students can explain them. The development of a formula is not necessarily the goal of this activity.

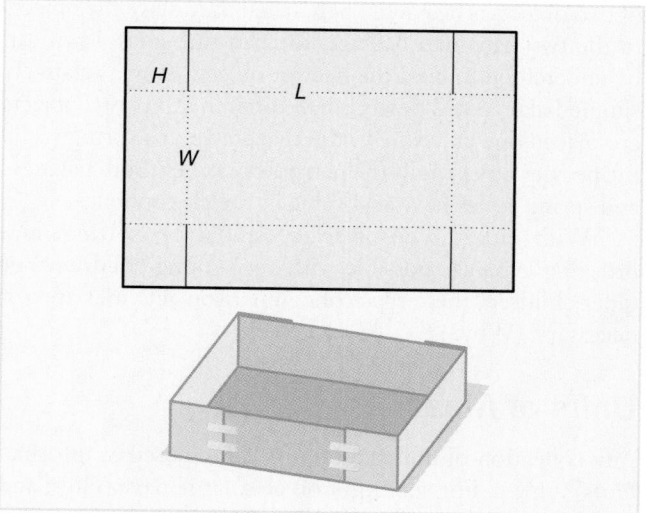

Figure 19.11 Make the small boxes by starting with a rectangle. Draw a square at each corner as shown. Cut on the solid lines and fold the box up, wrapping the corners around the outside; then tape or glue the corners to the sides, as shown.

Using Measuring Cups Instruments for measuring capacity, commonly found in kitchens and laboratories, are generally used for small amounts of liquids (e.g., water) or materials that can be poured (such as rice). A measuring cup can be made using a smaller container as the unit of measure. Students should use their measuring cups and compare their results with those made when the container is filled directly from the unit. It is likely that their measuring cups will produce errors due to inaccurate markings. This is an opportunity to point out that measuring instruments themselves can also be a source of error. The more accurate the instrument is, and the finer its calibration, the less the chance of error from that source.

Mass

Mass is the amount of matter in an object and a measure of the force needed to accelerate it. *Weight*, on the other hand, is a measure of the pull or force of gravity on an object. On the moon, where gravity is much less than on Earth, an object has a smaller weight but the identical mass as on Earth. For purposes of metric measure we will talk about mass.

Comparison Activities

The most conceptual way to compare the mass of two objects is to hold one in each hand, extend your arms, and experience the relative downward pull on each—effectively communicating to a pre-K to grade 1 child what "heavier" means. This personal experience can then be transferred to one of two basic types of scales—balances and spring scales.

Children should first use their hands to estimate which of two objects is heavier. Then, when they place the objects in the two pans of a balance, the pan that goes down can be understood to hold the heavier object. Even a relatively simple balance will detect small differences. If two objects are placed one at a time in the receptacle of a spring scale, the heavier object pulls the pan down farther. Both balances and spring scales have real value in the classroom.

With either type of scale estimating, sorting, and ordering tasks are possible with very young children. For older children, these types of comparison activities are not necessary. (Why?)

Units of Mass

Any collection of uniform objects can be used as informal units of mass. For very light objects, large paper clips, and wooden or plastic cubes work well. Large metal washers found in hardware stores are effective for finding the mass of slightly heavier objects. You will need to rely on standard units to find the mass of larger objects, as heavy as a kilogram or more.

To find the mass of an object, we use indirect measurement. Either a two-pan balance or spring scale is used. For the balance scale, place an object in one pan and enough of the unit of measure (e.g., plastic cubes, washers) in the other so that the two pans balance. For the spring scale, place the object being measured in the receptacle attached to the scale. Mark the position of the receptacle on a piece of paper taped behind the pan. Remove the object. Then, place just enough of the units of measure in the receptacle to pull it down to the same level it reached with the object being measured. Discuss how different objects of equal mass will pull the spring or rubber band with the same amount of force.

While the concept of heavier and lighter is learned rather early, the notion of units of mass is a bit more challenging. At any grade level, even a brief experience with informal units of mass is good preparation for standard units and scales.

Time

Time is somewhat different from other attributes commonly measured in school because it cannot be seen or felt. Also, it is more difficult for students to comprehend units of time or how they are paired with a given time period or interval.

Duration

Time can be thought of as the duration of an event from its beginning to its end. As with other attributes, for students to adequately understand the attribute of time, they need to compare events of different durations. If two events begin at the same time, the shorter one will end first while the other lasts longer. For example, if two tops are made to spin, which top spins longer? This type of comparison focuses on the ending of the time interval rather than on the duration itself. In order to think of time as something that can be measured, it is helpful to compare two events that do not start at the same time. Doing so requires that some form of measurement be used from the beginning.

An informal unit of time might be the duration of a swing of a pendulum, made from a tennis ball suspended on a long string from the ceiling. The long string produces a slow swing, keeping the counting manageable. The steady drip of a water faucet into an empty container is another option. The level of water is marked at the end of the time period. When the marked container is emptied and used to time a second duration, the two markings can be compared. One advantage of the water drip method is that there are no units to count. Simple tasks that address duration include the following:

- Stacking 10 blocks one at a time; then removing them one at a time

- Printing the alphabet
- Walking slowly around a designated path
- Making a bar of 15 interlocking cubes

Only one student does each task so that there is no competition or racing.

Clock Reading

The clock is the common instrument for measuring time. This has not necessarily been the case for Anishnaabe people who measured time by various other methods (Hopkins & Stonefish, 2003). However, learning to tell time has little to do with the measurement of time and more with the skills of learning to read a dial type of instrument. Clock reading can be a difficult skill to teach.

Some Challenges   Starting in grade 1, children are usually taught first to read clocks to the hour, then to the half and quarter hour, and finally to 5- and 1-minute intervals, in the grades that follow. In the early stages of this sequence, children are shown clocks set exactly to the hour or half-hour. Thus many children who can read a clock at 7:00 or 2:30 are initially challenged by 6:58 or 2:33.

Digital clocks permit students to read times easily but do not necessarily promote the concept of time very well. To understand that a digital reading of 7:58 is nearly 8 o'clock, the child must know that there are 60 minutes in an hour, that 58 is close to 60, and that 2 minutes is not a very long time. Most grade 2 and many grade 3 children have not yet developed these concepts. The analogue clock (with hands) allows a child to see that the time is close to the hour, without the need for understanding larger numbers or even knowing how many minutes are in an hour.

Suggested Approach   The following suggestions can help students better understand and read analogue clocks.

1. Begin with a one-handed clock. A clock with only an hour hand can be read with reasonable accuracy. As much as possible, use language that signifies approximation: "It's about 7 o'clock." "It's a little past 9 o'clock." "It's halfway between 2 o'clock and 3 o'clock" (see Figure 19.12).
2. Discuss what happens to the big hand as the little hand goes from one hour to the next. When the big hand is at 12, the hour hand is pointing exactly to a number. If the hour hand is about halfway between numbers, about where would the minute hand be? If the hour hand is a little past or before an hour (10 to 15 minutes), about where would the minute hand be?
3. Use two real clocks, one with only an hour hand and one with two hands. (Break off the minute hand from an old clock.) Cover the two-handed clock. Periodically, during the day, direct attention to the one-handed clock. Discuss the time using the language

"About 7 o'clock"   "Halfway between 2 o'clock and 3 o'clock"   "A little bit past 9 o'clock"

Figure 19.12 Approximate time with one-handed clocks.

of approximation. Have students predict where the minute hand should be. Uncover the other clock and check.
4. Teach time after the hour in 5-minute intervals. After step 3 has begun, count by fives going around the clock. Instead of predicting that the minute hand is pointing at the 4, encourage students to say it is about 20 minutes after the hour. As skills develop, suggest that students always look first at the little or hour hand to learn approximately what time it is and then focus on the minute hand for precision.
5. Predict the reading on a digital clock when shown an analogue clock, and vice versa. Set an analogue clock to match the time shown on a digital clock. This can be done with both one-handed and two-handed clocks.

As students learn more about two-digit numbers, the time after the hour can also be related to time remaining before the next hour. This is helpful not only for telling time but for number sense as well. Note that in the sequence suggested, time after the hour is stressed almost exclusively. Time before or until the hour can come later.

The following activity can be used to help students in grade 2 and beyond, even if the earlier sequence of one-handed clocks has not been followed.

Activity 19.17

One-Handed Clocks

Prepare a page of clock faces (see Blackline Master 33). On each clock draw an hour hand. Include placements that are approximately a quarter past the hour, a quarter before the hour, half-past the hour, and some that are close to the hour. For each clock face, the students' task is to write the digital time and draw a minute hand where they think it would be.

"One-Handed Clocks" is a good assessment of students' clock reading. If students in grade 3 or higher are having difficulty reading clocks, working with a one-handed clock, suggested earlier, will offer a different approach. ◆

Elapsed Time

Determining elapsed time is a skill required by most provincial and territorial curricula starting about grade 3. It is also a skill that can be challenging for students, especially when the period of time includes noon or midnight. Students must know how many minutes are in an hour. In one national assessment, only 26 percent of grade 4 students and 55 percent of grade 8 students could solve a problem involving the conversion of one measure of time to another (Blume, Galindo & Walcott, 2007). If given digital time or the time after the hour, students must be able to tell how many minutes to the next hour. This should certainly be a mental process of counting on for multiples of five minutes. Avoid having students use pencil and paper to subtract 25 from 60.

Figuring the time from, say, 8:15 A.M. to 11:45 A.M. is a multi-step task regardless of how it is done. Keeping track of the intermediate steps is difficult, as is deciding what to do first. In this case you could count hours from 8:15 to 11:15 and add on 30 minutes. But, what do you do if the endpoints are 8:45 and 11:15? To propose a singular method or algorithm is not helpful.

Next is the issue of A.M. and P.M. The problem is due less to students not understanding what happens on the clock at noon and midnight, than it is to having trouble counting the intervals.

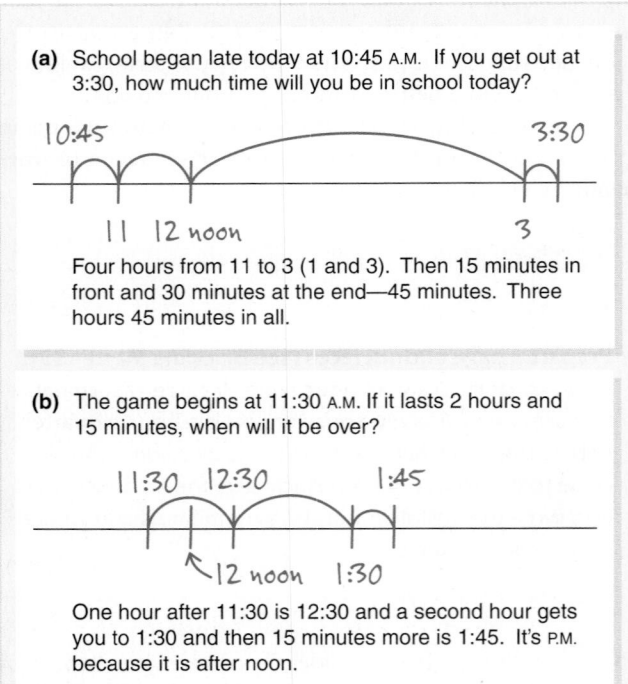

(a) School began late today at 10:45 A.M. If you get out at 3:30, how much time will you be in school today?

10:45   3:30

11 12 noon   3

Four hours from 11 to 3 (1 and 3). Then 15 minutes in front and 30 minutes at the end—45 minutes. Three hours 45 minutes in all.

(b) The game begins at 11:30 A.M. If it lasts 2 hours and 15 minutes, when will it be over?

11:30 12:30   1:45

12 noon   1:30

One hour after 11:30 is 12:30 and a second hour gets you to 1:30 and then 15 minutes more is 1:45. It's P.M. because it is after noon.

Figure 19.13 A sketch of an empty time line can be useful in solving elapsed time problems.

So far, only one form of the problem has been addressed. There is also the task of finding the end time given the start time and the elapsed time, or finding the start time given the end time and the elapsed time. In keeping with the spirit of problem solving and the use of models, consider the following.

As a general model for all these elapsed time problems, suggest that the students sketch an empty time line (similar to the empty number line for computation discussed in Chapter 12). Examples are shown in Figure 19.13. It is important not to be overly prescriptive in telling students how to use the time line since there are various alternatives (Dixon, 2008). For example in Figure 19.13a, a student might count by full hours from 10:45 (11:45, 12:45, 1:45, 2:45, 3:45) and then subtract 15 minutes.

Angles

Angle measurement can be challenging for two reasons: the attribute of angle size is often misunderstood, and protractors are introduced and used without students understanding how they work.

Comparison Activities

The attribute of angle size might be referred to as the "spread of the angle's rays," or the amount of rotation. Angles are composed of two rays whose lengths are infinite, with a common vertex. The only difference in their size is how widely or narrowly the two rays are spread apart.

To help children conceptualize the attribute of the spread of the rays, two angles can be compared directly by tracing one and placing it over the other. Be sure to have students compare angles whose sides vary in length. A wide angle with short sides may seem smaller than a narrow angle with long sides. This is a common misconception among students (Munier, Devichi, & Merle, 2008). As soon as students can tell the difference between a large angle and a small one, regardless of the length of the sides, you can move on to measuring angles.

Units of Angular Measure

A unit for measuring an angle must be an angle (a measure of rotation in some direction). Nothing else has the same attribute of spread or rotation that we want to measure. (Contrary to popular opinion, you do not need to use degrees to measure angles.)

Activity 19.18 illustrates that measuring an angle is the same as measuring length or area. Angular units are used to fill or cover the spread of an angle just as linear units are used to fill or cover a length. Once this concept is well understood, you can move on to using measuring instruments.

Activity 19.18

An Angle Unit

Give each student an index card or a small piece of tagboard. Have students draw a narrow angle on the tagboard using a straight edge, then cut it out. The resulting wedge can now be used as a unit of angular measure by counting how many of these will fit in a given angle, as shown in Figure 19.14. Pass out a worksheet with assorted angles on it and have students use their angle unit to measure them. Because students made their own angular units, the results will differ and can be discussed in terms of their size.

Using Protractors and Angle Rulers

The protractor is one of the most poorly understood measuring instruments found in schools. Part of the difficulty arises because the units of measure (degrees) are so very small. It would be physically impossible to cut out and use a single degree to measure an angle accurately. In addition, the numbers that appear on most protractors run both clockwise and counterclockwise along the marked edges, making the scale hard to interpret, without a strong conceptual foundation. By making a protractor with a large angle unit, all these mysterious features can be understood.

Students can make non-standard waxed paper protractors (see Figure 19.15). It is likely that they will soon be able to move to standard instruments after working with

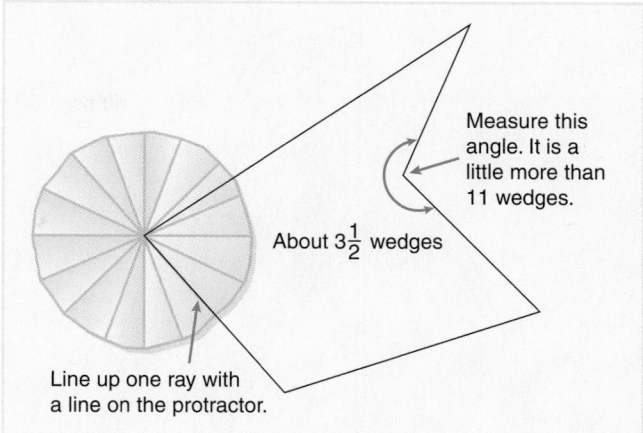

Figure 19.15   Measure angles in a polygon using a waxed-paper protractor.

non-standard protractors. For students to best understand the measures on a protractor or angle ruler, they need an approximate mental image of the size of an angle. False readings on the protractor scale will then be eliminated. One approach is to use a wheel similar to a rational number wheel in Figure 17.1 on page 340. Rather than measuring hundredths, the wheel, in this case, would be used as an "angle fixer." Two paper dessert plates, one white and the other a vivid colour, could be cut and merged as in Figure 17.1. You can then rotate the plates to create an "angle fixer" that could match angles of interest. Eventually, it could be used to estimate important benchmark angles such as 30, 45, 60, 90, 135, 180, and 270 degrees. If students have a strong grasp of the approximate sizes of angles, it will give them the background they need to move to standard measuring tools such as protractors and angle rulers (see Figure 19.16).

Introducing Standard Units

As pointed out earlier, there are a number of reasons for teaching measurement using non-standard units. However, measurement sense demands that children be familiar with standard units of measurement and that they be able to make estimates in terms of these units. It also requires that they be able to meaningfully interpret measures depicted with standard units.

Perhaps the biggest error that occurs with instruction in measurement is the failure to recognize and distinguish between two types of objectives: (1) understanding the meaning and technique of measuring a particular attribute, and (2) learning about the standard units commonly used to measure that attribute.

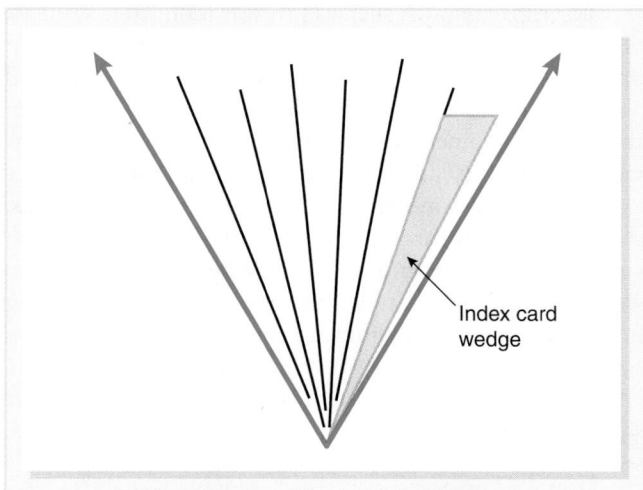

Figure 19.14   Using a small wedge cut from an index card as a unit angle, this angle measures about $7\frac{1}{2}$ wedges. Accuracy of measurement with these nonstandard angles is less important than the idea of how an angle is used to measure the size of another angle.

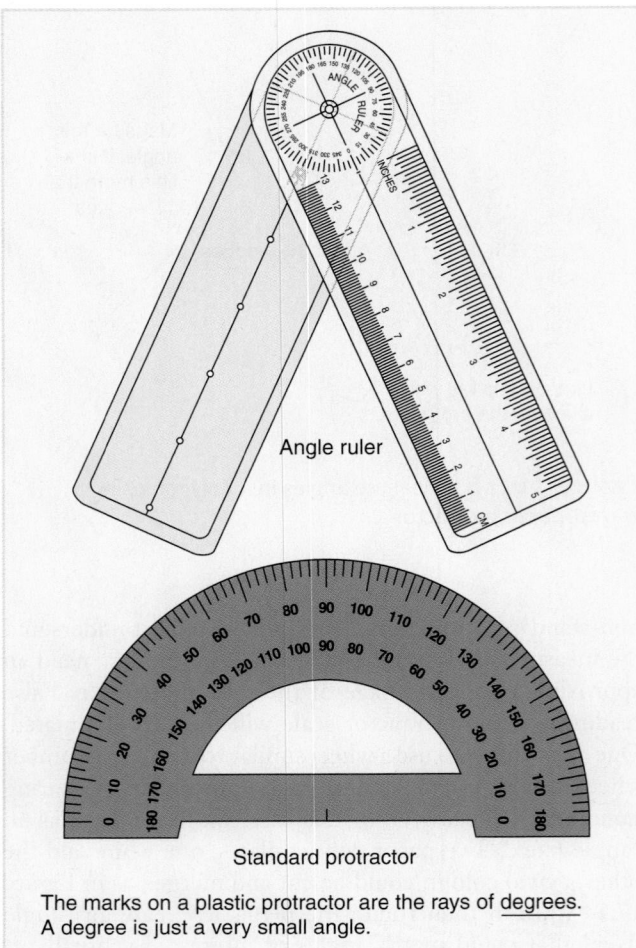

Angle ruler

Standard protractor

The marks on a plastic protractor are the rays of <u>degrees</u>. A degree is just a very small angle.

Figure 19.16 Different tools to measure angles (see Blackline Master 32).

Instructional Goals

Teaching standard units of measurement can be organized around three broad goals:

1. *Familiarity with the unit.* Students should have a basic idea of the size of commonly used units and what they measure. It is more important to know about how much 1 litre of water is, or to be able to estimate a shelf as 1 metre long, than to have the ability to measure either of these accurately.

2. *Ability to select an appropriate unit.* Students should know what a reasonable unit of measure is in a given situation. The choice of an appropriate unit is also a matter of required precision. (Would you measure your lawn for the purchase of grass seed with the same precision as you would use when measuring a window to buy a pane of glass?) Students need practice using common sense when selecting the appropriate standard units.

3. *Knowledge of a few important relationships between/among units.* Students should know those relationships that are commonly used, such as those between/among centi-

metres, metres, and kilometres; grams and kilograms; or millilitres and litres. Tedious conversion exercises do little to enhance measurement sense. The goal of unit relationships is the least important of all measurement objectives.

Developing Unit Familiarity Two types of activities can help students develop familiarity with the most frequently used standard units: (1) comparisons that focus on a single unit, and (2) activities that develop personal referents or benchmarks for single units or easy multiples of units.

Activity **19.19**

About One Unit

Give students a model of a standard unit and have them search for things that measure about the same as that one unit. For example, to develop familiarity with the metre, give students a piece of rope 1 metre long. Have them make lists of things that measure about 1 metre. Keep separate lists for things that are a little less (or more) or twice as long (or half as long). Encourage students to find familiar items in their daily lives. In the case of lengths, be sure to include circular lengths. Later, students can try to predict if a given object is more than, less than, or close to 1 metre in length.

The same activity can be done with other unit lengths. Families can be enlisted to help students find familiar distances that are about 1 kilometre. Suggest in a letter that they check distances around the neighbourhood, to the school or shopping centre, or along other frequently travelled paths.

For capacity units such as litres or millilitres, students need a container that holds or has a marking for a single unit. They should then find other containers at home and at school that hold about as much as, more than, or less than the given container. Remember that the shape of a container can be very deceptive when estimating its capacity.

For standard measures of mass, grams or kilograms, students can compare objects on a two-pan balance with single copies of these units. It may be more effective to work with 10 grams. Students can be encouraged to bring in familiar objects from home to compare on the classroom scale.

Standard area units such as square centimetres or square metres are reported in terms of their linear units, so familiarity with length is important. Familiarity with a single degree is not as important as having some idea of what 30, 45, 60, and 90 degrees might look like.

The second approach to unit familiarity is to begin with very familiar items and use their measures as referents or benchmarks. A doorway is a bit more than 2 metres tall. A bag of flour is a good referent for about 5 kilograms. Your bedroom may be about 3 metres long. A paper clip weighs about a gram and is about 1 centimetre wide.

Activity 19.20
Familiar References

For each unit of measure on which you wish to focus, have students make a list of at least five familiar things at home or in class and measure them using that standard unit of measure. For length, encourage them to include both long and short things; for mass, both light and heavy things; and so on. The measures should be rounded off to whole numbers (unless children suggest adding fractional units to be more precise). Discuss lists of familiar items and their measures, in class, so that different ideas and benchmarks are shared.

Benchmarks found on the body are of special interest for length. These become quite familiar over time and can be used as approximate rulers in many situations. Even though young children grow quite rapidly, it is useful for them to know the approximate lengths that they carry around with them.

Activity 19.21
Personal Benchmarks

Measure your body. About how long is your foot, your stride, your hand span (with fingers stretched and together), the width of your finger, your arm span (finger to finger and finger to nose), the distance around your wrist and your waist, and your height to waist, to shoulder, and to head? Some may prove to be useful benchmarks, and some may be excellent models for single units. (The average child's fingernail width is about 1 centimetre, and most people can find a 10-centimetre length somewhere on their hands.)

To help remember these references, they must be used in activities in which length, volume, and so on are compared to the benchmarks when estimating measurements.

Choosing Appropriate Units Should the room be measured in metres or centimetres? Should the concrete blocks be weighed in grams or kilograms? The answers to questions such as these involve more than simply knowing how big the units are, although that is certainly required. Another consideration involves the need for precision. If you were measuring your wall in order to cut a piece of moulding or woodwork to fit, you would need to be precise in your measurement. The smallest unit would be a centimetre, and you would also use small fractional parts. But if

you were determining how many moulding strips to buy, the nearest half-metre would probably be sufficient.

Activity 19.22
Guess the Unit

Find examples of measurements of all types in newspapers, on signs, or in other everyday situations. Present the context and the measures but without units. The task is to predict what units of measure were used. Have students discuss their choices.

Important Standard Units and Their Relationships

The relationship between units within the metric system is a convention. As such, students must simply be told what the relationships are, and instructional experiences must be devised to reinforce them. It can be argued that knowing about how much liquid makes a litre, or being able to pace off 3 metres—unit familiarity—is more important than knowing how many cubic centimetres are in a litre. However, in the intermediate grades, knowing basic relationships becomes more important. Your local curriculum document should be your guide.

Since the metric system was designed systematically around powers of ten, there is little advantage to teaching the relationships that exist in this system before students have developed a full understanding of decimal notation. As students begin to appreciate the structure of decimal notation, the metric system can and should be developed with all seven places: three prefixes for smaller units (*deci-*, *centi-*, and *milli-*) and three for larger units (*deca-*, *hecto-*, and *kilo-*). Table 19.2 lists the units that are most commonly used.

Table 19.2

Commonly Encountered Units of Measure	
	Metric Measure
Length	millimetre centimetre metre kilometre
Area	square centimetre square metre
Volume	cubic centimetre cubic metre
Capacity	millilitre litre
Weight	gram kilogram tonne

Perhaps one of the worst errors in teaching metric measurement prior to a complete development of decimal notation is to have students "move the decimal point" when converting from one metric unit to another. Avoid mechanical rules such as "To change centimetres to metres, move the decimal point two places to the left." When students do not develop conceptually meaningful methods for conversions themselves, arbitrary sounding rules are bound to be misused and forgotten.

 When assessing students' understanding of and familiarity with standard units, avoid focusing on traditional conversion tasks.

Consider these two tasks:

1. 540 millimetres = _____ centimetres
2. Estimate the length of the blackboard in metres and centimetres. How did you decide on your estimate?

Both tasks require that students have some familiarity with metric units. However, the second task requires students to have familiarity with the units themselves. The estimation task allows us to see whether the student uses the first estimate to make the second estimate (which is understanding and using the metre–centimetre relationship) or rather makes two separate estimates. This task also allows us to see how the student makes an estimate—information that cannot be gleaned from the first task. ◆

Estimating Measures

Estimation in measurement is the process of using mental and visual information to measure or make comparisons without the use of a measuring instrument. It is a practical skill. Almost every day, we make estimates of measures. Do I have enough sugar to make the cookies? How far can you throw the ball? Is the mass of this suitcase over the acceptable limit? About how long is the fence? Will this paper cover the box?

Besides its value outside the classroom, estimation in measurement activities helps students focus on the attribute being measured, adds intrinsic motivation, and helps develop familiarity with standard units. Consequently, estimation improves measurement instruction at the same time that it develops a valuable life skill.

Strategies for Estimating Measurement

Just as with computational estimation, specific strategies exist for estimating measurements. Four of these can be taught:

1. *Develop and use benchmarks or referents for important units.* Research has shown that students who have acquired mental benchmarks or reference points for measurements *and* have practised using them in class activities are much better estimators than students who have not learned to use benchmarks (Joram, 2003). Referents should be benchmarks that are easily envisioned by the student. One example is the cabinet shown in Figure 19.17. Students should have good referents for single units and for useful multiples of standard units.
2. *Use "chunking" when appropriate.* Figure 19.17 is an example. It may be easier to estimate the shorter chunks

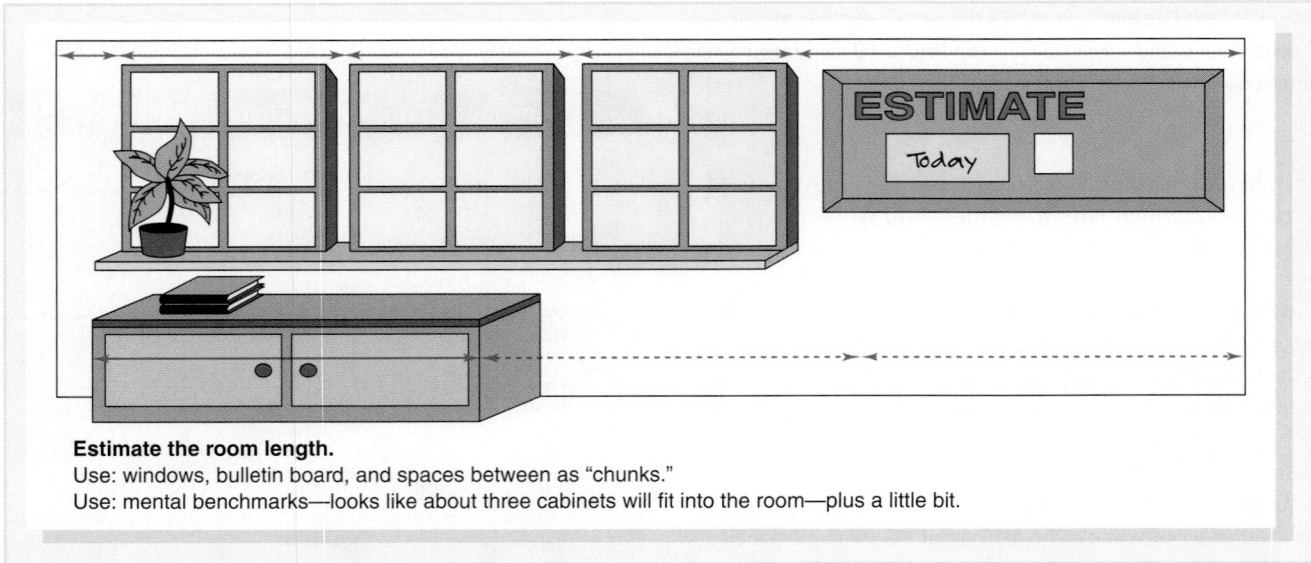

Estimate the room length.
Use: windows, bulletin board, and spaces between as "chunks."
Use: mental benchmarks—looks like about three cabinets will fit into the room—plus a little bit.

Figure 19.17 Estimating measurements by using benchmarks and chunking.

along the wall than to estimate the whole length as one. The mass of a stack of books is easier if some estimate is given of an "average" book.

3. *Use subdivisions.* This is a similar strategy to chunking, with the chunks imposed on the object by the estimator. For example, if the wall length to be estimated has no useful chunks, it can be mentally divided in half, then in fourths or even eighths by repeated halving in order to arrive at a more manageable length. Length, volume, and area measurements all lend themselves to this technique.

4. *Iterate a unit mentally or physically.* For length, area, and volume, it is sometimes easy to mark off single units visually. You might use your hands or make marks or folds to keep track as you go. If you know, for example, that your stride is about 1 metre, you can walk off a length and then multiply to get an estimate. Hand and finger widths are useful for shorter measures.

Tips for Teaching Estimation

Each of the four strategies just listed should be taught and discussed with students. Suggested benchmarks for useful measures can be developed and recorded on a class chart. Include items found at home. But the best approach to improving students' estimation skills is to have them practise a lot, keeping the following tips in mind:

1. Help students learn strategies by having them use a specified approach. Later activities should permit students to choose whatever techniques they wish.

2. Discuss how different students made their estimates. This practice will help students understand that there is no single right way to estimate. It will also remind them of different approaches that are useful.

3. Accept a range of estimates. Think in relative terms about what a good estimate is. Within 10 percent for length is quite good. Even 30 percent off may be reasonable for mass or volume. Do not promote a "winning" strategy.

4. Encourage students to give a range of measures that they believe includes the actual measure. Not only is this a practical approach in real life, but it also helps focus on the approximate nature of estimation.

5. Make estimation in measurement an ongoing activity. A daily measurement to be estimated can be posted on the bulletin board. Students can turn in their estimates on paper and discuss them in a 5-minute period. Older students can even be given the task of deciding what to estimate and a team of students can be assigned a task each week.

Measurement Estimation Activities

Estimation activities need not be elaborate. Any measurement activity can have an "estimate first" component. To increase the emphasis on the process itself, simply think of things that students can estimate; then have them do it. Here are a few suggestions.

Activity 19.23

Estimation Quickie

Select a single object such as a box, a pumpkin, or a jar. Each day, select a different attribute or dimension to estimate. For a pumpkin, for example, students can estimate its height, girth, mass, volume, and surface area.

Activity 19.24

Estimation Scavenger Hunt

Conduct estimation scavenger hunts. Give teams a list of measurements and have them find things with measurements close to those on the list. Do not permit the use of measuring instruments. A list might include the following items:

- **A length of 3.5 metres**
- **Something with a mass of more than 1 kilogram but less than 2 kilograms**
- **A container that holds about 200 millilitres**
- **An angle of 45 degrees or 135 degrees**

Let students suggest how accuracy of results should be judged.

Estimation tasks are a good way to assess students' understanding of both measurement and standard units. Use real objects and distances within the room as well as outside. Time and long distances should be estimated with comparison to events and distances that are meaningful to the students. Have students explain how they arrived at their estimates in order to get a more complete picture of their measurement knowledge. Providing only a numerical estimate can mask a lack of understanding and will not give you the information you need to provide appropriate remediation. ◆

Developing Formulas for Area and Volume

It is important not to bypass formula development with your students. Conceptual development does so much more than provide them with a strategy for plugging in numbers. When students develop formulas, they gain a conceptual understanding of the ideas and relationships involved. Moreover, they are engaging in one of the real processes of doing mathematics. There is less likelihood that students will confuse area and perimeter or that they will select the incorrect formulas on a test. General relationships are developed. For example, students are able to see how all area formulas are related to one idea: length of the base times the height. And students who understand where formulas come from do not see them as mysterious, tend to remember them, and formulas are reinforced by the idea that mathematics makes sense. The rote use of formulas from a book offers none of these advantages.

Students' Misconceptions

Results of testing clearly indicate that students do not have a very good understanding of formulas. For example, data from the 2004 Junior High Mathematics Program Assessment for Nova Scotia suggests that students experienced difficulty finding the area of a composite shape (a semi-circle, a rectangle, and a triangle) and solving multi-step problems involving perimeter and area (*Nova Scotia Elementary Mathematics Program Assessment Report, 2004*). Results of the National Assessment of Educational Progress (NAEP) testing clearly indicate that students do not have a very good understanding of formulas. In the 2007 NAEP, only 39 percent of grade 4 students were able to give the correct answer when asked to find the area of a carpet. A common error is to confuse formulas for area and perimeter. Results such as these are largely due to an overemphasis on formulas with little or no conceptual grounding.

The tasks in Figure 19.18 cannot be solved with simple formulas; they require an understanding of concepts and how formulas work. "Length times width" is not a definition of area that works.

Another common error when students use formulas comes from their inability to conceptualize the idea of height and base in both two- and three-dimensional geometric figures. The shapes in Figure 19.19 each have a given slanted side and a given height. Students tend to confuse these two. Any side or flat surface of a figure can be called a *base* of the figure. For each base that a figure has,

there is a corresponding height. If the figure were to slide into a room on its base, the *height* would be the height of the shortest door it could pass through without tipping over—that is, the perpendicular distance to the base. Students have a lot of early experiences with the length-multiplied-by-the-width formula for rectangles, where the height is actually the same as the length of a side. Perhaps this is the source of the confusion. Before formulas involving heights are discussed, students need to be able to identify where a height could be measured for the base of any figure.

Areas of Rectangles, Parallelograms, Triangles, and Trapezoids

The formula for the area of a rectangle is one of the first that is developed and is usually given as $A = L \times W$, "area equals length multiplied by width." Looking forward to other area formulas, an equivalent but more unifying idea might be $A = b \times h$, "area equals *base* multiplied by *height*." The base-multiplied-by-height formulation can be generalized to all parallelograms (not just rectangles) and is useful in developing the area formulas for triangles and trapezoids. Furthermore, the same approach can be extended to three dimensions, where volumes of cylinders are given in terms of the *area of the base* multiplied by the height. Base multiplied by height, then, helps connect a large family of formulas that otherwise must be mastered independently.

Rectangles Research suggests that it is a significant leap for students to move from counting squares inside a rectangle to the conceptual development of a formula. Battista (2003) found that students often try to fill in empty rectangles with drawings of squares, then count the result one square at a time.

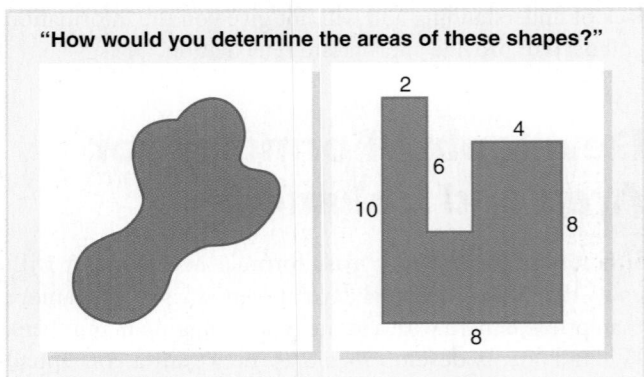

"How would you determine the areas of these shapes?"

Figure 19.18 Understanding the attribute of area.

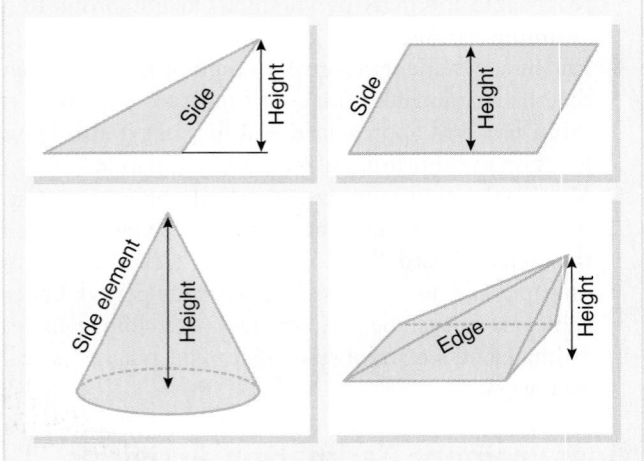

Figure 19.19 Heights of figures are not always measured along an edge or a surface.

An important concept to review is the meaning of multiplication as seen in arrays. Show students rows and columns of objects or of squares. Then, discuss how multiplication can be used to find the total amount. Students need to be aware that we are not multiplying squares by squares or dots by dots. Rather, we are counting either a single row or column and finding out how many columns or rows there are in all. This is the same concept they will need to apply to find the area of a rectangle. When we multiply a length by a width, we are not multiplying "squares by squares." Rather, the *length* of one side indicates how many squares will fit on that side. If this set of squares is taken as a unit, then the *length* of the other side (not a number of squares) will tell how many of these *rows of squares* can fit in the rectangle.

A good activity to begin your exploration of area formulas is to revisit Activity 19.11, "Rectangle Comparison— Square Units" (p. 394). Students who are drawing in all the squares and counting them have not thought about a row of squares as a single row that can be replicated. Related tasks based on the work of Battista (2003) are shown in Figure 19.20.

When your students have formulated an approach to area based on the idea of a row of squares (determined by the length of a side) multiplied by the number of these rows that will fit the rectangle (determined by the length of the other side), it is time to consolidate these ideas. Explain to students that you like the idea of measuring one side to tell how many squares will fit in a row along that side. You

would like them to call or think of this side as the *base* of the rectangle, even though some people call it the length or the width. You can then call the other side the *height*. But which side is the base? Be sure that students conclude that either side could be the base. If you use the formula $A = b \times h$, the same area will result using either side as the base.

From Rectangles to Other Parallelograms   Once students understand the base-multiplied-by-height formula for rectangles, the next challenge is to determine the area of parallelograms. Do not provide a formula or other explanation. Rather, try the following activity, which again asks students to devise their own formula.

Activity **19.25**

Area of a Parallelogram

Give students two or three parallelograms, drawn either on grid paper or, for a slightly harder challenge, on blank paper. If the parallelograms are drawn on blank paper, provide all dimensions (the length of all four sides and the height). The students' task is to apply what they have learned about the area of rectangles to determine the area of these parallelograms. Students should find a method that will work for any parallelogram, even if it is not drawn on a grid.

If students are stuck, ask them to examine ways in which the parallelogram is like a rectangle or how it can be changed into a rectangle. As shown in Figure 19.21, a parallelogram can always be transformed into a rectangle with the same base, the same height, and the same area. Thus, the formula for the area of a parallelogram is exactly the same as for a rectangle: base multiplied by height.

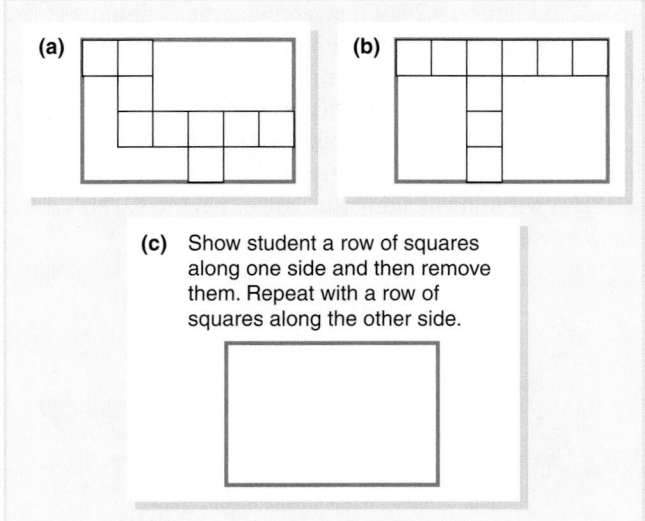

Figure 19.20 Three different activities in sequential order for determining area. In each case, students are to tell how many squares will fill the rectangles.

Source: Based on suggestions by Battista, M. T. (2003). "Understanding Students: Thinking about Area and Volume Measurement." In D. H. Clements (Ed.), *Learning and Teaching Measurement* (pp. 122–142). Reston, VA: NCTM.

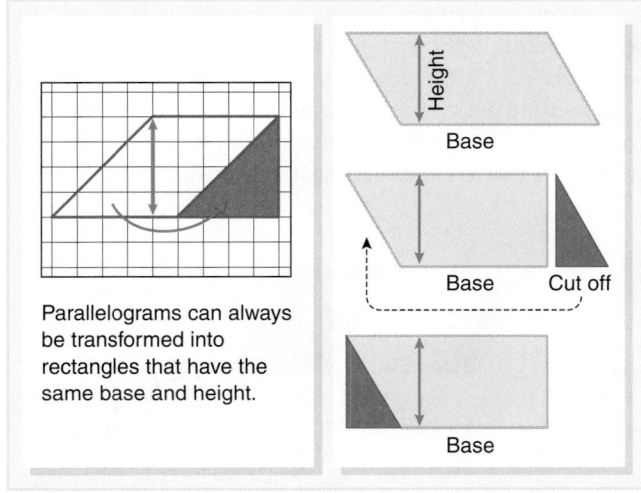

Figure 19.21 Transforming a parallelogram into a rectangle.

From Parallelograms to Triangles   With that background, the area of a triangle is relatively simple. Again, use a problem-based approach as in the next activity.

Activity **19.26**

Area of a Triangle

Provide students with at least two triangles drawn on grid paper. Avoid using right triangles because they are an easier special case. The challenge for students is to apply what they have learned about the area of parallelograms to find the area of each of the triangles and to develop a method that will work for any triangle. They should be sure that their method works for all the triangles given, as well as for at least one more that they draw.

There are several hints that you might offer if students are stuck. You might ask, *Can you find a parallelogram that is somehow related to your triangle?* If this is not sufficient, suggest that they fold a piece of paper in half, draw a triangle on the folded paper and cut it out, making two identical copies. They should use the copies to find out how a triangle is related to a parallelogram.

As shown in Figure 19.22, two congruent triangles can always be arranged to form a parallelogram with the same base and height as the triangle. The area of the triangle will therefore be one-half as much as the area of the parallelogram. Have students further explore all three possible parallelograms, one for each side of the triangle serving as the base. Will the computed areas always be the same?

From Parallelograms to Trapezoids   After developing formulas for parallelograms and triangles, your students may be interested in tackling trapezoids without any further assistance. (See Figure 3.1, p. 34, for an example of a completely open challenge.) There are at least ten different methods for arriving at a formula for trapezoids, each related to the area of parallelograms or rectangles. One method uses the same general approach that was used for triangles. Suggest that students try working with two trapezoids that are identical, just as they did with triangles.

Figure 19.23 shows how this method results in the formula. Not only are all of these formulas connected, but similar methods were used to develop them.

Here are a few hints, each of which leads to a different approach to finding the area of a trapezoid.

- Make a parallelogram inside the given trapezoid using three of the sides.
- Make a parallelogram using three sides that surround the trapezoid.
- Draw a diagonal forming two triangles.
- Draw a line through the midpoints of the sides that are not parallel. The length of that line is the average of the lengths of the two parallel sides.
- Draw a rectangle inside the trapezoid, leaving two triangles; then put those two triangles together.

 ——————— *Pause and Reflect*

Do you think that students should learn special formulas for the area of a square? Why or why not? Do you think students need formulas for the perimeters of squares and rectangles?

The relationship among the areas of rectangles, parallelograms, and triangles can be dramatically illustrated using a dynamic geometry program such as *The Geometer's Sketchpad* (Key Curriculum Press), *Cabri Geometry* (Texas Instrument), or *Wingeom* (free public domain program available on line). Draw two congruent segments on two parallel lines, as shown in Figure 19.24. Then, connect the endpoints of the segments to form a parallelogram and two triangles that form it. A segment between the parallel lines, which is perpendicular to each line, indicates the height of the parallelogram. Either of the two line segments can be dragged left or right to "shear" the parallelogram and each of the triangles without changing the base or height. All area measures remain fixed! ◆

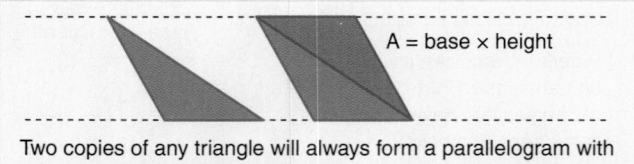

Two copies of any triangle will always form a parallelogram with the same base and height; therefore, the triangle has an area of half of the parallelogram, $A = \frac{1}{2}$ (base × height).

Figure 19.22 Two congruent triangles always make a parallelogram.

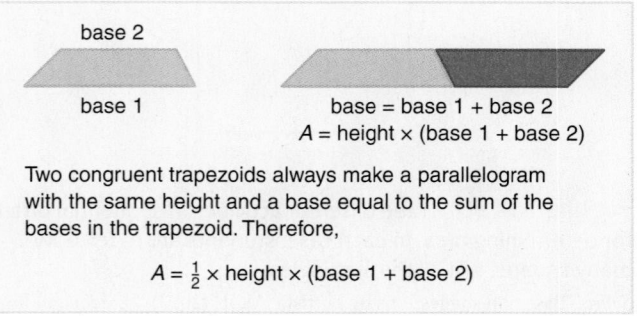

Two congruent trapezoids always make a parallelogram with the same height and a base equal to the sum of the bases in the trapezoid. Therefore,

$$A = \tfrac{1}{2} \times \text{height} \times (\text{base 1} + \text{base 2})$$

Figure 19.23 Two congruent trapezoids always form a parallelogram.

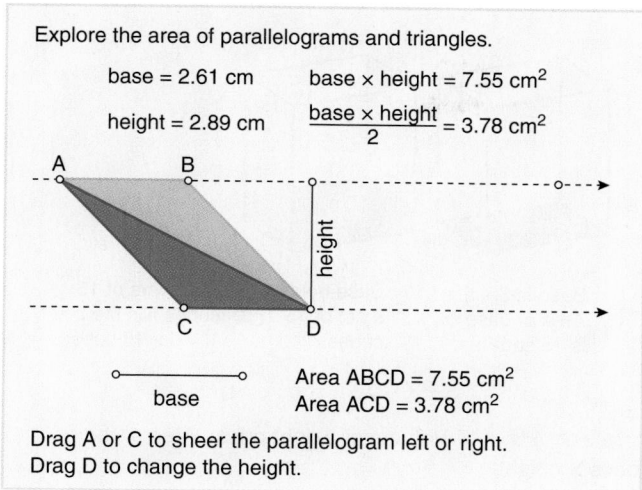

Explore the area of parallelograms and triangles.

base = 2.61 cm   base × height = 7.55 cm²

height = 2.89 cm $\dfrac{\text{base} \times \text{height}}{2}$ = 3.78 cm²

Area ABCD = 7.55 cm²
Area ACD = 3.78 cm²

Drag A or C to sheer the parallelogram left or right.
Drag D to change the height.

Figure 19.24 Dynamic geometry software shows that figures with the same base and height maintain the same area.

Circumference and the Area of Circles

The relationship between the *circumference* of a circle (the distance around or the perimeter) and the length of the *diameter* (a line through the centre joining two points on the circle) is one of the most interesting that children can discover. The circumference of every circle is about 3.14 times as long as the diameter. The exact ratio is an irrational number close to 3.14 and is represented by the Greek letter π. So $\pi = C/D$, the circumference divided by the diameter. In a slightly different form, $C = \pi D$. Half the diameter is the radius (r), so the same equation can be written $C = 2\pi r$. (Activity 20.10 on page 432 in Chapter 20 will discuss in detail the concept of π and how students can discover this important ratio.)

Figure 19.25 presents an argument for the area formula $A = \pi r^2$. This development is one commonly found in textbooks.

Regardless of the approach you use to develop the area formula for a circle, students should be challenged to figure it out on their own. For example, show students how to arrange 8 or 12 sectors of a circle into an approximation of a parallelogram. Their task then should be to use this as a hint toward developing an area formula for the circle. You may need to help them notice that the arrangement of sectors is an approximation of a parallelogram and that the smaller you make the sectors, the more closely the arrangement approaches a rectangle. But the complete argument for the formula should come from your students.

Tech NOTES The lesson component of the geometry unit in *Math Trek 7, 8* (Nectar Foundation, 2006) develops the relationship between the circumference and the diameter of a circle, in a sequential but interactive manner. The lesson begins by defining *circle*,

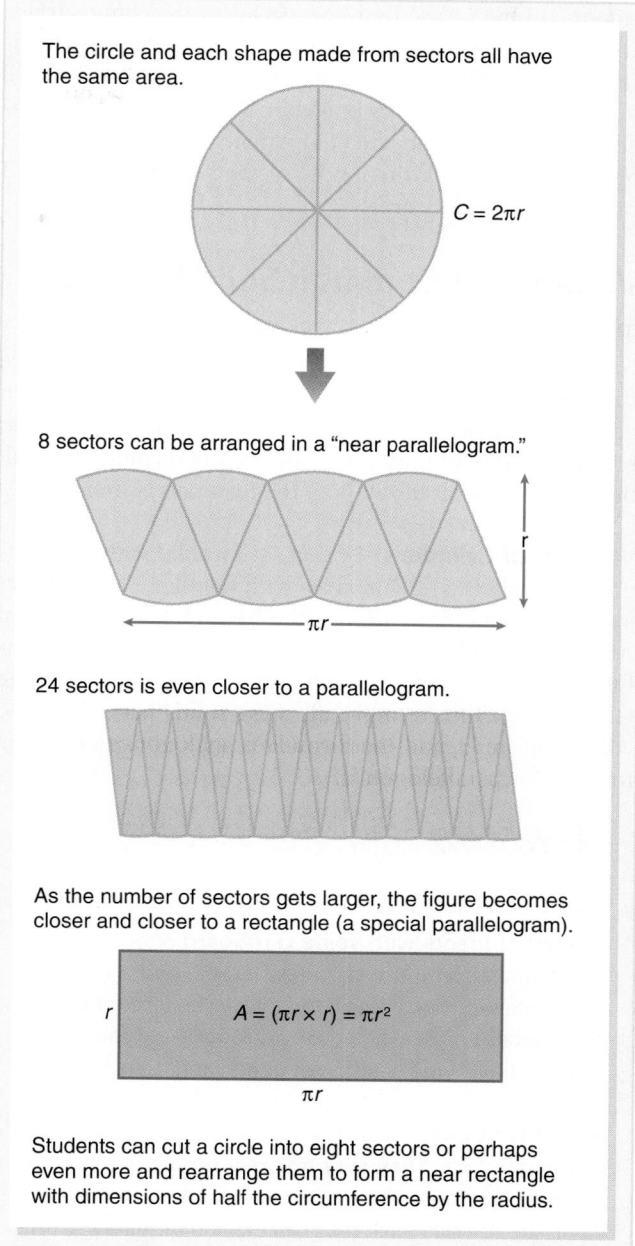

The circle and each shape made from sectors all have the same area.

$C = 2\pi r$

8 sectors can be arranged in a "near parallelogram."

πr

24 sectors is even closer to a parallelogram.

As the number of sectors gets larger, the figure becomes closer and closer to a rectangle (a special parallelogram).

$A = (\pi r \times r) = \pi r^2$

πr

Students can cut a circle into eight sectors or perhaps even more and rearrange them to form a near rectangle with dimensions of half the circumference by the radius.

Figure 19.25 Development of the formula for the area of a circle.

circumference, diameter, and *radius.* Through a series of steps, the area formula, similar to the one used in this book, is developed for the student. Practice questions are provided in the lesson and in the practice component of the program. ◆

Surface Area As students begin to explore the surface area of prisms and other figures, build on the knowledge they have of the area of two-dimensional figures. If they think of each face of a solid as its two-dimensional counterpart, they can find the area of each face and add the amounts. One of the best approaches to teaching surface area of three-dimensional figures is to create several cardstock rectangular prisms, cubes, or cylinders with sides held together by small pieces of Velcro®. In this way the students can think about the components of the "net" of the figure as they break the model of the solid into faces and calculate the surface area.

Volumes of Common Solid Shapes

The relationships between the formulas for volume are completely analogous to those for area. As you read, notice the similarities between rectangles and prisms, between parallelograms and "sheared" (oblique) prisms, and between triangles and pyramids. Not only are the formulas related, but the process for developing the formulas is similar.

Volumes of Cylinders A *cylinder* is a solid with two congruent parallel bases and sides with parallel elements that join corresponding points on the bases. There are several special classes of cylinders, including *prisms* (with polygons for bases), *right prisms*, *rectangular prisms*, and *cubes* (see Chapter 20). Interestingly, all these solids have the same volume formula, and the formula is analogous to the area formula for parallelograms.

Activity 19.27

Volume of a Box

Provide students with some cardboard shoe boxes or other similar type boxes, a few cubes, and a ruler. As was done with rectangles, the task is to determine how many cubes will fit inside the box. Most likely your boxes will not have whole number dimensions, so have the students ignore any fractional parts of a cube that may arise. Even though they may have seen or used a volume formula before, they may not rely on it for this task. Rather, they must come up with a method or formula, using the cubes, which they can explain or justify. If students require a hint, suggest that they begin by finding how many cubes will fit on the bottom of the box.

The development of the formula for volume from this box exploration exactly parallels the development of the formula for the area of a rectangle. Figure 19.26 illustrates how this development mirrors the one for area. The *area* of the base (instead of the *length* of the base, for rectangles) determines how many *cubes* can be placed on the base forming a single unit of measure—a *layer* of cubes (instead of *squares*). The *height* of the box then determines how many of these *layers* will fit in the box just as the height of the rectangle determined how many *rows* of squares would fill the rectangle.

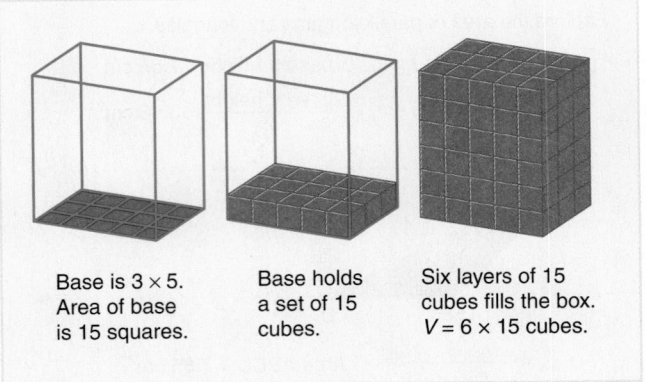

Base is 3 × 5. Area of base is 15 squares.

Base holds a set of 15 cubes.

Six layers of 15 cubes fills the box. $V = 6 \times 15$ cubes.

Figure 19.26 Volume of a right prism: Area of the base × height.

Recall that a parallelogram can be thought of as a "sheared" rectangle, as was illustrated with the dynamic geometry software (Figure 19.24). Show students a stack of three or four decks of playing cards (or a stack of books or paper). When stacked straight, they form a rectangular solid. The formula for volume, as just discussed, is $V = A \times h$, with A equal to the area of one playing card. Now if the stack is sheared or slanted to one side as shown in Figure 19.27, what will the volume of this new figure be? Students should be able to argue that this figure has the same volume (and same volume formula) as the original stack.

What if the cards in this activity were some other shape? If they were circular, the volume would still be the area of the base multiplied by the height; if they were triangular, still the same. The conclusion is that the volume of *any* cylinder is equal to the *area of the base* multiplied by the *height*.

Connections Among Formulas

The connectedness of mathematical ideas can hardly be better illustrated than with the connections of all of the formulas discussed, to the single concept of base times height.

As illustrated throughout this last section, a conceptual approach to the development of formulas helps students

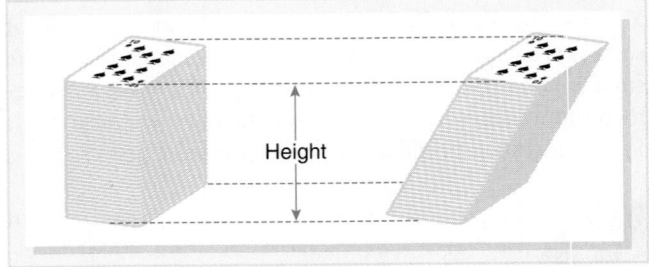

Height

Figure 19.27 Two cylinders with the same base and height have the same volume.

understand these tools as significant, yet efficient, ways to measure different attributes of objects around us. After having developed formulas in meaningful ways, students no longer need to memorize them as isolated pieces of math-

ematical facts. Instead, they can derive formulas from what they already know and realize that mathematics does make sense!

Reflections on Chapter 19

Writing to Learn

1. Explain what it means to measure something. Does your explanation work equally well for length, area, mass, volume, and time?
2. A general instructional plan for measurement has three parts. Explain how the type of activity that would be used with each part accomplishes the instructional goal.
3. Four reasons were offered for using non-standard units instead of standard units in instructional activities. Which of these seem most important to you, and why?

4. Develop in a connected way the area formulas for rectangles, parallelograms, triangles, and trapezoids. Draw pictures and provide explanations.
5. Explain how the area of a circle can be determined using the basic formula for the area of a parallelogram. (If you have a set of circular fraction pieces, these can be used as sectors of a circle.)

For Discussion and Exploration

1. Obtain a teacher's edition of a textbook for any grade level, and look at the chapters on measurement. How well does the book cover measurement ideas? How would you modify or expand on the lessons found in the book?

Resources for Chapter 19

Literature Connections

Counting on Frank   *Clement, 1991*

Although referenced previously, here is another excellent opportunity for connecting with this book.

Jim and the Beanstalk   *Briggs, 1970*

In this amusing variation on the classic tale of *Jack and the Beanstalk*, Jim (not Jack, as the author notes) helps the giant to deal with some of the problems of aging he is experiencing such as eyesight, teeth, and hair loss. He does so by measuring the giant for glasses, teeth, and a wig and taking these measurements to the appropriate professionals to have the items made for him. As well, the gold coins to pay for services are giant size also. Students can estimate the size of these items and make comparisons with the same ones for humans. Measuring these items would allow them to apply their knowledge of linear and area measure. There would also be opportunities to incorporate ratio concepts.

Every Minute on Earth: Fun Facts That Happen Every 60 Seconds   *Murrie & Murrie, 2007*

This is an amazing book that is not just about the concept of time. The authors provide fun facts about what can happen in 60 seconds: a snow avalanche travels 4.2 miles (6.8 kilometres); the adult heart pumps 3.3 litres (3.5 quarts) of blood; movie film travels 90 feet (27.4 metres) through a projector; a garden snail moves 0.31 inches (7.8 millimetres); people in the United States throw away 18,315 pounds (8325 kilograms) of food; and consumers spend $954.00 on chewing gum. Students can use the facts provided or identify others as they think about and discuss these relationships.

Fairy Tale Feasts: A Literary Cookbook
Yolen & Stemple, 2006,

This book offers a tasty blend of literary wizardry and creative cookery. There are 20 stories alongside 25 recipes from different parts of the world. The book provides students with an opportunity to examine food from different cultures and to possibly try out these recipes.

Up Up Down *Munsch, 2001*

This charming book about Anna, who likes to climb, could be connected to linear measure. In the story, Anna climbs up the refrigerator, her dresser, and a tree. Children could estimate the heights of the three items, then find the actual measure for the refrigerator and the dresser, at home. The different measurements they bring to class can lead to some good discussion. As a follow up, students could estimate and measure other items. Students can actually hear Robert Munsch narrate this story (as well as others) on his Web site.

Recommendations for Further Reading

Articles

Austin, R., Thompson, D., & Beckmann, C. (2005). Exploring measurement concepts through literature: Natural links across disciplines. *Mathematics Teaching in the Middle School, 10* (5), 218–224.

This article includes a rich collection of almost 30 children's books that emphasize overall systems of measurement, length, weight, capacity, speed, area, perimeter, and volume. Three books are described in detail as the authors share how to link measurement to science, history, geography, and economics.

National Council of Teachers of Mathematics. (2004). Measurement [Focus Issue]. *Mathematics Teaching in the Middle School, 9.*

This focus issue of NCTM's middle school journal is full of great information for teachers at that level. Of particular note are several articles that involve scale drawings or other aspects of proportional reasoning, which is a great way to integrate measurement into the curriculum.

Pumala, V. A., & Klabunde, D. A. (2005). Learning measurement through practice. *Mathematics Teaching in the Middle School, 10* (9), 452–460.

A mathematics teacher and a science teacher collaborated on a series of six activities to help their students learn about measurement. Included in the article are descriptions of the activities and detailed rubrics along with samples of student work.

Whitin, D. (2008). Learning our way to one million. *Teaching Children Mathematics, 14* (8), 448–453.

Through an exploration of the topic of one million, Whitin suggests ways for children in grades 2–5 to explore several mathematics topics, including length, area, and money. All investigations emphasize the need for active problem solving in real-world contexts that reflect students' interests.

Books

Clements, D. H. (Ed.) (2003). *Learning and teaching measurement: 2003 Yearbook.* Reston VA: National Council of Teachers of Mathematics.

This book offers a practical perspective and a research perspective on measurement that expands and provides additional details concerning the ideas in this chapter. Discussions include beginning measurement in the K–2 classroom, assessment strategies, and the importance of benchmarks in estimation.

Hopkins, R., & King-Stonefish, R. (2003). An Anishnaabe Look at Exploring Measurement. Owen Sound, ON: Ningwakwe Learning Press.

This book provides an Anishnaabe perspective on measurement integrating it with contemporary principles and concepts. It can serve as a useful tool for making mathematics more inclusive in the elementary classroom and broadening children's perspectives. Ningwakwe Learning Press also publishes other resources for teaching from a First Nations perspective.

Online Resources

Area Tool
http://illuminations.nctm.org/ActivityDetail.aspx?ID=108
There are three separate applets that explore how changes in the base and height of the shapes affect the area.

Clock Wise
www.shodor.org/interactivate/activities/ClockWise
A clock face is shown and the user enters the digital time. There are three difficulty levels.

Cubes
http://illuminations.nctm.org/ActivityDetail.aspx?ID=6
This is an excellent interactive applet that illustrates the volume of a rectangular prism (box). Units of single cubes, rows of cubes, or layers of cubes can be used to fill a prism.

Geoboard
http://nlvm.usu.edu/en/nav/frames_asid_279_g_4_t_3.html
This electronic geoboard measures the area and perimeter of any shape made. What is nice is that the measures are not shown until the user clicks the Measure button. Students can be challenged to make shapes with specified areas and/or perimeters.

How High
http://nlvm.usu.edu/en/nav/frames_asid_275_g_3_t_4.html
Two cylinders are shown along with the area of the base shown as a grid of squares. One cylinder is filled to a specified height. The task is to determine the height of this same liquid when it is poured into the second container.

Image Tool
www.shodor.org/interactivate/activities/ImageTool
The user can measure angles, distances, and areas in several different images (choices include maps, aerial photos, and others). A scale feature allows the user to set the scale used for measuring distances and areas. This site is unique!

Perimeter Explorer
www.shodor.org/interactive/activities/PerimeterExplorer
The user sets a fixed number of square units and the applet randomly creates shapes on a grid with this area. The object is to determine the perimeter. There is also an *Area Explorer* (fixes the perimeter) and a *Shape Explorer*, which asks the user for both the area and perimeter of the randomly produced shapes.

What Time Will It Be?

http://nlvm.usu.edu/en/nav/frames_asid_318_g_2_t_4.html

Elapsed time problems are presented in word format. Two clocks are shown, one with the start time and the other to be set. Some problems are digital, while others are analogue.

Wired Math—Free Math Games

http://cemc2.math.uwaterloo.ca/wired_math/english/grade7.shtml

This site provides math games followed by exercises that focus on measurement concepts.

---

myeducationlab *will help you improve your understanding of the concepts taught in this textbook and in your course. This online tool includes videos of real classroom experiences, sample lesson plans, simulations, case studies, and links to important educational and teaching Web sites that will help you make the transition from student to teacher. As you study in your course and with this textbook, please follow along in **MyEducationLab**. Use it! Explore it! And improve your knowledge and your grade!*

Chapter 20
Geometric Thinking and Geometric Concepts

Geometry is an important strand of the K–8 curriculum. This is due in part to the influence of the NCTM standards movement beginning in 1989 and the growing use of geometry in everything from global positioning systems to computer animation. Another significant influence is the increased attention to a theoretical perspective that has helped us understand how students reason about spatial concepts.

Big Ideas

1. What makes shapes alike and different can be determined by an array of geometric properties. For example, shapes have sides that are parallel, perpendicular, or neither; they have line symmetry, rotational symmetry, or neither; they are similar, congruent, or neither.

2. Shapes can be moved in a plane or in space. These changes can be described in terms of translations (slides), reflections (flips), and rotations (turns).

3. Shapes can be described in terms of their location in a plane or in space. Coordinate systems can be used to describe these locations precisely. In turn, the coordinate view of shape offers ways to understand certain properties of shapes, changes in position (transformations), and how they appear or change size (visualization).

4. Shapes can be seen from various perspectives. The ability to perceive shapes from different viewpoints helps us understand relationships between two- and three-dimensional figures and mentally change the position and size of shapes

Mathematics Content Connections

A rich understanding of geometry has clear and important implications for other areas of the curriculum. Take advantage of these connections whenever possible.

- **Algebra** (Chapter 14): Coordinate graphing provides an analytical view of the concept of slope, and in turn, of perpendicular and parallel relationships. Transformations of shapes (slides, flips, and turns) can be described in terms of coordinates, allowing for the digital manipulation of shapes. The entire world of computer animation is based on a marriage of geometry and algebra.

- **Proportional Reasoning** (Chapter 18): Similar geometric objects have proportional dimensions and provide visual representation of proportionality.

- **Measurement** (Chapter 19): Measurement is aligned in the development of area and volume formulas and in an understanding of area/perimeter and surface/volume relationships. Coordinate geometry provides new ways to determine lengths, areas, and volumes. The Pythagorean relationship is at once an algebraic, a geometric, and a metric relationship.

- **Integers** (Chapter 23): Both positive and negative numbers are used in the description of position in the plane and in space.

Geometry Goals for Students

It is useful to think about your geometry objectives in terms of two quite different, yet related, frameworks: (1) spatial sense and geometric reasoning, and (2) the specific geometric content most likely found in your provincial or territorial objectives. The first of these frameworks has to do with the way students think and reason about shape and space. There is a well-researched theoretical basis for organizing the development of geometric thought that guides this framework. The second framework is content in the more traditional sense—knowing about symmetry, triangles, parallel lines, and so forth. The NCTM *Principles and Standards for School Mathematics* authors have helped describe content goals across the grades. We need to understand both of these aspects of geometry—reasoning and content—so that we can best help students grow.

Spatial Sense and Geometric Reasoning

Spatial sense can be defined as an intuition about shapes and the relationships among shapes. Spatial sense includes the ability to mentally visualize objects and spatial relationships—to turn things around in your mind. It includes a comfort with geometric descriptions of objects and position. People with well-developed spatial sense appreciate geometric form in art, nature, and architecture. They are able to use geometric ideas to describe and analyze their world.

Some people say they aren't very good with shape or that they have poor spatial sense. The typical belief is that you are either born with spatial sense or not. This simply is not true! We now know that rich experiences with shape and spatial relationships, when provided consistently over time, can and do develop spatial sense. Without geometric experiences, most people do not grow in their spatial sense or spatial reasoning. Between 1990 and 2000, NAEP data indicated a steady, continuing improvement in students' geometric reasoning at grade 8 (Sowder & Wearne, 2006). It's unlikely that students suddenly got smarter. What is more likely is that the improvement is due to an increasing emphasis on geometry at all grades.

Results for the Trends in International Mathematics and Science Study (TIMSS) for Canadian students appear to corroborate American findings. From 1995 to 2007, grade 8 and grade 4 students, especially, for those provinces that participated, tested above the international mean in geometry.

⏸ ———— *Pause and Reflect*

Reflect for a moment about your own beliefs concerning an individual's abilities in the area of spatial sense. What do you think causes some people to have better spatial sense than others?

NCTM Standards *Standards* supports the notion that all students can grow in their geometric skills and understandings. "The notion of building understanding in geometry across the grades, from informal to more formal thinking, is consistent with the thinking of theorists and researchers" (p. 41).

Geometric Content

The growing emphasis placed on geometry has spawned a huge assortment of wonderful tasks for students. As with each of the NCTM content standards, the geometry stan-

dard has a number of goals that apply to all grade levels. The four content goals for geometry can be summarized according to the following four categories: *Shapes and Properties*, *Transformation*, *Location*, and *Visualization*.

- *Shapes and Properties* includes a study of the properties of shapes in both two and three dimensions, as well as a study of the relationships built on properties.
- *Transformation* includes a study of translations, reflections, rotations (slides, flips, and turns), the study of symmetries, and the concept of similarity.
- *Location* refers primarily to coordinate geometry or other ways of specifying how objects are located in the plane or in space.
- *Visualization* includes the recognition of shapes in the environment, developing relationships between two- and three-dimensional objects, and the ability to draw and recognize objects from different perspectives.

These content goals provide a framework that bridges grades so that both teachers and curriculum planners can examine growth from year to year. To get a more detailed look at these areas of the curriculum, turn to Appendix A in this book and examine the NCTM goals and expectations for each of these areas across the grades. The activities in this chapter are grouped according to these four categories.

The Development of Geometric Thinking

Although not all people think about geometric ideas in the same manner, we are all capable of growing and developing in our ability to think and reason in geometric contexts. The research of two Dutch educators, Pierre van Hiele and Dina van Hiele-Geldof, has provided insight into the differences in geometric thinking and how the differences come to be.

The van Hieles' work, which began in 1959, immediately attracted a lot of attention in the former Soviet Union. However, their work received little notice from American researchers for nearly two decades (Hoffer & Hoffer, 1992). In Canada, the van Hiele theory provides an important basis for the development of concepts in geometry curricula.

The van Hiele Levels of Geometric Thought

The most prominent feature of the model is a five-level hierarchy of ways of understanding spatial ideas. Each of the five levels describes the thought processes used in geometric contexts (see Figure 20.1). The levels describe how we think and what types of geometric ideas we think about, rather than how much knowledge we have. A significant difference from one level to the next is the

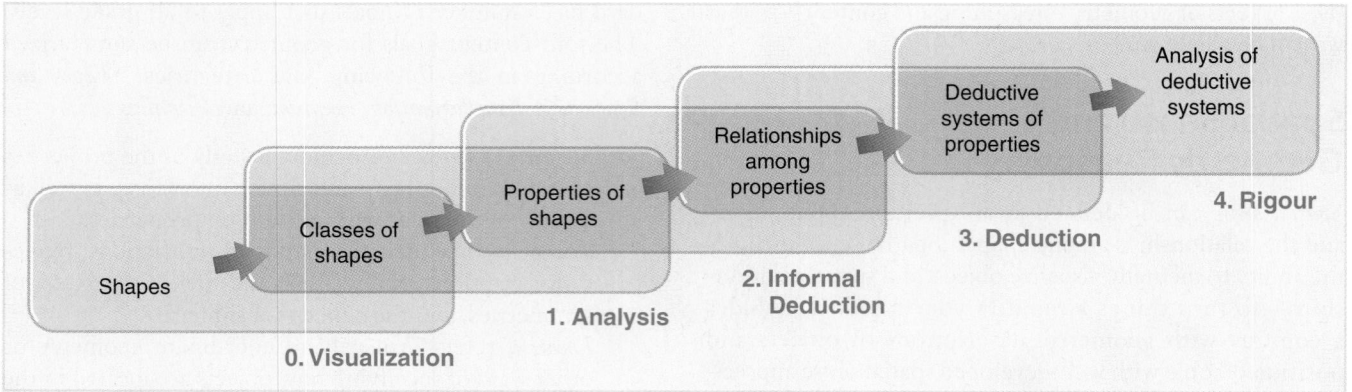

Figure 20.1 The van Hiele theory of geometric thought.

objects of thought—what we are able to think about geometrically.

Level 0: Visualization

The objects of thought at level 0 are shapes and what they "look like."

Students at level 0 recognize and name figures based on the global, visual characteristics of the figure. It is the appearance of the shape that defines it for the student. For example, a student at level 0 will define a square as a square, "because it looks like a square." Because appearance is dominant at this level, appearances can overpower properties of a shape. For instance, a square that has been rotated so that all sides are at a 45-degree angle to the vertical may now be a diamond and no longer a square. Students at this level will sort and classify shapes based on their appearances—"I put these together because they are all pointy" (or "fat," or "look like a house," or are "dented in sort of," and so on). With a focus on the appearances of shapes, students are able to see how shapes are alike and different. As a result, students at this level can create and begin to understand classifications of shapes.

The products of thought at level 0 are classes or groupings of shapes that seem to be "alike."

The emphasis at level 0 is on the shapes that students can observe, feel, build, take apart, or work with in some manner. The general goal is to explore how shapes are alike and different and to use these ideas to create classes of shapes (both physically and mentally). Some of these classes of shapes have names—rectangles, triangles, prisms, cylinders, and so on. Properties of shapes—such as parallel sides, symmetry, right angles, and so on, are included at this level but only in an informal, observational manner.

Although the van Hiele theory applies to students of all ages learning any geometric content, it may be easier to apply the theory to the shapes-and-property category. The following is a good representation of an activity appropriate for level 0.

Activity 20.1

Shape Sorts

Have students work in groups of four with a set of two-dimensional shapes similar to those in Figure 20.2, doing the following related activities in order:

- **Each student in the group selects a shape. In turn, the students tell one or two things they find interesting about their shape. There are no right or wrong responses.**
- **The students each randomly select two shapes. They try to find something that is alike about the two shapes and something that is different. (Have the students select their shapes before they know the task.)**
- **The group selects one shape at random and places it in the centre of the workspace. Their task is to find all other shapes that are like the target shape, according to the same rule. For example, if they say, "This shape is like our shape because it has a curved side and a straight side," then all other shapes that they put in the collection must have these properties. Challenge them to do a second sort with the same target shape using a different property.**
- **Do a "secret sort." You (or one of the students) create a small collection of about five shapes that fit a secret rule. Leave others that belong in your group in the pile. The other students try to find additional pieces that belong to the set and/or guess the secret rule.**

Depending on the grade level, these activities will elicit a wide variety of ideas as students examine the shapes. For the most part, these will be ideas such as "curvy" or "looks like a rocket" rather than typical geometric concepts. But students may begin to notice more sophisticated properties and the teacher can take the opportunity to attach appropriate names to them as the students describe them. For

Figure 20.2 An assortment of shapes for sorting. See Blackline Masters 41–47 for a larger collection of shapes.

example, students may notice that some shapes have corners "like a square" (right angles) or that "these shapes are the same on both sides" (line symmetry).

You might wish to have those students who easily use more sophisticated properties to describe the shapes complete the activity using only these descriptions to figure out a group member's secret rule.

What clearly makes this a level-0 activity is not the presence or the absence of traditional geometric properties or terms; rather, it is that students are operating on the shapes they see in front of them. Furthermore, for level-0 students, the shapes may even "change" or have different properties as they are rearranged or rotated. The objective of the activity is for students to begin to see that there are likenesses and differences in shapes. By forming groups of shapes, they may begin to imagine shapes belonging to these classes that are not there.

Level 1: Analysis

The objects of thought at level 1 are classes of shapes rather than individual shapes.

Students at the analysis level are able to consider all shapes within a class rather than a single shape. Instead of talking about *this* rectangle, it is possible to talk about *all* rectangles. By focusing on a class of shapes, students are able to think about what makes a rectangle a rectangle (four sides, opposite sides parallel, opposite sides same length, four right angles, congruent diagonals, etc.). The irrelevant

features (e.g., size or orientation) fade into the background. At this level, students begin to appreciate that a collection of shapes goes together because of properties. Ideas about an individual shape can now be generalized to all shapes that fit that class. If a shape belongs to a particular class such as cubes, it has the corresponding properties of that class. "All cubes have six congruent faces, and each of those faces is a square." These properties were only implicit at level 0. Students operating at level 1 may be able to list all the properties of squares, rectangles, and parallelograms. But they may not see that these are subclasses of one another; i.e., that all squares can be classified as rectangles and all rectangles can be classified as parallelograms. In defining a shape, level-1 thinkers are likely to list as many properties of a shape as they know.

The products of thought at level 1 are the properties of shapes.

A significant difference between level 1 and level 0 is the object of students' thought. While level-1 students will continue to use models and drawings of shapes, they begin to see these as representatives of classes of shapes. Their understanding of the properties of shapes—such as symmetry, perpendicular and parallel lines, and so on—continues to be refined.

In the following activity, students use the properties of shapes they learned in earlier activities, possibly while operating at level 0. These include ideas such as symmetry, angle classification (right, obtuse, acute), parallel and perpendicular, and the concept of congruent line segments and angles.

Activity 20.2

Property Lists for Quadrilaterals

Prepare worksheets for parallelograms, rhombi, rectangles, and squares. (See Blackline Masters 54–57 and Figure 20.3.) Assign students working in groups of three or four to one type of quadrilateral. Their task is to list as many properties as they can that are applicable to all of the shapes on their sheet. They will need an index card to check right angles, to compare side lengths, and to draw straight lines. Mirrors (for checking line symmetry) and tracing paper (for angle congruence and rotational symmetry) are also useful tools. Encourage students to use the words "at least" when describing how many of something: for example, "rectangles have at least two lines of symmetry," because squares—included in the rectangles—have four.

Have students prepare their property lists under these headings: Sides, Angles, Diagonals, and Symmetries. Groups then share their lists with the class and eventually a class list for each shape will be developed.

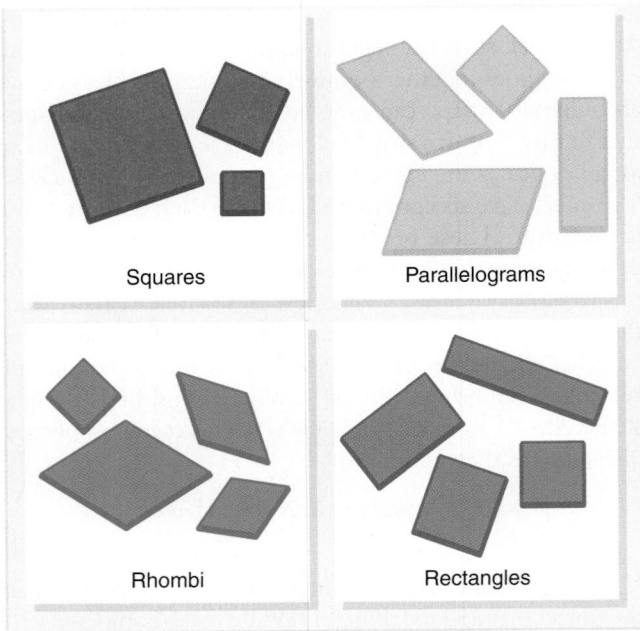

Figure 20.3 Shapes for the "Property Lists for Quadrilaterals" activity (see Blackline Masters 54–57).

Both this activity and the earlier classification activity involve an examination of shapes, focusing on geometric properties. What distinguishes this activity from the level-0 classification activity is the object of students' thinking. Students must assess whether the properties apply to all shapes in the category. For example, if they are working on the squares, they must be able to apply their observations to a square metre, as well as to a square centimetre.

Level 2: Informal Deduction

The objects of thought at level 2 are the properties of shapes.

As students begin to be able to think about properties of geometric objects without the constraints of a particular object, they are able to develop relationships between and among these properties. "If all four angles are right angles, then the shape must be a rectangle. If it is a square, then all angles are right angles. If it is a square, then it must be a rectangle." With greater ability to engage in "if–then" reasoning, shapes can be classified using only minimum defining characteristics. For example, four congruent sides and at least one right angle can be sufficient to define a square. Rectangles are parallelograms with a right angle. Observations go beyond properties themselves and begin to focus on logical arguments *about* the properties. Students at level 2 will be able to follow and appreciate an informal deductive argument about shapes and their properties. "Proofs" may be more intuitive than rigorously deductive. However, there is an appreciation that a logical argument is compelling. An appreciation of the axiomatic structure

of a formal deductive system, however, remains under the surface.

The products of thought at level 2 are relationships among properties of geometric objects.

The hallmark of level-2 activities is the inclusion of informal logical reasoning. Students have developed an understanding of various properties of shapes. Now it is time to encourage conjecture and to ask "Why?" or "What if?" Contrast the required thinking in the following activity with that of the "Property Lists" activity. (The two activities form a pair that can be done over several days.)

Activity 20.3

Minimal Defining Lists

(This activity must be done as a follow-up to Activity 20.2 "Property Lists.") Once property lists for the parallelogram, rhombus, rectangle, and square (and possibly the kite and trapezoid) have been agreed upon by the class, have these lists posted. Have students work in groups to find "minimal defining lists," or MDLs, for each shape. An MDL is a subset of the properties for a shape that is "defining" and "minimal." "Defining" here means that any shape that has all the properties on the MDL must be that shape. Thus, an MDL for a square will guarantee that you have a square. "Minimal" means that if any single property is removed from the list it is no longer defining. For example, one MDL for a square is a quadrilateral with four congruent sides and four right angles. Students should try to find at least two or three MDLs for their shape. A proposed list can be challenged as either not minimal or not defining. A list is not defining if a counterexample—a shape other than the one being described—can be produced using only the properties on the list.

The hallmark of this activity and other level-2 ones is the logic component. "*If* a quadrilateral has these properties, *then* it must be a square." Logic is also involved in proving that a list is faulty—either not minimal or not defining. Here students begin to learn the nature of a definition and the value of counterexamples. In fact, any minimal defining list (MDL) is a potential definition. The other aspect of this activity that clearly sets it into the level-2 category is that students are focusing here on the lists of properties of the shapes—the very things that were products of the earlier level-1 activity. As a result of the MDL activity, students are creating a collection of new relationships that exist between and among properties.

Level 3: Deduction

The objects of thought at level 3 are relationships among properties of geometric objects.

At level 3, students are able to examine more than just the properties of shapes. Their earlier thinking has produced conjectures concerning relationships among properties. Are these conjectures "true"? As this analysis of the informal arguments takes place, the structure of a system complete with axioms, definitions, theorems, corollaries, and postulates begins to develop and can be appreciated as the necessary means for establishing geometric truth. The student at this level is able to work with abstract statements about geometric properties and draw conclusions based more on logic than intuition. A student operating at level 3 is aware that the diagonals of a rectangle bisect each other. However, at level 3, there is an appreciation of the need to prove this from a series of deductive arguments. The level-2 thinker, by contrast, follows the argument but fails to appreciate the need.

The products of thought at level 3 are deductive axiomatic systems for geometry.

The type of reasoning that characterizes a level-3 thinker is the same as is required in a typical high school geometry course. There students build on a list of axioms and definitions to create theorems. They also prove theorems using clearly articulated logical reasoning, whereas the reasoning at level 2 may be quite informal. In the best geometry courses, students would engage in activities in which they would discover the relationships they later prove.

In a very global sense, high school geometry students are working on the creation of a complete geometric deductive system. Usually, this is the Euclidean system that best describes the world in which we live. They may also explore other geometric systems, such as the geometry where all lines are drawn on the surface of a sphere or "taxicab geometry" where lines may only follow a rectangular grid of "streets."

Level 4: Rigour

The objects of thought at level 4 are deductive axiomatic systems for geometry.

At the highest level of the van Hiele hierarchy, the objects of attention are axiomatic systems themselves, not just the deductions within a system. There is an appreciation of the distinctions and relationships between different axiomatic systems. For example, spherical geometry is based on lines drawn on a sphere rather than in a plane or ordinary space. This geometry has its own set of axioms and theorems. This is generally the level of a university mathematics major who is studying geometry as a branch of mathematical science.

The products of thought at level 4 are comparisons and contrasts among different axiomatic systems of geometry.

Characteristics of the van Hiele Levels You no doubt noticed that the products of thought at each level are the same as the objects of thought at the next. This object–product relationship between levels of the van Hiele theory is illustrated in Figure 20.1. The objects (ideas) must be created at one level so that relationships among these objects can become the focus of the next level. In addition to this key concept of the theory, the van Hiele levels have several common characteristics:

- The levels are sequential. To arrive at one level, students must move through prior levels.
- The products of thought at each level are the same as the objects of thought at the next level.
- The levels are not age dependent in the sense of the developmental stages of Piaget. A grade 3 student or a high school student could be at level 0.
- Geometric experiences are the greatest single factor influencing advancement through the levels. Students need to explore, talk about, and interact with content at the next level while increasing experiences at their current level.
- When instruction or language is at a level higher than that of the student, there will be a lack of communication. A student can memorize a fact (e.g., all squares are rectangles) without having constructed that relationship.

Implications for Instruction

If the van Hiele theory is correct—and there is much evidence to support it—then a major goal of the pre-K–8 curriculum must be to advance students' level of geometric thought. If students are to be adequately prepared for the deductive geometry curriculum of high school, then it is important for their thinking to have grown to level 2 by the end of grade 8.

All teachers should be aware that the experiences they provide are the single most important factor in moving children up this developmental ladder. Every teacher should be able to see some growth in geometric thinking over the course of the year.

The van Hiele theory and the developmental perspective of this book highlight the necessity of teaching at the child's level of thought. However, almost any activity can be modified to span two levels of thinking, even within the same classroom. For many activities, how we interact with individual children will adapt the activity to their levels while challenging them to operate at the next higher level.

The following sections contain descriptions of the types of activity and questioning that are appropriate for each of the first three levels. Apply these descriptors to the tasks that you pose to students, and use them to guide your interaction with students. The use of physical materials, drawings, and computer models is a must at every level.

All teachers should be aware that the experiences they provide are the single most important factor in moving children up the geometric developmental ladder. Teachers must be enthusiastic and show that mathematics can make a real-life difference. For example, as shown in these three photos, the four goals for geometry (Shapes and Properties, Transformation, Location, and Visualization) were certainly applied during the planning and construction of the Michael Lee-Chin Crystal geometric extension at the Royal Ontario Museum.

Instruction at Level 0 Instructional activities in geometry appropriate for level 0 should:

- Involve a lot of sorting and classifying. Seeing how shapes are alike and different is the primary focus of level 0. As students learn more content, the relationships that they notice will become more sophisticated.

- Students need ample opportunities to draw, build, make, put together (compose), and take apart (decompose) shapes in both two and three dimensions. These activities should be built around specific characteristics or properties so that students develop an understanding of geometric properties and begin to use them naturally.

To help students move from level 0 to level 1, students should be challenged to test ideas about shapes for a variety of examples from a particular category. Say to them, "Let's see if that is true for other rectangles," or "Can you draw a triangle that does *not* have a right angle?" In general, students should be challenged to see if observations made about a particular shape apply to other shapes of a similar kind.

Instruction at Level 1 Instructional activities in geometry appropriate for level 1 should:

- Focus more on the properties of figures rather than on simple identification. As new geometric concepts are learned, the number of properties that figures have can be expanded.
- Apply ideas to entire classes of figures (e.g., *all* rectangles, *all* prisms) rather than on individual models. For example, find ways to sort all possible triangles into groups. From these groups, define types of triangles.

To assist students in moving from level 1 to level 2, challenge them with questions such as "Why?" and those that involve some reasoning. For example, "If the sides of a four-sided shape are all congruent, will you always have a square?" and "Can you find a counterexample?"

Instruction at Level 2 Instructional activities in geometry appropriate for level 2 should:

- Encourage the making and testing of hypotheses or conjectures. "Do you think that will work all the time?" "Is that true for all triangles or just equilateral ones?"
- Examine properties of shapes to determine necessary and sufficient conditions for different shapes or concepts. "What properties of diagonals do you think will guarantee that you will have a square?"
- Use the language of informal deduction: *all, some, none, if ... then, what if,* and so on.
- Encourage students to attempt informal proofs. As an alternative, require them to make sense of informal proofs that other students or you have suggested.

Task Selection and Levels of Thought If you teach at the pre-K–3 level, nearly all your students will be at level 0. In the upper grades you may have children at two or even all three levels within the same classroom. How do you discover the level of each student? Once you know, how will you select the right activities to match your students' levels?

No simple assessment exists to identify the exact level at which a student is functioning. However, you can examine the descriptors for the first two levels. As you conduct an activity, listen to the students' observations. Can they talk about shapes as classes? Do they refer, for example, to "rectangles" rather than basing discussion around a particular rectangle? Do they understand that shapes do not change when the orientation or size changes? With careful observations such as these, you will soon be able to distinguish between levels 0 and 1.

At the upper grades, attempt to move students from level 1 to level 2. If students are not able to follow or appreciate logical arguments and are not comfortable with conjectures and if–then reasoning, these students are likely still at level 1 or below.

The remainder of this chapter offers a sampling of activities organized broadly around the four content goals of the NCTM standards: Shapes and Properties, Transformations, Location, and Visualization. Within each of these content groupings, activities are further sorted according to the first three van Hiele levels. Understand that all these subdivisions are quite fluid. An activity found at one level can easily be adapted to an adjacent level simply by the way it is presented to the students.

Learning About Shapes and Properties

This is the content area that most people think about when they think about geometry in the pre-K–8 classroom; children are working with both two- and three-dimensional shapes. They are finding out what makes these shapes alike and different. In the process they begin to discover properties of the shapes, including the conventional names for these properties. With sufficient experiences, students will develop classifications of special shapes—triangles, parallelograms, cylinders, pyramids, and so on—and learn that some properties apply to full classes. Eventually, they will investigate how properties of shapes impose logical consequences on geometric relationships and will develop the ability to reason about shapes and properties.

Shapes and Properties for Level-0 Thinkers

Young children need experience with a rich variety of both two- and three-dimensional shapes. Triangles should be more than just equilateral. Shapes should have curved sides, straight sides, and combinations of these. Along the way, the names of shapes and their properties can be introduced.

Sorting and Classifying As young students work at classification of shapes, be prepared for them to notice features that you do not consider to be "real" geometric attributes, such as "dented" or "looks like a tree." Children at this level

will also attribute to shapes ideas that are not part of the shape, such as "points up" or "has a side that is the same as the edge of the board."

For variety in two-dimensional shapes, create your own materials. A good set of assorted shapes is found in Blackline Masters 41–47. Make multiple copies so that groups of children can all work with the same shapes. Once you have your sets constructed, a good beginning activity is Activity 20.1, "Shape Sorts," on page 418.

In any sorting activity, the students, not the teacher, should decide how to sort. Doing so allows the students to do the activity using ideas *they* own and understand. By listening to the kinds of attributes that they use in their sorting, you will be able to tell what properties they know and use and how they think about shapes. Figure 20.4 illustrates a few of the many possible ways a set might be sorted.

The secret sorting portion of Activity 20.1 is one option for introducing a new property. For example, sort the shapes so that all have at least one right angle or "square corner." When students discover your rule, you have an opportunity to talk more about that property.

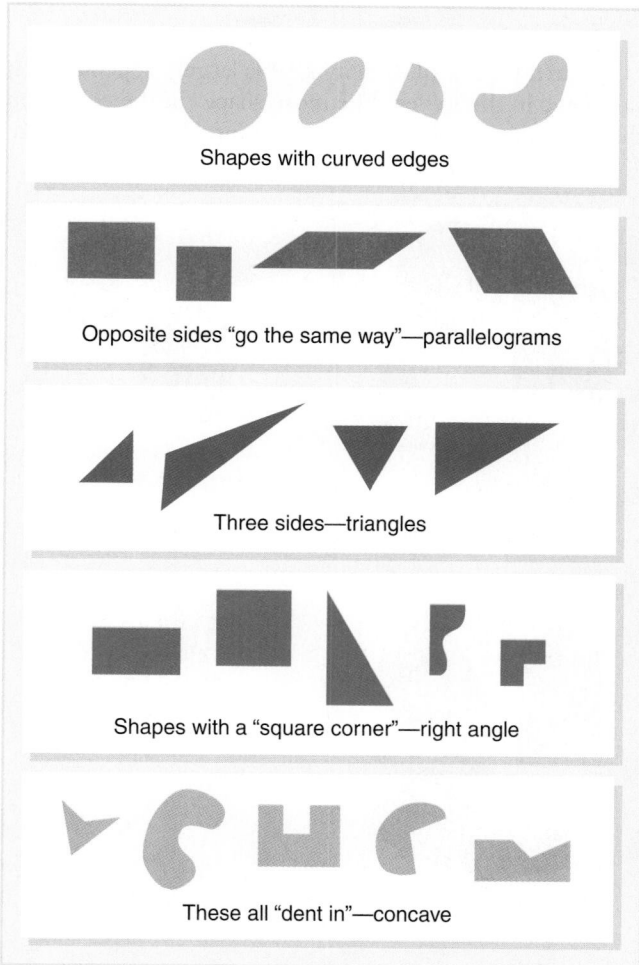

Shapes with curved edges

Opposite sides "go the same way"—parallelograms

Three sides—triangles

Shapes with a "square corner"—right angle

These all "dent in"—concave

Figure 20.4 By sorting shapes, students begin to recognize properties.

The following activity is also done with two-dimensional shapes.

Activity 20.4

What's My Shape?

From Blackline Masters 41-47, make a double set of two-dimensional assorted shapes on cardstock. Cut out one set of shapes and glue each inside a half-sheet of construction paper, folded to make "secret shape" folders.

Students work in groups. One student in the group is designated the leader and given a secret-shape folder. The other students need to find the shape that matches the shape in the folder. To this end, they ask questions to which the leader can answer only "yes" or "no." The group can eliminate shapes as they ask questions to help narrow down the possibilities. They are not allowed to point to a piece and ask, "Is it this one?" Rather, they must continue to ask questions that reduce the choices to one shape. The final piece is tested against the one in the leader's folder.

The difficulty of Activity 20.4 is largely dependent on the shape in the folder. The more shapes in the collection that resemble the secret shape, the more difficult the task.

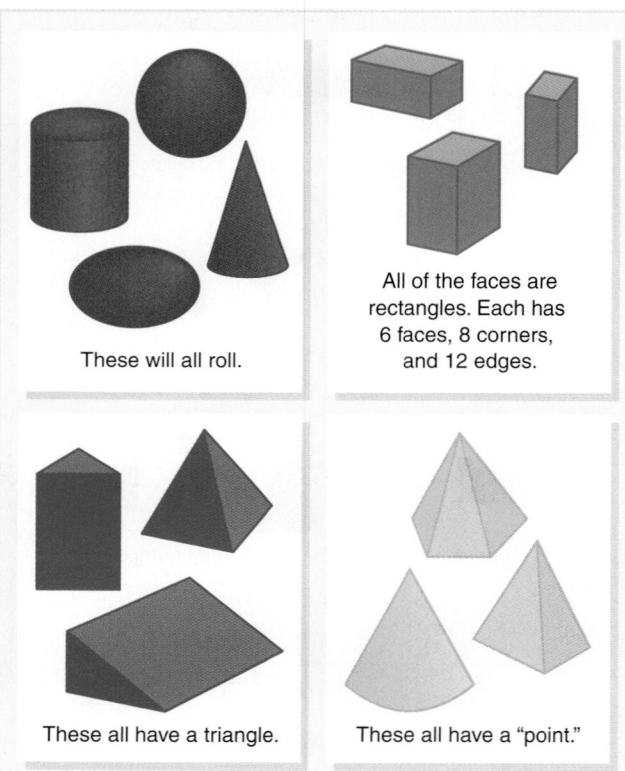

These will all roll.

All of the faces are rectangles. Each has 6 faces, 8 corners, and 12 edges.

These all have a triangle.

These all have a "point."

Figure 20.5 Early classifications of three-dimensional shapes.

Most of the activities in "Shape Sorts" can and should be done with three-dimensional shapes as well. The difficulty is finding or making a collection that has sufficient variability. Commercially produced wooden solids offer a good variety of three-dimensional shapes. If these are not available, you may consider combining several different sets of collections to get variation. Another option is to collect real objects such as cans, boxes, balls, and Styrofoam shapes. Figure 20.5 illustrates some classifications of solids.

 The ways in which children describe shapes in "Shape Sorts" and similar activities with three-dimensional shapes provide good evidence of their level of thinking. The classifications made by level-0 thinkers will generally be restricted to the shapes that they have in front of them. As they begin to think in terms of the properties of shapes, they will create categories based on properties and their language will indicate that there are many more shapes in the group than those that are physically present (Mack, 2007). Students may say things like, "These shapes have square corners sort of like rectangles," or "These look like boxes. All the boxes have square [rectangular] sides." ◆

Composing and Decomposing Shapes Children need to freely explore how shapes fit together to form larger shapes and how larger shapes can be made of smaller shapes. The best known two-dimensional shapes for these activities are pattern blocks and tangrams. In a 1999 article, Pierre van Hiele describes an interesting set of tiles he calls

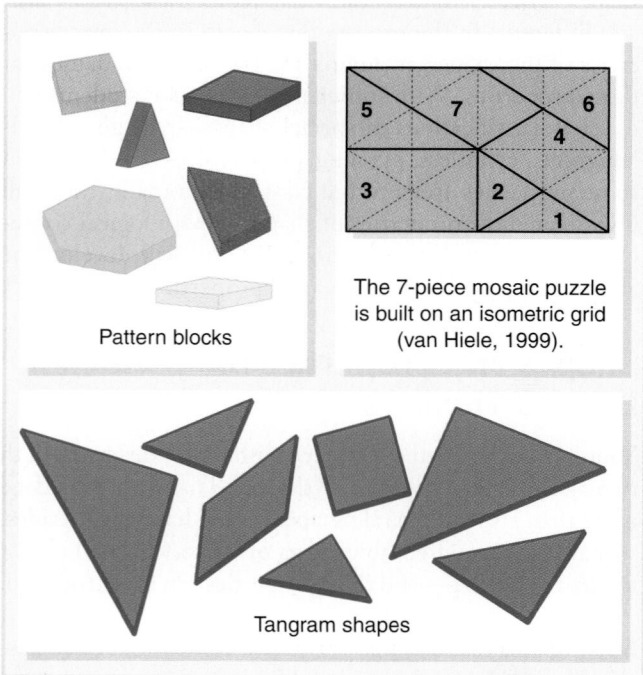

Pattern blocks

The 7-piece mosaic puzzle is built on an isometric grid (van Hiele, 1999).

Tangram shapes

Figure 20.6 Assorted two-dimensional shapes for activities.

the mosaic puzzle (see Figure 20.6). Patterns for the mosaic puzzle and tangrams can be found in Blackline Master 51.

Figure 20.7 shows four different types of tangram puzzles in increasing order of difficulty. Numerous resource books devoted entirely to tangrams are available, and NCTM's e-Examples includes a tangram applet (Example 4.4) with a set of challenges. One form of the applet includes eight puzzle figures that can be made using all seven of the pieces. The e-version of tangrams has the advantage of

being motivating and you must be much more deliberate in arranging the shapes.

The value of van Hiele's mosaic puzzle is partly due to the fact that the set contains five different angles (see Figure 20.8). You can use the pieces to talk about square corners (*right* angles) and angles that are more or less than a right angle (*obtuse* or *acute* angles).

The geoboard is one of the best devices for creating two-dimensional shapes. The following are just two of many possible activities appropriate for level 0.

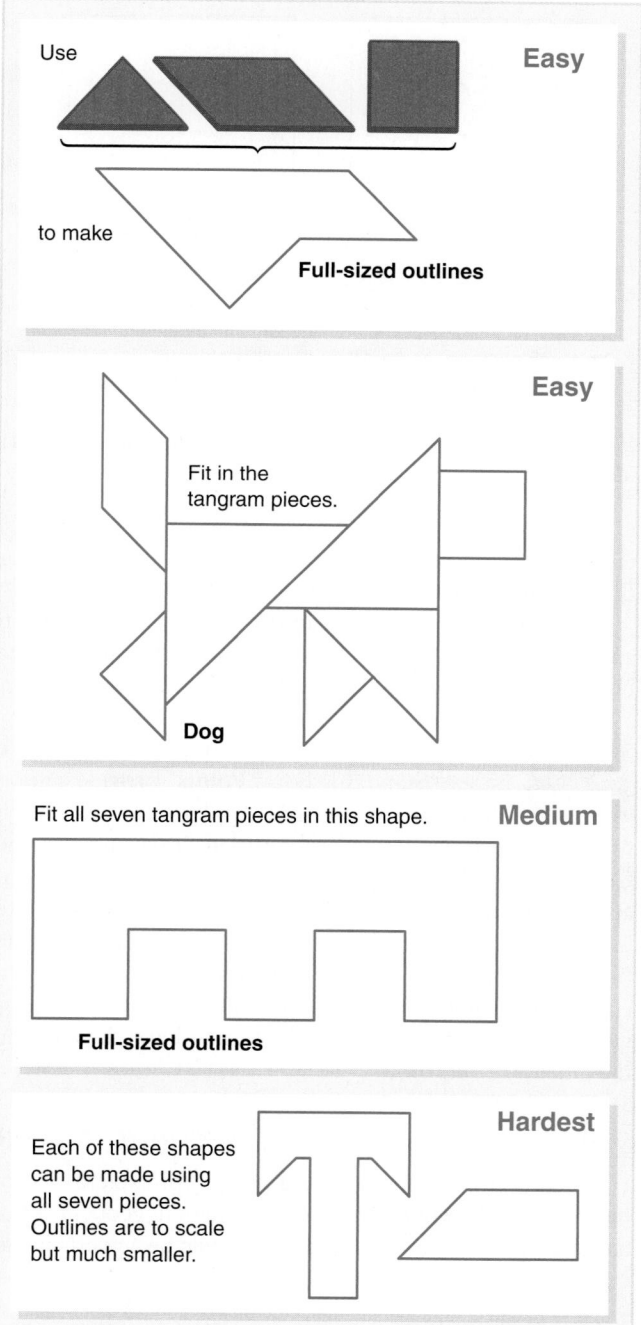

Figure 20.7 Four types of tangram puzzles (see Blackline Master 51).

Activity **20.5**

Geoboard Copy

Copy shapes, designs, and patterns from prepared cards onto geoboards, as shown in Figure 20.9. Begin with designs using one band; then create more complex designs.

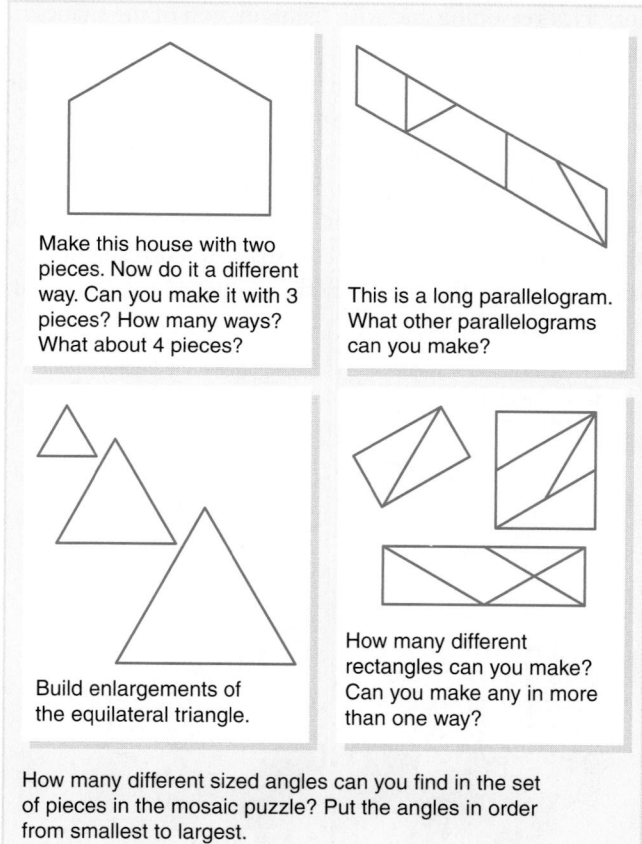

Figure 20.8 A sample of activities with the mosaic puzzle (see Blackline Master 51).

Source: Based on van Hiele, P. M. (1999). Developing Geometric Thinking Through Activities That Begin With Play. *Teaching Children Mathematics*, 5 (6), 310–316. Reprinted with permission. Copyright © 1999 by the National Council of Teachers of Mathematics, Inc. www.nctm.org. All rights reserved.

Activity 20.6

Congruent Parts

Copy a shape from a card onto a geoboard, and have students subdivide or decompose the shape on the geoboard into smaller shapes. Specify the number of smaller shapes to be made. Also specify whether they are all to be congruent or simply the same type, as shown in Figure 20.10.

Have a lot of geoboards available in the classroom. It is better for two or three children to have 10 or 12 boards at a station than for each to have only one. That way, a variety of shapes can be made and compared before they are changed.

In the full class discussion, students list all the different totals that they found. (There are eight different solutions.) Questions revolve around the possibility of a solution with even more blocks, or fewer blocks, or some additional solutions in between. The teacher is looking for students' comfort with reasoning and with manipulation of the shapes in making substitutions.

Teach students from the very beginning to copy their geoboard designs onto dot paper. Paper copies permit students to create complete sets of drawings that fulfill a particular task. To help children in the very early grades copy geoboard designs onto paper, suggest that they first mark the dots for the corners of their shape to correspond with the position of the shape on the geoboard ("second row,

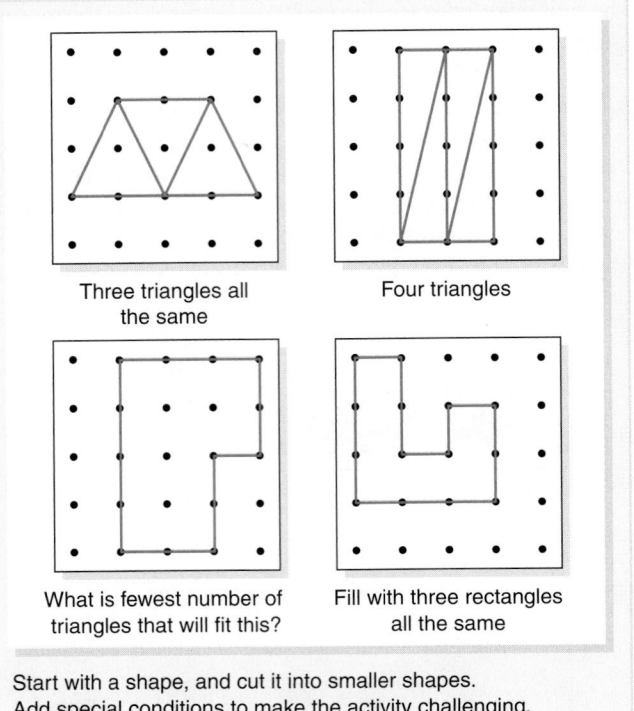

Three triangles all the same

Four triangles

What is fewest number of triangles that will fit this?

Fill with three rectangles all the same

Start with a shape, and cut it into smaller shapes.
Add special conditions to make the activity challenging.

Figure 20.10 Subdividing shapes (see Blackline Masters 49 and 50).

end peg"). With the corners identified, it is much easier for them to draw lines to make the shape.

Drawings can be placed into groups for classification and discussion, made into booklets to illustrate a new idea being discussed in class, and sent home to families.

NCTM Standards The e-Examples found at the NCTM Web site under "Standards Focal Points" provide a good electronic geoboard (Applet 4.2). Although found in the K–2 section and entitled "Investigating the Concept of a Triangle," this is actually a great geoboard applet for any grade. It allows you to select and delete bands, and select vertices. The *Geoboard* applet from the National Library of Virtual Manipulatives (http://nlvm.usu. edu/en/nav/vlibrary.html) is essentially the same, but provides instant calculation of perimeter and area by clicking the "measure" button.

Pause and Reflect

If you have never used a geoboard, explore one of these electronic geoboards. If you know about geoboards but have never used an e-geoboard, now would be a good time to try one.

Building three-dimensional shapes is a little more difficult compared with two-dimensional shapes. A variety of commercial materials permit fairly creative construc-

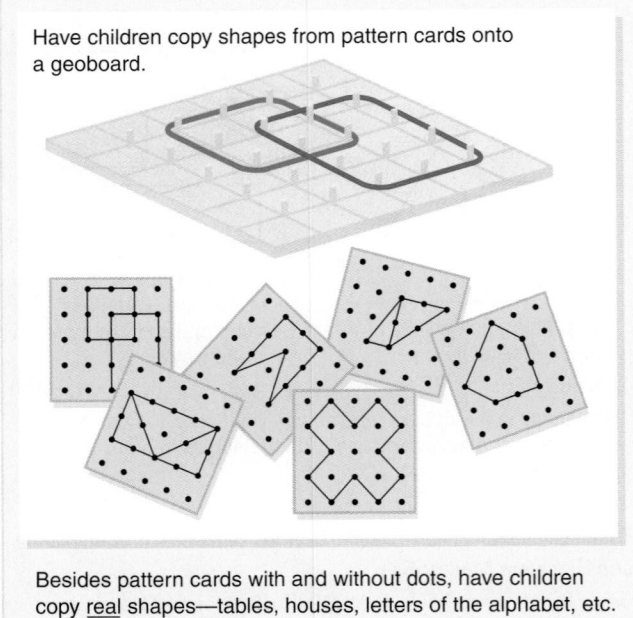

Have children copy shapes from pattern cards onto a geoboard.

Besides pattern cards with and without dots, have children copy <u>real</u> shapes—tables, houses, letters of the alphabet, etc.

Figure 20.9 Shapes on geoboards (see Blackline Masters 49 and 50).

tion of geometric solids (for example, three-dimensional Geoshapes, Polydron, and the Zome System). The following are three highly recommended homemade approaches to skeletal models.

- *Plastic coffee stirrers with modelling clay or twist ties.* Plastic stirrers can be easily cut to different lengths. Use twist ties inserted into the ends of small chunks of clay (about 2 centimetres in diameter) to connect the corners.
- *Plastic drinking straw.* Cut the straws lengthwise from the top down to the flexible joint with scissors. These slit ends can then be inserted into the uncut bottom ends of other straws, making a strong but flexible joint. Three or more straws are joined in this fashion to form two-dimensional polygons. Use tape or wire twist ties to join polygons.
- *Rolled newspaper rods.* Fantastic "super-large" skeletons can be built using newspaper and masking tape (see Figure 20.11).

With these class-made models, students should compare the rigidity of a triangle with the lack of rigidity of polygons with more than three sides. Point out that triangles are used in many bridges, in the long booms of construction cranes, in gates, and in the structural parts of buildings. Discuss why this may be so. As children build large skeletal structures, they will find that they need to add diagonals to form triangles for strength. The more triangles, the less likely their structure is to collapse. Primary-grade students can benefit from creating freeform structures. Older students can be challenged to make more well-defined shapes.

Tessellations   A *tessellation* is a tiling of the plane using one or more shapes in a repeated pattern with no gaps or overlaps. Making tessellations is an artistic way for level-0 students, from grades 1 to 8, to explore patterns in shapes and to see how shapes combine to form other shapes. Tessellation activities can vary considerably in difficulty.

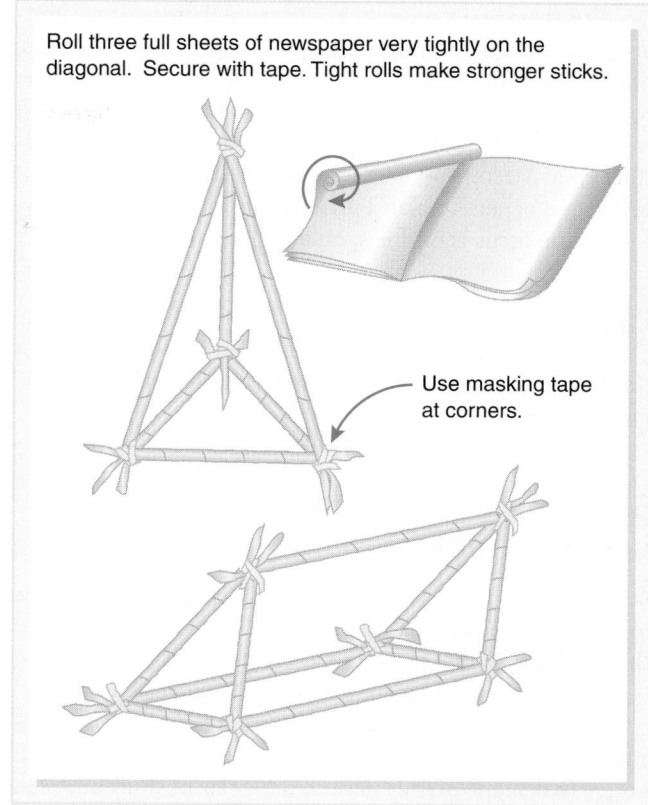

Roll three full sheets of newspaper very tightly on the diagonal. Secure with tape. Tight rolls make stronger sticks.

Use masking tape at corners.

Figure 20.11 Large skeletal structures and special shapes can be built with tightly rolled newspaper.

Single-shape tessellations are more easily made with some shapes than with others. For example, squares or equilateral triangles tessellate quite easily, although these provide only a minimal geometric challenge. When the shapes can be put together in more than one pattern, the level of problem solving and creativity increase. Literally hundreds of shapes can be used as tiles for tessellations (see Figure 20.12).

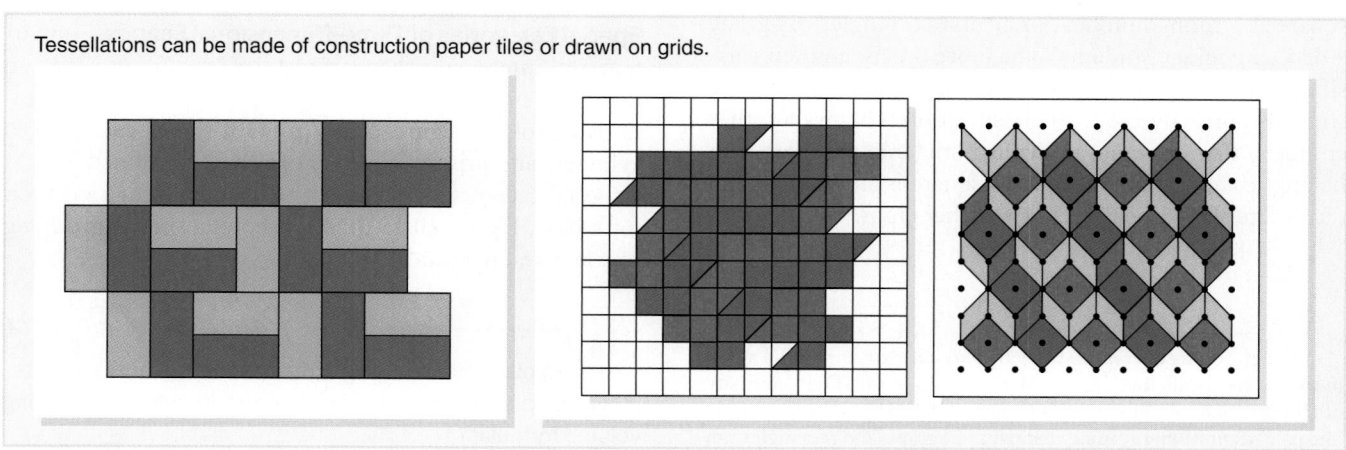

Tessellations can be made of construction paper tiles or drawn on grids.

Figure 20.12 Tessellations (see Blackline Masters 34–40).

For their first experiences with tessellations, most children will benefit from using actual tiles to create patterns. Simple construction paper tiles can be cut quickly on a paper cutter or several of the pattern block pieces can work well too. Older children may be able to use dot or line grids (Blackline Masters 34–40) and plan their tessellations with pencil and paper. To plan a tessellation, use only one colour so that the focus is on the spatial relationships.

Pause and Reflect

Look at the centre tessellation in Figure 20.12. What single tile (a combination of squares and half squares) made this pattern?

Shapes and Properties for Level-1 Thinkers

As students move to level-1 thinking, attention turns more to properties possessed by the traditional classifications of shapes. During this period, it makes sense for students to learn the proper names for shapes and their properties.

For the sake of clarity, the important definitions of two- and three-dimensional shapes are provided here. You will notice that shape definitions include relationships between and among shapes.

Special Categories of Two-Dimensional Shapes Table 20.1 lists some important categories of two-dimensional shapes. Examples of these shapes can be found in Figure 20.13 on page 426.

In the classification of quadrilaterals and parallelograms, some subsets overlap. For example, a square can be classified as a rectangle and a rhombus. All parallelograms can be classified as trapezoids, but not all trapezoids can be classified as parallelograms.[1] Children at level 1 continue to have difficulty seeing these more subtle types of relationships. They may quite correctly list all the properties of a square, a rhombus, and a rectangle and still identify a square as a "non-rhombus" or a "non-rectangle." By grade 4 or 5, encourage students to be more precise in their classifications. Burger (1985) points out that upper elementary students correctly use such classification schemes in other contexts. For example, individual students in a class can belong to more than one club. A square is an example of a quadrilateral that belongs to two other clubs.

---

[1]Some definitions of *trapezoid* specify *only one* pair of parallel sides, in which case parallelograms would not be trapezoids. The University of Chicago School Mathematics Project (UCSMP) uses the "at least one pair" definition, meaning that parallelograms and rectangles can be classified as trapezoids.

Table 20.1

Categories of Two-Dimensional Shapes	
Shape	Description
Simple Closed Curves	
Concave, convex	An intuitive definition of *concave* might be "having a dent in it." If a simple closed curve is not concave, it is *convex*. A more precise definition of *concave* may be interesting to explore with older students.
Symmetrical, non-symmetrical	Shapes may have one or more lines of symmetry and may or may not have rotational symmetry. These concepts will require more detailed investigation.
Polygons Concave, convex Symmetrical, non-symmetrical	Simple closed curves with all straight sides.
Regular	All sides and all angles are congruent.
Triangles	
Triangles	Polygons with exactly three sides.
Classified by sides	
Equilateral	All sides are congruent.
Isosceles	At least two sides are congruent.
Scalene	No two sides are congruent.
Classified by angles	
Right	Has a right angle.
Acute	All angles are smaller than a right angle.
Obtuse	One angle is larger than a right angle.
Convex Quadrilaterals	
Convex quadrilaterals	Convex polygons with exactly four sides.
Kite	Two opposing pairs of congruent adjacent sides.
Trapezoid	At least one pair of parallel sides.
Isosceles trapezoid	A pair of opposite sides is congruent.
Parallelogram	Two pairs of parallel sides.
Rectangle	Parallelogram with a right angle.
Rhombus	Parallelogram with all sides congruent.
Square	Parallelogram with a right angle and all sides congruent.

Special Categories of Three-Dimensional Shapes Important and interesting shapes and relationships also exist in three dimensions. Table 20.2 (p. 430) describes classifications of solids. Figure 20.14 (p. 430) shows examples of cylinders and prisms. Note that prisms are defined here as a special category of cylinders—a cylinder with a polygon for a base. Figure 20.15 (p. 431) shows a similar grouping of cones and pyramids.

Pause and Reflect

Explain the following: Prisms are to cylinders as pyramids are to cones. How is this relationship helpful in learning volume formulas?

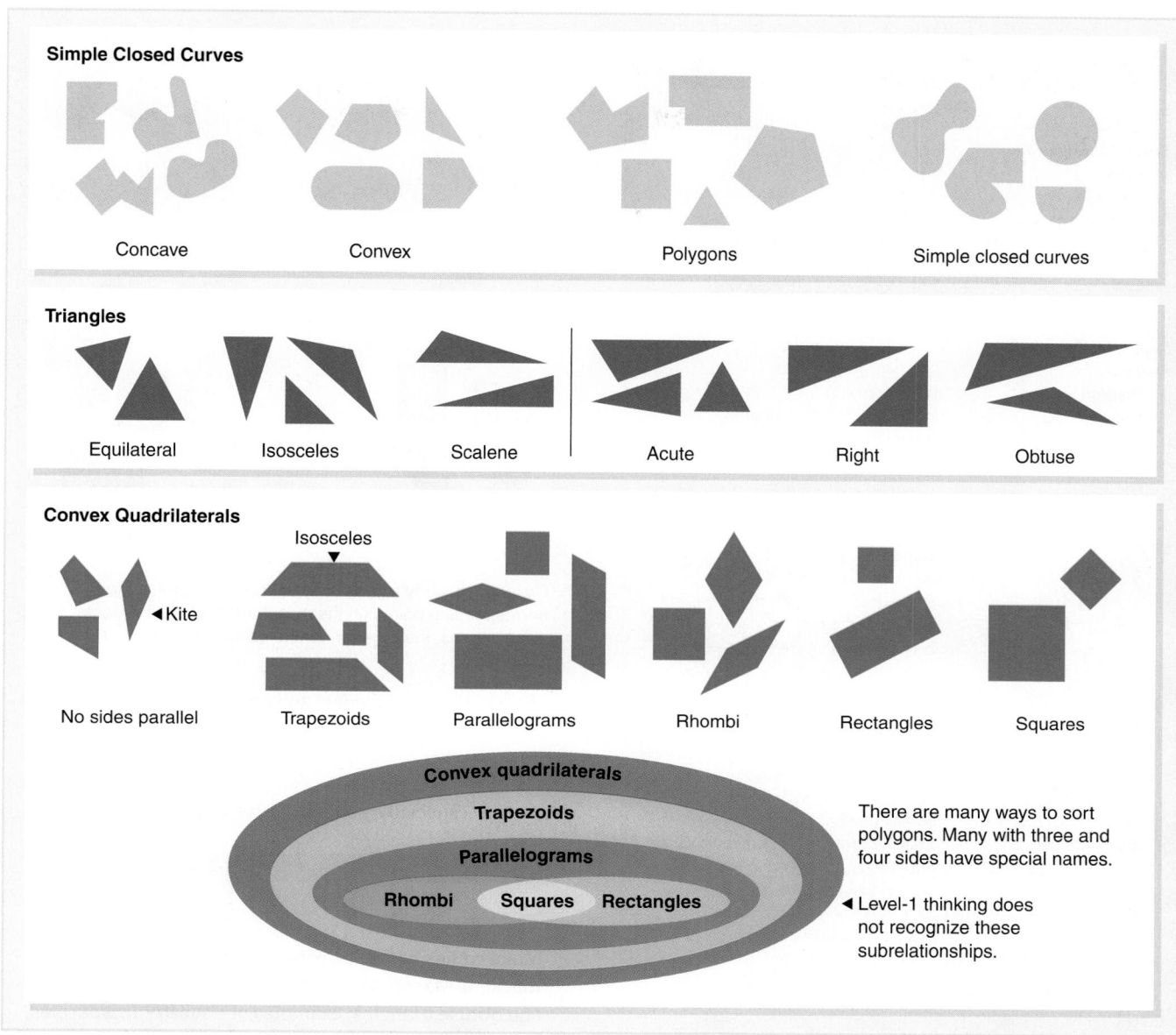

Figure 20.13 Classification of two-dimensional shapes.

Many textbooks define cylinders strictly as circular cylinders. These books do not have special names for other cylinders. Under that definition, the prism is not a special case of a cylinder. This situation highlights the fact that definitions are conventions, and not all conventions are universally agreed upon. If you return to the volume formulas in Chapter 19, you will see that the more inclusive definition of cylinders and cones given here allows one formula for any type of cylinder—hence, prisms—with a similar statement that is true for cones and pyramids.

Sorting and Classifying Activities The next activity provides a good method when you want to introduce a category of shapes.

Activity **20.7**

Mystery Definition

Use the overhead or whiteboard to conduct logic activities such as the example in Figure 20.16 (p. 431). For your first collection be certain that you have allowed for all possible variables. In Figure 20.16, for example, a square is included in the set of rhombi. Similarly, choose non-examples to be as close as necessary to examples that fit, to help with an accurate definition. The third, or mixed, set should also include those non-examples with which students are most likely to be confused. Students should write an explanation to justify their choices.

Table 20.2

Categories of Three-Dimensional Shapes	
Shape	**Description**
Sorted by Edges and Vertices	
Spheres and "egglike" shapes	Shapes with no *edges* and no *vertices* (corners).
	Shapes with *edges* but no *vertices* (e.g., a flying saucer).
	Shapes with *vertices* but no *edges* (e.g., a football).
Sorted by Faces and Surfaces	
Polyhedron	Shapes made of all faces (a *face* is a flat surface of a solid). If all surfaces are faces, all the edges will be straight lines.
	Some combination of faces and rounded surfaces (circular cylinders are examples, but this is not a definition of a cylinder).
	Shapes with all curved surfaces.
	Shapes with and without edges and with and without vertices.
	Faces can be parallel. Parallel faces lie in planes that never intersect.
Cylinders	
Cylinder	Two congruent, parallel faces called *bases*. Lines joining corresponding points on the two bases are always parallel. These parallel lines are called *elements* of the cylinder.
Right cylinder	A cylinder with elements perpendicular to the bases. A cylinder that is not a right cylinder is an *oblique cylinder*.
Prism	A cylinder with polygons for bases. All prisms are special cases of cylinders.
Rectangular prism	A cylinder with rectangles for bases.
Cube	A square prism with square sides.
Cones	
Cone	A solid with exactly one face and a vertex that is not on the face. Straight lines (elements) can be drawn from any point on the edge of the base to the vertex. The base may be any shape at all. The vertex need not be directly over the base.
Circular cone	Cone with a circular base.
Pyramid	Cone with a polygon for a base. All faces joining the vertex are triangles. Pyramids are named by the shape of the base: *triangular* pyramid, *square* pyramid, *octagonal* pyramid, and so on. All pyramids are special cases of cones.

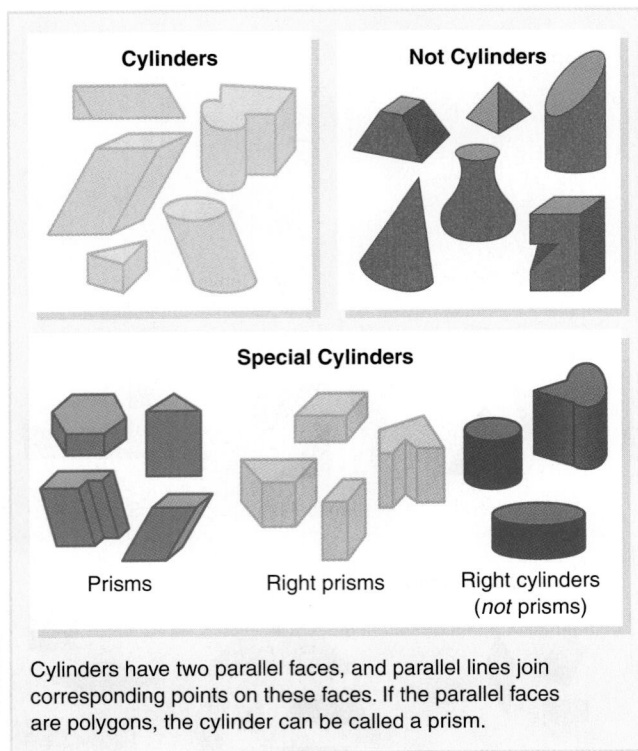

Cylinders have two parallel faces, and parallel lines join corresponding points on these faces. If the parallel faces are polygons, the cylinder can be called a prism.

Figure 20.14 Cylinders and prisms

The value of the "Mystery Definition" approach is that students develop ideas and definitions based on their own concept development. After their definitions have been discussed and compared, you can offer the usual "book" definition for the sake of clarity.

For defining types or categories of triangles, the next activity is especially good and uses a different approach.

Activity 20.8

Triangle Sort

Make copies of the Assorted Triangles sheet found (see Blackline Master 58). Note the examples of right, acute, and obtuse triangles; examples of equilateral, isosceles, and scalene triangles; and triangles that represent every possible combination of these categories. Have students cut them out. The task is to sort the entire collection into three groups so that no triangle belongs to two groups. When this is done and descriptions of the groupings have been written, students should then find a second criterion for creating three different groupings.

Accommodation

Students who find this activity challenging may need hints such as, "look only at angle sizes or only at the issue of congruent sides." For those students who are easily able to sort the triangles according to different criteria, hold these hints.

"Triangle Sort" will result in the formulation of definitions of the six different types of triangles without having to list these definitions on the board and without having

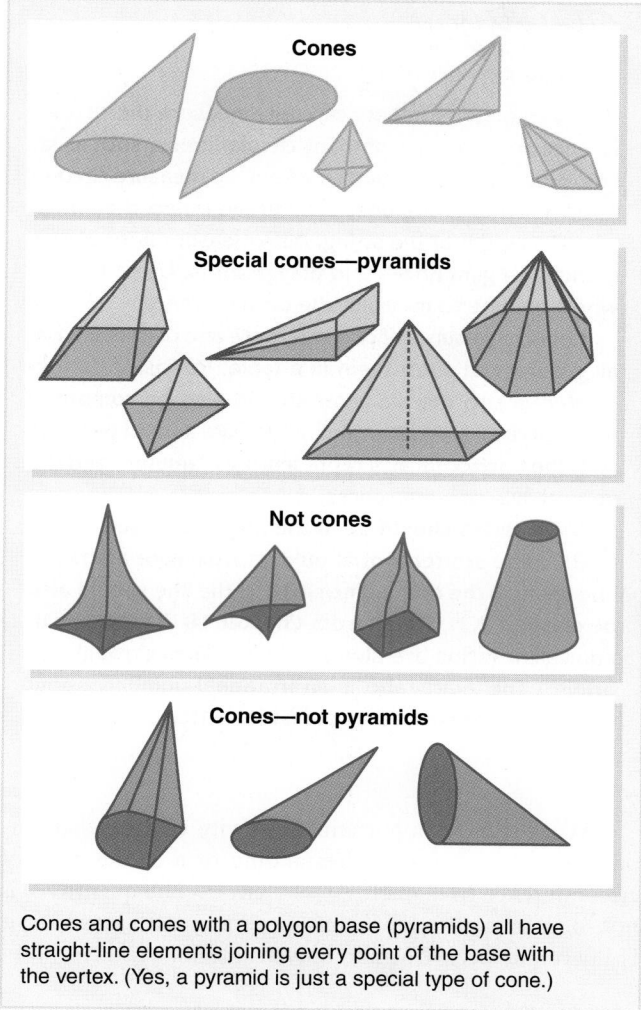

Cones and cones with a polygon base (pyramids) all have straight-line elements joining every point of the base with the vertex. (Yes, a pyramid is just a special type of cone.)

Figure 20.15 Cones and pyramids.

students memorize them. As a follow-up activity, make a chart such as the one shown here. Challenge students to sketch a triangle in each of the nine cells.

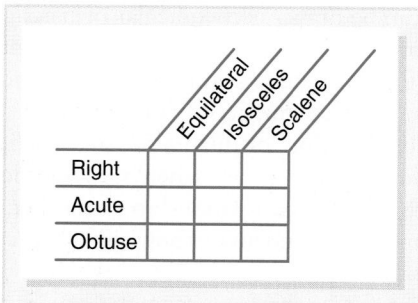

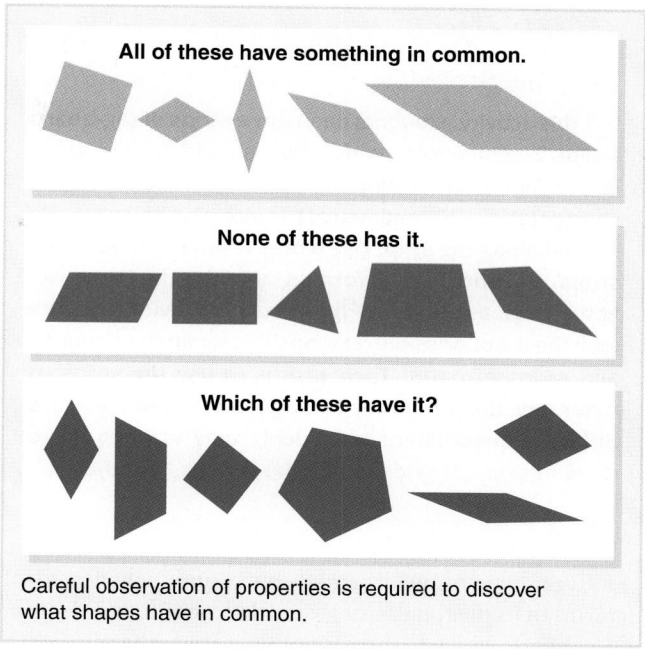

Careful observation of properties is required to discover what shapes have in common.

Figure 20.16 A mystery definition.

Quadrilaterals (polygons with four sides) are an especially rich source for investigations. Once students are familiar with the concepts of right, obtuse, and acute angles, congruence of line segments and angles, and symmetry (both line and rotational), Activity 20.2, "Property Lists for Quadrilaterals," on page 419 is a good way to bring these ideas together and to begin to see how different collections of properties apply to special classes of shapes. In this activity, students work to create lists of all the properties that they can find for a particular class of shapes. Students should share lists beginning with parallelograms, then rhombi, then rectangles, and finally squares.

The class must agree with everything that is put on the list. As new relationships come up in this presentation-and-discussion period, you can introduce proper terminology. For example, if two diagonals intersect in a square corner, then they are *perpendicular.* Other terms such as *parallel, congruent, bisect, midpoint,* and so on can be clarified as you help students write their descriptions. This is also a good time to introduce symbols such as ≅ for "congruent" or | | for "parallel." As an extension, repeat Activity 20.2 using kites and trapezoids. Furthermore, similar activities can be used to introduce three-dimensional shape definitions.

Construction Activities Having students build or draw shapes continues to be important at level 1. Dynamic geometry software (*The Geometer's Sketchpad, Cabri Geometry II,* and *Wingeom*) dramatically enhances the exploration of shapes at this level.

In the next activity, students examine the diagonals of various classes of quadrilaterals.

❚❚ ———————————— *Pause and Reflect*

Of the nine cells in the chart, two of them are impossible to fill. Can you tell which ones and why?

Activity 20.9

Diagonal Strips

For this activity, students need three strips of tag-board about 2 centimetres wide. Two should be the same length (about 30 centimetres) and the third somewhat shorter (about 20 centimetres). Punch nine holes equally spaced along the strip. Use a brass fastener to join two strips. A quadrilateral is formed by joining the four holes at the ends, as shown in Figure 20.17. Provide students with the list of possible relationships for angles, lengths, and ratios of parts. Their task is to use the strips to determine the properties of diagonals that will produce different quadrilaterals. Students may want to make drawings on dot grids to test the various hypotheses.

Every type of quadrilateral can be uniquely described in terms of its diagonals using only the conditions of length, ratio of parts, and whether or not they are perpendicular. A dynamic geometry program is an excellent vehicle for this investigation.

Circles Many interesting relationships can be observed among measures of different parts of the circle. One of the most astounding and important is the ratio between measures of the circumference and the diameter.

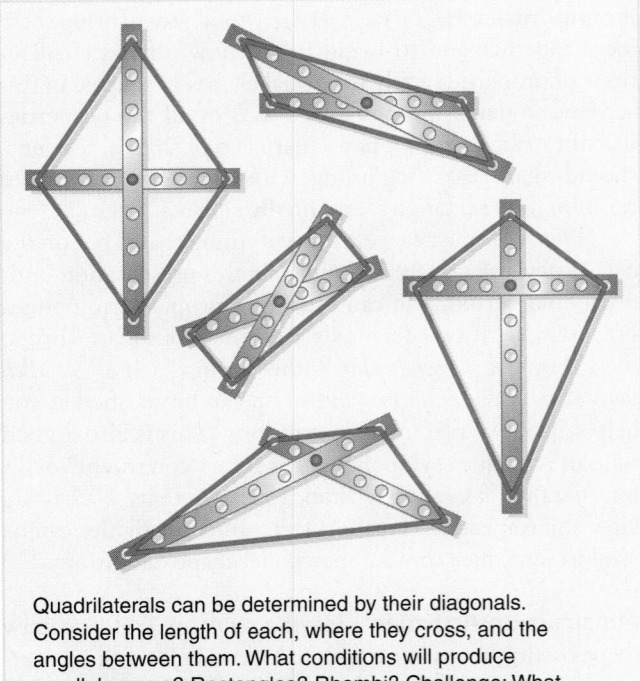

Quadrilaterals can be determined by their diagonals. Consider the length of each, where they cross, and the angles between them. What conditions will produce parallelograms? Rectangles? Rhombi? Challenge: What properties will produce a non-isosceles trapezoid?

Figure 20.17 Diagonals of quadrilaterals.

Activity 20.10

Discovering Pi

Have groups of students carefully measure the circumference and diameter of many circular items, such as jar lids, tubes, cans, and wastebaskets. To measure circumference, wrap string once around the object then measure the length of the string. Also measure large circles marked on gym floors and playgrounds. Use a trundle wheel or rope to measure the circumference.

Collect measures of circumference and diameter from all groups and enter them in a table. Ratios of the circumference to the diameter should also be computed for each circle. A scatter plot of the data should be made with the horizontal axis representing diameters and the vertical axis circumferences.

Most ratios should be in the neighbourhood of 3.1 or 3.2. The scatter plot should approximate a straight line through the origin. The slope of the line should also be close to 3.1. (Recall from Chapter 18 that graphs of equivalent ratios are always straight lines through the origin.) The exact ratio is an irrational number, about 3.14159, represented by the Greek letter π (pi).

What is most important in Activity 20.10 is that students develop a clear understanding of π as the ratio of circumference to diameter in any circle. The quantity π is not some strange number that appears in math formulas; it is a naturally occurring and universal ratio.

Dynamic Geometry Software In a dynamic geometry program, points, lines, and geometric figures are easily constructed on the computer using only the mouse. Once drawn, the geometric objects can be moved about and manipulated in endless variety. Distances, lengths, areas, angles, slopes, and perimeters can be measured. As the figures are changed, the measurements update instantly.

Lines can be drawn perpendicular or parallel to other lines or segments. Angles and segments can be drawn congruent to other angles and segments. A point can be placed at the midpoint of a segment. A figure can be produced that is a reflection, rotation, or dilation of another figure. The most significant thing is that when a geometric object is created with a particular relationship to another, that relationship is maintained no matter how either object is moved or changed.

The best known dynamic geometry programs are *The Geometer's Sketchpad* (Key Curriculum Press), *Wingeom* (open source from Peanut Software*), *Geogebra* (open source), and *Cabri Geometry II* (Texas Instruments). Originally designed for high school students, all can be used starting about grade 4.

Dynamic Geometry Examples To appreciate the potential (and the fun) of dynamic geometry software, you really need to experience it. In the meantime, an example is offered here in an attempt to illustrate how these programs work.

In Figure 20.18, the midpoints of a freely drawn quadrilateral ABCD have been joined. The diagonals of the resulting quadrilateral (EFGH) are also drawn and measured. No matter how the points A, B, C, and D are dragged around the screen, even inverting the quadrilateral, the other lines will maintain the same relationships (joining midpoints and diagonals), and the measurements will be instantly updated on the screen.

Remember that at level 1, the objects of thought are *classes* of shapes. In a dynamic geometry program, if a quadrilateral is drawn, only one shape is observed, as would be the case on paper or on a geoboard. But now that quadrilateral can be stretched and altered in endless ways. Students actually explore not one shape but an enormous number of examples from that class of shapes. If a property or constructed relationship does not change when the figure changes, the property is attributable to the *class* of shapes rather than any particular shape.

Another example in Figure 20.19 shows how dynamic geometry software can be used to investigate quadrilaterals starting with the diagonals. By creating the drawing in this manner, the diagonals of ACBD will always bisect each other no matter how the drawing is altered. By dragging point C around, ACBD can be made into a parallelogram, rectangle, rhombus, or square. For each of these figures, additional information about the diagonals can be determined by looking at the drawing.

Dynamic geometry programs are also powerful for investigating concepts of symmetry and transformations

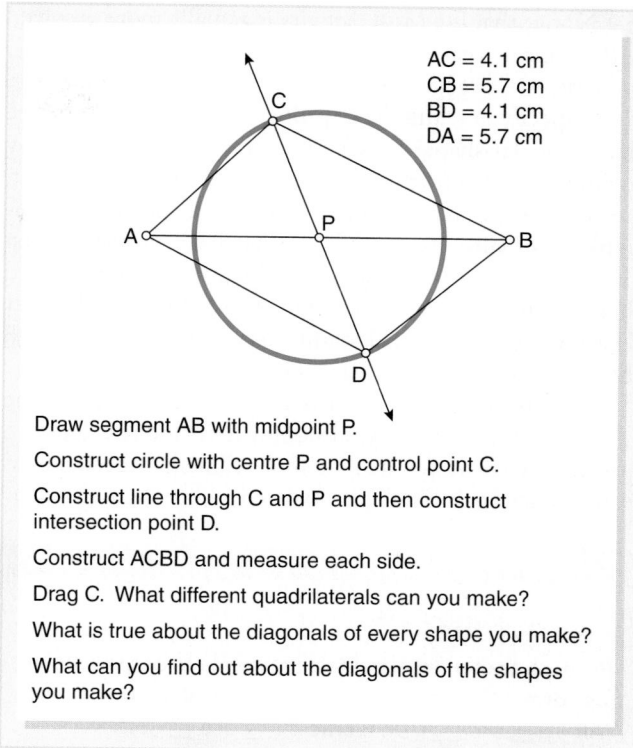

AC = 4.1 cm
CB = 5.7 cm
BD = 4.1 cm
DA = 5.7 cm

Draw segment AB with midpoint P.

Construct circle with centre P and control point C.

Construct line through C and P and then construct intersection point D.

Construct ACBD and measure each side.

Drag C. What different quadrilaterals can you make?

What is true about the diagonals of every shape you make?

What can you find out about the diagonals of the shapes you make?

Figure 20.19 Quadrilaterals with diagonals that bisect each other.

(slides, flips, and turns). There are many excellent activities that are appropriate for level-1 investigations found in supplemental publications and on the Web.

Shapes and Properties for Level-2 Thinkers

At level 2, the focus shifts from simply examining properties of shapes to explorations that include logical reasoning. As students develop an understanding of various geometric properties and attach these properties to important categories of shapes, it is essential to encourage conjecture and to explore informal deductive arguments. Students should begin to attempt—or at least follow—simple proofs and explore ideas that connect directly to algebra.

Definitions and Proofs The previously described activities of "Property Lists for Quadrilaterals" (Activity 20.2), which is a level-1 activity, and "Minimal Defining Lists" (Activity 20.3), a level-2 activity, really clarify the distinction between these two levels. (See Groth, 2006, for more information.) The parallelogram, rhombus, rectangle, and square each have at least four MDLs. One of the most interesting MDLs for each shape consists only of the properties of its diagonals. For example, a quadrilateral with diagonals that bisect each other and are perpendicular (intersect at right angles) is a rhombus.

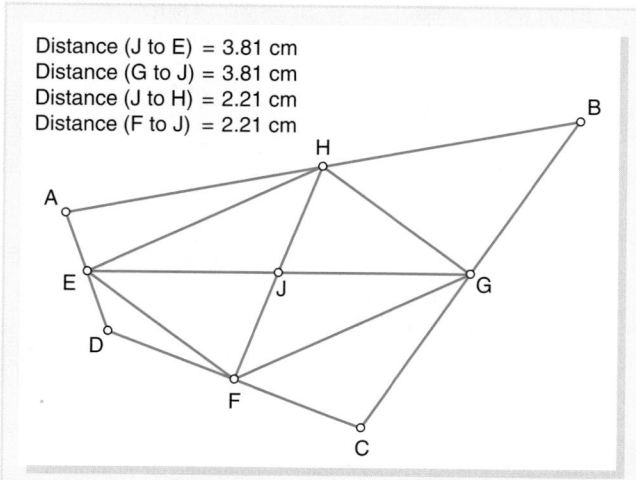

Distance (J to E) = 3.81 cm
Distance (G to J) = 3.81 cm
Distance (J to H) = 2.21 cm
Distance (F to J) = 2.21 cm

Figure 20.18 A *Geometer's Sketchpad* construction illustrating an interesting property of quadrilaterals.

Notice that the MDL activity is actually more involved with logical reasoning than with examining shapes. Students are engaged in the general process of deciding, "*If* we specify only this list of properties, will that guarantee this particular shape?" A second feature is the opportunity to discuss what constitutes a definition of the shape. In fact, any MDL could be the definition of the shape. The definitions we usually use are MDLs that have probably been chosen because of the ease with which we can understand them. A quadrilateral with diagonals that bisect each other does not immediately call to mind a parallelogram although that is part of a defining list of properties.

The next activity is also a good follow-up to the "Property Lists" activity, although it is not restricted to quadrilaterals and can include three-dimensional shapes as well. Notice again the logic involved.

Activity 20.11

True or False?

Prepare a set of true and false statements of the following forms: "If it is a(n) _____, then it is also a(n) _____." "All _____ are _____." "Some _____ are _____."

A few examples are suggested here but numerous possibilities exist.

- If it is a square, then it is a rhombus.
- All squares are rectangles.
- Some parallelograms are rectangles.
- All parallelograms have congruent diagonals.
- If it has exactly two lines of symmetry, it must be a quadrilateral.
- If it is a cylinder, then it is a prism.
- All prisms have a plane of symmetry.
- All pyramids have square bases.
- If a prism has a plane of symmetry, then it is a right prism.

The task is to decide if the statements are true or false and to present an argument to support the decision. Four or five true-or-false statements will make a good lesson. Once this format is understood, let students challenge their classmates by making their own lists of five statements. Each list should have a mix of true and false statements. Students' lists can then be used in subsequent lessons.

II ———————— *Pause and Reflect*

Use the property list for squares and rectangles to prove "All squares are rectangles." Notice that you must use logical reasoning to understand this statement. It does little good simply to force it on students who are not ready to develop the relationship.

The following activity was designed by Sconyers (1995) to demonstrate that students can create proofs in geometry well before high school.

Activity 20.12

Two Polygons from One

Pose the following problem:

Begin with a convex polygon with a given number of sides. Connect two points on the polygon with a line segment forming two new polygons. How many sides do the resulting two polygons have altogether?

Demonstrate with a few examples (see Figure 20.20). Have students explore by drawing polygons and slicing them. Encourage students to make a table showing the number of sides in the original polygon and in the resulting polygon. Students should first make conjectures about a general rule. When groups are comfortable with their conjecture, they should try to reason why their statement is correct—that is, to prove their conjecture.

Obviously, the number of resulting sides depends on where the slice is made. With the exception of triangles, there are three possibilities. For each case, a clear argument can be made. The appropriate conjecture and proof are left to you, but trust that students working together can do this task.

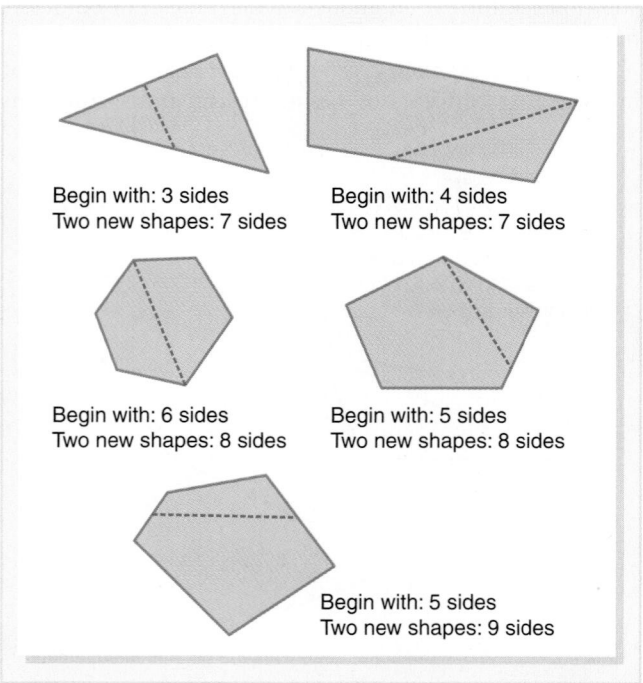

Figure 20.20 Start with a polygon, and draw a segment to divide it into two polygons. How many sides will the two new polygons have?

Notice that in this task, as in others we have explored, the statements to be proven come from students. If you write a theorem on the board and ask students to prove it, you have already told them that it is true. If, by contrast, a student makes a statement about a geometric situation the class is exploring, it can be written on the board with a question mark as a *conjecture*, a statement whose truth has not yet been determined. You can ask, "Is it true? Always? Can we prove it? Can we find a counterexample?" Reasonable deductive arguments can be forged out of discussions (Boats, Dwyer, Laing, & Fratella, 2003).

The Pythagorean Relationship   The *Pythagorean relationship* is so important that it deserves some special attention. In geometric terms, this relationship states that if a square is constructed on each side of a right triangle, the areas of the two smaller squares will together equal the area of the square on the longest side, the hypotenuse. To discover this relationship, consider the following activity.

Activity 20.13

The Pythagorean Relationship

Have students draw a right triangle on half-centimetre grid paper (see Blackline Master 36). Assign each student a different triangle, specifying the lengths of the two legs. Students are to draw a square on each leg and on the hypotenuse and find the area of all three squares. (For the square on the hypotenuse, the exact area can be found by making each of the sides the diagonal of a rectangle. See Figure 20.21.) Make a table of the area data (Sq. on leg 1, Sq. on leg 2, Sq. on hyp.), and ask students to look for a relationship among the squares.

As an extension to the last activity, students can explore drawing other figures on the legs of right triangles and

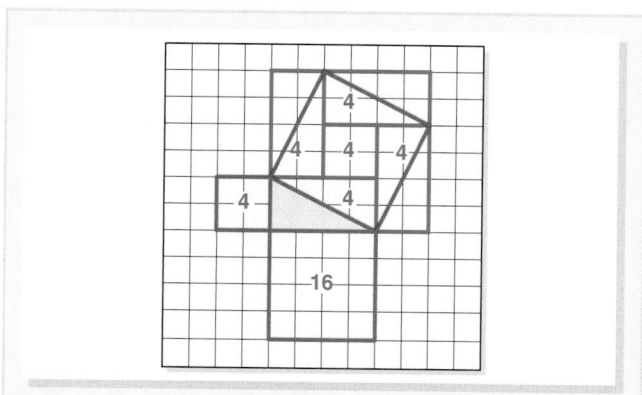

Figure 20.21 The Pythagorean relationship. Note that if drawn on a grid, the areas of all squares are easily determined. Here, 4 + 16 = area of the square on the hypotenuse.

computing areas. For example, draw semicircles or equilateral triangles instead of squares. The areas of any regular polygons drawn on the three sides of right triangles will have the same relationship.

What about proof? Both large congruent squares in Figure 20.22 together show a pictorial representation for a proof of the Pythagorean Theorem (Nelson, 2001). Note that both squares contain four triangles that are the same, but arranged differently. By adding up the areas of the squares and the triangles and setting them equal, the Pythagorean relationship can be found by subtracting the common areas in both squares. An algebraic recording of the thinking process is shown below the drawings.

⏸ ──────── *Pause and Reflect*

Use the two drawings in Figure 20.22 to create proof of the Pythagorean relationship.

The e-Examples found at the NCTM Web site under "Standards & Focal Points" includes a dynamic proof without words that is worth sharing with your students (Applet 6.5). Because it requires knowing that parallelograms and rectangles with the same base and height have the same area (see Chapter 19), it is a good review. ◆

Finding Versus Explaining Relationships   At level 2, the focus is on reasoning or deductive thinking. Can dynamic geometry software programs help students develop deductive arguments to support the relationships they come to believe through inductive reasoning? Consider the following situation.

Suppose that you have students use a dynamic geometry program to draw a triangle, measure all the angles, and add them up. As the triangle vertices are dragged around, the sum of the angles would remain steadfast at 180 degrees. Students can conjecture that the sum of the interior angles of a triangle is always 180 degrees, and they would be

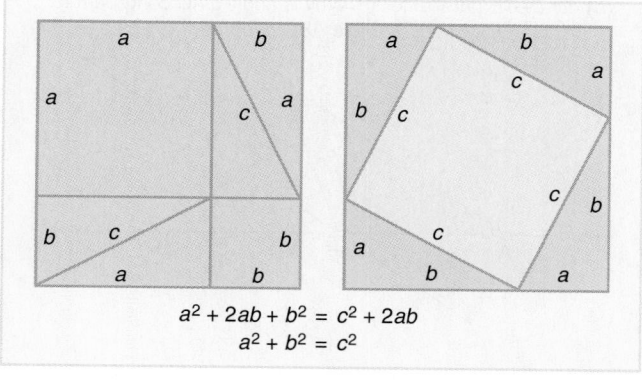

$$a^2 + 2ab + b^2 = c^2 + 2ab$$
$$a^2 + b^2 = c^2$$

Figure 20.22 The two squares together are a "proof without words." Can you supply the words?

completely convinced of the truth of this conjecture based on this inductive experience. (Several non-computer activities lead to the same conclusion.) However, the experience just described fails to explain *why it is so.* Consider the following activity, which can be done easily with paper and scissors or quite dramatically with a dynamic geometry program.

Activity 20.14

Angle Sum in a Triangle

Have all students cut out three congruent triangles. (Stack three sheets of paper, and cut three shapes at one time.) Place one triangle on a line and the second directly next to it in the same orientation. Place the third triangle in the space between the triangles, as shown in Figure 20.23(a). Based on this experience, what conjecture can you make about the sum of the angles in a triangle?

In a dynamic geometry program, the three triangles in Figure 20.23(a) can be drawn by starting with one triangle, translating it to the right the length of AC, and then rotating the same triangle about the midpoint of side BC. When vertices of the original triangle are dragged, the other triangles will change accordingly and remain congruent. We still do not know why the angle sum is always a straight angle, but this exploration allows students to see why it might be so. In the figure, there are lines parallel to each side of the original triangle. By using properties of angles formed by cutting parallel lines with a transverse line, it is easy to argue that the sum of the angles will always be a straight line (see Figure 20.23(b); the proof is left to you).

Dynamic geometry software can be enormously powerful for helping students observe geometric relationships and make conjectures. The truth of the conjectures will often be obvious. At level 2, however, we must begin to ask why. The following activity further illustrates the point.

Activity 20.15

Triangle Midsegments

Using a dynamic geometry program, draw a triangle and label the vertices A, B, and C. Draw the segment joining the midpoints of AB and AC, and label this segment DE, as in Figure 20.24. Measure the lengths of DE and BC. Also measure angles ADE and ABC. Drag points A, B, and C. What conjectures can you make about the relationships between segment DE, the *midsegment* of ABC, and BC, the base of ABC?

It is very clear that the midsegment is half the length of the base and parallel to it. But why is this so? Students will need a bit more guidance. However, you should not necessarily have to provide the argument for them. Suggest that they draw a line through A parallel to BC. List all pairs of angles that they know are congruent. Why are they congruent? Note that triangle ABC is similar to triangle ADE. Why is it similar? With hints such as these, many upper grade students can begin to make logical arguments for why the things they observe to be true are in fact true.

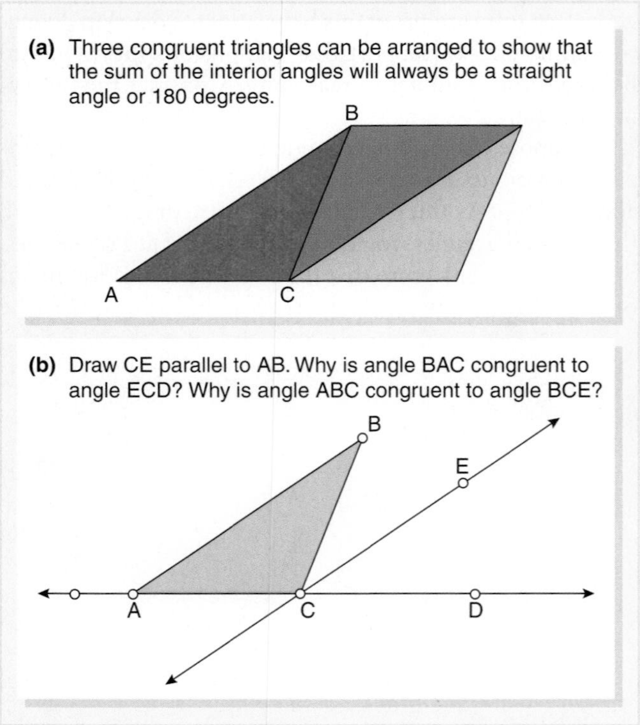

(a) Three congruent triangles can be arranged to show that the sum of the interior angles will always be a straight angle or 180 degrees.

(b) Draw CE parallel to AB. Why is angle BAC congruent to angle ECD? Why is angle ABC congruent to angle BCE?

Figure 20.23 Deductive, logical reasoning is necessary to prove relationships that appear true from observation.

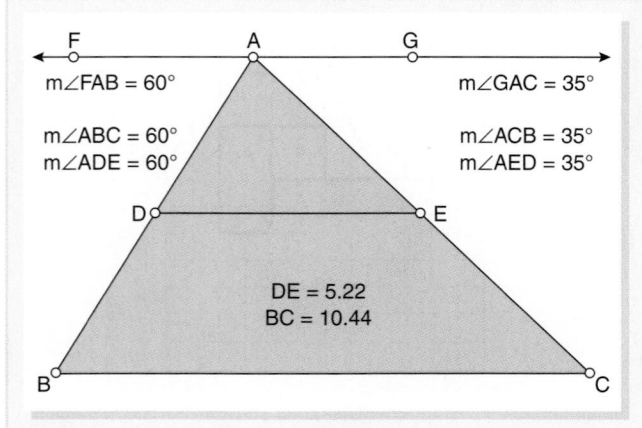

Figure 20.24 The midsegment of a triangle is always parallel to the base and half as long.

Learning About Transformations

Transformations are changes in position or size of a shape. Movements that do not change the size or shape of the object are called "rigid motions." Usually, three rigid-motion transformations are discussed: *translations* or slides, *reflections* or flips, and *rotations* or turns. Interestingly, the study of symmetry is also included under the study of transformations. Do you know why?

Transformations for Level-0 Thinkers

Transformations at this level involve an introduction to the basic concepts of slides, flips, and turns and the initial development of line symmetry and rotational symmetry.

Slides, Flips, and Turns   At the primary level, the terms *slide, flip,* and *turn* are adequate. The early goal is to help students recognize these transformations and begin to explore their effect on simple shapes. You can use a non-symmetrical shape on the overhead to introduce these terms (see Figure 20.25). Most likely your textbook will use only the centre of a shape as the point of rotation and restrict reflections to vertical and horizontal lines through the centre. These restrictions are not necessary and may even be misleading.

The Motion Man described in the next activity can also be used to introduce students to the terms *slide, flip,* and *turn*. In the activity, rotations are restricted to $\frac{1}{4}$, $\frac{1}{2}$, and $\frac{3}{4}$ turns in a clockwise direction. The centre of the turn will be the centre of the figure. Reflections will be flips over vertical or horizontal lines. These restrictions are for simplicity. In the general case, the centre of rotation can be

anywhere on or off the figure. Lines of reflection can also be anywhere.

Activity **20.16**

Motion Man

Using Blackline Masters 52 and 53, make copies of the first Motion Man then copy the mirror image on the backs of these copies. (See Figure 20.26.) Experiment first. You want the back image to match the front image when held to the light. Cut off the excess paper to leave a square. Give all students a two-sided Motion Man.

Demonstrate each of the possible motions. A slide is simply that. The figure does not rotate or turn over. Demonstrate $\frac{1}{4}$, $\frac{1}{2}$, and $\frac{3}{4}$ turns. Emphasize that only clockwise turns will be used for this activity. Similarly, demonstrate a horizontal flip (top goes to bottom) and a vertical flip (left goes to right). Practise by having everyone start with his or her Motion Man in the same orientation. As you announce one of the moves, students slide, flip, or turn Motion Man accordingly.

Then display two Motion Men side by side in any orientation. The task is to decide what motion or combination of motions will get the man on the left to match the man on the right. Students use their own man to work out a solution. Test the solutions that students offer. If both men are in the same position, call that a slide.

⏸ ———————————— *Pause and Reflect*

Begin with the Motion Man in the left position shown in Figure 20.26. Now place a second Motion Man next to the first. Will it take one move or more than one move (transformation) to get from the first to the second Motion Man? Can you describe all the positions that require more than one move? Are there any positions that require more than two moves?

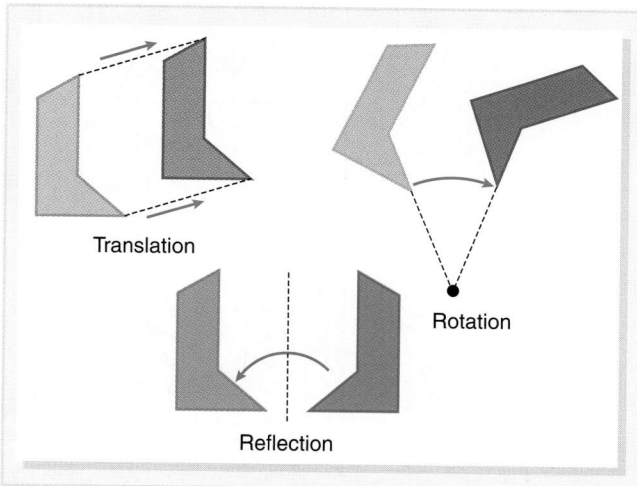

Figure 20.25 Translation (slide), reflection (flip), rotation (turn).

Figure 20.26 The Motion Man is used to show slides, flips, and turns. (See Blackline Masters 52 and 53.)

At first, students will be confused when they can't get their Motion Man into the new position with one move. This causes an excellent problem. Don't be too quick to suggest that it may take two moves. If flips across each of the two diagonals are added to the motions along with vertical and horizontal flips, Motion Man can assume any new position in exactly one move. This provides a challenge for students. Two students begin with their Motion Man figures in the same position. One student then changes his or her Motion Man and challenges the other student to say what motion is required to make the two Motion Men match. The solution is then tested and the roles reversed.

Line and Rotational Symmetry If a shape can be folded on a line so that the two halves match, then it is said to have *line symmetry* (or mirror symmetry). Notice that the fold line is actually a line of reflection—the portion of the shape on one side of the line is reflected onto the other side. That is the connection between line symmetry and transformations.

One way to introduce line symmetry to children is to show examples and non-examples using an all-of-these/none-of-these approach, as in Figure 20.16 on page 431. Another possibility is to have students fold a sheet of paper in half and cut out a shape of their choosing. When they open the paper, the fold line will be a line of symmetry. A third way is to use mirrors or Miras (red, plastic image reflectors that can be used to explore concepts of symmetry and congruence). When you place a mirror on a picture or design so that the mirror is perpendicular to the table, you see a shape with symmetry when you look in the mirror.

The following activity explores line symmetry.

Activity 20.17

Pattern Block Mirror Symmetry

Students need a plain sheet of paper with a straight line through the middle. Using about six to eight pattern blocks, students complete on one side of the line a design that touches the line in some way. The task is to make the mirror image of the design on the other side of the line. When finished, students use a mirror or Mira to check their work. They place the mirror on the line and look into it from the side of the original design. With the mirror in place they should see exactly the same image as they see when they lift the mirror. You can also challenge them to make designs with more than one line of symmetry.

Building symmetrical designs with pattern blocks tends to be easier if the line is vertical. If the line is oriented horizontally or diagonally, the task is harder.

The same task can be done with a geoboard. First, stretch a band down the centre or from corner to corner. Make a design on one side of the line and its mirror image on the other. Check with a mirror. This can also be done on either isometric or square dot grids (Blackline Masters 34 and 38), as shown in Figure 20.27 or with dynamic geometry software.

A plane of symmetry in three dimensions is analogous to a line of symmetry in two dimensions. Figure 20.28 illustrates a shape built with cubes that has a plane of symmetry.

Activity 20.18

Plane Symmetry Buildings

With cubes, construct a building that has a plane of symmetry. If the plane of symmetry goes between cubes, slice the shape by separating the building into two symmetrical parts.

Accommodation

For those students who require an added challenge, have them make buildings with two or three planes of symmetry. They can build various prisms. Remember that a plane can slice diagonally through the blocks.

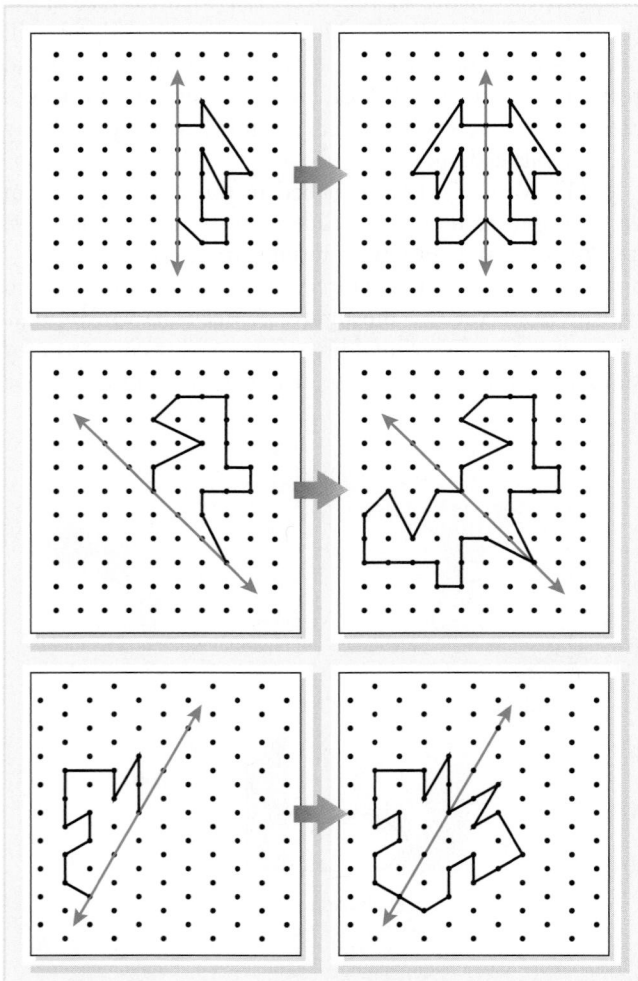

Figure 20.27 Exploring symmetry on dot grids.

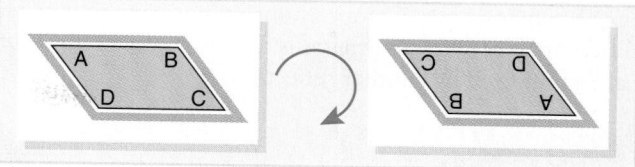

Figure 20.29 This parallelogram fits in its footprint two ways without flipping it over. Therefore, it has rotational symmetry of order 2.

see. Two types of activities seem appropriate at this level: compositions of transformations, and using transformations to create tessellations.

Composition of Transformations One transformation can be followed by another. For example, a figure can be reflected over a line, then that figure can be rotated about a point. A combination of two or more transformations is called a *composition*.

Have students experiment with compositions of two or even three transformations using a simple shape on a rectangular dot grid. For example, have students draw an L-shape on a dot grid and label it L_1. (Refer to Figure 20.30.) Reflect it through a line then rotate the image $\frac{1}{4}$ turn clockwise about a point not on the shape. Call this image L_2, the image of a composition of a reflection followed by a rotation. Notice that if L_1 is rotated $\frac{1}{4}$ turn clockwise about the same point used before to L_3 there is a relationship between L_2 and L_3. Continue to explore different combinations of transformations. Remember to include translations (slides)

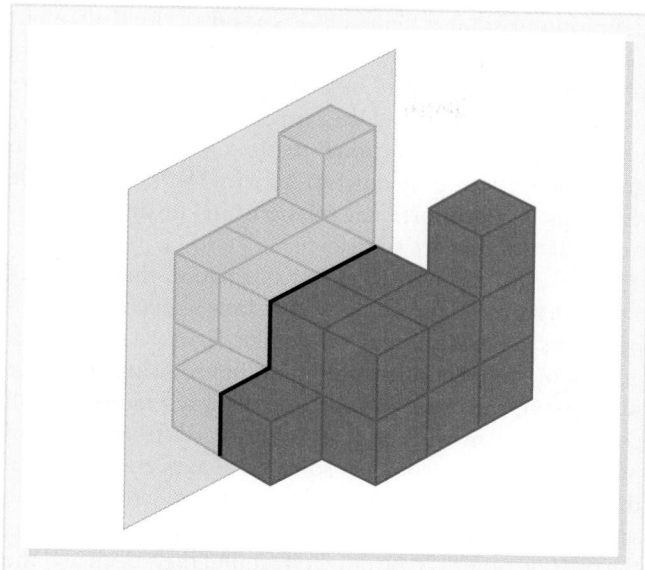

Figure 20.28 A block building with one plane of symmetry.

A shape has *rotational symmetry* (also referred to as *point symmetry*) if it can be rotated about a point and land in a position exactly matching the one in which it began. A square has rotational symmetry, as does an equilateral triangle.

A good way to understand rotational symmetry is to take a shape with rotational symmetry, such as a square, and trace around it on a piece of paper. Call this tracing the shape's "footprint." The order of rotational symmetry will be the number of ways that the shape can fit into its footprint without flipping it over. A square has rotational symmetry of *order* 4, whereas an equilateral triangle has rotational symmetry of *order* 3. The parallelogram in Figure 20.29 has rotational symmetry of order 2. Some books would call order 2 symmetry "180-degree symmetry." The degrees refer to the smallest angle of rotation required before the shape matches itself or fits into its box. A square has 90-degree rotational symmetry.

Activity **20.19**

Pattern Block Rotational Symmetry

Have students construct designs with pattern blocks with different rotational symmetries. They should be able to make designs with rotational symmetry of order, 2, 3, 4, 6, or 12. Which of the designs have mirror symmetry as well?

Transformations for Level-1 Thinkers

Within the context of transformations, students moving into level-1 thinking can begin to look at transformations a bit more analytically and to apply them to shapes that they

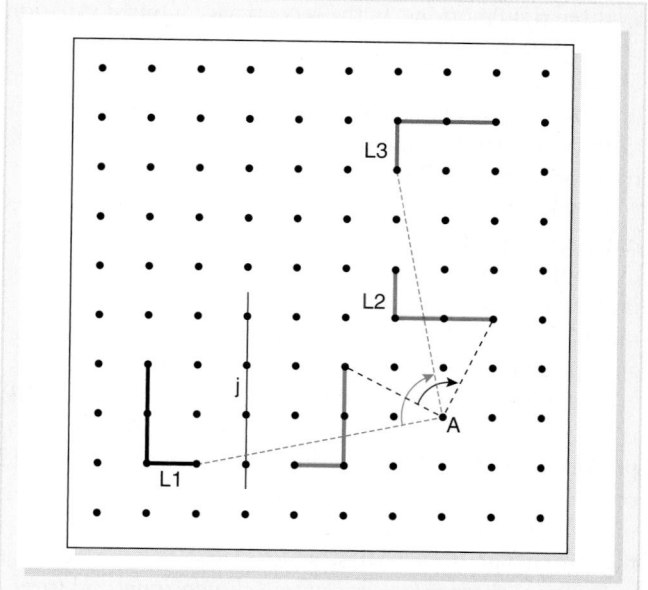

Figure 20.30 Shape L_1 was reflected across line j and rotated $\frac{1}{4}$ turn about point A resulting in L_2. L_1 was also rotated $\frac{1}{4}$ turn about point A. How are L_2 and L_3 related? Will this always work?

in the compositions. Compositions do not have to involve different types of transformations. For example, a reflection can be followed by another reflection.

Activity 20.20

Mystery Transformations

Draw a small L-shaped figure near one corner of a rectangle dot grid. On this page, students draw a congruent L-shape somewhere near the centre of the page. The second L can be flipped or turned in any orientation they wish. Then students trade papers with a partner. The task is to find some combination of slides, flips, and $\frac{1}{4}$ or $\frac{1}{2}$ turns that will take the shape in the corner onto the shape drawn by the students.

This is a challenging activity. To help students, ask if the L has been flipped over or not. If it has been flipped over, then there will have to be one or three reflections. Regardless of how the two shapes are oriented, it can always be done in three or fewer transformations.

For those students who are having difficulty with this activity, you might have them go back and do some earlier level-0 transformation activities.

 In NCTM's e-Examples, found at the NCTM Web site under "Standards and Focal Points," Applet 6.4, "Understanding Congruence, Similarity, and Symmetry" is one of the best examples of a simple yet valuable interactive applet. In the first part of the applet, students develop an understanding of all three rigid motions. In the second part, a transformation is complete and the student uses a guess-and-check procedure to determine what exact transformation was carried out. In the last two parts, students can explore compositions of reflections then other compositions of up to three transformations. This applet is strongly recommended.

In *Math Trek 4, 5, 6* (Nectar Foundation, 2006) students have an opportunity to work with transformations in different contexts. The lesson component provides learning about slides, flips, and turns in an interactive environment. Students then apply this learning sliding, flipping, and turning pentomino pieces in the activities that follow.

Mathville Middle School (Courseware Solutions, 2004) is one of the series in the virtual village of Mathville where practice is offered with slides, flips, and turns in a real-world context. Students engage in sliding, flipping, and turning to solve different puzzles. Students also have an opportunity to engage in activities, which focus on symmetry of polygons and other features of two-dimensional and three-dimensional figures. ◆

Similar Figures and Proportional Reasoning In Chapter 18 on proportional reasoning, we saw a good first

definition of similar figures as shapes that "look alike but are different sizes" (see Activity 18.3, page 365). More precisely, two figures are *similar* if all their corresponding angles are congruent and the corresponding sides are proportional. Other proportional reasoning activities are also good connections to geometry. Activity 18.9 involves scale drawings and proportional relationships in three-dimensional figures that are similar.

A *dilation* is a non-rigid transformation that produces similar figures. Figure 20.31 shows how a given figure can be *dilated* to make larger or smaller figures. If different groups of students dilate the same figure using the same scale factor, they will find that the resulting figures are all congruent, even with each group using different dilation points. Dynamic geometry software makes the results of this exercise quite dramatic. The software allows for the scale factors to be set at any value. Once a dilation is made, the dilation point can be dragged around the screen and the size and shape of the image clearly stay unchanged. Scale factors less than 1 produce smaller figures.

Tessellations Revisited Either by using transformations or by combining compatible polygons, students at level 1 can create tessellations that are artistic and quite complex.

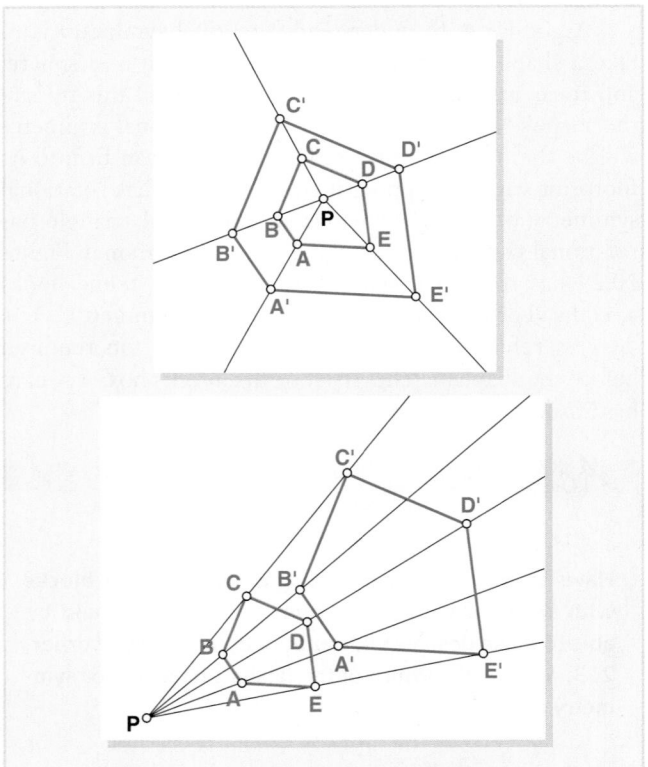

Figure 20.31 Begin with figure ABCDE and place point P anywhere at all. Draw lines from P through each vertex. Place point A' twice as far from P as A is from P (scale factor of 2). Do similarly for the other points. ABCDE is congruent with A'B'C'D'E'.

The Dutch artist M.C. Escher is well known for his tessellations, in which the tiles are very intricate and often take the shape of objects such as birds, horses, angels, or lizards. Escher took a simple shape such as a triangle, parallelogram, or hexagon and performed transformations on the sides. For example, a curve drawn along one side might be translated (slid) to the opposite side. Another idea was to draw a curve from the midpoint of a side to the adjoining vertex. This curve was then rotated about the midpoint to form a totally new side of the tile. These two ideas are illustrated in Figure 20.32. Dot paper is used to help draw the lines. *Escher-type tessellations*, as these have come to be called, are important applications of transformations for students in grades 5 and up. Once a tile has been designed, it can be cut from two different colours of construction paper instead of drawing the tessellation on a dot grid.

A *regular tessellation* is made of a single tile that is a regular polygon (all sides and angles are congruent). Each vertex of a regular tessellation has the same number of tiles meeting at that point. A checkerboard is a simple example of a regular tessellation. A *semi-regular tessellation* is made of two or more tiles, each of which is a regular polygon. At each vertex of a semi-regular tessellation, the same arrangement of regular polygons comes together in the same order. A vertex (and, therefore, the complete semi-regular tessellation) can be described by the series of shapes that meet at it. Students can figure out what polygons are possible at a vertex and design their own semi-regular tessellations.

Transformations for Level-2 Thinkers

The following activity is a challenge for students to use their understanding of symmetries and transformations to establish an interesting relationship between these two ideas. The shapes used for this activity are called *pentominoes*—shapes made from 5 squares, with each square touching at least one other square by sharing a full side with these adjacent squares. The search to see how many different pentominoes there are is a well-known geometry activity (see Activity 20.27 on page 446). For our purposes in discussing transformations and symmetries, the collection of 12 pentominoes simply serves as a convenient collection of shapes. These are shown in Figure 20.33.

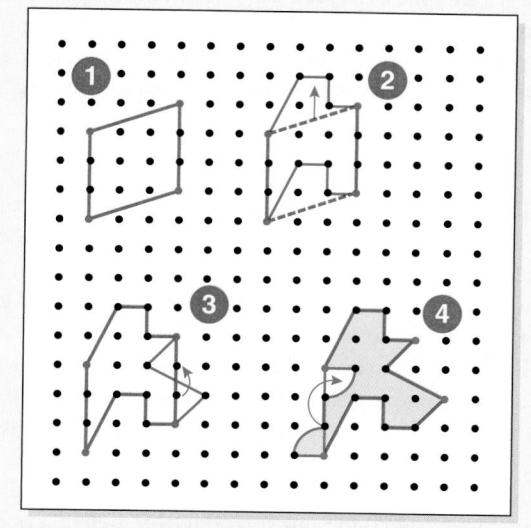

① Start with a simple shape.

② Draw the same curve on two opposite sides. This tile will stack up in columns.

③ Rotate a curve on the midpoint of one side.

④ Rotate a curve on the midpoint of the other side. Use this tile for tessellation (below).

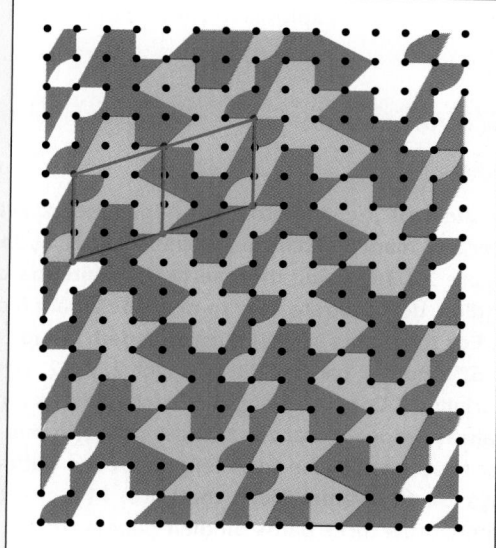

A column of the resulting tile will now match a like column that is rotated one complete turn. Find these rotated columns in the tessellation shown here.

Figure 20.32 Creating Escher-type tessellations.

Activity 20.21

Pentomino Positions

Have students cut out a set of 12 pentominoes from 2-centimetre grid paper (see Figure 20.33). Mark one side of each piece to help remember if it has been flipped over. The first part of the task is to determine how many different positions on the grid each piece has. Call positions "different" if a reflection or a turn is required to make them match. Therefore, the cross-shaped piece has only one position. The strip of five squares has two positions. Some pieces have as many as eight positions. The second part of the task is to find a relationship between the line symmetries and rotational symmetries for each piece and the number of positions it can have on the grid. Students may need to make a table of what they know.

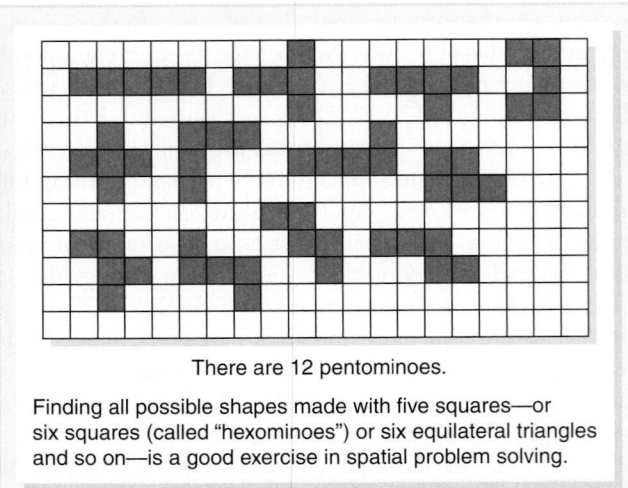

There are 12 pentominoes.

Finding all possible shapes made with five squares—or six squares (called "hexominoes") or six equilateral triangles and so on—is a good exercise in spatial problem solving.

Figure 20.33 There are 12 different pentomino shapes. An exploration to find these shapes is found in Activity 20.27 on page 446.

Learning About Location

The location standard in *Principles and Standards* says that students should "specify locations and describe spatial relationships using coordinate geometry and other representational systems" (NCTM, 2000, p. 42). After some early development of terms for how objects are located with respect to other objects (e.g., the ball is *under* the table), location activities involve the analysis of paths from point to point as on a map and the use of coordinate systems.

Location for Level-0 Thinkers

In pre-K and kindergarten, children learn about everyday positional descriptions—*over, under, near, far, between, left,* and *right*. These are the beginnings of the *Standards'* goal of specifying locations. However, helping students refine the way they answer questions of direction, distance, and location enhances spatial understandings. Geometry, measurement, and algebra are all supported by the use of a grid system with numbers or coordinates attached that can specify the location on a grid. As students become more sophisticated, their use of coordinates progresses along with them. It is important that students at the primary level begin to think in terms of a grid system to identify location.

The next activity can serve as a readiness task for coordinates and help students see the value of having a way to specify location without pointing.

Activity 20.22

Hidden Positions

To make the game boards, draw 18-centimetre squares on tag-board. Subdivide the squares into 3 × 3 grids.

To play the game, students work in twos sitting with a "screen" separating their desktop space so that neither student can see the other's grid (see Figure 20.34). Each student has four different pattern blocks. The first player places a block on each of four different sections of the grid. He or she then tells the other player where to put blocks in matching positions on her or his blank grid. When all four pieces are positioned, students check the two grids to see if they are alike. Then, the players switch roles. Model the game once by taking the part of the first student. Use words such as *top row, middle, left,* and *right*. Students can play in pairs as a station activity.

The "Hidden Positions" game can easily be extended to grids up to 6 × 6. As the grid size increases, the need for a system of labelling positions increases. Students can begin to use a simple coordinate system as early as the first grade. Use a coordinate grid like the one shown in Figure 20.35 (see Blackline Master 48). Explain how to use two numbers to designate a point of intersection on the grid. The first number tells how far to move to the right. The second number tells how far to move up. For younger children use the words along with the numbers: 3 right and 0 up. Be sure to include 0 in your introduction. Select a point on the grid and have students decide what two numbers name that point. If your point is at (2, 4) and students incorrectly say "four, two," then simply indicate where the point is that they named. Emphasize that when they say or write the two numbers, the first number is the number of steps to the right and the second is the number of steps up.

The next activity explores the notion of different paths on a grid.

Activity 20.23

Paths

On a sheet of 2-centimetre grid paper (see Blackline Master 34), mark two different points A and B, as shown in Figure 20.36. Using the overhead, whiteboard, or floor tiles, demonstrate how to describe a path from A to B. For the points in the figure, one path is "up 5 and right 6." Another path might be "right 2, up 2, right 2, up 3, right 2." Count the length of each path. As long as you always move toward the target point (in this case either right or up), the total lengths of the paths will always be the same. Here they are 11 units long. Students draw three paths on their papers from A to B using different coloured crayons. For each path they write directions describing their paths. Ask, "What is the greatest number of turns that you can make in your path?" "What is the smallest number?" Where would A and B have to be in order to get there with no turns?"

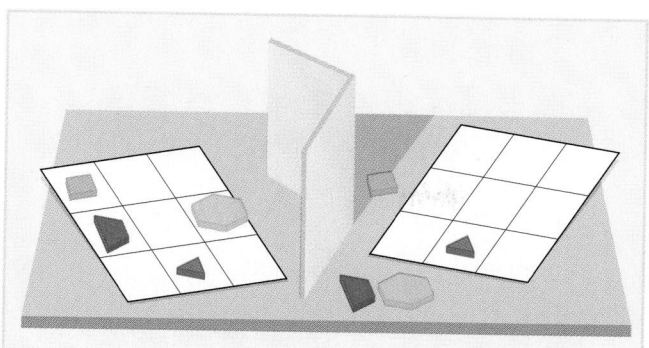

Figure 20.34 The "Hidden Positions" game.

If you add a coordinate system on the grid in "Paths," students can describe their paths with coordinates: For example: $(1, 2) \rightarrow (3, 2) \rightarrow (3, 5) \rightarrow (7, 5) \rightarrow (7, 7)$

 The e-Examples found at the NCTM Web site under "Standards & Focal Points" contain a nice applet (Applet 4.3) that is similar to the previous activity but offers some additional challenges. Students move a ladybug by issuing directions. The task is to make a list of directions to hide the ladybug beneath a leaf. When the directions are complete, the ladybug is set in motion to follow them. The ladybug is also used to draw shapes such as a rectangle in a tilted position or to travel through mazes. This applet is a very basic version of the powerful computer programming language Logo. ◆

Location for Level-1 Thinkers

At level 1, one use of the coordinate grid is to examine transformations in a more analytic manner. There is not a lot of new knowledge about coordinates to learn except for the extension to four quadrants with the use of negative numbers. Even grade 4 and 5 students can use negative

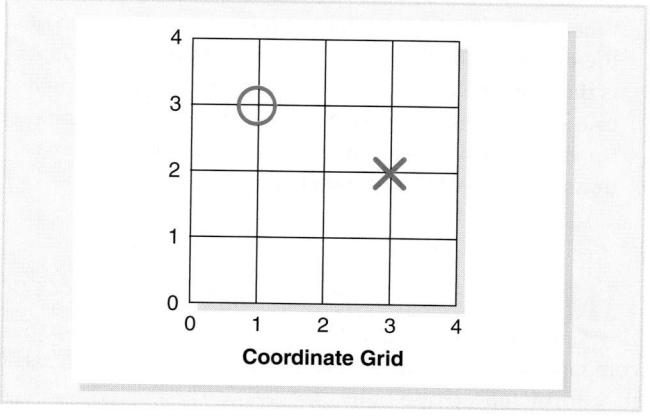

Figure 20.35 A simple coordinate grid. The X is at (3, 2) and the O is at (1, 3). Use the grid to play Three in a Row (like Tic-Tac-Toe). Put marks on intersections, not spaces.

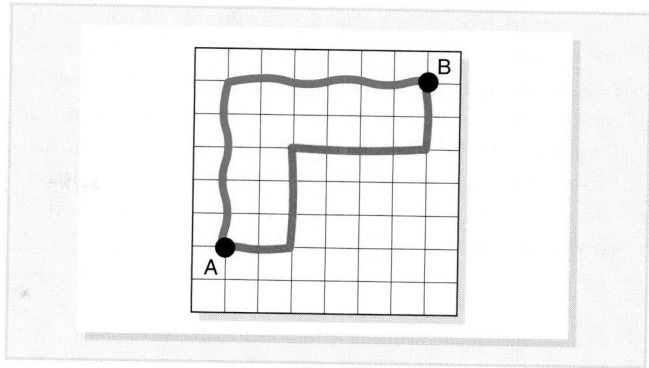

Figure 20.36 Different paths from A to B.

integers so that the full plane can be represented. The activities here suggest how coordinates can be used to examine transformations.

Activity 20.24

Coordinate Slides

Students will need a sheet of centimetre grid paper on which to draw two coordinate axes near the left and bottom edges. Have them plot and connect about five or six points on the grid to form a small shape (see Figure 20.37). If you direct them to use only coordinates between 5 and 12, the figure will be reasonably small and near the centre of the paper. Next, students make a new shape by adding 6 to each of the first coordinates (called the *x*-coordinates) of their shape, leaving the second coordinates the same. That is, for the point (5, 10) a new point (11, 10) is plotted. When new points for each point in the figure have been plotted, these are connected as before. This new figure should be congruent to the original and translated to the right. Students then create a third figure by adding 9 to each second coordinate of the original.

With these two slides as initial guidance, stop and discuss what should be done to the coordinates to move the figure along a diagonal line up and to the right. Have students make and test their conjectures. Figure 20.37 shows a slide that was created by adding 6 to all the first coordinates and adding 9 to all the second coordinates. As long as all first coordinates are changed by the same amount, the figure will be translated without distortion. Challenge students to figure out how to change the coordinates to make the figure slide down and to the left. (Subtract from the coordinates instead of add.) Students' papers should show their original shape and four copies, each in a different location on the grid.

Help students summarize what they've learned: What does adding (or subtracting) a number from the first coordinates cause? What if the number is added or subtracted from the second coordinates? From both coordinates? Have students draw lines connecting corresponding points in the original figure with one of those where both coordinates were changed. What do they notice? (The lines are parallel and the same length.) Pick any two of the five shapes in the final drawing. How can you begin with one of the shapes and change the coordinates to get to the other?

In "Coordinate Slides" the figure did not twist, turn, flip over, or change size or shape. The shape "slid" along the path that matched the lines between the corresponding points. Reflections can be explored on a coordinate grid just as easily as translations. At this beginning level, it is advisable to restrict the lines of reflection to the *x*-axis or *y*-axis, as in the following activity.

Activity 20.25

Coordinate Reflections

Have students draw a five-sided shape, using grid points for vertices, in the first quadrant on coordinate grid paper. Label the figure **ABCDE** and call it **Figure 1**. Use the *y*-axis as a line of symmetry and draw the reflection of the shape in the second quadrant. Call it **Figure 2** (for second quadrant) and label the reflection points **A'B'C'D'E**. Now use the *x*-axis as the line of symmetry. Reflect both Figure 2 and Figure 1 into the third and fourth quadrants, respectively. Call these **Figures 3** and **4**. Label the points of these figures with double and triple primes (**A″** and **A‴**, and so on). Write in the coordinates for each vertex of all four figures.

- How is Figure 3 related to Figure 4? How else could you have gotten Figure 3? How else could you have found Figure 4?
- How are the coordinates of Figure 1 related to its image across the *y*-axis, Figure 2? What can you say about the coordinates of Figure 4?
- Make a conjecture about the coordinates of a shape reflected across the *y*-axis and a different conjecture about the coordinates of a shape reflected across the *x*-axis.
- Draw lines from the vertices of Figure 1 to the corresponding vertices of Figure 2. What can you say about these lines? How is the *y*-axis related to each of these lines?

Refer to Figure 20.38 to answer these questions.

Students who have done the preceding activities should have a general way to describe translations and reflections across an axis, all in terms of coordinates. Rotations can also be explored with the use of coordinates. In the following

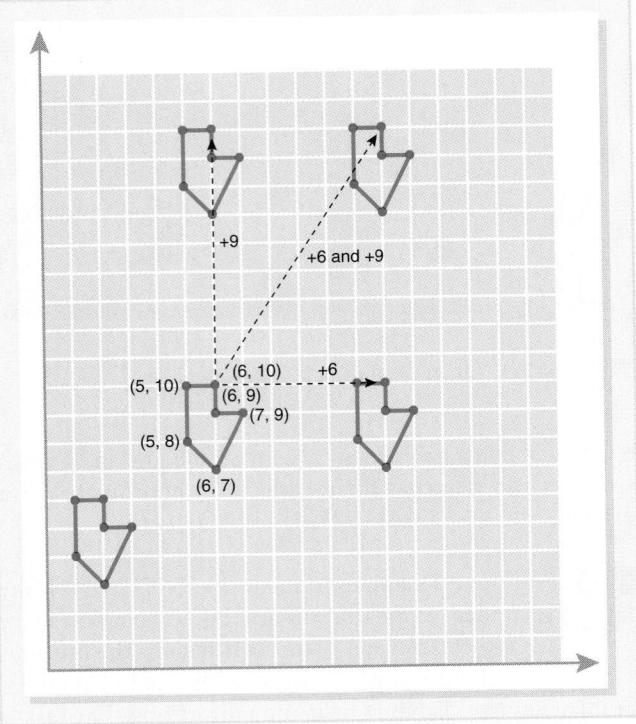

Figure 20.37 Begin with a simple shape and record the coordinates. By adding or subtracting from the coordinates, new shapes are found that are translations (slides) of the original.

activity, multiplying by a constant is a transformation that is not a rigid motion.

Activity 20.26

Coordinate Dilations

Students begin with a four-sided shape in the first quadrant. They then make a list of the coordinates, and make a new set of coordinates by multiplying each of the original coordinates by 2. They plot the resulting shape. What is the result? Now have students multiply each of the original coordinates by $\frac{1}{2}$ and plot that shape. What is the result? Next, students draw a line from the origin to a vertex of the largest shape on their paper. Repeat for one or two additional vertices and ask for observations. (An example is shown in Figure 20.39.)

Pause and Reflect

How do the lengths of sides and the areas of the shapes compare when the coordinates are multiplied by 2? What if they are multiplied by 3 or by $\frac{1}{2}$?

When the coordinates of a shape are multiplied as in the last activity, each by the same factor, the shape either

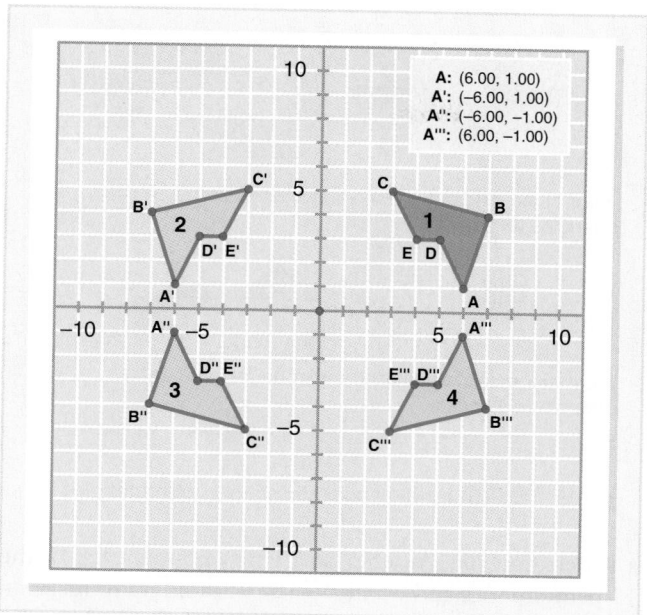

Figure 20.38 Exploring reflections on a coordinate grid.

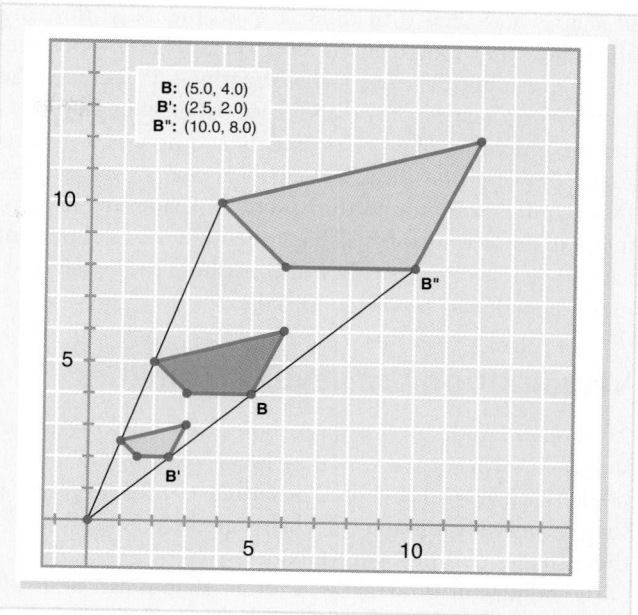

Figure 20.39 Dilations with coordinates.

gets larger or smaller. The size is changed but not the shape. The new shape is similar to the old shape. This is called a *dilation*, a transformation that is *not* rigid because the shape changes.

Your students may enjoy exploring this phenomenon a bit further. If they start with a line drawing of a simple face, boat, or some other shape drawn with straight lines connecting vertices, they will create an interesting effect by multiplying just the first coordinates, just the second coordinates, or using a different factor for each. When only the second coordinate is multiplied, the vertical dimensions alone are dilated, so the figure is proportionately stretched (or shrunk) in a vertical manner. Students can explore this process to distort shapes in various ways.

It is impressive to see how an arithmetic operation can control a figure. Imagine being able to control slides, flips, turns, and dilations, not just in the plane but also for three-dimensional figures. The process is identical to computer animation techniques.

Location for Level-2 Thinkers

On the surface, there may not be a clear distinction between coordinate activities for level 1 and those for level 2. However, the move to level-2 thinking is highlighted by the infusion of logical reasoning into the activities.

Coordinate Transformations Revisited   It is quite reasonable that a class has both level-1 and level-2 thinkers or at least students who are ready to move on to logical reasoning. While exploring the transformation activities in the last section, students who are ready might be challenged

with questions that are a bit more than simple explorations, such as the following:

- How should the coordinates be changed to cause a reflection if the line of reflection is not the *y*-axis but is parallel to it?
- Can you discover a single rule for coordinates that would cause a reflection across one of the axes followed by a rotation of a quarter turn? Is that rule the same for the reverse order—a quarter turn followed by a reflection?
- If two successive slides are made with coordinates and you know what numbers were added or subtracted, what number should be added or subtracted to get the figure there in only one move?
- What do you think will happen if, in a dilation, different factors are used for different coordinates?

   Once students begin to explore questions of this type, they may well come up with their own questions and explorations. Dynamic geometry software includes an optional coordinate grid. If drawings are made with the points "snapped" to the grid, coordinate transformations can be explored much more easily. ◆

Learning About Visualization

Visualization might be called "geometry done with the mind's eye." It involves being able to create mental images of shapes and then turn them around mentally, thinking about how they look from different perspectives—predicting the results of various transformations. It includes the mental coordination of two and three dimensions—predicting the unfolding of a box or understanding a two-dimensional drawing of a three-dimensional shape. Any activity that requires students to think about a shape mentally, to manipulate or transform a shape mentally, or to represent a shape as it is seen visually will contribute to the development of students' visualization skills.

Visualization for Level-0 Thinkers

At level 0, students are quite bound to thinking about shapes in terms of the way they look. Visualization activities at this level will have students using a variety of physical shapes and drawings and will challenge them to think about these shapes in different orientations.

Finding out how many different shapes can be made with a given number of simple tiles demands that students mentally flip and turn shapes in their minds and find ways to decide if they have found them all. This is the focus of the next activity.

Activity 20.27

Pentominoes

A pentomino is a shape formed by joining five squares as if cut from one square grid. Each square must have at least one side in common with another. Provide students with five square tiles and a sheet of square grid paper for recording. Challenge them to see how many different pentomino shapes they can find. (Each square in a shape can touch adjacent squares on one side only.) Shapes that are flips or turns of other shapes are not considered different. Do not tell students how many pentomino shapes there are. Good discussions will come from deciding if some shapes are really different and if all shapes have been found.

Once students have decided that there are just 12 pentominoes (revisit Figure 20.33 on page 442), the 12 pieces can then be used in a variety of activities. Glue the grids with the children's pentominoes onto tag-board, and let them cut out the 12 shapes.

It is also fun to explore the number of shapes that can be made from six equilateral triangles or from four 45-degree right triangles (halves of squares), as shown in Figure 20.40. With the right triangles, sides that touch must be the same length. How many of each of these "ominoes" do you think there are?

A lot of activities can be done with pentominoes. For example, try to fit all 12 pieces into a 6 × 10 or a 5 × 12 rectangle. Also, each of the 12 shapes can be used as

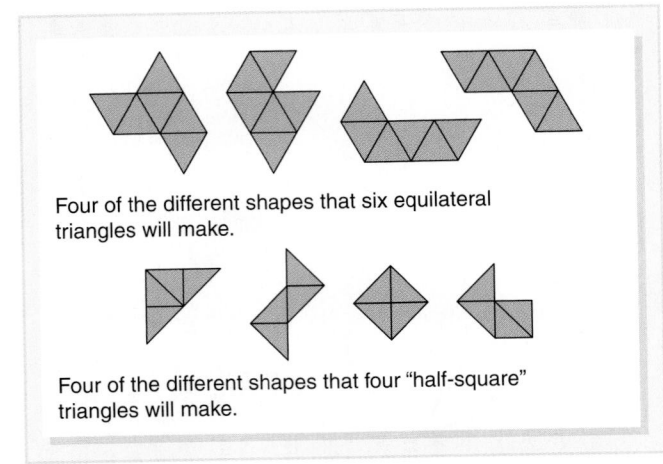

Four of the different shapes that six equilateral triangles will make.

Four of the different shapes that four "half-square" triangles will make.

Figure 20.40 Finding possible shapes with triangles.

a tessellation tile. Another task is to examine each of the 12 pentominoes and decide which will fold up to make an open box. For those that are "box makers," which square is the bottom?

Another aspect of visualization for young children is to be able to think about solid shapes in terms of their faces or sides. For these activities you will need to make "face cards" by tracing around the different faces of a shape, either making all faces on one card or using a set of separate cards with one face per card (see Figure 20.41).

Activity 20.28

Face Matching

There are two versions of the task: Given a face card, find the corresponding solid, or given a solid, find the face card. With a collection of single-face cards, students can select the cards that go with a particular solid. For another variation, stack all of the single-face cards for one solid face down. Turn them up one at a time as clues to finding the solid.

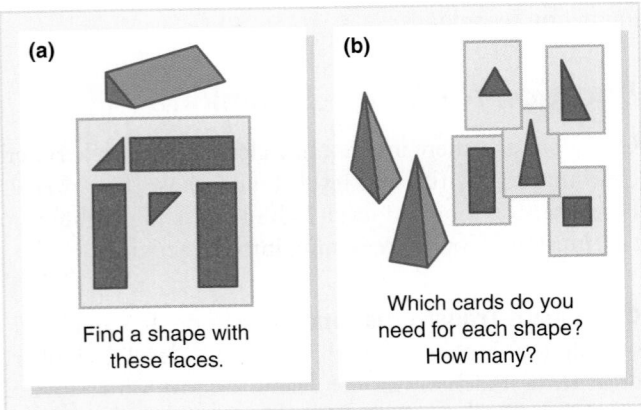

(a) Find a shape with these faces.

(b) Which cards do you need for each shape? How many?

Figure 20.41 Matching face cards with solid shapes.

The following activity has been adapted from NCTM's *Principles and Standards* book and is found in the pre-K–2 section on geometry (NCTM, 2000, p. 101).

Activity 20.29

Quick Images

Draw some simple sketches on transparencies so that they can be shown one figure at a time to the students. They should be drawings that students can easily reproduce. Some examples are shown in Figure 20.42. Display one of the sketches on the overhead projector for about 5 seconds. Then have students attempt to reproduce the sketch on their own paper. Show the same sketch again for a few seconds and allow students to modify their drawings. Repeat with additional sketches.

In your discussions with students, ask them to tell how they thought about the figure or to describe it in words that helped them remember what they saw. As students learn to describe orally what they see, their visual memory will improve.

In the last activity, visual memory as well as the ability to think about positions of lines and features of the figure are important.

Visualization for Level-1 Thinkers

In identifying a visualization task as either level 0 or level 1, one consideration is the degree of attention that must be given to the particular properties of shapes. The activities in this section are almost certainly too difficult for students at level 0.

One of the main goals of the visualization strand of the Geometry Standard is to be able to identify and draw two-dimensional images of three-dimensional figures and to build three-dimensional figures from two-dimensional images. Activities aimed at this goal often involve drawings of small "buildings" made of centimetre cubes.

Activity 20.30

Viewpoints

In the first version, students begin with a building and draw the direct views of the left, right, front, and back of the building. In Figure 20.43, the building plan shows a top view of the building and the number of blocks in each position. After students construct a building from a plan like this, their task is to draw the direct views of the front, right, left, and back, as shown in the figure. In the reverse versions of the task, students are given a right and front view. The task is to construct the building that has those views. To record their solution, they draw a building plan (top view with numbers).

Notice that front and back direct views are symmetrical, as are the left and right views. That is why only one of each is given in the second part of the activity.

In "Viewpoints," students made "buildings" out of wooden cubes (interlocking cubes will also work) and coordinated these with direct views of the sides and top. For those students who require an added challenge, a significantly more demanding activity is to draw perspective views of these buildings or to match perspective drawings with a building. Isometric dot grids (Blackline Masters 38 and 39) are used for the drawings. The next activity provides a glimpse of this form of visualization activity.

For those students who are experiencing difficulty with the "Viewpoints" activity, have them work with less complex structures such as those that resemble rectangular prisms.

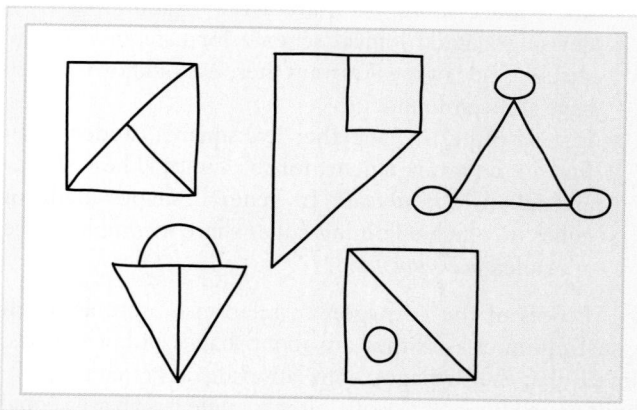

Figure 20.42 Examples of designs to use in the "Quick Images" activity.

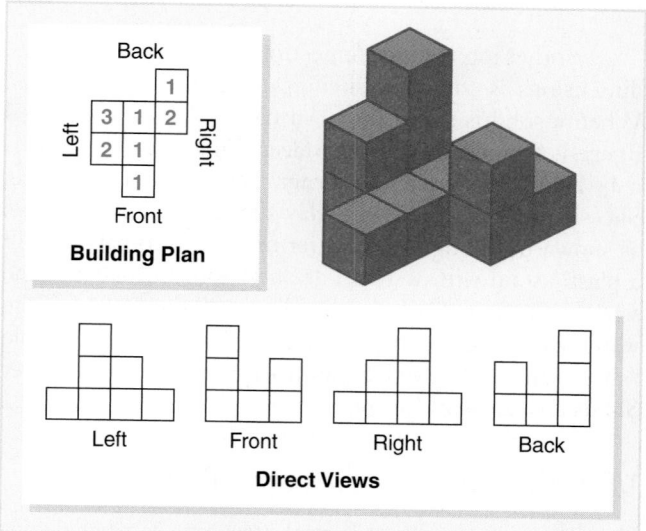

Figure 20.43 "Viewpoints" task.

Activity 20.31

Perspective Drawings

In the first version, students begin with a perspective drawing of a building. The assumption is that there are no hidden blocks. From the drawing the students construct the actual building with their blocks. To record the result, they draw a building plan indicating the number of blocks in each position.

In the second version, students are given either a plan or the five direct views (see Figure 20.44). They construct the building accordingly and draw two or more perspectives of it. There are four possible perspectives from above the table: the front left and right, and the back left and right. It is useful to build the building on a sheet of paper with the words "front," "back," "left," and "right" written on the edges to keep from getting different viewpoints confused.

Accommodation

For students who are experiencing difficulty with this activity, have them work with more regular structures, as suggested in Activity 21.30.

An amazing computer tool for drawing two- and three-dimensional views of block buildings is the "Isometric Drawing Tool," available on the *Illuminations* Web site (http://illuminations.nctm.org/ActivityDetail.aspx?ID=125). This applet requires only mouse clicks to draw either whole cubes, any single face of a cube, or just lines. The drawings, however, are actually "buildings" and can be viewed as three-dimensional objects. They can be rotated in space so that they can be seen from any vantage. Prepared investigations are informative and also lead students through the features of the tool. ◆

Another interesting connection between two and three dimensions is found in slicing solids in different ways. When a solid is sliced into two parts, a two-dimensional figure is formed on the slice faces. Figure 20.45 shows a cube being sliced off at the corner, leaving a triangular face. Slices can be explored with clay sliced with a piano wire, as shown in the figure. A niftier method is to partially fill a plastic solid with water. The surface of the water is the same as the face of a slice coinciding with the surface of the water. By tilting the shape in different ways, every possible "slice" can be observed. Small plastic solids such as Power Solids are excellent for this.

Visualization for Level-2 Thinkers

Once again, we see that logical reasoning is what distinguishes activities for level-2 thinkers from those for level 1.

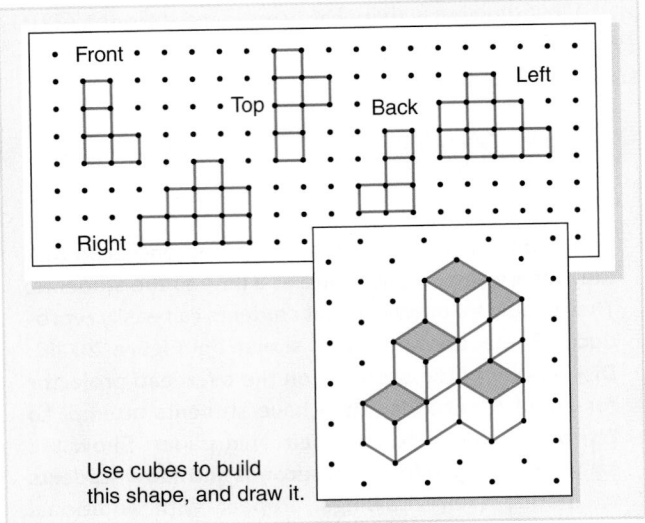

Use cubes to build this shape, and draw it.

Figure 20.44 Block "buildings" on isometric grids.

It is important to note, however, that visualization is an area of geometry where the distinction is not particularly sharp. The activities described for level 1 can easily be modified to challenge level-2 thinkers. Likewise, the activities in this section will help to push level-1 students forward in their thinking.

Connecting Earlier Activities to Level-2 Visualization Students who are ready can be challenged to make predictions about the types of slices that are possible. For example, given a particular solid, they might go through a list of the types of triangles and quadrilaterals, prior to testing, as previously described, with water. They then decide which can be made and which are not possible. For those they think are impossible, they should offer a reason for their hypothesis.

The following are extensions of pentomino activities that are appropriate visualization tasks for level 2:

- How many *hexominoes* are there? A hexomino is made of six squares following the same rule as for pentominoes. Since there are quite a few hexominoes (35), devising a good logical scheme for categorizing the shapes is one of the few ways there are of knowing they have all been found.
- Instead of putting together five squares, students can find all the arrangements for five cubes. These shapes are called *pentominoids*. In general, shapes made of cubes in which adjoining cubes share a complete face are called *polyominoids*.

Proofs of the Pythagorean relationship are as much visualization tasks as they are about shapes and properties. Recall that the Pythagorean relationship says that a square built on the hypotenuse of a right triangle has an area equal to the sum of the areas of the squares built on the two legs. Figure 20.46 can be used to devise a proof for this relation-

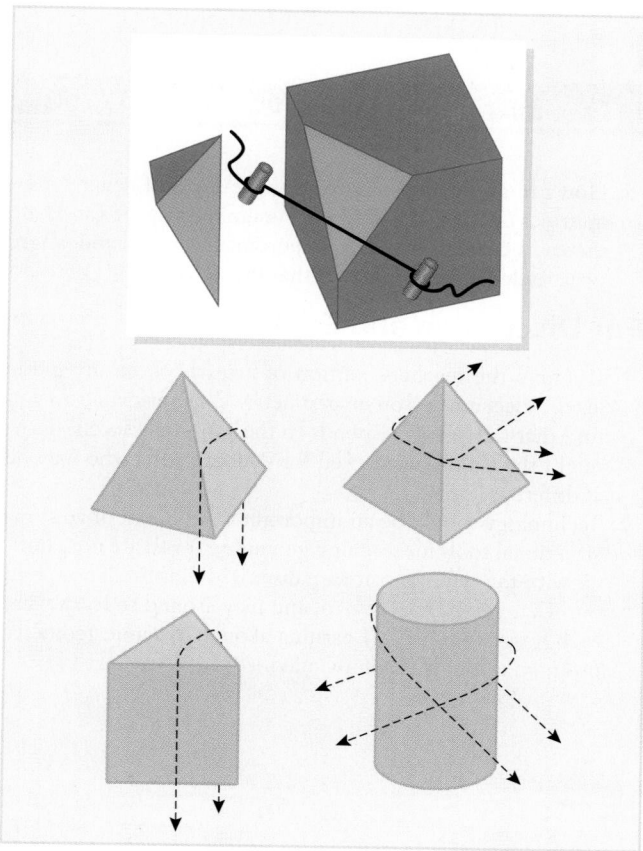

Figure 20.45 Cutting a clay model with a piano wire.

ship. As a visualization task, students may or may not be given any hints to help discover this proof. Once found, they can also explain how the proof will work for any right triangle, not just the one on which this figure is based.

The Platonic Solids   A *polyhedron* is a three-dimensional shape with polygons for all faces. Among the various polyhedra, the Platonic solids are especially interesting. *Platonic solids* is the name given to the set of completely regular polyhedra. "Completely regular" means that each face is a regular polygon and every vertex has exactly the same number of faces joining at that point. An interesting visualization task appropriate for this level is to find and describe all of the Platonic solids.

Activity **20.32**

Search for the Platonic Solids

Provide students with a supply of equilateral triangles, squares, regular pentagons, and regular hexagons. These can be cut from tag-board, or plastic sets for building solids (e.g., *Polydron* or *Geofix*) can be used. Explain what a completely regular solid is. The task is to find as many different completely regular solids as possible.

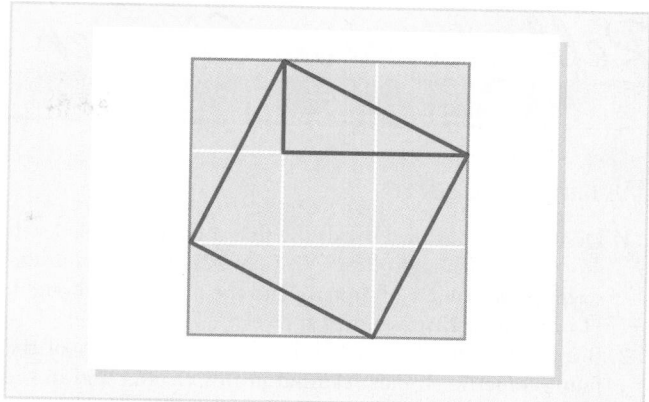

Figure 20.46 Figure for proving the Pythagorean relationship.

Some students, particularly those with special needs, may need additional structure. Therefore, you might suggest a systematic approach as follows. Since the smallest number of sides a face can have is three, begin with triangles, then squares, then pentagons, and so on. Furthermore, since every vertex must have the same number of faces, try three faces at a point, then four, and so on. (Clearly, it is impossible to have only two faces at a point.)

With this plan, students will find that for triangles they can have three, four, or five triangles coming to a point. For each of these, they can begin with a "tent" of triangles then add more triangles so that each vertex has the same number. With three at a point you get a four-sided solid called a *tetrahedron* (in Greek, *tetra* = four). With four at each point you get an eight-sided solid called an *octahedron* (*octa* = eight). It is really exciting to build the solid with five triangles at each point. It will have 20 sides and is called an *icosahedron* (*icosa* = twenty).

In a similar manner, students will find that there is only one solid made of squares—three at each point and six in all—a *hexahedron* (*hex* = six), also called a cube. And there is only one solid with pentagons, three at each point, 12 in all. This is called a *dodecahedron* (*dodeca* = twelve).

ll ─────────────── *Pause and Reflect*

Why are there no regular polyhedra with six or more triangles or four or more squares? Why are there no regular polyhedra made with hexagons or with polygons with more than six sides? The best way to answer these questions is to experiment with the polygons and explain the answers in your own words. Students should do the same.

A fantastic skeletal icosahedron can be built out of the newspaper rods described earlier (see Figure 20.11, page 427). Since five triangles converge at each point, there are also five edges at each point. Simply work at bringing five rods to each vertex and remember that each face is a triangle. This icosahedron will be about 1 metre across and will be amazingly sturdy.

Reflections on Chapter 20

Writing to Learn

1. Describe in your own words the first three van Hiele levels of geometric thought (levels 0, 1, and 2). Note in your description the object of thought and the product of thought. How would activities aimed at levels 0, 1, and 2 differ?
2. Briefly describe the nature of the content in each of the four geometric strands featured in this chapter and in the *Standards:* Shapes and Properties, Location, Transformations, and Visualization.
3. What can you do when the students in your classroom are at different van Hiele levels of thought?
4. Find one of the suggested applets for geometry or an example of geometry software and explain how it can be used. What are the advantages of using the computer in geometry instead of the corresponding hands-on materials or drawings?

5. How can a teacher assess students in terms of general geometric growth or spatial sense? Assuming that the van Hiele theory is correct, why is it important to understand where your students are in terms of that theory?

For Discussion and Exploration

1. Examine the teacher's edition of a textbook at any grade level. Select any lesson on geometry. What evidence do you find that the lesson responds to the van Hiele levels? How might the lesson be adapted for your students who may be at different levels?
2. Technology should be an important component of your instructional tools for teaching geometry. If you are not familiar with the types of software discussed in this chapter, find out what you have access to, and play around to learn what each program can do. (Learning about a dynamic geometry program is highly recommended.)

Resources for Chapter 20

Literature Connections

A Circle Is Not a Valentine *Zimmerman, 1990*

This picture book, by Canadian author Zimmerman, offers a simple, funny introduction to four basic shapes: square, circle, triangle, and valentine heart. Preschool students can paint, label, and sort the four shapes as well as explore the concept of symmetry. It is a perfect book for a Valentine's Day theme.

Circles: Shapes in Mathematics, Science and Nature *Ross, 1992*

This book, also by a Canadian author, is appropriate for grades 4–8. Humorous text and excellent illustrations are employed to discuss circles. The book offers just about everything there is to know about circles, from pi to discs, from cones to spheres, as Ross takes us on a whirlwind tour around the world and through history.

Selina and the Bear Paw Quilt *Smucker, 1996*

This enchanting story, by another Canadian author, of a grandparent's love for her grandchild will captivate young

children's attention. The quilt plays a central role in this story. At the same time, it can serve as a jumping off point for working with two-dimensional geometric figures. A detailed lesson plan on how to connect this book with geometry can be found at www.saskschools.ca/~mathnews/grkto2/bearquilt.html.

The Greedy Triangle *Burns, 1995*

This delightful book starts off with the story of a triangle that is very busy being a sail or musical instrument, or fitting into the crook of someone's arm when standing with hand on hip. It isn't long before he becomes bored and travels to the local shapeshifter for a change. Adding a new side and angle and becoming a quadrilateral gives the triangle new things to try as he fits into different four-sided figures in the environment. The greedy triangle goes through several other shape-shifts. This book links well with activities at level 0 and level 1. Using a metre-long loop of yarn for every pair of students, have students follow and discuss events in the book by creating appropriate shapes with the loop (holding it in the air between their hands). First they can explore the different triangles that were made and eventually they can investigate properties as they shift from one shape to the next.

Color Farm *Ehlert, 1990*

Color Zoo *Ehlert, 1998*

These visually motivating books can engage young children in thinking about shapes. Using cut-out overlays of circles, rectangles, ovals triangles, and other familiar shapes, images of either farm or zoo animals are created The reader turns the page to remove a shape, transforming the image into a new animal. Because this book reinforces shapes, animals, and colours, it is a good vocabulary development book to engage English language learners and their families.

Cubes, Cones, Cylinders and Spheres
Hoban, 2000

Shapes, Shapes, Shapes *Hoban, 1996*

So Many Circles, So Many Squares *Hoban, 1998*

These books without words are a collection of vivid photographs on a geometric theme. Each one can engage students of all ages into thinking about and locating shapes in the environment. It is easy to see how students can use digital cameras to create their own Hoban-like books that invite readers to seek and identify two- and three-dimensional shapes in the world around them. Student-made books are great for children to take home to their families, for students in upper grades to make for younger children, or are great to add to the collection in the school classroom or library.

Recommendations for Further Reading

Articles

Glass, B. (2004). Transformations and technology: What path to follow? *Mathematics Teaching in the Middle School, 9* (7), 393–397.

Glass explores compositions of transformations with his middle-school students. Part of their discourse revolves around this question: Is a composition of two or more transformations the same as the single transformation that will accomplish the same thing? For those exploring transformations at the upper grades, this is a useful article.

Koester, B. A. (2003). Prisms and pyramids: Constructing three-dimensional models to build understanding. *Teaching Children Mathematics, 9* (8), 436–442.

Koester's activities and explorations with grade 3–5 students involves building models using straws and pipe cleaners. The activities described involve classification and definitions of shapes and also Euler's formula relating faces, vertices, and edges.

Renne, C. G. (2004). Is a rectangle a square? Developing mathematical vocabulary and conceptual understanding. *Teaching Children Mathematics, 10* (5), 258–263.

The voices of children in this article are clear examples of the difficulty that students at level-1 reasoning have in attempting to draw logical conclusions about geometric properties and relationships.

Books

Findell, C. R., Small, M., Cavanagh, M., Dacey, L., Greenes, C. E., & Sheffield, L. J. (2001). *Navigating through geometry in prekindergarten–grade 2.* Reston, VA: NCTM.

Gavin, M. K., Sinelli, A. M., & St. Marie, J. (2001). *Navigating through geometry in grades 3–5.* Reston, VA: NCTM.

Pugalee, D. K., Frykholm, J., Johnson, A., Slovin, H., Malloy, C., & Preston, R. (2002). *Navigating through geometry in grades 6–8.* Reston, VA: NCTM.

Each of these three excellent books from the Navigations Series provides both a perspective on the geometry standard and also a collection of excellent activities appropriate for the grade band of the book

Online Resources

Suggested Applets and Web Links

Cube Nets

http://illuminations.nctm.org/tools/tool_detail.aspx?id=84

This site provides a great visualization challenge! It shows arrangements of squares. The challenge is to find the 11 arrangements that will fold into a cube.

Cutting Corners

http://illuminations.nctm.org/tools/CutTool/CutTool.asp

A cutting tool allows any one of three simple shapes to be sliced into parts along any straight line. Shapes can be rearranged, rotated, and flipped.

Exploring the Pythagorean Theorem

www.learnalberta.ca/content/mejhm/html/video_interactives/pythagoras/pythagorasSmall.html

There are two parts to the site: (1) a video that illustrates real-life application of the Pythagorean Theorem, and (2) an interactive part where students have a chance to construct right triangles of various sizes to explore calculations of the Pythagorean Theorem.

Exploring Transformations

www.learnalberta.ca http://www.learnalberta.ca/content/mejhm/html/video_interactives/transformations/transformationsSmall.html

There are two parts to the site: (1) a video that illustrates real-life places where transformations can be found, and (2) an interactive part where students have a chance to explore and work with transformations.

Geoboards

http://nlvm.usu.edu/en/nav/category_g_2_t_3.htm

The NLVM library has four geoboards. The first measures areas and perimeters. The circular board has pins in a circular arrangement. The isometric board has pins in a triangular arrangement (like isometric dot paper). The coordinate board shows coordinates for each peg when the cursor is on it. It measures the slope and distance between two points joined by a band and then the perimeter and area of banded shapes.

GeoGebra

www.geogebra.org/cms

This is free, downloadable dynamic geometry software that emphasizes geometry and algebra. Like *Geometer's Sketchpad*, you can construct with points, segments, and lines.

Maze Game

www.shodor.org/interactivate/activities/coords/index.html

The maze game provides practice with coordinates. The user plots points to guide a robot through a mine field.

Mirror Tool

http://illuminations.nctm.org/ActivityDetail.aspx?ID=24

A nice tool for early investigations of mirror or line symmetry.

Space Blocks

http://nlvm.usu.edu/en/nav/frames_asid_195_g_3_t_3. html?open=activities

This applet allows the user to create "buildings" made of cubic blocks rather easily. Each new block snaps to a block in the ongoing construction.

Tangrams

http://nlvm.usu.edu/en/nav/frames_asid_292_g_3_t_1.html

These virtual tangrams can be manipulated freely. Plus, there are 14 puzzle shapes to fill in with all 7 tangrams.

Transformations in the Coordinate Plane

http://argyll.epsb.ca/jreed/math7/strand3/3301.htm

This site has numerous applets on translations, reflections, rotations, and plotting points in the coordinate plane.

Visualizing Transformations

http://standards.nctm.org/document/eexamples/chap6/6. 4/index.htm

This four-part applet provides an excellent exploration of the three rigid-motion transformations, including composition of two transformations.

---

myeducationlab *will help you improve your understanding of the concepts taught in this textbook and in your course. This online tool includes videos of real classroom experiences, sample lesson plans, simulations, case studies, and links to important educational and teaching Web sites that will help you make the transition from student to teacher. As you study in your course and with this textbook, please follow along in* **MyEducationLab**. *Use it! Explore it! And improve your knowledge and your grade!*

Chapter 21
Developing Concepts of Data Analysis

Graphs and statistics bombard the public in areas such as advertising, opinion polls, reliability estimates, population trends, health risks, and progress of students in schools. We hear that the average amount of rainfall this summer is more than it was last summer; that the average Canadian household consists of 2.6 people. We can read on Statistics Canada Web site (www.statcan.gc.ca) that in 2003, Canadian households spent just over $3.0 billion shopping on the Internet on everything from airplane tickets to books. Knowing this statistical information should raise a variety of questions such as, "How were these data gathered?" "What was the purpose?" "What does it mean to have an average of 2.6 people per household?" "How many households does $3.0 billion represent?"

Statistical literacy is critical to understanding the world around us. To deal with this information, students in pre-K–8 should have meaningful experiences with the basic concepts of data analysis throughout their school years. At the pre-K–3 level, students can begin this understanding by learning how data can be categorized and displayed in various graph forms. By the time students are in grade 5, they should have had many experiences collecting and organizing sets of data as well as representing data in frequency tables, bar graphs, line plots, and picture graphs. As they mature in understanding, they should be introduced to new data representations, such as box-and-whisker plots, scatter plots, and stem-and-leaf plots. Students should also study measures of central tendency—for example, median and mean (NCTM, 2006; Schielack & Seeley, 2007).

Big Ideas

1. Doing statistics involves a four-step process: formulating questions, collecting data, analyzing data, and interpreting results.

2. Data are gathered and organized in order to answer questions about the populations from which the data come. With data from only a sample of the population, inferences are made about the population.

3. Different types of graphs and other ways of organizing data provide different information about the data; hence, the population from which the data were taken. The choice of graphical representation can affect how well the data are understood.

4. Measures that describe data with numbers are called *statistics*. Data can be organized in various graph forms to visually convey information. The use of a particular graph or statistic can mediate what the data tell about the population.

5. Both graphs and statistics can provide a sense of the shape of the data, including how spread out or how clustered they are. Having a sense of the shape of data is like having a big picture of the data rather than a collection of numbers.

Mathematics Content Connections

Statistics involves using data in the form of numbers and graphs to describe our world. Certainly, there are connections to the numerical areas of the curriculum. However, the connection to algebra is perhaps one of the most important mathematical connections.

- **Number Sense** (Chapter 8): Young children create graphs of class data (such as "What colour socks?" or "How many buttons?") and use the graphs to talk about quantity.

- **Algebra** (Chapter 14): Algebra is used to analyze and describe relationships. Whenever data are gathered on two related variables (e.g., height and arm span, age and growth), algebra can be used to describe the relationship between the variables. The resulting relationship can then be used to predict outcomes for which no data have yet been gathered. The better that the data are approximated by the algebraic relationship or function, the more predictive value the function has.

- **Fractions, Decimal Numbers, and Percents** (Chapters 15 and 17): Fractions, decimals, and percents are used to describe data.

- **Proportional Reasoning** (Chapter 18): Statistical reasoning is proportional reasoning. When a population is sampled (a subset selected), that sample is assumed to be proportional to the larger population.

- **Measurement** (Chapter 19): Much of the real-world data that are gathered consist of measurements. Pedagogically, measurement can be interwoven with data analysis as students make measurements to answer questions and create data to be analyzed.

What Does It Mean to Do Statistics?

Doing statistics is a different process from doing mathematics, a notion that has recently received much attention by standards documents and research (Burrill & Elliott, 2006; Franklin et al., 2005; Shaugnessy, 2003):

> *Mathematics is about numbers and their operations, generalizations and abstractions, spatial configurations and their measurement, transformations and abstractions .... Statistics is also about numbers—but numbers in context. These contexts are called data (Schaeffer, 2006).*

In statistics, the context is essential to analyzing and interpreting the data. Looking at the spread or shape of data and considering the meaning of the unusual data points (outliers) are determined based on the context.

The Shape of Data

A major concept in data analysis is referred to as the *shape of data:* a sense of how data are spread out or grouped, what characteristics of the data set, as a whole, can be described, and what the data tell us in a global way about the population from which they are taken.

There is no single technique that will tell us what the shape of the data is. Across the K–8 curriculum, students begin looking at the shape of data by looking at various graphs. Different graphing techniques or types of graphs can provide a different snapshot of the data as a whole. For example, bar graphs and circle graphs (percentage graphs) each show how the data cluster in different categories. The circle graph focuses more on the relative values of this clustering, whereas the bar graph adds a dimension of quantity. The choice of which categories and how many to use in these graphs will result in different pictures of the shape of the data.

Part of understanding the shape of data is being aware of how spread out or clustered the data are. In the early grades, this can be discussed informally by looking at almost any graph.

For numerical data, there are statistics that tell us how data are spread. The simplest of these is the *range*. Averages (the *mean* and the *median*) tell us where the "centre" of the data is. In secondary school, students will learn about the standard deviation statistic, which is a measure of spread. At the upper elementary school level, a simple graphical technique called the *box-and-whisker plot* is designed to give us visual information about the spread of data.

Process of Doing Statistics

To engage students meaningfully in learning and doing statistics, they should be involved in the following four-step process: formulating questions, collecting data, analyzing data, and interpreting results.

Formulating Questions

Statistics is about more than making graphs and analyzing data. It includes both asking and answering questions about our world. To answer the questions, data must be gathered and organized then analyzed. The first goal in the Data Analysis and Probability standard of *Principles and Standards* says that students should "formulate questions that can be addressed with data and collect, organize, and display relevant data to answer them" (NCTM, 2000, p. 48). Notice that data collection should be for a purpose, to answer a question, just as in the real world. Then the analysis of data actually adds information about some aspect of our world. This is what political pollsters, advertising agencies, market researchers, census takers, wildlife managers, medical researchers, and hosts of others do: gather data to answer questions.

Students should be given opportunities to generate their own questions, decide on appropriate data to help answer these questions, and determine methods of collecting the data. For example, in a grade 2 class, studied by Susan Jo Russell, a student wanted to know how many houses were on her street (Russell, 2006). It might be that a teacher asks, "How many sisters or brothers do you have?" Whether the question is teacher or student initiated, students should engage in conversations about how well defined a question is. In the house example, students wondered whether they should include houses that weren't finished yet or whether apartments counted. In the second case, there could be a need, for example, to discuss half-siblings.

When students formulate the questions they want to ask, the data they gather become more meaningful. How they organize the data and the techniques for analyzing them have a purpose.

Ideas for Questions

Often the need to gather data will come from the class naturally in the course of discussion or from questions arising in other content areas. Science, of course, is full of measurements and thus abounds in data requiring analysis. Social studies is also full of opportunities to pose questions requiring data analysis. The next few sections suggest some additional ideas.

Classroom Questions Students often want to learn about themselves, their families and pets, measures such as arm span or time to get to school, their likes and dislikes, and so on. The easiest questions to deal with are those that can be answered by each class member contributing one piece of data. Here are a few ideas:

- *Favourites:* TV shows, games, movies, ice cream, video games, sports teams, music CDs. (When there are a lot of possibilities, suggest that students restrict the number of choices.)
- *Numbers:* Number of pets, sisters, or brothers; hours watching TV or hours of sleep; birthdays (month or day of month); bedtime; time spent on the computer.
- *Measures:* Height, arm span, area of foot, long-jump distance, shadow length, seconds to run around the track, minutes spent on the bus.

Beyond One Classroom The questions in the previous section are designed for students to contribute data about themselves. These questions can be expanded by asking, "How would this compare to data from another class?" Comparison questions are a good way to focus on the data they have collected and the variability within the data (Russell, 2006). As children get older, they can begin to think about various populations and differences among them. For example, how are grade 5 students similar to or different from grade 8 students? Students might examine questions related to adults versus children or categories of animals. In addition, students an ask questions about things beyond the classroom. Discussions about communities provide a good way to integrate social studies and mathematics.

The newspaper suggests all sorts of data-related questions. For example, how many full-page ads occur on different days of the week? What types of stories are on the front page? Which comics are really for kids and which are not?

Science is another area where questions can be asked and data gathered. For example, what is the width of an oak leaf that falls to the ground? How many times do different types of balls bounce when each is dropped from the same height? How many days does it take for different types of bean, squash, and pea seeds to germinate when kept in moist paper towels?

Data Collection

Gathering data is not easy for students, especially young students. In a grade 1 class, a teacher asked students to gather data on "Are you 6?" Upon receiving the prompt, 18 eager students began asking others in the class if they were 6 and tallying the yes and no responses. The problem? They had no idea whom they had asked more than once or whom they had not asked at all. This situation provided an excellent entry into a discussion about how data must be gathered. Carolyn Cook, a kindergarten teacher, asked her students to help think of an organized manner to gather the data from their classmates on favourite ice cream flavours. These students decided a class list (see Figure 21.1) would allow them to keep track (Cook, 2008).

Gathering data must also take into consideration variability. Young children can understand that asking a group of grade 1 students what their favourite TV show is will produce different answers than if they asked the same questions of grade 5 students. For older students, planning data collection should include gathering data from more than one classroom in order to achieve a more representative sample.

Using Existing Data Sources

Data do not have to be collected by survey. Data abound in various places such as the following print sources and on the Web.

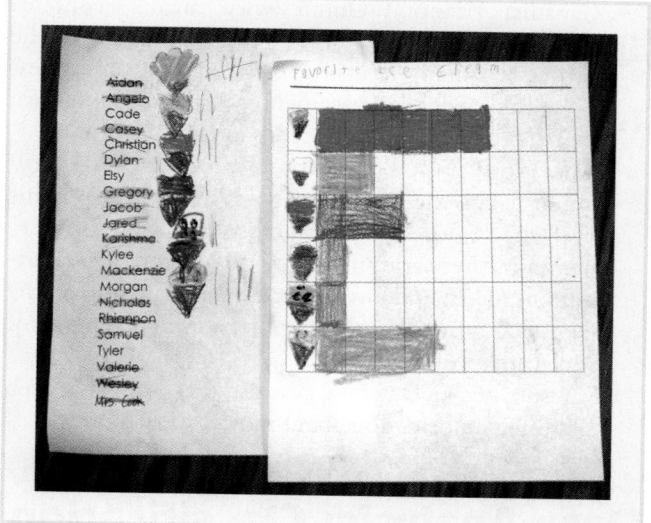

Figure 21.1 Kindergartners collect data on ice cream flavour choices, keeping track of who they have surveyed, tallying the data, and then creating a horizontal bar graph.
Source: Cook, C. D. (2008). "I Scream, You Scream: Data Analysis with Kindergartners." *Teaching Children Mathematics, 14*(9), p. 539. Reprinted with permission. Copyright © 2008 by the National Council of Teachers of Mathematics, Inc. www.nctm.org. All rights reserved.

Print Resources Newspapers, almanacs, sports record books, maps, and various government publications are possible sources of data that may be used to answer student-formulated questions.

Children's literature is an excellent and engaging resource. Young students can tally words in a repeating verse like "Hickory, Dickory, Dock" (Niezgoda & Moyer-Packenham, 2005). Similarly, books like *Good Night Moon* (Brown, 1947) or *Green Eggs and Ham* (Dr. Seuss, 1960) have many repeated words or phrases. Non-fiction literature can be a source of data, especially for older students. For example, the *Book of Lists: Fun Facts, Weird Trivia, and Amazing Lists on Nearly Everything You Need to Know!* (Buckley & Stremme, 2006) reports on various statistics and includes surveys at the end of every section. Books on sports can also have very interesting statistics about historic periods that students can explore and compare.

Web Sites

- Statistics Canada (www.statcan.gc.ca) is Canada's national statistical agency. Along with providing census information, the agency provides data about virtually all aspects of Canadian life. The statistics produced help Canadians better understand their country—its population, resources, economy, society, and culture. Statistics Canada also includes features such as Stats Can Learning Resources, Census at School and Kids' Zone, which provide information, learning resources, and activities appropriate for use by elementary teachers and students.
- Canadian Economy Online (www.canadianeconomy.gc.ca/english/economy/) is a one-stop guide to the national economy. It lets you check out statistics, access a wealth of federal government information, and learn more about economic concepts and events.
- The World Fact Book (https://www.cia.gov/library/publications/the-world-factbook/index.html): This Web site provides demographic information for every nation in the world, including population, age distributions, death and birth rates, and information on the economy, government, transportation, and geography. Maps are included as well.
- Internet Movie Database (www.imdb.com): This Web site offers information about movies of all genres.

Data Analysis: Classification

Classification involves making decisions about how to categorize things. This basic activity is fundamental to data analysis. In order to formulate questions and decide how to represent data that have been gathered, decisions must be made about how things might be categorized. Young children might group farm animals, for example, by number of legs; by type of product they provide; by those that work, provide food, or are pets; by size or colour; by the type of food they eat; and so on. Each of these groupings is based on a different attribute of the animals.

Young children need experiences with categorizing things in different ways in order to learn to make sense of real-world data. Attribute activities are explicitly designed to develop this flexible reasoning about the characteristics of data.

Attribute Materials

Attribute materials are sets of objects that lend themselves to being sorted and classified in different ways. Such things might include seashells, leaves, the children themselves, or the set of the children's shoes. The *attributes* determine the ways that the materials can be sorted. For example, hair colour, height, and gender are attributes of children. Each attribute has a number of different *values:* for example, black, blond, brown, or red (for the attribute of hair colour); tall or short (for height); male or female (for gender). An example of a teacher-made attribute set is displayed in Figure 21.2. These cards are available in Blackline Master 59.

Commercially available attribute blocks, that come in sets of 60, have four attributes: colour (red, yellow, blue), shape (circle, triangle, rectangle, square, hexagon), size (big,

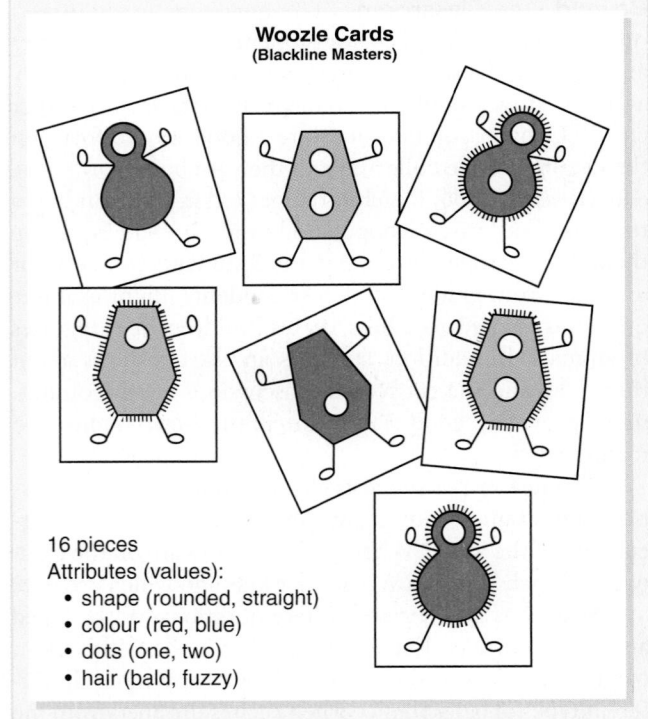

Woozle Cards
(Blackline Masters)

16 pieces
Attributes (values):
- shape (rounded, straight)
- colour (red, blue)
- dots (one, two)
- hair (bald, fuzzy)

Figure 21.2 Woozle Cards can be duplicated on card stock coloured with red and blue bodies, then laminated, and cut into individual cards (see Blackline Master 59).

little), and thickness (thick, thin). The specific values, number of values, or number of attributes that a set may have is not important.

 "Organizing data into categories should begin with informal sorting experiences, such as helping to put away groceries.... Young children should continue activities that focus on attributes of objects and data so that by the second grade, they can sort and classify simultaneously, using more than one attribute" (pp. 109–110).

Activities with Attribute Materials Most attribute activities are best done with young children sitting on the floor in a large circle where all can see and have access to the materials. Children as young as kindergarten can have fun with simple Venn diagram activities. With the use of words such as *and*, *or*, and *not*, the loop activities become quite challenging even for grade 5 students.

Before children can use loops in a problem-solving activity, the scheme itself must be understood. A good way to accomplish this is to do a few activities that involve the loops. Children find these interesting and fun. After several days of working with these initial activities, you can move on to problem-solving activities involving the same formats.

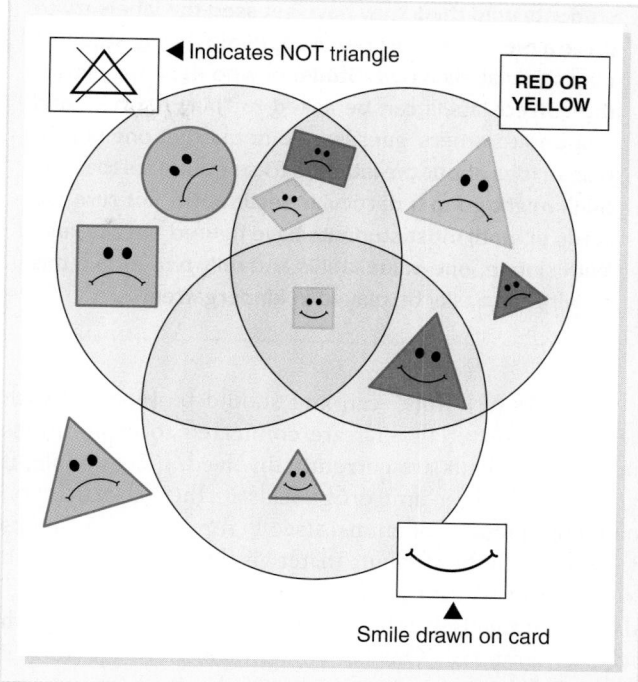

Figure 21.3 A Venn diagram activity with attribute pieces. A rule is written on each card.

Activity 21.1

What about "Both"?

Give children two large loops of yard or string. Direct them to put all the red pieces inside one loop and all triangles inside the other. Let the children try to resolve the difficulty of what to do with the red triangles. When the notion of overlapping the loops to create an area common to both is clear, more challenging activities can be explored.

Affix or draw labels on each loop and have students take turns placing pieces in the appropriate regions. As shown in Figure 21.3, the labels need not be restricted to single attributes. If a piece does not fit in any region, it is placed outside of all the loops.

It is important to introduce labels for negative attributes such as "not red" or "not small." Also important is the use of *and* and *or* connectives, as in "red and square" or "big or happy." This use of *and*, *or*, and *not* significantly widens children's classification schemes.

An engaging and challenging activity is to infer how things have been classified when the loops are not labelled.

The following activities require students to make and test conjectures about how things are being classified.

Activity 21.2

Guess My Rule

For this activity, try using the students instead of the shapes as attribute "pieces." Decide on an attribute such as "blue jeans" or "stripes on clothing" for grouping your students but do not tell them your rule. Silently sort the children, one at a time, by moving each child to the left or right according to this attribute rule. After a number of students have been sorted, have the next child come up and ask students to predict in which group he or she belongs. Continue the activity for a while before the rule is articulated, so that others in the class will have an opportunity to determine the rule. This same activity can be done with virtually any material that can be sorted such as students, students' shoes, shells, or buttons.

Activity 21.3

Hidden Labels

Select label cards for the loops of string, and place them face down. Ask students to select a piece for you to place. Begin to sort pieces according to the labels that have been turned down. As you sort, have students try to determine what labels are for each of the loops. Let

students who think they have guessed the labels try to place a piece in the proper loop. Avoid having students guess the labels aloud. Students who think they know the correct labels can be asked to "play teacher" and respond to others' guesses. Point out that one way to test an idea about the labels is to select pieces that you think might go in a particular section. Do not turn the cards up until most students have figured out the rule. With simple, one-value labels and only two loops, this activity can easily be played in kindergarten.

"Guess My Rule" can and should be repeated with real-world materials that are connected to explorations in which students are currently involved. For example, if you were doing a unit on animals in the backyard, you could use pictures of animals (see Figure 21.4). The loops together with the attribute materials provide students with a first form of data presentation. The class can "graph" data about themselves by placing information in loops with labels. A graph of "Our Pets" might consist of a picture of each student's pet or favourite stuffed animal (in lieu of a pet) affixed to a wall display showing how the pets were classified.

Data Analysis: Graphical Representations

How data are organized should be directly related to the question that caused you to collect the data in the first place. For example, suppose that students want to know how many pockets they have on their clothing (Burns, 1996; Russell et al., 2007). Each student in the room counts his or her pockets and the data are collected.

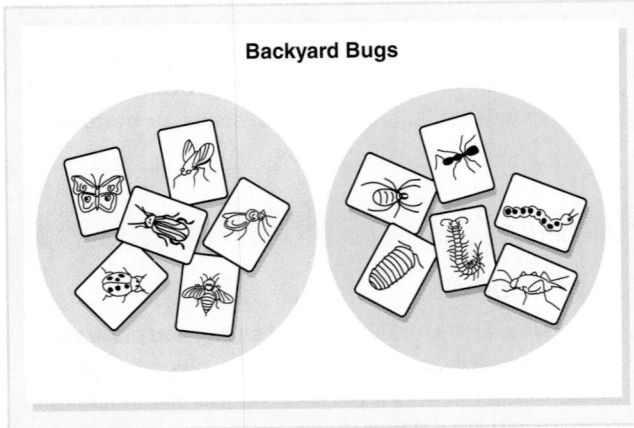

Backyard Bugs

Figure 21.4 Can you guess the rule that was used to sort these bugs?

Pause and Reflect

If your grade 2 class had collected these data, what methods might you suggest they use for organizing and graphing them? Is one of your ideas better than others for answering the question about how many pockets?

If a large bar graph were made with a bar for every student, it would certainly tell how many pockets each student has. However, is it the best way to answer the question? If the data were categorized by number of pockets, then a graph showing the number of students with two pockets, three pockets, and so on would easily show which number of pockets is most common and how the number of pockets varies across the class.

Students should be involved in deciding how they want to represent their data. However, for children with little experience with the various methods of picturing data, you can suggest alternatives.

Once students have displayed the data, they can discuss its value. Analyzing data that are numerical (number of pockets) versus categorical (colour of socks) is an added challenge for students as they struggle to make sense of the graphs (Russell, 2007). If, for example, the graph has seven stickers above the five, students may think that five people have seven pockets or seven people have five pockets.

The emphasis or goal of this instruction should be to help children see that graphs and charts tell about information, and that different types of representations tell different things about the same data. The value of having students actually construct their own graphs is not so much that they learn the techniques but that they are personally invested in the data and that they learn how a graph conveys information. Once a graph is constructed, the most important activity is discussing what it tells the people who see it, especially those who were not involved in making the graph. Discussions about graphs of real data that the children themselves have been involved in gathering will help them analyze and interpret other graphs and charts that they see in newspapers and on TV.

What we should *not* do is get overly anxious about the tedious details of graph construction. The issues of analysis and communication should be your agenda. They are much more important than the technique! In the real world, technology will take care of the details.

Students should construct graphs or charts by hand and with technology. First you can encourage students to make charts and graphs that make sense to them—that they feel communicate the information they wish to convey. Young students may feel more personally invested in their work when they create graphs by hand and are not distracted by the techniques of technology. The intent is to get the students involved in accurately communicating a message about their data.

Across the K–8 curriculum, students begin looking at the shape of data by looking at various graphs. From bar graphs and tally charts to pie charts and scatter plots, students' work will prepare them for encounters with the graphs and statistics that bombard the public in areas such as advertising, weather, opinion polls, reliability estimates, population trends, health risks, and progress of students in schools.

 Technology use is very common in graphical representations. Computer programs and graphing calculators can provide various graphical displays with very little effort. Discussion can then focus on the information that each display provides. Students can select their own graphs and justify their choice based on their intended purposes. ◆

Bar Graphs and Tally Charts

Bar graphs and tally charts are among the first ways to group and present data and are especially useful in grades pre-K–3. At this early level, bar graphs should be made so that each bar consists of countable parts such as squares, objects, tallies, or pictures of objects. Figure 21.5 illustrates a few techniques that can be used to make a graph quickly with the whole class.

A "real graph" uses the actual objects being graphed. Examples include types of shoes, seashells, and books. Each item can be placed in a square or on a floor tile so that comparisons and counts are easily made.

Picture graphs use a drawing of some sort that represents what is being graphed. Students can make their own drawings, or you can duplicate drawings to be coloured or cut out to suit particular needs.

Symbolic graphs use something like squares, blocks, tallies, or Xs to represent the things being counted in the

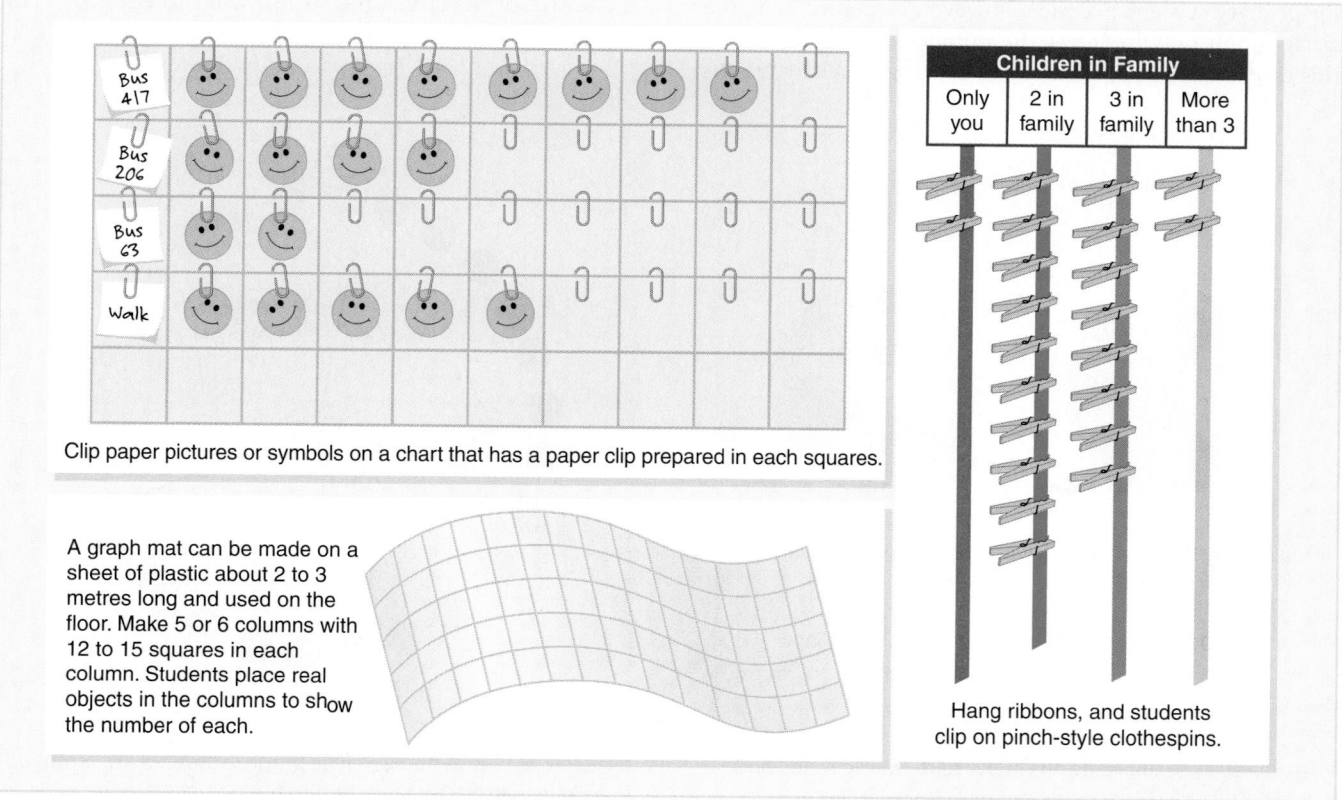

Clip paper pictures or symbols on a chart that has a paper clip prepared in each squares.

A graph mat can be made on a sheet of plastic about 2 to 3 metres long and used on the floor. Make 5 or 6 columns with 12 to 15 squares in each column. Students place real objects in the columns to show the number of each.

Hang ribbons, and students clip on pinch-style clothespins.

Figure 21.5 Some ideas for quick graphs that can be used again and again.

graph. An easy idea is to use sticky notes as elements of a graph. These can be attached directly to the chalkboard or to other charts and rearranged if needed.

Analyzing data in this way is step 3 of the process of doing statistics. A question is posed and data are collected based on the categories to be graphed. Figure 21.5 illustrates two quick ways to gather information so that it is already displayed in a bar. A class of 25 to 30 students can make a graph in less than 10 minutes, leaving ample time to use it for questions and observations.

Once a graph has been constructed, engage the class in a discussion of what information the graph tells or conveys. "What can you tell about our class by looking at this shoe graph?" Graphs convey factual information (e.g., more people wear sneakers than any other kind of shoe) and also provide opportunities for making inferences that are not directly observable in the graph (e.g., children in this class do not like to wear leather shoes). The difference between facts and inferences is an important idea in graph construction and is also an important idea in science. Older students can examine graphs found in newspapers or magazines and discuss the *facts* in the graphs and the *message* that may have been intended by the person who made the graph.

Circle Graphs

Typically, we think of circle graphs as showing percentages. As such, these would probably not be appropriate for primary students. Notice, however, in Figure 21.6, the circle graph only indicates the number of data points (in this case, students) in each of five categories. Many graph-

ing programs will create a similar graph. An understanding of percentages is not required when the computer creates the graph.

Notice also that the circle graph shows information that is not as easily obtained from the other graphs. For example, when comparisons are made between two populations of very different size, the circle graph offers a visual that allows for the comparison of the part–whole ratios. In Figure 21.6, each of the two graphs shows the percents of students with different numbers of siblings. One graph is based on classroom data and the other on school-wide data. Because circle graphs display ratios rather than quantities, the small set of class data can be compared to the large set of school data. This could not be done with bar graphs.

Easily Made Circle Graphs Circle graphs of the students in your classroom can be made quickly and quite dramatically. Suppose, for example, that each student picked his or her favourite hockey team in the Stanley Cup semi-final playoffs (the Conference finals). Line up all the students in the room so that students favouring the same team are together. Now form the entire group into a circle of students. Tape the ends of four long strings to the floor in the centre of the circle, and extend each string to a point along the circumference of the circle where the teams change. Voilà! Now you have a very nice circle graph with no measuring and no percentages. If you copy and cut out a rational number wheel (see Blackline Master 28) and place it on the centre of the circle, the strings will show approximate percentages for each part of your graph (see Figure 21.7).

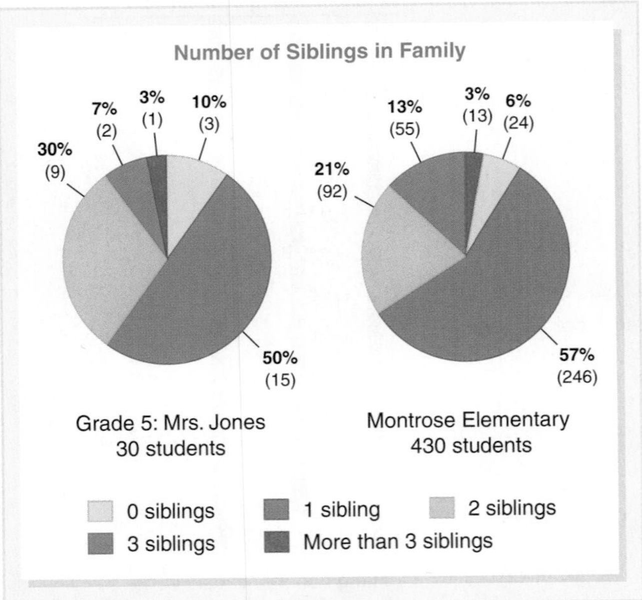

Number of Siblings in Family

7% (2) 3% (1) 10% (3)
30% (9)
50% (15)

Grade 5: Mrs. Jones
30 students

13% (55) 3% (13) 6% (24)
21% (92)
57% (246)

Montrose Elementary
430 students

☐ 0 siblings ■ 1 sibling ☐ 2 siblings
■ 3 siblings ■ More than 3 siblings

Figure 21.6 Circle graphs show part–whole ratios and can be used to compare ratios of different populations.

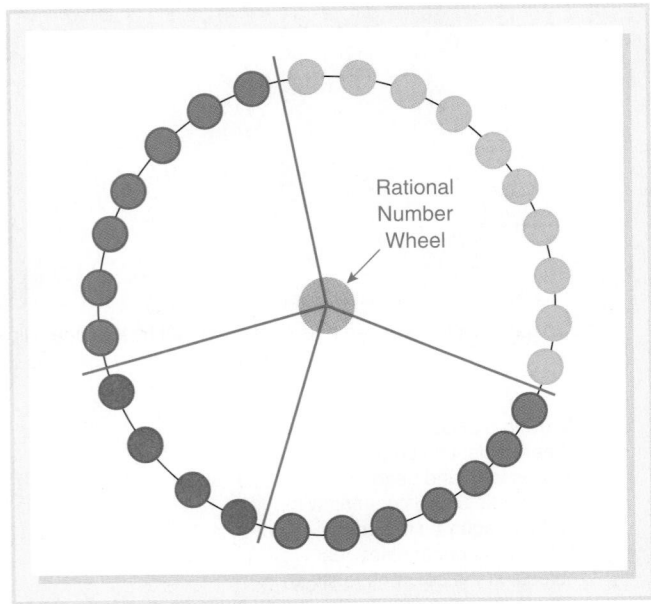

Figure 21.7 A human circle graph: Students are arranged in a circle, with string stretched to the points were the information changes.

Another easy approach to circle graphs is similar to the human circle graph. Begin by having students make a bar graph of the data. Cut out the bars themselves, and tape them together end to end. Next, tape the two ends together to form a circle. Estimate where the centre of the circle is, draw lines to the points where different bars meet, and trace around the full loop. The result is a circle graph, again. You can estimate percentages using the rational number wheel, as before.

Determining Percents If students have experienced either of the two methods just described, using their own calculations to make pie graphs will make more sense. The numbers in each category are added to form the total or whole. (That's the same as taping all the strips together or lining up the students.) By dividing each of the parts by the whole with a calculator, students will find the decimal values and convert them to percents. Since one value is out of 100 and the other out of 360, converting percents to degrees is an interesting proportional problem for students.

 As you evaluate students in the area of graphing, it is important not to focus undue attention on the skills of constructing a graph. It is more important to think about the choice of graphs that the students make to help answer their questions or complete their projects. Your goal is for students to understand that a graph helps answer a question and provides a picture of the data. Different graphs tell us different things about the data.

Students should write about their graphs, explaining what the graph tells and why they selected that type of graph to illustrate the data. Use this information for your assessment. ◆

Continuous Data Graphs

Bar graphs or picture graphs are useful for illustrating categories of data that have no numerical ordering, for example, colours or TV shows. When data are grouped along a continuous scale, they should be ordered along a number line. Examples of such information include temperatures that occur over time, height or mass over age, and percentages of test takers who score at different intervals along the scale of possible scores.

Line Plots *Line plots* are counts of things along a numerical scale. To make a line plot, a number line is drawn and an X is made above the value on the line for every corresponding data element. One advantage of a line plot is that every piece of data is shown on the graph. It is also a very easy type of graph for students to make. It is essentially a bar graph with a potential bar for every possible value. A simple example is shown in Figure 21.8.

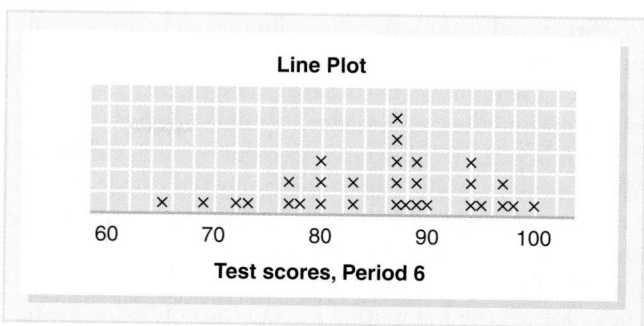

Figure 21.8 Line plot of test scores.

Stem-and-Leaf Plots *Stem-and-leaf plots* are a form of bar graph in which numerical data are graphed and displayed using the actual numbers in the data to form the graph. By way of example, suppose that the average points scored per game for each team in the Canadian Football League (CFL) for the 2008 season was posted.

British Columbia	31
Calgary	33
Edmonton	29
Hamilton	32
Montreal	34
Saskatchewan	28
Toronto	35
Winnipeg	24

If the data are to be grouped by tens, list the tens digits in order and draw a line to the right, as in Figure 21.9(a). These form the "stem" of the graph. Next, go through the list of scores, and write the ones digits next to the appropriate tens digit, as in Figure 21.9(b). These are the "leaves." The process of making the graph groups the data for you. Furthermore, every piece of data can be retrieved from the graph. (*Note:* stem-and-leaf plots are best made on grid paper, so that each digit takes up the same amount of space.) To provide more information, the graph can be quickly rewritten, ordering each leaf from least to most, as in Figure 21.9(c).

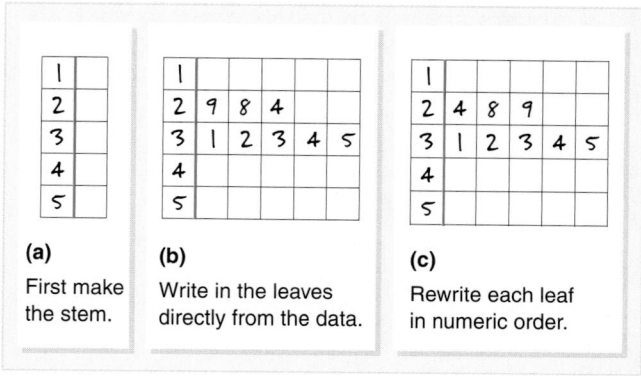

Figure 21.9 Making a stem-and-leaf plot.

Stem-and-leaf plots are not limited to two-digit data. For example, if the data ranged from 600 to 1300, the stem could be the numbers from 6 to 13 and the leaves made of two-digit numbers separated by commas.

Figure 21.10 illustrates two additional variations. When two sets of data are to be compared, the leaves can extend in opposite directions from the same stem. In the same example, notice that the data are grouped by fives instead of tens. When plotting 62, the 2 is written next to the 6; for 67, the 7 is written next to the dot below the 6.

Notice that the stem-and-leaf plot in Figure 21.10 clearly shows the shape of the data. You can observe how the data are spread and how they cluster. From observation, students can find the range, median, mode, and any outliers. Figure 21.10, using rows grouped by fives instead of by tens, illustrates the spread of the data, possibly to show particular grades (e.g., B vs. B+). Determining how to set up the stem-and-leaf plot depends on the context and on the question being asked.

Histograms A *histogram* is a form of bar graph in which the categories are consecutive equal intervals along a numerical scale. The height or length of each bar in the graph is determined by the number of data elements that fall into that particular interval (see Figure 21.11). Histograms are not difficult in concept but can cause problems for the students constructing them. What is the appropriate interval to use for the bar width? What is a good scale to use for the length of the bars? That all the data must be grouped and counted within each interval causes further difficulty. Histograms can be created with graphing calculators or by computer software, making the process more immediate.

Line Graphs A *line graph* is used when there is a numerical value associated with points equally spaced along a continuous number scale. The points are plotted to represent two related pieces of data, and a line is drawn to connect these points. For example, a line graph might be used to show how the length of a flagpole shadow changed from one hour to the next during the day. The horizontal scale would represent the time, and the vertical scale would represent the length of the shadow. Discrete points can be plotted and straight lines drawn to connect them. In the example of the shadow, a shadow did exist at all times. But its length did not jump or drop from one plotted value to the other. It changed continuously, as suggested by the graph. See the example in Figure 21.12 for a similar context, that of temperature change. Line graphs were discussed in detail in Chapter 14.

Students have a tendency to graph discrete data using continuous data graphs such as the line graph. For example, consider Figure 21.13, in which a student has graphed the number of siblings of each of his classmates using a line graph. The arrows, which have been added to the graph, highlight the problem with using a line graph to display

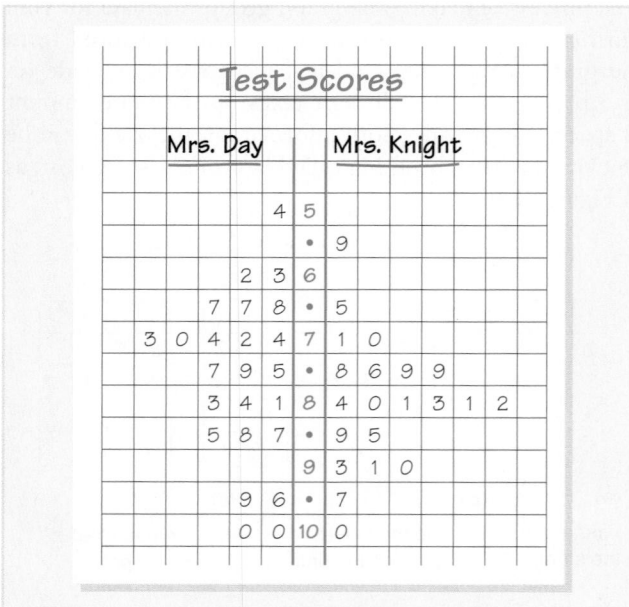

Figure 21.10 Stem-and-leaf plots can be used to compare two sets of data.

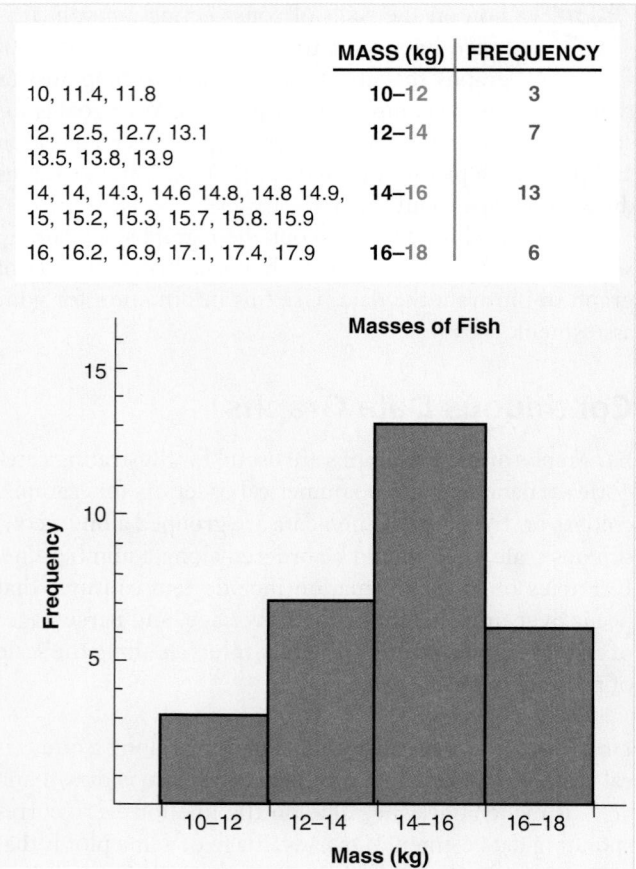

	MASS (kg)	FREQUENCY
10, 11.4, 11.8	10–12	3
12, 12.5, 12.7, 13.1 13.5, 13.8, 13.9	12–14	7
14, 14, 14.3, 14.6 14.8, 14.8 14.9, 15, 15.2, 15.3, 15.7, 15.8. 15.9	14–16	13
16, 16.2, 16.9, 17.1, 17.4, 17.9	16–18	6

Figure 21.11 Histogram for the masses in kilograms of 29 fish caught in a lake.

Source: www.worsleyschool.net/science/files/bargraphs/page.html

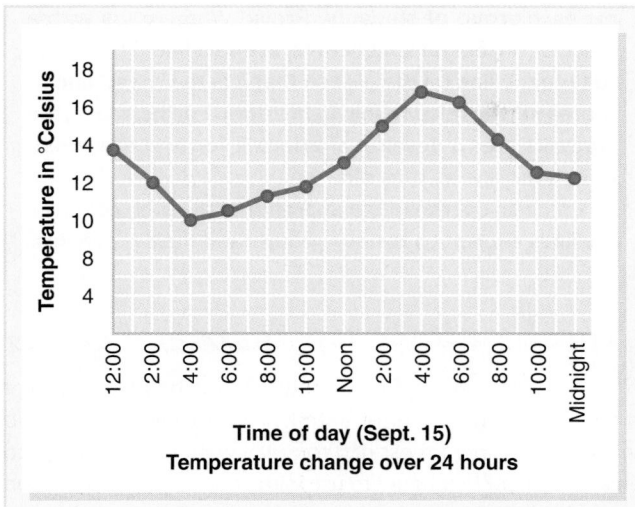

Figure 21.12 Line graph of one day's temperatures.

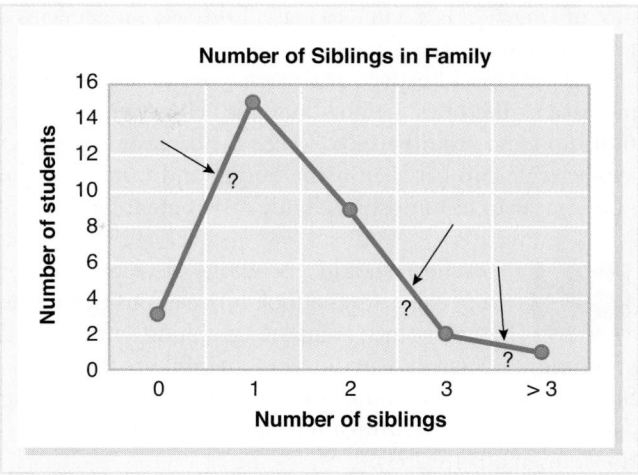

Figure 21.13 A line graph is used inappropriately to graph discrete data. What would the values be for the points indicated by the arrows?

these types of data. Every point on the line should have a value. What are the values where the arrows are pointing? A more appropriate choice would be a bar graph or a circle graph.

Similarly, a line graph would not be appropriate for a graph of students' favourite colours. There is no natural ordering, nor are there values between the colours. For this type of data, a bar graph would be more appropriate.

Scatter Plots

Data are often analyzed to search for or demonstrate relationships between two sets of data or phenomena. For example, what are the relationships, if any, between time spent watching television and overall grades?

There are all sorts of real situations where we are interested in relationships between two variables or two numerical phenomena. How far does a toy car roll beyond an inclined plane as compared to the angle of the plane? Is

there a relationship between the volume of air in a balloon and the time it takes to deflate? Such data are generally gathered as a result of some sort of experiment that is set up and observed, with measurements taken.

Data that may be related are gathered in pairs. For example, if you were going to examine the possible relationship between hours of TV watched and grades, each person in the survey or sample would produce a pair of numbers, one for TV time and one for grade point average.

Data involving two variables can be plotted on a *scatter plot*, a graph of points on a coordinate grid with each axis representing one of the two variables. Each pair of numbers from the two sets of data, when plotted, produces a visual image of the data as well as a hint concerning any possible relationships. Suppose that the following information was gathered from 25 grade 8 boys: height in centimetres, mass in kilograms, and number of letters in their last name. The two graphs in Figure 21.14 show two possibilities. Graph (a) is a scatter plot of height to mass, and graph (b) is a

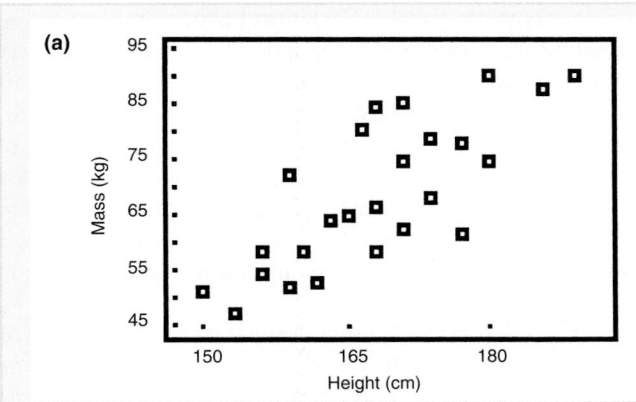

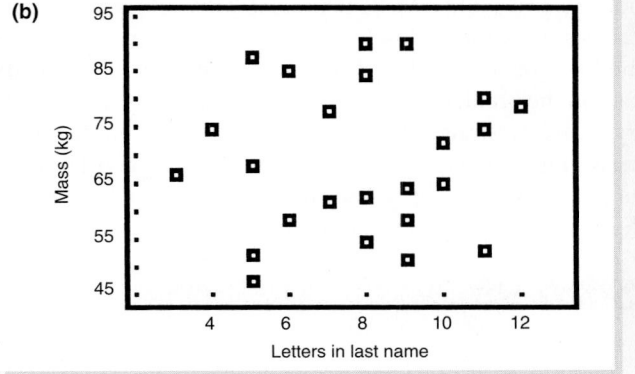

Figure 21.14 Scatter plots show potential relationships or lack of relationships.

plot of length of last name to mass. Both were made with a graphing calculator.

As you would expect, the masses of the boys seem to increase as the boys' heights increase. However, the relationship is far from perfect. There is no reason to expect any relationship between name length and mass, and the dots appear to be almost randomly distributed.

 "Teachers should encourage students to plot many data sets and look for relationships in the [scatter] plots; computer graphing software and graphing calculators can be very helpful in this work. Students should see a range of examples in which plotting data sets suggests linear relationships, and no apparent relationships at all" (p. 253).

Best-Fit Lines If your scatter plot indicates a relationship, it can be simply described in words. "As boys get taller, they tend to get heavier." This is correct but not particularly useful. What exactly is the relationship? If I knew the height of a boy, could I predict what his mass might be, based on this information? Like much of statistical analysis, the value of a statistic is to predict what has not yet been observed. We poll a small sample of voters before an election to predict how the full population will vote. Here, can a sample of 30 students predict the mass of other students? The line of best fit helps students develop conjectures.

The relationship in these cases is not a number like a mean or a standard deviation but rather a line or curve. Is there a line that can be drawn through the scatter plot that represents the "best" approximation of all the dots and reflects the observed trend? If the scatter plot seems to indicate a steadily increasing or steadily decreasing relationship (as in the height–mass graph), you would probably try to find a straight line that approximates the dots. Sometimes the plot will indicate a curved relationship, in which case you might try to draw a smooth curve like a parabola to approximate the dots.

What Determines Best Fit? From a strictly visual standpoint, the line you select defines the observed relationship and could be used to predict other values not in the data set. The more closely the dots in the scatter plot hug the line you select, the greater the confidence you would have in the predictive value of the line. Certainly, you could try to draw a straight line somewhere in the name-length–mass graph However, you would not have much faith in its predictive capability because the dots would be quite dispersed from any line you might draw.

Activity 21.4

Best-Fit Line

Once students have collected related data and prepared a scatter plot, duplicate an accurate version of the plot

for each group of students. Provide the groups with a piece of uncooked spaghetti to use as a line. The task is to tape the line on the plot so that it is the "best" line to represent the relationship in the dots. Furthermore, the students are to develop a rationale for why they positioned the line as they did.

Using an overhead transparency of the plot, compare the lines chosen by various groups and their rationales.

Pause and Reflect

Before reading further, return to the height–mass plot in Figure 21.14(a) and draw a straight line that you think would make a good line of best fit. (You may want to make a photo enlargement of that figure to use with your class.) What reason would you offer for why you drew the line where you did?

Encourage students to use a more "mathematical" reason for why a line might be best. Since a good line is one around which most dots cluster, a well-fitting line is one where the distances from all the dots to the line are minimal. This general notion of least distance to the line for all points can lead to an algorithm that will always produce a unique line for a given set of points. Two such algorithms are well known and used in statistics. The more complicated approach is called the *least squares regression* line. It is an algebraic procedure that is not accessible to middle-grade students and is also rather tedious to compute. The second algorithm produces what is called the *median median* line, which is easier to determine. It basically involves dividing the data into three sets and finding the median of each. The medians are plotted and further manipulated to find a best-fit line.

 Data analysis is an area of the curriculum in which technology really changes the way we teach. In the past, the emphasis was on *how* to create the graph and *how* to compute the statistic. Students had to labour over grid paper, drawing scales, labelling axes, colouring the graphs, and so on. Today, every graphing technique and every statistic mentioned in this chapter is readily available in a variety of technologies. An exception may be stem-and-leaf plots. With the help of technology, the focus of instruction in data analysis can and should shift to the big ideas of using graphs and statistics: to describe data, to get a sense of the shape of data, to answer questions with data, and to communicate this information to others.

A spreadsheet will compute any statistic for columns or rows of data. If the data are changed, the statistics change instantly. Spreadsheets also make very nice bar graphs, line graphs, and circle graphs. Teachers should check to see if the publisher of their textbook offers graphing software.

The graphing calculator puts data analysis technology in the hands of every student. The TI-73 calculator is designed for upper-grade students. It will produce eight different kinds of plots or graphs, including circle graphs, bar graphs, and picture graphs, and will compute and graph best-fit lines.

An argument can be made for having students do some graphing and computing of statistics without technology. Appropriate methods have been suggested in this chapter. However, the intent of by-hand methods should always be to analyze the question and interpret results. ◆

Data Analysis: Measures of Centre

Although graphs provide visual images of data, measures of the data are a different and important way to describe them. The most common numerical descriptions of a set of data relate to the spread (the *range*), the centre of the data (*mean*, *median*, or *mode*), and the dispersion within the range (the *variance* or *dispersion*). Students can get an idea of the importance of these statistics by exploring the ideas informally.

Averages

The term *average* is heard quite frequently in everyday usage. Sometimes it refers to an exact arithmetic average, as in "the average daily rainfall." Sometimes it is used quite loosely, as in "She is about average height." In either situation, an average is a single number or measure that represents a larger collection of numbers. If your test average is 92, it is assumed that somehow this number reflects all your test scores.

The *mean*, *median*, and *mode* are specific types of averages, also called *measures of centre* or *measures of central tendency*. The *mode* is the value that occurs most frequently in the data set.

The *mean* is computed by adding all the numbers in the set and dividing the sum by the number of elements added.

The *median* is the middle value in an ordered set of data. Half of all values lie at or above the median and half below. The median is easier to understand and to compute and is not affected, as the mean is, by one or two extremely large or extremely small values outside the range of the rest of the data. Moreover, the concept of median is also more accessible to elementary age students.

As mentioned earlier, the context in statistics is important. The context of a situation will determine whether the mode, mean, or median is the measure you want to use. For example, in reporting home prices, the median is quite different from the mean, with the mean being higher. Which better portrays the cost of housing? Very expensive homes can drive the mean up, so typically the median is a more common measure for describing the centre of housing costs. If a travel agent gathered data on the number of days that families usually travel as part of planning a promotional vacation package, the agent would be more interested in the mode, because the other measures would not be as helpful in answering the question.

Understanding the Mean: Two Interpretations

There are actually two different ways to think about the mean. First, it is a number that represents what all the data items would be if they were levelled out. In this sense, the mean represents all the data items. Statisticians prefer to think of the mean as a central balance point. This concept of the mean is more in keeping with the notion of a measure of the "centre" of the data, or a measure of central tendency. Both concepts are discussed in the following sections.

Levelling Interpretation   Suppose that the average number of family members for the students in your class is 5. One way to interpret this is to think about distributing the entire collection of moms, dads, sisters, and brothers to each of the students so that each would have a "family" of the same size. To say that you have an average of 93 for the four tests in your class is like spreading the total of all your points evenly across the four tests. It is as if each student had the same size family and each test score was the same, but the totals matched the actual distributions. This concept of the mean is easy to understand and explain and has the added benefit that it leads directly to the algorithm for computing the mean.

Activity **21.5**

Levelling the Bars

Have students make a bar graph of some data using interlocking cubes. Choose a situation with 5 or 6 values. For example, the graph in Figure 21.15 shows prices for six toys. The task for students is to use the graph to determine how much each toy would cost if all the toys were the same price, assuming that the total remained the same. Students will use various techniques to rearrange the cubes in the graph and will eventually create six equal bars, possibly with some leftovers that could mentally be distributed in fractional amounts.

Explain to students that the size of the levelled bars is the *mean* of the data—the amount that each item would cost if all items cost the same amount and the total of the prices remained fixed.

Follow "Levelling the Bars" with the next activity to help students develop an algorithm for finding the mean.

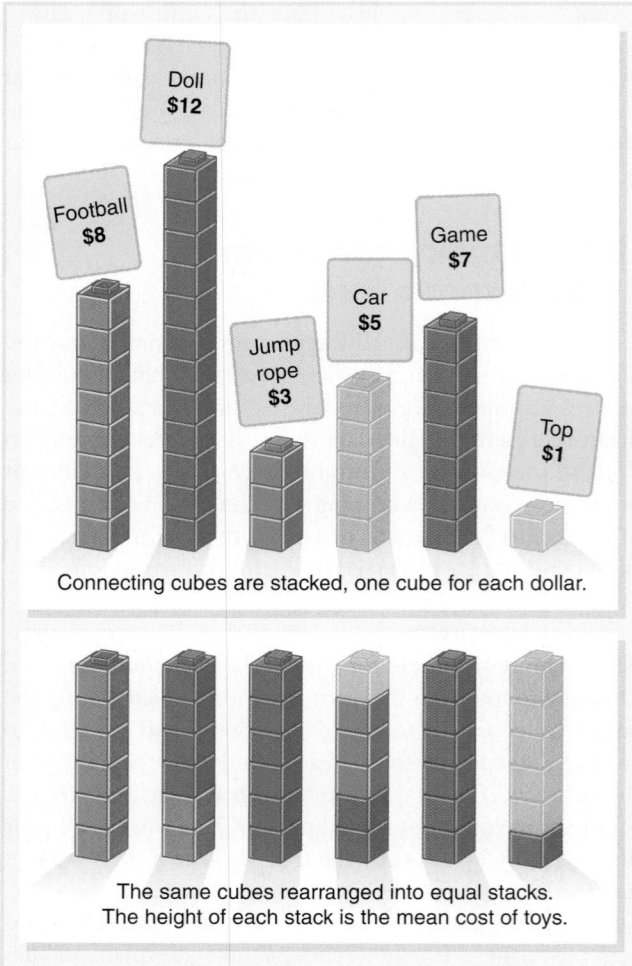

Doll
$12

Football
$8

Game
$7

Car
$5

Jump
rope
$3

Top
$1

Connecting cubes are stacked, one cube for each dollar.

The same cubes rearranged into equal stacks.
The height of each stack is the mean cost of toys.

Figure 21.15 Understanding the mean as a leveling of the data.

Activity 21.6

Our Foot Mean

Pose the following question: What is the mean in centimetres of the length of your feet? Have each student cut a strip of adding machine tape that matches the length of her or his foot. Students record their name and the length of their foot in centimetres on their strip. Suggest that before finding a mean for the class, you will first collect the means for smaller groups. Put students into groups of four, six, or eight. (Groups of five or seven will prove to be problematic.) In each group, have the students tape the lengths of their foot strips end to end. The task for each group is to come up with a method of finding the mean without using any of the individual measurements written on the strips. They can only use the taped strip of the combined foot measures. Each group will share their method for finding the mean with the class. Doing this work will offer students an opportunity to devise a method for determining the mean for the whole class.

II ———————————————— *Pause and Reflect*

Before reading on, what method for determining the mean could the students use in "Our Foot Mean"?

To evenly distribute the centimetre measure for each student's foot among the members of the group, they can fold the strip into equal parts so that there are as many sections as students in the group. Then they can measure the length of any one part.

How can you find the mean for the whole class? Suppose there are 23 students in the class. Using the taped strips of the combined foot measures, make one very long strip for the whole class. It is not reasonable to fold this long strip into 23 equal sections. But, if you wanted to know the length of this long strip, how could you do it? The total length of the strip is equal to the sum of the lengths of the 23 individual foot strips. To find the length of one section, if the strip was actually folded in 23 parts, simply divide by 23. In fact, students can mark off "mean feet" along the strip. There should be very close to 23 equal-length "feet." This dramatically illustrates the usual add-up-and-divide algorithm for finding the mean.

Balance Point Interpretation Statisticians think about the mean as a point on a number line where the data on either side of the point are balanced. To help think about the mean in this way, it is useful to think about the data as a line plot rather than as a bar graph. What is important is not how many pieces of data are on either side of the mean or balance point, but the distances of data from the mean that must balance.

To illustrate, draw a number line on the board, and arrange eight sticky notes above the number 3 as shown in Figure 21.16(a). Each sticky note represents one family. The notes are positioned on the line to indicate how many pets each family owns. Stacked up like this, it appears that all families have the same number of pets. The mean is three pets. But different families are likely to have different numbers of pets. So we could think of eight families with a range of numbers of pets. Some may have zero pets, and some may have as many as ten, or even more. How could you change the number of pets for these eight families so that the mean remains at 3? Students will suggest moving the sticky notes in opposite directions, probably in pairs. This will result in a symmetrical arrangement. But what if one of the families has eight pets, a move of five spaces from the 3? This might be balanced by moving two families to the left, one three spaces to 0 and one two spaces to 1. Figure 21.16(b) shows one way the families could be re-arranged to maintain a mean of 3. You should stop here and find at least two other distributions for the families, each with a mean of 3.

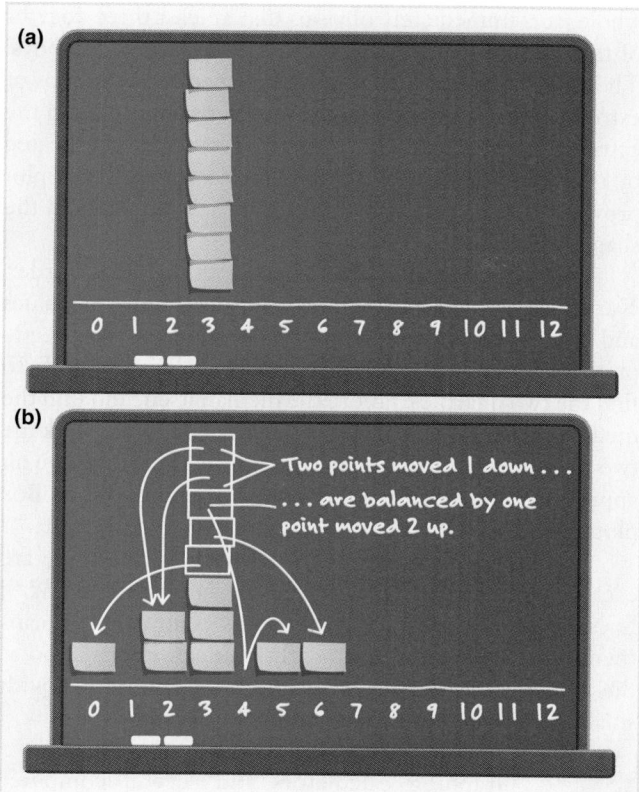

Figure 21.16 (a) If all data points are the same, the mean is that value. (b) By moving data points away from the mean in a balanced manner, different distributions can be found that have the same mean.

Use the next activity to find the mean or balance point, given the data.

Activity 21.7

Finding the Balance Point

Have students draw a number line from 0 to 12 with about 2–3 centimetres between the numbers. Use six small sticky notes to represent the prices of six toys, as shown in Figure 21.17. Have students place a light pencil mark on the line where they think the mean might be. For the moment, avoid the add-up-and-divide computation. The task is to determine the actual mean by moving the notes in toward the "centre." In so doing, the students are finding out what price or point on the number line balances out the six prices on the line. For each move of a sticky note one space to the left (a toy with a lower price), a different note must be moved one space to the right (a toy with a higher price). Eventually, all sticky notes should end up stacked above the same number: the balance point or mean.

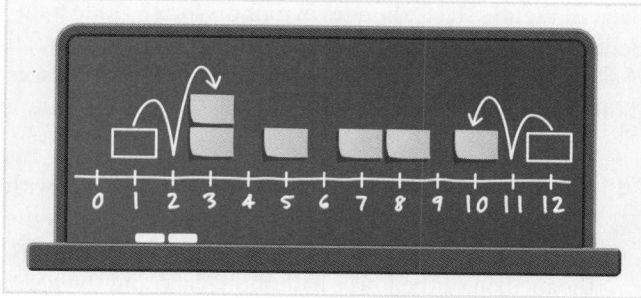

Figure 21.17 Move data points in toward the centre or balance point without changing the balance around that point. When you have all points at the same value, that is the balance or the mean.

⏸ ——————————— *Pause and Reflect*

Stop now and try this exercise yourself. Notice that after any pair of moves that keep the distribution balanced, you actually have a new distribution of prices but still the same mean. The same was true when you moved the sticky notes out from the mean when they were all stacked on the same point.

Changes in the Mean Notice that the mean only defines a "centre" of a set of data. So by itself, it is not a very useful description of the shape of the data. The balance approach to the mean clearly illustrates that many different distributions can have the same mean.

Especially for small sets of data, the mean is significantly affected by extreme values. For example, suppose that another toy with a price of $20 is added to the six we have been using in the examples. How will doing so change the mean? If the $1 toy were removed, how would the mean be affected? Suppose that one new toy that increases the mean from $6 to $7 is added. How much does the new toy cost? Students should be challenged with questions such as these, using small sets of data and either the balance or the levelling concept.

In the *e-Standards* on the NCTM Web site, Applet 6.6 (under Standards and Focal Points), "Comparing Properties of the Mean and the Median" shows seven data points that can be dragged back and forth along a number line with the mean and median updated instantly. The applet allows students to see how stable the median is and how changing one point can affect the mean.

Box-and-Whisker Plots

Box-and-whisker plots (or just *box plots*) are a method for visually displaying not only the median statistic (centre) but also information about the range and distribution or variance of data. In Figure 21.18, the ages in months for 27 grade 6 students are given, along with stem-and-leaf plots for the full class and for the boys and girls separately. Box-and-whisker plots are shown in Figure 21.19.

Each box-and-whisker plot has these three features:

1. A box that contains the "middle half" of the data, with one-fourth to the left and one-fourth to the right of the median. The ends of the box are at the *lower quartile*, the median of the lower half of the data, and the *upper quartile*, the median of the upper half of the data.
2. A line inside the box at the median of the data.
3. A line extending from the end of each box to the *lower extreme* and *upper extreme* of the data. Each line, therefore, covers the upper and lower fourths of the data.

Look at the information these box plots provide at a glance! The box and the lengths of the lines provide a quick indication of how the data are spread out or bunched together. Since the median is shown, this spreading or bunching can be determined for each quarter of the data. The entire class in this example is much more spread out in the upper half than the lower half. The girls are much more closely grouped in age than either the boys or the class as a whole. It is immediately obvious that at least three-fourths of the girls are younger than the median age of the boys. The *range* of the data (difference between upper and lower extremes) is represented by the length of the plot, and the extreme values can be read directly. The mean is indicated by the small marks above and below each box. A box plot provides useful visual information to help understand the shape of a data set.

To make a box-and-whisker plot, put the data in order. Next, find the median. Simply count the number of values and determine the middle one. This can be done directly on the stem-and-leaf plots as was done in Figure 21.18. To find the two quartiles, ignore the median itself, and find the medians of the upper and lower halves of the data. Mark the two extremes, the two quartiles, and the median above an appropriate number line. Draw the box and the lines. Box plots can also be drawn vertically.

Note that the means for the data in our example are each just slightly higher than the medians (class = 132.4; boys = 133.9; girls = 130.8). For this example, the means themselves do not provide nearly as much information as the box plots. In Figure 21.19, the means are shown with small marks extending above and below each box.

 Graphing calculators and several computer programs draw box-and-whisker plots, making this relatively simple process even more accessible. The TI-73 and TI-84 calculators can draw box plots for up to three sets of data on the same axis. Remember that a box-and-whisker plot, like any graph, is a tool for learning about the question posed, not an end in itself (McClain, Leckman, Schmitt, & Regis, 2006). Because a box-and-whisker plot offers so much information on the spread and centre of the data, much can be learned from careful examination, and particularly from comparing two box-and-whisker plots with related data. ◆

The following numbers represent the ages in months of a class of grade 6 students.

Boys		Girls	
132	122	140	131
140	130	129	128
133	134	141	131
142	125	134	132
134 Joe B.	147	124	130
(137)	131	129 Whitney	127
139	129	(125)	

All students

```
12 | 2, 4
 • | 5, 5, 7, 8, (9,) 9, 9,
13 | 0, 0, 1,  1, (1,) 2, 2, 3, 4, 4, 4
 • | (7,) 9
14 | 0, 0, 1, 2
 • | 7
```

Boys

```
12 | 2
 • | 5, 9
13 | (0,) 1, 2, 3, |4, 4
 • | 7, (9)
14 | 0, 2
 • | 7
```

Girls

```
12 | 4
 • | 5, 7,|8, 9, 9
13 | (0,) 1, 1, 2, |4
 • |
14 | 0, 1
 • |
```

Figure 21.18 Ordered stem-and-leaf plots grouped by fives. Medians and quartiles are circled or are represented by a bar (|) if they fall between two elements.

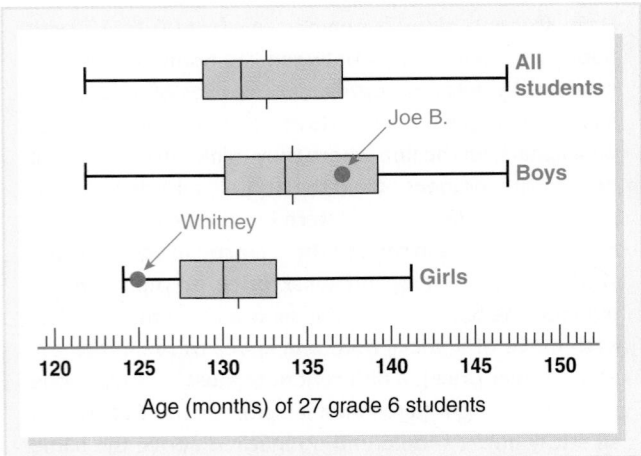

Figure 21.19 Box-and-whisker plots show a lot of information. In addition to showing how data are distributed, data points of particular interest can be shown.

|| ———————— *Pause and Reflect*

Notice that in Figure 21.19 the box for the boys is actually a bit longer than the box for the whole class. How can that be when there are clearly more students in the full class than there are boys? How would you explain this apparent discrepancy to a class of grade 7 students?

Interpreting Results

Interpretation is the fourth step in the process of doing statistics. As seen in the test items shown earlier, sometimes questions focus on mathematical ideas rather than statistical ideas. Although it is helpful to ask mathematical questions, it is essential to ask questions that are statistical in nature. That means the questions focus on the context of the situation and seeing what can be learned or inferred from the data. In addition, they should focus on the key ideas of statistics, such as variability, the centre of the data, and the shape of the data. During interpretation, students might want to loop back and create a different data display to get a different look at the data, or might want to gather data from a different population to see if their results are representative.

Different researchers have recommended questions that focus on statistical thinking (Franklin et al., 2005; Friel, O'Conner, & Mamer, 2006; Russell, 2006; Shaughnessy, 2006). Here are some ideas from their lists to get you started on having meaningful discussions interpreting data:

- What do the numbers (symbols) tell us about our class (or other population)?

- If we asked another class (population), how would our data look? What if we asked a larger group, how would the data look?
- How do the numbers in this graph (population) *compare* to the numbers in this other graph (population)?
- Where are the data "clustering"? How much of the data are in the cluster? How much are *not* in the cluster? About what percent is or is not in the cluster?
- What kinds of variability might need to be considered in interpreting these data?
- Would the results be different if... [change of population/sample or setting] (Example: Would gathered data on word length in a grade 3 book be different for a grade 5 book? Would a science book give different results than a reading book?)
- How strong is the association between two variables (scatter plot)? How do you know? What does that mean if you know *x*? If you know *y*?
- What does the graph *not* tell us? What might we infer?
- What new questions arise from these data?

This section is shorter than the sections on data analysis, only because these prompts apply across many data displays. It certainly should be a major focus of your instruction. Consider it the *follow up* phase of your lesson, though some of these questions will be integrated in the *development* phase as well.

Our world is inundated with data, from descriptive statistics to different graphs. It is essential that we prepare students to be literate about what can be interpreted from data and what cannot be interpreted from data, what is important to pay attention to, and what can be discarded as misleading or poorly designed statistics. This is important for success in school, as well as for being a literate citizen.

Reflections on Chapter 21

Writing to Learn

1. How is statistics different from mathematics? What four steps are involved in the process of doing statistics?
2. What is meant by the "shape of data?"
3. Explain why attribute activities are important in the development of data analysis skills.
4. Data should be collected to answer questions. What are some examples of questions that students might explore about data at the K–2 level? What are some appropriate questions for the upper grades?
5. What kinds of graphs can be used for data that can be put into categories?
6. Describe the difference between a bar graph and a histogram.
7. What kinds of data are required for a histogram?
8. What are three ways to make a circle graph? What does a circle graph tell you that a bar graph does not? What does it not tell?
9. Give an example of a context in which you would choose to use median over mean. When would you choose mean over median (other than the ones given in the text)?
10. Describe two different concepts of the mean. How can each be developed? Which idea leads to the method of computing the mean?

For Discussion and Exploration

1. Select a popular news weekly such as *Maclean's* magazine. Look through at least one issue carefully to see what graphs and statistical information a typical reader would be expected to understand. Note that you will not be able to do this by simply looking for graphs. Statistics are frequently used without any corresponding graphs.
2. The process of doing statistics must be clear to students, even when they are working on a piece (e.g., circle graphs) within the process. Choose a division within the elementary curriculum (K–3, 4–6, 7–9) and consider possible engaging and authentic (and researchable) questions to investigate. Then, discuss how you would plan instruction to include the four-step process as well as engage students in statistical thinking.

Resources for Chapter 21

Literature Connections

Literature is full of situations in which things must be sorted, compared, or measured. Each of these can be the springboard for a data collection and representation activity. Books of lists and interesting data also provide fruitful beginnings for data explorations. Students can use the data in the books and/or compare similar data they collected.

Canada Votes: How We Elect Our Government   *Granfield, 2000*

This excellent non-fiction book about the Canadian election process is suitable for grades 5–9. Students learn about who is eligible to vote, the political parties, and related historical features. The book is ideal for connecting to data analysis related to the voting process. Connections can also be made to social studies, where a mock election can be held.

One Well: The Story of Water on Earth
Strauss, 2007

This beautifully illustrated book, by Canadian author Strauss, is appropriate for grades 4–8. It uses real data to describe the dependence of all living things on water and is liberally sprinkled with interesting facts and plentiful statistical snippets. The book is perfect for an introduction to statistics and works well as a foundation for statistical activities that are connected to the real world. A learning resource document that provides ideas regarding how to use the book for instruction is also available.

The Best Vacation Ever   *Murphy, 1997*

This is just one book in the MathStart series, designed as a collection of single-concept books to generate simple activities in mathematics. In this book, appropriate for grade 1–2 students, a little girl gathers data from her family to try to decide what is important to them. Her purpose is to use the data to decide where the family should go in order to have the best vacation and please everyone.

This book nicely introduces the concept of gathering data to answer a question. Use the book as an introduction to this important topic.

Frog and Toad Are Friends *Lobel, 1970*

When Frog and Toad go walking, Frog loses a button. As they search to find the button, they find many buttons. Whenever one of Frog's friends asks, "Is this your button?" Frog responds (with a touch of frustration), "No, that is not my button! That button is ____, but my button was ____."

This classic story is a perfect lead-in to sorting activities as described in this chapter. Young students can model the story directly with sets of buttons, shells, attribute blocks, Woozle Cards (Blackline Master 59), or other objects with a variety of attributes.

200% of Nothing: An Eye-Opening Tour Through the Twists and Turns of Math Abuse and Innumeracy *Dewdney, 1993*

This chapter book, suitable for upper elementary, has explanations of the many ways that "statistics are turned" to mislead the common person. Because the examples, provided by readers of *Scientific American*, are *real*, this book is an excellent tool for showing the power of statistics and how important it is to be statistically literate in today's society. Reading the examples can launch a mathematics project into looking for error in advertisements and at how overlapping groups (as in a Venn diagram) can be reported separately to mislead readers. (See Bay-Williams and Martinie, 2008, for more ideas connected to this topic.)

Recommendations for Further Reading

Articles

Harper, S. R. (2004). Students' interpretations of misleading graphs. *Mathematics Teaching in the Middle Grades, 9*, 340–343. *Harper explores some of the types of misleading graphing techniques that are often seen in the popular press and discusses how she explored these graphs with students. This is a very short version of a few of the ideas found in the classic book* How to Lie with Statistics *(Huff, 1954/1993).*

Manchester, P. (2002). The lunchroom project: A long-term investigative study. *Teaching Children Mathematics, 9*, 43–47. *A grade 3 teacher describes how her class decided to do something about their dislike of the cafeteria food. She explains the difficulty of designing appropriate questions and gathering the data. Student work shows how the students dealt with the data collected.*

Books

Burrill, G. F., & Elliott, P. C. (Eds.). (2006). *Thinking and reasoning about data and chance: Sixty-eighth yearbook.* Reston, VA: National Council of Teachers of Mathematics. *This NCTM Yearbook is full of excellent articles that can inform and improve your understanding and teaching of statistics. Many of the articles are cited in this chapter.*

Sheffield, L. J., Cavanagh, M., Dacey, L., Findell, C. R., Greenes, C. E., & Small, M. (2002). *Navigating through data analysis and probability in prekindergarten–grade 2.* Reston, VA: NCTM.

Chapin, S., Koziol, A., MacPherson, J., & Rezba, C. (2002). *Navigating through data analysis and probability in grades 3–5.* Reston, VA: NCTM

Bright, G. W., Brewer, W., McClain, K., & Mooney, E. S. (2003). *Navigating through data analysis in grades 6–8.* Reston, VA: NCTM. *Each of these books is strongly suggested as a reference for excellent activities and explorations with students.*

Online Resources

Bar Graph
www.shodor.org/interactivate/activities/BarGraph
The user of this applet can enter data as well as manipulate the *y*-axis values to create a bar graph. The ability to manipulate the *y*-axis values allows the creation of potentially misleading graphs, a good source of discussion.

Box Plotter
http://illuminations.nctm.org/ActivityDetail.aspx?ID=77
The user can enter data and create box-and-whisker plots.

Exploring Measures of Central Tendency
www.learnalberta.ca/content/mejhm/index. html?l=0&ID1=AB.MATH.JR.STAT&ID2=AB.MATH. JR.STAT.CENT&lesson=html/video_interactives/ centralTendency/centralTendencysmall.html
Central tendencies are explored in this multimedia mathematics resource. An interactive component, as well as a print activity, is included.

Circle Grapher
http://illuminations.nctm.org/ActivityDetail.aspx?ID=60
Make your own circle graph with your own data, or display a circle graph from a given set of data.

Collecting, Representing, and Interpreting Data Using Spreadsheets and Graphing Software: Collecting and Examining Weather Data
http://standards.nctm.org/document/eexamples/chap5/ 5.5/index.htm
Data are provided in a spreadsheet. The data can be changed and/or ordered in different ways with simple buttons. Scatter plots and bar graphs are also easily made with various combinations of data. Lesson suggestions are provided.

Histogram Tool
http://illuminations.nctm.org/ActivityDetail.aspx?ID=78

This site offers an interactive applet allowing the user to create and manipulate histograms. User data can be entered or data are supplied.

Statistics and Probability
www.learnalberta.ca/content/mejhm/index.
html?l=0&ID1=AB.MATH.JR.STAT

This site provides both videos and interactive activities on concepts related to statistics and probability (data display and graphs, central tendency and distribution, probability).

Stem-and-Leaf Plot
www.shodor.org/interactivate/activites/
StemAndLeafPlotter

Enter data and calculate mean, median, and mode.

myeducationlab *will help you improve your understanding of the concepts taught in this textbook and in your course. This online tool includes videos of real classroom experiences, sample lesson plans, simulations, case studies, and links to important educational and teaching Web sites that will help you make the transition from student to teacher. As you study in your course and with this textbook, please follow along in* **MyEducationLab**. *Use it! Explore it! And improve your knowledge and your grade!*

Chapter 22
Exploring Concepts of Probability

References to probability are all around us: The weather forecaster predicts a 60 percent chance of snow; medical researchers predict people with certain diets have a high chance of heart disease; investors calculate risks of specific stocks; and so on. Simulations of complex situations are frequently based on probabilities and are then used in the design process of such things as spacecraft, highways, and storm sewers, or plans for reactions to disasters. Because the ideas and methods of probability are so prevalent in today's world, this strand of mathematics has risen in visibility in the school curriculum.

Realistic concepts of chance require considerable development before children are ready to construct formal ideas about the probability of a future event. This development best occurs as children consider and discuss with their peers the outcomes of a wide variety of probabilistic situations. The emphasis should be on exploration rather than on rules and formal definitions. If done well, these informal experiences will provide a useful background from which more formal ideas can be developed. Without these explorations, students will find it difficult to move from the relatively simple (and at times faulty) reasoning prevalent in elementary school to the more formal reasoning that will be developed in high school.

Big Ideas

1. Chance has no memory. For repeated trials of a simple experiment, the outcomes of prior trials have no impact on the next ones. The chance occurrence of six heads in a row has no effect on getting heads on the next toss of the coin. That chance remains 50–50.

2. The probability that a future event will occur can be characterized along a continuum from impossible to certain.

3. The probability of an event occurring is a number between 0 and 1. It is a measure of the chance that the given event will occur. A probability of 0 indicates impossibility and that of 1 indicates certainty. A probability of $\frac{1}{2}$ indicates an even chance of the event occurring.

4. The relative frequency of outcomes of an event (from experiments) can be used as an estimate of the exact probability of an event. The larger the number of trials, the better the estimate will be. The results for a small number of trials may be quite different from those experienced in the long run.

5. For some events, the exact probability can be determined by an analysis of the event itself. A probability determined in this manner is called a *theoretical probability*.

6. *Simulation* is a technique used for answering real-world questions or making decisions in complex situations in which an element of chance is involved. To see what is likely to happen in the real event, a model must be designed that has the same probabilities as the real situation.

Mathematics Content Connections

Probability and data analysis have long been joined when talking about the mathematics curriculum and there is a real mathematical connection as students reach the upper grades.

- **Fractions and Percents** (Chapters 15 and 17): Since probability is measured with numbers between 0 and 1, there is a natural connection with fractions and percents. Students can see fractional parts when working with spinners or sets of counters in a bag and use these fractions to determine probabilities. Percents are useful because they are the most convenient common denominator for comparing ratios that do not have the same whole (e.g., rolling a 7 three times in the first 20 rolls, or 15 percent, and 16 times in 80 rolls, or 20 percent).

- **Ratio and Proportion** (Chapter 19): Comparing probabilities often involves comparing ratios that are parts of different wholes as in the example just illustrated. To understand these comparisons requires proportional reasoning.
- **Data Analysis** (Chapter 21): When performing a probability experiment, the results are data—a sample of the theoretically infinite experiments that could be done. The more experiments conducted, the better the observed frequencies will coincide with the actual probability. In the reverse situation, gathering data and finding a best-fit line is a data-analysis activity. The greater the sample size, the greater the probability is that the observed relationship reflects the actual population.

Introducing Probability

Young children's concept of the likelihood of a future event is often bewildering to adults. Children can be absolutely convinced that the next roll of the die will be a 3 "because I just know it's going to happen" or "because 3 is my lucky number."

Likely or Not Likely

To change these early misconceptions, a good place to begin is with a focus on possible and not possible (Activity 22.1) and later impossible, possible, and certain (Activity 22.2). In preparation for these activities, discuss the words *impossible* and *certain*. *Certain* is the more difficult of these words for children.

Activity 22.1

Nursery Rhyme Possibilities

Create a table, labelling one column "Impossible" and the other "Possible." Take a nursery rhyme verse, such as "Hey, Diddle, Diddle" (or a picture book). For each line, ask students if it goes in the impossible or possible column. Record each statement in the appropriate column.

Activity 22.2

Is It Likely?

Ask students to judge various events as *certain, impossible,* or *possible* ("might happen"). Consider these examples:

- It will rain tomorrow.
- Drop a rock in water and it will sink.
- Trees will talk to us in the afternoon.
- The sun will rise tomorrow morning.

- Three students will be absent tomorrow.
- Sumia will go to bed before 8:30 tonight
- You will have two birthdays this year.

Have children describe or make up events that are certain, impossible, or possible. For each event, they should justify their choice of likelihood.

The key idea to developing chance or probability on a continuum is to help children see that some of these possible events are more likely or less likely than others. For instance, if a group of students have a race, the chance that Mei Lin, a really fast runner, will be first is not certain but is very likely. It is more likely that she will be near the front of the group than near the back of the pack.

The use of random devices that can be analyzed (e.g., spinners, number cubes, coins to toss, coloured cubes drawn from a bag) can help students make predictions about the likelihood of an event. The process of exploring the likelihood of an event maps onto the three-phase lesson format described in Chapter 3. In the *introductory* phase, students make predictions of what they think is likely to happen. In the *development* phase, students experiment to explore the likelihood of the event. And in the *follow up* phase, students analyze the experimental results to determine the likelihood of the event.

The following activity or variations of it should be repeated often using the same random devices, and with a variety of devices.

Activity 22.3

Race to the Top

Show students the spinners in Figure 22.1 and ask, "If we count spins that land on red and on blue, which colour will have the highest number of spins (reach the top) first?" Two players take turns spinning the spinner. Each game requires a simple recording sheet with ten rows or spaces. Figure 22.1 shows a sheet for recording the number of spins for the two-colour spinner. In the simplest version of the game, use only one spinner: one-fourth red and three-fourths blue. Before playing, each student predicts which colour will win, red or blue. (Note that it is *colour* that wins, not a player!) After each spin, an X is drawn in the appropriate column. Play continues until the number of spins for one colour reaches the top of the chart.

Students should play "Race to the Top" several times. After all students have played, ask "Which colour came up the most times? Why do you think so? If you play again, which colour do you think will win?"

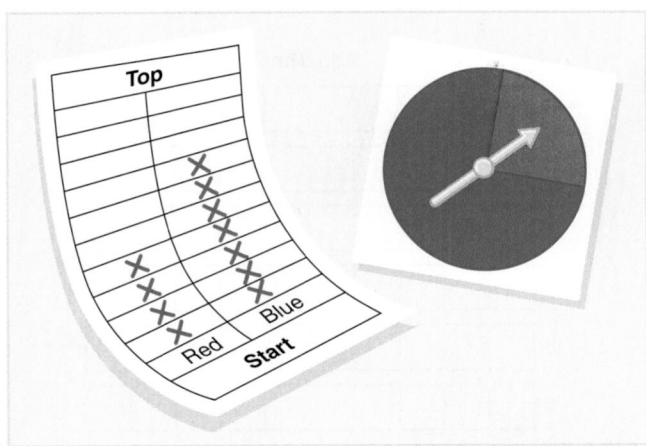

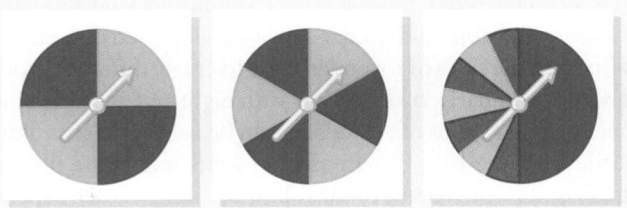

Figure 22.1 Students take turns spinning a spinner and recording the result. The first colour to reach the top is the winner.

In activities such as "Race to the Top," use a variety of spinners. Use spinners that have two colours with the same area, and colours covering different areas, as shown here.

As a random device, spinners have the advantage that students can see the relative portion of the whole devoted to each colour or outcome. Students do not always see that the first two spinners, or a spinner divided into just two equal sections, have the same likelihood of getting blue (Cohen, 2006; Jones, Langrall, Thornton, & Magill, 1997; Nicolson, 2005). Therefore, it is important to use spinners that are partitioned in different ways. Spinner faces can be easily made to adjust the chances of different outcomes. An effective way to connect the idea that the larger region on the spinner is more likely to have a spin land there is to have students use frequency charts to record data. In Figure 22.2 a student explains how she knows which frequency table goes with which circle graph.

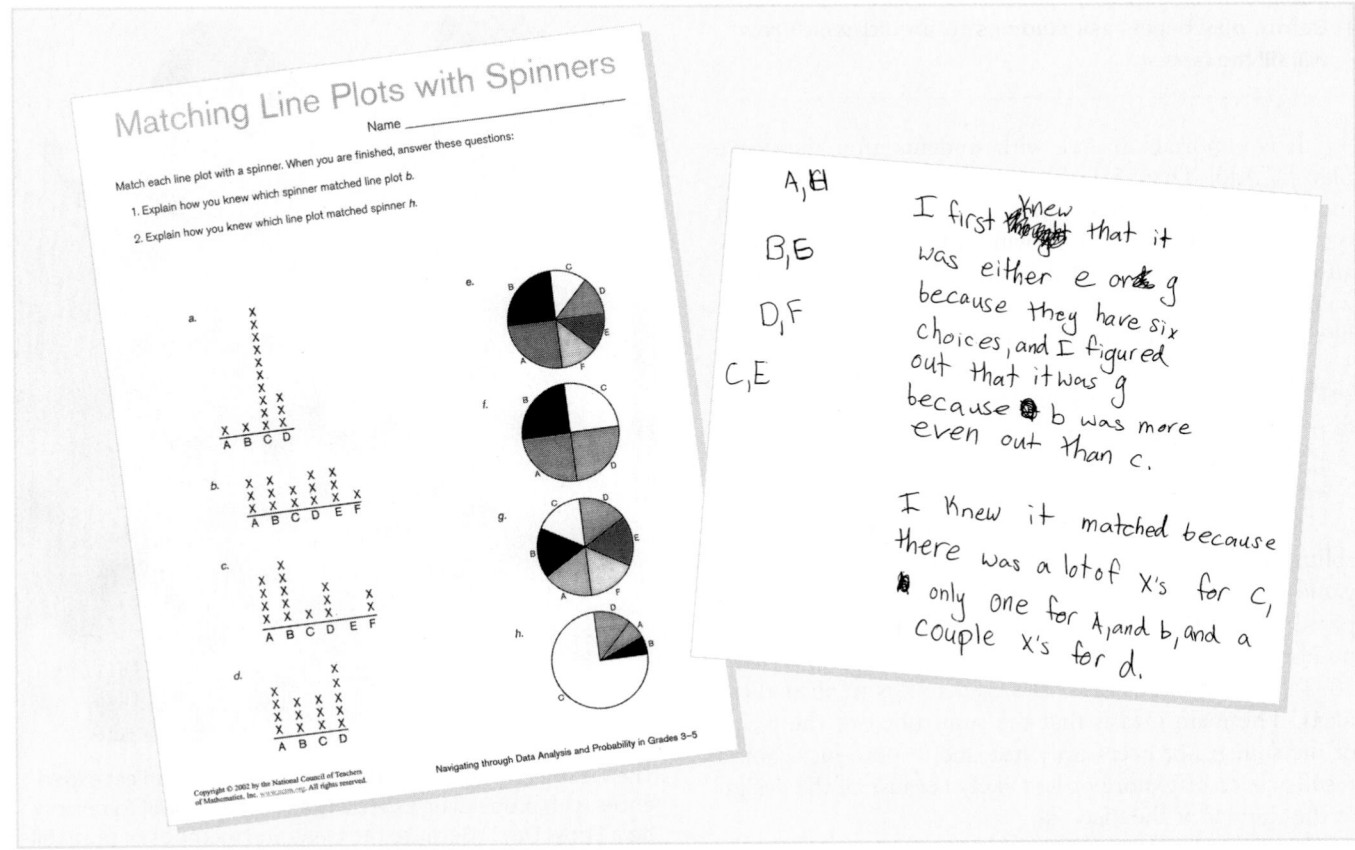

Figure 22.2 Student explanations connecting frequency charts to spinners.

Source: Adapted from Chapin, S., Kozial, A., MacPherson, J., & Rezba, C. (2002). *Navigating Through Data Analysis and Probability in Grades 3–5*. Reston, VA: NCTM, p. 116. Reprinted with permission. Copyright © 2002 by the National Council of Teachers of Mathematics, Inc. www.nctm.org. All rights reserved.

Devices other than spinners should also be used for "Race to the Top" and similar activities. Coloured dots can be affixed to the sides of a wooden cube to create different probabilities. Similarly, opaque bags with eight red and two blue tiles or other ratios of red to blue can be used. Students draw a tile from the bag. Be sure that students return the tiles to the bag after each draw. In the follow up phase of each experience, focus on what is likely/unlikely and certain/impossible.

The following activity is a game of chance with unequal outcomes. However, students will not readily be able to predict which result is most likely, thus providing a good opportunity for discussion.

Activity 22.4

Add, Then Tally

Make number cubes with sides labelled as follows: 1, 1, 2, 3, 3, 3. Each game requires two cubes. Students take turns rolling the two cubes and recording the sum of the two numbers that occur. Results are recorded on tally sheets that have six rows of ten squares, labelled 1 through 6. (See Figure 22.3.) Students continue to roll the cubes until one of the rows is full. The game can be repeated on a new tally sheet, as long as time permits. Before play begins ask students to predict which row will fill the fastest.

It is important to talk with students after they have played "Add, Then Tally." Which numbers came up the most and the least often? If they were to play again, which number would they pick to win and why? Furthermore, although an outcome of 1 is impossible, all the other outcomes, 2 through 6, are possible. A sum of 4 is the most likely. Sums of 2 or 3 are the least likely.

 Students' ideas about chance must develop from experience. At the same time though, their experiences with likely events can lead to misconceptions about chance. For example, some students think that rolling a 1 is not as likely as rolling a 5 on a die. It might be because they are playing a game where 1 is desirable. The 1 is probably not likely compared to the other 5 choices. Yet it is as likely as any other number to come up (Nicolson, 2005; Watson & Moritz, 2003). During discussions, it is your task is to elicit these ideas. The main idea is that the sum rolled or the result of the spin is not necessarily just due to pure luck. Some results are clearly more or less likely because of the design of the spinner or the dice. ◆

The Probability Continuum

To begin refining the concept that some events are more or less likely to occur than others, introduce the idea of a

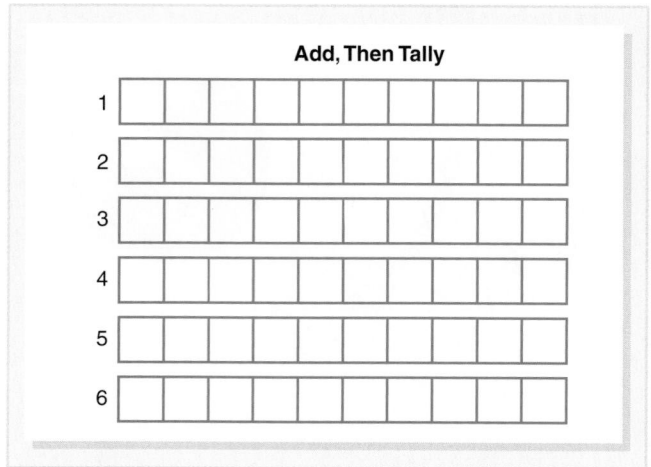

Figure 22.3 A recording sheet for "Add, Then Tally."

continuum of likelihood between impossible and certain. Draw a long line on the board, as in Figure 22.4. Label the left end "Impossible" and the right end "Certain." Write "Chances of Spinning Blue" above the line. Discuss various positions on the line and what a spinner would look like

The weather forecast may be one of students' earliest experiences with probability, especially as they ask, "Will tomorrow be a Snow Day?" Because the ideas and methods of probability are so prevalent in today's world, this strand of mathematics has risen in visibility in the school curriculum. Try to use an experimental approach in the classroom whenever possible. If a theoretical analysis is possible, it should also be examined, and the results compared.

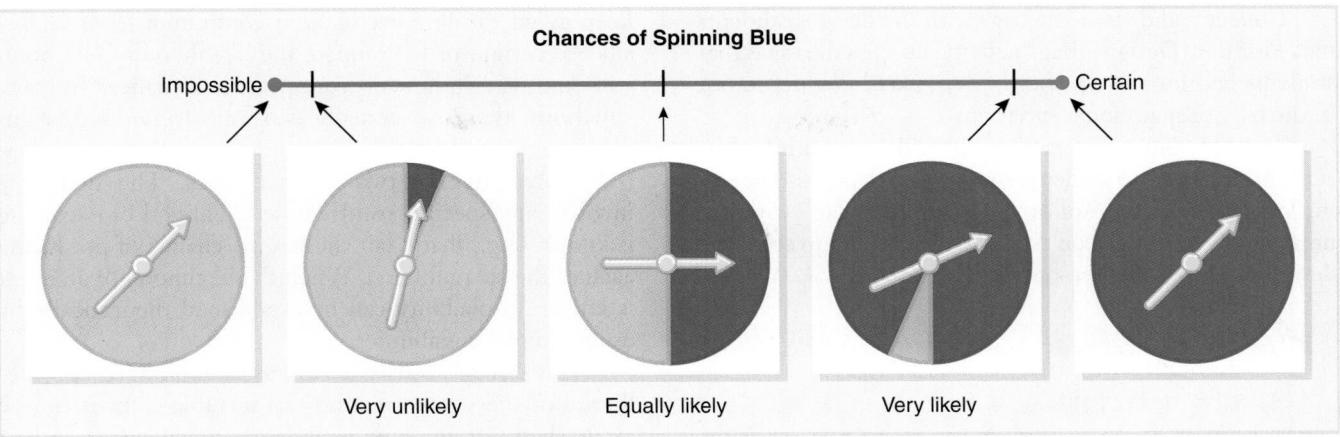

Figure 22.4 The probability continuum. Use these spinner faces to help students see how chance can occur at different places on a continuum between impossible and certain.

in order to match with these points. For example, show students a spinner that is all yellow and ask, "What is the chance of spinning blue with this spinner?" Indicate the left end of the probability line as showing this chance. Show other spinners (e.g., all blue, half blue, and half yellow) one at a time and discuss the chance of spinning blue with the spinner. Ask students where they would put a mark on the line to indicate the chance of spinning blue for each of these spinners. To review these ideas, show the spinners and ask which marks represent the chance of getting blue for that spinner. You might also name events (e.g., chance of having a Snow Day) and ask where they would go on the line.

In the next activity, students design random devices that they think will create chances for various designated positions on the probability line.

Activity 22.5

Design a Bag

(*Note*; Students must be introduced to the idea of a probability continuum as just described.)

Use the worksheet shown in Figure 22.5 (see Blackline Master 60) and provide students with a copy. On the board, mark a place on a probability line at roughly the 20 percent position. At this time do not use percent or fraction language with the children. Students are to mark this position on their probability line worksheets. Students should colour the square indicated by "Colour" at the top of the page. Explain that they are going to decide what colour tiles should be put in bags of 12 tiles, so that the chance of drawing this designated colour is about the same as the chance indicated on the probability line. Before students begin to design their bags, ask for ideas regarding what colour tiles might be put in the bag if the mark was placed very close to the middle of the line. Show how the real bags will be filled to match the bags on the worksheets.

Demonstrate with tiles, a bag, and a completed worksheet. Emphasize that the bags will be shaken up so that the way the particular squares appear on their bags will have no bearing on what occurs in the bag.

At the bottom of each sheet (and on the reverse if needed), students explain why they chose their tiles. Give them an example: *We put in 8 red and 4 of other colours because _____.*

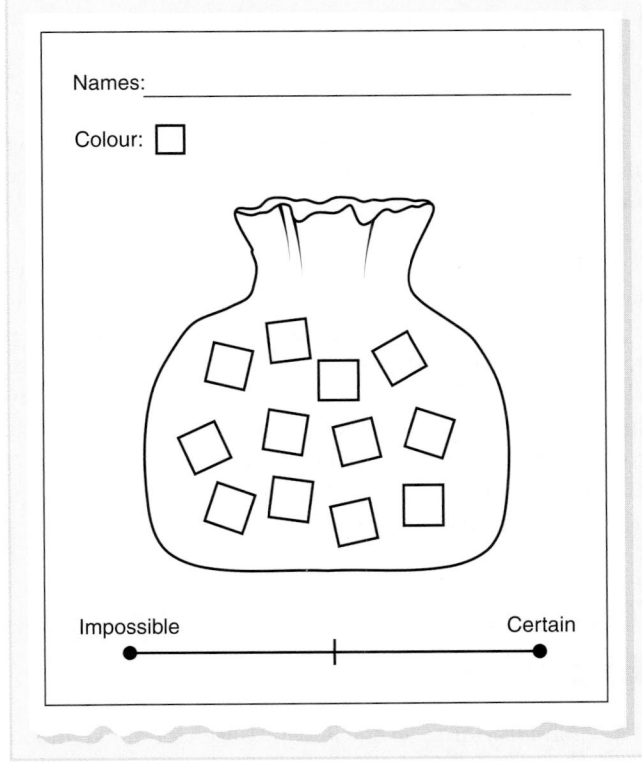

Figure 22.5 A possible recording sheet for the "Design a Bag" activity.

Collect and display the bags with the designs students made for the "Design a Bag" activity. Discuss the ideas that students had for the number of designated colours to put in the bag. (Expect some variation.)

The "Design a Bag" activity provides useful information about how your students conceive of chance as appearing on a continuum. Follow up "Design a Bag" with the next activity. It focuses on doing an experiment to see if the design predicted was reasonable.

Activity 22.6

Testing Bag Designs

Select a bag with a design (from Activity 22.5) that most students seem to agree on for the 20 percent mark. Then distribute paper bags and coloured tiles or cubes to pairs of students to fill according to the selected design. Once filled, students shake the bag and draw one tile. Tally marks are used to record a Yes (if the designated colour is drawn) or No (if any other colour is drawn). This is repeated at least ten times. Be sure that students replace each tile after it is drawn.

Discuss with the class how their respective experiments turned out. Did it turn out the way they expected? With the small number of trials, there will be groups that get rather unexpected results.

Next, make a large bar graph or tally graph of all the groups' data. This should show many more Nos and Yeses. Here the discussion can help students see that if the experiment is repeated many times, it becomes more evident that the chances are about as predicted.

The dual activities of "Design a Bag" and "Testing Bag Designs" can and should be repeated for two or three other marks on the probability line. Try marks at about $\frac{1}{3}$, $\frac{1}{2}$, and $\frac{3}{4}$.

"Design a Bag" and "Testing Bag Designs" are important activities. Because no numbers are used for the probabilities, there are no "right" answers. The small-group testing of a design shows students that chance is not an absolute predictor in the short run. The group graphs may help students with the difficult concept that chance tends to approach what is expected in the long run.

A variation of "Design a Bag" is to have students design a spinner instead of a bag of tiles.

Theoretical Probability and Experiments

The *probability* of an event is a measure of the likelihood of an event occurring. It is a measure of the certainty of the event (Franklin, 2005). Students to this point have only

been asked to place events on a continuum from impossible to certain or to compare the likelihood of one event with another. So how do you measure a chance? In many situations, there are actually two ways to determine this measure.

Probability has two distinct types. The first type involves any specific event whose likelihood of occurring is known (e.g., that a fair die has a $\frac{1}{6}$ chance of producing each of the six numbers). When the likelihood of an event is known, probability can be established theoretically by examining all possibilities.

The second case involves any event where the likelihood of the occurrence isn't observable—but it can be established through empirical data, or evidence from past experiments of data collection (Colgan, 2006; Nicolson, 2005). Examples include a basketball player's likelihood of making free throws in a game (based on the player's previous record), the chance that a telecommunicator will be successful (based on prior rates of success) or the chance of rain (based on how often it rained under equivalent conditions). Although this latter type of probability is less common in the school curriculum, it is the most applicable to most fields that use probability. However, it is important to include in your teaching (Franklin et al., 2005).

In both cases, *experiments* or *simulations* can be designed to explore the phenomenon being examined. (In the K–12 curriculum, this terminology may be referred to as *experimental probability*. However, it is not used by statisticians.)

Coin flips have a known likelihood of occurrence. Logically, we could argue that if it is a fair coin, obtaining a head is just as likely as obtaining a tail. Since there are two possible outcomes that are equally likely, each has a probability of $\frac{1}{2}$. Hence, the theoretical probability of obtaining a head is $\frac{1}{2}$. When all possible outcomes of a simple experiment are equally likely, the *theoretical probability* of an event is

$$\frac{\text{Number of outcomes in the event}}{\text{Number of possible outcomes}}$$

Instead consider the question, "Is this coin fair?" This is a statistics problem that can only be answered by doing an experiment and establishing the frequency of heads and tails over the long run (Franklin et al., 2005). The answer requires empirical data and the probability will be:

$$\frac{\text{Number of observed occurrences of the event}}{\text{Total number of trials}}$$

Because it is impossible to conduct an infinite number of trials, we can only consider the relative frequency for a very large number of trials as an approximation of the theoretical probability. This emphasizes the notion that probability is more about predictions over the long term than predictions of individual events.

Theoretical Probability

A problem-based way to introduce theoretical probability is to engage students in an activity with an unfair game. After, have them examine the possibilities within the game to determine theoretically if it is fair. In the following activity, the results of the game (the experimental probability) will very likely be contrary to students' intuitive ideas. This in turn will provide a real reason to analyze the game in a logical manner and find out why things happened as they did—theoretical probability.

Activity 22.7

Fair or Unfair?

Three students take turns tossing 2 like coins (e.g., 2 pennies or 2 nickels) and are assigned points according to the following rules: Player A gets 1 point if the coin toss results in "two heads"; player B gets 1 point if the toss results in "two tails"; and player C gets 1 point if the toss results are "mixed" (one head, one tail). The game is over after 20 tosses. The player who has the most points wins. Have students play the game at least two or three times. After each game, the players stop and discuss if they think the game is fair and make predictions about who will win the next game.

When the class has played the game several times, conduct a discussion on the fairness of the game. Challenge students to present an argument, *not* based on the data, whether the game is fair or not and why.

A common analysis of the game in Activity 22.7 goes something like this: There are three outcomes: two tails, one head and one tail, or two heads. Each has an equal chance. The game should be fair. However, after playing "Fair or Unfair?" students will find that player C (gets points for a mixed result) appears to have an unfair advantage (especially if they have played several games or the class has pooled its data). This observation seems to contradict the notion that the outcomes are equally likely.

Rubel (2006, 2007) used a similar two-coin task with students in grades 5–11, asking for the probability of getting a head and a tail with two coins. She found that about half (54 percent) answered this problem correctly (across grades). Yet many of the grade 5 and 7 students, having picked that answer, used faulty reasoning. They believed that there is a 50–50 chance in any experiment. About 25 percent of the students said the probability was $\frac{1}{3}$—because three things could happen (two heads, one of each, or two tails).

Encourage students to analyze the situation and generate all the possible outcomes. A student explanation may be as follows:

There is only one way for two heads to occur and one way for two tails to occur, but there are two ways for a

First Coin	Second Coin
Head	Head
Head	Tail
Tail	Head
Tail	Tail

Figure 22.6 Four possible outcomes of flipping two coins.

head and a tail to occur: Either the first coin is heads and the second tails, or vice versa. That makes a total of four possible outcomes, not three. (See Figure 22.6.) Getting a head and a tail happens in two out of the four possible outcomes. Since each outcome is equally likely, getting a head and a tail has a probability of $\frac{2}{4}$ or $\frac{1}{2}$.

This theoretical probability is based on a logical analysis of the experiment, not on experimental results.

Another great context is the game of "rock, paper, scissors," which can be played in the normal way, or adapted so "same" scores 1 point and "different" scores 1 point for the other player. Decide whether this is a fair game (Ellis, Yeh, & Stump, 2007).

Experiments

As noted earlier, some situations cannot be analyzed mathematically to determine the theoretical likelihood of the event or the theoretical probability. The probability of these events can be determined only through empirical data, which may be pre-existing or may be established through experimentation. Doing so requires conducting a sufficiently large number of trials to ensure that the resulting relative frequency is an approximation of the theoretical probability. The following activity provides students with such a situation.

Activity 22.8

Cup Toss

Provide a small cup, such as a portion cup, to pairs of students. Ask them to list the possible ways that the cup could land if they tossed it in the air and let it land on the floor. Which of the possibilities (upside down, right side up, or on its side) do they think are most and least likely? Why? Have students toss the cup 20 times, each time recording how it lands on the floor. Students should agree on a uniform method of tossing the cups to ensure unbiased data (e.g., dropping the cups from the same height). Record each pair of students' data in

a class chart. Discuss the differences and generate reasons for these differences. Have students predict what will happen if they pool their data. Then pool the data and compute the three ratios (upside down, right side up, and on the side) for the total number of tosses at various points, say, after 100, 200, 300, 400, 500, and so on, up to 1000 tosses. The relative frequency of the combined data should begin to approximate the actual probability.

In the cup-tossing experiment, there is no practical way to determine the results before you start. However, once you have results for 200 tosses (empirical data), you would undoubtedly feel more confident in predicting the results of the next 100 tosses. After gathering data for 1000 trials, you would feel even more confident. The more tosses that are made, the more confident you become. You have determined a *probability (theoretical)* of $\frac{4}{5}$ or 80 percent for the cup to land on its side. It is empirical data because it is based on the results of an experiment rather than a theoretical analysis of the cup.

The Law of Large Numbers   The phenomenon in which the relative frequency becomes a closer approximation of the actual probability or the theoretical probability, as the size of the data set (sample) increases, is referred to as *the law of large numbers*. The larger the size of the data set, the more representative the sample is of the population. Thinking about statistics, a survey of 1000 people provides more reliable and convincing data about the larger population than a survey of 5 people. The larger the number of trials (people surveyed), the more confident you can be that the data reflect the larger population. The same is true when you are attempting to determine the probability of an event through data collection.

Although critical to understanding probability, this concept is difficult for students to grasp. Students commonly think that a probability should play out in the short term, a misconception sometimes referred to as "the law of small numbers" (Flores, 2006; Tarr, Lee, & Rider, 2006). For example, students think that if a coin has had a series of heads, it is more likely to have several tails. But a coin has no memory, and the likelihood of heads and tails is still 50–50. The next activity emphasizes the large variability of data when only a small number of trials occurs.

Activity 22.9

Get All 6!

Have students list the numbers 1 through 6 at the bottom of a frequency table. Then have them roll a die and mark an X above each number until each has been rolled at least once. Repeat this process five or six times. Discuss how the results of the frequency charts compare in each case. Students will see, for example, that in some cases many 4s were rolled. Also, it took 25 rolls before all numbers were secured. In other cases, it took only 10 rolls to get all six numbers. Discuss that, in the short run, data can vary a lot. However in the long run data "even out." This activity can also be done on a graphing calculator (Flores, 2006).

Truly random events often occur in unexpected groups; a fair coin may turn up heads five times in a row. A 100-year flood may hit a town twice in ten years. Hands-on random devices such as spinners, dice, or cubes drawn from a bag give students an intuitive feel for the imperfect distribution of randomness. Students believe in the unbiased outcomes of these devices. The downside is that hands-on devices require a lot of time to produce a large number of trials. This is where technology can help enormously.

The next activity is designed to help students with this difficult idea without resorting to comparing ratios expressed as fractions.

Activity 22.10

What Are the Chances?

Make a transparency of Blackline Master 61 shown in Figure 22.7. Provide pairs of students with a spinner face that is half red and half blue. Discuss the chances of spinning blue. Mark the $\frac{1}{2}$ point on the Impossible–Certain continuum. Then, draw a vertical line down through all the lines below this point. Have each pair of students spin their spinner 20 times, tallying the number of red and blue spins. Mark the number of blue spins on the second line. For example, if there are 13 blue and 7 red, place a mark at about 13 on the 0-to-20 number line. If the result of these 20 spins was not exactly 10 and 10, discuss possible reasons why this may be so.

Now have pairs of students each spin their spinners 20 more times. Collect these results and add them to the tallies for the first 20 spins. Mark the total in the right-hand box of the third line and indicate the number of blue spins on the line as before. Repeat this at least two more times. Continue to add the results of new spins to the previous results. Each time, enter the total in the right-hand box to create a new number line but with the same length as before. If possible, try to get the total number of spins to be at least 200. With a graphing calculator, even 1000 trials is possible in a short amount of time.

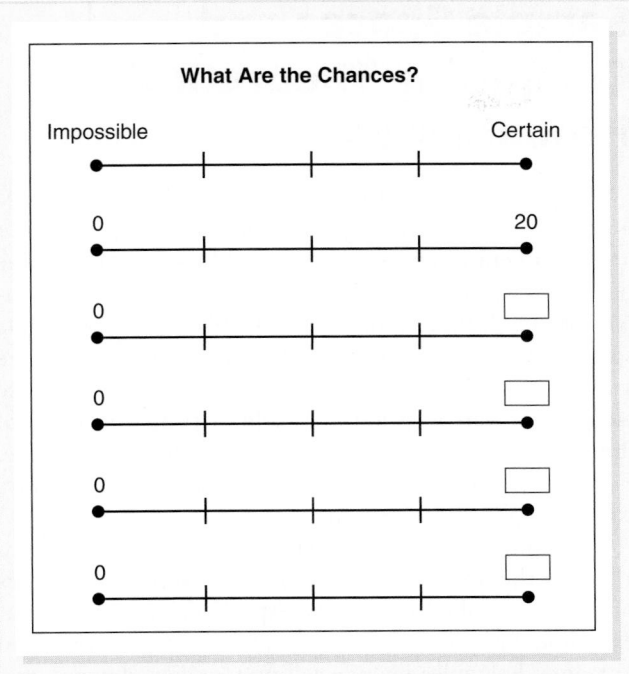

What Are the Chances?

Impossible .... Certain

0 20

0 .... ☐

0 .... ☐

0 .... ☐

0 .... ☐

Figure 22.7 This activity is used to explore probability in the short and the long run (see Blackline Master 61).

Each successive number line used in "What Are the Chances" has the same length and represents the total number of trials at each stage of the experiment. When the results are plotted on any one number line, the position illustrates the fraction of the total spins as a portion of the whole line. With more trials the marks will almost certainly get closer and closer to the $\frac{1}{2}$ mark you drew at the top of the page. Note that 240 blue spins out of 500 is 48 percent, or very close to one-half. This is so even though there are 20 more red spins (260) than blue. To be that close with only 100 spins, the results would need to be 48 and 52.

The same Blackline Master and the same method of accumulating data in stages can and should be used for other experiments as well. For example, try using this approach with the "Cup Toss" experiment. Rather than drawing a vertical line before collecting data, decide on the best guess at the actual probability after the numbers have gotten large. Then draw the vertical line and observe how more and more trials bring the results closer to it. Students who have an understanding of percentages can express the probabilities at each stage as percents. For those students who are experiencing difficulty expressing the probabilities as percents, a review lesson on percent concepts would be helpful.

 Pose the following situation to students to assess their ideas about long-run results versus short-run results. Then have students write about their ideas.

Margaret spun the spinner 10 times. Blue turned up on 3 spins. Red turned up on 7 spins. Margaret says that there is a 3-in-10 chance of spinning blue. Carla then spun the same spinner 100 times. Carla recorded 53 spins of blue and 47 spins of red. Carla says that the chance of spinning blue on this spinner is about even.

Who do you think is more likely correct: Margaret or Carla? Explain. Draw a spinner that you think they may have been using.

Look for evidence that students understand that 10 spins is not very good evidence of the probability and that 100 spins tells us more about the chances. Also, to assess whether students understand the big idea that chance has no memory, have students either write about or discuss the following:

Jeremy has a lucky coin that he has tossed many, many times. He is sure that it is a fair coin—that there is an even chance of heads or tails. Jeremy tosses his coin six times and heads come up six times in a row. Jeremy is sure that the next toss will be tails because he has never been able to toss heads seven times in a row. What do you think his chances of tossing heads on the next toss are? Explain your answer.

In this case, you are looking for the idea that each toss of the coin is independent of prior tosses. ◆

Implications for Instruction

There are many reasons why an experimental approach to probability, actually conducting experiments and examining outcomes, is important in the classroom.

- It develops an appreciation for a simulation approach to solving problems. Many real-world problems are actually solved by conducting experiments or simulations.
- It is significantly more intuitive. Results begin to make sense and do not come from some abstract rule.
- It eliminates guessing at probabilities and wondering, "Did I get it right?" Counting or trying to determine the number of elements in a sample space can be very difficult without some intuitive background information.
- It provides an experiential background for examining the theoretical model. When you begin to sense that the probability of two heads is $\frac{1}{4}$ instead of $\frac{1}{3}$, the analysis in Figure 22.6 seems more reasonable.
- It helps students see how the ratio of a particular outcome to the total number of trials begins to converge toward a fixed number. For an infinite number of trials, the relative frequency and theoretical probability would be the same.
- It is a lot more fun and interesting! Even searching for a correct explanation in the theoretical model is more interesting.

Try to use an experimental approach in the classroom whenever possible. If a theoretical analysis (such as with the two-coin experiment in "Fair or Unfair?") is possible, it should also be examined, and the results compared to the expected outcome.

The experimental approach is much like the inquiry approach that is the basis of the three-part lesson format (*introduction*, *development*, and *follow up*). In an experiment, you start with a problem (*introduction*), design and implement a way to explore the problem (*development*), and analyze the results of the experiment (*follow up*).

Use of Technology in Experiments

Electronic devices, including some relatively simple calculators and graphing calculators, are designed to produce random outcomes at the press of a button. Computer software that flips coins, spins spinners, or draws numbers from a hat is available. Calculators produce random numbers that can then be interpreted in terms of the desired device. As long as students accept the results generated by the technology as truly random or equivalent to the hands-on device, they offer significant advantages for performing experiments.

Technology makes some content more accessible, and this is certainly the case with probability experiments. Using software or a graphing calculator has the advantage of enabling many more trials in much less time. These devices can also explore across a variety of tools (virtual dice, coins, cards, etc.) and show graphical displays of the trials. For teachers, technology means that dice can be "loaded" and that spinners can easily be created with different partitions (Beck & Huse, 2007; Phillips-Bey, 2004). One particular Web site to explore is the National Library of Virtual Manipulatives. This site has been recommended in many chapters, but it is worth emphasizing here, as it is an outstanding site for doing virtual experiments.

Software for exploring probability concepts can generally be described as computer-animated random devices. Graphics show students the coins being flipped or the spinner being spun. Most allow different speeds. In a slow version, students may watch each spin of a spinner or flip of a coin. Faster speeds show the recording of each trial but omit the graphics. An even quicker mode simply shows the cumulative results. The number of trials can be set by the user.

Math Trek (Nectar Foundation, 2006) software offers a series of structured activities presented in meaningful contexts. For primary children, *Math Trek 1, 2, 3* presents probability in the context of games in a toy store. The games of chance involve spinning a spinner or rolling dice to find out if there is an equal chance of landing on a particular colour or getting a certain number. In *Math Trek 4, 5, 6,* also Canadian computer software, students apply learning acquired from interactive tutorials to activities that involve spinning spinners, rolling dice, and tossing coins.

Sample Spaces and Computing Theoretical Probabilities

Understanding the concepts of outcome and sample space is central to understanding probability. The *sample space* for an experiment or chance situation is the set of all possible outcomes for that experiment. For example, if a bag contains two red, three yellow, and five blue tiles, the sample space consists of all ten tiles. An *event* is a subset of the sample space. The event of drawing a yellow tile has three elements or outcomes in the sample space and the event of drawing a blue tile has five elements in the sample space. For rolling a single number cube, the sample space always consists of the numbers 1 to 6.

Rolling a single die, drawing one coloured chip from a bag, or the occurrence of rain tomorrow are all examples of what are called one-event experiments. A two-event experiment requires two or more activities to determine an outcome. Examples include rolling two dice, drawing two cubes from a bag, or the occurrence of rain and forgetting your umbrella.

When exploring two-stage experiments, there is another factor to consider: Does the occurrence of the event in one stage have an effect on the occurrence of the event in the other? In the following sections we will consider two-stage experiments of both types—those with *independent* events and those with *dependent* events.

Independent Events

Recall that in Activity 22.7, "Fair or Unfair?," students explored the results of tossing two coins. The toss of one coin had no effect on the other. These were examples of *independent events*; the occurrence or non-occurrence of one event has no effect on the other. The same is true of rolling two dice—the result on one die does not affect the other. The common error that occurs for tossing two coins or rolling two dice is a failure to distinguish between the two events, especially when the outcomes are combined, as in "a head and a tail" or adding the numbers on two dice.

We've already solved the problem of tossing two coins. Let's explore rolling two dice and adding the results. Suppose that your students tally the sums that they get for two dice. The results might look like Figure 22.8. Clearly, these events are not equally likely and in fact the sum of 7 appears to have the best chance of occurring. To explain this, students might look for the combinations that make 7: 1 and 6, 2 and 5, and 3 and 4. But there are also three combinations for 6 and for 8. It seems as though 6 and 8 should be just as likely as 7, and yet they are not.

Now suppose that the experiment is repeated. This time, for the sake of clarity, suggest students roll two different-

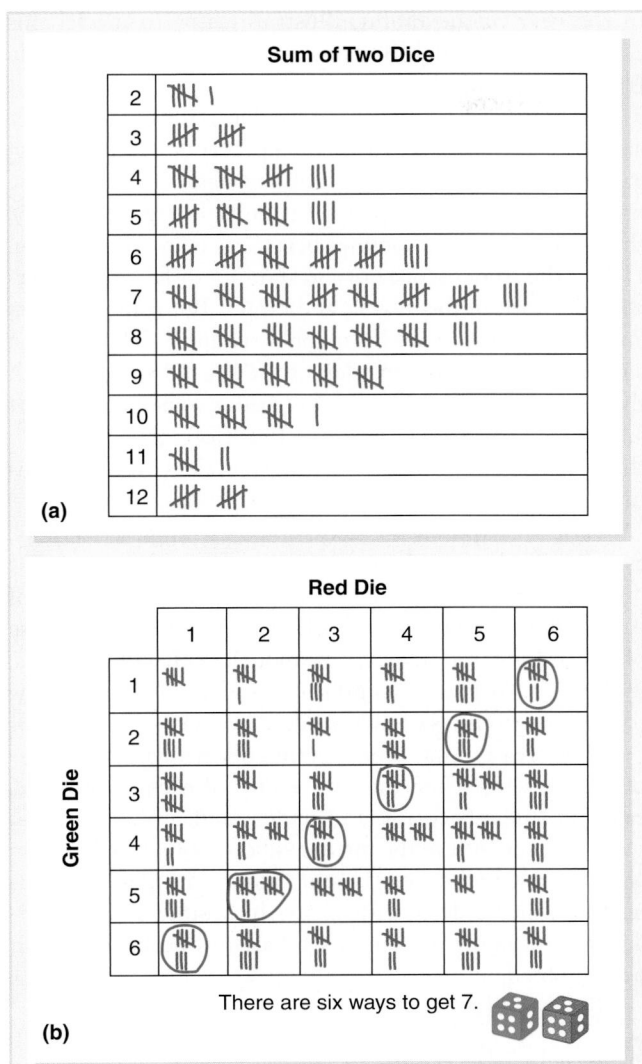

Figure 22.8 Tallies can account only for the total (a) or keep track of the individual dice (b).

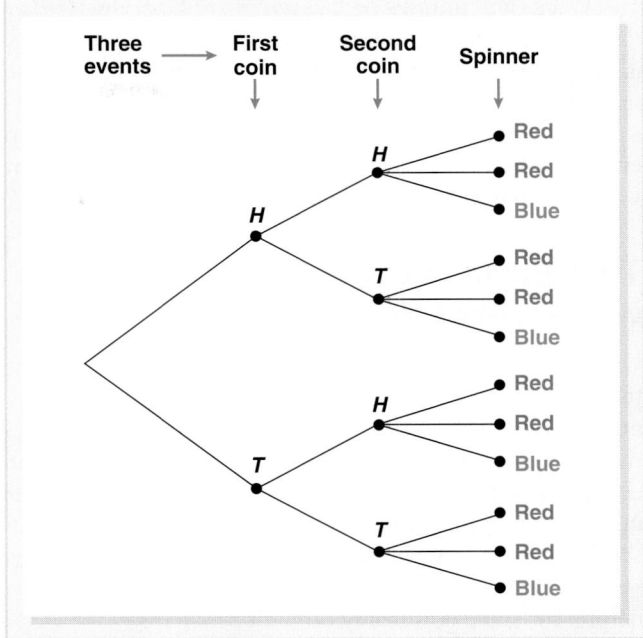

Figure 22.9 A tree diagram showing all possible outcomes for two coins and a spinner that is $\frac{2}{3}$ red.

colour dice and that they keep the tallies in a chart like the one in part (b) of Figure 22.8.

The results of a large number of rolls of the dice indicate what one would expect, namely, that all 36 cells of this chart are equally likely. But there are more cells with a sum of 7 than any other number. Therefore, students were really looking for the event consisting of any six ways, not three ways, in which two dice can add to make 7. There are six outcomes in the desired event out of a total of 36, for a probability of $\frac{6}{36}$, or $\frac{1}{6}$.

To create the sample space for two independent events, it is helpful to use a chart or diagram that keeps the two events separate and illustrates all possible combinations. The matrix in Figure 22.8(b) is one good suggestion when there are only two events. A tree diagram (Figure 22.9) is another method of creating sample spaces that can be used with any number of events. For example, consider building

an ice cream cone. You can begin with a waffle or a regular cone, choose any of three flavours, then have it dipped or not. This can be simulated using coins and a spinner, as illustrated in Figure 22.9.

Pause and Reflect

Use a chart and/or tree diagram to analyze the sum of two number cubes, each with sides 1, 1, 2, 3, 3, and 3. (These were the cubes used in "Add, Then Tally," Activity 22.4, page 476.) What is the probability of each sum, 1 through 6?

Activity **22.11**

Exploring Multistage Events

The following are examples of multistage events composed of independent events.

- **Rolling an even sum with two dice**
- **Spinning blue twice on a spinner**
- **Having a tack or a cup land right way up if each is tossed once**
- **Getting *at least* two heads from a toss of four coins**

Have students first make and defend a prediction for the probability of an event. Then have them conduct an experiment with a large number of trials, comparing their results to their predicted probabilities. Finally, they should reconcile differences. Where appropriate, students can try to determine the theoretical probability as part of their final analysis of the experiment.

Words and phrases such as *and, or, at least,* and *no more than* can also cause children some trouble. Of special note is the word *or,* since its everyday usage is generally not the same as its strict logical use in mathematics. In mathematics, *or* includes the case of *both.* So in the tack-and-cup example, the event includes tack right way up, cup right way up, and *both* tack *and* cup right way up.

Two-Event Probabilities with an Area Model

One way to determine the theoretical probability of a multistage event is to list all possible outcomes and count the number of outcomes that make up the event. This is effective; however, it has some limitations. First, what if the events are not all equally likely? For example, the spinner may be only $\frac{1}{4}$ blue. Second, it can become tedious when there are many possibilities. An area model approach has been used successfully with grade 5 students and is quite helpful for some reasonably difficult problems.

Students like to explore data about themselves. Consider the context of birthdays of the entire grade 7 class. Asking students which animal represents their Chinese birth year and in which season they were born represents two independent events. Figure 22.10, with 64 percent of the class born in the year of the tiger and 36 percent born

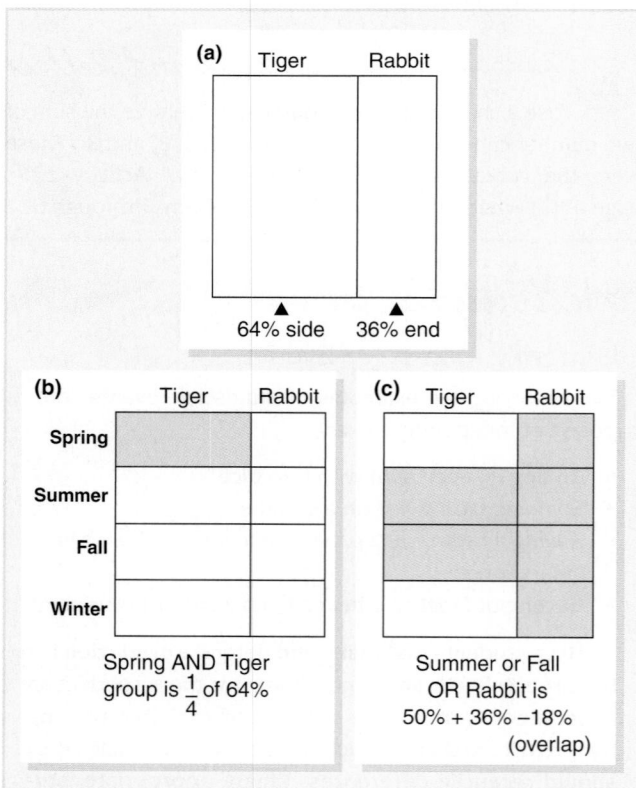

Figure 22.10 An area model for determining probabilities.

in the year of the rabbit, illustrates how to model this using an area model, Seasons are assumed to be equally likely.

In Figure 22.10(b) you can see that students in the tiger and spring groups make up $\frac{1}{4}$ of 64 percent or 16 percent of the population. This should look very familiar, as the same process is used for multiplying fractions. In Figure 22.10(c), the situation is more complex because it is an OR situation. Half of the students are born in summer or fall and 36 percent are born in the year of the rabbit. But some students are both, and they have been double counted. The diagram shows this case as the overlap of the shaded columns with the shaded rows. In the situation under consideration that amount is $\frac{1}{2}$ of 36, or 18 percent. Therefore, the population that is born in summer or fall or born in the year of the rabbit is $50 + 36 - 18 = 68$ percent of the population.

The area approach is accessible to a range of learners, as it is less abstract than equations or tree diagrams. For more than two independent events, further subdivision of each region is required but is still quite reasonable. The use of *and* and *or* connectives can be modelled effectively. Thus, it is clear to students, without memorizing formulas, how to find probabilities of independent events.

The area approach for experiments involving two independent events when the probability of each is known is easy for students to use and understand. For more than two independent events, further subdivision of each region is reasonable and necessary and the use of *and* and *or* connectives can be dealt with easily. It is quite clear to students, without memorizing formulas, how probabilities can be combined.

Dependent Events

Dependent events occur when the second event depends on the result of the first. For example, suppose that there are two identical boxes. In one box is a five dollar bill and two counterfeit bills. In the other box is one of each. You may choose one box and select one bill from it without looking. What are your chances of getting a genuine five dollar bill? Here there are two events: selecting a box and selecting a bill. The probability of getting a genuine bill in the second event depends on which box is chosen in the first event. These events are *dependent,* not independent.

As a whimsical but engaging context, suppose that you are held captive in a faraway land. The queen has pity on you and gives you a chance to leave. She shows you the maze in Figure 22.11. At the start and at each fork in the path, you must spin the spinner and follow the path to which it points. You may request that the key to freedom be placed in one of the two rooms. In which room should you place the key to have the best chance of freedom? Notice that the probability of ending the maze in any one room is dependent on the result of the first spin.

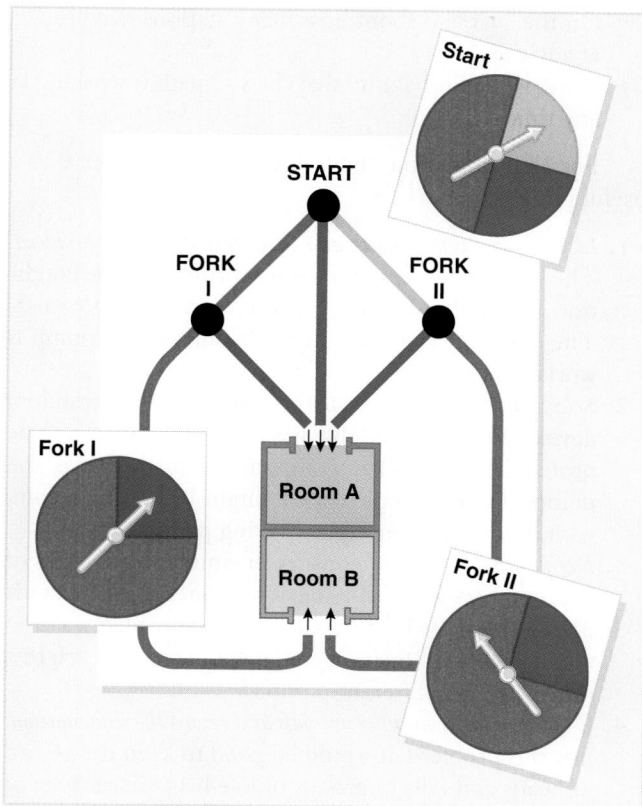

Figure 22.11 Should you place your key to freedom in Room A or Room B? At each fork, the spinner determines your path.

Either of these two problems could be explored with an experimental approach, a simulation. Remember that experiments are a good lead-in to theoretical probability. You can use the area model to determine the theoretical probabilities. An area model solution to the prisoner problem is shown in Figure 22.12. How would the area model for the prisoner problem be different if the spinner at Forks I and II were $\frac{1}{3}$ A and $\frac{2}{3}$ B spinners?

🎵 *Pause and Reflect*

Try the area approach for the problem of the counterfeit bills. The chance of getting real money is $\frac{5}{12}$. Can you get this result?

The area model will not solve all probability problems. However, it fits very well into a developmental approach to the subject because it is conceptual, it is based on existing knowledge of fractions, and more symbolic approaches can be derived from it. Figure 22.13 shows a tree diagram for the same problem, with the probability of each path of the tree written in. After some experience with probability situations, the tree diagram model is probably easier to use and

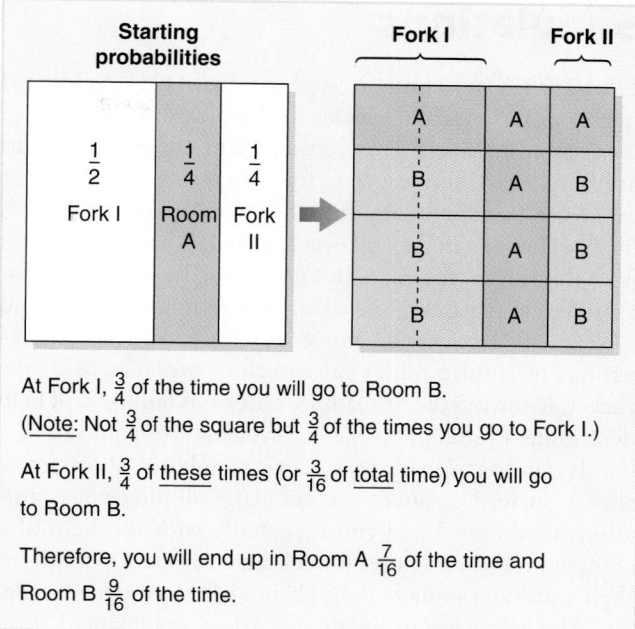

At Fork I, $\frac{3}{4}$ of the time you will go to Room B.
(Note: Not $\frac{3}{4}$ of the square but $\frac{3}{4}$ of the times you go to Fork I.)

At Fork II, $\frac{3}{4}$ of these times (or $\frac{3}{16}$ of total time) you will go to Room B.

Therefore, you will end up in Room A $\frac{7}{16}$ of the time and Room B $\frac{9}{16}$ of the time.

Figure 22.12 Using the area model to solve the maze problem.

adapts to a wider range of situations. You should be able to match up each branch of the tree diagram in Figure 22.13 with a section of the square in Figure 22.12. Use the area model to explain why the probability for each complete branch of the tree is determined by multiplying the probabilities along the branch.

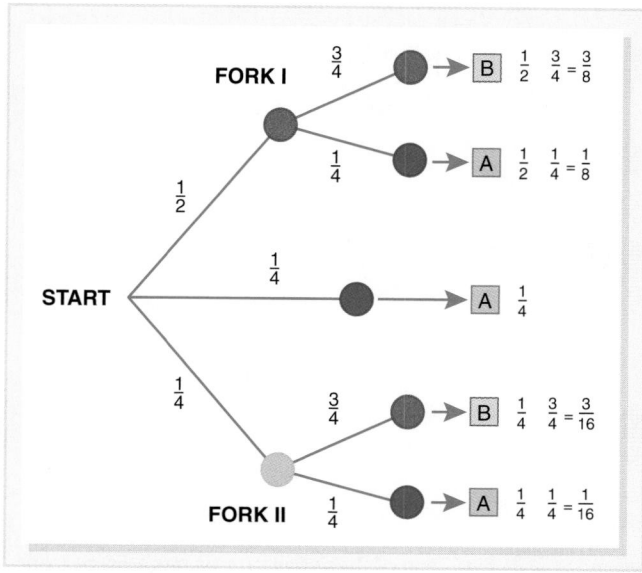

Figure 22.13 A tree diagram is another way to model the outcomes of two or more dependent events.

Simulations

Simulation is a technique used for answering real-world questions or making decisions in complex situations where an element of chance is involved. Many times simulations are conducted because it is too dangerous, complex, or expensive to manipulate the real situation. To see what is likely to happen in the real event, a model that has the same probabilities as the real situation must be designed. For example, in designing a rocket, a large number of related systems all have some chance of failure. Various combinations of failures might cause serious problems with the rocket. Knowing the probability of serious failures will help determine if redesign or backup systems are required.

It is not reasonable to make repeated tests of the actual rocket. Instead, a model that simulates all the chance situations is designed and run repeatedly with the help of a computer. The computer model can simulate thousands of flights, and an estimate of the chance of failure can be made.

The following problem and model are adapted from the excellent materials developed by the Quantitative Literacy Project (Gnanadesikan, Schaeffer, & Swift, 1987). In Figure 22.14, a diagram shows water pipes for a pumping system connecting A to B. The five pumps are aging, and it is estimated that at any given time, the probability of pump failure is $\frac{1}{2}$. If a pump fails, water cannot pass through that station. For example, if pumps 1, 2, and 5 fail, water can flow only through 4 and 3. Consider the following questions that might well be asked about such a system:

- What is the probability that water will flow at any time?

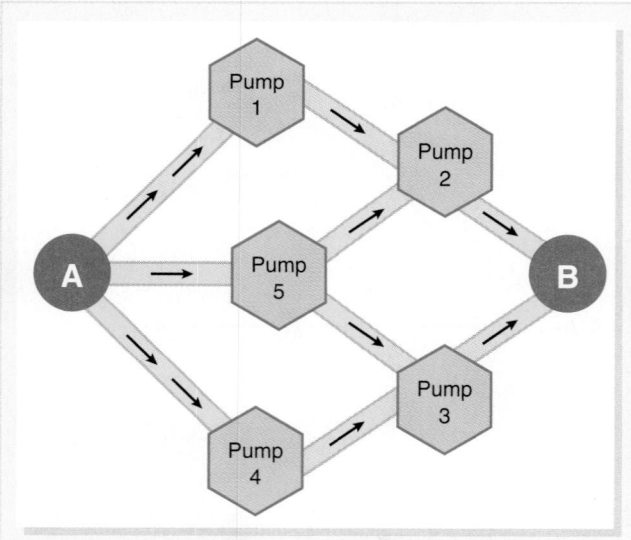

Figure 22.14 Each of these five pumps has a 50 percent chance of failure. What is the probability that some path from A to B is working?

- On the average, about how many stations need repair at any time?
- What is the probability that the 1–2 path is working at any time?

For any simulation, the following steps can serve as a useful guide:

1. *Identify key components and assumptions of the problem.* The key component in the water problem is the condition of a pump. Each pump is either working or not. The assumption is that the probability that a pump is working is $\frac{1}{2}$.
2. *Select a random device for the key components.* Any random device can be selected that has outcomes with the same probability as the key component—in this case, the pumps. Here a simple choice might be tossing a coin, with heads representing a working pump.
3. *Define a trial.* A *trial* consists of simulating a series of key components until the situation has been completely modelled one time. In this problem, a trial could consist of tossing a coin five times, with each toss representing a different pump.
4. *Conduct a large number of trials and record the information.* For this problem, it would be good to keep the record of heads and tails in groups of five because each set of five is one trial and represents all the pumps.
5. *Use the data to draw conclusions.* There are four possible paths for the water, each flowing through two of the five pumps. As they are numbered in the drawing, if any one of the pairs 1–2, 5–2, 5–3, and 4–3 is open, it makes no difference whether the other pumps are working. By counting the trials in which at least one of these four pairs of coins both came up heads, we can estimate the probability of water flowing. To answer the second question, the number of tails per trial can be averaged.

II ———————— *Pause and Reflect*

How would you answer the third question concerning the 1–2 path's being open?

The interesting problem-solving aspects of simulation activities are in the first three steps, where the real-world situation is translated into a model. Steps 4 and 5 are the same as solving a probability problem by experimental means. Translation of real-world information into models is the essence of applied mathematics.

Here are a few more examples of problems for which a simulation can be used to gather empirical data.

In a true-or-false test, what is the probability of getting 7 out of 10 questions correct by guessing alone? (*Key component:*

Answering a question. *Assumption:* **Chance of getting it correct is $\frac{1}{2}$.**)
    Simulation option: **Flip a coin 10 times for one trial.**

In a group of five people, what is the chance that two were born in the same month? (*Key component:* Month of birth. *Assumption:* All 12 months are equally likely.)
    Simulation option: **12-sided dice or 12 cards. Draw/roll one, replace, and draw/roll again.**

Casey's batting average is .350. What is the chance he will go hitless in a complete nine-inning game? (*Key component:* Getting a hit. *Assumptions:* Probability of a hit for each at-bat is 35. Casey will get to bat four times in the average game.)
    Simulation option: **Spinner with 35 percent shaded. Spin 4 times for one trial.**

Students often have trouble selecting an appropriate random device for their simulations. Spinners are an obvious choice since faces can be adjusted to match probabilities. Coins or two-coloured chips are useful for probabilities of $\frac{1}{2}$. A standard die can be used for probabilities that are multiples of $\frac{1}{6}$. There are also dice available from educational distributors with 4, 8, 12, and 20 sides.

Many relatively simple calculators include a key *Tech NOTES* that will produce random numbers that can be used to simulate experiments (e.g., 1 means true, 2 means false). Usually, the random numbers generated are between 0 and 1. Students who are going to use these random number generators will need some direction in using them to their advantage. Each number generated will likely have eight or more decimal places. A list of five numbers might look like this:

    0.8904433368
    0.0232028877
    0.1669322714
    0.1841957303
    0.5523714952

How could a list of decimals like this replace flipping a coin or spinning a spinner? Suppose each number was multiplied by 2. The results would be between 0 and 2. If you ignore the decimal part and focus only on the whole number part of these numbers, you would have a series of zeros and ones that could stand for heads and tails, boys

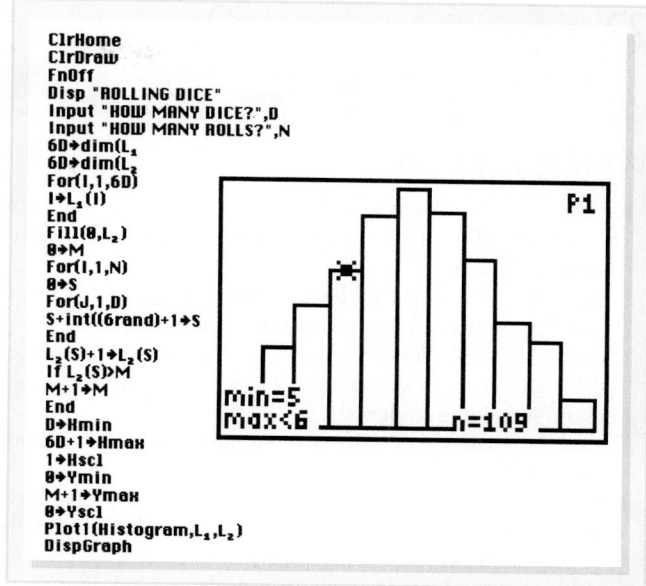

Figure 22.15 This TI-83 program can be used to simulate thousands of dice rolls and accumulate the results.

and girls, true and false, or any other pair of equally likely outcomes. For three outcomes, the same as a quarter–quarter–half spinner, you might decide to look at the first two digits of the number and assign values from 0 to 24 and 25 to 49 to the two quarter portions and values 50 to 99 for the one-half portion. Alternatively, each number could be multiplied by 4, ignoring the decimal part, which would result in random numbers 0, 1, 2, and 3. These numbers could then be assigned to the desired outcomes. In effect, random numbers can simulate any simple random device.

With graphing calculators, the random number generator can be used within a simple program that produces the numbers and stores them in a list. The list can then be displayed graphically. The program in Figure 22.15 is for a TI-83 calculator. It will "roll" as many dice as you request. At the end of the program, a histogram displays the totals for each sum. With the TRACE feature, the value for each bar in the graph is displayed. The figure shows the result of rolling two dice 1000 times. It took about $2\frac{1}{2}$ minutes to run the program and produce the graph. (Computer programs produce the result almost instantly.) The TI-73 calculator has a built-in coin and dice function that will graph the results of flipping a coin or rolling dice. ◆

Reflections on Chapter **22**

Writing to Learn

1. What are the first ideas about probability that students should develop? How can you help students with these ideas?
2. Activities 22.3 and 22.4 ("Race to the Top" and "Add, Then Tally") are each designed to help students see that some outcomes are more likely than others. What is the difference between these two activities? Why might this difference be useful in helping students?
3. Explain what is meant by the statement "Chance has no memory."
4. Describe the difference between experimental probability and theoretical probability. Will these ever be the same? Which is the "correct" probability?
5. What are the advantages of having students conduct experiments even before they attempt to figure out a theoretical probability?
6. Explain the law of large numbers. Describe an activity that might help students to appreciate this idea.
7. Describe the difference between a single-stage and a multi-stage experiment. Among multi-stage experiments, what are independent events and dependent events? Give an example of each.
8. Use an area model and a tree diagram to determine the probability for the following situation:

   Dad puts a $10 bill and three $5 bills in the first box. In a second box, he puts another $10 bill with just one $5 bill. For washing the car, Nathaniel gets to take one bill from the first box without looking

   and put it in the second box. After these have been well mixed, he then gets to take one bill from the second box. What is the probability that he will get $10?

   Design a simulation for the problem and try it out. Does your simulation agree with your theoretical probability?
9. The three outcomes of a sample space have probabilities of $\frac{1}{3}$, $\frac{1}{6}$, and $\frac{1}{2}$. Describe how you could use a random number generator on a calculator or computer to simulate these probabilities.

For Discussion and Exploration

1. The "Monty Hall Problem" has become a classic. In the game show, the contestant chooses from one of three doors. Behind one of the three doors is a big prize. Monty shows the contestant a goat behind one of the doors not selected, then offers the contestant the opportunity to switch doors. Does the contestant have a better chance of winning the big prize by switching, staying with the original choice, or is there no difference? There are numerous methods of answering this question. Make a convincing argument for your own answer based on the ideas and techniques in this chapter.
2. Go to the *Illuminations* Web site and find activities related to probability. Explore the tasks for various trials. Discuss (a) the advantages and disadvantages of virtual experiments, and (b) content within this chapter that could be discussed following student exploration on these applets.

Resources for Chapter **22**

Literature Connections

The books described here offer both fanciful and real-life data for investigating probability. Also listed in Recommended Readings is an article with two more great literature links.

Hockey Trivia for Kids   *Zweig, 2007*

Hockey Trivia for Kids 2   *Zweig, 2008*

These books are full of fun facts about everyone's favourite players and teams. The many facts that the author provides about male and female hockey players offer opportunities for students to make mathematical predictions and look at chances of occurrences.

Extreme Canadian Weather: Freakish Storms and Unexpected Disasters   *Dixon, 2005*

This non-fiction book describes extreme Canadian weather events from the past century and their implications for local people in the affected regions. Students can look at these events to make their own predictions. They can also investigate the role of probability/chance in predicting weather patterns.

Go Figure! A Totally Cool Book About Numbers   *Ball, 2005*

This wonderful book could be placed in every chapter of this book. About 40 different topics are covered, one of which is called "Take a Chance." This two-page spread is full of interesting contexts for probability, including a match-dropping experiment and genetics.

Do You Wanna Bet? Your Chance to Find Out About Probability   *Cushman, 1991*

The two characters in this book, Danny and Brian, become involved in everyday situations both in and out of school. Each situation has an element of probability involved. For example, two invitations to birthday parties are for the same day. What is the chance that two friends would have the same birthday? In another situation, Danny flips heads several times and readers are asked about Brian's chance on the next flip; an excellent opportunity to explore this possible misconception. These and other situations woven into an interesting story can each lead to a probability experiment or discussion. Students might create simulations to examine some of the same ideas.

My Little Sister Ate One Hare   *Grossman, 1996*

This counting book will appeal to elementary school students of all ages due to the somewhat gross thought of a little girl eating one rabbit, two snakes, three ants, and so on, including bats, mice, worms, and lizards. Upon eating ten peas, she throws up everything she ate.

Bay-Williams and Martinie (2004) used this tale with primary-grade students to create a wonderful introductory lesson on probability. If one of the things the little sister "spilled" on the floor is picked up at random in the process of cleaning up, what is the probability of getting a polliwog (or other animal or category of animal)? Students can use cards for the correct number of each thing eaten and approach the task experimentally and also compare the results to the theoretical probability.

Recommendations for Further Reading

Articles

Coffey, D. C., & Richardson, M. G. (2005). Rethinking fair games. *Mathematics Teaching in the Middle School, 10* (6), 298–303.
  Students explore the fairness of a matching game both experimentally and using a theoretical model. They then set out to create a variation of the game that would be fair by assigning points to a match and to a mismatch. A TI-73 program is included that simulates the revised game.

Edwards, T. G., & Hensien, S. M. (2000). Using probability experiments to foster discourse. *Teaching Children Mathematics, 6* (8), 524–529.
  Grade 5 students experiment with outcomes of flipping a coin, spinning a spinner, and rolling a die. The discourse is directed to the disparity between the observed outcomes and the theoretical probabilities. For example, is it reasonable that there are 77 heads out of 150 tosses?

Lawrence, A. (1999). From *The Giver* to *The Twenty-one Balloons*: Explorations with probability. *Mathematics Teaching in the Middle School, 4* (8), 504–509.
  Lawrence uses two award-winning books to motivate some nontrivial explorations for her middle school students. One task was to decide how often in a series of 50 births there will be 25 boys and 25 girls. In a related task, students tried to find out if it was more likely to have the same number of girls and boys in a small family or a large family. The ideas here are quite challenging and the results are interesting.

McMillen, S. (2008). Predictions and probability. *Teaching Children Mathematics, 14* (8), 454–463.
  This article provides a series of high-quality probability lessons—various contexts and models are used, as well as calculators. The lessons include a number of key concepts discussed in this chapter. Two handouts are provided.

Books

Currah, J., & Felling, J. (2001). *Probability and Statistics.* Edmonton: Box Cars & One-Eyed Jacks.
  This teacher resource book includes activities for grades 6–8 that present and review counting techniques, probability notation, and both theoretical and experimental probability. Activities using spinners and game rules are compared to theoretical calculation. Mean, median, and mode; graphs; range puzzles; and more are offered.

Shaughnessy, J. M. (2003). Research on students' understanding of probability. In J. Kilpatrick, W. G. Martin, & D. Schifter (Eds.), *A research companion to Principles and Standards for School Mathematics* (pp. 216–226). Reston, VA: NCTM.
  Shaughnessy's chapter offers interesting insights from research and makes useful recommendations. Teachers serious about the teaching of probability will benefit from checking this out.

Online Resources

Adjustable Spinner (Shodor)
www.shodor.org/interactivate/activities/AdjustableSpinner
  A virtual spinner can be adjusted to have any number of sections of any size. It can then be spun any number of times in increments of 100 000.

A Better Fire!! (Shodor's Project Interactivate)
www.shodor.org/interactivate/activities/ABetterFire
  This site offers a realistic simulation of actual forest fires, with controls for wind speed and direction to add more realism. The simulation uses virtual "die" to see if a tree should be planted for each square. Then the fire is set and allowed to burn. An excellent authentic use of simulations.

Box Model (NLVM)
http://nlvm.usu.edu/en/nav/frames_asid_146_g_3_t_5.html
  The applet permits creating a box of up to 16 coloured cubes including the possibility of duplicates. Cubes can then be drawn at random (with replacement). A bar graph shows the results that can be compared to the theoretical results.

Coin Tossing (NLVM)
http://nlvm.usu.edu/en/nav/frames_asid_305_g_3_t_5.
html

A single coin can be "tossed" any number of times. The results are shown in order, which can help with the concept of randomness. A bar graph shows results.

Marble Mania
www.sciencenetlinks.com/interactives/marble/
marblemania.html

This applet explores randomness and probability. You'll be able to control how many and what colour marbles to place in a virtual marble bag. An advantage of this applet is that you can run a large number of different trials in a short amount of time.

Probability (Shodor)
www.shodor.org/interactivate/activities/ExpProbability/

A spinner can be created with up to four regions or two like dice can be made with each side adjustable from 1 to 6. The devices can then be used in experiments.

Exploring Probability (Jim Reed)
http://argyll.epsb.ca/jreed/math8/strand4/201.htm

This applet provides opportunities for students to work with the concepts of experimental and theoretical probability. Activities involve working with dice and spinners as they engage in different motivating games. Other probability-related concepts are also available at this site.

Games from the Aboriginal People of North America
http://MathCentral.uregina.ca/RR/database/RR.09.00/
treptau1/

This site offers provides access to games of chance originating from Aboriginal people's culture.

Spinner Game
http://cemc2.math.uwaterloo.ca/mathfrog/english/kidz/
index.shtml

Spinner game is just one of the many games and activities for the different strands of math found at this site, maintained by the University of Waterloo.

Spinners (NLVM)
http://nlvm.usu.edu/en/nav/frames_asid_186_g_l_t_l.html

This site provides a spinner that can be customized and used for experiments.

PEARSON
myeducationlab will help you improve your understanding of the concepts taught in this textbook and in your course. This online tool includes videos of real classroom experiences, sample lesson plans, simulations, case studies, and links to important educational and teaching Web sites that will help you make the transition from student to teacher. As you study in your course and with this textbook, please follow along in *MyEducationLab*. Use it! Explore it! And improve your knowledge and your grade!

Chapter 23
Developing Concepts of Exponents, Integers, and Real Numbers

Students in the upper elementary grades need to develop a more complete understanding of the number system, extending whole numbers to integers, starting to think of fractions as rational numbers (both positive and negative), and beginning to appreciate the completeness of the real number system.

The ideas presented in this chapter build on ideas that have been developed throughout this book. Exponents are used in algebraic expressions and add to the operations. Scientific notation expands how large and small numbers are represented, building on place-value concepts. Integers open up the counting numbers less than 0 and therefore extend the number line (as well as operations) to include negative values. In grade 7, students should be developing an understanding of operations with rational numbers. In grade 8, students use exponents and scientific notation to describe very large and very small numbers. As well, they apply their knowledge of square root to work with concepts such as the Pythagorean theorem.

Big Ideas

1. Exponential notation is a way to express repeated products of the same number. Specifically, powers of 10 express very large and very small numbers in an economical manner.

2. Integers add the negative (and positive) counting numbers to the number system, so that every number has both size and a positive or negative relationship to other numbers. A negative number is the opposite of the positive number of the same size.

3. Whole numbers, fractions, and integers are rational numbers. Every rational number can be expressed as a fraction.

4. Many numbers are not rational; the irrationals can be expressed only symbolically or approximately using a close rational number. Examples: $\sqrt{2} \approx 1.41421...$ and $\pi \approx 3.14159....$

Mathematics Content Connections

The ideas in this chapter represent an expansion of the ways in which we represent numbers. These representations expand or enhance earlier ideas of whole numbers, fractions, and decimals.

- **Whole-Number Place Value, Fractions, and Decimals** (Chapters 11, 15, and 17): When exponential notation is combined with decimal notation, very small and very large numbers can be written efficiently. Decimals and fractions help to describe the difference between rational and irrational numbers. Negative numbers extend the number line in both directions.

- **Algebra** (Chapter 14): The symbolic manipulation of numbers, including the rules for order of operations, is exactly the same as is used with variables. The study of integers helps with the notion of "opposite," represented by a negative sign: $^-6$ is the opposite of $^+6$ and ^-x is the opposite of ^+x, regardless of whether x is negative or positive. Exponents can also be variables, giving rise to exponential functions.

Exponents

As numbers in our technological world get very small or very large, expressing them in standard form is cumbersome. Exponential notation is much more efficient for conveying numerical or quantitative information.

Exponents in Expressions and Equations

Students often get confused in algebra trying to remember the rules of exponents. For example, when you raise numbers to powers, do you add or multiply the exponents? This is an example of procedural knowledge that is often learned without supporting conceptual knowledge. Before algebra, students should have ample opportunity to explore working with exponents on whole numbers rather than with letters or variables. By doing so, they are able to deal directly with the concept and actually generate the rules themselves.

A *whole-number exponent* is simply shorthand for repeated multiplication of a number times itself; for example, $3^4 = 3 \times 3 \times 3 \times 3$.

Conventions of symbolism must also be learned. These are arbitrary rules with no conceptual basis. The first is that *an exponent applies to its immediate base*. For example, in the expression $2 + 5^3$, the exponent 3 applies only to the 5, so the expression is equal to $2 + (5 \times 5 \times 5)$. However, in the expression $(2 + 5)^3$, the 3 is an exponent of the quantity $2 + 5$ and is evaluated as $(2 + 5) \times (2 + 5) \times (2 + 5)$, or $7 \times 7 \times 7$.

Students' first encounter with exponents should be squares and cubes, numbers that can be represented geometrically. For example, consider the following problem:

Mina knows that square pens are the most economical for the amount of space they provide. Can you construct for Mina a table that shows the areas of square pens whose fencing measures between 4 and 10 metres on each side.

Students may set up a table similar to Figure 23.1, showing possible areas for the pen.

Students can also explore algebraic growing patterns involving squares and/or cubes. The Painted Cube Problem, which involves both squares and cubes, is a popular investigation that appears in many places (see Figure 23.2). In this problem the faces of the cube are squares. Therefore, the sides getting painted are also squares, and the growth pattern is a square. The cubes getting no sides painted are those hidden inside the painted cube. In a $2 \times 2 \times 2$ structure, there are 0 cubes inside. However, in a $3 \times 3 \times 3$ structure, there is one cube hidden inside that will not get painted. This "hidden cube" grows at a cubic rate. In exploring the pattern, students get experience with squares and cubes.

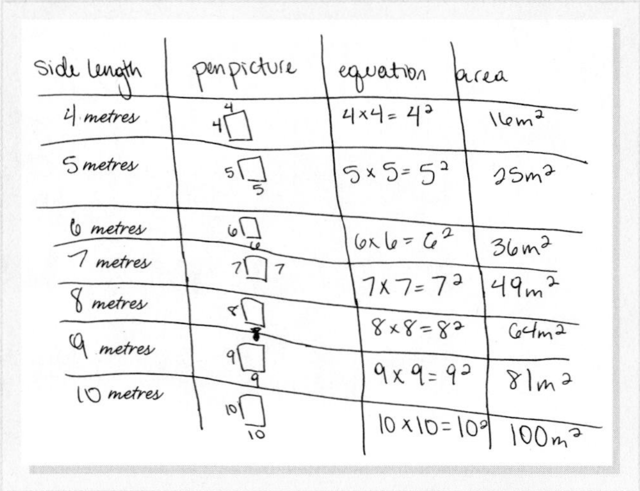

Figure 23.1 A student records possibilities for making a square pen.

Order of Operations   The other convention involves the *order of operations:* Multiplication and division are always done before addition and subtraction. Since exponentiation is repeated multiplication, it also is done before addition and subtraction. In the expression $5 + 4^2 - 6 \div 3$, 4^2 and $6 \div 3$ are done first. Therefore, the expression is evaluated as $5 + 16 - 2 = 21 - 2 = 19$.

Pause and Reflect

Try evaluating the same expression in left-to-right order. Do you get 4?

Parentheses are used to group operations that are to be done first. Therefore, in $(5 + 4) \times 2 - 6 \div 3$, the addition inside the parentheses can be done first, or the distributive property can be used, and the final result is 16. The phrase "*P*lease *e*xcuse *m*y *d*ear *A*unt *S*ally" is sometimes used to help students recall that operations inside *p*arentheses are done first, then *e*xponentiation, then *m*ultiplication and *d*ivision before *a*ddition and *s*ubtraction.

Although this phrase is a good mnemonic, it can lead students to think that addition is done before subtraction and multiplication comes before division. An improvement might involve writing it as a verse in rows that show the last four words as pairs. Another option is to just use the acronym "BEDMAS," with the letters listed in rows to indicate order:

B = brackets
E = exponents
DM = division and multiplication
   (whichever is first from left to right)
AS = addition and subtraction
   (whichever is first from left to right)

Sometimes, students' only experience is to simplify expressions applying the order. You can both assess and strengthen

Organize your data in a table like the one below.

Edge Length of Large Cube	Number of Centimetre Cubes	Number of Centimetre Cubes Painted On			
		3 faces	2 faces	1 face	0 faces
2					
3					
4					
5					
6					

Study the patterns in the table.

1. Describe the relationship between the edge length of the large cube and the total number of centimetre cubes.

2. Describe the relationship between the edge length of the large cube and the number of centimetre cubes painted on.

    a. three faces   **b.** two faces   **c.** one face   **d.** zero faces

Figure 23.2 The Painted Cube Problem provides a context for exploring squares and cubes.

Source: Adapted from *Connected Mathematics: Frogs, Fleas and Painted Cubes: Quadratic Relationships.* by Glenda Lappan, James T. Fey, William M. Fitzgerald, Susan N. Friel, & Elizabeth Difanis Phillips. Copyright © 2006 by Michigan State University. Used by permission of Pearson Education, Inc. All rights reserved.

their understanding of this process by having them write equations that indicate the proper order of operations, as in the activity below.

Activity 23.1

Guess My Number

This algebraic activity involves the teacher giving hints about a number and students thinking backwards to find it (using logical reasoning). Students create equations, as in the following three examples, using brackets appropriately, to reflect the teacher's clues:

- **I am thinking of a number; I add 5, double it, and get 22. [$(n + 5) \times 2 = 22$]**
- **I am thinking of a number; I subtract 2, square it, and get 36. [$(n - 2)^2 = 36$]**
- **I am thinking of a number; I double it, add 2, cube it, and get 1000. [$(2n + 2)^3 = 1000$]**

The writing stories activity is another excellent tool for learning and applying the order of operations. Students can

be asked to write an expression using all the operations and brackets, for example, $(4 + 2)^2 \times 2 \div 4$. They then write a story, using a context of their choice to fit the expression they created (Golembo, 2000).

 Writing stories is an excellent assessment of students' understanding of the order of operations. Golembo (2006) includes a student page and assessment pages. As students write expressions or stories, determine whether they realize that multiplication and division (and addition and subtraction) are equal in order and should be solved left to right. Also, ask students questions to see whether they understand when brackets are optional and when they are necessary. ◆

Exponential Notation on the Calculator   Most scientific calculators employ "algebraic logic" that evaluates expressions using the order of operations and also allows grouping with parentheses. However, with the exception of the TI-Math-Mate and other newer calculators designed specifically for school use, most simple four-function calculators do not use algebraic logic. Operations are processed as they are entered. On calculators without algebraic logic, the following two keying sequences produce the same results:

Key: → 3 [+] 2 [×] 7 [=]
Display → 3   2 (5   7   35

Key: → 3 [+] 2 [=] [×] 7 [=]
Display → 3   2   5   7   35

Whenever an operation sign is pressed, the effect is the same as pressing [=] and then the operation. Of course, neither result is correct for the expressions $3 + 2 \times 7$, which should be evaluated as $3 + 14$, or 17. Calculators designed for upper grades do use algebraic logic and include parenthesis keys so that both $3 + 2 \times 7$ and $(3 + 2) \times 7$ can be keyed in the order that the symbols appear. See the difference in the following displays:

Key: → 3 [+] 2 [×] 7 [=]
Display → 3   2   7   17

Notice that the following display does not change when [×] is pressed and a right parenthesis is never displayed. Instead, the expression that the right parenthesis encloses is calculated and that result displayed.

Key: → [(] 3 [+] 2 [)] [×] 7 [=]
Display → [3   2 [5]   7   35

Some basic calculators and graphing calculators show the expression $3 + 2 \times (6^2 - 4)$. Nothing is evaluated until you press [Enter] or [EXE]. Then the result appears on the next line to the right of the screen:

3 + 2 * (6² − 4)
                          67

Moreover, the last expression entered can be recalled and edited so that students can see how different expressions are evaluated. Only minimum key presses are required.

3 + 2 * (6² − 4)   67
(3 + 2) * (6² − 4)   160
(3 + 2) * 6² − 4   176
3 + 2 * 6² − 4   71

The simple four-function calculator remains a powerful tool regardless of its limitations. For example, to evaluate 3^8, press 3 [×] [=] [=] [=] [=] [=] [=] [=]. (The first press of [=] will result in 9, or 3×3.) Students will be fascinated by how quickly numbers grow. Enter any number, press [×], and then repeatedly press [=] Try two-digit numbers. Try 0.2.

Give students ample opportunity to explore expressions involving exponents. When experience has provided a firm background, the rules of exponents will make sense and should not require rote memorization.

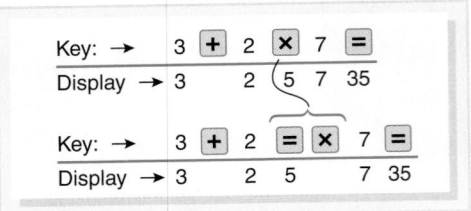

Activity 23.2

Entering Expressions

Provide students with numerical expressions to evaluate with simple four-function calculators. Ask: "How will you have to enter these correctly in order to apply the order of operations?" Rewrite the expression the way it will be entered. Here are some examples of expressions.

$3 + 4 \times 8$	$3^6 + 2^6$	$3^4 \times 7 - 5^2$	$3^4 \times 5^2$
$4 \times 8 + 3$	$(3 + 2)^6$	$(3 \times 7)^4 - 5 \times 2$	$(3 \times 5)^6$

$\dfrac{5^3 \times 5^2}{5^6}$	$4 \times 3 - 2^3 \times 5 + 23 \times 9$	$\dfrac{4 \times 3^5}{2}$ $4 + \dfrac{3^5}{2}$

Accommodation

For those students experiencing difficulty with exponents, have them write equivalent expressions without exponents or include parentheses to indicate explicit groupings. For example:

$$(7 \times 2^3 - 5)^3 = (7 \times (2 \times 2 \times 2) - 5) \times$$
$$(7 \times (2 \times 2 \times 2) - 5) \times$$
$$(7 \times (2 \times 2 \times 2) - 5)$$
$$= ((7 \times 8) - 5) \times$$
$$((7 \times 8) - 5) \times$$
$$((7 \times 8) - 5)$$
$$= (56 - 5) \times (56 - 5) \times (56 - 5)$$
$$= 51 \times 51 \times 51$$

When discussing results, emphasize the procedures rather than the answer. For many expressions, there is more than one way to proceed, and one may be easier to do or to understand than another. Sharing different strategies is important.

Of course, calculators with algebraic logic will automatically produce correct results. Yet it remains important for students to know the rules for the order of operations. The calculator should not replace an understanding of the rules. The rules apply to symbolic manipulation in algebra and must be understood for mental calculations or for using with a basic calculator.

Negative Exponents

When students begin to explore exponents and have also experienced negative integers, it is interesting to consider what it might mean to raise a number to a negative power. For example, what does 2^{-4} mean? The following are two related options for exploring the possibilities of negative exponents. First, in the spirit of patterns in mathematics, examine a pattern of numbers, and see how it might best be expanded. As with large numbers, the powers of 10 are good to explore because they are directly related to place value. Have students consider 10^n as follows:

$$10^4 = 10\ 000$$
$$10^3 = 1000$$
$$10^2 = 100$$
$$10^1 = 10$$
$$10^0 = ?$$
$$10^{-1} = ?$$

In this sequence, the most obvious entry for 10^0 is 1, which is the *definition* of 10^0. That is, it is a convention that 10 or any other non-zero number raised to the power 0 is 1.

So what is 10^{-1}? If the pattern is to continue, the 1 should move to the right of the decimal:

$$10^0 = 1$$
$$10^{-1} = 0.1$$
$$10^{-2} = 0.01$$
$$10^{-3} = 0.001$$

and so on. Notice how each of these numbers is written as a fraction:

$$10^{-1} = 0.1 \quad = \frac{1}{10}$$
$$10^{-2} = 0.01 \quad = \frac{1}{100} \quad = \frac{1}{10^2}$$
$$10^{-3} = 0.001 \quad = \frac{1}{1000} \quad = \frac{1}{10^3}$$

Second, students can explore negative exponents on a calculator. For example, tell students, "Use a calculator to see if you can figure out what things like 4^{-3} or 2^{-5} equal." The calculator should, of course, never be seen as the *reason* for anything in mathematics, but here you are searching for a notation convention. If the calculator has decimal-to-fraction conversion, suggest that students use that feature to help develop the meaning of negative exponents. Figure 23.3 gives an example of how this might look on a graphing calculator.

Scientific Notation

The more common it becomes to find very large or very small numbers in our daily lives, the more important it is to have convenient ways to represent them. One option is to say and write numbers in their common form. However, this practice can at times be cumbersome. Another option is to use exponential notation and our base-ten place-value

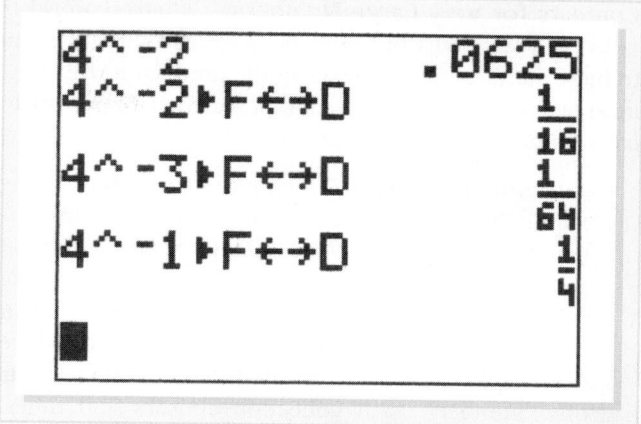

Figure 23.3 Graphing calculators routinely evaluate expressions as decimals. However, they also convert decimals to fractions. This figure shows the screen of a TI-73 calculator. The F–D key converts fractions to decimals (and decimals to fractions) as shown here.

system—scientific notation. In scientific notation, a number is expressed as a product of a decimal number between 1 and 10, with only one digit to the left of the decimal place times a power of 10. The power of 10 is equal to the place value of the digits to the right of the decimal number. For example, 3 414 000 000 can be written as 3.414×10^9. Because the decimal point has been moved nine places to the left (divided by 1 billion) in the original number, it is necessary to multiply by 1 billion (10^9) in order not to change its value.

Different notations have different purposes and values. Consider this fact: In 1990, the population of the world was more than 5 050 700 000 persons, about 1 billion fewer than in the year 2000. This can be expressed in various ways:

- 5 billion 50 million 700 thousand
- 5 050 700 000
- 5.0507×10^9
- Less than 5.1 billion
- A little more than 5 billion

Each way of stating the number has value and purpose in different contexts. Rather than spending time on exercises converting numbers from standard form to scientific notation, consider large numbers found in newspapers, magazines, and atlases. How are they written? How are they said aloud? When are they rounded? When not and why? What forms of the numbers seem best for the purposes?

 *Standards* reminds us that large numbers and scientific notation are used in various contexts. "A newspaper headline may proclaim, 'Clean-Up Costs from Oil Spill Exceed $2 Billion!' or a science textbook may indicate that the number of red blood cells in the human body is about 1.9×10^{13}" (p. 217).

Contexts for Very Large Numbers The real world is full of very large quantities and measures. We see references to huge numbers in the media all the time. Unfortunately, most of us have not developed an appreciation for extremely large numbers. Here are a few examples:

- A provincial lottery in which players pick 6 numbers out of 49 allows over 10 billion possible number combinations. There are $49 \times 48 \times 47 \times 46 \times 45 \times 44$ possible ways that the balls could come out of the hopper (10 068 347 520). But generally the order in which they are picked is not important. Since there are $6 \times 5 \times 4 \times 3 \times 2 \times 1 = 720$ different arrangements of 6 numbers, each collection appears 720 times. Therefore, there are *only* 10 068 347 520 divided by 720 possible lottery numbers, or in other words, 1 out of 13 983 816 chances to win.
- An estimate of the size of the universe is 40 billion light-years. One light-year is the number of kilometres light travels in *one year*. The speed of light is 298 050.7 kilometres per *second*, or 25 751 580 480 kilometres in a single day.
- The human body has about 100 billion cells.
- The distance to the sun is about 150 million kilometres.
- The population of the world in 2008 was about 6.71 billion.

Connecting these large numbers to meaningful points of reference can help students get a handle on their true magnitude. For example, suppose students determine that the population in their city or town is about 500 000 people. They can then figure that it would take about 12 500 cities of the same population size to generate the population of the world. Or suppose students determine that there are about 4600 km between Fredericton, New Brunswick, and Edmonton, Alberta. This calculation would mean that it would take over 32 000 trips back and forth between these two cities to equal the distance between the earth and the sun. Building from such familiar or meaningful reference points can help students develop benchmarks to work with and make sense of large numbers.

The following activity uses real data and asks students to use scientific notation and to create a scale drawing.

Activity 23.3

How Far Away Is the Sun?

A problem-based way to explore scientific notation is to have students research planetary distances from the sun (in kilometres), record the data in scientific notation, and create a scale illustration of the distances. Alternatively, the following figures can be provided:

Mercury	57 909 000	Jupiter	778 400 000
Venus	108 200 000	Saturn	1 423 600 000
Earth	149 600 000	Uranus	2 867 000 000
Mars	227 940 000	Neptune	4 488 400 000

Connecting very large and very small numbers to meaningful points of reference can help students get a handle on the numbers' true magnitude. For example, a typical rain or water drop, such as the one shown here, spans about 3 millimetres. By contrast, NGC 1309, a face-on spiral galaxy, spans about 30 000 light-years (a light year is approximately 9.46 trillion kilometres). Comparing familiar things such as raindrops and the night sky may help students grasp the concepts of *miniscule* and *infinite*.

Contexts for Very Small Numbers   As with large numbers, it is extremely important to use real examples of very small numbers. Without real contexts, you may be tempted to resort to drill exercises that have little meaning for students. Connecting these small numbers to points of reference can help students conceptualize how very tiny these numbers really are, as shown by the following real-world examples:

- The length of a DNA strand in a cell is about 10^{-7} metres. This is also measured as 1000 *angstroms*. (Based on this information, how long is an angstrom?) For perspective, the diameter of a human hair is about 2.54×10^{-5} metres.
- Human hair grows at the rate of 10^{-8} kilometres per hour.
- Garden snails have been clocked at about 4.8×10^{-2} kilometres per hour.
- The chances of winning a lottery, based on selecting six numbers from a possible 44 (1 to 44), is 1 in 7.059 million. That is a probability of less than 1.4×10^{-10}.
- The mass of one atom of hydrogen is 0.000 000 000 000 000 000 000 001 675 grams, while the mass of one paper clip is about 1 gram.
- It takes sound 0.28 seconds (2.8×10^{-1}) to travel the length of a football field. In contrast, a TV signal travels 1.6 kilometres in about 0.000 005 368 seconds, or 5.3×10^{-6} seconds. A TV viewer at home hears the football being kicked before the receiver on the field does.

Scientific Notation on the Calculator   Students in elementary school learn how to multiply by 10, by 100, and by 1000 by simply adding the appropriate number of zeros. Help students expand this idea by examining powers of 10 on a calculator that handles exponents.

Activity **23.4**

Exploring Powers of 10

Have students use any calculator that permits entering exponents to explore some of the following:

a. Explore 10^n for various values of *n*. What patterns do you notice? What does 1E15 mean? (1E15 is the typical calculator form of 1×10^{15}.)

b. Find different expressions for one thousand, one million, one billion, one trillion. What patterns are there in expressions you found?

c. Enter 45 followed by a string of zeros. How many will your calculator permit? What happens when you press [Enter]? What does 4.5E10 mean?

d. What does 5.689E6 mean? Can you enter this another way?

e. Try sums like $(4.5 \times 10^n) + (27 \times 10^k)$ for different values of *n* and *k*. What can you find out?

f. What happens with products of numbers like those in item (e)?

It is useful to become comfortable with the power-of-10 expressions in Activity 23.4. Students should eventually discover that when scientific or graphing calculators display numbers with more digits than the display will hold, they use scientific notation. For example, on a TI-73, the product of 45 000 000 × 8 000 000 is displayed as 3.6E14, meaning 3.6×10^{14}, or 360 000 000 000 000 (360 trillion).

Ask students why there are only 13 zeros. What happens when the numbers in the computation do not involve a lot of zeros?

 ——————— *Pause and Reflect*

With each factor in the product expressed in scientific notation—$(4.5 \times 10^7) \times (8 \times 10^6)$, or 4.5E7 × 8.0E6—can you compute the result mentally?

Notice the advantages of scientific notation, especially for multiplication and division. Here the significant digits can be multiplied mentally ($4.5 \times 8 = 36$) and the exponents added to produce almost instantly 36×10^{13} or 3.6×10^{14}.

Integers

Almost daily, students have some interaction with negative numbers or experience phenomena that negative numbers can model. Some examples:

- A loss of money
- Negative acceleration of a car
- Below-zero temperature
- Below sea level

In fact, almost any concept that is quantified and has direction probably has both a positive and a negative value.

Generally, negative values are introduced with *integers—*the whole numbers and their negatives or opposites—instead of with fractions or decimals.

However, it is a mistake to stop with integer values, because students must understand where numbers like $^-4.5$ and $^-1\frac{3}{4}$ belong in relation to the integers. In fact, research has shown that students often place $^-1\frac{3}{4}$ between $^-1$ and 0 instead of between $^-2$ and $^-1$.

Contexts for Exploring Integers

As with any new types of numbers that students encounter, it is important to start with familiar contexts so that students can use prior knowledge to build meaning. Often, when working with integers, students become confused regarding which number is bigger or in which direction they are moving when carrying out operations. Therefore, having a context is particularly important. As students learn to compare and compute, they can use contexts to ground their thinking and justify their answers. Some contexts for integers involve quantities while others involve contexts that are linear.

Pause and Reflect

Review the list of contexts in the introduction to this section. Which do you think are quantity contexts and which are linear contexts? In the following sections, both quantity and linear contexts are discussed, followed by models for illustrating integers for both types.

Quantity Contexts *Golf Scores.* In golf, scores are often written in relationship to a number considered par for the course. So, if par is 70 for the course, a golfer who ends the day at 67 has a score of $^-3$. Consider a player in a tournament with day-end scores of $^+5$, $^-2$, $^-3$, $^+1$. What would be her or his final result for the tournament? How did you think about it? You could match up the positive and the negatives (in this case, $^+5$ with $^-2$ and $^-3$ to get a net result of 0), then see what is left (in this case, $^+1$). The notion that opposites (5 and $^-5$) equal zero is a big idea in the teaching of integers. You can post a mixed-up leader board of golf scores and ask students to order them from first through tenth place. Emphasize that first place is the *lowest* score—and therefore the *smallest* number. As you can see, golf scores provide a great context for comparing and computing with integers.

Money in the Bank: *Debits and Credits*. Suppose that you are looking at your bank statement. At any time, it shows how many dollars you have in your account. Each month there are dollars deposited into the account (credited) and dollars taken out of the account (debited) for personal use and to pay bills. At the end of the month, the difference between the debit total and the credit total plus the opening balance tells you how much money you have in the bank. If the total of the opening balance plus the credits is more than the debits, the account has a positive balance, or it is "in the black." If there are more debits than the total of the opening balance plus the credits, the account has a negative cash value, or it is "in the red." With the bank statement context, it is possible to explore addition and subtraction of integers (signed quantities), as in the example illustrated in Figure 23.4.

Hockey. A hockey player's plus/minus (+/−) rating is one of the statistics that contributes to an overall season ranking. It comes into play when two teams are at even strength in a game (i.e., neither team has a penalty against it). If a player is on the ice when his team scores a goal he receives a plus (or $^+1$) rating. If a goal is scored against the team, then a minus (or $^-1$) is given. Plus/minus scores are calculated for every game and a single value assigned. This single value contributes to the player's overall season rating, which is based on the total of every plus/minus

Credits		Debits		Balance
In	Out	In	Out	**Begin** 0
50				+50
		30		+20
	10			+10
		50		−40
25				−15
			20	+5

Figure 23.4 A simplified bank statement.

game score. Similar to the debits and credits scenario, the plus/minus scores can be used for discussing positive and negative quantities. The table below shows the plus/minus scores for 12 of the top 30 NHL players for 10 (of approximately 80) games played during the 2008–2009 season. Students could work in pairs to choose three favourite players and figure out for each player possible single value scores for each of the 10 games that resulted in the plus/minus score shown in the table. Students could then compare with other pairs the 10 numbers they chose that resulted in the plus/minus score shown in the chart for a player.

NHL Player	Plus/Minus (1/−) Score
Evgeni Malkin	17
Alex Ovechkin	8
Sidney Crosby	3
Ilya Kovalchuk	−12
Ryan Getzlaf	5
Jarome Iginla	−2
Nicklas Backstrom	16
Martin St. Louis	4
Rick Nash	11
Marc Savard	22
Jason Spezza	−14
Eric Staal	15

Linear Contexts Many of the real contexts for negative numbers are linear. In addition, the number line provides a good tool for learning the operations that relates well to what the students have done with whole number and fraction operations.

Temperature. The "number line" measuring temperature is vertical. Since most students have experienced temperatures below zero, demonstrating negative integers, or know about temperatures at the North or South Pole, this context may be the most familiar to students. A good starting activity for students is finding where various temperatures belong on a thermometer. For example, Figure 23.5 displays a thermometer marked in increments of five degrees, and students are asked to place on the number line the following temperatures from a week in Saskatchewan: 8, ⁻2, ⁻2, 4, ⁻8. Ask students to order them from the coldest to the warmest (least to greatest). Temperatures as a context have the advantage that you can also use fraction and decimal values.

Altitude. Altitude, another vertical number-line model, is also a good context for integers. The altitudes of sites below sea level are negative. The Dead Sea, Israel, with an altitude of ⁻481 metres is considered to be the lowest point on Earth. Badwater, California, in Death Valley, with an altitude of ⁻86 metres, is the lowest point in North America. Positive values for altitude include Mount Everest, the tallest mountain in the world at 8848 metres and Mount McKinley, the tallest mountain in North America at 6194 metres. Students can order the altitudes of various places around the world (data easily found through a Google search on the Web) or find the difference between the altitudes of two different places—a good context for subtraction of integers. Beyond exploring real altitudes, using a model of a hill and a valley over which a toy car moves up and down can be a graphic way to explore integer operations.

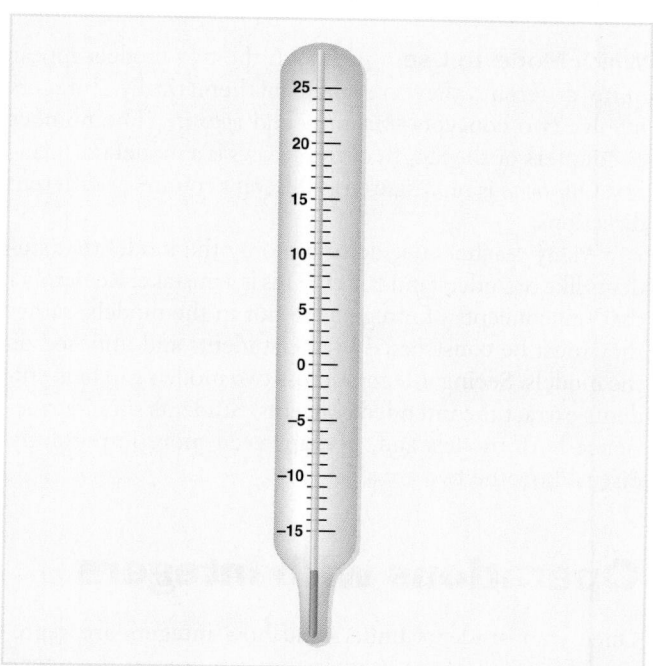

Figure 23.5 Thermometers are an excellent tool for exploring positive and negative numbers.

 The calculator is another model that might be explored early in the discussion of signed numbers. It gives correct and immediate results that students can justify on a number line or with one of the contexts described.

Have students explore subtraction problems such as 5 – 8 = ? and discuss the results. (Be aware that the negative sign appears in different places on different calculators.)

Students can benefit by using the calculator along with the intuitive models and questions mentioned earlier. For example, how can you get from ⁻5 to ⁻17 by addition? 13 minus *what* is 15?

Meaning of Negative Numbers

Negative numbers are defined in terms of whole numbers. Therefore, the definition of negative 3 is the solution to the equation 3 + ? = 0. In general, the *opposite of n* is the solution to $n + ? = 0$. If n is a positive number, the *opposite of n* is a negative number. Therefore, the set of integers consists of the positive whole numbers, the opposites of the positive whole numbers, or negative numbers, and 0, which is neither positive nor negative. This is the definition found in student textbooks. Like many aspects of mathematics, abstract or symbolic definitions are best understood when conceptual connections link to the formal ideas.

Absolute Value   The distance between two points, either on the number line or in the plane, is often an important concern, especially in applications of mathematics. We need to be able, for example, to tell a computer how far a train is from a station regardless of whether it is to the north or the south on the track. "Distance" can also refer to a mathematical distance as in the amount of possible error between a measurement and the true value, and the measures could be time, voltage, and so on.

The *absolute value of a number* is defined as the distance between that number and zero. The notation for absolute value consists of two vertical bars, one on either side of the number. Thus, the absolute value of a number n is $|n|$. Opposites, such as ⁻12 and ⁺12, are the same distance from zero, and therefore have the same absolute value.

Notations   Because students have only seen the negative sign when doing subtraction, the symbolic notation for integers may be confusing. It is important to help students understand and use the appropriate symbols. Sometimes students may find it confusing to see the negative sign appear at different heights (e.g., −7 and ⁻7). There are instances where parentheses (brackets) are placed around a number to separate it from the operation (e.g., 8 − (−5). Students have not seen parentheses used in this way and may think there is multiplication involved. It is important to connect to their prior knowledge and add to it. In this case, you might then ask students, "When do we use parentheses in mathematics?" Students might say they are used for grouping a series of computations to show what to do first and that it can also mean multiplication. Point out that parentheses are also used to make a number sentence more readable—separating the negative number from the operation.

On graphing calculators these expressions are entered using the "negative" key and the "subtraction" key. The difference between those two symbols is evident in the display. The redundant superscript plus signs are not shown. Students can see that 3 + ⁻5 and 3 – 5 each results in –2 and that 3 – ⁻5 and 3 + 5 are equal. ◆

Two Models for Integer Operations

Two models, one denoted by quantity and the other by linear operations, are popular for helping students understand comparisons and the four operations ($+$, $-$, $\times$, and $\div$) with integers.

Counters   One model consists of counters in two different colours: yellow for positive counts and red for negative counts. Two different coloured counters cancel each other out, resulting in zero (⁺1 + ⁻1 = 0). Now consider money: If yellows are credits and reds are debits, 5 yellows and 7 reds represent the same amount as 2 reds or 2 debits. This is an equivalent representation of ⁻2 (see Figure 23.6). It is important with this model that students understand that it is always possible to add to or remove from a pile of counters any number of pairs consisting of one positive and one negative counter, without changing its value. (Intuitively, this is like adding equal quantities of debits and credits.) The actions of addition and subtraction are the same as for whole numbers; addition is joining or adding counters, and subtraction is removing or taking away counters.

Number Lines   The other commonly used model is the number line. A number line has several advantages. First, it shows the distance from 0 (or the absolute value of the number). In addition, it is an excellent tool for modelling the operations. Jumps can be shown in the same way as with whole numbers and fractions (see Chapters 12 and 16). Students can see that integer moves to the left go to smaller

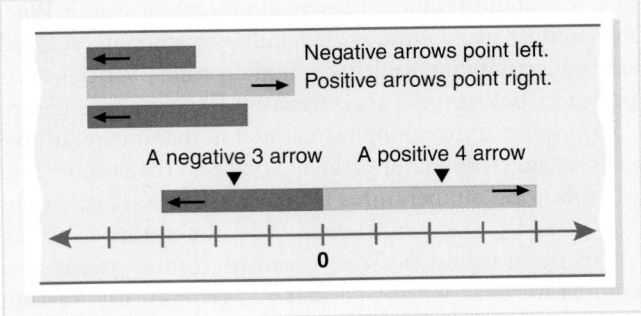

Figure 23.7 Number-line model for integers.

numbers and moves to the right go to larger numbers. Also, the number line allows students to explore non-integer negative and positives values (e.g., $-4\frac{1}{2} + 3\frac{1}{4}$) that cannot be modelled very well with counters. A thermometer could be considered a vertical model of a number line.

It is important for students to understand that directed distances, not points on the number line, are the models of the integers. Arrows to show distance and direction can be used to model operations on the number line. For example, 4 can be modelled with an arrow four units long pointing to the right, and ⁻3 can be modelled with an arrow three units long pointing to the left (see Figure 23.7). The arrows help students think of integer quantities as directed distances. A positive arrow never points left, and a negative arrow never points right. Furthermore, each arrow is a quantity with both length (magnitude or absolute value) and direction (sign). These properties are constant for each arrow, regardless of its position on the number line.

Which Model to Use   Although the two models appear quite different, they are alike mathematically. Integers involve two concepts—*quantity* and *opposite*. The number of counters or the length of the arrows is a model for quantity. Opposite is represented as different colours or different directions.

Many teachers decide to use only the model that students like or understand better. This is a mistake! Remember that the concepts of integers are not in the models; rather they must be constructed by the students and imposed on the models. Seeing integers across two models can help students extract the intended concepts. Students should experience both models and, perhaps even more importantly, discuss how the two are alike.

Operations with Integers

Once your students understand how integers are represented by each of the models, you can present the operations for the integers in the form of problems. In other words, rather than explaining how addition of integers

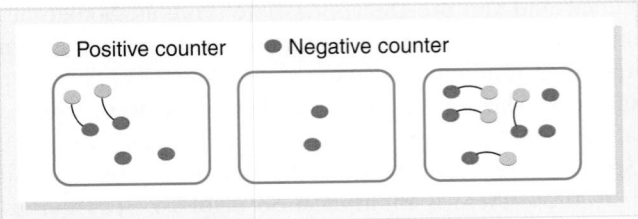

Figure 23.6 Each collection is a model of negative 2.

works and showing students how to solve exercises with the models, you pose an integer computation and let students use their models to find a solution. When solutions have been reached, the groups can compare and justify their results using one of the contexts or models described earlier in this chapter.

Addition and Subtraction

Since grade 7–8 students may not have used counters or number lines for a while, it would be good to begin work with either of these models using positive whole numbers. After a few examples to help students become familiar with the model for addition or subtraction with whole numbers, have them work through an example with integers using exactly the same reasoning. Remember, the emphasis should be on the rationale and not on how quickly students can get correct answers.

Introduce negative values using one of the contexts discussed earlier in this chapter. For example, golf scores

can be used as a context. Personalize the story by telling students that each weekend you golf a round on Saturday and on Sunday. The first weekend your results were $^+3$ and $^+5$; the next weekend you scored $^-6$ and $^+2$. How did you do overall this weekend? Because this is a quantity model, counters are a good choice for modelling (though number lines could also be used). Altitude could be used for a linear, albeit vertical, context. Students could compare points of interest above and below sea level. See Figure 23.8 for illustrations of how to use both models for addition.

Several examples of addition are modelled in Figure 23.8, each in two ways: with positive and negative counters and with the number-line-and-arrow model. First examine the counter model. After the two quantities are joined, any pairs of positive and negative counters combine to equal zero (cancel each other out). Students can remove these, making it easier to see the result.

To add using the arrow model, note that each arrow that is added begins at the point where the previous arrow ends. Recall that subtraction can be used for take-away

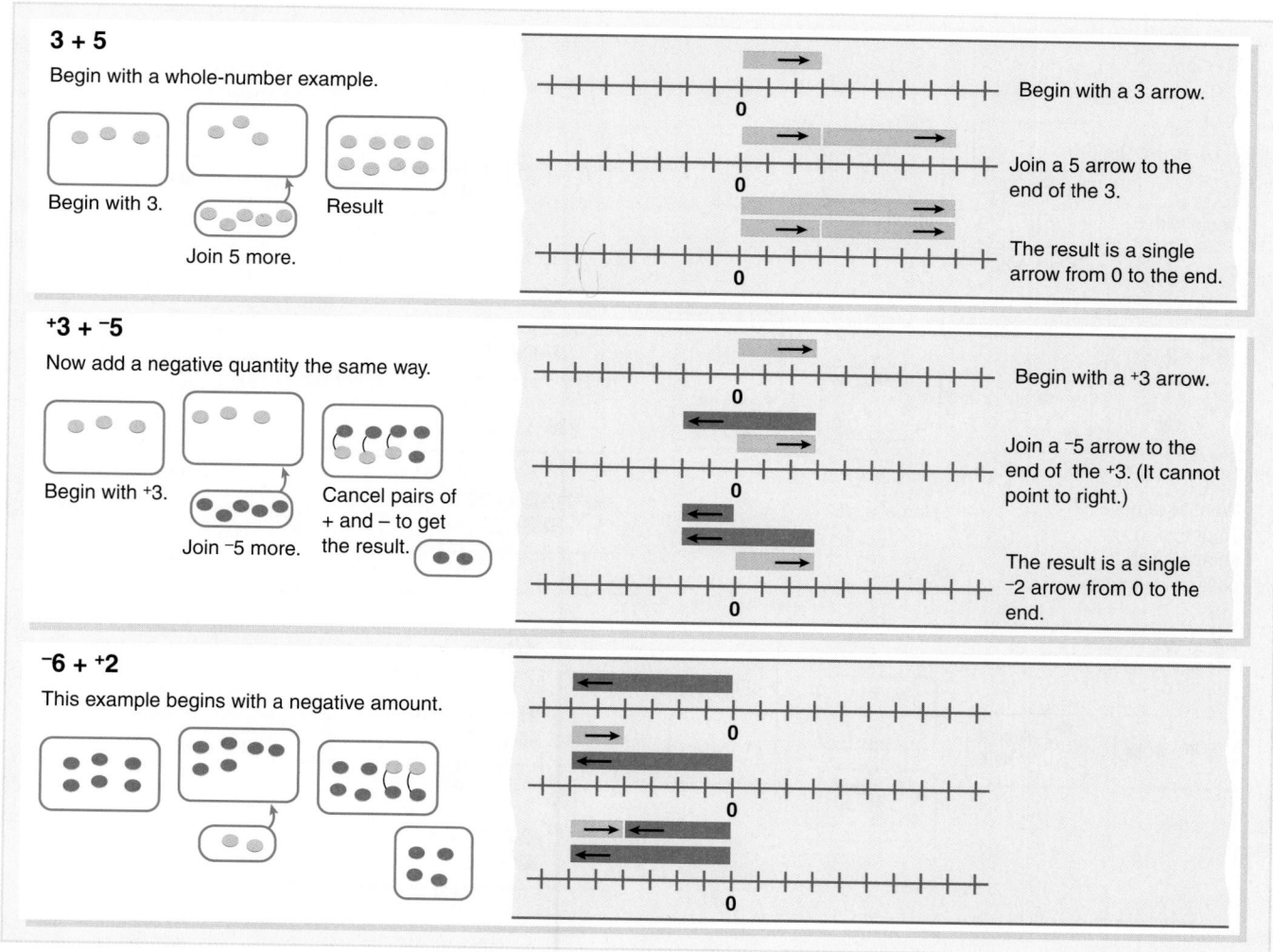

Figure 23.8 Relate integer addition to whole-number addition with counters and number lines.

situations (e.g., start with 7 and take away 10) or in comparisons. (What is the difference between 7 and ⁻3?)

Consider the problem ⁻5 − ⁺2, the second example modelled in Figure 23.9 (the first being a whole number example for the sake of making the connection). If using a quantity model, the context could be money, such as, "I start with an overdraft of $5 and then take out $2 more from my account. What balance will my bank account show (if no fees have been charged yet for my overdrawn account)? To model it, you start with the five red counters. To remove two positive counters from a set that has none, a different representation of ⁻5 must first be made. Since any number of neutral pairs (one positive, one negative) can be added without changing the value of the set, two pairs are added so that two positive counters can be removed. The net effect is to have more negative counters.

In a number model, subtraction can be modelled using arrows. When subtracting positive values, as in the second example in Figure 23.9, this works just as with whole numbers, moving to the left. Using temperature as a context, the explanation could be: "The day begins at 5 below zero.

Then the temperature drops +2 degrees, which means it just got colder and is now ⁻7 degrees." The difficulty comes when trying to provide an authentic explanation of subtracting a negative value. An example is ⁻4 − ⁻7 (see Figure 23.9, third example). In this case, you start with thinking about taking away, but because it is negative temperature (or coldness) that is being taken away, you are in fact doing the opposite—warming up by 7 degrees. Modelling on the number line, you start at ⁻4, then reverse the arrow going left to one going right 7 moves. Number lines can also be used for comparison or distance. What is the difference between ⁻7 and ⁻4? In other words, how do you get from ⁻7 to ⁻4? You count up 3.

Pause and Reflect

Before reading further, go through each example in Figures 23.8 and 23.9. Explain each problem using both a quantity and linear context. You should become comfortable with both models.

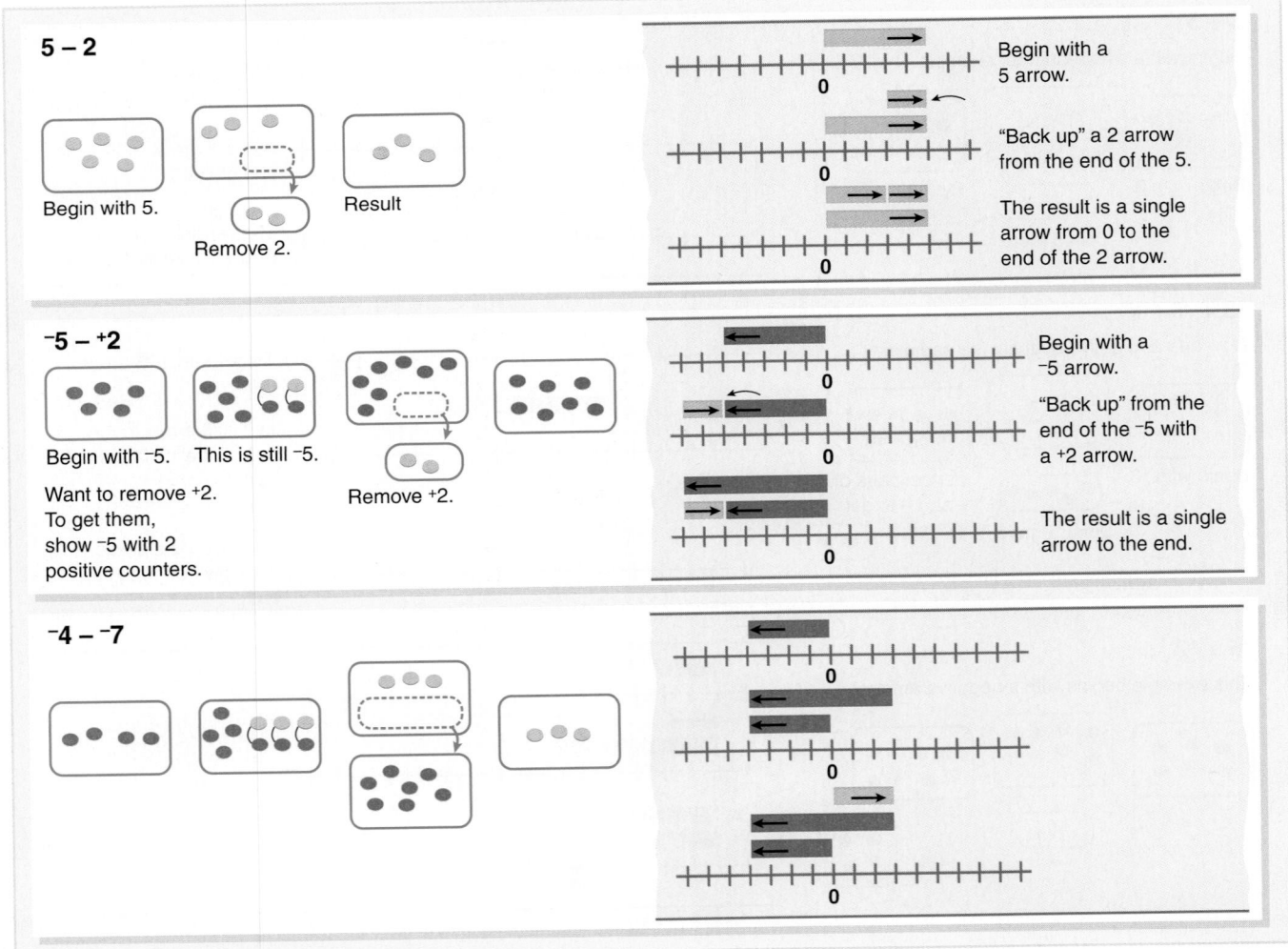

Figure 23.9 Integer subtraction is also related to whole numbers.

Have your students draw pictures to accompany integer computations. Set pictures are easy enough; they may consist of Xs and Os, for example. For the number line, arrows can be used. Figure 23.10 illustrates how a student might draw arrows for simple addition and subtraction exercises without even sketching the number line.

It is important for students to see that $^+3 + {}^-5$ is the same as $^+3 - {}^+5$ and that $^+2 - {}^-6$ is the same as $^+2 + {}^+6$. By modelling addition and subtraction problems in both ways, students will see the connection. They will then recognize that, while these expressions are quite distinguishable, they have the same result.

Multiplication and Division

Multiplication of integers should be treated as a direct extension of multiplication with whole numbers, just as addition and subtraction were connected to whole-number concepts. We frequently refer to whole-number multiplication as repeated addition. The first factor tells how many sets there are or how many in all, beginning with 0, are added. This translates quite readily to integer multiplication when the first factor is positive, regardless of the sign of the second factor. The first example in Figure 23.11 illustrates a positive first factor and a negative second factor.

What could the meaning be when the first factor is negative, as in $^-2 \times {}^-3$? If a positive first factor means

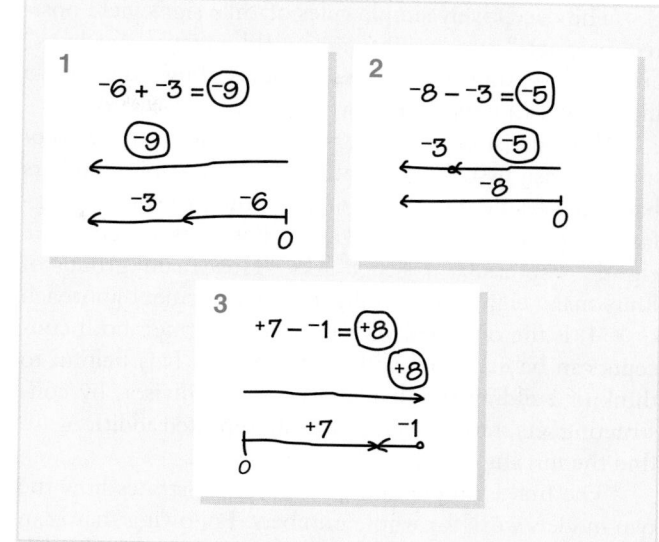

Figure 23.10 Students can use simple arrow sketches to represent addition and subtraction with integers.

repeated addition (how many times added to 0), a negative first factor should mean repeated subtraction (how many times subtracted from 0). The second example in Figure 23.11 illustrates how multiplication, with the first factor negative, can be modelled.

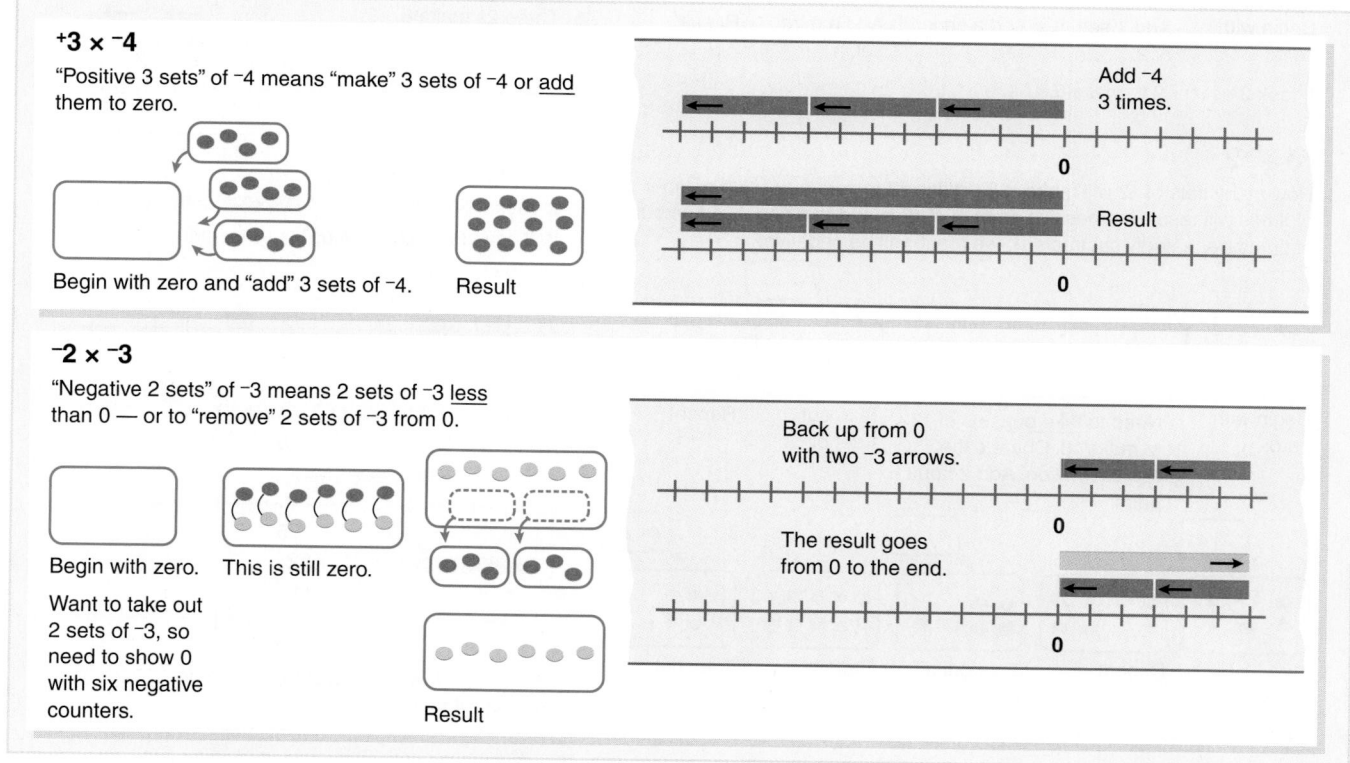

Figure 23.11 Multiplication by a positive first factor is repeated addition. Multiplication by a negative first factor is repeated subtraction.

The deceptively simple rules of "like signs yield positive products" and "unlike signs yield negative products" are quickly established. These models allow students to understand why those rules work.

With division of integers, again explore the whole-number case first. Recall that $8 \div 4$ with whole numbers has two possible meanings corresponding to two missing-factor expressions: $4 \times ? = 8$ asks, "Four sets of *what* make eight?" whereas, $? \times 4 = 8$ asks, "How many groups of fours make eight?" Generally, the measurement approach ($? \times 4$) is the one used with integers, although both concepts can be exhibited with either model. It is helpful to think of building the dividend using the divisor, by constructing sets starting from 0, or with repeated addition—to find the missing factor.

The first example in Figure 23.12 illustrates how the two models work for whole numbers. Following that is an example where the divisor is positive but the dividend is negative.

Pause and Reflect

Try using both models to compute $^-8 \div {}^+2$. Draw pictures using Xs and Os and also arrows. Check your understanding with the examples in Figure 23.12. Once you understand that example, try $9 \div {}^-3$ and also $^-12 \div {}^-4$.

Understanding of integer division rests on a good concept of a negative first factor for multiplication and knowledge of the relationship between multiplication and division.

Do not rush your students into difficult problem solving. It is much better that they first think about how to model the whole-number situation then figure out, with some guidance from you, how to deal with integers.

NCTM Standards "Positive and negative integers should be seen as useful for noting relative changes or values. Students can also appreciate the utility of nega-

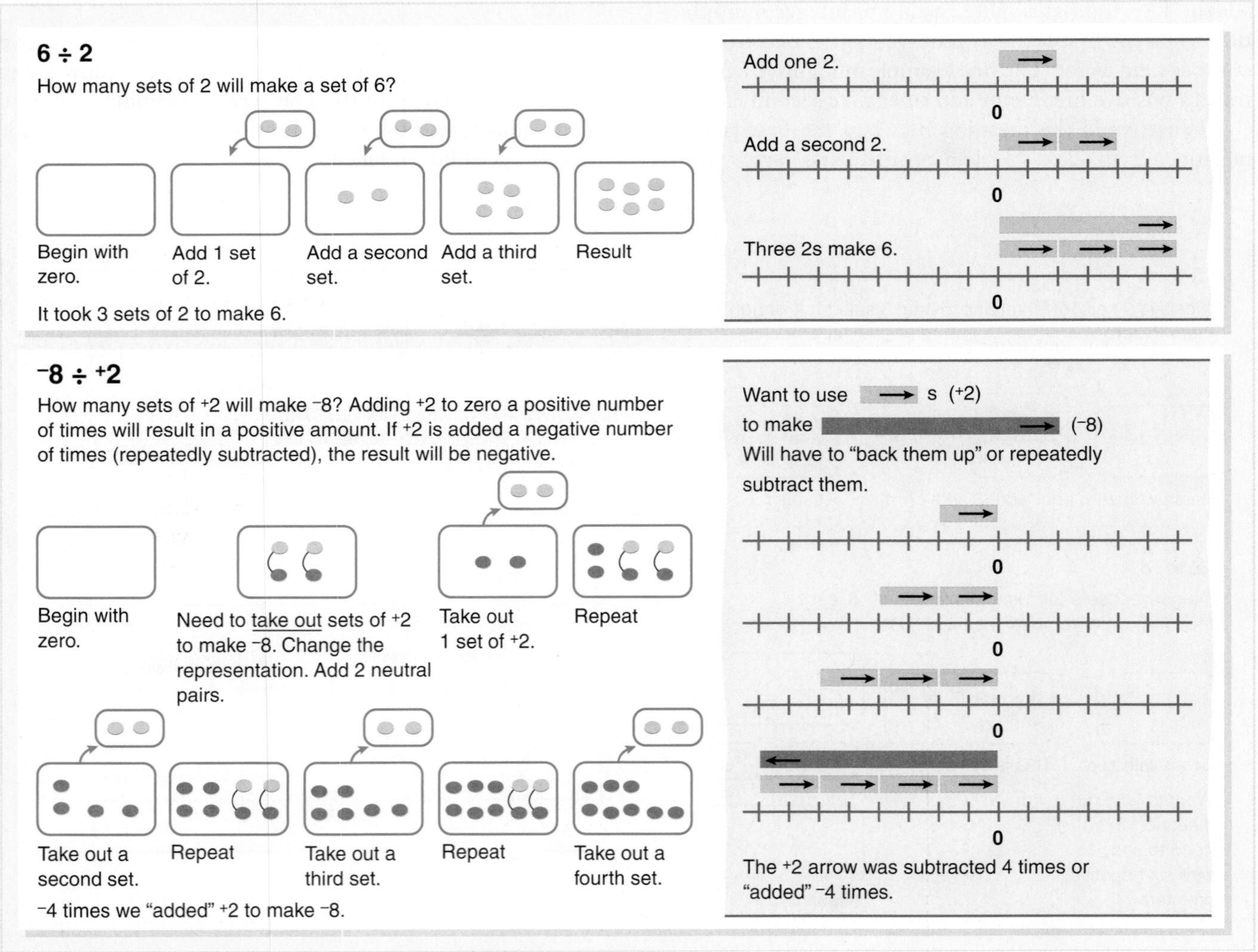

6 ÷ 2

How many sets of 2 will make a set of 6?

Begin with zero. | Add 1 set of 2. | Add a second set. | Add a third set. | Result

It took 3 sets of 2 to make 6.

Add one 2.

0

Add a second 2.

0

Three 2s make 6.

0

⁻8 ÷ ⁺2

How many sets of ⁺2 will make ⁻8? Adding ⁺2 to zero a positive number of times will result in a positive amount. If ⁺2 is added a negative number of times (repeatedly subtracted), the result will be negative.

Begin with zero. | Need to <u>take out</u> sets of ⁺2 to make ⁻8. Change the representation. Add 2 neutral pairs. | Take out 1 set of ⁺2. | Repeat

Take out a second set. | Repeat | Take out a third set. | Repeat | Take out a fourth set.

⁻4 times we "added" ⁺2 to make ⁻8.

Want to use ⟶ s (⁺2) to make ▬▬▬⟶ (⁻8) Will have to "back them up" or repeatedly subtract them.

0

0

0

0

The ⁺2 arrow was subtracted 4 times or "added" ⁻4 times.

Figure 23.12 Division of integers following a measurement approach.

tive integers when they work with equations whose solution requires them, such as $2x + 7 = 1$" (p. 218).

Real Numbers

Section ll of this book began with whole numbers then moved to rational numbers. Now, in this chapter integers are explored. All these are rational numbers. Irrational numbers are numbers such as the square root of 2—numbers whose value cannot be written as a fraction and whose value can only be estimated. All these numbers are part of the *real numbers*, which are the only types of numbers students explore until high school where they consider the square roots of negative numbers. Each of these sets of numbers is interrelated, and some are subsets of other sets. Figure 23.13 provides an illustration of the types of numbers and how they are interrelated

Rational Numbers

Rational numbers comprise the set of all numbers that can be represented as fractions—or as a ratio of one integer to another. Even when numbers are written as whole numbers or as terminating decimals, they can also be written as fractions. Hence, they are rational numbers. In most textbooks, the term *rational numbers* is often used to refer to fractions, decimal numbers (terminating and repeating), and percents. These are rational numbers, but so are integers, including whole numbers. To help build this notion of rational numbers, it is important to be able to move between fractions and decimals and between fractions and whole numbers.

Moving Among Representations Because children tend to think of fractions as parts of sets or objects, they remain more physical object than number, for them. This is one reason that students can have such a difficult time placing fractions on a number line. A significant leap toward thinking about fractions as numbers is made when students begin to understand that a decimal number is a representa-

tion of a fraction. In Chapter 17, we explored the idea of the "friendly" fractions (halves, thirds, fourths, fifths, eighths) in terms of their decimal equivalents.

For students in grades 6–8, it is time to combine all these ideas:

- $4\frac{3}{5}$ is 4.6 because $\frac{3}{5}$ is six-tenths of a whole, so 4 wholes and six-tenths is 4.6.
- $4\frac{3}{5}$ is $\frac{23}{5}$, and that is the same as $23 \div 5$, or 4.6 if I use decimal numbers.
- 4.6 is read "four and six-tenths," so I can write that as $\frac{46}{10} = 4\frac{3}{5}$.

Similarly, compare these three expressions:

$$\frac{1}{4} \text{ of } 24 \qquad \frac{24}{4} \qquad 24 \div 4$$

This discussion can lead to a general development of the idea that a fraction can be thought of as division of the numerator by the denominator or that $\frac{a}{b}$ is the same as $a \div b$.

What becomes clear in a discussion building on students' existing ideas is that any number, positive or negative, that can be written as a fraction can also be written as a decimal number. You can also reverse this idea and convert decimal numbers to fractions. Keep in mind that the purpose is to see that there are different symbolic notations for the same quantities—not to become skilled at conversions.

When a fraction is converted to a decimal number, it is interesting to note that the decimal number either terminates (e.g., 3.415) or repeats (e.g., 2.514 1414...).

Is there a way to tell if a given fraction is a terminating decimal or a repeating decimal? The answer lies in the denominator. The following activity can be used to discover the rule.

Activity **23.5**

Repeater or Terminator

Have students generate a table listing in one column the first 20 unit fractions ($\frac{1}{2}$, $\frac{1}{3}$, $\frac{1}{4}$, ... $\frac{1}{21}$). In the second column they list the prime factorization of the denominators and in the third column the decimal equivalent for the fraction. Have students use calculators to get the decimal form.

After completing the table, the task is to see if they can discover a rule that will tell in advance if the decimal will repeat or terminate. They can test the rule with fractions with denominators beyond 21. They may also wish to confirm that it makes no difference what the numerator is.

If you try the last activity yourself, you will quickly discover that only fractions that have terminating decimal

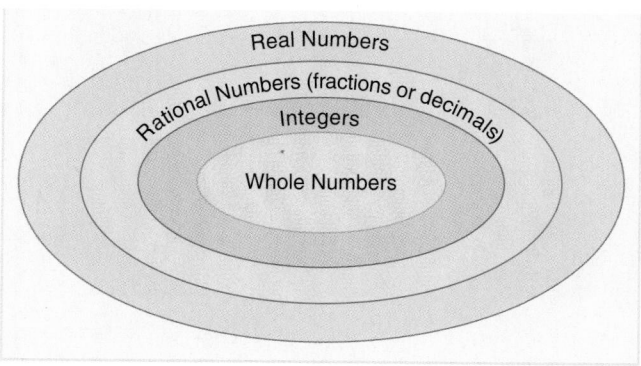

Figure 23.13 An illustration of the real numbers.

equivalents have denominators whose factors are all 2s and/ or 5s. The explanation for why this is so is also within the reach of students. As students work on this task, they will notice various patterns, as can be seen in the student work provided in Figure 23.14.

Irrational Numbers

When students learn about π in their investigation of circumference and area of a circle, they are gaining familiarity with *irrational numbers*. Unlike rational numbers, *irrational* numbers cannot be put in fraction form. The irrational numbers together with the rational numbers make up the *real* numbers. The real numbers fill in all the holes on the number line even though the holes are infinitesimally small. Students' first experience with irrational numbers typically occurs when exploring roots of whole numbers.

Introducing the Concept of Roots   The following activity provides a good introduction to square roots and cube roots. From this beginning, the notion of roots of any degree is easily developed.

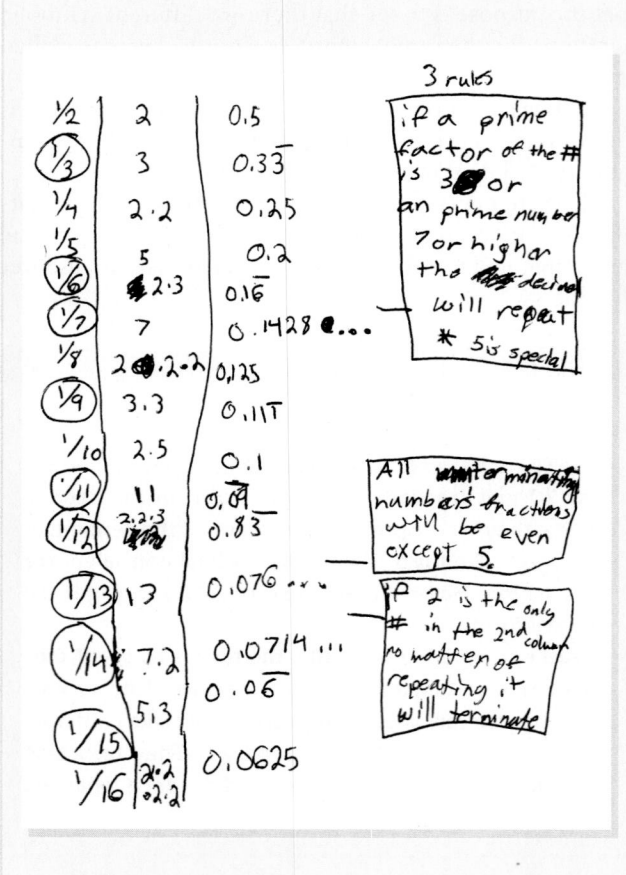

Figure 23.14 A student notes patterns as he explores the "Repeater or Terminator" activity.

Activity 23.6

Edges of Squares and Cubes

Show students pictures of three squares (or three cubes) as in Figure 23.15. The edges of the first and last figure are consecutive whole numbers. The areas (volumes) of all three figures are provided. The students' task is to use a calculator to find the edge of the figure in the centre. Explain to students that use of the square root key is not permitted. Rather they are to estimate what they think the measure of the side would be and to test it by squaring it, Ask students to continue estimating until they have found a value in the hundredths that is as close to 45 as possible (or to 30, in the case of the cube.)

Solutions will satisfy these equations:

$\square \times \square = 45,$ or $\square^2 = 45$

and

$\square \times \square \times \square = 30,$ or $\square^3 = 30$

For example, to solve the cube problem, students might start with 3.5 and find that 3.5^3 is 42.875, which is much too large. Quickly, they will find that the solution is between 3.1 and 3.2. But where? Although a calculator can find these square or cube roots quickly, the estimation activity strengthens students' understanding of squares and square roots and the relative size of numbers.

▌▌ ———————— *Pause and Reflect*

Use a calculator to continue getting a better approximation of the cube root of 30 to two decimal places.

From this simple introduction, students can be challenged to find solutions to equations such as $\square^2 = 8$. These students are now prepared to understand the general defini-

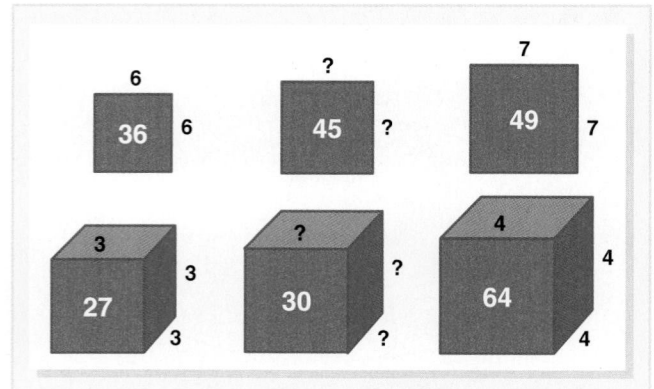

Figure 23.15 A geometric interpretation of square roots and cube roots.

tion of the *nth root* of a number *N*, which, when raised to the *n*th power, equals *N*. The *square* and *cube* roots are simply other names for the second and third roots. The notational convention of the radical sign comes last. It should then be clear that $\sqrt{6}$ is a number and not a computation. The cube root of eight is the same as $\sqrt[3]{8}$, which is just another way of writing 2.

 "In grades 6–8, students frequently encounter squares and square roots when they use the Pythagorean relationship. They can use the inverse relationship to determine the approximate location of square roots between whole numbers on a number line" (p. 220). As examples, the authors note that 27 is a little more than 5 because $5^2 = 25$, and 99 is a little less than 10 since $10^2 = 100$.

Discussing Real Numbers

Grade 8 students probably do not need a very sophisticated knowledge of the real number system. A few powerful ideas, however, deserve to be explored informally.

Density of the Real Numbers

One important aspect of real numbers that is not well understood by students is that they are infinite. This means that for two values such as $\frac{7}{9}$ and $\frac{8}{9}$, there is an infinite amount of rational numbers between them. This is a concept that warrants exploration and discussion, which is the intent of Activity 23.7.

If the density of the rationals is impressive, even more astounding is that the irrationals are also dense. And the irrationals and the rationals are all mixed up together. The density of the irrationals is not as easy to demonstrate and is not within the scope of elementary school.

The following activity can help students develop a better understanding of the structure of the rational number system.

Activity **23.7**

How Close Is Close?

Have students select any two fractions or any two decimal numbers that they think are "really close." It makes no difference which numbers students pick or even how close together they really are. Now challenge them to find at least 10 more numbers (fractions or decimals) that are between these two numbers.

"How Close Is Close?" provides an opportunity to find out how your students understand fractions and decimals. (Eventually, the activity should be done in both forms.) This activity offers a great opportunity for discussion, assessment of individual students' fraction and decimal concepts, and the introduction of perhaps the most interesting feature of the rational number system: density. The rational numbers are said to be *dense* because between any two rational numbers there exists an *infinite* number of other rational numbers.

 Ask students, "How many numbers are between these two numbers?" for each of the following:

$$\frac{3}{5} \text{ and } \frac{4}{5}$$
$$0.6 \text{ and } 0.7$$
$$-2 \text{ and } -3$$

As part of this "interview" assessment, ask students to provide examples and to explain how they are finding the numbers in between. Students should be able to manipulate the numbers to find values in between and should know there are an infinite number of values.

If they are stuck and say there are none, ask if they could write an equivalent form of the numbers that would help them find a number in between.◆

Reflections on Chapter 23

Writing to Learn

1. What strategies can you use to help students understand and appropriately use the order of operations?

2. How can a calculator be used to explore the order-of-operations convention?

3. Explain how powers of 10 are used to write very small and very large numbers. What is the particular form of the power-of-10 symbolism used in scientific notation and on calculators?

4. Use a context and a model to solve the following:
$$^-10 + {}^+13 = {}^+3 \qquad ^-4 - {}^-9 = {}^+5 \qquad ^+6 - {}^-7 = {}^+13$$
$$^-4 \times {}^-3 = {}^+12 \qquad ^+15 \div {}^-5 = {}^-3 \qquad ^-12 \div {}^-3 = {}^+4$$

5. For each of the following numbers, list the different ways it can be categorized (real, rational, integer, whole). For example, $^-8\frac{1}{2}$ is real and rational.
$$^-3 \qquad 120 \qquad \frac{4}{5} \qquad \sqrt{5} \qquad .323232... \qquad ^-1.4$$

6. How would you explain the difference between a rational number and an irrational number to a grade 8 student?

7. What does $\sqrt{6}$ mean? How is $\sqrt{6}$ different from $\sqrt{4}$? How are they the same?

8. What does it mean to say that the rational numbers are dense?

For Discussion and Exploration

1. How might a teacher help students become fluent in moving between equivalent representations of numbers such as changing fractions to decimals flexibly to fit the situation?

2. Some exponent values are easily confused by students. Two of the most common cases are listed below. For each example,

   • Explain how the values are different in meaning.
   • Draw representations to show how they are different.
   • Describe what investigation you would plan to help students see the differences in these values.

   Case 1: 2^3 and 2×3 and 3^2

   Case 2: $2n$ and n^2 and 2^n

Resources for Chapter 23

Literature Connections

Some topics in this chapter present opportunities for "playing around" with ideas and numbers. Literature can be a great springboard for doing mathematics in grades 6–8. The following ideas offer a change of pace at this level.

The Number Devil *Enzensberger, 1997*

Full of humour and wit, *The Number Devil* lays out a collection of interesting ideas about numbers in 12 easily read chapters. Robert, a boy who hates mathematics, meets up with a crafty number devil in each of 12 dreams. On the fourth night's dream, Robert learns about infinitely repeating decimals and the "Rutabaga of two" (the square root of two), providing a connection to rational and irrational numbers.

Oh Yikes! History's Grossest, Wackiest Moments *Masoff, 2006*

In this picture-rich reference book, the author describes important historical events and people with facts that are interesting to elementary school students. Her topics include "Aztec Antics," "Cruel Constructions," "Humongous Hoaxes," "pirates," and so on. In several cases, she takes topics such as brushing teeth and briefly describes how this

was handled across all of history. Doing so provides the opportunity to create time lines that include dates such as 2500 BC. Students can create a proportionally accurate time line representing events related to their chosen topic. In addition to integers, this lesson includes measuring, proportional reasoning, and fractions.

The Kids Book of Canadian History *Hacker, 2000*

This book provides students with an informative overview of the people, places, and events that have shaped our country. The book features fact boxes, mini-profiles, maps, a timeline, and more. Similar to the Masoff book, students can create timelines that focus on Canadian historical facts.

Recommendations for Further Reading

Articles

Graeber, A. O., & Baker, K. M. (1992). Little into big is the way it always is. *Arithmetic Teacher, 39* (8), 18–21.
   This is one of the few articles that discusses the issue of a fraction as an indicated division. The authors look at practices in elementary school that suggest why the difficulty exists and make practical suggestions for working with middle-school students.

Reeves, C. A., & Webb, D. (2004). Balloons on the rise: A problem-solving approach to integers. *Mathematics Teaching in the Middle School, 9,* 476–482.

Expanding on a discussion of the possibility of helium party balloons making you weigh less if held while on a scale, the grade 5 students in this article generalize the concepts of integers and use their ideas for addition and subtraction. The authors point clearly to the value of a context to help students develop a new concept.

Online Resources

Integers and Exponents
http://www.learnalberta.ca/content/mejhm/index.html?l=0&ID1=AB.MATH.JR.NUMB&ID2=AB.MATH.JR.NUMB.EXPO&lesson=html/object_interactives/patterning_the_powers_of_10/use_it.html

Both video and interactive activities that focus on integers and exponents can be found at this site.

Wired Math
http://cemc2.math.uwaterloo.ca/mathfrog/english/kidz/index.shtml

This site provides links to a variety of math games and resources for grades 7, 8, and 9. Among the offerings are games that focus on exponents and integers.

The Evolution of the Real Numbers
www.themathpage.com/aReal/real-numbers.htm

This is an interesting description of many topics related to the real number system. Although mostly text, the pages are filled with interactive questions and useful information that is not too technical.

National Library of Virtual Manipulatives (NLVM)
http://nlvm.usu.edu

Among the many applets on this site are "Colour Chips—Addition," "Colour Chips—Subtraction," "Rectangle Multiplication of Integers," and "Integer Arithmetic." These applets focus on using models for integer computation.

Tic-Tac-Go Negative Numbers (Freudenthal Institute)
www.fi.uu.nl/toepassingen/03088/toepassing_wisweb.en.html

In this game, students pick addition, subtraction, or multiplication and find the equation to match an answer, trying to get three in a row.

Volt Meter (*Illuminations*)
http://illuminations.nctm.org/ActivityDetail.aspx?ID=152

Click and drag batteries with negative and positive voltage to explore integer addition and subtraction.

Exponential Growth (Otherwise)
www.otherwise.com/population/exponent.html

This site offers an applet to experiment with population (exponential growth).

The Next Billion (*Illuminations*)
http://illuminations.nctm.org/LessonDetail.aspx?id=L715

In 1999 the world population passed 6 billion. In this lesson, students predict when it will reach 7 billion. Students discuss their predictions, past trends in population growth, and social factors—a good interdisciplinary opportunity.

Working with Exponents (Jim Reed)
http://argyll.epsb.ca/jreed/math8/strand1/1101.htm

This site has numerous applets on powers of numbers, scientific notation, and number system descriptions. The Munchers game asks students to correctly identify all numbers on a game board that belong to a given number system (natural numbers, whole numbers, integers, rational numbers, or irrational numbers).

myeducationlab will help you improve your understanding of the concepts taught in this textbook and in your course. This online tool includes videos of real classroom experiences, sample lesson plans, simulations, case studies, and links to important educational and teaching Web sites that will help you make the transition from student to teacher. As you study in your course and with this textbook, please follow along in *MyEducationLab*. Use it! Explore it! And improve your knowledge and your grade!

Appendix

Guide to Blackline Masters

This Appendix contains images of all of the Blackline Masters that are listed below. The actual masters can be found on MyEducationLab (www.myeducationlab.com).

Suggestions for Use and Construction of Materials

Card Stock Materials

A good way to have many materials made quickly and easily for students is to have them duplicated on card stock at a photocopy store. Card stock is a heavy paper that comes in a variety of colors. It is also called cover stock or index stock. The price is about twice that of paper.

Card stock can be laminated and then cut into smaller pieces, if desired. The laminate adheres very well. Laminate first, and then cut into pieces afterward. Otherwise you will need to cut each piece twice.

Materials are best kept in plastic bags with zip-type closures. Freezer bags are recommended for durability. Punch a hole near the top of the bag so that you do not store air. Lots of small bags can be stuffed into the largest bags. You can always see what you have stored in the bags.

The following list is a suggestion for materials that can be made from card stock using the masters in this section. Quantity suggestions are also given.

Dot Cards

One complete set of cards will serve four to six children. Duplicate each set in a different colour so that mixed sets can be separated easily. Laminate and then cut with a paper cutter.

Five-Frames and Ten-Frames

Five-frames and ten-frames are best duplicated on light-coloured card stock. Do not laminate; if you do, the mats will curl and counters will slide around.

10 × 10 Multiplication Array

Make one per student in any colour. Lamination is suggested. Provide each student with an L-shaped piece of tagboard.

Base-Ten Pieces (Centimetre Grid)

Use the grid (number 11) to make a master as directed. Run copies on white card stock. One sheet will make 4 hundreds and 10 tens or 4 hundreds and a lot of ones. Mount the printed card stock on white poster board using either a dry-mount press or permanent spray adhesive. (Spray adhesive can be purchased in art supply stores. It is very effective but messy to handle.) Cut into pieces with a paper cutter. For the tens and ones pieces, it is recommended that you mount the index stock onto mount board or illustration board, also available in art supply stores. This material is thicker and will make the pieces easier to handle. It is recommended that you not laminate the base-ten pieces. A kit consisting of 10 hundreds, 30 tens, and 30 ones is adequate for each student or pair of students.

Little Ten-Frames

There are two masters for these materials. One has full ten-frames and the other has 1 to 9 dots, including two with 5 dots. Copy the 1-to-9 master on one colour of card stock and the full ten-frames on another. Cut off most of the excess stock and then laminate. Cut into little ten-frames. Each set consists of 20 pieces: 10 full ten-frames and 10 of the 1-to-9 pieces, including 2 fives. Make a set for each child.

Place-Value Mat (with Ten-Frames)

Mats can be duplicated on any pastel card stock. It is recommended that you not laminate these because they tend to curl and counters slide around too much. Make one for every child.

Circular Fraction Pieces

First make three copies of each page of the master. Cut the disks apart and tape onto blank pages with three of the same type on a page. You will then have a separate master for each size with three full circles per master. Duplicate each master on a different colour card stock. Laminate and then cut the circles out. A kit for one or two students should have two circles of each size piece.

Hundredths Disk

These disks can be made on paper but are much more satisfying on card stock. Duplicate the master on two contrasting colours. Laminate and cut the circles and also the slot on the dotted line. Make a set for each student. It's easy and worthwhile.

Tangrams and Mosaic Puzzle

Both tangrams and the Mosaic Puzzle should be copied on card stock. For younger children, the card stock should first be mounted on poster board to make the pieces a bit thicker and easier to put together in puzzles. You will want one set of each per student.

Woozle Cards

Copy the Woozle Card master on white or off-white card stock. You need two copies per set. Before laminating, colour one set one colour and the other a different colour. An easy way to colour the cards is to make one pass around the inside of each Woozle, leaving the rest of the creature white. If you colour the entire Woozle, the dots may not show up. Make one set for every four students.

Transparencies and Overhead Models

A copy of any page can be made into a transparency with a photocopier. Alternatively, the PDF files can be printed directly onto transparency masters (use the appropriate transparency film for your printer). This method will avoid the minor distortions and blurring that sometimes occur with photocopying.

Some masters make fine transparency mats to use for demonstration purposes on the overhead. The 10 10 array, the blank hundreds board, and the large geoboard are examples. The five-frame and ten-frame work well with counters. The place-value mat can be used with strips and squares or with counters and cups directly on the overhead. The missing-part blank and the record blanks for the four algorithms are pages that you may wish to use as write-on transparencies.

A transparency of the 10,000 grid is the easiest way there is to show 10,000 or to model four-place decimal numbers.

A transparency of the degrees and wedges page is the very best way to illustrate what a degree is and also to help explain protractors.

All of the line and dot grids are useful to have available as transparencies. You may find it a good idea to make several copies of each and keep them in a folder where you can get to them easily.

For the Woozle Cards, dot cards, little ten-frames, and assorted shapes, make a reduction of the master on a photocopy machine. Then make transparencies of the small cards, cut them apart, and use them on the overhead.

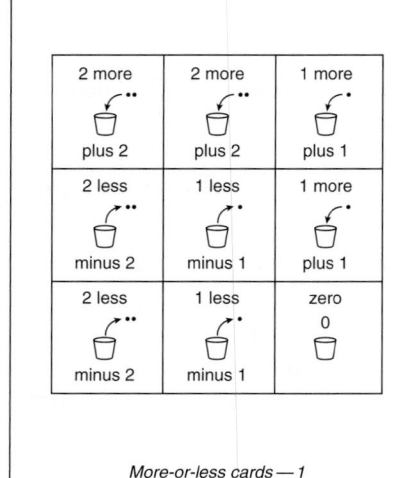

More-or-less cards — 1

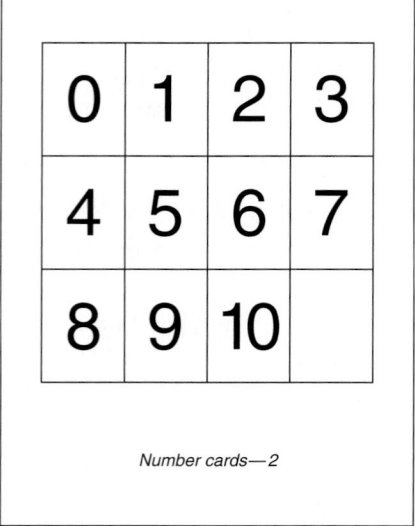

Number cards—2

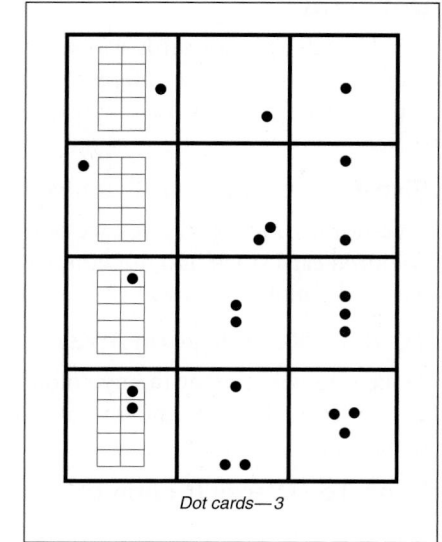

Dot cards—3

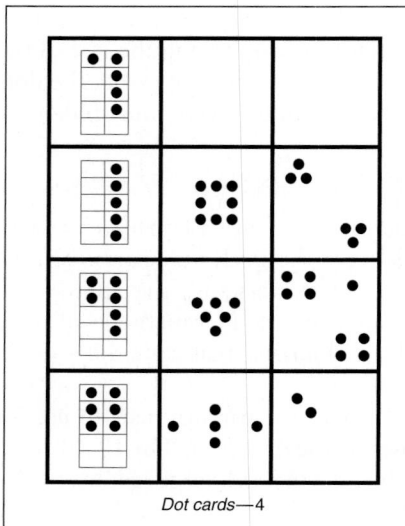

Dot cards—4

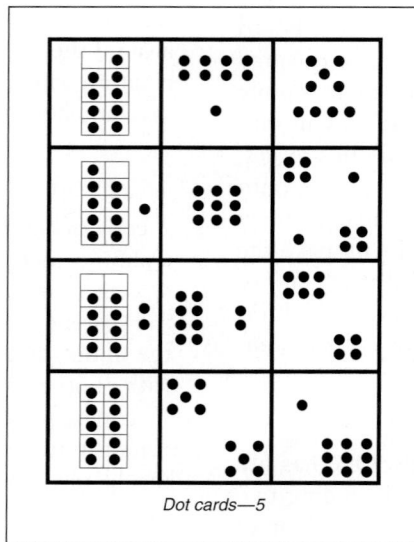

Dot cards—5

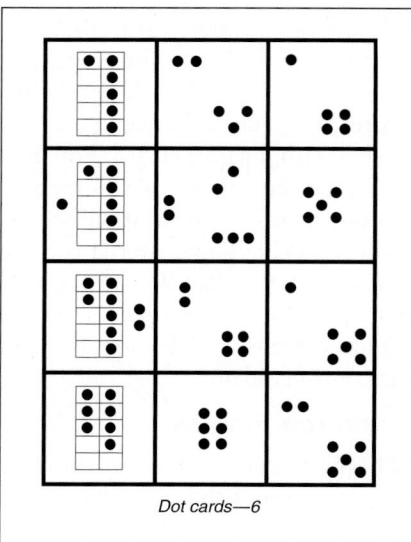

Dot cards—6

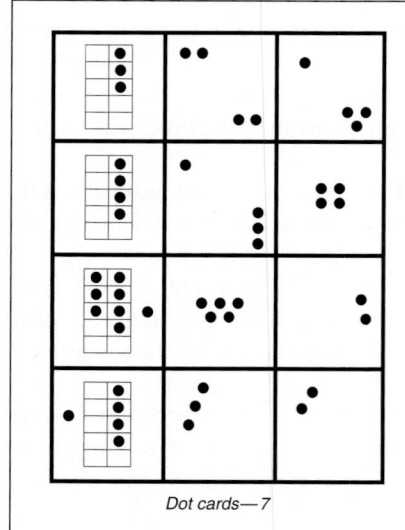

Dot cards—7

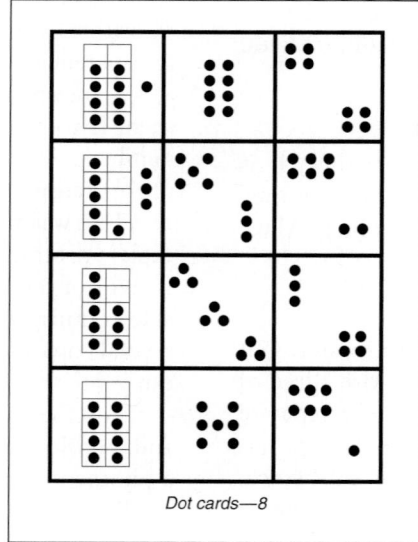

Dot cards—8

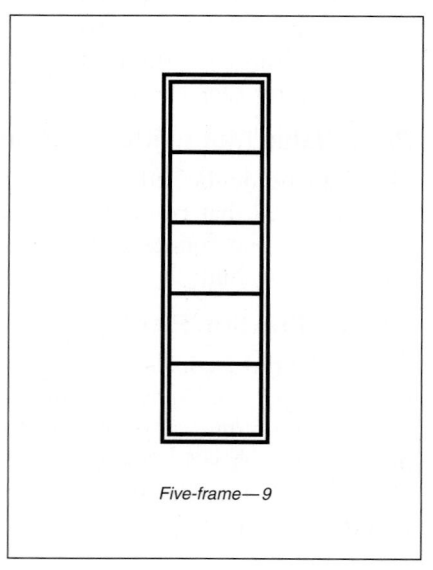

Five-frame—9

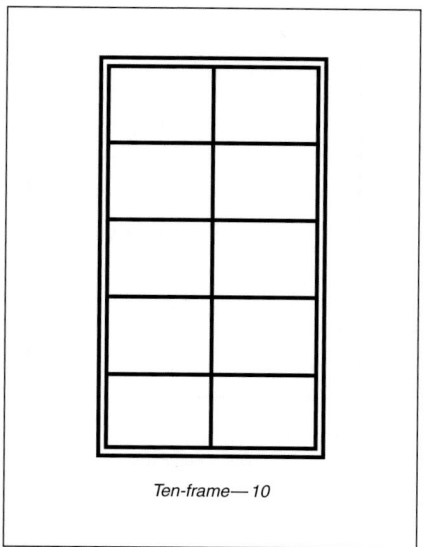

Ten-frame—10

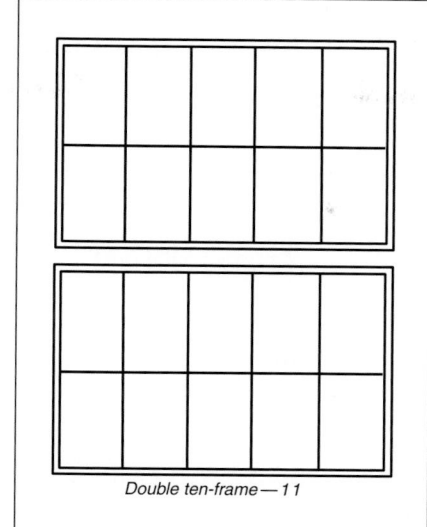

Double ten-frame—11

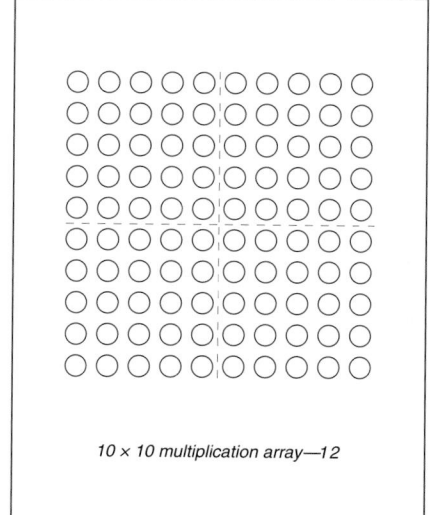

10 × 10 multiplication array—12

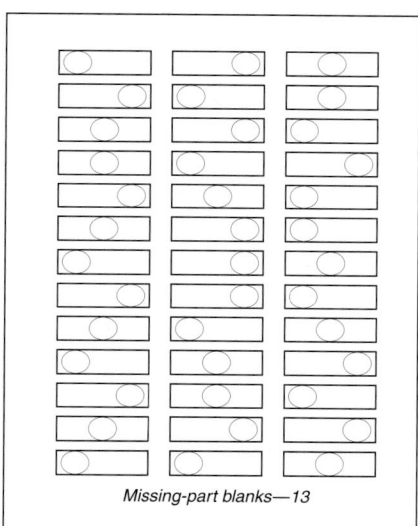

Missing-part blanks—13

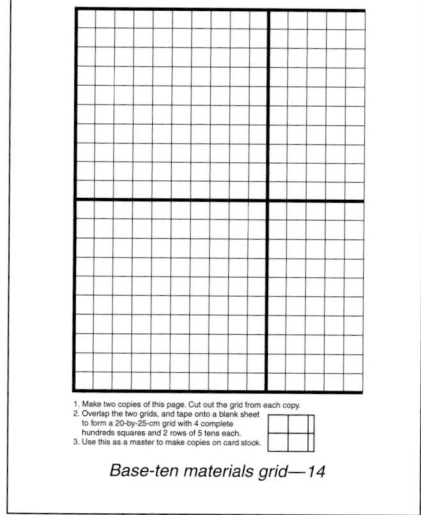

Base-ten materials grid—14

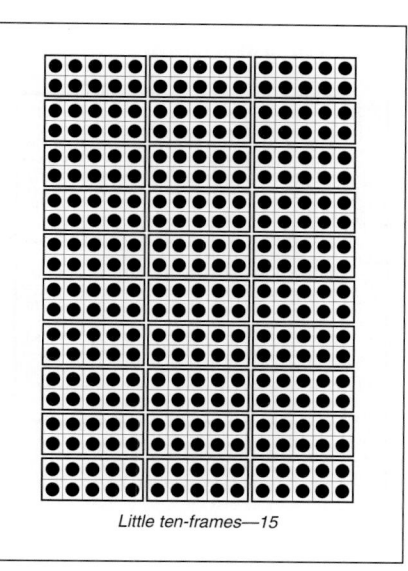

Little ten-frames—15

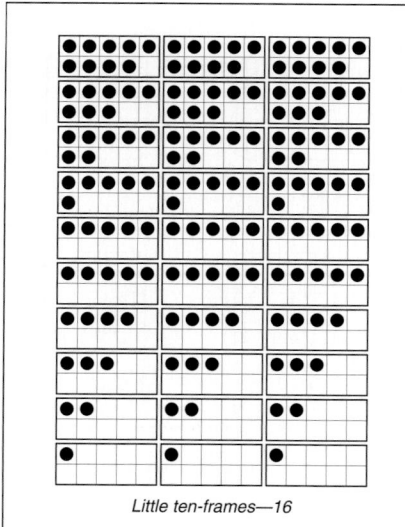

Little ten-frames—16

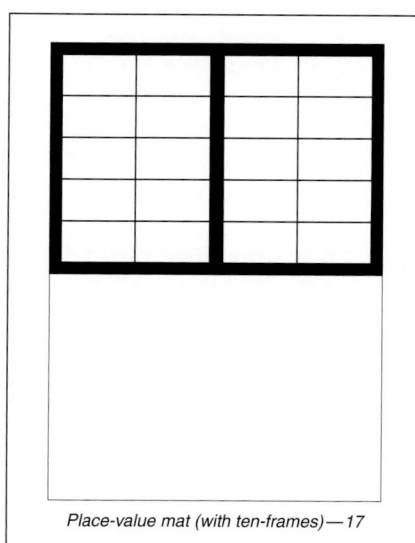

Place-value mat (with ten-frames)—17

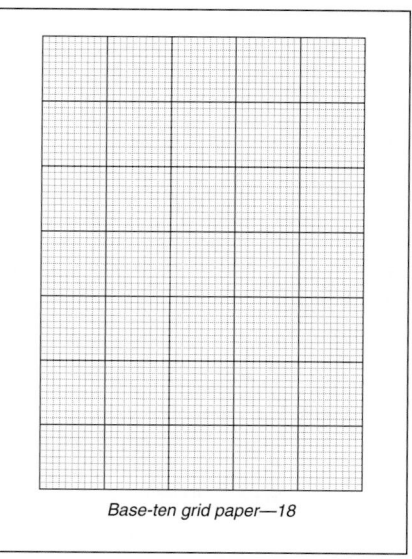

Base-ten grid paper—18

Addition and subtraction record blanks—19

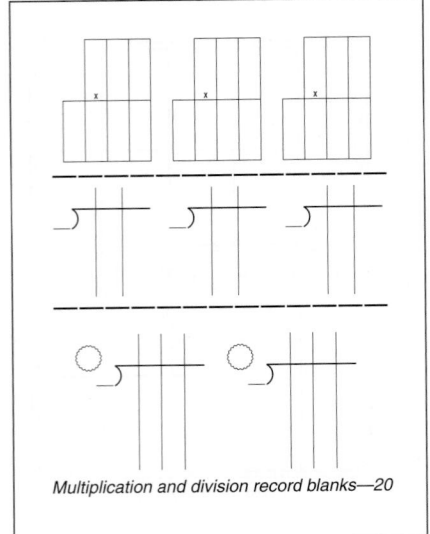

Multiplication and division record blanks—20

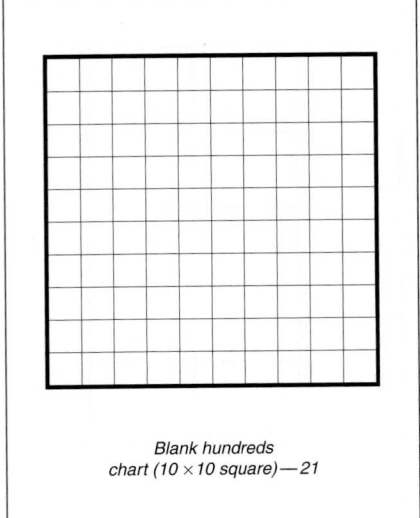

Blank hundreds chart (10 × 10 square)—21

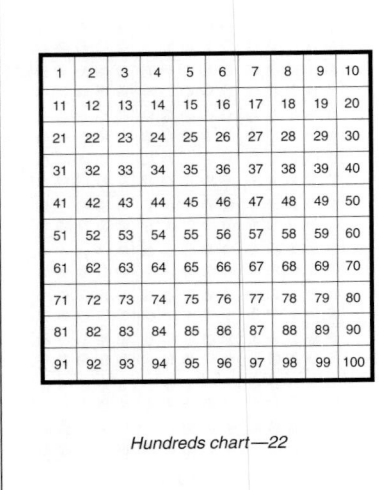

Hundreds chart—22

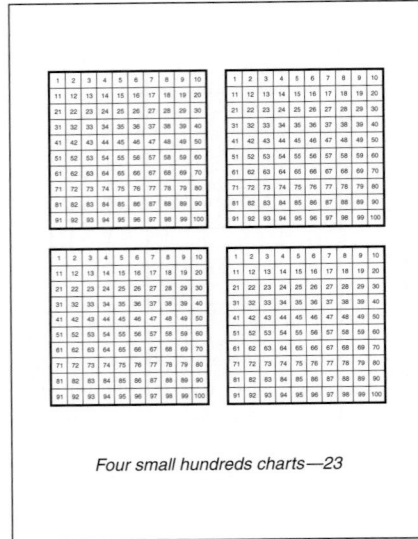

Four small hundreds charts—23

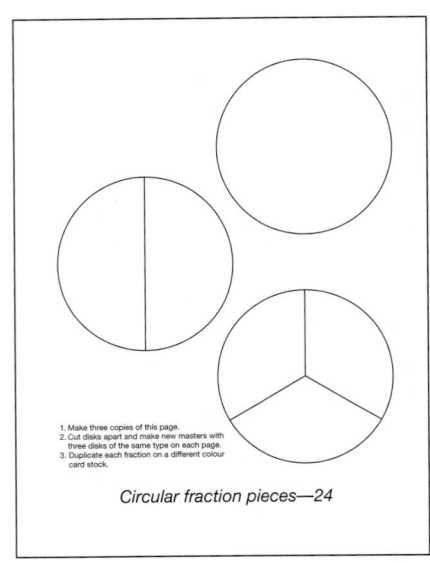

Circular fraction pieces—24

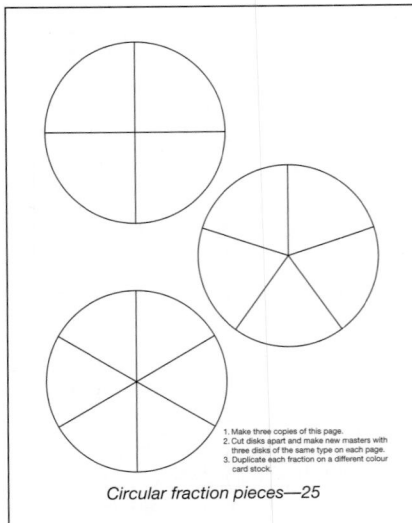

Circular fraction pieces—25

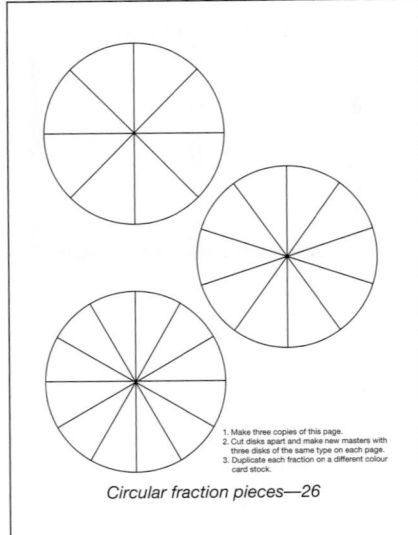

Circular fraction pieces—26

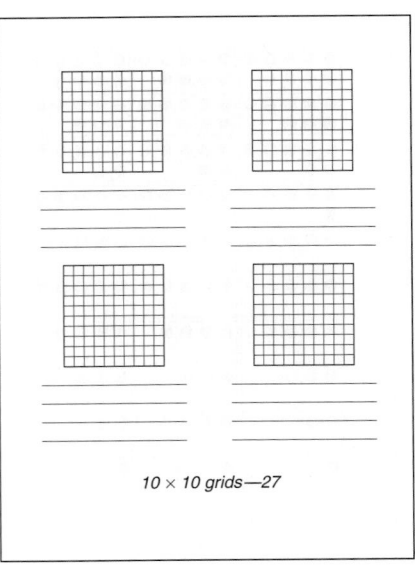

10 × 10 grids—27

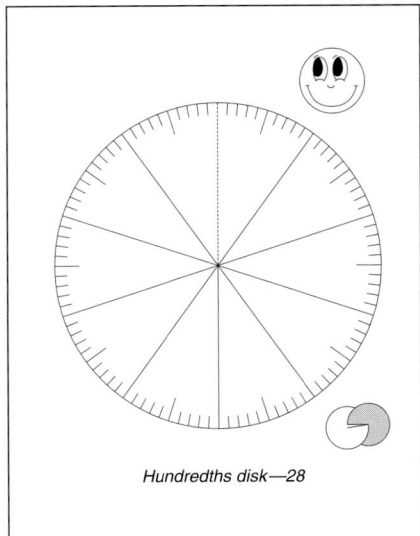

Hundredths disk—28

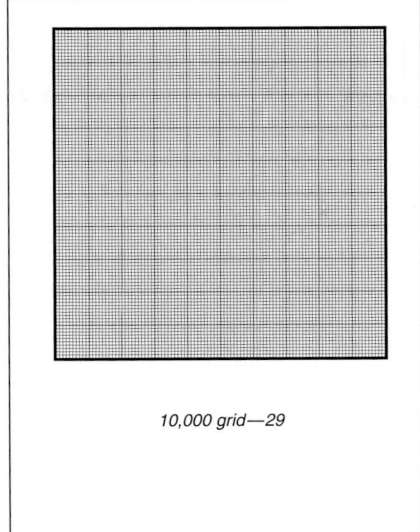

10,000 grid—29

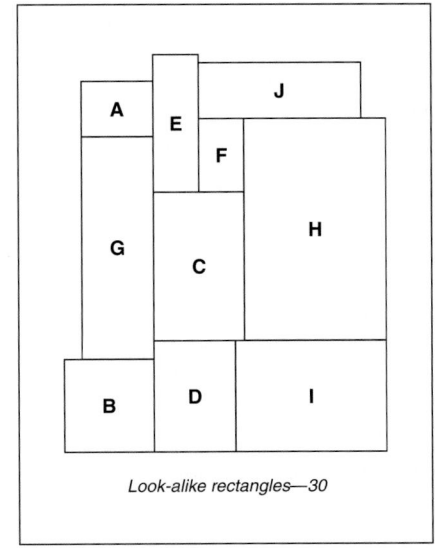

Look-alike rectangles—30

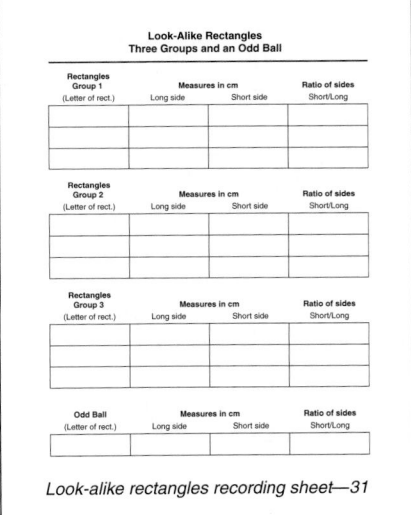

Look-alike rectangles recording sheet—31

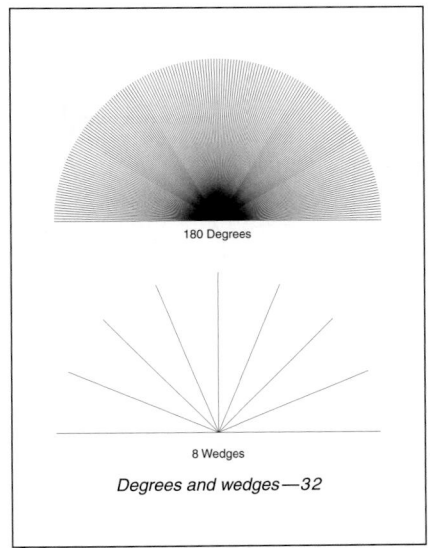

Degrees and wedges—32

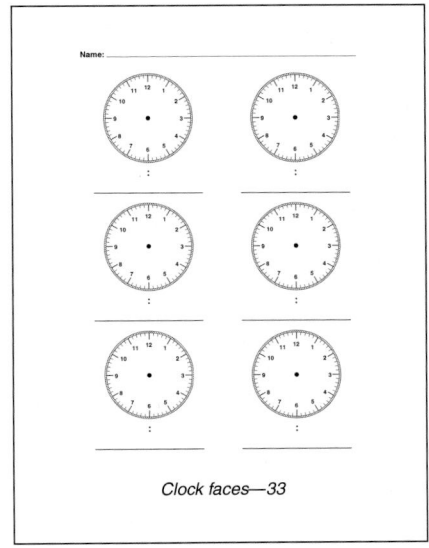

Clock faces—33

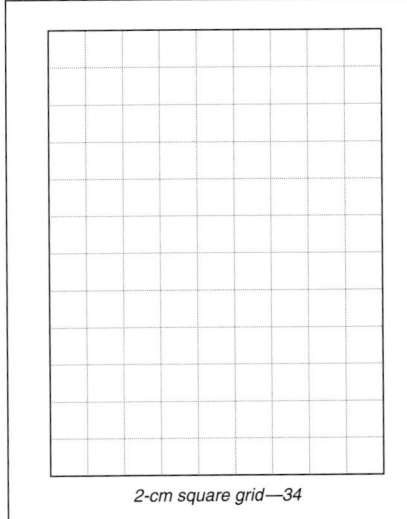

2-cm square grid—34

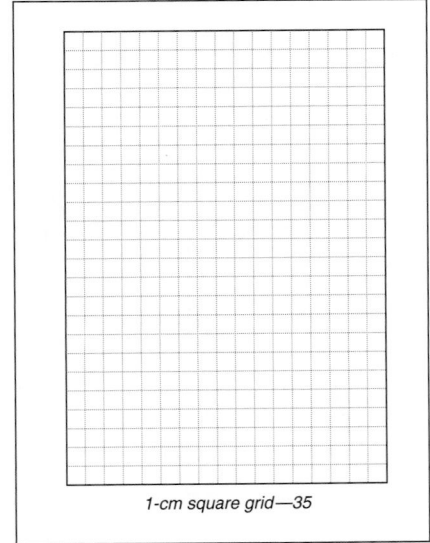

1-cm square grid—35

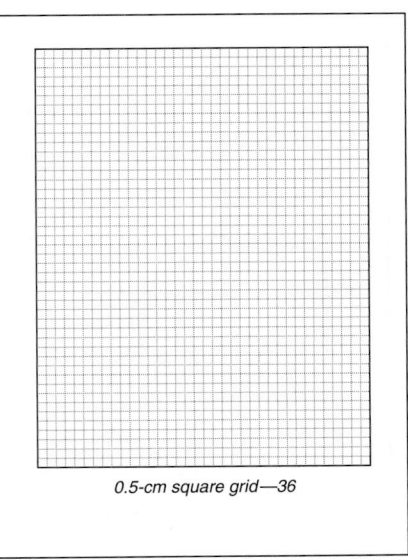

0.5-cm square grid—36

1-cm square dot grid—37

2-cm isometric grid—38

1-cm isometric dot grid—39

1-cm square/diagonal grid—40

Assorted shapes—41

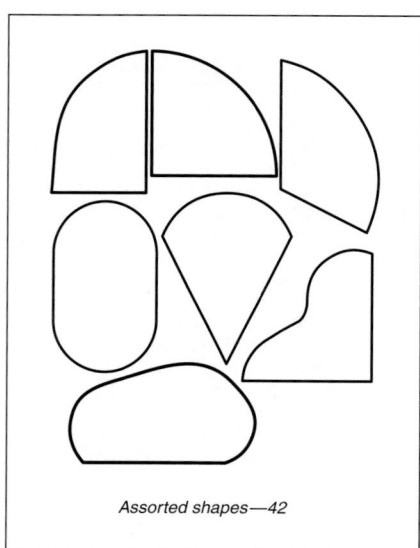

Assorted shapes—42

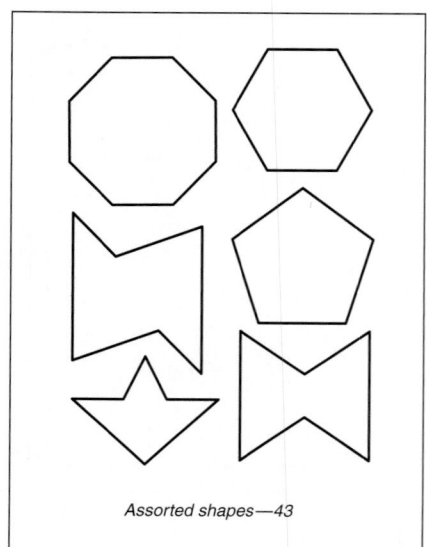

Assorted shapes—43

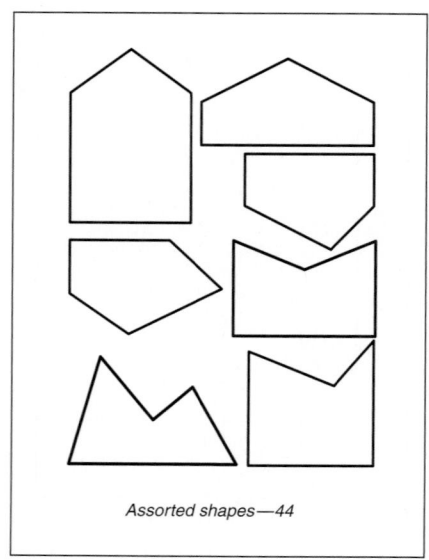

Assorted shapes—44

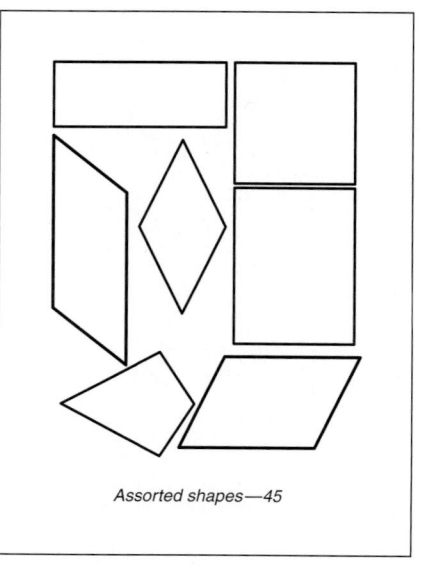

Assorted shapes—45

Assorted shapes—46

Assorted shapes—47

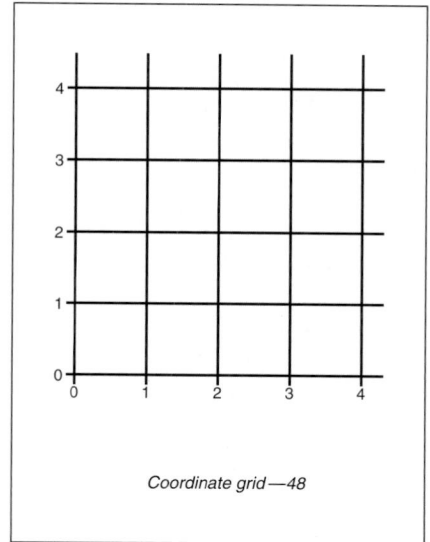

Coordinate grid—48

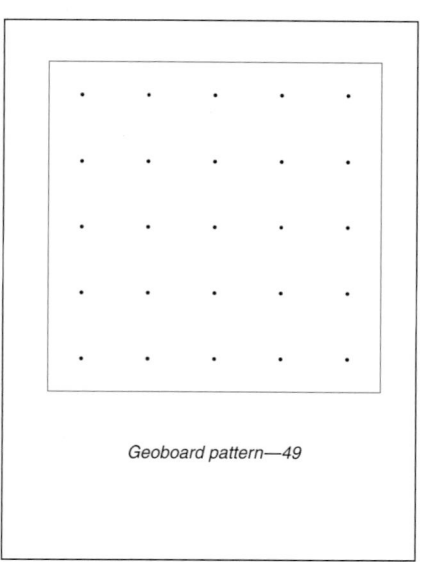

Geoboard pattern—49

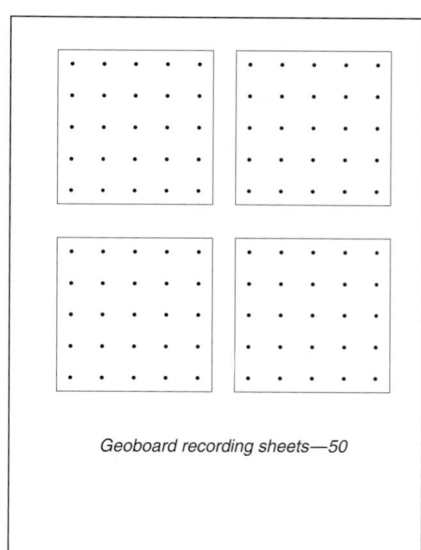

Geoboard recording sheets—50

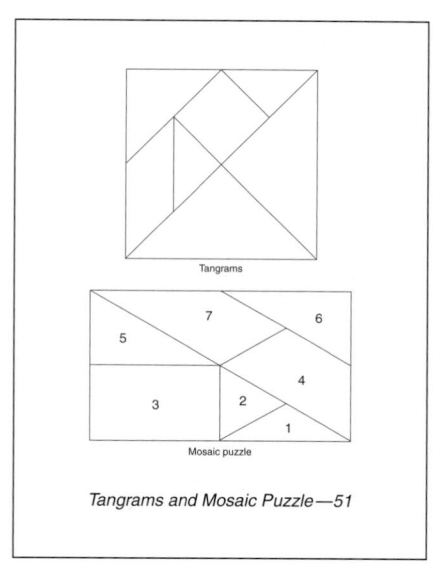

Tangrams and Mosaic Puzzle—51

Motion Man—52

Motion Man—53

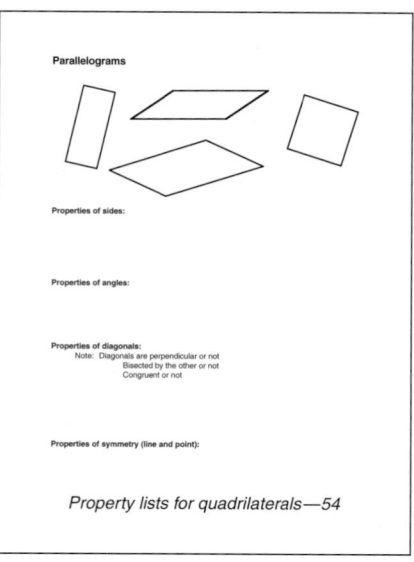

Property lists for quadrilaterals—54

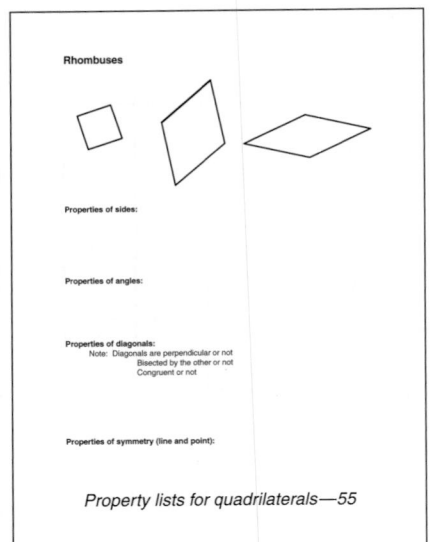

Property lists for quadrilaterals—55

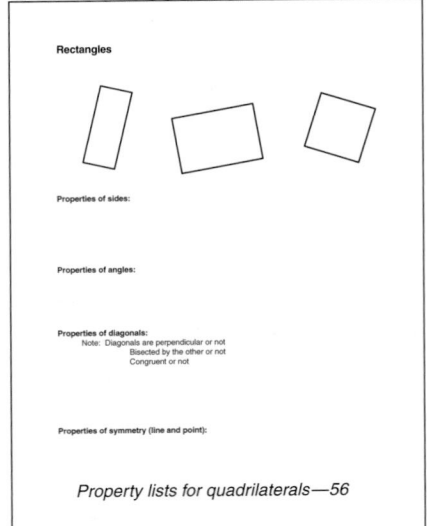

Property lists for quadrilaterals—56

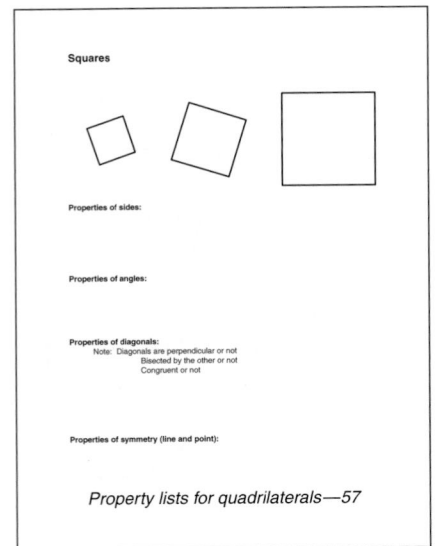

Property lists for quadrilaterals—57

Assorted triangles—58

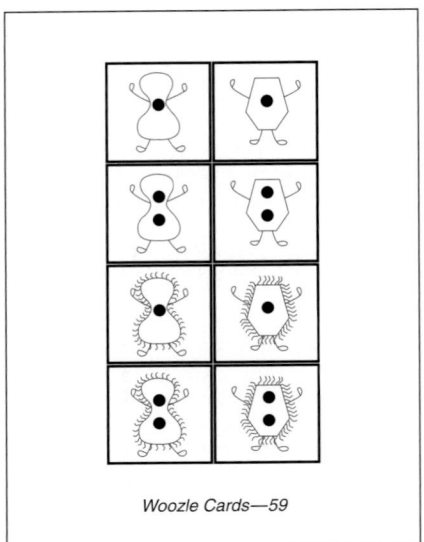

Woozle Cards—59

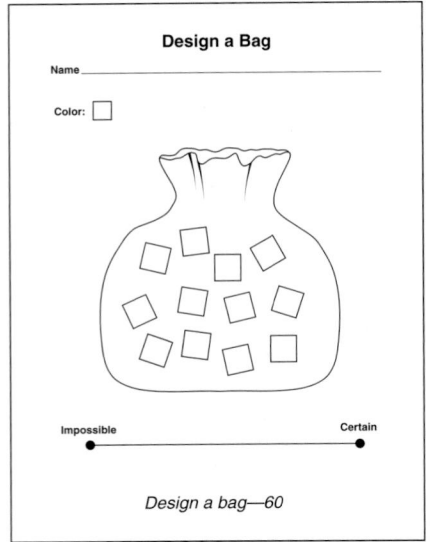

Design a bag—60

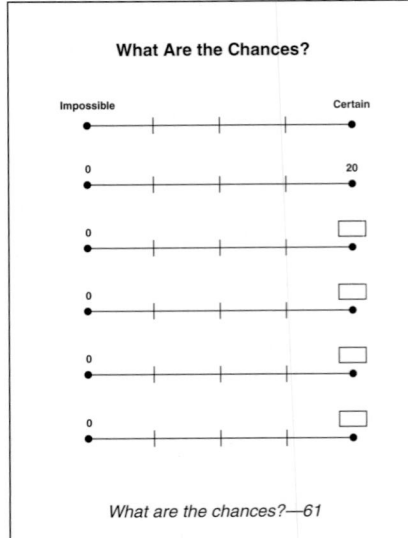

What are the chances?—61

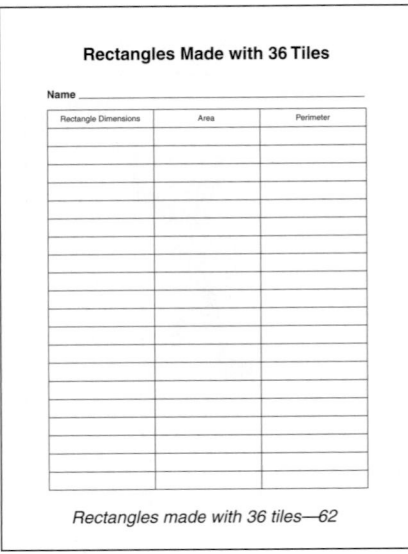

Rectangles made with 36 tiles—62

My Sandwich Recipe Sheet

Number of Ingredients	BREAD	CHEESE	TOMATO	LETTUCE	CUCUMBER
6					
5					
4					
3					
2					
1					

References

Ambrose, R., Baek, J., & Carpenter, T. P. (2003). Children's invention of multidigit multiplication and division algorithms. In A. J. Baroody & A. Dowker (Eds.), *The development of arithmetic concepts and skills: Constructing adaptive expertise* (pp. 305–336). Mahwah, NJ: Erlbaum.

ARC Center (2002). *The ARC tri-state student achievement study* [online]. www.comap/elementary/projects/arc.

Ashcraft, M. H., & Christy, K. S. (1995). The frequency of arithmetic facts in elementary texts: Addition and multiplication in grades 1–6. *Journal for Research in Mathematics Education, 26,* 396–421.

Austin, R., & Thompson, D. (1997). Exploring algebraic patterns through literature. *Mathematics Teaching in the Middle School, 2,* 274–281.

Backhouse, J., Haggarty, L., Pirie, S., & Stratton, J. (1992). *Improving the learning of mathematics.* Portsmouth, NH: Heinemann.

Baek, J. (1998). Children's invented algorithms for multidigit multiplication problems. In L. J. Morrow (Ed.), *The teaching and learning of algorithms in school mathematics* (pp. 151–160). Reston, VA: NCTM.

Baek, J. M. (2006). Children's mathematical understanding and invented strategies for multidigit multiplication, *Teaching Children Mathematics, 12* (5), 242–247.

Baker, A., & Baker, J. (1991). *Math's in the mind: A process approach to mental strategies.* Portsmouth, NH: Heinemann.

Baker, J., & Baker, A. (1990). *Mathematics in process.* Portsmouth, NH: Heinemann.

Ball, D. L. (1992). Magical hopes: Manipulatives and the reform of math education. *American Educator, 16* (2), 14–18, 46–47.

Ball, D. L. (2008). *The work of teaching and the challenges for teacher education.* Presentation at the American Association of Colleges of Teacher Education annual meeting, New Orleans, LA, February 2008.

Ball, L., & Bass, H. (2003). Making mathematics reasonable in school. In J. Kilpatrick, W. G. Martin, & D. Schifter (Eds.), *A research companion to* Principles and Standards for School Mathematics (pp. 27–44). Reston, VA: NCTM.

Ball, L., & Stacey, K. (2005). Teaching strategies for developing judicious technology use. In W. J. Masalski & P. C. Elliott (Eds.), *Technology-supported mathematics learning environments* (pp. 3–15). Reston, VA: NCTM.

Baratta-Lorton, M. (1976). *Mathematics their way.* Menlo Park, CA: AWL Supplemental.

Baroody, A. J. (1985). Mastery of the basic number combinations: Internalization of relationships or facts? *Journal for Research in Mathematics Education, 16,* 83–98.

Baroody, A. J. (1987). *Children's mathematical thinking: A developmental framework for preschool, primary, and special education teachers.* New York: Teachers College Press.

Baroody, A. J. (2003). The development of adaptive expertise and flexibility: The integration of conceptual and procedural knowledge. In A. J. Baroody & A. Dowker (Eds.), *The development of arithmetic concepts and skills: Constructing adaptive expertise* (pp. 1–34). Mahwah, NJ: Erlbaum.

Baroody, A. J., & Hume, J. (1991). Meaningful mathematics instruction: The case of fractions. *Remedial and Special Education, 12,* 54–68.

Baroody, A. J., & Wilkins, J. L. M. (1999). The development of informal counting, number, and arithmetic skills and concepts. In J. V. Copley (Ed.), *Mathematics in the early years* (pp. 48–65). Reston, VA: NCTM.

Barrett, J. E., Jones, G., Thornton, C., & Dickson, S. (2003). Understanding children's developing strategies and concepts of length. In D. H. Clements (Ed.), *Learning and teaching measurement* (pp. 17–30). Reston, VA: NCTM.

Battista, M. C. (1999). The mathematical miseducation of America's youth: Ignoring research and scientific study in education. *Phi Delta Kappan, 80,* 424–433.

Battista, M. T. (2003). Understanding students' thinking about area and volume measurement. In D. H. Clements (Ed.), *Learning and teaching measurement* (pp. 122–142). Reston, VA: NCTM.

Bay-Williams, J. M., & Martinie, S. L. (2004). *Math and literature: Grades 6–8.* Sausalito, CA: Math Solutions Publications.

Bay-Williams, J. M. & Martinie, S. L. (2008). Mathematics and Nonfiction: Grades 6–8. Sausalito, CA: Math Solutions Publications.

BC Ministry of Education. (2002). *BC Performance Standards Numeracy,* Revised Edition. Victoria, BC: Ministry of Education, Student Assessment and Program Evaluation Branch, Province of British Columbia. www.bced.gov.bc.ca/perf_stands/nintro.pdf

BC Special Education Branch. (1995). Gifted education: A resource guide for teachers. Victoria, BC: Author.

Beck, S. A., & Huse, V. E. (2007). A virtual spin on probability. Teaching Children Mathematics, 13 (9), 482–486.

Becker, J. P., & Shimada, S. (Eds.). (1997). *The open-ended approach: A new proposal for teaching mathematics.* Reston, VA: NCTM.

Becker, J. R., & Jacobs, J. E. (2001). Introduction. In J. E. Jacobs, J. R. Becker, & G. F. Gilmer (Eds.), *Changing the faces of mathematics: Perspectives on gender* (pp. 1–8). Reston, VA: NCTM.

Beckman, C. E., Thompson, D., & Austin, R. A. (2004). Exploring proportional reasoning through movies and literature. *Mathematics Teaching in the Middle School, 9,* 256–262.

Behr, M. J., Erlwanger, S. H., & Nicholls, E. (1975). How Children View Equality Sentences, *PMDC Technical Report, 3,* Florida State University.

Behr, M. J., Lesh, R., Post, T. R., & Silver, E. A. (1983). Rational number concepts. In R. Lesh & M. Landau (Eds.), *Acquisition of Mathematics Concepts and Processes* (pp. 91–126). New York: Academic Press.

Bell, M. (1998–1999, Winter). Problems with implementing new curricula: The example of the K–6 *Everyday Mathematics* Curriculum. *UCSMP Newsletter, 24,* 1–2.

Bell, E. S., & Bell, R. N. (1985). Writing and mathematical problem solving: Arguments in favor of synthesis. *School Science and Mathematics, 85* (3), 210–21.

Bley, N. S. (1994). Accommodating special needs. In C. A. Thornton & N. S. Bley (Eds.), *Windows of opportunity: Mathematics for students with special needs* (pp. 137–163). Reston, VA: NCTM.

Bley, N. S., & Thornton, C. A. (1995). *Teaching mathematics to students with learning disabilities* (3rd ed.). Austin, TX: Pro-Ed.

Blume, G., Galindo, E., & Walcott, C. (2007). Performance in measurement and geometry from the viewpoint of Principles and Standards for School Mathematics. In P. Kloosterman and F. Lester, Jr. (Eds.), *Results and interpretations of the 2003 mathematics assessment of the National Assessment of Educational Progress* (pp. 95–138). Reston, VA: NCTM.

Boaler, J. (1998). Open and closed mathematics: Student experiences and understandings. *Journal for Research in Mathematics Education, 29,* 41–62.

Boaler, J., & Humphreys, C. (2005). *Connecting mathematical ideas: Middle school video cases to support teaching and learning.* Portsmouth, NH: Heinemann.

Boats, J., Dwyer, N., Laing, S., & Fratella, M. (2003). Geometric conjectures: The importance of counterexamples. *Mathematics Teaching in the Middle School, 9* (4), 210–215.

Borasi, R. (1994, April). Implementing the NCTM *Standards* in "inclusive" mainstream classrooms. Presented at the annual meeting of the National Council of Teachers of Mathematics, Indianapolis, IN.

Bransford, J., Brown, A., & Cocking, R., Eds. (2000). *How people learn: Brain, mind, experience, and school: Expanded edition.* Washington, DC: National Academy Press.

Bresser, R. (1995). *Math and literature (grades 4–6).* White Plains, NY: Cuisenaire (distributor).

Bright, G. W., Behr, M. J., Post, T. R., & Wachsmuth, I. (1988). Identifying fractions on number lines. *Journal for Research in Mathematics Education, 19,* 215–232.

Bright, G. W., Joyner, J. M., & Wallis, C. (2003). Assessing proportional thinking. *Mathematics Teaching in the Middle School, 9,* 166–172.

Brooks, J. G., & Brooks, M. G. (1993). *In search of understanding: The case for the constructivist classroom.* Alexandria, VA: Association for Supervision and Curriculum Development.

Brownell, W., & Chazal, C. (1935). The effects of premature drill in third grade arithmetic. *Journal of Educational Research, 29,* 17–28.

Burger, W. F. (1985). Geometry. *Arithmetic Teacher, 32* (6), 52–56.

Burns, M. (1982). *Math for smarty pants.* New York: Little, Brown.

Burns, M. (1992). *Math and literature (K–3).* Sausalito, CA: Math Solutions Publications.

Burns, M. (1995a). Timed tests. *Teaching Children Mathematics, 1,* 408–409.

Burns, M. (1995b). *Writing in math class.* White Plains, NY: Cuisenaire (distributor).

Burns, M. (1996). *50 problem-solving lessons: Grades 1–6.* White Plains, NY: Cuisenaire (distributor).

Burns, M. (1999). *Making sense of mathematics: A look toward the twenty-first century.* Presentation at the annual meeting of the National Council of Teachers of Mathematics, San Francisco.

Burns, M. (2000). *About teaching mathematics: A K–8 resource* (2nd ed.). Sausalito, CA: Math Solutions Publications.

Burns, M., & McLaughlin, C. (1990). *A collection of math lessons from grades 6 through 8.* Sausalito, CA: Math Solutions Publications.

Burrill, G. F., & Elliot, P. (2006). *Thinking and reasoning with data and chance: The 68th yearbook of the National Council of Teachers of Mathematics.* Reston, VA: NCTM.

Buschman, L. (2003). *Share and compare: A teacher's story about helping children become problem solvers in mathematics.* Reston, VA: NCTM.

Cai, J., & Sun, W. (2002). Developing students' proportional reasoning: A Chinese perspective. In B. Litwiller (Ed.), *Making sense of fractions, ratios, and proportions* (pp. 195–205). Reston, VA: NCTM.

Cai, J., & Wang, T. (2006). U.S. and Chinese teachers' conceptions and constructions of representations: A case of teaching ratio concept. *International Journal of Science and Mathematics Education, 4* (1), 145–186.

Campbell, P. B. (1995). Redefining the "girl problem in mathematics." In W. G. Secada, E. Fennema, & L. B. Adajian (Eds.), *New directions for equity in mathematics education* (pp. 225–241). New York: Cambridge University Press.

Campbell, P. F. (1996). Empowering children and teachers in the elementary mathematics classrooms of urban schools. *Urban Education, 30,* 449–475.

Campbell, P. F. (1997, April). Children's invented algorithms: Their meaning and place in instruction. Presented at the annual meeting of the National Council of Teachers of Mathematics, Minneapolis, MN.

Campbell, P. F., & Johnson, M. L. (1995). How primary students think and learn. In I. M. Carl (Ed.), *Prospects for school mathematics* (pp. 21–42). Reston, VA: NCTM.

Campbell, P. F., Rowan, T. E., & Suarez, A. R. (1998). What criteria for student-invented algorithms? In L. J. Morrow (Ed.), *The teaching and learning of algorithms in school mathematics* (pp. 49–55). Reston, VA: NCTM.

Campione, J. C., Brown, A. L., & Connell, M. L. (1989). Metacognition: On the importance of understanding what you are doing. In R. I. Charles & E. A. Silver (Eds.), *The teaching and assessing of mathematical problem solving* (pp. 93–114). Reston, VA: NCTM.

Carey, D. A., Fennema, E., Carpenter, T. P., & Franke, M. L. (1995). Equity and mathematics education. In W. G. Secada, E. Fennema, & L. B. Adajian (Eds.), *New directions for equity in mathematics education* (pp. 93–125). New York: Cambridge University Press.

Carpenter, T. P. (1985). Learning to add and subtract: An exercise in problem solving. In E. A. Silver (Ed.), *Teaching and learning mathematical problem solving: Multiple research perspectives* (pp. 17–40). Hillsdale, NJ: Lawrence Erlbaum.

Carpenter, T. P., Ansell, E., Franke, M. L., Fennema, E., & Weisbeck, L. (1993). A study of kindergarten children's problem-solving processes. *Journal for Research in Mathematics Education, 24*, 428–441.

Carpenter, T. P., Carey, D. A., & Kouba, V. L. (1990). A problem-solving approach to the operations. In J. N. Payne (Ed.), *Mathematics for the young child* (pp. 111–131). Reston, VA: NCTM.

Carpenter, T. P., Fennema, E., Franke, M. L., Levi, L., & Empson, S. B. (1999). *Children's mathematics: Cognitively guided instruction.* Portsmouth, NH: Heinemann.

Carpenter, T. P., Franke, M. L., Jacobs, V. R., Fennema, E., & Empson, S. B. (1998). A longitudinal study of invention and understanding in children's multidigit addition and subtraction. *Journal for Research in Mathematics Education, 29*, 3–20.

Carpenter, T. P., Franke, M. L., & Levi, L. (2003). *Thinking mathematically: Integrating arithmetic & algebra in elementary school.* Portsmouth, NH: Heinemann.

Carpenter, T. P., & Moser, J. M. (1984). The acquisition of addition and subtraction concepts in grades one through three. *Journal for Research in Mathematics Education, 15,*179–202.

Carroll, W. M., & Porter, D. (1997). Invented strategies can develop meaningful mathematical procedures. *Teaching Children Mathematics, 3*, 370–374.

Chapin, S. H., O'Conner, C., & Anderson, N. C. (2003). *Classroom discussions: Using math talk to help students learn.* Sausalito, CA: Math Solutions Publications.

Charles, R. I., Chancellor, D., Harcourt, L., Moore, D., Schielack, J. F., Van de Walle, J., & Wortzman, R. (1998). *Scott Foresman—Addison Wesley MATH (Grades K to 5).* Glenview, IL: Addison Wesley Longman, Inc.

Chick, C., Tierney, C., & Storeygard, J. (2007). Seeing students' knowledge of fractions: Candace's inclusive classroom. *Teaching Children Mathematics,14* (1), 52–57.

Clark, F. B., & Kamii, C. (1996). Identification of multiplicative thinking in children in grades 1–5. *Journal for Research in Mathematics Education, 27*, 41–51.

Clarke, D. M., Roche, A., & Mitchell, A. (2008). 10 practical tips for making fractions come alive and make sense. *Mathematics Teaching in the Middle School, 13* (7), 373–380.

Clement, L., & Bernhard, J. (2005). A problem-solving alternative to using key words. *Mathematics Teaching in the Middle School, 10* (7), 360–365.

Clements, D. H., & Battista, M. T. (1990). Constructivist learning and teaching. *Arithmetic Teacher, 38* (1), 34–35.

Clements, D. H., & Battista, M. T. (2001). *Logo and geometry.* Reston, VA: NCTM.

Clements, D. H., & Sarama, J. (2005). Young children and technology: What's appropriate? In W. Masalski & P. C. Elliott (Eds.), *Technology-supported mathematics learning environments: 67th yearbook* (pp. 51–73). Reston, VA: NCTM.

Cobb, P. (1988). The tension between theories of learning and instruction in mathematics education. *Educational Psychologist, 23*, 87–103.

Cobb, P. (1994) Where is the mind? Constructivist and sociocultural perspectives on mathematical development. *Educational Researcher, 23* (7), 13–20.

Cohen, R. (2006). How do students think? *Mathematics Teaching in the Middle School, 11* (9), 434–436.

Colgan, M. D. (2006). March math madness: The mathematics of the NCAA basketball tournament. *Mathematics Teaching in Middle School, 11* (7), 334–342.

Cook, C. D. (2008). I scream, you scream: Data analysis with kindergartners. *Teaching Children Mathematics, 14* (9), 538–540.

Council of Ministers of Education. (2001). *School Achievement Indicators Program SAIP mathematics III 2001.* Toronto: Council of Ministers of Education.

Cramer, K., & Henry, A. (2002). Using manipulative models to build number sense for addition of fractions. In B. Litwiller (Ed.), *Making sense of fractions, ratios, and proportions* (pp. 41–48). Reston, VA: NCTM.

Cramer, K., Wyberg, T., & Leavitt, S. (2008). The role of representations in fraction addition and subtraction. *Mathematics Teaching in the Middle School, 13* (8), 490–496.

Crespo, S., Kyriakides, A. O., & McGee, S. (2005). Nothing "basic" about basic facts: Exploring addition facts with fourth graders. *Teaching Children Mathematics, 12* (2), 60–67.

Cummins, J. (1994). Primary language instruction and the education of language minority students. In C. F. Leyba (Ed.), *Schooling and language minority students: A theoretical framework* (pp. 3–46). Los Angeles, CA: California State University, National Evaluation, Dissemination and Assessment Center.

Curcio, F. R., & Bezuk, N. S. (1994). *Understanding rational numbers and proportions: Addenda Series, grades 5–8.* Reston, VA: NCTM.

Damarin, S. K. (1995). Gender and mathematics from a feminist standpoint. In W. G. Secada, E. Fennema, & L. B. Adajian (Eds.), *New directions for equity in mathematics education* (pp. 242–257). New York: Cambridge University Press.

Davies, A. (2007). Making classroom assessment work, 2nd edition. Courtenay, BC: Connections Publishing.

Davis, R. B. (1986). *Learning mathematics: The cognitive science approach to mathematics education.* Norwood, NJ: Ablex.

Dixon, J. (2008) Tracking time: Representing elapsed time on an open timeline. *Teaching Children Mathematics, 15* (1), 18–24.

Drake, J., & Barlow, A. (2007). Assessing students' level of understanding multiplication through problem writing. *Teaching Children Mathematics, 14* (5), 272–277.

Earl, L. (2006). Classroom assessment for deep understanding. In Leithwood, K., McAdie, P., Bascia, N., & Rodrigue, A., *Teaching for deep understanding: What every educator should know*, pp. 116–122. Thousand Oaks, CA: Corwin Press.

Earnest, D., & Balti, A. A. (2008). Instructional strategies for teaching algebra in elementary school: Findings from a research–practice partnership. *Teaching Children Mathematics, 14* (9), 518–522.

Echevarria, J., Vogt, M., & Short, D. J. (2004). *Making content comprehensible for English learners: The SIOP model* (2nd ed.). Boston: Pearson.

Ellington, A. (2003). A meta-analysis of the effects of calculators on students' achievement and attitude levels in precollege mathematics classes. *Journal for Research in Mathematics Education, 34* (5), 433–463.

Elliott, P., & Garnett, C. (1994). Mathematics power for all. In C. A. Thornton & N. S. Bley (Eds.), *Windows of opportunity: Mathematics for students with special needs* (pp. 3–17). Reston, VA: NCTM.

Ellis, M., Yeh, C., & Stump, S. (2007/2008). Rock–paper–scissors and solutions to the broken calculator problem. *Teaching Children Mathematics, 14* (5), 309–314.

Empson, S. B. (2002). Organizing diversity in early fraction thinking. In B. Litwiller (Ed.), *Making sense of fractions, ratios, and proportions* (pp. 29–40). Reston, VA: NCTM.

Erlwanger, S. H., & Berlanger, M. (1983). Interpretations of the Equal Sign among Elementary School Children, *Proceedings of the North American Chapter of the International Group for the Psychology of Mathematics Education*, Montreal.

Falkner, K. P., Levi, L., & Carpenter, T. P. (1999). Children's understanding of equality: A foundation for algebra. *Teaching Children Mathematics, 6*, 232–236.

Fernandez, M. L., & Schoen, R. C. (2008). Teaching and learning mathematics through hurricane tracking. *Mathematics Teaching in the Middle School, 13* (9), 500–512.

Findell, C. R., Small, M., Cavanagh, M., Dacey, L., Greenes, C. E., & Sheffield, L. J. (2001). *Navigations*, Reston, VA: NCTM.

Fischer, F. E. (1990). A part-part-whole curriculum for teaching number in the kindergarten. *Journal for Research in Mathematics Education, 21*, 207–215.

Flewelling, G., & Higginson, W. (2001). *A Handbook on Rich Learning Tasks*, Kingston, ON: Centre for Mathematics, Science, and Technology Education, Queen's University.

Flores, A. (2006). Using graphing calculators to redress beliefs in the "law of small numbers." *Thinking and reasoning about data and chance: Sixty-eighth yearbook* (pp. 139–149). Reston, VA: NCTM.

Flores, A., & Klein, E. (2005). From students' problem solving strategies to connections with fractions. *Teaching Children Mathematics, 11* (9), 452–457.

Flores, A., Samson, J., Yanik, H. B. (2006). Quotient and measurement interpretations of rational numbers. *Teaching Children Mathematics, 13* (1), 34–39.

Forman, E. A. (2003). A sociocultural approach to mathematics reform: Speaking, inscribing, and doing mathematics within communities of practice. In J. Kilpatrick, G. Martin, & D. Schifter (Eds.) *A research companion to the NCTM Standards* (pp. 333–352). Reston, VA: NCTM.

Forman, E. A., & McPhail, J. (1993). A Vygotskian perspective on children's collaborative problem-solving activities. In E. A. Forman, N. Minick, & C. A. Stone (Eds.), *Contexts for learning: Sociocultural dynamics in children's development* (pp. 213–229). New York: Oxford University Press.

Fosnot, C. T. (1996). Constructivism: A psychological theory of learning. In C. T. Fosnot (Ed.), *Constructivism: Theory, perspectives, and practice* (pp. 8–33). New York: Teachers College Press.

Fosnot, C. T., & Dolk, M. (2001). *Young mathematicians at work: Constructing number sense, addition, and subtraction.* Portsmouth, NH: Heinemann.

Franklin, C., Kader, G., Mewborn, D., Moreno, J., Peck, R., Perry, M., & Scheaffer, R. (2005). *Guidelines for assessment and instruction in statistics education (GAISE) report.* Alexandria, VA: American Statistical Association.

Friedman, Thomas (2007). The world is flat 3.0: A brief history of the twenty-first century. New York: Picador.

Friel, S. N., Mokros, J. R., & Russell, S. J. (1992). *Statistics: Middles, means, and in-betweens.* A unit of study for grades 5–6 from *Used numbers: Real data in the classroom.* White Plains, NY: Cuisenaire—Dale Seymour.

Friel, S. N., O'Conner, W., & Mamer, J. D. (2006). More than "meanmedianmode" and a bar graph: What's needed to have a statistical conversation? In G. F. Burrill & P. C. Elliott (Eds.) *Thinking and reasoning about data and chance: Sixty-eighth yearbook* (pp. 117–138). Reston, VA: NCTM.

Fuson, K. C. (1984). More complexities in subtraction. *Journal for Research in Mathematics Education, 15*, 214–225.

Fuson, K. C. (1988). *Children's counting and concepts of number.* New York: Springer-Verlag.

Fuson, K. C. (1992). Research on whole number addition and subtraction. In D. A. Grouws (Ed.), *Handbook of research on teaching and learning* (pp. 243–275). Old Tappan, NJ: Macmillan.

Fuson, K. (2003). Developing mathematical power in whole number operations. In J. Kilpatrick, W. G. Martin, and D. Schifter (Eds.), *A research companion to Principles and Standards in School Mathematics* (pp. 68–94). Reston, VA: NCTM.

Fuson, K. C., Carroll, W. M., & Drueck, J. V. (2000). Achievement results for second and third graders using the *Standards*-based curriculum *Everyday Mathematics. Journal for Research in Mathematics Education, 31*, 277–295.

Fuson, K. C., & Hall, J. W. (1983). The acquisition of early number word meanings: A conceptual analysis and review. In H. P. Ginsburg (Ed.), *The development of mathematical thinking* (pp. 49–107). Orlando, FL: Academic Press.

Fuson, K. C., & Kwon, Y. (1992). Korean children's single digit addition and subtraction: Numbers structured by ten. *Journal for Research in Mathematics Education, 23*, 148–165.

Fuson, K. C., Wearne, D., Hiebert, J. C., Murray, H. G., Human, P. G., Olivier, A. I., Carpenter, T. P., & Fennema, E. (1997). Children's conceptual structures for multidigit numbers and methods of multidigit addition and subtraction. *Journal for Research in Mathematics Education, 28*, 130–162.

Fuys, D., Geddes, D., & Tischler, R. (1988). The van Hiele model of thinking in geometry among adolescents. *Journal for Research in Mathematics Education Monograph, 3*.

Garofalo, J. (1987). Metacognition and school mathematics. *Arithmetic Teacher, 34* (9), 22–23.

Garrison, L. (1997). Making the NCTM's Standards work for emergent English speakers. *Teaching Children Mathematics, 4*, 132–138.

Geddes, D., & Fortunato, I. (1993). Geometry: Research and classroom activities. In D. T. Owens (Ed.), *Research ideas for the classroom: Middle grades mathematics* (pp. 199–222). New York: Macmillan.

Gelman, R., & Gallistel, C. R. (1978). *The child's understanding of number.* Cambridge, MA: Harvard University Press.

Gelman, R., & Meck, E. (1986). The notion of principle: The case of counting. In J. Hiebert (Ed.), *Conceptual and procedural knowledge: The case of mathematics* (pp. 29–57). Hillsdale, NJ: Erlbaum.

Gibbs, J. (2006). *Reaching all by creating tribes of learning communities*. California: Centersource Systems, LLC.

Gill, B. P. & Schlossman, S. L. (2003). A Nation at Rest: The American Way of Homework. *Educational Evaluation and Policy Analysis, 25*(3), 319–337.

Gill, B. P. & Schlossman, S. L. (2004). Villain or Savior? The American Discourse on Homework, 1850–2003, *Theory Into Practice, 43*(3), pp. 174-181.

Ginsburg, H. P. (1977). *Children's arithmetic: The learning process*. New York: Van Nostrand.

Gnanadesikan, M., Schaeffer, R. L., & Swift, J. (1987). *The art and techniques of simulation: Quantitative literacy series*. Palo Alto, CA: Dale Seymour.

Goldin, G. A. (1985). Thinking scientifically and thinking mathematically: A discussion of the paper by Heller and Hungate. In E. A. Silver (Ed.), *Teaching and learning mathematical problem solving: Multiple research perspectives* (pp. 113–122). Hillsdale, NJ: Lawrence Erlbaum.

Golembo, V. (2000). Writing a PEMDAS story. *Mathematics Teaching in the Middle School, 5* (9), 574–579.

Goos, M. (2004). Learning mathematics in a classroom community of inquiry. *Journal for Research in Mathematics Education, 35* (4), 258–291.

Goral, M. B., & Wiest, L. R. (2007). An arts-based approach to teaching fractions. *Teaching Children Mathematics, 14* (2), 74–80.

Gravemeijer, K., & van Galen, F. (2003). Facts and algorithms as products of students' own mathematical activity. In J. Kilpatrick, W. G. Martin, & D. Schifter (Eds.), *A research companion to* Principles and Standards for School Mathematics (pp. 114–122). Reston, VA: NCTM.

Greenes, C., & Findell, C. (1999a). *Groundworks: Algebra puzzles and problems* (separate books for grades 4 to 7). Chicago: Creative Publications.

Greenes, C., & Findell, C. (1999b). *Groundworks: Algebraic thinking* (separate books for grades 1, 2, and 3). Chicago: Creative Publications.

Greer, B. (1992). Multiplication and division as models of situations. In D. A. Grouws (Ed.), *Handbook of research on mathematics teaching and learning* (pp. 276–295). Old Tappan, NJ: Macmillan.

Gregg, J., & Gregg, D. W. (2007). Measurement and Fair-Sharing Models for Dividing Fractions. *Mathematics Teaching in the Middle School, 12* (9), 490–496

Groff, P. (1996). It is time to question fraction teaching. *Mathematics Teaching in the Middle School, 1,* 604–607.

Groth, R. E. (2006). Expanding teachers' understanding of geometric definition: The case of the trapezoid. *Teaching Children Mathematics, 12* (7), 376–380.

Gutstein, E., & Romberg, T. A. (1995). Teaching children to add and subtract. *Journal of Mathematical Behavior, 14,* 283–324.

Hanson, S. A., & Hogan, T. P. (2000). Computational estimation skill of college students. *Journal for Research in Mathematics Education, 31* (4), 483–499.

Hawes, K. (2007). Using error analysis to teach equation solving. *Mathematics Teaching in the Middle School, 12* (5), 241.

Hashimoto, Y., & Becker, J. (1999). The open approach to teaching mathematics—Creating a culture of mathematics in the classroom: Japan. In L. J. Sheffield (Ed.), *Developing mathematically promising students* (pp. 101–119). Reston, VA: NCTM.

Heck, T. *Team building games on a shoestring*. Retrieved August 22, 2008, www.teachmeteamwork.com.

Heinz, K., & Sterba-Boatwright, B. (2008). The When and Why of Using Proportions. *Mathematics Teacher, 101* (7), 528–533.

Hembree, R., & Dessert, D. (1986). Effects of hand-held calculators in precollege mathematics education: A meta analysis. *Journal of Research in Mathematics Education, 17* (2), 83–99.

Henry, V. J., & Brown, R. S. (2008). First-grade basic facts: An investigation into teaching and learning of an accelerated, high-demand memorization standard. *Journal for Research in Mathematics Education, 39* (2), 153–183.

Hiebert, J. (2003). What research says about the NCTM standards. In J. Kilpatrick, W. G. Martin, & D. Schifter (Eds.), *A research companion to* Principles and Standards for School Mathematics (pp. 5–23). Reston, VA: NCTM.

Hiebert, J., & Carpenter, T. P. (1992). Learning and teaching with understanding. In D. A. Grouws (Ed.), *Handbook of research on mathematics teaching and learning* (pp. 65–97). Old Tappan, NJ: Macmillan.

Hiebert, J., Carpenter, T. P., Fennema, E., Fuson, K., Human, P., Murray, H., Olivier, A., & Wearne, D. (1996). Problem solving as a basis for reform in curriculum and instruction: The case of mathematics. *Educational Researcher, 25* (May), 12–21.

Hiebert, J., Carpenter, T. P., Fennema, E., Fuson, K., Wearne, D., Murray, H., Olivier, A., & Human, P. (1997). *Making sense: Teaching and learning mathematics with understanding*. Portsmouth, NH: Heinemann.

Hiebert, J., Gallimore, R., Garnier, H., Givvin, K. B., Hollingsworth, H., Jacobs, J., Chui, A. M–Y., Wearne, D., Smith, M., Kersting, N., Manaster, A., Tseng, E., Etterbeek, W., Manaster, C., Gonzales, P., & Stigler, J. (2003). *Teaching mathematics in seven countries: Results from the TIMSS 1999 video study*. Washington, D.C.: National Center for Education Statistics, U.S. Department of Education.

Hiebert, J. & Lefevre, P. (1986). Conceptual and Procedural Knowledge in Mathematics: an Introductory Analysis. In J. Hiebert (Ed.), *Conceptual and Procedural Knowledge: The Case of Mathematics* (pp. 1–27). Hillsdale, NJ: Erlbaum.

Hiebert, J., & Lindquist, M. M. (1990). Developing mathematical knowledge in the young child. In J. N. Payne (Ed.), *Mathematics for the young child* (pp. 17–36). Reston, VA: NCTM.

Hiebert, J., & Wearne, D. (1996). Instruction, understanding, and skill in multidigit addition and subtraction. *Cognition and Instruction, 14,* 251–283.

Hoffer, A. R., & Hoffer, S. A. K. (1992). Ratios and proportional thinking. In T. R. Post (Ed.), *Teaching mathematics in grades K–8: Research-based methods* (2nd ed.) (pp. 303–330). Boston: Allyn & Bacon.

House, P. A. (1999). Promises, promises, promises. In L. J. Sheffield (Ed.), *Developing mathematically promising students* (pp. 1–7). Reston, VA: NCTM.

Howden, H. (1989). Teaching number sense. *Arithmetic Teacher, 36* (6), 6–11.

Huinker, D. (1994, April). Multi-step word problems: A strategy for empowering students. Presented at the annual meeting of the National Council of Teachers of Mathematics, Indianapolis, IN.

Huinker, D. (1998). Letting fraction algorithms emerge through problem solving. In L. J. Morrow (Ed.), *The teaching and learning of algorithms in school mathematics* (pp. 170–182). Reston, VA: NCTM.

Hutchinson, N. L. (2002). *Inclusion of exceptional learners in Canadian schools: A practical handbook for teachers.* Toronto: Prentice Hall.

Hyde, A., George, K., Mynard, S., Hull, C., Watson, S., & Watson, P. (2006). "Creating multiple representations in algebra: All chocolate, no change," *Mathematics Teaching in the Middle School, 11* (6), 262–268.

Ineson, G. (2007). Year 6 children: Has the new British mathematics curriculum helped their mental calculation? *Early Child Development and Care, 177* (5), 541–555.

Izsak, A., Tillema, E., Tunc-Pekkam, Z. (2008). Teaching and learning fraction addition on number lines. *Journal for Research in Mathematics Education, 39* (1), 1, 33–62.

Janvier, C. (Ed.). (1987). *Problems of representation in the teaching and learning of mathematics.* Hillsdale, NJ: Erlbaum.

Johanning, D. J. (2008). Learning to use fractions: Examining middle school students' emerging fraction literacy. *Journal for Research in Mathematics Education, 39* (3), 281–310.

Jones, A. (1998). *Team building activities for every group.* Richland, WA: Rec Room Publishing.

Jones, G., Langrall, C., Thornton, C., & Mogill, A. (1997). A framework for assessing and nurturing young children's thinking in probability. *Educational Studies in Mathematics, 32* (3), 101–125.

Jones, G. A., Thornton, C. A., Langrall, C. W., & Tarr, J. E. (1999). Understanding students' probabilistic reasoning. In L. V. Stiff (Ed.), *Developing mathematical thinking in grades K–12* (pp. 146–155). Reston, VA: NCTM.

Jones, G., Langrall, C., Thornton, C., & Mogill, A. (1997). A framework for assessing and nurturing young children's thinking in probability. *Educational Studies in Mathematics, 32* (3), 101–125.

Joram, E. (2003). Benchmarks as tools for developing measurement sense. In D. H. Clements (Ed.), *Learning and teaching measurement* (pp. 57–67). Reston, VA: NCTM.

Kamii, C. K. (1985). *Young children reinvent arithmetic.* New York: Teachers College Press.

Kamii, C. K. (1989). *Young children continue to reinvent arithmetic: 2nd grade.* New York: Teachers College Press.

Kamii, C. K., & Clark, F. B. (1995). Equivalent fractions: Their difficulty and educational implications. *The Journal of Mathematical Behavior, 14,* 365–378.

Kamii, C. K., & Dominick, A. (1997). To teach or not to teach the algorithms. *Journal of Mathematical Behavior, 16,* 51–62.

Kamii, C. K., & Dominick, A. (1998). The harmful effects of algorithms in grades 1–4. In L. J. Morrow (Ed.), *The teaching and learning of algorithms in school mathematics* (pp. 130–140). Reston, VA: NCTM.

Kaput, J. J. (1998). Transforming algebra from an engine of inequity to an engine of mathematical power by "algebrafying" the K–12 curriculum. In *The nature and role of algebra in the K–12 curriculum: Proceedings of national symposium* (pp. 25–26). Washington, DC: National Academy Press.

Kaput, J. J. (1999). Teaching and learning a new algebra. In E. Fennema & T. A. Romberg (Eds.), *Mathematics classrooms that promote understanding* (pp. 133–155). Mahwah, NJ: Erlbaum.

Karp, K., Brown, E. T., Allen, L., & Allen, C. (1998). *Feisty females: Inspiring girls to think mathematically.* Portsmouth, NH: Heinemann.

Karp, K., & Howell, P. (2004). Building responsibility for learning in students with special needs. *Teaching Children Mathematics, 11* (3), 118–126.

Karplus, R., Pulos, S., & Stage, E. K. (1983). Proportional reasoning of early adolescents. In R. A. Lesh & M. Landau (Eds.), *Acquisition of mathematics concepts and processes* (pp. 45–90). Orlando, FL: Academic Press.

Khisty, L. L. (1997). Making mathematics accessible to Latino students: Rethinking instructional practice. In M. Kenney & J. Trentacosta (Eds.), *Multicultural and gender equity in the mathematics classroom: The gift of diversity* (pp. 92–101). Reston, VA: NCTM.

Kingore, B. (2006, Winter). Tiered instruction: Beginning the process. *Teaching for High Potential,* pp. 5–6.

Klein, A. S., Beishuizen, M., & Treffers, A. (1998). The empty number line in Dutch second grade: *Realistic* versus *gradual* program design. *Journal for Research in Mathematics Education, 29,* 443–464.

Kliman, M., & Russell, S. J. (1998). *The number system: Building number sense (Grade 1).* Glenview, IL: Scott Foresman.

Kloosterman, P., Warfield, J., Wearne, D., Koc, Y., Martin, W. G., & Strutchens, M. (2004). Fourth-grade students' knowledge of mathematics and perceptions of learning mathematics. In P. Kloosterman & F. K. Lester, Jr., *Results and interpretations of the 1990–2000 mathematics assessments of the National Assessment of Educational Progress* (pp. 71–103). Reston, VA: NCTM.

Knuth, E. J., Stephens, A. C., McNeil, N. M., & Alabali, M. W. (2006). Does understanding the equal sign matter? Evidence from solving equations. *Journal for Research in Mathematics Education, 37* (4), 297–312.

Kohn, A. (1993). *Punished by rewards: The trouble with gold stars, incentive plans, A's, praise, and other bribes.* Boston: Houghton Mifflin.

Kouba, V. L. (1989). Children's solution strategies for equivalent set multiplication and division word problems. *Journal for Research in Mathematics Education, 20,* 147–158.

Kouba, V. L., Brown, C. A., Carpenter, T. P., Lindquist, M. M., Silver, E. A., & Swafford, J. O. (1988a). Results of the fourth NAEP assessment of mathematics: Number, operations, and word problems. *Arithmetic Teacher, 35* (8), 14–19.

Kouba, V. L., Zawojewski, J. S., & Strutchens, M. E. (1997). What do students know about numbers and operations? In

P. A. Kenney & E. Silver (Eds.), *Results from the sixth mathematics assessment of the National Assessment of Educational Progress* (pp. 87–140). Reston, VA: NCTM.

Kribs Zaleta, C. (2008). Oranges, poster, ribbons, & lemonade: Concrete computational strategies for dividing fractions. *Mathematics Teaching in the Middle School, 13* (8), 453–457.

Kulm, G. (1994). *Mathematics and assessment: What works in the classroom.* San Francisco: Jossey-Bass.

Labinowicz, E. (1985). *Learning from children: New beginnings for teaching numerical thinking.* Menlo Park, CA: AWL Supplemental.

Lamon, S. J. (1993). Ratio and proportion: Connecting content and children's thinking. *Journal for Research in Mathematics Education, 24,* 41–61.

Lamon, S. J. (1996). The development of unitizing: Its role in children's partitioning strategies. *Journal for Research in Mathematics Education, 27,* 170–193.

Lamon, S. J. (1999a). *More: In-depth discussion of the reasoning activities in "Teaching fractions and ratios for understanding."* Mahwah, NJ: Lawrence Erlbaum.

Lamon, S. J. (1999b). *Teaching fractions and ratios for understanding: Essential content knowledge and instructional strategies for teachers.* Mahwah, NJ: Lawrence Erlbaum.

Lamon, S. J. (2002). Part-whole comparisons with unitizing. In B. Litwiller (Ed.), *Making sense of fractions, ratios, and proportions* (pp. 79–86). Reston, VA: NCTM.

Lannin, J. K., Townsend, B. E., Armer, N., Green, S., & Schneider, J. (2008). Developing meaning for algebraic symbols: Possibilities and pitfalls. *Mathematics Teaching in the Middle School, 13* (8), 478–483.

Lappan, G., & Briars, D. (1995). How should mathematics be taught? In I. M. Carl (Ed.), *Prospects for school mathematics* (pp. 115–156). Reston, VA: NCTM.

Lappan, G., & Even, R. (1989). *Learning to teach: Constructing meaningful understanding of mathematical content* (Craft Paper 89–3). East Lansing: Michigan State University.

Lappan, G., & Mouck, M. K. (1998). Developing algorithms for adding and subtracting fractions. In L. J. Morrow (Ed.), *The teaching and learning of algorithms in school mathematics* (pp. 183–197). Reston, VA: NCTM.

Leder, G. C. (1995). Equity inside the mathematics classroom: Fact or artifact? In W. G. Secada, E. Fennema, & L. B. Adajian (Eds.), *New directions for equity in mathematics education* (pp. 209–224). New York: Cambridge University Press.

Leeming, C. (November 3, 2007). 'Cool Cash' card confusion. *Manchester Evening News,* Manchester, England. Retrieved September 4, 2008, www.manchestereveningnews.co.uk/news/s/1022757_cool_cash_card_confusion

Lesh, R. A., Post, T. R., & Behr, M. J. (1987). Representations and translations among representations in mathematics learning and problem solving. In C. Janvier (Ed.), *Problems of representation in the teaching and learning of mathematics* (pp. 33–40). Hillsdale, NJ: Erlbaum.

Lester, F. K., Jr. (1989). Reflections about mathematical problem-solving research. In R. I. Charles & E. A. Silver (Eds.), *The teaching and assessing of mathematical problem solving* (pp. 115–124). Reston, VA: NCTM.

Lester, F. K., Jr. (1994). Musings about mathematical problem-solving research, 1970–1994. *Journal for Research in Mathematics Education, 25,* 660–675.

Lo, J., & Watanabe, T. (1997). Developing ratio and proportion schemes: A story of a fifth grader. *Journal for Research in Mathematics Education, 28,* 216–236.

Ma, L. (1999). *Knowing and teaching elementary mathematics: Teachers' understanding of fundamental mathematics in China and the United States.* Mahwah, NJ: Lawrence Erlbaum.

Mack, N. K. (1995). Confounding whole-number and fraction concepts when building on informal knowledge. *Journal for Research in Mathematics Education, 26,* 422–441.

Mack, N. K. (2001). Building on informal knowledge through instruction in a complex content domain: Partitioning, units, and understanding multiplication of fractions. *Journal for Research in Mathematics Education, 32,* 267–295.

Mack, N. K. (2004). Connecting to develop computational fluency with fractions. *Teaching Children Mathematics, 11* (4), 226–232.

Mack, N. K. (2007). Gaining insights into children's geometric knowledge. *Teaching Children Mathematics, 14* (4), 238–245.

Madell, R. (1985). Children's natural processes. *Arithmetic Teacher, 32* (7), 20–22.

Manitoba Education, Citizenship and Youth. (2007). *Middle years assessment of key competencies in mathematics, reading comprehension, expository writing, and student engagement.* Winnipeg, MB: Author. www.edu.gov.mb.ca/k12/assess/docs/my_policy/my_policy_doc.pdf

Manitoba Education, Citizenship and Youth. (2007). *Western and Northern Canadian Protocol for Collaboration in Education (WNCP), 2006.* Winnipeg, MB: Author. www.edu.gov.mb.ca/k12/assess/docs/my_policy/my_policy_doc.pdf

Mann, R. L. (2004). Balancing act: The truth behind the equal sign. *Teaching Children Mathematics, 11* (2), 65–69.

Marks-Krpan, K. (2001). *The write math: Writing about math in the classroom.* Parsippany, NJ: Dale Seymour Publications.

Martin, R., Sexton, C., Wagner, K., & Gerlovich, J. (1997). *Teaching science for all children.* Boston: Allyn & Bacon.

Martinie, S. L. (2007). *Middle school rational number knowledge.* Unpublished doctoral dissertation, Kansas State University.

Martinie, S. L., & Bay-Williams, J. (2003). Investigating students' conceptual understanding of decimal fractions using multiple representations. *Mathematics Teaching in the Middle School, 8,* 244–247.

Martinie, S., & Coates, G. D. (2007). A push for number sense makes good sense. *Mathematics Teaching in the Middle Schools, 13* (2), 88–90.

Mathematical Sciences Education Board, National Research Council. (1989). *Everybody counts: A report to the nation on the future of mathematics education.* Washington, DC: National Academy of Sciences Press.

Mau, T. S., & Leitze, A. R. (2001). Powerless gender or genderless power? The promise of constructivism for females in the mathematics classroom. In J. E. Jacobs, J. R. Becker, & G. F. Gilmer (Eds.), *Changing the faces of mathematics: Perspectives on gender* (pp. 37–41). Reston, VA: NCTM.

McClain, K., Leckman, J., Schmitt, P., & Regis, T. (2006). Changing the face of statistical data analysis in the middle grades: Learning by doing. In G. F. Burrill & P. C. Elliott (Eds.), *Thinking and reasoning about data and chance: Sixty-eighth yearbook* (pp. 229–240). Reston, VA: NCTM.

McCoy, L. (1997). Algebra: Real-life investigations in a lab setting. *Mathematics Teaching in the Middle School, 2,* 220–224.

Middleton, J. A., van den Heuvel-Panhuizen, M., & Shew, J. A. (1998). Using bar representations as a model for connecting concepts of rational number. *Mathematics Teaching in the Middle School, 3* (4), 302–312.

Mishra, P., & Koehler, M. J. (2006). Technological pedagogical content knowledge: A new framework for teacher knowledge. *Teachers College Record, 108* (6), 1017–1054.

Ministry of Education, Ontario. (2005). *The Ontario Curriculum Grades 1–8 Mathematics.* Toronto, ON: Author.

Mokros, J., Russell, S. J., & Economopoulos, K. (1995). *Beyond arithmetic: Changing mathematics in the elementary classroom.* Palo Alto, CA: Dale Seymour Publications.

Mulligan, J. T., & Mitchelmore, M. C. (1997). Young children's intuitive models of multiplication and division. *Journal for Research in Mathematics Education, 28,* 309–330.

Munier, V., Devichi, C., & Merle, H. (2008). A physical situation as a way to teach angle. *Teaching Children Mathematics, 14* (7), 402–407.

National Council of Teachers of Mathematics. (1989). *Curriculum and evaluation standards for school mathematics.* Reston, VA: Author.

National Council of Teachers of Mathematics. (1991). *Professional standards for teaching mathematics.* Reston, VA: Author.

National Council of Teachers of Mathematics. (1995). *Assessment standards for school mathematics.* Reston, VA: Author.

National Council of Teachers of Mathematics. (2000). *Principles and standards for school mathematics.* Reston, VA: Author.

National Council of Teachers of Mathematics. (2004). *News Bulletin 40*(6). Reston, VA: The Council.

National Council of Teachers of Mathematics. (2006). *Curriculum focal points for prekindergarten through grade 8 mathematics: A quest for coherence.* Reston, VA: NCTM.

National Council of Teachers of Mathematics. (2007). *Mathematics teaching today.* Reston, VA: NCTM.

National Council of Teachers of Mathematics. (March 2008). *NCTM position statement on the role of technology and learning of mathematics.* Reston, VA: Author.

National Mathematics Advisory Panel. (2008). *Foundations for success.* Jessup, MD: U.S. Department of Education. (Also at www.ed.gov/MathPanel.)

National Research Council. (2001). *Adding it up: Helping children learn mathematics.* J. Kilpatrick, J. Swafford, & B. Findell (Eds.). Mathematics Learning Study Committee, Center for Education Division of Behavioral and Social Sciences and Education. Washington, DC: National Academy Press.

Nelson, R. (2001). *Proofs without words II: More exercises in visual thinking.* Washington, DC: Mathematical Association of America.

Neumer, C. (2007). Mixed numbers made easy: Building and converting mixed numbers and improper fractions. *Teaching Children Mathematics, 13* (9), 488–492.

Nicolson, C. P. (2005). Is chance fair? One student's thoughts on probability. *Teaching Children Mathematics, 12* (2), 83–89.

Niess, M. (2008). Guiding preservice teachers in developing TPCK. In AACTE Committee on Innovation and Technology (Eds.), *Handbook of Technological Pedagogical Content Knowledge (TCPK) for Educators* (pp. 223–250). Routledge/Taylor and Francis Group.

Niezgoda, D. A., & Moyer-Packenham, P. S. (2005). Hickory, dickory, dock: Navigating through data analysis. *Teaching Children Mathematics, 11*(6), 292–300.

Noddings, N. (1993). Constructivism and caring. In R. B. Davis & C. A. Maher (Eds.), *Schools, mathematics, and the world of reality* (pp. 35–50). Boston: Allyn & Bacon.

Noelting, G. (1980). The development of proportional reasoning and the ratio concept: 1. Differentiation of stages. *Educational Studies in Mathematics, 11,* 217–253.

Nyquist, J. B. (2003). The benefits of reconstruing feedback as a larger system of formative assessment: A meta-analysis. Unpublished master's thesis. Vanderbilt University, Nashville, TN.

O'Brien, T. C. (1999). Parrot math. *Phi Delta Kappan, 80,* 434–438.

Oppedal, D. C. (1995). Mathematics is something good. *Teaching Children Mathematics, 2,* 36–40.

Outhred, L., & Mitchelmore, M. (2004). Students' structuring of rectangular arrays. In M. J. Hoines & A. B. Fuglestad (Eds.), *Proceedings of the 28th PME International Conference, 3,* 465–472.

Papert, S. (1980). *Mindstorms: Children, computers, and powerful ideas.* New York: Basic Books.

Parker, M. (2004). Reasoning and working proportionally with percent. *Mathematics Teaching in the Middle School, 9,* 326–330.

Perkins, I., & Flores, A. (2002). Mathematical notations and procedures of recent immigrant students. *Mathematics Teaching in the Middle School, 7* (6), 346–351.

Petersen, J. (2004). *Math and Nonfiction: Grades K–2.* Sausalito, CA: Math Solutions Publications.

Philipp, R. A., Schappelle, B., Siegfried, J., Jacobs, V., & Lamb, L. (2008). *The effects of professional development on the mathematical content knowledge of K–3 teachers.* Paper presented at the American Educational Research Association annual meeting, New York City, NY, April 2008.

Phillips-Bey, C. K. (2004). TI-73 calculator activities. *Mathematics Teaching in the Middle School, 9* (9), 500–508.

Pirie, S., & Kieren, T. (1992). Creating constructivist environments and constructing creative mathematics. *Educational Studies in Mathematics, 23,* 505–528.

Popham, W. J. (2008). *Transformative assessment.* Alexandria, VA: Association for Supervision and Curriculum Development.

Poplin, M. S. (1988a). Holistic/constructivist principles of the teaching/learning process: Implications for the field of learning disabilities. *Journal of Learning Disabilities, 21,* 401–416.

Poplin, M. S. (1988b). The reductionistic fallacy in learning disabilities: Replicating the past by reducing the present. *Journal of Learning Disabilities, 21,* 389–398.

Post, T. R. (1981). Fractions: Results and implications from the national assessment. *Arithmetic Teacher, 28*(9), 26–31.

Post, T. R., Behr, M. J., & Lesh, R. A. (1988). Proportionality and the development of prealgebra understandings. In A. F. Coxford (Ed.), *The ideas of algebra, K–12* (pp. 78–90). Reston, VA: NCTM.

Post, T. R., Wachsmuth, I., Lesh, R. A., & Behr, M. J. (1985). Order and equivalence of rational numbers: A cognitive analysis. *Journal for Research in Mathematics Education, 16,* 18–36.

Pothier, Y., & Sawada, D. (1983). Partitioning: The emergence of rational number ideas in young children. *Journal for Research in Mathematics Education, 14,* 307–317.

Powell, C. A., & Hunting, R. P. (2003). Fractions in the early-years curriculum: More needed, not less. *Teaching Children Mathematics, 10,* 6–7.

Pugalee, D. K. (2005). Writing for mathematical understanding. Norwood, MA: Christopher Gordon Publishers.

Pugalee, D. K., Arbaugh, F., Bay-Williams, J. M., Farrell, A., Matthews, S., & Royster, D. (2008) *Navigating through mathematical connections in grades 6–8.* Reston, VA: NCTM.

Quinn, R., Lamberg, T., & Perrin, J. (2008). Teacher perceptions of division by zero. *Clearing House, 81* (3), 101–104.

Rasmussen, C., Yackel, E., & King, K. (2003). Social and sociomathematical norms in the mathematics classroom. In H. L. Schoen & R. I. Charles (Eds.), *Teaching mathematics through problem solving: Grades 6–12* (pp. 143–154). Reston, VA: NCTM.

Rathmell, E. C. (1978). Using thinking strategies to teach the basic skills. In M. N. Suydam (Ed.), *Developing computational skills* (pp. 13–38). Reston, VA: NCTM.

Rathmell, E. C., Leutzinger, L. P., & Gabriele, A. (2000). *Thinking with numbers.* (Separate packets for each operation.) Cedar Falls, IA: Thinking With Numbers.

Resnick, L. B. (1983). A developmental theory of number understanding. In H. P. Ginsburg (Ed.), *The development of mathematical thinking* (pp. 109–151). New York: Academic Press.

Reys, B. J., & Reys, R. E. (1995). Japanese mathematics education: What makes it work. *Teaching Children Mathematics, 1* (8), 474–475.

Reys, B. J., Reys, R. E., & Penafiel, A. F. (1991). Estimation performance and strategy use of Mexican 5th and 8th grade student sample. *Educational Studies in Mathematics, 22* (4), 353–375.

Reys, B. J., Robinson, E., Sconiers, S., & Mark, J. (1999). Mathematics curricula based on rigorous national standards: What, why, and how? *Phi Delta Kappan, 80,* 454–456.

Reys, R. E. (1998). Computation versus number sense. *Mathematics Teaching in the Middle School, 4*(2), 110–113.

Reys, R. E., & Reys, B. J. (1983). *Guide to using estimation skills and strategies (GUESS)* (Boxes I and II). Palo Alto, CA: Dale Seymour.

Reys, R. E., Reys, B. J., Nohda, N., Ishida, J., Yoshikawa, S., & Shimizu, K. (1991). Computational estimation performance and strategies used by fifth- and eighth-grade Japanese students. *Journal for Research in Mathematics Education, 22* (1), 39–58.

Riordin, J. E. & Noyce, P. E. (2001). The impact of two *Standards*-based mathematics curricula on student achievement in Massachusetts. *Journal for Research in Mathematics Education, 32,* 368–398.

Robitaille, D. F., Beaton, A. E., & Plomp, T. (Eds.) (2000). *The impact of TIMSS on the teaching and learning of mathematics and science.* Vancouver: Pacific Educational Press.

Robitaille, D. F., Taylor, A. R., & Orpwood, G. (1996). *The TIMMS-Canada report Volume 1: grade 8.* Vancouver: University of British Columbia.

Robitaille, D. F., Taylor, A. R., & Orpwood, G. (1996). *The TIMMS-Canada report Volume 2: grade 4.* Vancouver: University of British Columbia.

Rogers, T. W. (1996). Principles for fair student assessment practices for education in Canada. *Assessment in Education: Principles, Policy & Practice, 3* (3), 413–432.

Rolheiser, C., Bower, B. & Stevahn, L. (2000). *The portfolio organizer.* Alexandria, VA: Association for Supervision and Curriculum Development.

Ross, S. H. (1986). *The development of children's place-value numeration concepts in grades two through five.* Presented at the annual meeting of the American Educational Research Association, San Francisco. (ERIC Document Reproduction Service No. ED 2773 482.)

Ross, S. H. (1989). Parts, wholes, and place value: A developmental perspective. *Arithmetic Teacher, 36*(6), 47–51.

Rowan, T. E. (1995, March). Helping children construct mathematical understanding with IMPACT. Presented at the regional meeting of the National Council of Teachers of Mathematics, Chicago, IL.

Rowan, T. E., & Bourne, B. (1994). *Thinking like mathematicians: Putting the K–4 standards into practice.* Portsmouth, NH: Heinemann.

Roy, J. A., & Beckmann, C. E. (2007). Batty functions: Exploring quadratic functions through children's literature. *Mathematics Teaching in the Middle School, 13* (1), 52–64.

Rubel, L. (2006). Students' probabilistic thinking revealed: The case of coin tosses. In G. Burrill & P. C. Elliott (Eds.), *Thinking and reasoning about data and chance: Sixty-eighth yearbook* (pp. 49–60). Reston, VA: NCTM.

Rubel, L. (2007). Middle school and high school students' probabilistic reasoning on coin tasks. *Journal for Research in Mathematics Education, 38*(5), 531–557.

Rubenstein, R. N. (2000). Word origins: Building communication connections. *Mathematics Teaching in the Middle School, 5,* 493–498.

Russell, S. J. (1997, April). *Using video to study students' strategies for whole-number operations.* Paper presented at the annual meeting of the National Council of Teachers of Mathematics, Minneapolis, MN.

Russell, S. J. (2006). What does it mean that "5 has a lot"? From the world to data and back. In G. F. Burrill, & P. C. Elliott (Eds.) *Thinking and reasoning about data and chance: Sixty-eighth yearbook* (pp. 17–30). Reston VA: NCTM.

Russell, S. J., & Economopoulos, K. (2008). *Investigations in number, data, and space.* New York: Pearson.

Sáenz-Ludlow, A. (2004). Metaphor and numerical diagrams in the arithmetical activity of a fourth-grade class. *Journal for Research in Mathematics Education, 35,* 34–56.

Saskatchewan Education. (1996). *Mathematics 6–9: A Curriculum Guide for the Middle Level.* Saskatchewan: Saskatchewan Education.

Scheaffer, R. L. (2006). Statistics and mathematics: On making a happy marriage. In G. F. Burrill, & P. C. Elliott (Eds.) *Thinking and reasoning about data and chance: Sixty-eighth yearbook* (pp. 309–322). Reston, VA: NCTM.

Schielack, J., & Seeley, C. (2007). A look at the development of data representation and analysis in *Curriculum Focal Points: A Quest of Coherence. Mathematics Teaching in the Middle School, 13* (4), 208–210.

Schifter, D. (1999). Reasoning about operations: Early algebraic thinking, grades K through 6. In L. Stiff & F. Curcio (Eds.), *Developing mathematical reasoning in grades K–12* (pp. 62–81). Reston, VA: NCTM.

Schifter, D. (2001). Perspectives from a mathematics educator. In Center for Education, *Knowing and Learning Mathematics for Teaching* (pp. 69–71). Washington, DC: National Academies Press.

Schifter, D., Bastable, V., & Russell, S. J. (1999a). *Developing mathematical understanding: Numbers and operations, Part 1, Building a system of tens (Casebook).* Parsippany, NJ: Dale Seymour Publications.

Schifter, D., Bastable, V., & Russell, S. J. (1999b). *Developing mathematical understanding: Numbers and operations, Part 2, Making meaning for operations (Casebook).* Parsippany, NJ: Dale Seymour Publications.

Schifter, D., Bastable, V., & Russell, S. J. (1999c). *Developing mathematical understanding: Numbers and operations, Part 2, Making meaning for operations (Facilitator's Guide).* Parsippany, NJ: Dale Seymour Publications.

Schifter, D., Bastable, V., & Russell, S. J. (2002). *Developing mathematical ideas: Numbers and operations, Part I: Building a system of tens—Casebook.* Parsippany, NJ: Dale Seymour Publications.

Schifter, D., Bastable, V., Monk, S., & Russell, S. J. (2007) *Developing mathematical ideas: Number and operations, Part 3, Reasoning algebraically about operations (Facilitator's Guide).* Parsippany, NJ: Dale Seymour Publications.

Schifter, D., & Fosnot, C. T. (1993). *Reconstructing mathematics education: Stories of teachers meeting the challenge of reform.* New York: Teachers College Press.

Schmidt, W. H., McKnight, C. C., & Raizen, S. A. (1996). *Executive summary of a splintered vision: An investigation of U.S. science and mathematics education.* Boston: Kluwer.

Schoenfeld, A. H. (1992). Learning to think mathematically: Problem solving, metacognition, and sense making in mathematics. In D. A. Grouws (Ed.), *Handbook of research on teaching and learning* (pp. 334–370). Old Tappan, NJ: Macmillan.

Schroeder, T. L., & Lester, F. K., Jr. (1989). Developing understanding in mathematics via problem solving. In P. R. Trafton (Ed.), *New directions for elementary school mathematics* (pp. 31–42). Reston, VA: NCTM.

Schwartz, S. L. (1996). Hidden messages in teacher talk: Praise and empowerment. *Teaching Children Mathematics, 2,* 396–401.

Sconyers, J. M. (1995). Proof and the middle school mathematics student. *Mathematics Teaching in the Middle School, 1,* 516–518.

Shaughnessy, J. M. (2003). Research on students' understanding of probability. In J. Kilpatrick, W. G. Martin, & D. Schifter (Eds.), *A research companion to Principles and Standards for School Mathematics* (pp. 216–226). Reston, VA: NCTM.

Shaughnessy, J. M. (2006). Research on students' understanding of some big concepts in statistics. In G. F. Burrill, & P. C. Elliott (Eds.), *Thinking and reasoning about data and chance: Sixty-eighth yearbook* (pp. 77–98). Reston VA: NCTM.

Sheffield, L. J. (1999). Serving the needs of the mathematically promising. In L. J. Sheffield (Ed.), *Developing mathematically promising students* (pp. 43–55). Reston, VA: NCTM.

Sheffield, S. (1995). *Math and literature (K–3)* (Vol. 2). Sausalito, CA: Math Solutions Publications.

Sheffield, S., & Gallagher, K. (2004). *Math and nonfiction: Grades 3–5.* Sausalito, CA: Math Solutions Publications.

Shoecraft, P. (1982, April). "Bowl-A-Fact: A game for reviewing the number facts," *Arithmetic Teacher.*

Shulman, L. (1986). Those who understand: Knowledge growth in teaching. *Educational Researcher, 15* (2), 4–14.

Siebert, D., & Gaskin, N. (2006). Creating, naming, and justifying fractions. *Teaching Children Mathematics, 12* (8), 394–400.

Sikes, S. (1995). *Feeding the zircon gorilla and other team building activities.* Tulsa, OK: Learning Unlimited Corporation.

Silver, E. A., Smith, M. S., & Nelson, B. S. (1995). The QUASAR project: Equity concerns meet mathematics education reform in the middle school. In W. G. Secada, E. Fennema, & L. B. Adajian (Eds.), *New directions for equity in mathematics education* (pp. 9–56). New York: Cambridge University Press.

Silver, E. A., & Stein, M. K. (1996). The QUASAR project: The "revolution of the possible" in mathematics instructional reform in urban middle schools. *Urban Education, 30,* 476–521.

Skemp, R. (1978). Relational understanding and instrumental understanding. *Arithmetic Teacher, 26*(3), 9–15.

Smith, A. (1997a). Testing the surf: Criteria for evaluation internet information resources, The Public-Access Computer Systems Review, 8(3), 5–23.

Smith, B. A. (1997b). A meta-analysis of outcomes from the use of calculators in mathematics education. (Doctoral dissertation, Texas A&M University, 1996). Dissertation Abstracts International, 58, 787A.

Smith, J. P., III. (2002). The development of students' knowledge of fractions and ratios. In B. Litwiller (Ed.), *Making sense of fractions, ratios, and proportions* (pp. 3–17). Reston, VA: NCTM.

Soares, J., Blanton, M. L., & Kaput, J. J. (2006). Thinking algebraically across the elementary school curriculum. *Teaching Children Mathematics, 12* (5), 228–234.

Sowder, J. (1989). Developing understanding of computational estimation. *Arithmetic Teacher, 36* (5), 25–27.

Sowder, J., & Wearne, D. (2006). What do we know about eighth-grade student achievement? *Mathematics Teaching in the Middle School, 11* (6), 285–293.

Sowder, J. T., Wearne, D., Martin, W. G., & Strutchens, M. (2004). What do 8th-grade students know about mathematics? Changes over a decade. In P. Kloosterman & F. K. Lester, Jr., *Results and interpretations of the 1990–2000 mathematics assessments of the National Assessment of Educational Progress* (pp. 105–143). Reston, VA: NCTM.

Steele, D. F. (2005). Using schemas to develop algebraic thinking. *Mathematics Teaching in the Middle School, 11* (1), 40–46.

Steele, D. F. (2007). Understanding students' problem-solving knowledge through their writing. *Mathematics Teaching in the Middle School, 13* (2), 102–109.

Steen, L. A. (1997). "The New Literacy" from *Why Numbers Count: Quantitative Literacy for Tomorrow's America*, College Entrance Examination Board (p. xv).

Steffe, L. (1988). Children's construction of number sequences and multiplying schemes. In J. Hiebert & M. J. Behr (Eds.), *Number concepts and operations in the middle grades* (pp. 119–140). Hillsdale, NJ: Erlbaum.

Stein, M. K., & Bovalino, J. W. (2001). Manipulatives: One piece of the puzzle. *Teaching Children Mathematics, 6* (6), 356–359.

Stein, M. K., Grover, B. W., & Henningsen, M. (1996). Building student capacity for mathematical thinking and reasoning: An analysis of mathematical tasks used in reform classrooms. *American Educational Research Journal, 33*, 455–488.

Stein, M. K., & Lane, S. (1996). Instructional tasks and the development of student capacity to think and reason: An analysis of the relationship between teaching and learning in a reform mathematics project. *Educational Research and Evaluation, 2* (1), 50–58.

Steinle, V., & Stacey, K. (2004). Persistence of decimal misconceptions and readiness to move to expertise. *Proceedings of the 28th conference of the International Groups for the Psychology of Mathematics Education, 4*, 225–232.

Stenmark, J. K. (1989). *Assessment alternatives in mathematics: An overview of assessment techniques that promote learning.* Berkeley: EQUALS, University of California.

Stenmark, J. K., & Bush, W. S. (Eds.) (2001). *Mathematics assessment: A practical handbook for grades 3–5.* Reston, VA: NCTM.

Stephan, M., & Whitenack, J. (2003). Establishing classroom social and sociomathematical norms for problem solving. In F. K. Lester, Jr. & R. I. Charles (Eds.), *Teaching mathematics through problem solving: grades pre-K–6* (pp. 149–162). Reston, VA: NCTM.

Stephens, A. C. (2005). Developing students' understanding of variable. *Mathematics Teaching in the Middle School, 11* (2), 96–100.

Stoessiger, R., & Edmunds, J. (1992). *Natural learning and mathematics.* Portsmouth, NH: Heinemann.

Suh, J. M. (2007). Developing "algebra-'rithmetic" in the elementary grades. *Teaching Children Mathematics, 14* (4), pp. 246–253.

Suh, J. M. (2007). Tying it all together: Building mathematics proficiency for all students. *Teaching Children Mathematics, 14* (3), 163–169.

Sulentic-Dowell, M. M., Beal, G., & Capraro, R. (2006). How do literacy experiences affect the teaching propensities of elementary pre-service teachers? *Journal of Reading Psychology, 27* (2–3), 235–255.

Taber, S. B. (2002). Go ask Alice about multiplication of fractions. In B. Litwiller (Ed.), *Making sense of fractions, ratios, and proportions* (pp. 61–71). Reston, VA: NCTM.

Taber, S. B. (2007). Using Alice in Wonderland to teach multiplication of fractions. *Mathematics Teaching in the Middle School, 12* (5), 244–250.

Tarr, J. E., Lee, H. S., & Rider, R. L. (2006). When data and chance collide: Drawing inferences from empirical data. In G. Burrill & P. C. Elliott (Eds.) *Thinking and reasoning about data and chance: Sixty-eighth yearbook* (pp. 139–149). Reston VA: NCTM.

Taylor, A. R., & Tubianosa, T. S. (2001). *Student assessment in Canada.* Kelowna, BC: Society for the Advancement of Excellence in Education.

Teachers of English to Speakers of Other Languages (TESOL). (1997). *TESOL ESL standards for pre-K–12 students.* Alexandria, VA: Author.

Theissen, D., Matthias, M., & Smith, J. (1998). *The wonderful world of mathematics: A critically annotated list of children's books in mathematics* (2nd ed.). Reston, VA: NCTM.

Thomas, K. R. (2006). Students THINK: A Framework for improving problem solving. *Teaching Children Mathematics, 13* (2), 86–95.

Thompson, C. S. (1990). Place value and larger numbers. In J. N. Payne (Ed.), *Mathematics for the young child* (pp. 89–108). Reston, VA: NCTM.

Thompson, P. W. (1994). Concrete materials and teaching for mathematical understanding. *Arithmetic Teacher, 41*, 556–558.

Thompson, T. D., & Preston, R. V. (2004). Measurement in the middle grades: Insights from NAEP and TIMSS. *Mathematics Teaching in the Middle School, 9*, 514–519.

Thornton, C. A. (1982). Doubles up—easy! *Arithmetic Teacher, 29* (8), 20.

Thornton, C. A. (1990). Strategies for the basic facts. In J. N. Payne (Ed.), *Mathematics for the young child* (pp. 133–151). Reston, VA: NCTM.

Thornton, C. A. (1990). Strategies for the basic facts. In J. N. Payne (Ed.), *Mathematics for the young child* (pp. 133–151). Reston, VA: NCTM.

Thornton, C. A., & Toohey, M. A. (1984). *A matter of facts: (Addition, subtraction, multiplication, division).* Palo Alto, CA: Creative Publications.

Tirosh, D. (2000). Enhancing prospective teachers' knowledge of children's conceptions: The case of division of fractions. *Journal for Research in Mathematics Education, 31* (1), 1, 5–25.

Tomlinson, C. A. (1999). *The differentiated classroom: Responding to the needs of all learners.* Alexandria, VA: Association for Supervision and Curriculum Development.

Torrence, E. (2003). Learning to think: An American third grader discovers mathematics in Holland. *Teaching Children Mathematics, 10*, 90–93.

Trafton, P. R., & Claus, A. S. (1994). A changing curriculum for a changing age. In C. A. Thornton & N. S. Bley (Eds.), *Windows of opportunity: Mathematics for students with special needs* (pp. 19–39). Reston, VA: NCTM.

Tsuruda, G. (1994). *Putting it together: Middle school math in transition.* Portsmouth, NH: Heinemann.

Tzur, R. (1999). An integrated study of children's construction of improper fractions and the teacher's role in promoting learning. *Journal for Research in Mathematics Education, 30,* 390–416.

Usiskin, Z. (2007). Some thoughts about fractions. *Mathematics Teaching in the Middle School, 12* (7), 370–373.

Van de Walle, J. A., & Lovin, L. H. (2006). *Teaching student-centered mathematics: Grades 5–8.* Boston: Allyn and Bacon.

van Hiele, P. M. (1999). Developing geometric thinking through activities that begin with play. *Teaching Children Mathematics, 5* (6), 310–316.

Varol, F., & Farran, D. (2007). Elementary school students' mental computation proficiencies, *Early Childhood Education Journal, 35* (1), 89–94.

von Glasersfeld, E. (1990). An exposition of constructivism: Why some like it radical. In R. B. Davis, C. A. Maher, & N. Noddings (Eds.), *Constructivist views on the teaching and learning of mathematics* (pp. 19–29). Reston, VA: NCTM.

von Glasersfeld, E. (1996). Introduction: Aspects of constructivism. In C. T. Fosnot (Ed.), *Constructivism: Theory, perspectives, and practice* (pp. 3–7). New York: Teachers College Press.

Vygotsky, L. S. (1978). *Mind and society.* Cambridge, MA: Harvard University Press.

Wallace, A. H. (2007). Anticipating student responses to improve problem solving. *Mathematics Teaching in the Middle School, 12* (9), 504–511.

Wallace, A. H., & Gurganus, S. P. (2005). Teaching for mastery of multiplication. *Teaching Children Mathematics, 12* (1), 26–33.

Walter, M. I. (1970). *Boxes, squares and other things: A teacher's guide for a unit in informal geometry.* Reston, VA: NCTM.

Wandt, E. & Brown, G. W. (1957). Non-occupational uses of mathematics: Mental and written—Approximate and exact. *Arithmetic Teacher, 4* (4), 151–154.

Ward, R. A. (2006). Numeracy and literacy: Teaching K–8 mathematics using children's literature. Colorado Springs, CO: PEAK Parent Center.

Wareham, K. (2005). *Hand-held calculators and mathematics achievement: What the 1996 national assessment of educational progress eighth-grade mathematics exam scores tell us.* Unpublished doctoral dissertation, Utah State University.

Warren, E., & Cooper, T. J. (2008). Patterns that support early algebraic thinking in elementary school. In C. E. Greenes & R. Rubenstein (Eds.), *Algebra and algebraic thinking in school mathematics: NCTM 70th yearbook,* (pp. 113–126). Reston, VA: NCTM.

Watanabe, T. (2001). Let's eliminate fractions from the primary curricula! *Teaching Children Mathematics, 8,* 70–72.

Watanabe, T. (2006). The teaching and learning of fractions: A Japanese perspective. *Teaching Children Mathematics, 12* (7), 368–374.

Watson, J. M., & Moritz, J. B. (2003). Fairness of dice: A longitudinal study of students' beliefs and strategies for making judgments. *Journal for Research in Mathematics Education, 34* (4), 270–304.

Watson, J. M., & Shaughnessy, J. M. (2004). Proportional reasoning: Lessons learned from research in data and chance. *Mathematics Teaching in the Middle School, 10,* 104–109.

Wearne, D., & Kouba, V. L. (2000). Rational numbers. In E. A. Silver & P. A Kenney (Eds.), *Results from the seventh mathematics assessment of the National Assessment of Educational Progress* (pp. 163–191). Reston, VA: NCTM.

Welchman-Tischler, R. (1992). *How to use children's literature to teach mathematics.* Reston, VA: NCTM.

Wheatley, G. H., & Hersberger, J. (1986). A calculator estimation activity. In H. Schoen (Ed.), *Estimation and mental computation* (pp. 182–185). Reston, VA: NCTM.

Whitin, D. J., & Whitin, P. (2004). New visions for linking literature and mathematics. Urbana, IL: National Council of Teachers of Mathematics; Reston, VA: NCTM.

Whitin, D. J., & Wilde, S. (1992). *Read any good math lately? Children's books for mathematical learning, K–6.* Portsmouth, NH: Heinemann.

Whitin, D. J., & Wilde, S. (1995). *It's the story that counts: More children's books for mathematical learning, K–6.* Portsmouth, NH: Heinemann.

Whitin, P., & Whitin, D. J. (2006). Making connections through math-related book pairs. *Teaching Children Mathematics, 13* (4), 196–202.

Whitin, P., & Whitin, D. (2008). Learning to solve problems in the primary grades. *Teaching Children Mathematics, 14* (7), 426–432.

Wickett, M., Kharas, K., & Burns, M. (2002). *Lessons for algebraic thinking.* Sausalito, CA: Math Solutions Publications.

Wiliam, D. (2007). Content then process: Teacher learning communities in the service of formative assessment. In D. B. Reeves (Ed.), *Ahead of the curve: The power of assessment to transform teaching and learning* (pp. 183–204). Bloomington, IN: Solution Tree.

Williams, L. (2008). Tiering and scaffolding: Two strategies for providing access to important mathematics. *Teaching Children Mathematics, 14* (6), 324–330.

Wood, T., Cobb, P., Yackel, E., & Dillon, D. (Eds.). (1993). *Rethinking elementary school mathematics: Insights and issues* (*Journal for Research in Mathematics Education* Monograph No. 6). Reston, VA: NCTM.

Wood, T., & Sellers, P. (1996). Assessment of a problem-centered mathematics program: Third grade. *Journal for Research in Mathematics Education, 27,* 337–353.

Wood, T., & Sellers, P. (1997). Deepening the analysis: Longitudinal assessment of a problem-centered mathematics program. *Journal for Research in Mathematics Education, 28,* 163–168.

Wood, T., & Turner-Vorbeck, T. (2001). Extending the conception of mathematics teaching. In T. Wood, B. S. Nelson, & Warfield, J. (Eds.), *Beyond classical pedagogy: Teaching elementary school mathematics* (pp. 185–208). Mahwah, NJ: Erlbaum.

Wood, T., Williams, G., & McNeal, B. (2006). Children's mathematical thinking in different classroom cultures, *Journal for Research in Mathematics Education, 37* (3), 222–255.

Yackel, E. (1997). A foundation for algebraic reasoning in the early grades. *Teaching Children Mathematics, 3* (6), 276–280.

Yackel, E., & Cobb, P. (1996). Sociomathematical norms, argumentation, and autonomy in mathematics. *Journal for Research in Mathematics Education, 27,* 458–477.

Zambo, R. (2008). Percents can make sense. *Mathematics Teaching in the Middle School, 13* (7), 418–422.

Children's Literature References

Andrews, J., Jolliffe, S. R. (2005). *The Twelve Days of Summer.* Victoria, B.C.: Orca Book Publishers.

Anno, M. (1982). *Anno's counting house.* New York: Philomel Books.

Anno, M. (1994). *Anno's magic seeds.* New York: Philomel Books.

Anno, M., & Anno, M. (1983). *Anno's mysterious multiplying jar.* New York: Philomel Books.

Appelt, K., Sweet, M. (1999). *Bats on parade.* Toronto: Harper Collins Publishers.

Ash, R. (1996). *Incredible comparisons.* New York: Dorling Kindersley.

Ball, J. (2005). *Go figure! A totally cool book about numbers.* Brookfield, CT: DK Children.

Bowers, V., Eastman, D. (2006). *Crazy about Canada! Amazing things kids want to know.* Toronto: Maple Tree Press.

Briggs, R. (1970). *Jim and the beanstalk.* New York: Coward-McCann.

Brown, M. W. (1947). *Goodnight moon.* New York: Harper and Row.

Buckley, J. Jr., & Stremme, R. (2006). *Book of lists: Fun facts, weird trivia, and amazing lists on nearly everything you need to know!* Santa Barbara, CA: Scholastic.

Burns, M . (1995). *The greedy triangle.* New York: Scholastic.

Carle, E. (1969). *The very hungry caterpillar.* New York: Putnam.

Carroll, L. (1865 and 1982). *Alice's adventures in Wonderland.* London: Hodder and Stoughton.

Chalmers, M. (1986). *Six dogs, twenty-three cats, forty-five mice, and one hundred sixteen spiders.* New York: HarperCollins.

Chwast, S. (1993). *The twelve circus rings.* San Diego, CA: Gulliver Books, Harcourt Brace Jovanovich.

Clement, R. (1991). *Counting on Frank.* Milwaukee: Gareth Stevens Children's Books.

Cushman, R. (1991). *Do you wanna bet? Your chance to find out about probability.* New York: Clarion Books.

Cuyler, M., Howard, A. (2000). *100th Day Worries.* New York: Simon and Schuster Children's Publishing.

Dee, R. (1988). *Two ways to count to ten.* New York: Holt.

Dewdney, A.K. (1993). *200% of nothing: An eye-opening tour through the twists and turns of math abuse and innumeracy.* New York: Wiley.

Dixon, J . (2005). *Extreme Canadian weather: Freakish storms and unexpected disasters.* Calgary: Altitude Publishing Canada.

Ehlert, L . (1990). *Color farm.* New York: HarperCollins.

Ehlert, L . (1998). *Color zoo.* New York: HarperCollins.

Enzensberger, H. M. (1997). *The number devil.* New York: Metropolitan Books.

Forster, M. (2004). *100 Canadian heroines.* Toronto: Dundurn Press.

Friedman, A. (1994). *The king's commissioners.* New York: Scholastic.

Gag, W. (1928). *Millions of cats.* New York: Coward-McCann.

Gifford, S., & Thaler, S. (2008). *Piece = part = portion: Fraction = decimal = percent.* New York: Tricycle Press.

Granfield, L. (2000). *Canada votes: How we elect our government.* Toronto: Kids Can Press.

Giganti, P. (1988). *How many snails? A counting book.* New York: Greenwillow.

Giganti, P. (1992). *Each orange had 8 slices.* New York: Greenwillow.

Grossman, B. (1996). *My little sister ate one hare.* New York: Crown.

Hacker, C. (2000). *The kids book of Canadian history.* Toronto, ON: Kids Can Press.

Hamm, D. J. (1994). *How many feet in the bed? New York:* Aladdin.

Harris, T. (1999). 100 days of school. Brookfield, CT: Millbrook Press.

Hoban, T. (1981). *More than one.* New York: Greenwillow.

Hoban, T. (1996). *Shapes, shapes, shapes.* New York: Harper Trophy.

Hoban, T. (1998). *So many circles, so many squares.* New York: Greenwillow.

Hoban, T. (2000). *Cubes, cones, cylinders and spheres.* New York: Greenwillow.

Hoffman, D. (2005). *The breakfast cereal gourmet.* Kansas City, MO: Andrews McMeel Publishing.

Hong, L. T. (1993). *Two of everything: A Chinese folktale.* Morton Grove, IL: Albert Whitman & Company.

Hutchins, P. (1986). *The doorbell rang.* New York: Greenwillow.

Isaacs, A., Zelinsky, P. O. (1999). *Swamp angel.* New York: Dutton Juvenile.

Jaspersohn, W. (1993). *Cookies.* Old Tappan, NJ: Macmillan.

Jocelyn, M. (2000). *Hannah's collection.* New York: Random House.

Juster, N. (1961). *The phantom tollbooth.* New York: Random House.

Kusugak, M., Krykorka, V. (1996). *My arctic 1, 2, 3.* Toronto: Annick Press.

Kyi, T. L., Bagley, T. (2007). *Canadian boys who rocked the world.* North Vancouver: Walrus Books.

Landau, E. (2006). *The history of everyday life.* Minneapolis: Lerner Press.

Lobel, A. (1970). *Frog and Toad are friends.* New York: HarperCollins.

Masoff, J. (2006). *Oh yikes! History's grossest, wackiest moments.* New York: Workman Publishing Company.

Mathews, L. (1979). *Gator pie.* New York: Dodd, Mead.

McKissack, P. C. (1992). *A million fish ... more or less.* New York: Knopf.

Munsch, R. (1987). *Moira's birthday.* Toronto: Annick Press.

Munsch, R. (2001). *Up up down.* New York: Cartwheel.

Munsch, R. (2002). *More pies.* New York: Cartwheel.

Murphy, S. J., Westcott, N. B. (1997). *The best vacation ever.* New York: HarperCollins.

Murrie, S., Murrie, & M. (2007). *Every minute on Earth: Fun facts that happen every 60 seconds.* New York: Scholastic.

Myller, R. (1990). *How big is a foot?* New York: Dell.

Osborne, M. P. (2000). *Kate and the beanstock.* New York: Atheneum/Anne Schawrtz Books.

Nolan, H. (1995). *How many, how much, how far, how heavy, how long, how tall is 1000?* Toronto: Kids Can Press.

Norton, M. (1953). *The borrowers.* New York: Harcourt Brace.

Numeroff, L. J., Bond, F. (1985). *If you give a mouse a cookie.* New York: HarperCollins.

Patkau, K. (2006). *Creatures great and small.* New York: Random House.

Pinczes, E. J. (1995). *Remainder of one.* New York: Houghton Mifflin Books for Children.

Pinczes, E. J. (1999). *One hundred hungry ants.* San Anselmo, CA: Sandpiper.

Pluckrose, H. (1988). *Pattern.* New York: Franklin Watts.

Reid, B. (1992). *Two by two.* New York: Scholastic.

Ross, C. S. (1992). *Circles: Shapes in mathematics, science and nature.* Sydney: Ashton Scholastic.

Ruurs, M. (2007). *In my backyard.* Toronto: Tundra Books.

Sachar, L. (2000). *Holes.* New York: Yearling.

St. John, G. (1975). *How to count like a Martian.* New York: Walck.

Schwartz, D. (1985). *How much is a million?* New York: Lothrop, Lee & Shepard.

Schwartz, D. (1989). *If you made a million.* New York: Lothrop, Lee & Shepard.

Schwartz, D. (1999). *On beyond a million: An amazing math journey.* New York: Doubleday Books for Young Readers.

Schwartz, D. M. (1999). *If you hopped like a frog.* New York: Scholastic Press.

Schwartz, D., & Whitin, D. (1998). *Magic of a million activity book—grades 2–5.* Scholastic.

Scieszka, J., & Smith, L. (1995). *Math curse.* New York: Viking Penguin.

Seuss, Dr. (1960). *Green eggs and ham.* New York: Random House.

Sharmat, M. W. (1979). *The 329th friend.* New York: Four Winds Press.

Silverstein, S. (1981). "How much, how many" from *A light in the attic.* New York: HarperCollins.

Smucker, B . (1996). *Selina and the bear paw quilt.* Dragonfly Books.

Strauss, R. (2007). *One well: The story of water on Earth.* Toronto: Kids Can Press.

Tahan, M. (1993). *The man who counted: A collection of mathematical adventures* (Trans. L. Clark & A. Reid). New York: Norton.

Tang, G. (2001). *The grapes of math.* Scholastic.

Toft, K. M. (1998). *One less fish.* Charlesbridge Publishing.

Tompert, A. (1997). *Grandfather Tang's story.* New York: Dragonfly Books.

Weiss, A. E. (1991). *Lotteries: Who wins, who loses.* Hillsdale, NJ: Enslow.

Wells, R. E. (2005). *Is a blue whale the biggest thing there is?* Morton Grove, IL: Whitman.

Wishinsky, F. (1999). *The man who made parks.* Toronto: Tundra Books.

Wishinsky, F. (2007). *Beware pirates.* Toronto: Tundra Books.

Wolkstein, D. (1972). *8,000 stones.* New York: Doubleday.

Yolen, J., & Semple, H. (2006). *Fairy tale feasts: A literary cookbook.* Northampton, MA: Crocodile Books.

Zimmerman, H. W. (1990). *A circle is not a valentine.* Markham, ON: Fitzhenry & Whiteside.

Zweig, E. (2007). *Hockey trivia for kids.* Toronto: Scholastic Canada.

Zweig, E. (2008). *Hockey trivia for kids 2.* Toronto: Scholastic Canada.

Computer Software

AutoSkill. *Academy of Math.*

Clements, D. H., & Meredith, J. S. (1994). *Turtle math.* Highgate Springs, VT: Logo Computer Systems.

Clements, D. H., & Sarama, J. (1995). *Shapes—Mathematical Thinking.* Highgate Springs, VT: Logo Computer Systems Inc. (LCSI).

CompassLearning. (2008). *Odyssey Math.* Courseware Solutions. (2004). *Mathville middle school.*

Courseware Solutions. *Mathville one.*

Courseware Solutions. (2006). *Mathville.*

Geogebra.org. *GeoGebra.* Open source.

Hickey, A. (1996). *Unifix software.* Rowley, MA: Didax Educational Resources.

Inspiration Software. (2008). *Kidspiration.*

Key Curriculum Press. (2001). *The geometer's sketchpad* (Version 4.0). Berkeley, CA: Key Curriculum Press.

Key Curriculum Press. (2005). *Tinkerplots.*

Knowledge Adventure. *Math blaster.*

National Center for Technology Innovation. (2008). TechMatrix. www.techmatrix.org

Nectar Foundation. (2006). *Math trek 1, 2, 3, 4, 5, 6, 7, 8.*

Nectar Foundation. *Math strategies—primary.*

Peanut Software. *Wingeom.* Open source. http://math.exeter.edu/rparris/wingeom.html

Pearson Education. (2004). *eTools.*

Riverdeep Interactive Learning. (2005). *Math munchers.*

Riverdeep Interactive Learning Limited. (2008). *Destination Math.*

Sunburst Technology. (1995). *Shape up.* Pleasantville, NY: Author.

Sunburst Technology. (1998). *Representing fractions* [Computer Software]. Pleasantville, NY: Author.

Sunburst. *Factory Deluxe.*

Sunburst Technology. (n.d.). *The cruncher 2.0.* Pleasantville, NY: Author.

Tenth Planet. (1998a). *Combining and breaking apart numbers.* Pleasantville, NY: Sunburst Communications.

Tenth Planet. (1998b). *Fraction operations.* Pleasantville, NY: Sunburst Communications.

Tenth Planet. (1998c). *Number meanings and counting.* Pleasantville, NY: Sunburst Communications.

Tenth Planet. (1998d). *Representing fractions.* Pleasantville, NY: Sunburst Communications.

Texas Instruments. (1994). *Cabri geometry II* [Computer Software]. Dallas: Author.

Thinkerport. No other info.

Tom Snyder. (1993). *The graph club* [Computer Software]. Watertown, MA: Author.

Tom Snyder Productions. (1998). *Fizz & Martina's math adventures: Lights, camera, fractions* [Computer Software]. Watertown, MA: Author.

Tom Snyder Productions. *FASTT Math.* www.tomsnyder.com/fasttmath/overview.html

Tom Snyder Productions. *Math Adventures.*

Tom Snyder Productions. (1999). *Prime time math.* Watertown, MA: Author.

Index

Note: Entries for figures and tables are followed by "*f*" and "*t*," respectively.